TEACHER'S EDITION

Volume 1　　　　Chapters 1–6

PRENTICE HALL

COURSE 1

MATHEMATICS

Randall I. Charles

Judith C. Branch-Boyd

Mark Illingworth

Darwin Mills

Andy Reeves

PEARSON

Prentice
Hall

Boston, Massachusetts
Upper Saddle River, New Jersey

Pearson Prentice Hall™ is a trademark of Pearson Education, Inc.
Pearson® is a registered trademark of Pearson plc.
Prentice Hall® is a registered trademark of Pearson Education, Inc.

Teacher's Edition package (Volumes 1 and 2): ISBN 0-13-063137-X
Volume 1: ISBN 0-13-180756-0
Volume 2: ISBN 0-13-180757-9

7 8 9 10   07

Teacher's Edition Contents
Volume I

Teacher Handbook

Student Edition With Teacher Notes
Volume 1

Volume 2

PRENTICE HALL
The *right path* makes

The right path across the grade levels . . .

Vertical Alignment K–12

Prentice Hall Mathematics is the grades 6–12 companion of the Scott Foresman elementary series. The continuity of design, content, and pedagogy extends from K–12. The scope and sequence of the series addresses both today's curriculum guidelines and teacher expectations. (See pages T36–T41.)

Proven Authorship

Series author Randy Charles ensures continuity of content from course to course, while program authors ensure integrity of content within each course. (See pages T14–T15.)

Proven Track Record

Prentice Hall Mathematics builds on the combined experience and heritage of three respected names in mathematics publishing—Prentice Hall, Scott Foresman, and Addison Wesley.

MATHEMATICS
all the difference

The right path
every day, in every lesson . . .

Reach Your Students

Math is made relevant and meaningful through *Dorling Kindersley Real-World Snapshots*. Watch students' excitement build as they make the connection between mathematics and real-world situations. (See pages T6–T7.)

Empower Your Students

Every student has the opportunity to excel through our unique *Instant Check System™*. No other program makes it this easy for you to assess readiness, progress, and mastery. (See pages T8–T9.)

Prepare Your Students

Daily Test Prep allows students to approach high-stakes tests with confidence. And because it's built into every lesson, you don't have to stop teaching to prepare them for the test! (See pages T10–T11.)

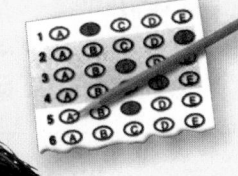

. . . and *Prentice Hall Mathematics*
provides you with the **teaching support**
you deserve—every day, in every lesson.

"How can I reach

Dorling Kindersley Real-World Snapshots

grab students' attention with a captivating visual style.

■ Take It to the Net

Data at PHSchool.com further develop concepts and skills.

DK Real-World Snapshots

Swimming to Win

Applying Mixed Numbers Suppose you want to build a set of shelves to hold the trophies and photographs for your school's swim team. Knowing how to work with fractions and mixed numbers can help you design and build shelves.

Put It All Together

1. Suppose you are building a trophy case $36\frac{1}{2}$ inches tall with three evenly spaced shelves each $\frac{3}{4}$ inch thick. Let h represent the height of each shelf. Calculate h.

$8\frac{1}{2}$ in. $28\frac{3}{4}$ in.

Side $36\frac{1}{2}$ in.

A, B, Brace, C, C, A

Front

2. Calculate the lengths of each of the boards needed to build the trophy case, including the top and bottom (A), the shelves (B), and the sides (C). Sketch each piece with its dimensions labeled.

3. **a.** The lumberyard sells boards that are 8 feet long and boards that are 10 feet long. How many 8-foot boards would you need to buy? How many 10-foot boards? Draw a diagram to support your answers.

   b. The price of the lumber is $3.25 per foot. How much would the lumber for the project cost?

Hands
To make yourself more streamlined during a turn, overlap and lock your hands as you stretch your arms out underwater.

Turns
As you approach the wall, begin to curl your body. Use the momentum from your approach to power your kick-off from the wall.

Take It to the NET For more information about school sports, go to **www.PHSchool.com**.
Web Code: abg-0804

The Butterfly Stroke
The butterfly was invented in the early 1930s but was considered a form of the breaststroke until 1952. Originally the kick was similar to the breaststroke kick, but now swimmers use the more efficient "dolphin kick."

Off the Block
To power your dive off the starting block, grip the block with your hands and toes and put your weight on your back foot. Next, pull hard with your arms and push with your feet.

As your arms sweep backward, raise your head out of the water and take a breath.

294   295

■ Activities

Students gather data to apply the mathematics from the chapter to real-world situations.

T6

all of my students?"

Connect to Their World

Real-World Connections
within each lesson make skills and concepts relevant.

You can use the GCF of two numbers to find the scale of a drawing or a model.

3 EXAMPLE Finding the Scale

Models Refer to the model boxcar shown at the right. The actual length of a boxcar is 609 in. What is the scale of the model?

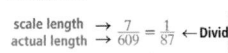

— 7 in. —

$$\begin{array}{ll}\text{scale length} \to \\ \text{actual length} \to\end{array} \frac{7}{609} = \frac{1}{87} \leftarrow \text{Divid}$$

The scale is 1 in. : 87 in.

✔ **Check Understanding** 3 The length of a room in an archi... 15 ft. What is the scale of the dra...

276 Chapter 5 Ratios, Rates, and Proportions

If the equation includes mixed numbers, write them as improper fractions.

3 EXAMPLE Writing and Solving Equations 🌐 Real World

Spelling Bee Students are making banners to support friends who are finalists in a national spelling bee. They have $8\frac{3}{4}$ yards of material. Each banner takes $\frac{5}{8}$ yards of material. How many banners can they make?

17

Real-World 🌐 Connection
The first national spelling bee was held in 1925. Today more than 10 million students participate in local spelling bees.

Words   yards per banner × number of banners = total yards

⬇

Let b = number of banners.

Equation $\frac{5}{8}$ × b = $8\frac{3}{4}$

$\frac{5}{8}b = 8\frac{3}{4}$ ← Write the equation.

$\frac{5}{8}b = \frac{35}{4}$ ← Write $8\frac{3}{4}$ as an improper fraction.

$\frac{8}{5} \cdot \left(\frac{5}{8}b\right) = \frac{35}{4} \cdot \frac{8}{5}$ ← Multiply each side by $\frac{8}{5}$, the reciprocal of $\frac{5}{8}$.

$b = \frac{\overset{7}{\cancel{35}}}{\underset{1}{\cancel{4}}} \cdot \frac{\overset{2}{\cancel{8}}}{\underset{1}{\cancel{5}}}$ ← Simplify and multiply.

$b = 14$

The students can make 14 banners.

✔ **Check Understanding** 3 **Estimation** Explain how you could estimate the number of banners the students can make without solving the equation in Example 3.

270 Chapter 5 Multiplying and Dividing Fractions

Plus...

Take It to the NET
Online lesson quiz at
www.PHSchool.com
····· Web Code: aag-0804

Built-in Web Support

PHSchool.com supports students as they learn. Built-in **Web Codes** take them directly to components of the Web site, including:

• Self-grading tests and lesson quizzes

• Updated data sources

• Support for chapter projects

"How can I *empower* to learn

INSTANT CHECK SYSTEM™

Instant Check System™

enables students to check their understanding at key points during instruction. No other program provides such an easy-to-use way to measure students' progress.

✓ Before lessons
Check Skills You'll Need

✓ During lessons
Check Understanding after _every_ example

✓ After lessons
Checkpoint Quizzes

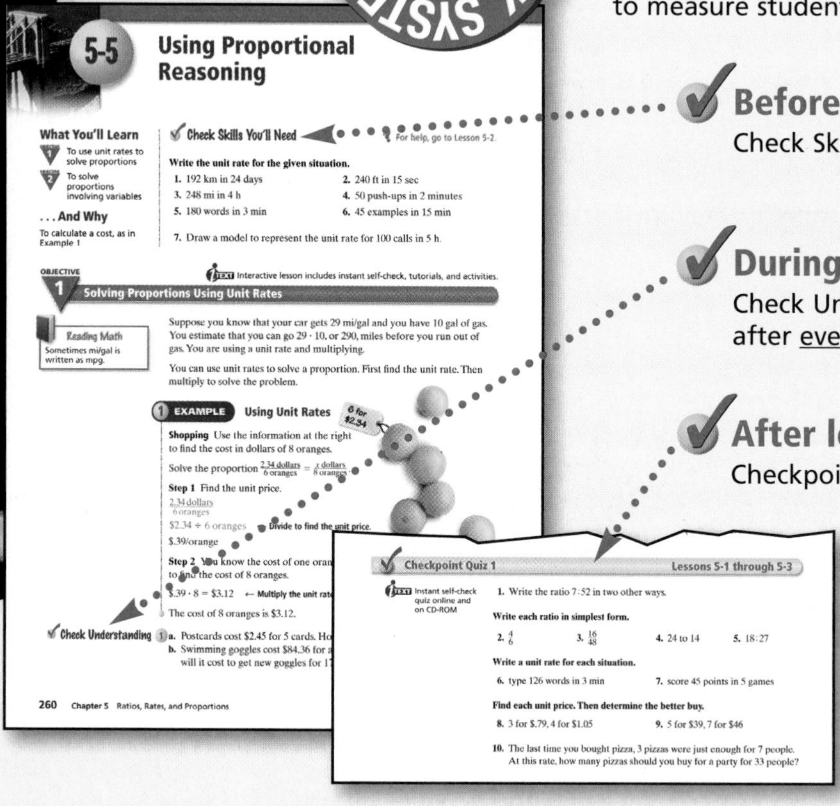

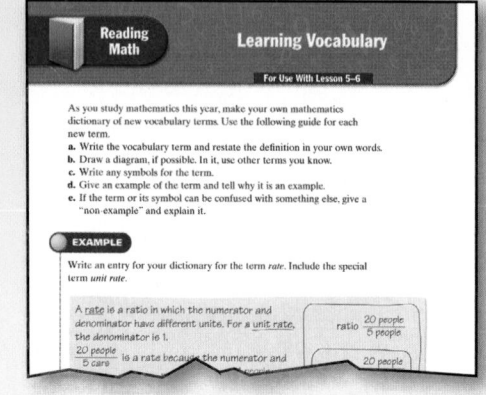

5-5 Using Proportional Reasoning

What You'll Learn
1 To use unit rates to solve proportions
2 To solve proportions involving variables

. . . And Why
To calculate a cost, as in Example 1

✓ Check Skills You'll Need   For help, go to Lesson 5-2.

Write the unit rate for the given situation.
1. 192 km in 24 days   2. 240 ft in 15 sec
3. 248 mi in 4 h   4. 50 push-ups in 2 minutes
5. 180 words in 3 min   6. 45 examples in 15 min

7. Draw a model to represent the unit rate for 100 calls in 5 h.

OBJECTIVE
1 Solving Proportions Using Unit Rates

Interactive lesson includes instant self-check, tutorials, and activities.

Reading Math
Sometimes mi/gal is written as mpg.

Suppose you know that your car gets 29 mi/gal and you have 10 gal of gas. You estimate that you can go 29 · 10, or 290, miles before you run out of gas. You are using a unit rate and multiplying.

You can use unit rates to solve a proportion. First find the unit rate. Then multiply to solve the problem.

1 EXAMPLE Using Unit Rates

Shopping Use the information at the right to find the cost in dollars of 8 oranges.

Solve the proportion $\frac{2.34\ dollars}{6\ oranges} = \frac{x\ dollars}{8\ oranges}$

Step 1 Find the unit price.
$\frac{2.34\ dollars}{6\ oranges}$
$\$2.34 \div 6\ oranges$ ← Divide to find the unit price.
$\$.39/orange$

Step 2 You know the cost of one orange. ... to find the cost of 8 oranges.

$\$.39 \cdot 8 = \$3.12$ ← Multiply the unit rate ...

The cost of 8 oranges is $3.12.

✓ Check Understanding 1 a. Postcards cost $2.45 for 5 cards. Ho...
b. Swimming goggles cost $84.36 for ... will it cost to get new goggles for 1...

260   Chapter 5 Ratios, Rates, and Proportions

✓ Checkpoint Quiz 1   Lessons 5-1 through 5-3

Instant self-check quiz online and on CD-ROM

1. Write the ratio 7 : 52 in two other ways.

Write each ratio in simplest form.
2. $\frac{4}{6}$ 3. $\frac{16}{48}$ 4. 24 to 14   5. 18 : 27

Write a unit rate for each situation.
6. type 126 words in 3 min   7. score 45 points in 5 games

Find each unit price. Then determine the better buy.
8. 3 for $.79, 4 for $1.05   9. 5 for $39, 7 for $46

10. The last time you bought pizza, 3 pizzas were just enough for 7 people. At this rate, how many pizzas should you buy for a party for 33 people?

Reading Math

Learning Vocabulary
For Use With Lesson 5-6

As you study mathematics this year, make your own mathematics dictionary of new vocabulary terms. Use the following guide for each new term.
a. Write the vocabulary term and restate the definition in your own words.
b. Draw a diagram, if possible. In it, use other terms you know.
c. Write any symbols for the term.
d. Give an example of the term and tell why it is an example.
e. If the term or its symbol can be confused with something else, give a "non-example" and explain it.

EXAMPLE

Write an entry for your dictionary for the term *rate*. Include the special term *unit rate*.

A _rate_ is a ratio in which the numerator and denominator have different units. For a _unit rate_, the denominator is 1.
$\frac{20\ people}{5\ cars}$ is a rate because the numerator and ...

ratio $\frac{20\ people}{5\ people}$

Reading Math

Built-in Reading Help

Reading Math lessons and side-column features provide help where students often struggle:
• Math Vocabulary
• Understanding Word Problems
• Understanding Formulas and Symbols

students independently?"

Built-in Homework Help

Leveled exercise sets

allow you to easily craft just the right assignments for your classes. Plus, we've built in homework helpers along the way.

■ Student Help features

throughout the text — consistently labeled in green — assist your students in becoming independent learners.

Ⓐ Practice by Example

Refers students directly back to the examples in the lesson. (Also great for parents trying to help with homework!)

Ⓑ Apply Your Skills

Richer skill exercises and multi-step application problems combine skills from earlier lessons.

Ⓒ Challenge

Exercises extend and stretch students' thinking.

EXERCISES

❓ For more practice, see *Extra Practice*.

Ⓐ Practice by Example

Example 1 (page 256)

Determine whether the ratios in each pair can form a proportion by writing each ratio in simplest form. Exercise 1 has been started for you.

1. $\frac{1}{2}, \frac{14}{28}$ 2. $\frac{6}{8}, \frac{4}{3}$ 3. $\frac{8}{18}, \frac{20}{45}$ 4. $\frac{21}{24}, \frac{56}{64}$

$\frac{14}{28} = \frac{14^{1}}{_{2}28} = \ldots$

5. $\frac{15}{45}, \frac{3}{15}$ 6. $\frac{45}{9}, \frac{10}{2}$ 7. $\frac{19}{76}, \frac{5}{20}$ 8. $\frac{17}{34}, \frac{2}{3}$

Example 2 (page 257)

Determine whether the ratios in each pair can form a proportion by finding a common multiplier.

9. $\frac{2}{8}, \frac{18}{72}$ 10. $\frac{5}{2}, \frac{65}{26}$ 11. $\frac{40}{12}, \frac{160}{3}$ 12. $\frac{7}{9}, \frac{35}{45}$

13. $\frac{11}{20}, \frac{3}{5}$ 14. $\frac{45}{60}, \frac{3}{4}$ 15. $\frac{16}{9}, \frac{96}{54}$ 16. $\frac{3}{10}, \frac{15}{25}$

Example 3 (page 258)

Determine whether the ratios in each pair can form a proportion by using cross products.

17. $\frac{6}{10}, \frac{9}{15}$ 18. $\frac{4}{5}, \frac{10}{13}$ 19. $\frac{7}{8}, \frac{15}{24}$ 20. $\frac{6}{14}, \frac{3}{7}$

21. $\frac{7}{22}, \frac{28}{77}$ 22. $\frac{12}{15}, \frac{20}{25}$ 23. $\frac{6}{10}, \frac{24}{42}$ 24. $\frac{5}{9}, \frac{15}{27}$

Ⓑ Apply Your Skills

25. Decorating A certain shade of green paint requires 4 parts blue to 5 parts yellow. If you mix 16 quarts of blue paint with 25 quarts of yellow paint,

26. Physical Science An astronaut who weighs 174 lb on Earth weighs 29 lb on the moon. If you weigh 102 lb on Earth, would you weigh 17 lb on the moon? Explain.

Determine whether the ratios in each pair are proportional.

27. $\frac{56}{2}, \frac{110}{3}$ 28. $\frac{18}{12}, \frac{4.8}{3.6}$ 29. $\frac{20}{1.5}, \frac{60}{4.5}$ 30. $\frac{3.5}{35}, \frac{2.04}{204}$

Geometry Show that the ratio of *b* to *h* is the same in each pair of figures.

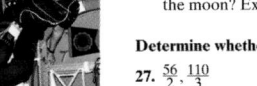

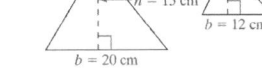

Real-World Connection

Astronauts learn to work even when they are weightless.

31. ($h = 9$ cm, $h = 15$ cm, $b = 12$ cm, $b = 20$ cm)

32. ($h = 4.5$ in., $h = 9$ in., $b = 9.75$ in., $b = 19.5$ in.)

Ⓒ Challenge

33. Do $\frac{\text{length of side } s \text{ of square } ABCD}{\text{perimeter of square } ABCD}$ and $\frac{\text{length of side } x \text{ of square } EFGH}{\text{perimeter of square } EFGH}$ *always*, *sometimes*, or *never* form a proportion? Explain.

34. **Writing in Math** Explain why $\frac{a}{b}$ and $\frac{a+b}{b}$ can *never* form a proportion.

35. **Stretch Your Thinking** If it takes you one minute to cut one board, how long will it take you to cut a 10-ft board into 10 equal pieces?

"How can I prepare hig

Test Prep Every Day Builds Readiness

Standardized Test Prep

in *every lesson* makes test prep a powerful part of every-day instruction. Includes all major problem types:

- **Multiple Choice**
- **Gridded Response**
- **Short and Extended Response (rubric-based)**
- **Reading Comprehension**

Test Prep

Multiple Choice

45. Which rate gives the best price for potatoes?

A. $.69/lb   B. $\frac{\$2.13}{3 \text{ lb}}$ C. $\frac{\$3.35}{5 \text{ lb}}$ D. $\frac{\$6.80}{10 \text{ lb}}$

46. Which rate gives the best price for oranges?

F. $.95/lb   G. $\frac{\$3.15}{3 \text{ lb}}$ H. $\frac{\$4.95}{5 \text{ lb}}$ I. $\frac{\$9.80}{10 \text{ lb}}$

47. A carpenter renovating a house is sanding the dining room floor. She sands 300 ft^2 of wood floor in 1 h 40 min. What is the unit rate in square feet per minute?

A. 0.3   B. 0.9   C. 3   D. 9

48. A farmer sells artichokes for $1.54 each. How much will it cost to buy one artichoke each for seven people?

F. $.22   G. $1.54   H. $7.28   I. $10.78

Short Response

49. An airplane travels 1,824 miles in 4 hours 45 minutes. Find the airplane's speed in miles per minute. Show your work.

50. You can buy a plain white T-shirt for $6.25. After printing your school mascot on it, you can sell the T-shirt for $9.50. If you sell 12 T-shirts at a basketball game, how much profit do you make?

Writing in Math

 **Writing in Math**

Writing to Compare

For Use With Exercise 37, page 263

Sometimes you are asked to compare two or more quantities, methods, or concepts. When you are writing to compare two quantities, it is important to make sure that quantities are similar.

On page 263, you will find the following exercise:

37. Writing in Math You estimate that it will take you 75 min to bike 15 mi to a state park. After 30 min, you have traveled 5 mi. Compare your actual rate to your estimate. At your current rate, will you arrive sooner or later than your estimate? Explain.

Here is one student's response.

> My actual speed was $\frac{5 \text{ mi}}{30 \text{ min}}$, while my estimated speed was $\frac{15 \text{ mi}}{75 \text{ min}}$.
>
> Since the rates have different denominators, I cannot compare the numerators directly. I can set up a proportion to get a common denominator.
>
> $$\frac{5 \text{ mi}}{30 \text{ min}} = \frac{x \text{ mi}}{75 \text{ min}}$$
> $$30x = 5 \cdot 75$$

Writing Math Strand

No other program provides this unique combination of practice and instruction.

- **Daily Writing Practice** — Every lesson contains Writing in Math exercises.
- **Writing Instruction** — Special Writing in Math lessons provide direct instruction in how to more effectively communicate using words and mathematics.

my students for high-stakes tests?"

Test-Taking Strategies Build Confidence

Test-Taking Strategies / Eliminating Answers

After you read a multiple-choice problem, you often can eliminate some of the answer choices. Be sure to cross out the answers you eliminate in the test booklet, and *not* on the answer sheet.

1 EXAMPLE

Mary jogged $4\frac{1}{2}$ miles. Dan jogged $\frac{2}{3}$ as far as Mary. How far did Dan jog?

A. $\frac{2}{3}$ miles   **B.** 3 miles   **C.** 6 miles   **D.** $6\frac{3}{4}$ miles

- The phrase "$\frac{2}{3}$ as far as Mary" means Dan jogged a shorter distance than Mary. Eliminate choices C and D, since they are greater than Mary's distance.
- Dan actually jogged $\frac{2}{3} \times 4\frac{1}{2}$ miles. Using benchmarks, a low estimate is $\frac{1}{2} \times 4$, or 2 miles. Eliminate choice A, which is too small.
- By elimination, the correct answer is B.

2 EXAMPLE

A truck carries machines that each weigh $\frac{4}{5}$ ton. If the total load is $5\frac{3}{5}$ tons, how many machines are on the truck?

F. 2 machines   **G.** 4 machines   **H.** 7 machines   **I.** 11 machines

- To solve this problem, divide the total weight of the load by the weight of one machine: $5\frac{3}{5} \div \frac{4}{5}$.
- Estimate the quotient: $5 \div 1 = 5$ machines. Eliminate choices F and I, since they are far from the estimate.

Test-Taking Strategies

give students the tools they need to approach tests with confidence. Each mini-lesson is supported with transparencies and practice masters.

Plus...

Prentice Hall Assessment System

enables you to easily prescribe a unique plan for each of your classes through a three-step process:

1. Diagnose & Prescribe
2. Review & Reteach
3. Practice & Assess

The teaching support

Presentation Assistant Plus!

All the materials you need to teach a lesson from beginning to end—in two easy-to-use formats: transparencies and PowerPoint®.

1. **Introduce**

   Check Skills You'll Need questions assess student understanding of prerequisite skills.

2. **Teach**

   Additional Examples have been reproduced from the Teacher's Edition.

3. **Check Homework**

   All answers are provided for all the home-work exercises in the Student Edition.

4. **Assess**

   Lesson Quizzes are reproduced from the Teacher's Edition and include answers.

Here's the "Plus!"

Presentation Pro CD-ROM

contains all the transparencies on **PowerPoint** to allow you to tailor your presentations for maximum effectiveness.

The interactive text online and on CD-ROM takes learning to a new level.

Try iText today at **PHSchool.com/Math**

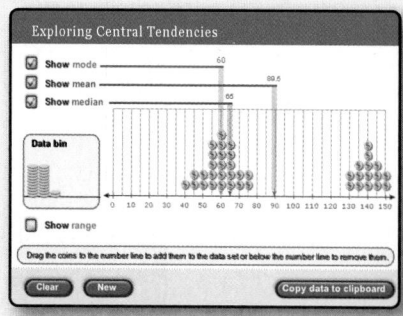

iText includes:

- **Activities and videos**

  at point-of-use bring math to life.

- **Reading support with audio**

  helps you reach students struggling with math vocabulary.

- **Instant-feedback assessments**

  let students know right away whether they're on track.

t you deserve

Complete Program Resources

Student Edition
iText—Interactive text
    online and on CD-ROM
Teacher's Edition
Teaching Resources
- Grab & Go
  Chapter Support Files
  – Practice
  – Reteaching
  – Enrichment
  – Chapter Projects
  – Checkpoint Quizzes
  – Chapter Tests
  – Alternative Assessment
  – Cumulative Review
- Cumulative Assessment
- Solution Key

Reaching All Students

Practice Workbook
Reading and Math Literacy Masters
Guided Problem-Solving Masters
Hands-on Activities
Technology Activities
Prentice Hall MathNotes Folders
Skills Intervention Kit

Teacher Time Savers

Presentation Assistant Plus!
- Additional Examples on Transparencies
- Daily Skills Check and Lesson Quiz Transparencies
- Problem of the Day Transparencies
- Student Edition Answers on Transparencies
- Classroom Aid Transparencies
- Prentice Hall Presentation Pro CD-ROM

Assessment and Test Prep

Prentice Hall Assessment System
- Computer Test
  Generator CD-ROM
- Algebra Readiness Tests
- Assessment Resources
  – Checkpoint Quizzes
  – Chapter Tests, Forms A & B
  – Alternative Assessment
  – Cumulative Assessment
- Content Diagnostic Tests
- Skills and Concepts Review
- Test Preparation Workbook with Teacher's Guide
- Test-Taking Strategies with Transparencies

Spanish Support

Student Edition, Spanish Version
Spanish Practice Workbook
Spanish Reading and Math Literacy Masters
Spanish Assessment Resources

Technology

iText—Interactive text online
    and on CD-ROM
Prentice Hall
    Presentation Pro CD-ROM
Resource Pro® with
    Planning Express® CD-ROM
Computer Test Generator CD-ROM
PH SuccessNet
    Teacher Center Web Site
PHSchool.com
    Textbook Site
Scientific Calculator
    TI–34 II
Graphing Calculator
    TI-73

Take a virtual tour
of the program at
PHSchool.com/Math

Authors

Series Author

Randall I. Charles, Ph.D., is Professor Emeritus in the Department of Mathematics and Computer Science at San Jose State University, San Jose, California. He began his career as a high school mathematics teacher, and he was a mathematics supervisor for five years. Dr. Charles has been a member of several NCTM committees and is the former Vice President of the National Council of Supervisors of Mathematics. Much of his writing and research has been in the area of problem solving. He has authored more than 75 mathematics textbooks for kindergarten through college. *Scott Foresman-Prentice Hall Mathematics Series Author Kindergarten through Algebra 2*

Program Authors

Judith C. Branch-Boyd, Ph.D., is the Area 24 Mathematics Coordinator for the Chicago Public School District. She works with high school teachers to provide quality instruction to students who are mandated to take Algebra, Geometry, and Advanced Algebra-Trigonometry. She also works with middle school and high school teachers to help students transition to Algebra 1. Dr. Branch-Boyd is active in several professional mathematics organizations at the state and national levels, including the National Council of Teachers of Mathematics. She believes, "All children can learn to love mathematics if it is taught with energy!"

PEARSON
Prentice
Hall

ISBN 0-13-063136-1

3 4 5 6 7 8 9 10   07 06 05 04 03

Mark Illingworth has taught fifth-graders and enrichment programs for fifteen years. During this time, he received the Christa McAullife sabbatical to develop problem-solving materials and projects for middle-grades math students, and he was granted the Presidential Award for Excellence in Mathematics Teaching. In addition to serving as the district math task force coordinator for the last six years, he has written two of his own books and has contributed to both math and science textbooks at Prentice Hall. Mr. Illingworth has recently shifted from teaching fifth-graders to teaching math to high school students.

Darwin Mills is a mathematics lead teacher for the public schools in Newport News, Virginia, and a mathematics adjunct professor at Thomas Nelson Community College in Hampton, Virginia. He has received various teaching awards, including teacher of the year for the 1999–2000 school year and an Excellence in Teaching Award from the College of Wooster, Ohio, in 2002. He is a frequent presenter for staff development, especially in the area of graphing calculator usage in the classroom. He believes that all students can learn mathematics if given the proper instruction.

Andy Reeves, Ph.D., teaches at the University of South Florida in St. Petersburg. His career in education spans 30 years and includes seven years as a middle grades teacher. He subsequently served as Florida's K–12 mathematics supervisor and more recently he supervised the publication of the *Mathematics Teacher, Mathematics Teaching in the Middle School,* and *Teaching Children Mathematics* for NCTM. Prior to entering education, he worked as an engineer for Douglas Aircraft.

Contributing Author

Denisse R. Thompson, Ph.D., is Associate Professor of Mathematics Education at the University of South Florida. She has particular interests in the connections between literature and mathematics and in the teaching and learning of mathematics in the middle grades. Dr. Thompson contributed to the Reading Math lessons and features.

Reviewers

Course 1 Reviewers

Donna Anderson
Math Supervisor 7–12
West Hartford Public Schools
West Hartford, Connecticut

Nancy L. Borchers
West Clermont Local Schools
Cincinnati, Ohio

Kathleen Chandler
Walnut Creek Middle School
Erie, Pennsylvania

Jane E. Damaske
Lakeshore Public Schools
Stevensville, Michigan

Frank Greco
Parkway South Middle School
Manchester, Missouri

Rebecca L. Jones
Odyssey Middle School
Orlando, Florida

Marylee R. Liebowitz
H. C. Crittenden Middle School
Armonk, New York

Kathy Litz
K. O. Knudson Middle School
Las Vegas, Nevada

Don McGurrin
Wake County Public School
    System
Raleigh, North Carolina

Ron Mezzadri
K–12 Mathematics Supervisor
Fair Lawn School District
Fair Lawn, New Jersey

Sylvia O. Reeder-Tucker
Prince George's County Math
    Department
Upper Marlboro, Maryland

Julie A. White
Allison Traditional Magnet
    Middle School
Wichita, Kansas

Charles Yochim
Bronxville Middle School
Bronxville, New York

Course 2 Reviewers

Cami Craig
Prince William County Public
    Schools
Marsteller Middle School
Bristow, Virginia

Donald O. Cram
Lincoln Middle School
Rio Rancho, New Mexico

Pat A. Davidson
Jacksonville Junior High School
Jacksonville, Arkansas

Yvette Drew
DeKalb County School System
Open Campus High School
Atlanta, Georgia

Robert S. Fair
K–12 District Mathematics
    Coordinator
Cherry Creek School District
Greenwood Village, Colorado

Michael A. Landry
Glastonbury Public Schools
Glastonbury, Connecticut

Nancy Ochoa
Weeden Middle School
Florence, Alabama

Charlotte J. Phillips
Wichita USD 259
Wichita, Kansas

Mary Lynn Raith
Mathematics Curriculum
    Specialist
Pittsburgh Public Schools
Pittsburgh, Pennsylvania

Tammy Rush
Consultant, Middle School
    Mathematics
Hillsborough County Schools
Tampa, Florida

Judith R. Russ
Prince George's County
    Public Schools
Capitol Heights, Maryland

Tim Tate
Math/Science Supervisor
Lafayette Parish School
    System
Lafayette, Louisiana

Dondi J. Thompson
Alcott Middle School
Norman, Oklahoma

Candace Yamagata
Hyde Park Middle School
Las Vegas, Nevada

Course 3 Reviewers

Linda E. Addington
Andrew Lewis Middle School
Salem, Virginia

Jeanne Arnold
Mead Junior High School
Schaumburg, Illinois

Sheila S. Brookshire
A. C. Reynolds Middle School
Asheville, North Carolina

Jennifer Clark
Mayfield Middle School
Putnam City Public Schools
Oklahoma City, Oklahoma

Nicole Dial
Chase Middle School
Topeka, Kansas

Christine Ferrell
Lorin Andrews Middle School
Massillon, Ohio

Virginia G. Harrell
Education Consultant
Hillsborough County, Florida

Jonita P. Howard
Mathematics Curriculum Specialist
Lauderdale Lakes Middle School
Lauderdale Lakes, Florida

Patricia Lemons
Rio Rancho Middle School
Rio Rancho, New Mexico

Susan Noce
Robert Frost Junior High School
Schaumburg, Illinois

Carla A. Siler
South Bend Community School
  Corp.
South Bend, Indiana

Kathryn E. Smith-Lance
West Genesee Middle School
Camillus, New York

Kathleen D. Tuffy
South Middle School
Braintree, Massachusetts

Patricia R. Wilson
Central Middle School
Murfreesboro, Tennessee

Patricia Young
Northwood Middle School
Pulaski County Special School
  District
North Little Rock, Arkansas

Content Consultants

Courtney Lewis
Mathematics
Prentice Hall Senior National Consultant
Baltimore, Maryland

Deana Cerroni
Mathematics
Prentice Hall National Consultant
Las Vegas, Nevada

Kimberly Margel
Mathematics
Prentice Hall National Consultant
Scottsdale, Arizona

Sandra Mosteller
Mathematics
Prentice Hall National Consultant
Anderson, South Carolina

Rita Corbett
Mathematics
Prentice Hall Consultant
Elgin, Illinois

Cathy Davies
Mathematics
Prentice Hall Consultant
Laguna Niguel, California

Sally Marsh
Mathematics
Prentice Hall Consultant
Baltimore, Maryland

Addie Martin
Mathematics
Prentice Hall Consultant
Upper Marlboro, Maryland

Rose Primiani
Mathematics
Prentice Hall Consultant
Brick, New Jersey

Loretta Rector
Mathematics
Prentice Hall Consultant
Foresthill, California

Charlotte Samuels
Mathematics
Prentice Hall Consultant
Lafayette Hill, Pennsylvania

Margaret Thomas
Mathematics
Prentice Hall Consultant
Indianapolis, Indiana

Contents in Brief

Decimals

Patterns and Variables

Number Theory and Fractions

Contents   **ix**

Chapter 4

Adding and Subtracting Fractions

Multiplying and Dividing Fractions

Table of Contents

Ratios, Proportions, and Percents

Chapter 7

Data and Graphs

Student Support

 Instant Check System

Diagnosing Readiness, 320

Check Skills You'll Need, 322, 326, 331, 335, 341, 347, 352, 358

Check Understanding, 322, 323, 326, 327, 331, 335, 336, 342, 347, 348, 352, 353, 358, 359

Checkpoint Quiz, 333, 350

Comprehensive Test Prep

Daily Test Prep, 325, 330, 333, 339, 345, 350, 355, 362

Test-Taking Strategies, 363

Cumulative Test Prep, 367

 Reading Math

Reading Math, 322, 342

Reading Graphs, 334

Understanding Vocabulary, 364

Reading Comprehension, 325, 367

Writing in Math

Daily Writing Practice, 324, 328, 332, 338, 344, 349, 354, 361, 366

Writing to Persuade, 346

Real-World Problem Solving

Strategy: Make an Organized List, 332–334
Geography, 327
Nutrition, 335
Practice Game, 339
Music, 347
. . . and more!

Table of Contents

Tools of Geometry

Chapter 9

Geometry and Measurement

Student Support

 Instant Check System

Diagnosing Readiness, 430

Check Skills You'll Need, 431, 436, 440, 446, 452, 456, 462, 467, 472, 477

Check Understanding, 431, 432, 433, 436, 437, 440, 441, 442, 447, 448, 452, 453, 457, 463, 467, 468, 469, 472, 473

Checkpoint Quiz, 450, 476

 **Comprehensive Test Prep**

Daily Test Prep, 435, 439, 445, 450, 455, 459, 466, 471, 475–476, 479–480

Test-Taking Strategies, 481

Cumulative Test Prep, 485

Reading Math

Reading Math, 441, 452, 458

Using Concept Maps to Connect Ideas, 460

Understanding Vocabulary, 482

Reading Comprehension, 459, 485

Writing in Math

Daily Writing Practice, 434, 438, 444, 449, 454, 458, 465, 470, 475, 479, 484

 Real-World Problem Solving

Strategy: Work Backward, 477–480
Landscaping, 441
Conservation, 447
Archery, 453
Math at Work, 480
. . . and more!

Table of Contents

Contents   **XV**

Chapter 10

Integers

Chapter

11

Exploring Probability

Table of Contents

Equations and Inequalities

From the Authors

Dear Student,

We have designed this unique mathematics program with you in mind. We hope that Prentice Hall Mathematics will help you make sense of the mathematics you learn. We want to enable you to tap into the power of mathematics.

Examples in each lesson are broken into steps to help you understand how and why math works. Work the examples so that you understand the concepts and the methods presented. Then do your homework. Ask yourself how new concepts relate to old ones. Make connections! As you practice the concepts presented in this text, they will become part of your mathematical power.

The many real-world applications will let you see how you can use math in your daily life and give you the foundation for the math you will need in the future. The applications you will find in every lesson will help you see why it is important to learn mathematics. In addition, the Dorling Kindersley Real-World Snapshots will bring the world to your classroom.

This text will help you be successful on the tests you take in class and on high-stakes tests required by your state. The practice in each lesson will prepare you for the format as well as for the content of these tests.

Ask your teacher questions! Someone else in your class has the same question in mind and will be grateful that you decided to ask it.

We wish you the best as you use this text. The mathematics you learn this year will prepare you for your future as a student and your future in our technological society.

Sincerely,

Randy Charles.

Andy Reeves

Darwin E. Mills

Mark Illingworth

Judith C. Branch-Boyd

Connect Your Learning
Through Problem Solving, Activities, and the Web

Applications: Real-World Applications

***And Over 100 More Topics!
See Real World Applications in
the Index, Page 746.***

Applications: Careers

Applications: Interdisciplinary Connections

Problem-Solving Strategies

Course 1 Students learn to apply a single problem-solving strategy in each lesson.

Course 2 Students learn to use more than one strategy to solve a problem. They also compare strategies to determine which one is most appropriate in a given situation.

Course 3 Students continue to combine and compare strategies to solve problems. Throughout the text, a greater focus on the strategy *write an equation* helps prepare students for success in algebra.

The problem-solving lessons included in each chapter of *Prentice Hall Mathematics* progress in depth and sophistication within a course and from course to course.

> *Prentice Hall Mathematics contains ample opportunities for you to actively explore mathematics, either working as a whole class, in groups, or individually.*

Activities: Investigations

Activities: Real-World Snapshots

Activities: Chapter Projects

Activities: Technology

Take It to the Net

Throughout this book, you will find links to the Prentice Hall Web site. Use the Web Code provided with each link to gain direct access to online material.

Here's how to **Take It to the NET**:
• Go to **www.PHSchool.com**.
• Enter the Web Code.
• Click. Go!

For a complete list of online features, use Web Code aak-0099.

Lesson Quiz Web Codes

There is an online quiz for each lesson. Access these quizzes with Web Codes aaa-0101 through aaa-1206 for Lesson 1-1 through Lesson 12-6. *See page 7.*

102 Lesson Quizzes
Web Code format: aaa-0204
02 = Chapter 2   04 = Lesson 4

Chapter Resource Web Codes

Chapter	Vocabulary Quizzes See page 54.	Chapter Tests See page 56.	Dorling Kindersley Real-World Snapshots See pages 58-59.	Chapter Projects
1	aaj-0151	aaa-0152	aae-0153	aad-0161
2	aaj-0251	aaa-0252	aae-0253	aad-0261
3	aaj-0351	aaa-0352	aae-0353	aad-0361
4	aaj-0451	aaa-0452	aae-0453	aad-0461
5	aaj-0551	aaa-0552	aae-0553	aad-0561
6	aaj-0651	aaa-0652	aae-0653	aad-0661
7	aaj-0751	aaa-0752	aae-0753	aad-0761
8	aaj-0851	aaa-0852	aae-0853	aad-0861
9	aaj-0951	aaa-0952	aae-0953	aad-0961
10	aaj-1051	aaa-1052	aae-1053	aad-1061
11	aaj-1151	aaa-1152	aae-1153	aad-1161
12	aaj-1251	aaa-1252	aae-1253	aad-1261
End-of-Course		aaa-1254		

Additional Resource Web Codes

Data Updates   Use Web Code aag-2041 to get up-to-date government data for use in examples and exercises. *See page 28.*

Math at Work   For information about each Math at Work feature, use Web Code aab-2031. *See page 12.*

iTEXT Complete student textbook available online. Includes interactivities and videos.

Scope and Sequence for Prentice Hall Mathematics

This scope and sequence of content is organized around the major strands and specific objectives in the **National Assessment of Educational Progress (NAEP) 2005 Assessment Specifications**. These NAEP skills are an important benchmark for No Child Left Behind. Also included here are the process skills referenced in the **NCTM Principles and Standards for School Mathematics 2000**.

Since **Prentice Hall Mathematics** is a complete Grades 6–12 program, a detailed scope and sequence chart for the entire program—middle school through high school—is available at PHSchool.com/math. Also available is a Grades Pre-K–8 scope and sequence chart that shows the careful articulation between **Prentice Hall Mathematics Courses 1–3** and **Scott Foresman-Addison Wesley Mathematics Grades Pre-K–5**, which together provide a complete mathematics curriculum for Grades Pre-K–8.

Course	1	2	3
Number Properties and Operations			
Number Sense			
• **Use place value to model numbers**			
— whole numbers	Maintain & Apply	Maintain & Apply	Maintain & Apply
— decimals	Develop	Develop	Maintain & Apply
• **Model rational numbers or numerical relationships**			
— number line models	Develop	Develop	Develop
— other models	Develop	Develop	Develop
• **Write or rename rational numbers**			
— read and write decimals	Develop	Develop	Maintain & Apply
— read and write integers	Develop	Maintain & Apply	Maintain & Apply
— read and write rational numbers	Develop	Maintain & Apply	Maintain & Apply
— irrational numbers		Maintain & Apply	Introduce
— real numbers			Introduce
• **Express multiple representations of rational numbers and translate between them**			
— equivalent decimals	Develop	Maintain & Apply	Maintain & Apply
— equivalent fractions	Develop	Maintain & Apply	Maintain & Apply
— simplest form	Develop	Maintain & Apply	Maintain & Apply
— mixed numbers and improper fractions	Develop	Maintain & Apply	Maintain & Apply
— convert between fractions and decimals	Develop	Develop	Maintain & Apply
• **Use scientific notation**			
— scientific notation	Introduce	Develop	Develop
• **Find or model absolute value**			
— absolute value	Introduce	Develop	Maintain & Apply
• **Compare and order rational numbers**			
— whole numbers	Maintain & Apply	Maintain & Apply	Maintain & Apply
— decimals	Develop	Maintain & Apply	Maintain & Apply

Course	1	2	3
— fractions	Develop	Develop	Maintain & Apply
— integers	Introduce	Maintain & Apply	Maintain & Apply
— rational numbers		Introduce	Develop
— irrationals numbers			Maintain & Apply
Estimation			
• **Establish benchmarks**			
— fractions	Develop	Develop	Maintain & Apply
• **Make appropriate estimates**			
— rounding	Develop	Develop	Maintain & Apply
— operations	Develop	Develop	Maintain & Apply
— clustering	Develop	Develop	Maintain & Apply
— compatible numbers	Introduce	Develop	Maintain & Apply
— front-end	Introduce	Develop	Maintain & Apply
• **Determine reasonableness of results**			
— determine reasonableness of answers	Develop	Develop	Develop
• **Estimate square and cube roots**			
— squares and square roots	Introduce	Develop	Develop
Number Operations			
• **Perform computation with rational numbers**			
— add, subtract, multiply, and divide whole numbers	Maintain & Apply	Maintain & Apply	Maintain & Apply
— add and subtract decimals	Develop	Develop	Maintain & Apply
— multiply and divide decimals	Develop	Develop	Maintain & Apply
— add and subtract fractions, like denominators	Develop	Maintain & Apply	Maintain & Apply
— add and subtract fractions, unlike denominators	Develop	Maintain & Apply	Maintain & Apply
— add and subtract mixed numbers	Develop	Develop	Maintain & Apply
— multiply and divide fractions	Develop	Develop	Maintain & Apply
— multiply and divide mixed numbers	Develop	Develop	Maintain & Apply
— add and subtract integers	Develop	Develop	Maintain & Apply

INTRODUCE   **DEVELOP**   **MAINTAIN & APPLY**

Course

Skill	1	2	3
— multiply and divide integers	→	→	→
— use mental math	→	→	→
— choose a computation method	→	→	→
• Describe the effect of operations			
— check for reasonableness	→	→	→
• Interpret rational number operations			
— add and subtract	→	→	→
— multiply and divide	→	→	→
• Solve application problems			
— solve problems using rational numbers	→	→	→

Ratios and Proportional Reasoning

Skill	1	2	3
• Use ratios to describe problem situations			
— read and write	→	→	→
— equal ratios	→	→	→
• Use fractions to represent ratios and proportions			
— equivalent forms for ratios	→	→	→
• Use proportional reasoning			
— solve proportions	→	→	→
— estimate solutions to proportions	→	→	→
— reasoning with proportions	→	→	→
— unit rate	→	→	→
— unit price	→	→	→
— distance, rate, time problems	→	→	→
• Solve problems involving percent			
— use percent models	→	→	→
— write as ratio and decimal	→	→	→
— greater than 100%	→	→	→
— less than 1%	→	→	→
— estimate	→	→	→
— find using a proportion	→	→	→
— find using an equation	→	→	→
— find percent of a number	→	→	→
— find percent one number is of another		→	→
— find number when percent is known		→	→
— percent change		→	→

Properties of Number and Operations

Skill	1	2	3
• Describe odd and even integers			
— integers	→	→	→

Course

Skill	1	2	3
• Use factors, multiples, or prime factorization			
— factors	→	→	→
— prime factorization	→	→	→
— greatest common factor	→	→	→
— multiples	→	→	→
— least common multiple	→	→	→
• Use prime and composite numbers			
— prime and composite numbers	→	→	→
• Use divisibility or remainders			
— divisibility rules	→	→	→
• Apply basic properties of operations			
— order of operations	→	→	→
— positive exponents	→	→	→
— negative exponents		→	
• Explain a mathematical concept or relationship			
— verbalize and define concepts	→	→	→

Measurement

Measuring Physical Attributes

Skill	1	2	3
• Compare objects by attribute (length, area, volume, angle, weight, mass)			
— use customary units of length, area, volume, weight, capacity	→	→	→
— use metric units of length, area, volume, weight, capacity	→	→	→
• Estimate size by attribute			
— estimate length	→	→	→
— estimate area of irregular figures	→	→	→
— estimate volume	→	→	→
— estimate time	→	→	→
• Use appropriate measurement instruments			
— compasses	→	→	→
— graph paper	→	→	→
— protractors	→	→	→
— rulers (metric and customary)	→	→	→
• Solve measurement problems			
— area of squares and rectangles	→	→	→
— area of parallelograms	→	→	→
— area of triangles	→	→	→
— area of trapezoids	→	→	→
— area of circles	→	→	→

Course	1	2	3
— area of composite figures	Introduce	Develop	Maintain & Apply
— surface area of prism	Introduce	Develop	Maintain & Apply
— surface area of cylinders	Maintain & Apply	Develop	Maintain & Apply
— volume of prisms	Develop	Develop	Maintain & Apply
— volume of cylinders	Introduce	Develop	Maintain & Apply
— volume of cones and pyramids			Develop
— volume of spheres			Develop
— dimension analysis		Introduce	Develop

Systems of Measurement

● Select appropriate type of unit for a particular attribute

Course	1	2	3
— use length, area, or volume	Develop	Develop	Develop

● Use conversion to solve problems

Course	1	2	3
— convert within customary system	Develop	Develop	Maintain & Apply
— convert within metric system	Develop	Develop	Maintain & Apply
— convert units of time	Develop	Maintain & Apply	Maintain & Apply

● Estimate measurement from one system to another

Course	1	2	3
— use conversion factors		Introduce	Develop

● Determine appropriate size of measurement units

Course	1	2	3
— choose appropriate units	Develop	Develop	Maintain & Apply

● Determine accuracy of measurement

Course	1	2	3
— precision		Introduce	Develop
— significant digits			Maintain & Apply

● Solve problems using scale drawings

Course	1	2	3
— scale drawing	Introduce	Develop	Develop

Geometry

Dimension and Shape

● Describe/draw shortest length between points

Course	1	2	3
— line	Develop	Develop	Maintain & Apply
— line segment	Develop	Develop	Maintain & Apply
— points on a line	Develop	Develop	Maintain & Apply

● Identify geometric object by description of its properties

Course	1	2	3
— identify polygons	Develop	Develop	Maintain & Apply
— classify quadrilaterals	Develop	Develop	Maintain & Apply
— classify triangles	Develop	Develop	Maintain & Apply
— congruent angles	Develop	Develop	Develop

● Identify geometric objects in plane and space by visual representation

Course	1	2	3
— spatial visualization	Introduce	Develop	Develop

● Draw figures from written description

Course	1	2	3
— polygons	Develop	Develop	Develop
— circles, semicircles	Develop	Develop	Develop
— similar triangles	Introduce	Develop	Develop

● Represent 3-dimensional figures in 2-dimensional space

Course	1	2	3
— use nets	Develop	Develop	Develop

● Demonstrate understanding of 2- and 3-dimension shapes in the real world

Course	1	2	3
— different viewpoints	Develop	Develop	Maintain & Apply
— spatial visualization	Develop	Develop	Maintain & Apply

Transformation of Shapes and Preservation of Properties

● Identify lines of symmetry and classify types of symmetry

Course	1	2	3
— symmetry	Develop	Develop	Develop

● Recognize effect of transformations on 2-dimensional shapes

Course	1	2	3
— reflections across lines of symmetry	Introduce	Develop	Develop
— rotations	Introduce	Develop	Develop
— translations	Introduce	Develop	Develop
— enlargements			Introduce
— reductions			Introduce
— dilations			Introduce

● Predict results of combining, subdividing, and changing shapes

Course	1	2	3
— plane figures	Introduce	Develop	Develop

● Justify and apply relationships of congruence and similarity

Course	1	2	3
— congruence	Introduce	Develop	Develop
— congruent polygons		Develop	Develop
— similarity	Introduce	Develop	Develop
— similar polygons	Introduce	Develop	Develop

● Use relationships of proportionality and conservation of angle

Course	1	2	3
— congruent angles	Introduce	Develop	Maintain & Apply
— proportions in similar figures	Introduce	Develop	Develop

Relationships Between Geometric Figures

● Use properties and relationships to solve problems

Course	1	2	3
— draw a diagram	Develop	Develop	Develop
— use a proportion	Develop	Develop	Develop
— congruent angles	Introduce	Develop	Develop

Legend: ▰ INTRODUCE ▱ DEVELOP ◼ MAINTAIN & APPLY

Topic	1	2	3
— similar triangles	➤	➤	➤
— trigonometric ratios (sine, cosine, tangent)			➤

● **Use geometric models to solve problems**

Topic	1	2	3
— make a model	➤	➤	➤

● **Use Pythagorean theorem to solve problems**

Topic	1	2	3
— Pythagorean theorem	➤	➤	➤
— trigonometric ratios			➤

● **Describe properties and relationships among polygonal plane figures**

Topic	1	2	3
— angles	➤	➤	➤
— congruence	➤	➤	➤
— similarity	➤	➤	➤
— ratio of sides and areas		➤	➤
— ratio of sides and volume		➤	➤

● **Describe properties and relationships of parallel or intersecting lines**

Topic	1	2	3
— parallel lines	➤	➤	➤
— perpendicular lines	➤	➤	➤

Position and Direction

● **Describe relative positions of points and lines**

Topic	1	2	3
— coordinate geometry	➤	➤	➤

● **Describe intersection of two or more figures in a plane**

Topic	1	2	3
— coordinate geometry			➤

● **Represent figures in the coordinate plane**

Topic	1	2	3
— coordinate geometry	➤	➤	➤

Mathematical Reasoning

● **Make and test a conjecture about regular polygons**

Topic	1	2	3
— make and test conjectures	➤	➤	➤

Data Analysis and Probability

Data Representation

● **Read and interpret data**

Topic	1	2	3
— analyze and interpret data	➤	➤	➤

● **Represent data set graphically and then solve a problem**

Topic	1	2	3
— decide how to present data	➤	➤	➤
— tables and charts	➤	➤	➤
— frequency tables	➤	➤	➤
— line plots	➤	➤	➤

Topic	1	2	3
— histograms	➤	➤	➤
— bar graphs	➤	➤	➤
— double bar graphs	➤	➤	➤
— stacked bar graphs			➤
— sliding bar graphs			➤
— line graphs	➤	➤	➤
— multiple line graphs	➤	➤	➤
— circle graphs	➤	➤	➤
— scatter plots	➤	➤	➤
— stem-and-leaf plots	➤	➤	➤
— back-to-back stem-and-leaf plots			➤
— box-and-whisker plots	➤	➤	➤
— draw and compare different representations	➤	➤	➤

● **Use estimation and computation to solve problems from data sets**

Topic	1	2	3
— interpolation and extrapolation	➤	➤	➤
— determine trends from data	➤	➤	➤

● **Determine appropriateness and effectiveness of data representations**

Topic	1	2	3
— choose an appropriate graph or statistic	➤	➤	➤

● **Compare and contrast different representations of same data**

Topic	1	2	3
— draw and compare different representations	➤	➤	➤

Characteristics of Data Sets

● **Calculate, use, interpret mean, median, mode, range**

Topic	1	2	3
— mean, median, mode	➤	➤	➤
— range	➤	➤	➤
— quartiles	➤	➤	➤
— analyze data	➤	➤	➤

● **Identify outliers and determine their effect**

Topic	1	2	3
— outlier	➤	➤	➤

● **Compare two or more data sets using appropriate statistical measures**

Topic	1	2	3
— identify misleading graphs and statistics	➤	➤	➤
— choose an appropriate graph or statistic	➤	➤	➤

● **Select "best fit" line and use it to make predictions**

Topic	1	2	3
— trend lines		➤	➤
— make predictions from graphs		➤	➤

Experiments and Samples

● **Identify sources of bias in sampling**

Topic	1	2	3
— analyze bias in surveys		➤	➤

Course 1 2 3

Probability

	1	2	3
● Distinguish between random and non-random samples			
— *analyze sampling techniques*		Develop	Develop
● Evaluate design of an experiment			
— *plan and analyze surveys*		Develop	Develop

Probability

	1	2	3
● Analyze probability of independent events			
— *theoretical probability*	Develop	Develop	Maintain & Apply
— *experimental probability*	Develop	Develop	Maintain & Apply
— *probability of complements*	Introduce	Develop	Develop
— *odds*	Introduce	Develop	Develop
● Determine theoretical probability of simple and compound events			
— *counting principle*	Introduce	Develop	Develop
● Estimate probability of simple and compound events			
— *estimate probability*	Introduce	Develop	Develop
— *simulations*	Introduce	Develop	Develop
● Distinguish between experimental and theoretical probability			
— *analyze probability*	Introduce	Develop	Maintain & Apply
● Determine sample space for a given situation			
— *tree diagrams/sample space*	Develop	Develop	Develop
● Use sample space to determine probability of possible outcomes			
— *simple probability*	Introduce	Develop	Develop
— *compound probability*	Introduce	Develop	Develop
● Represent probability using fractions, decimals, percents			
— *find and write probability*	Develop	Develop	Develop
— *permutations*	Introduce	Develop	Develop
— *combinations*		Introduce	Develop
● Determine probability of dependent and independent events			
— *independent events*	Introduce	Develop	Develop
— *dependent events*		Introduce	Develop
● Interpret probability within a given context			
— *conduct experiments and simulations*	Develop	Develop	Develop

Algebra

Patterns, Relations, and Functions

	1	2	3
● Use, describe, extend numerical and geometric patterns			
— *numerical patterns*	Develop	Develop	Develop
— *geometric patterns*	Introduce	Develop	Develop

Patterns, Relations, and Functions (continued)

	1	2	3
● Generalize pattern in a number sequence, table or graph			
— *look for and describe a pattern*	Develop	Develop	Develop
● Analyze or create patterns, sequences, functions			
— *write a rule*	Introduce	Develop	Develop
— *input-output tables*	Develop	Develop	Develop
— *sequences*	Introduce	Develop	Develop
— *Fibonacci sequence*	Introduce		
● Identify linear and nonlinear functions			
— *functions*	Introduce	Develop	Develop
— *linear*	Introduce	Develop	Develop
— *quadratic*		Introduce	Introduce
— *other nonlinear*	Introduce	Develop	
● Interpret meaning of slope or intercepts in linear functions			
— *using slope*		Introduce	Develop
— *graphing and using intercepts*			Introduce

Algebraic Representations

	1	2	3
● Translate between different linear expressions			
— *evaluate*	Develop	Develop	Develop
● Analyze or interpret linear relationships			
— *use linear relationships*	Introduce	Develop	Develop
● Graph or interpret points represented by ordered pairs			
— *ordered pairs*	Develop	Develop	Maintain & Apply
● Solve problems in the coordinate system			
— *graphing equations*	Introduce	Develop	Develop
— *graphing inequalities*		Introduce	Develop
● Make conclusions and generalizations about linear relationships			
— *make generalizations*	Introduce	Develop	Develop
● Represent functional relationships			
— *linear functions*	Introduce	Develop	Develop
— *quadratic functions*		Introduce	Introduce

Variables, Expressions, and Operations

	1	2	3
● Write algebraic expressions, equations, inequalities			
— *write from word phrases*	Develop	Develop	Maintain & Apply
— *write from word sentences*	Develop	Develop	Maintain & Apply
— *write inequalities*	Introduce	Develop	Develop
● Perform basic operations on linear algebraic expressions			
— *evaluate*	Develop	Develop	Develop
— *simplify*	Develop	Develop	Develop

■ INTRODUCE   ▨ DEVELOP   ■ MAINTAIN & APPLY

— commutative property
— associative property
— distributive property

Equations and Inequalities

● Solve linear equations or inequalities

— solve one-step equations
— solve two-step equations
— solve systems of linear equations
— solve one-step inequalities
— solve two-step inequalities

● Understand the concept of equivalence

— properties of equations
— properties of inequalities

● Solve problems using equations and inequalities with coefficients

— write from word sentences
— solve equations with integer solutions
— solve inequalities

● Relate linear expressions and graphs of lines using slope, intercept

— write and graph equations

● Use and evaluate common formulas

— formulas

Mathematical Processes

Problem Solving

● Problem-solving skills

— use a problem-solving plan
— too much or too little information
— check for reasonableness
— use a proportion
— use a calculator
— use a computer
— use estimation
— use formulas
— use graphs

● Problem-solving strategies

— choosing a strategy
— draw a diagram
— look for a pattern

— make a graph
— make an organized list
— make a table
— simulate a problem
— solve a simpler problem
— try, check, and revise
— use logical reasoning
— use multiple strategies
— work backward
— write an equation

Reasoning and Proof

— justify answers
— make and test conjectures
— make generalizations
— reason from graphs
— reason with proportions
— recognize patterns
— use logical reasoning
— evaluate mathematical arguments
— use or construct Venn diagrams

Communication

— interpret mathematical ideas through discussing, writing, reading
— make convincing arguments using mathematical ideas
— relate mathematical language to everyday language
— analyze and evaluate mathematical thinking of others

Connections

— use connections among mathematical ideas
— apply mathematics in contexts outside of mathematics
— use technology

Representation

— use representations to develop mathematical ideas
— use tables, graphs, words, and symbols interchangeably
— solve problems using pictures/diagrams
— algebra tiles
— decimal models
— fraction models
— number line models
— two-color chips

Scope and Sequence

Prentice Hall Mathematics programs are research-based and proven to work

The stakes for mathematics educators are high. You are expected to raise student achievement. Prentice Hall understands your dedicated efforts and gives you the confidence to meet this challenge. In developing Prentice Hall programs, the use of research studies is a central, guiding construct. Research on *Prentice Hall Mathematics* indicated key elements of a textbook program that ensure student success: constant review within instruction, support for reading and writing in mathematics, and an ongoing assessment strand. This research was conducted in three phases:

Phase ❶: Exploratory Needs Assessment

Phase ❷: Formative, Prototype Development and Field Testing

Phase ❸: Summative, Validation Research

❶ Exploratory Needs Assessment

Along with periodic surveys concerning curriculum issues and challenges, we conducted specific product development research, which included discussions with teachers and advisory panels, focus groups, and quantitative surveys. We explored the specific needs of teachers, students, and other educators regarding each book we developed in *Prentice Hall Mathematics*.

In conjunction with Prentice Hall authors, secondary research was done to explore educational research about learning. This research was incorporated into our instructional strategy and pedagogy to make a more effective mathematics program.

❷ Formative, Prototype Development and Field Testing

During this phase of research, we worked to develop prototype materials for each course in *Prentice Hall Mathematics*. Then we tested the materials, including field testing with students and teachers, and qualitative and quantitative evaluations of different kinds. We received solid feedback about our lesson structure in our early prototype testing. Results were channeled back into the program development for improvement. For example, teachers commented positively on motivational quality and richness of the mathematics in the Dorling Kindersley features.

❸ Summative, Validation Research

Finally, we conducted and continue to conduct longer-term research based on scientific, experimental designs under actual classroom conditions. This research identifies what works and what can be improved in revisions. We also continue to monitor the program in the market. We talk to our users about what works, and then we begin the cycle over again. Highlights of this research follow in the next section.

The new federal education law "No Child Left Behind" dictates that math programs be supported by research showing their efficacy. The research behind *Prentice Hall Mathematics* provides the evidence you deserve.

Prentice Hall Research Time Line

Market Needs Assessment
(Quantitative & Qualitative)
- Teacher Interviews
- Classroom Observations
- Mail Surveys
- Conference Participation

Formative Research
(Quantitative & Qualitative)
- Field Testing of Prototypes
- Classroom Observations
- Teacher Reviews
- Supervisor Reviews
- Educator Advisory Panels
- Prentice Hall Sales Force Input

Summative Research
(Experimental and Quasi-Experimental Study Designs & Qualitative Research)
- Pre-Publication Learner Verification Research
- Post-Publication Validation Studies
- Classroom Observations
- Evaluation of In-Market Results on Standardized Tests

Prentice Hall Math programs get results at middle grades and high school!

Standardized Test End-of-Year Results
(adjusted for differences in pre-test levels)

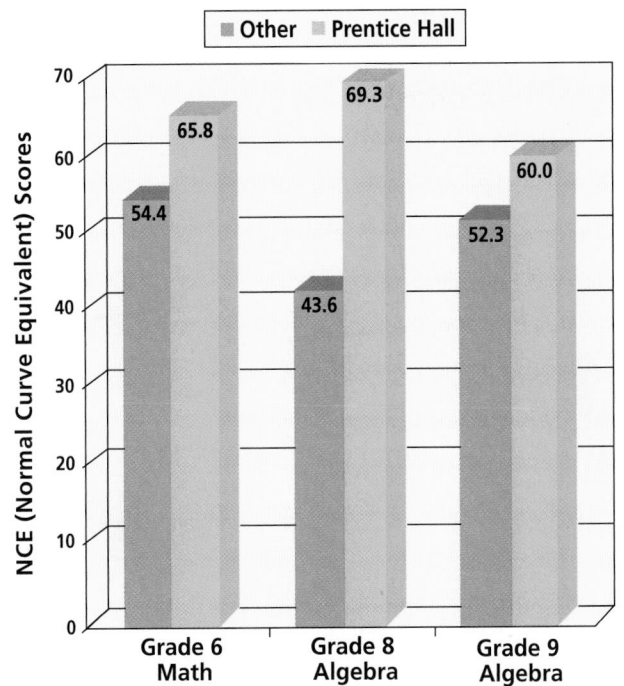

Prentice Hall mathematics programs are continually researched to determine "what works." Our programs are regularly revised to keep the best of what has worked in prior editions, and to improve them to meet changing market and curriculum needs. For example . . .

In a year-long study conducted in six states, students using Prentice Hall mathematics programs at grades 6 (math) and 8 and 9 (algebra) outscored students using other math programs on a nationally normed standardized test.

The study followed a scientific, experimental design with two classes per school. The classes selected were of similar ability levels. A total of eight schools (a mix of rural, suburban, and urban) participated, with 350 students involved in the study.

Classes were tested at the beginning of the school year using the TerraNova™ CTBS Basic Battery, and they were re-tested at the end of the school year. The final results, shown in the graph at the left, have been adjusted (via ANCOVA) to eliminate any contribution of higher or lower starting points on the pre-test to the observed post-test score.

All tests were scored by CTB/McGraw-Hill, the publisher of the TerraNova™ exam. Statistical analyses were conducted by an independent statistician from Pulse Analytics, Inc.

Additional studies of program effectiveness are under way, and many districts have demonstrated math improvement since adopting Prentice Hall mathematics programs.

Detailed results of this study can be obtained at **www.PHSchool.com/MathResearch**.

A unique progress-monitoring system that gives every student the opportunity to excel

What Research Indicates: Students' learning progresses to higher levels of understanding only if they have mastered a foundational understanding of preliminary concepts. If students are not functioning at a particular level of understanding, they are not ready to move on. Review plays a key role in promoting retention. Research clearly indicates that review should be systematically planned and incorporated into instruction. Before a new chapter or topic is begun, an inventory can help you ascertain whether any prerequisite knowledge is missing. Review should be continuous for students to attain mastery.

(Suydam, Marilyn N. *The Role of Review in Mathematical Instruction*. Columbus, Ohio: ERIC Clearinghouse for Science, Mathematics, and Environmental Education.)

Prentice Hall's Response: *Prentice Hall Mathematics* provides a unique **Instant Check System**™ that is built right into the text to assess mastery and diagnose weaknesses before, during, and after each lesson's instruction. This ongoing monitoring strand allows students to check their understanding of skills before moving on to the next topic. If students have misconceptions or need to reinforce their skills, the green type throughout the text clearly indicates where they can go for help. All the answers for the *Instant Check System*™ questions are available at the back of the student edition so students can check their work.

✔ Diagnosing Readiness

At the beginning of every chapter, students complete the *Diagnosing Readiness* exercises to see what prerequisite skills they may need to review before they begin the chapter. The Teacher's Edition prescribes specific *Examples* and *Exercises* that students can do for intervention.

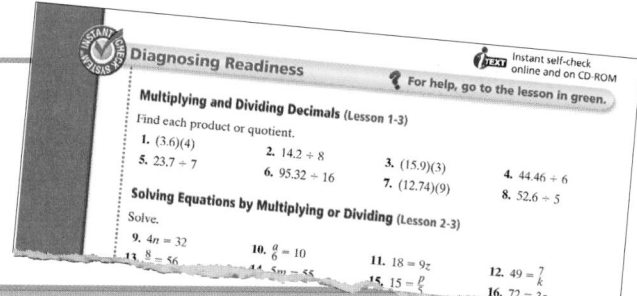

✔ Check Skills You'll Need

To begin each lesson, students complete the *Check Skills You'll Need* exercises to make sure they have the skills needed to successfully learn the concepts in the lesson. These questions with worked-out solutions are conveniently available as transparencies and on CD-ROM.

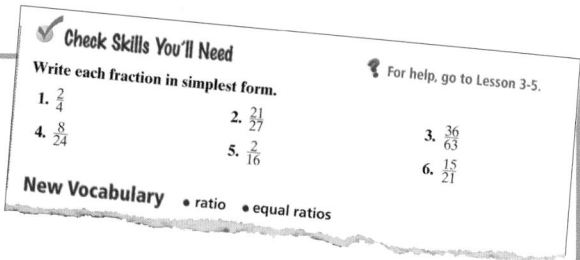

> "The Instant Check System™ enables teachers and students to know exactly what mathematics students are ready for, what they understand, and when more teaching is needed. Prior to starting a chapter, before each lesson, and during mid-lesson, student understanding is effectively evaluated, giving instant feedback. 'Know what you know and what you don't know' is a feature of this series."
>
> —Andy Reeves, *Prentice Hall Mathematics* program author

✔ Check Understanding

Every lesson includes numerous *Examples*, each followed by *Check Understanding* questions that students can do on their own. As skills and concepts are introduced, these questions focus students on the mathematics being presented and allow them to assess their understanding. More importantly, these questions will raise misconceptions that students have so that you may immediately address them.

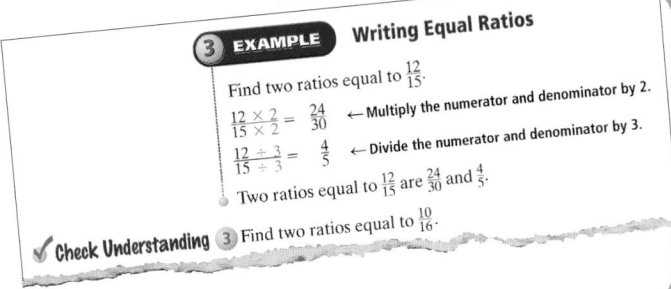

Leveled Exercises

The abundant *Exercises* in every lesson are organized by level to provide ample opportunity for students of all abilities to master the concepts. The *A: Practice by Example* exercises directly relate to the *Examples* in the lesson. Some *A* exercises are partially solved to help students get started. The *B: Apply Your Skills* and *C: Challenge* exercises provide richer skill and application problems to extend students' thinking.

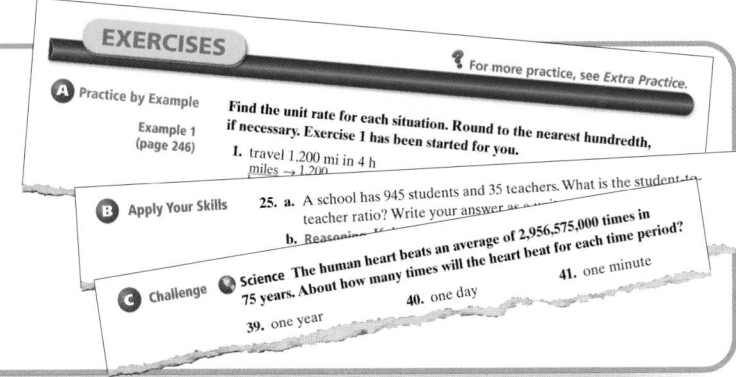

✔ Checkpoint Quizzes

Two *Checkpoint Quizzes* in every chapter provide students with opportunities for ongoing assessment. Each quiz provides a cumulative review of skills within specific lessons. Alternate versions are available in the Teaching Resources and online.

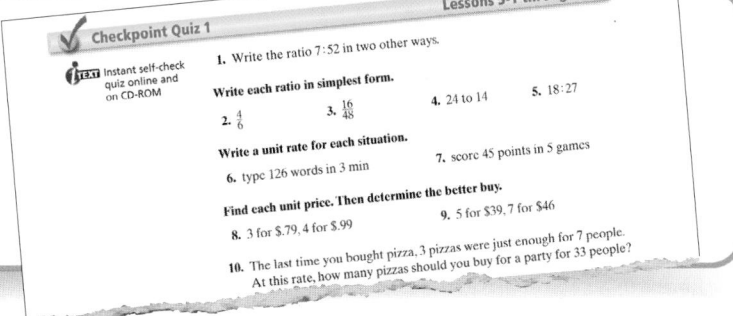

Prentice Hall Mathematics *iText* with Self-Grading Assessments

The *iText* provides the complete Student Edition online and on CD-ROM. The unique *Instant Check System™* is made interactive in the *iText* to allow students ongoing opportunities for checking their learning. Also, the click of a button lets students go back to a lesson or Example for additional help. Students get instant feedback so they know whether they're on track and where to go to get help.

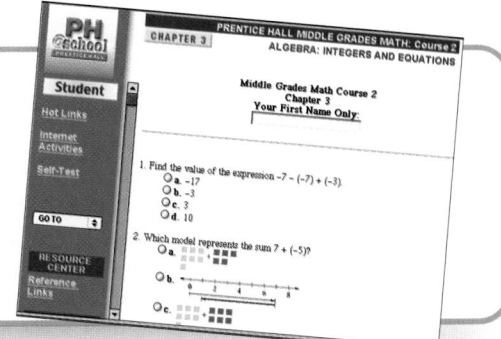

Reading and writing throughout build communication skills

What Research Indicates: Reading mathematics requires the same skills as reading in other content areas—decoding and comprehending what is read, analyzing and evaluating the content based on one's prior knowledge, and making inferences and generating conclusions. Mathematics text demands that readers also use additional, content-specific reading skills, for example, reading graphs. Students need to learn to focus on significant details, explanations, and the underlying logic in texts where there are more concepts per word, per sentence, and per paragraph than in any other kind of text.

(Barton, Mary Lee & Heidema, Clare. *Teaching Reading in Mathematics:* A Supplement to Teaching Reading in the Content Areas Teacher's Manual, 2nd Ed. Aurora, Colorado: Mid-continent Research for Education and Learning.)

The development of a student's power to use mathematics also involves learning the signs, symbols, and terms of mathematics. This is best accomplished in problem-solving situations in which students have an opportunity to read, write, and discuss ideas so that the use of the language of mathematics becomes natural. As students communicate their ideas, they learn to clarify, refine, and consolidate their thinking.

(*Curriculum and Evaluation Standards for School Mathematics.* Reston, Virginia: The National Council of Teachers of Mathematics, Inc.)

Prentice Hall's Response: *Prentice Hall Mathematics* provides a consistent emphasis on mathematics literacy with a special focus on reading and writing in mathematics. This program integrates even more ways for you to develop your students' ability to read and write mathematically so that they are successful in this course and on state tests.

Reading Math

The *Reading Math* hints within lessons help students to read and understand the language of mathematics. The *Reading Math* lessons help students read more effectively, so that they can write, speak, and think mathematically. Understanding Word Problems, Reading Prefixes, Using Concept Maps, and Reading a Lesson are just a few of the strategies included.

Writing in Math

Writing in Math lessons help students learn to explain, describe, justify, or compare in a mathematical situation. Every lesson incorporates *Writing in Math* exercises to give students daily writing practice. Instruction in writing answers to rubric-scored questions helps students communicate successfully on today's tests.

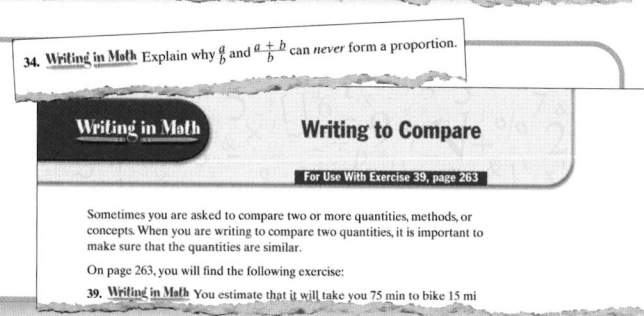

> "Success in subsequent mathematics courses and on standardized tests depends greatly on a student's ability to communicate in mathematics. The emphasis on reading and writing in Prentice Hall Mathematics through the Reading Tips and Reading Math features and through the Writing in Math opportunities enables all students to develop their communication skills."
>
> —Randy Charles, *Prentice Hall Mathematics* series author

Understanding Vocabulary

The text carefully develops the skill of reading math vocabulary. New vocabulary is conveniently listed at the beginning of each chapter and each lesson. Each new term is highlighted in yellow. The Chapter Review exercises help students to correctly use the chapter vocabulary. The iText reinforces students' vocabulary skills with an online vocabulary quiz for every chapter and an audio version of all glossary terms.

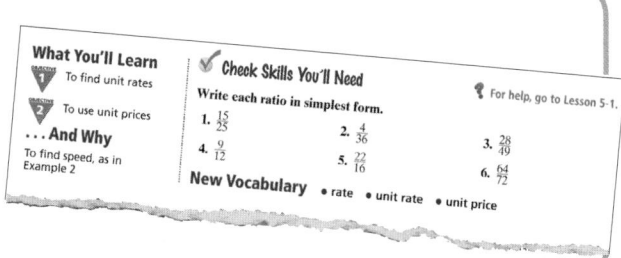

Reading and Math Literacy Masters

These unique blackline masters supplement the coverage of reading and math in the textbook. Students learn a variety of techniques to master mathematics vocabulary and symbols, read for problem solving, and increase comprehension.

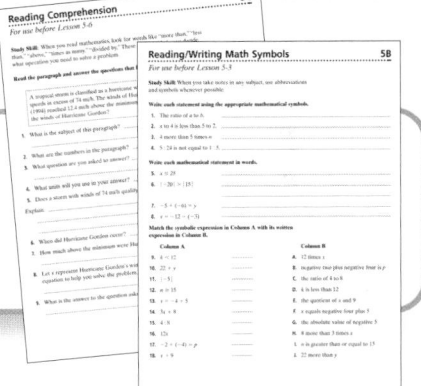

Guided Problem Solving Masters

Within the text, students learn to use a wealth of problem-solving strategies. More importantly, they learn to choose, compare, and combine strategies to solve problems. The *Guided Problem Solving Masters* provide a step-by-step guide to help students read, understand, solve, and check a problem. With one master for each lesson, students can develop their reading and problem-solving skills on a daily basis.

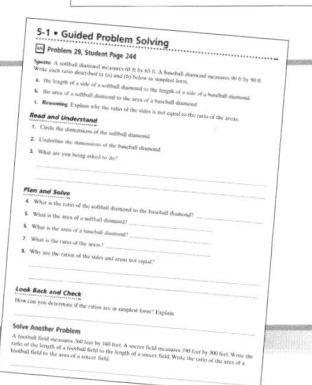

Reading for problem solving through Real-World Connections

Prentice Hall Mathematics incorporates abundant real-world connections within *Examples* and *Exercises* to provide a problem-solving context for applications of mathematics. Dorling Kindersley Real-World Snapshots bring math to life, with activities in which students gather data they need by reading graphic displays and captions.

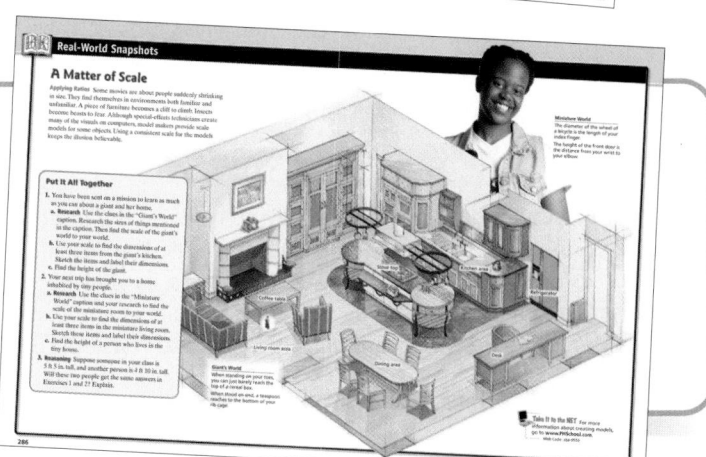

Ongoing assessment and test preparation guarantee testing success

What Research Indicates: We assess students most fairly when we assess often and with a variety of different answers. Research also shows that assessment needs to measure and describe a student's growth and achievement in all domains of mathematics and at three levels of thinking. Because of this, there should be questions at all levels of thinking, of varying degrees of difficulty, and in all content domains.

(Shafer, Mary C. & Foster, Sherian. "The Changing Faces of Assessment." *Principled Practice in Mathematics and Science Education,* Volume 1, No. 2.)

Prentice Hall's Response: *Prentice Hall Mathematics* provides an ongoing assessment strand that begins within the lesson instruction and continues throughout the program components. The program exposes students to questions of varying difficulty and at different levels of thinking in the daily *Check Understanding* questions and in the leveled *Exercises.*

A variety of question formats, including those found on today's standardized tests, is built into the Student Edition to assess student learning and prepare students for high-stakes tests. The ability to demonstrate knowledge in short-answer and open-ended formats increases opportunities for students to be successful on today's tests and in gaining admission to higher schooling and to the workplace.

✓ Check Understanding

Check Understanding questions after worked-out *Examples* allow students to assess their progress on a daily basis. These questions often emphasize the processes of explaining or reasoning—mirroring the types of questions that students will encounter on today's tests. You can use these questions to address any misconceptions or weaknesses before moving on to new topics.

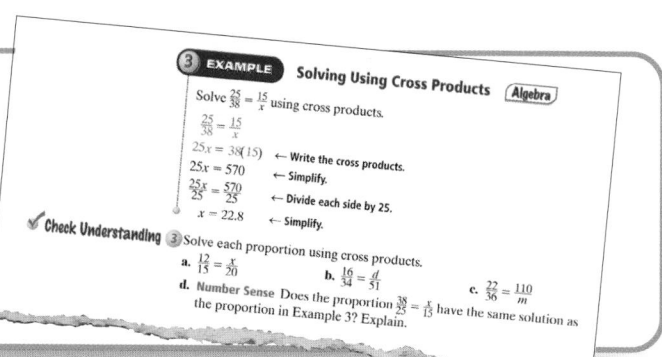

Quizzes and Tests—In Print and Online

You can assess student progress at key points with the *Lesson Quizzes, Checkpoint Quizzes,* and *Chapter Tests.* The Teaching Resources provides additional quizzes and tests, as well as alternative assessments. Online self-grading quizzes and tests are available on the Prentice Hall Web site at **www.PHSchool.com.**

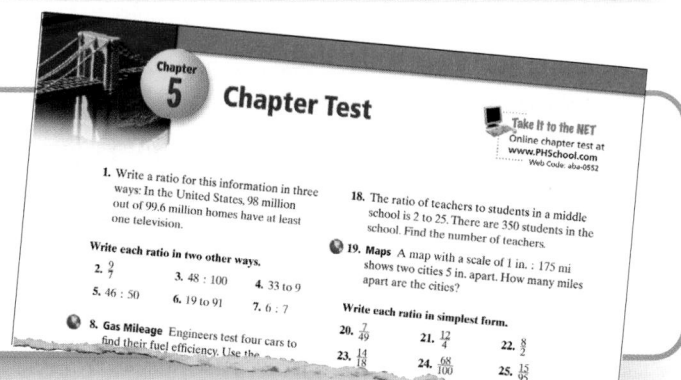

> "Assessment is a major strand in the series. Guided practice (Check Understanding) and quizzes help the student build the content needed to perform well on tests. The Test Prep exercises and instruction on strategies are essential in helping students familiarize themselves with the language and format of high-stakes assessments."
>
> —Darwin Mills, *Prentice Hall Mathematics* program author

Standardized Test Prep Exercises

Test Prep exercises in every lesson give students daily practice with the types of test item formats that they will encounter on state tests. You can also provide students with the *Test Prep* page at the end of each chapter.

The daily exercises and the test prep pages include these most common test item formats:

- Multiple Choice
- Gridded Response
- Reading Comprehension
- Short Response
- Extended Response

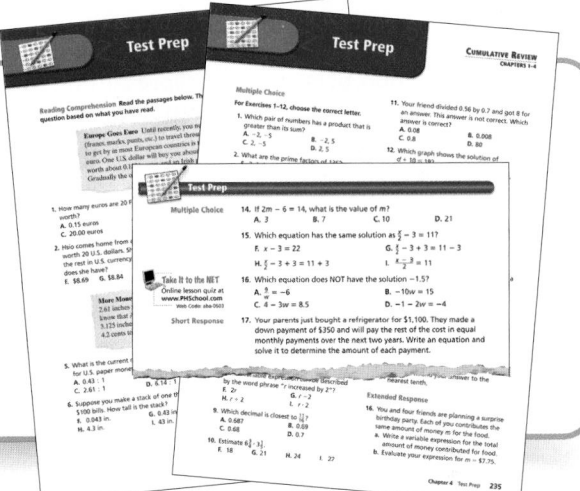

Test-Taking Strategies

Test-Taking Strategies in every chapter teach students strategies to be successful and give them practice in the skills they need to pass state tests and standardized national exams. Several lessons focus on helping students answer rubric-based questions.

The *Test-Taking Strategies With Transparencies* provide instruction on overheads and include additional practice sheets for the strategies taught in each chapter.

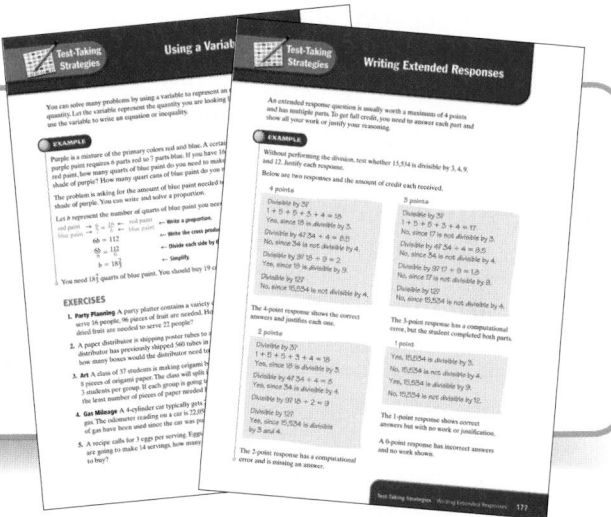

Prentice Hall Assessment System

An innovative *Assessment System* gives you everything you need to assess student progress on the content covered in the course, and to prepare students for high-stakes testing. The system contains the program Assessment Resources and the Computer Test Generator CD-ROM with unlimited questions and ready-to-use Instant Chapter Tests™.

You can diagnose and monitor student progress with *Diagnostic and Benchmark Tests*, prescribe intervention with the *Skills and Concept Review*, and provide practice for standardized assessments with the *Test Prep* booklet. A *Teacher's Guide* gives correlations and answers. Also included is the *Test-Taking Strategies With Transparencies* described above.

Mathematical Strands

Overview and Background

Number and Operations

NCTM Standard for Grades 6–8

- Understand numbers, ways of representing numbers, relationships among numbers, and number systems
- Understand meanings of operations and how they relate to one another
- Compute fluently and make reasonable estimates

Key Content in Prentice Hall
Course 1, Course 2, Course 3

- Represent, compare, compute, and solve problems with decimals (**C1:** Ch 1, 3; **C2:** Ch 1; **C3:** Ch 4)
- Represent, compare, compute, and solve problems with fractions (**C1:** Ch 3, 4, 5; **C2:** Ch 3, 4) and rational numbers (**C2:** Ch 3; **C3:** Ch 4)
- Represent, compare, compute, and solve problems with integers (**C1:** Ch 10; **C2:** Ch 1, 2, 9; **C3:** Ch 1, 2, 3, 12)
- Represent, compute, and solve problems with ratios, proportions, and percents (**C1:** Ch 6, **C2:** Ch 5, 6; **C3:** Ch 5, 6)
- Represent large numbers in various forms; use exponents (**C1:** Ch 1; **C2:** Ch 3; **C3:** Ch 7)
- Use mental math and estimation to solve problems and to judge the reasonableness of computations (throughout **C1, C2, C3**)
- Use properties of numbers to simplify computations and understand relationships (throughout **C1, C2, C3**)

Background and Progression

Students usually enter middle grades with computational facility with whole numbers, and varying degrees of mastery of fractions and decimals.

In **Course 1,** students reach mastery of all decimal and fraction operations. They work with percents and develop estimation skills. Concepts of scale and ratio are introduced. Integers are introduced with appropriate models.

In **Course 2,** students reach mastery of integer operations, rates, ratios, and proportions. They work with percent applications and exponents. Estimation skills are maintained.

In **Course 3,** students reach mastery of percent and proportion applications, as well as computation with exponents. Estimation skills are maintained.

Data Analysis and Probability

NCTM Standard for Grades 6–8

- Formulate questions that can be addressed with data and collect, organize, and display relevant data to answer them
- Select and use appropriate statistical methods to analyze data
- Develop and evaluate inferences and predictions that are based on data
- Understand and apply basic concepts of probability

Key Content in Prentice Hall
Course 1, Course 2, Course 3

- Select, make, and use appropriate graphical representations of data (**C1:** Ch 7; **C2:** Ch 9, 11; **C3:** Ch 10)
- Find, use, and interpret measures of center and spread (**C1:** 7; **C2:** Ch 1; **C3:** Ch 1)
- Compute probabilities for simple and compound events, and for complementary and mutually exclusive events (**C1:** Ch 11; **C2:** Ch 12; **C3:** Ch 11)
- Use proportionality and probability to make and test conjectures (**C1:** Ch 11; **C2:** Ch 12; **C3:** Ch 11)
- Use observations about samples to make conjectures about the parent populations (**C1:** Ch 11; **C2:** Ch 11; **C3:** Ch 11)
- Use scatterplots and approximate lines of fit to make conjectures (**C2:** Ch 11; **C3:** Ch 11)

Background and Progression

Students entering middle grades have experience with gathering, displaying, and analyzing data. They have used probabilities to express the likelihood of an event as a number from 0 through 1.

In **Course 1,** students master measures of center, simple line graphs, bar graphs, and probabilities. They make circle graphs, stem-and-leaf plots, and box-and-whisker plots.

In **Course 2,** students master double bar graphs, double line graphs, stem-and-leaf plots, and box-and-whisker plots. They analyze survey techniques for bias, group data into intervals, and make scatter plots to analyze data.

In **Course 3,** students master measures of spread, histograms, and circle graphs. They place and interpret lines of fit on scatter plots.

 *For more **Math Background** on every lesson, see pages C–D before each chapter and see each lesson's teaching notes.*

Algebra

- Understand patterns, relations, and functions
- Represent and analyze mathematical situations and structures using algebraic symbols
- Use mathematical models to represent and understand quantitative relationships
- Analyze change in various contexts

Key Content in Prentice Hall
Course 1, Course 2, Course 3

- Represent, analyze, and generalize a variety of patterns with tables, graphs, words, and symbolic rules (**C1:** Ch 2, 10; **C2:** Ch 2, 9, 10; **C3:** Ch 1,2, 3, 12)
- Use graphs, tables, and patterns to analyze the changes in quantities in linear relationships (**C1:** Ch 2, 10; **C2:** Ch 9, 10; **C3:** Ch 3, 5, 12)
- Explore properties of nonlinear relationships (**C2:** Ch 10; **C3:** Ch 12)
- Model and solve problems using diagrams, tables, and graphs (throughout **C1**, **C2**, **C3**)
- Use symbolic algebra to represent and solve problems (throughout **C1**, **C2**, **C3**)
- Recognize and generate equivalent forms for simple algebraic expressions (**C1:** Ch 2, 12; **C2:** Ch 2, 6; **C3:** Ch 2, 3, 7, 12)
- Solve linear equations (**C1:** Ch 2, 12; **C2:** Ch 2, 5, 6; **C3:** Ch 2, 3, 12)

Background and Progression

Students usually enter middle grades having represented patterns and relationships through words, tables, and graphs. They also have some experience with symbolic representation of an unknown quantity in equations or a varying quantity in relationships.

In **Course 1,** students use variables (1) to represent a specific unknown number (as in an equation), and (2) to generalize patterns in numeric relationships (as in input/output tables). Models that support algebraic notation are introduced for percents, proportions, integers, and properties of equality.

In **Course 2,** students continue to use models, tables, graphs, and symbolic notation to represent algebraic relationships. They solve two-step equations, work with like terms, and interpret slope in linear functions.

In **Course 3,** students solve multi-step equations and use equivalent forms for expressions containing parentheses, like terms, and exponents. They relate rate of change, slope, and *y*-intercept to graphs, tables, and symbolic forms. They use tables, graphs, and equations to explore nonlinear relationships.

Geometry

- Analyze characteristics and properties of two- and three-dimensional geometric shapes and develop mathematical arguments about geometric relationships
- Specify locations and describe spatial relationships using coordinate geometry and other representational systems
- Apply transformations and use symmetry to analyze mathematical situations
- Use visualization, spatial reasoning, and geometric modeling to solve problems

Key Content in Prentice Hall
Course 1, Course 2, Course 3

- Describe, classify, and use relationships among two- and three-dimensional objects (**C1:** Ch 8, 9; **C2:** Ch 7, 8; **C3:** Ch 8, 9)
- Draw inferences about angles, side lengths, perimeters, areas, and volumes of similar objects (**C3:** Ch 8, 9)
- Use two-dimensional representations of three-dimensional objects to visualize and solve problems (**C1:** Ch 9; **C2:** Ch 8; **C3:** Ch 9)
- Use number lines to represent various numbers and operations (**C1:** Ch 1, 3, 10; **C2:** Ch 1, 3; **C3:** Ch 1)
- Use coordinate geometry to represent and examine properties of geometric shapes (**C2:** Ch 10; **C3:** Ch 3)
- Describe size, position, and orientation of shapes under various transformations (**C1:** Ch 8, 10; **C2:** Ch 10; **C3:** Ch 3)
- Recognize and describe symmetries and congruence (**C1:** Ch 8; **C2:** Ch 5, 7, 10; **C3:** Ch 3, 5, 8)

Background and Progression

Students entering middle grades have usually mastered names and characteristics of angles, common polygons, circles, and simple solids.

In **Course 1,** students use grids, nets, and block diagrams to build concepts of area and volume. They explore symmetry and transformations and through slides, flips, and turns. They use number lines and other geometric models for fractions, decimals, and integers. The coordinate plane is introduced.

In **Course 2,** students continue to use two-dimensional representations of three-dimensional figures. Congruent and similar figures are studied and transformations are presented on a coordinate plane.

In **Course 3,** students continue to study two- and three-dimensional figures. They draw inferences about lengths, areas, and volumes of similar figures and study both reflective and rotational symmetry.

Mathematical Strands

 *For more **Math Background** on every lesson, see pages C–D before each chapter and see each lesson's teaching notes.*

Measurement

NCTM Standard for Grades 6–8

- Understand measurable attributes of objects and the units, systems, and processes of measurement
- Apply appropriate techniques, tools, and formulas to determine measurements

Key Content in Prentice Hall
Course 1, Course 2, Course 3

- Understand and use metric and customary systems of measurement (**C1:** Ch 5, 9; **C2:** Ch 1, 4)
- Convert among units within a system of measurement (**C1:** Ch 5, 9; **C2:** Ch 1, 4)
- Select and use units of the appropriate size and type to measure angles, perimeter, area, surface area, and volume (**C1:** Ch 8, 9; **C2:** Ch 7, 8; **C3:** Ch 8, 9)
- Estimate measures (**C1:** Ch 5, 8, 9; **C2:** Ch 4, 8; **C3:** Ch 8, 9)
- Develop strategies and use formulas to find the perimeter (circumference) and the area of triangles, various quadrilaterals, circles, and compound plane figures (**C1:** Ch 9; **C2:** Ch 8; **C3:** Ch 8)
- Develop strategies and use formulas to find the surface area and volume of various prisms, pyramids, cylinders, cones, and spheres (**C1:** Ch 9; **C2:** Ch 8; **C3:** Ch 9)
- Solve problems involving scale factors and rates (**C2:** Ch 5, 8; **C3:** Ch 5, 9)

Background and Progression

Students entering middle grades have usually worked with customary and metric units of length, weight, capacity, and temperature. They often know formulas for the perimeter and area of simple figures.

In **Course 1,** students choose appropriate units, convert units, and estimate measures within the customary system and the metric system. They develop and use formulas for measurement of triangles, rectangles, squares, parallelograms, and circles. They explore surface area and volume of three-dimensional figures.

In **Course 2,** students use dimensional analysis. They develop and use formulas to find areas of trapezoids and other irregular figures, and to find surface area and volume of prisms and cylinders. They explore the relationship between scale factors and corresponding lengths and areas in similar figures.

In **Course 3,** students continue to use dimensional analysis. They extend their understanding of formulas to include pyramids, cones, and spheres. They apply scale factors in similar figures to changes in surface area and volume.

Problem Solving

NCTM Standard for Grades 6–8

- Build new mathematical knowledge through problem solving
- Solve problems that arise in mathematics and in other contexts
- Apply and adapt a variety of appropriate strategies to solve problems
- Monitor and reflect on the process of mathematical problem solving

Key Processes in Prentice Hall
Course 1, Course 2, Course 3

- Solve problems taken from the student's current and future world (Real-World Problem-Solving Examples throughout **C1, C2, C3**)
- Use a problem-solving plan that supports flexibility, analysis, choice of strategies, evaluation, and checks for reasonableness (Problem Solving lessons in each chapter)
- Choose from and use a variety of appropriate methods to solve problems (More Than One Way features, Method 1/Method 2 examples, and Problem Solving lessons that compare strategies throughout **C1, C2, C3**)
- Construct an appropriate expression or equation to solve a problem (Examples using the "Words to Equation" or "Words to Expression" models throughout **C1, C2, C3**)
- Build understanding of new topics through problem solving (Investigations, Understanding Word Problems, and Real-World Snapshots throughout **C1, C2, C3**)
- Reflect on the process of problem solving (Look Back and Check, checks for reasonableness, and Writing-in-Math and Error Analysis exercises throughout **C1, C2, C3**)

Background and Progression

The Prentice Hall Mathematics program builds problem-solving skills through (1) a consistent framework for the problem-solving process, (2) a wide range of specific strategies, and (3) a variety of problems. The framework identifies a three-phase process: Read and Understand, Plan and Solve, Look Back and Check.

In **Course 1,** students learn to use the framework. Students use checks for both reasonableness and accuracy. They apply ten specific strategies to a variety of problems.

In **Course 2,** students learn to use more than one strategy to solve a problem. They compare strategies to determine which one is most appropriate in a given situation.

In **Course 3,** students continue to combine and compare strategies to solve problems. Throughout the text, a greater focus on the strategy Write an Equation helps prepare students for algebra.

 *For more **Math Background** on every lesson, see pages C–D before each chapter and see each lesson's teaching notes.*

Reasoning and Proof

NCTM Standard for Grades 6–8

- Recognize reasoning and proof as fundamental aspects of mathematics
- Make and investigate mathematical conjectures
- Develop and evaluate mathematical arguments and proofs
- Select and use various types of reasoning and methods of proof

Key Processes in Prentice Hall
Course 1, Course 2, Course 3

- Use inductive reasoning to make and investigate conjectures (Investigations throughout **C1, C2, C3**)
- Apply appropriate reasoning to analyze mathematical statements (Reasoning exercises throughout **C1, C2, C3**)
- Explain work and justify conclusions (Writing-in-Math, Error Analysis, Short Response and Extended Response exercises throughout **C1, C2, C3**)
- Construct logical arguments to support conclusions (Writing in Math lessons and exercises throughout **C1, C2, C3**)

Background and Progression

At the elementary level, mathematical reasoning is present in the development of number sense with operations, classification skills in geometry, and the use of variables in algebraic notation. Problem-solving strategies such as *work backward* also require reasoning skills.

In **Prentice Hall Mathematics,** reasoning is an integral part of students' daily work. Every lesson contains a mix of Reasoning, Number Sense, and Error Analysis exercises. These exercises are found both in the Check Understanding questions that follow each worked-out Example and in the B-level practice exercises.

Investigations provide students with opportunities to use inductive reasoning while exploring topics in number sense, operations, algebraic patterns, geometric properties, data analysis, and probability.

Throughout the texts, students are encouraged to state properties as specific instances and as generalizations using variables. Students also have the opportunity to justify steps in various procedures by citing the supporting properties.

Most lessons contain Short Response and Extended Response questions. These require students to justify conclusions or explain their work.

Finally, every lesson contains a Writing-in-Math exercise, along with specific instruction in each text to help students write to explain, to justify, to compare, or to persuade.

Communication

NCTM Standard for Grades 6–8

- Organize and consolidate their mathematical thinking through communication
- Communicate their mathematical thinking coherently and clearly to peers, teachers, and others
- Analyze and evaluate the mathematical thinking and strategies of others
- Use the language of mathematics to express mathematical ideas precisely

Key Processes in Prentice Hall
Course 1, Course 2, Course 3

- Write about mathematical concepts by summarizing, comparing, analyzing, and explaining (Writing in Math exercises and lessons; Reasoning, Short Response, and Extended Response exercises throughout **C1, C2, C3**)
- Understand the language and notations of mathematics (Reading Math hints and lessons, Vocabulary and Reading Comprehension exercises throughout **C1, C2, C3**)
- Use appropriate notation to express mathematical relationships in real-world contexts ("Words to Equations" model throughout **C1, C2, C3**)
- Analyze sample work to find errors (Error Analysis exercises throughout **C1, C2, C3**)

Background and Progression

To effectively communicate in the language of mathematics, students need ample opportunity to express mathematics in words, in symbols, through models, and orally.

Prentice Hall Mathematics contains a Reading Math strand with tips related to vocabulary and symbols as well as full-page lessons. The lessons include concept maps, vocabulary, and how to read examples, graphs, and real-context word problems.

Frequent Writing in Math exercises ask students to justify their work, explain a process, compare concepts, or draw a conclusion. Full-page Writing in Math lessons focus on writing to explain, compare, justify, or persuade.

Many examples use Prentice Hall's "Words to Equations" model to help students translate real-world situations into precise mathematical language.

Test Prep exercises in every lesson and at the end of each chapter include Short Response, Extended Response, and Reading Comprehension. These exercises require students to explain their work, justify their conclusions, and interpret mathematics found in everyday situations. In each text, students also learn how to write rubric-based responses.

 *For more **Math Background** on every lesson, see pages C–D before each chapter and see each lesson's teaching notes.*

Mathematical Strands

Connections

NCTM Standard for Grades 6–8

- Recognize and use connections among mathematical ideas
- Understand how mathematical ideas interconnect and build on one another to produce a coherent whole
- Recognize and apply mathematics in contexts outside of mathematics

Key Processes in Prentice Hall
Course 1, Course 2, Course 3

- Solve problems in more than one way (Problem-Solving Strategy lessons, More Than One Way features, Method 1/Method 2 examples throughout **C1, C2, C3**)
- Solve problems arising from real-world contexts (Data Files and related exercises, Real-World examples and exercises, Real-World Snapshots, and Reading Comprehension exercises throughout **C1, C2, C3**)
- Use various models to represent numeric, geometric, and algebraic concepts (throughout **C1, C2, C3**)
- Use symbolic algebra to represent generalizations and problems about numbers (**C1:** Ch 2, 10, 12; **C2:** Ch 2, 9; **C3:** Ch 1, 2, 7, 12)
- Use algebraic formulas to represent properties of geometric figures (**C1:** Ch 9; **C2:** Ch 8; **C3:** Ch 8, 9)
- Use concepts of ratio and proportionality to solve problems in geometry, probability, and algebra (**C1:** Ch 6, 11; **C2:** Ch 5, 12; **C3:** Ch 5, 9, 11)

Background and Progression

By the upper elementary grades, most students can master alternative methods for certain procedures and distinguish which of several approaches might be most appropriate.

In **Prentice Hall Mathematics,** students use alternative methods in More Than One Way features (every chapter), in Method 1/Method 2 presentations (worked-out examples), and in Problem Solving lessons in *Courses 2 and 3*. These situations provide a rich mix of numeric, algebraic, geometric, and experimental approaches to problems.

Every lesson contains real-world applications that provide contexts for mathematics. In addition, the Data Files and Real-World Snapshots in each chapter provide rich contexts that require students to apply what they have learned.

Models for decimals, fractions, percents, and proportions help students make connections among numbers and operations. Two-dimensional nets help link an object and its surface area.

By *Course 3*, students have made connections from the coordinate plane to algebraic equations and to geometric transformations.

Representation

NCTM Standard for Grades 6–8

- Create and use representations to organize, record, and communicate mathematical ideas
- Select, apply, and translate among mathematical representations to solve problems
- Use representations to model and interpret physical, social, and mathematical phenomena

Key Processes in Prentice Hall
Course 1, Course 2, Course 3

- Organize mathematical information in order to make and support conjectures (Investigations throughout **C1, C2, C3**)
- Make and use tables, graphs or other visual models, verbal rules, and symbolic rules to represent operations and relationships (throughout **C1, C2, C3**)
- Choose an appropriate graphical display for data; use one and two variables to express relationships within data (**C1:** Ch 7, 10; **C2:** Ch 10, 11; **C3:** Ch 3, 10, 12)
- Solve real-world problems by creating a mathematical model to represent the essential mathematics involved (Examples using the "Words to Equations" model, Reading Comprehension exercises, and Real-World Snapshots throughout **C1, C2, C3**)

Background and Progression

For younger students, concrete or visual representations of concepts are most effective.

Visualization continues as a strong strand in **Prentice Hall Mathematics,** with consistent modeling of numbers, operations, and relationships. Visual models are presented for fractions, decimals, percents, addition/subtraction, multiplication/division, equations, proportions, probabilities, and algebraic expressions.

Function relationships are represented through input/output visuals, tables, patterns, graphs, words, and symbols. The use of variables to represent functions is introduced gradually from *Course 1* through *Course 3*.

The presentation of data also includes a wide range of choices. By the end of *Course 3*, students have learned to identify the most appropriate display of data involving one or two variables or to compare data from two or more samples. They choose from bar graphs, histograms, line graphs, circle graphs, box-and-whisker plots, stem-and-leaf plots, and scatter plots.

Finally, students are given many opportunities to choose their own representation for real-life contextual mathematics in the Real-World Snapshots and numerous Real-World Problem-Solving examples.

 *For more **Math Background** on every lesson, see pages C–D before each chapter and see each lesson's teaching notes.*

Pacing Options for Course 1

Pacing Guide

This chart is provided merely as a guide to help you customize your course. To accommodate flexible scheduling, most lessons are subdivided into objectives. Within the lessons of the Student Edition, these objectives are indicated in red by the symbol ▼. The Assignment Guide for each lesson indicates which exercises in the Student Edition correspond to each objective of the lesson.

Detailed Chapter Pacing Options precede each chapter and give you lesson-by-lesson pacing suggestions for that specific chapter.

CHAPTER	Traditional (45-minute class periods)	Block (90-minute class periods)
1	15 days	7 days
2	15 days	7 days
3	14 days	7 days
4	14 days	7 days
5	13 days	7 days
6	15 days	7 days
7	13 days	7 days
8	13 days	7 days
9	14 days	7 days
10	15 days	7 days
11	11 days	6 days
12	8 days	4 days
Total	160 days	80 days

Differentiated Scope of Course

B = Basic Course   C = Core Course   A = Advanced Course

	B	C	A
Chapter 1 Decimals			
1-1: Understanding Whole Numbers	✓	✓	
• Investigation: Exploring Decimal Models	✓	✓	
1-2: Reading and Writing Decimals	✓	✓	
1-3: Comparing and Ordering Decimals	✓	✓	✓
1-4: Estimating With Decimals	✓	✓	✓
• Investigation: Using Models	✓	✓	
1-5: Adding and Subtracting Decimals	✓	✓	✓
1-6: Using a Problem-Solving Plan	✓	✓	✓
• Investigation: Modeling Multiplication of Decimals	✓	✓	
1-7: Multiplying Decimals	✓	✓	✓
1-8: Multiplying and Dividing Decimals by 10, 100, and 1,000	✓	✓	✓
1-9: Dividing Decimals	✓	✓	✓
1-10: Order of Operations	✓	✓	✓
• Technology: Exploring Order of Operations	✓	✓	✓
Chapter 2 Patterns and Variables			
2-1: Describing a Pattern	✓	✓	✓
2-2: Variables and Expressions	✓	✓	✓
2-3: Writing Algebraic Expressions	✓	✓	✓
• Technology: Using Formulas	✓	✓	✓
2-4: Make a Table and Look for a Pattern	✓	✓	✓
2-5: Using Number Sense to Solve One-Step Equations	✓	✓	✓
• Investigation: Using Models to Solve Equations	✓	✓	✓
2-6: Solving Addition and Subtraction Equations	✓	✓	✓
2-7: Solving Multiplication and Division Equations	✓	✓	✓
2-8: Exponents	✓	✓	✓
• Extension: Scientific Notation		✓	✓
2-9: The Distributive Property	✓	✓	✓
Chapter 3 Number Theory and Fractions			
3-1: Divisibility and Mental Math	✓	✓	✓
3-2: Prime Numbers and Prime Factorization	✓	✓	✓
• Extension: The Sieve of Eratosthenes		✓	✓
3-3: Greatest Common Factor	✓	✓	✓
• Investigation: Modeling Fractions	✓	✓	
3-4: Equivalent Fractions	✓	✓	✓

	B	C	A
• Technology: Simplifying Fractions	✓	✓	✓
3-5: Mixed Numbers and Improper Fractions	✓	✓	✓
3-6: Least Common Multiple	✓	✓	✓
3-7: Comparing and Ordering Fractions	✓	✓	✓
3-8: Fractions and Decimals	✓	✓	✓
3-9: Try, Check, and Revise	✓	✓	✓
Chapter 4 Adding and Subtracting Fractions			
4-1: Estimating Sums and Differences	✓	✓	✓
4-2: Fractions With Like Denominators	✓	✓	✓
• Investigation: Modeling Unlike Denominators	✓	✓	✓
4-3: Fractions With Unlike Denominators	✓	✓	✓
4-4: Adding Mixed Numbers	✓	✓	✓
4-5: Subtracting Mixed Numbers	✓	✓	✓
4-6: Equations With Fractions	✓	✓	✓
• Technology: Computing With a Fraction Calculator	✓	✓	✓
4-7: Measuring Elapsed Time	✓	✓	✓
4-8: Draw a Diagram	✓	✓	✓
Chapter 5 Multiplying and Dividing Fractions			
5-1: Multiplying Fractions	✓	✓	✓
5-2: Multiplying Mixed Numbers	✓	✓	✓
• Investigation: Fraction Division	✓	✓	✓
5-3: Dividing Fractions	✓	✓	✓
5-4: Dividing Mixed Numbers	✓	✓	✓
• Technology: Using a Calculator for Fractions	✓	✓	✓
5-5: Solving Fraction Equations by Multiplying	✓	✓	✓
5-6: Solve a Simpler Problem	✓	✓	✓
5-7: The Customary System	✓	✓	✓
5-8: Changing Units in the Customary System	✓	✓	✓
Chapter 6 Ratios, Proportions, and Percents			
6-1: Ratios	✓	✓	✓
6-2: Unit Rates	✓	✓	✓
6-3: Understanding Proportions	✓	✓	✓
6-4: Using Cross Products	✓	✓	✓
6-5: Scale Drawings	✓	✓	✓
• Investigation: Modeling Percents	✓	✓	
6-6: Percents, Fractions, and Decimals	✓	✓	✓
6-7: Finding a Percent of a Number	✓	✓	✓

	B	C	A
6-8: Estimating With Percents	✓	✓	✓
6-9: Write an Equation	✓	✓	✓
• Extension: Percents Under 1% or Over 100%			✓
Chapter 7 Data and Graphs			
• Investigation: Exploring the Mean	✓	✓	✓
7-1: Mean, Median, and Mode	✓	✓	✓
7-2: Organizing and Displaying Data	✓	✓	✓
7-3: Make an Organized List	✓	✓	✓
7-4: Bar Graphs and Line Graphs	✓	✓	✓
• Extension: Double Bar and Line Graphs		✓	✓
7-5: Circle Graphs	✓	✓	✓
7-6: Using Spreadsheets to Organize Data	✓	✓	✓
• Technology: Making a Graph From a Spreadsheet	✓	✓	✓
7-7: Stem-and-Leaf Plots		✓	✓
• Extension: Box-and-Whisker Plots			✓
7-8: Misleading Graphs and Statistics	✓	✓	✓
Chapter 8 Tools of Geometry			
8-1: Points, Lines, Segments, and Rays	✓	✓	✓
8-2: Angles	✓	✓	✓
• Extension: Basic Constructions			✓
8-3: Special Pairs of Angles	✓	✓	✓
• Technology: Investigating Angles in a Triangle		✓	✓
8-4: Classifying Triangles	✓	✓	✓
8-5: Exploring and Classifying Polygons	✓	✓	✓
8-6: Use Logical Reasoning	✓	✓	✓
8-7: Congruent and Similar Figures	✓	✓	✓
8-8: Line Symmetry		✓	✓
8-9: Transformations		✓	✓
• Extension: Tessellations			✓
Chapter 9 Geometry and Measurement			
9-1: Metric Units of Length, Mass, and Capacity	✓	✓	✓
9-2: Converting Units in the Metric System	✓	✓	✓
9-3: Perimeters and Areas of Rectangles	✓	✓	✓
9-4: Areas of Parallelograms and Triangles	✓	✓	✓
• Investigation: Exploring Circles	✓	✓	✓
9-5: Circles and Circumference	✓	✓	✓
9-6: Area of a Circle	✓	✓	✓
9-7: Three-Dimensional Figures and Spatial Reasoning	✓	✓	✓

	B	C	A
• Investigation: Views of Three-Dimensional Objects		✓	✓
9-8: Surface Areas of Prisms and Cylinders	✓	✓	✓
9-9: Volumes of Rectangular Prisms and Cylinders	✓	✓	✓
9-10: Work Backward	✓	✓	✓
Chapter 10 Integers			
10-1: Using a Number Line	✓	✓	✓
• Investigation: Modeling Addition of Integers	✓	✓	
10-2: Adding Integers	✓	✓	✓
• Investigation: Modeling Subtraction of Integers	✓	✓	
10-3: Subtracting Integers	✓	✓	✓
10-4: Multiplying Integers	✓	✓	✓
10-5: Dividing Integers	✓	✓	✓
10-6: Graphing in the Coordinate Plane	✓	✓	✓
• Extension: Reflections in the Coordinate Plane			✓
10-7: Applications of Integers			✓
10-8: Tables and Graphs of Functions	✓	✓	✓
10-9: Make a Graph	✓	✓	✓
Chapter 11 Exploring Probability			
11-1: Probability	✓	✓	✓
• Extension: Odds			✓
11-2: Experimental Probability	✓	✓	✓
11-3: Making Predictions From Data	✓	✓	✓
11-4: Simulate a Problem	✓	✓	✓
• Technology: Simulations		✓	✓
11-5: Tree Diagrams and the Counting Principle	✓	✓	✓
11-6: Exploring Permutations			✓
11-7: Independent Events			✓
Chapter 12 Equations and Inequalities			
12-1: Solving Two-Step Equations		✓	✓
12-2: Inequalities		✓	✓
12-3: Solving One-Step Inequalities		✓	✓
12-4: Comparing Strategies	✓	✓	✓
• Investigation: Exploring Squares			✓
12-5: Exploring Square Roots and Rational Numbers			✓
• Investigation: Exploring Right Triangles			✓
12-6: Introducing the Pythagorean Theorem			✓

Using Your Book for Success

Welcome to *Prentice Hall Mathematics, Course 1*. There are many features built into the daily lessons of this text that will help you learn the important skills and concepts you will need to be successful in this course. Look through the following pages for some study tips that you will find useful as you complete each lesson.

Instant Check System™
An *Instant Check System*, built into the text and marked with a ✔, allows you to check your understanding of skills before moving on to the next topic.

✔ Diagnosing Readiness
Complete the *Diagnosing Readiness* exercises to see what topics you may need to review before you begin the chapter.

✔ Check Skills You'll Need
Complete the *Check Skills You'll Need* exercises to make sure you have the skills needed to successfully learn the concepts in the lesson.

✔ Check Understanding
Every lesson includes several *Examples*, each followed by a *Check Understanding* question that you can do on your own to see if you understand the skill being introduced. Check your progress with the answers at the back of the book.

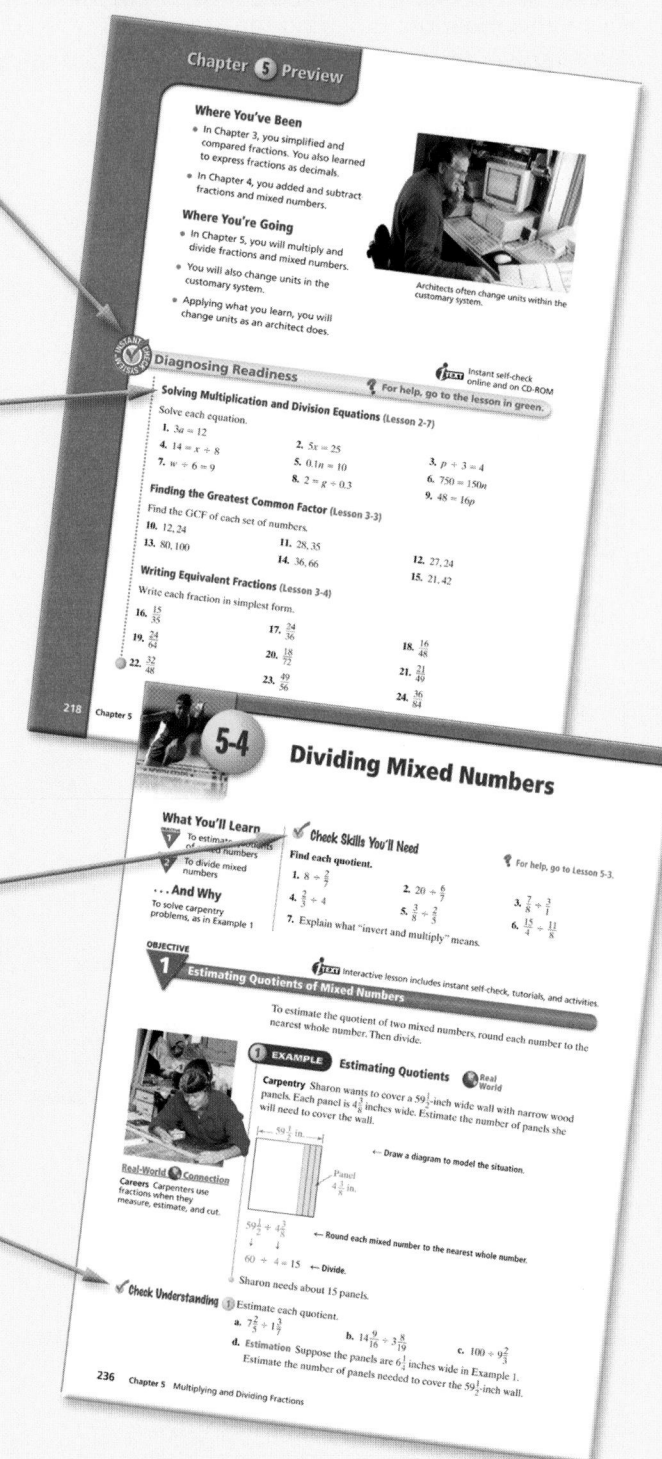

Need Help?

Need Help? notes provide a quick review of a concept you need to understand the topic being presented. Look for the green labels throughout the book that tell you where to "Go" for help.

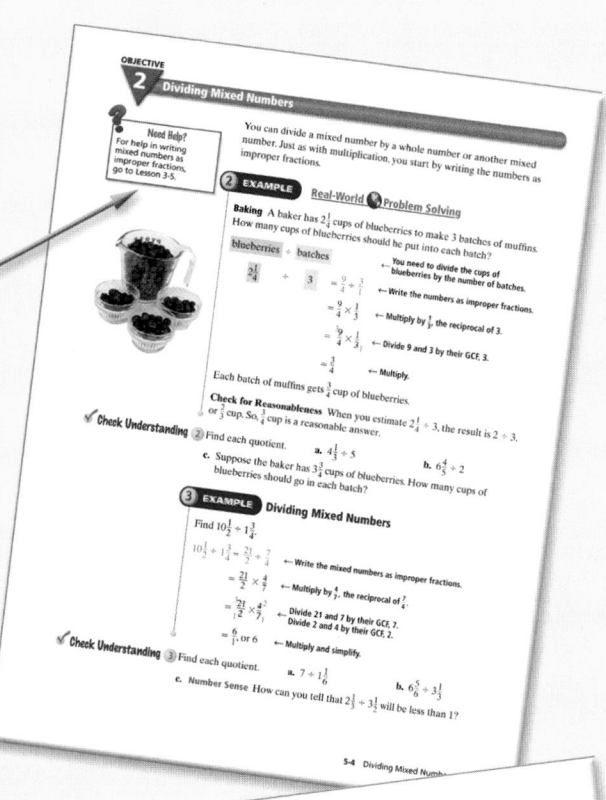

More Than One Way

The *More Than One Way* features show you two different methods to solve a problem. By analyzing each student's method, you can think critically about the solution and then choose the method you would use to solve a similar problem.

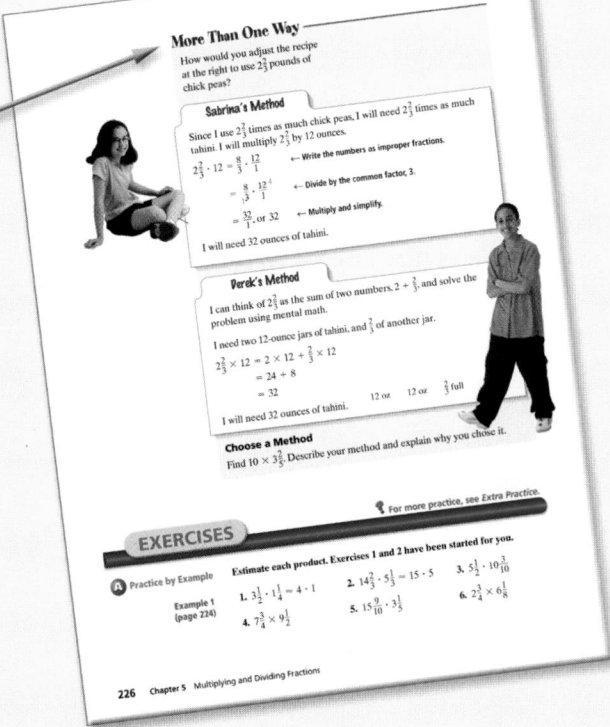

Exercise Sets

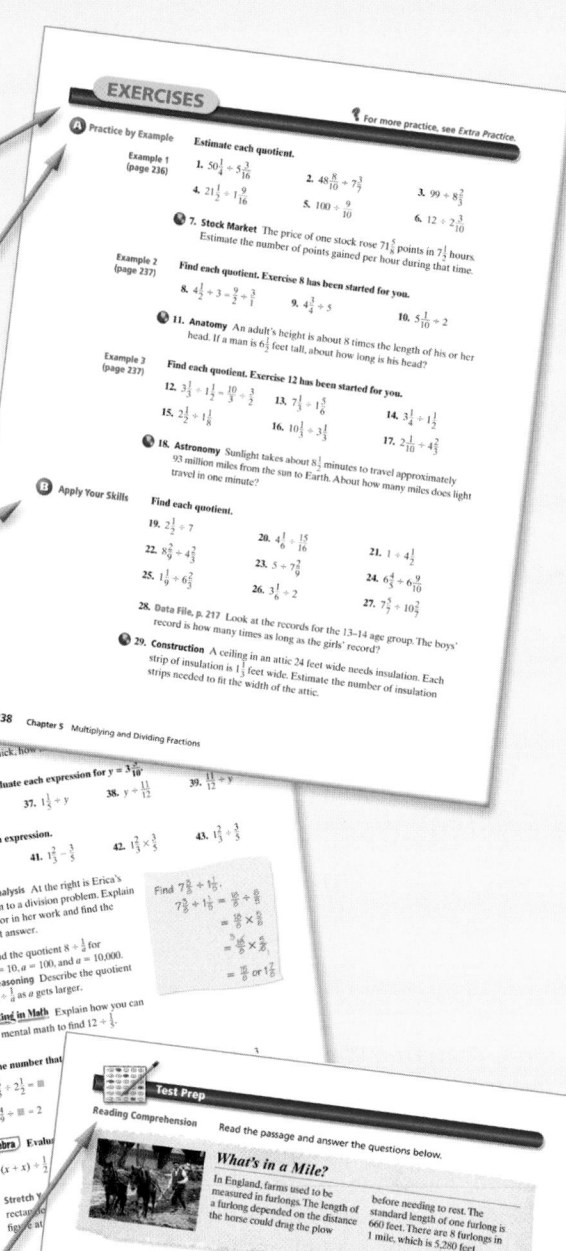

Exercises

There are numerous *Exercises* in each lesson that give you the practice you need to master the concepts in the lesson. Each practice set includes the following sections.

A: Practice by Example

The *A: Practice by Example* exercises refer you to the Examples in the lesson, in case you need help completing these exercises.

B: Apply Your Skills

The *B: Apply Your Skills* exercises combine skills from earlier lessons to offer you richer skill exercises and multi-step application problems.

C: Challenge

The *C: Challenge* exercises give you an opportunity to solve problems that extend and stretch your thinking.

Test Prep

The *Test Prep* exercises give you daily practice with the types of test question formats that you will encounter on state and national tests.

Preparing for Tests

Test-Taking Strategies
Test-Taking Strategies in every chapter teach you strategies to be successful and give you practice in the skills you need to pass state tests and standardized national exams.

Test Prep
In addition to the exercises in every lesson, the *Test Prep* pages in every chapter give you more opportunities to prepare for the tests you will have to take.

Test Item Formats
The *Test Prep* exercises in your book give you the practice you need to answer all types of test questions.
- *Multiple Choice*
- *Gridded Response* (answers are written in a grid)
- *Short Response* (answers are scored with a rubric)
- *Extended Response* (answers are scored with a rubric)
- *Reading Comprehension*

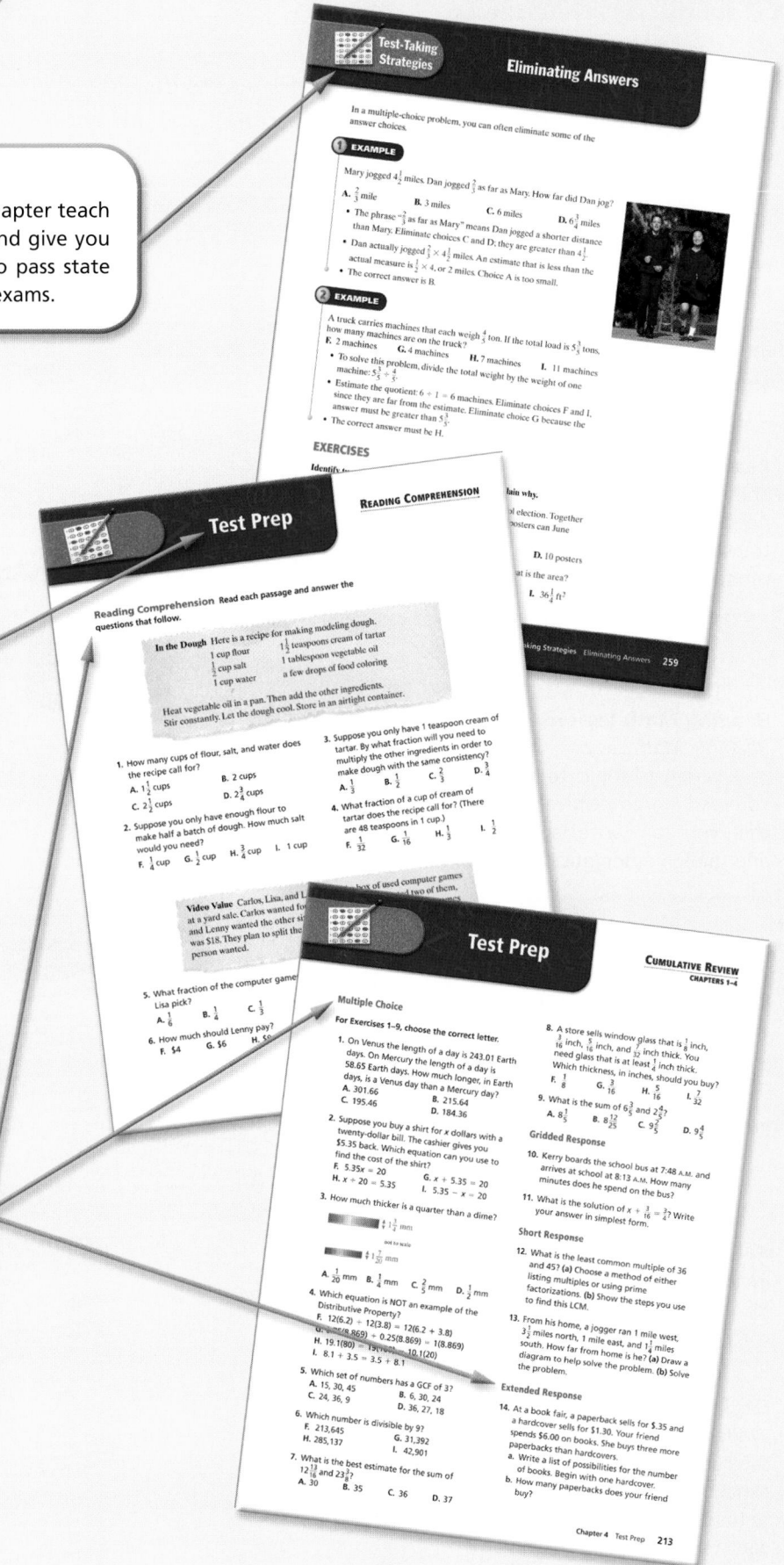

Student's Guide

Reading and Writing to Learn

Your *Course 1* text provides even more ways for you to develop your ability to read and write mathematically so that you are successful in this course and on state tests.

New Vocabulary
New Vocabulary is listed for each lesson so you can pre-read the text. As each term is introduced, it is highlighted in yellow.

Reading Math hints
These *hints* help you to use the mathematical notation correctly, understand vocabulary, and translate symbols into everyday English so you can talk about what you've learned.

Reading Math lessons
Reading Math lessons focus on a variety of topics to help you read more effectively, so that you can write, speak, and think mathematically.

Writing in Math lessons
Writing in Math lessons help you write more effectively about the mathematics you are learning.

For more help:

- **Reading Math exercises**
  Reading Math exercises in the Chapter Review help you to understand and correctly use the vocabulary presented in the chapter.

- **English/Spanish Illustrated Glossary**
  While you are learning, use this handy reference that contains a written explanation and an illustrated example to help you understand and remember each term.

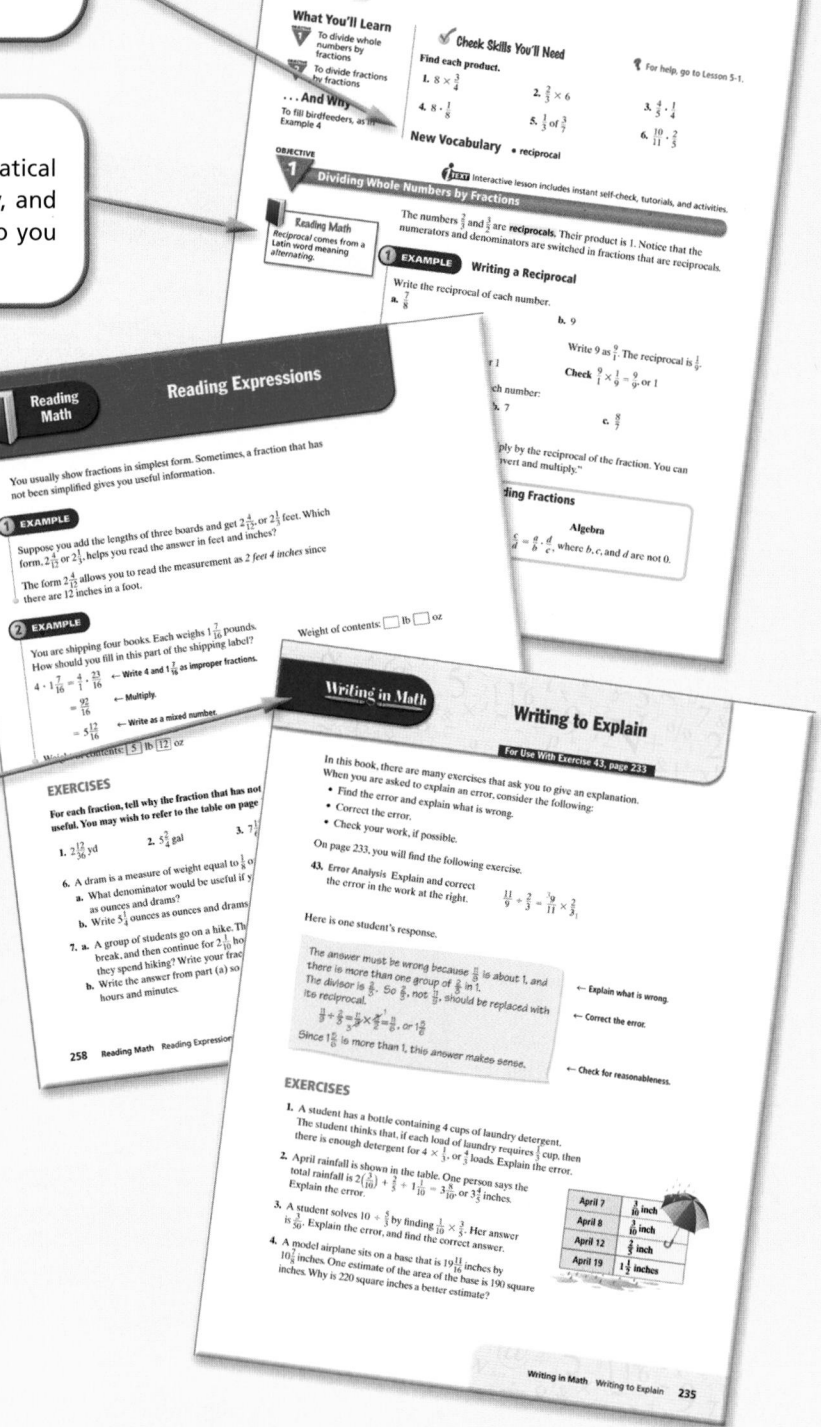

Dorling Kindersley (DK) is an international publishing company that specializes in the creation of high-quality, illustrated information books for children and adults. DK is part of the Pearson family of companies.

Real-World Snapshots
The *Real-World Snapshots* feature applies the exciting and unique graphic presentation style found in Dorling Kindersley books to show you how mathematics is used in real life.

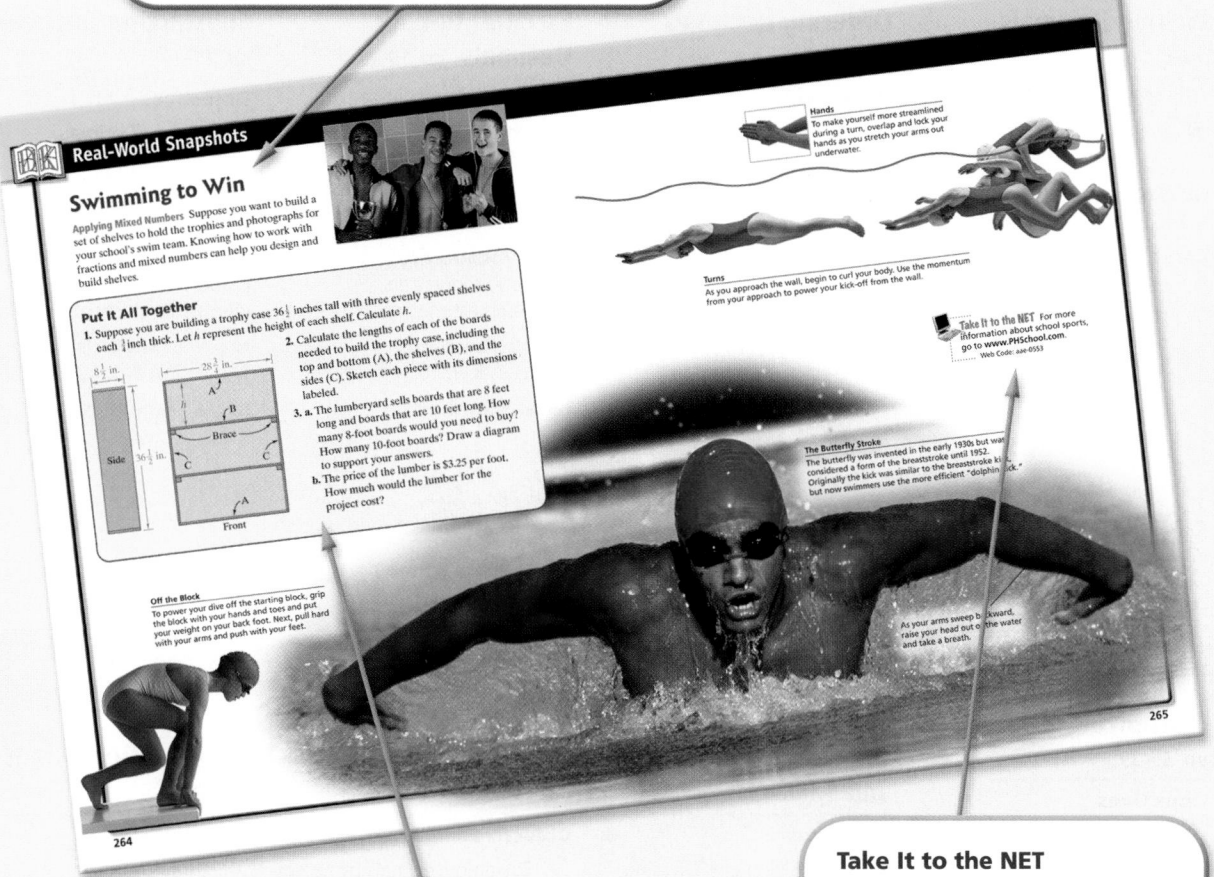

Put It All Together
Using data that you gather as well as data from these pages and the Data File, complete the hands-on activities to apply the mathematics you are learning in real-world situations.

Take It to the NET
Enter the Web Code for online information you can use to learn more about the topic of the feature.

Student's Guide

CHAPTER 1

Decimals

Chapter at a Glance

1-1
Understanding Whole Numbers
pp. 5–7

Objectives
- Writing and Comparing Whole Numbers

New Vocabulary
standard form, expanded form

NCTM Standards
1, 6, 7, 8, 9, 10

Local Standards

1-2
Reading and Writing Decimals
pp. 9–12

Objectives
- Reading and Writing Decimals

NCTM Standards
1, 3, 6, 7, 8, 9, 10

Local Standards

1-3
Comparing and Ordering Decimals
pp. 13–17

Objectives
- Using Models
- Using Place Value

Optional Materials
graph paper

NCTM Standards
1, 3, 6, 7, 8, 9, 10

Local Standards

✔ Checkpoint Quiz 1

1-4
Estimating With Decimals *pp. 19–23*

Objectives
- Estimating by Rounding and Compatible Numbers
- Using Front-End Estimation

New Vocabulary
compatible numbers, front-end estimation

NCTM Standards
1, 4, 6, 7, 8, 9, 10

Local Standards

1-5
Adding and Subtracting Decimals
pp. 25–29

Objectives
- Adding Decimals
- Subtracting Decimals

New Vocabulary
Commutative Property of Addition, Associative Property of Addition, Identity Property of Addition

NCTM Standards
1, 3, 4, 6, 7, 8, 9, 10

Local Standards

1-6 Problem Solving
Using a Problem-Solving Plan
pp. 30–33

Objectives
- Using a Problem-Solving Plan

NCTM Standards
1, 6, 7, 8, 9, 10

Local Standards

1-7
Multiplying Decimals
pp. 35–39

Objectives
- Multiplying Decimals
- Using Properties of Multiplication

New Vocabulary
Commutative Property of Multiplication, Associative Property of Multiplication, Identity Property of Multiplication

NCTM Standards
1, 3, 4, 6, 7, 8, 9, 10

Local Standards

✔ Checkpoint Quiz 2

1-8
Multiplying and Dividing by 10, 100, and 1,000 *pp. 40–42*

Objectives
- Multiplying and Dividing by 10, 100, and 1,000

NCTM Standards
1, 2, 6, 7, 8, 9, 10

Local Standards

1-9
Dividing Decimals
pp. 43–47

Objectives
- Dividing Decimals by Whole Numbers
- Dividing Decimals by Decimals

New Vocabulary
terminating decimal, repeating decimal

Optional Materials
graph paper

NCTM Standards
1, 3, 4, 6, 7, 8, 9, 10

Local Standards

1-10
Order of Operations
pp. 48–51

Objectives
- Using the Order of Operations

New Vocabulary
expression, order of operations

NCTM Standards
1, 2, 6, 7, 8, 9, 10

Local Standards

Reaching All Students
Additional Instructional Options in Chapter 1

Reading and Math Literacy

Reading Math
Reading Your Textbook, p. 18

Reading Math hints, pp. 9, 19, 26, 36, 43

Reading Comprehension, p. 57

Understanding Vocabulary, p. 54

Writing in Math
Writing Gridded Responses, p. 53

Daily Writing Practice, pp. 7, 11, 16, 22, 23, 28, 38, 42, 50, 56

Above Level

C Challenge exercises
pp. 7, 12, 17, 23, 29, 33, 38, 42, 47, 51

Hands-On and Technology

Investigations
Exploring Decimal Models, p. 8

Finding an Exact or Estimated Answer, p. 21

Using Models, p. 24

Modeling Multiplication of Decimals, p. 34

Multiplying by 10, 100, and 1,000, p. 40

Technology
Exploring Order of Operations, p. 52

Activities and Projects

Real-World Snapshots
Applying Decimals pp. 58–59

Chapter Project
Celebration, p. 636

Test Prep

Daily Test Prep
pp. 7, 12, 17, 23, 29, 33, 39, 42, 47, 51

Test-Taking Strategies
Writing Gridded Responses, p. 53

Test Prep
Reading Comprehension, p. 57

Chapter Assessment

Checkpoint Quiz
pp. 17, 39

Chapter Review
pp. 54–55

Chapter Test
p. 56

Pacing Options

This chart suggests pacing only for the core lessons and their parts. It is provided as a possible guide. It will help you determine how much time you have in your schedule to cover the additional features and assessment, as described at the left.

Day	Traditional 45-minute class periods	Block 90-minute class periods
1	1-1 ▽	1-1 ▽
		1-2 ▽
2	1-2 ▽	1-3 ▽ ▽
		1-4 ▽
3	1-3 ▽ ▽	1-4 ▽
		1-5 ▽
4	1-3 ▽ ▽	1-5 ▽
		1-6 ▽
5	1-4 ▽	1-7 ▽ ▽
6	1-4 ▽ ▽	1-8 ▽
		1-9 ▽
7	1-5 ▽	1-9 ▽
		1-10 ▽
8	1-5 ▽	
9	1-6 ▽	
10	1-7 ▽	
11	1-7 ▽	
12	1-8 ▽	
13	1-9 ▽ ▽	
14	1-9 ▽ ▽	
15	1-10 ▽	

NCTM STANDARDS 2000

1 Number and Operations
2 Algebra
3 Geometry
4 Measurement
5 Data Analysis and Probability
6 Problem Solving
7 Reasoning and Proof
8 Communication
9 Connections
10 Representation

Math Background

Skills Trace

BEFORE Chapter 1
Grade 5 presented operations with whole numbers and decimals.

DURING Chapter 1
Course 1 extends operations with decimals to estimating, comparing, and ordering.

AFTER Chapter 1
Throughout this course students use decimal operations to solve real-world problems.

1-1 Understanding Whole Numbers

Math Understandings
- Our numeral system is a base-10 system that uses these ten digits: 0, 1, 2, 3, 4, 5, 6, 7, 8, 9.
- The position of a digit in a numeral determines its value.
- You can write a numeral in standard form, using digits and place value, or in expanded form with a sum that shows the place and value of each digit.

In the numeral 254, the *place* of the digit 5 is the tens place. The *value* of the digit 5 is 5 tens, or 50. Use commas to separate the periods in a numeral. This chart shows the periods.

Trillions Period			Billions Period			Millions Period			Thousands Period			Ones Period		
Hundreds	Tens	Ones	Hundreds	Tens	Ones	Hundreds	Tens	Ones	Hundreds	Tens	Ones	Hundreds	Tens	Ones
		2,	6	2	3,	6	8	4,	6	0	8,	0	0	0

You can write a numeral in *standard form*, in *expanded form*, or as words.

Standard form	3,256
Expanded form	3,000 + 200 + 50 + 6
Words	three thousand, two hundred fifty-six

1-2 Reading and Writing Decimals

Math Understandings
- Digits to the left of the decimal point have whole number values; digits to the right have decimal values.
- When you read a decimal greater than 1, you read the decimal point as "and".

You can extend the place-value chart to include values for decimal places.

Hundreds	Tens	Ones		Tenths	Hundredths	Thousandths	Ten-Thousandths	Hundred-Thousandths	Millionths
		1	.	7	5	9			

1-3 1-4 Comparing and Ordering Decimals Estimating With Decimals

Math Understandings
- Estimation is used when an exact answer is not needed.
- Most estimation techniques involve replacing numbers with ones that are close and easy to compute with mentally.
- Methods and results from estimating can vary.
- Rounding decimals is similar to rounding whole numbers: values greater than or equal to 5 round up.

To compare two decimals, first write them so that each number has the same number of decimal places, and then compare from left to right. You can estimate decimal calculations by rounding, by using compatible numbers, or by using front-end estimation.

Compatible numbers are numbers that are easy to compute with mentally. To use **front-end estimation,** you add the "front-end digits," estimate the sum of the remaining digits, and adjust the estimate as necessary.

1-5 Adding and Subtracting Decimals

Math Understandings
- When you find sums or differences of decimals, you line up the decimal points, annex zeros, and rename as needed.
- You can simplify an expression by replacing it with the simplest name for its value.

You can use the properties of addition to reorder and regroup sums and differences to make calculations easier.

PROPERTIES OF ADDITION

Commutative Property
Changing the order of the addends does not change the sum.
$$2.5 + 3 = 3 + 2.5$$

Associative Property
Changing the grouping of the addends does not change the sum.
$$(2.5 + 3) + 4 = 2.5 + (3 + 4)$$

Identity Property
The sum of 0 and any number is that number.
$$2.5 + 0 = 0 + 2.5 = 2.5$$

1-6 Using a Problem-Solving Plan

A problem-solving plan can help you solve more challenging problems.

A Problem-Solving Plan

1. Read and understand the problem.
2. Plan how to solve the problem, then solve it.
3. Look back and check to see if your answer makes sense.

1-7 1-8 Multiplying Decimals Multiplying and Dividing Decimals by 10, 100, and 1000

Math Understandings

• The fact that our numeral system is a base-10 system means that you can multiply or divide by a power of 10 by moving the decimal point.

You can use the properties of multiplication to reorder, regroup, and simplify so that multiplications are easier.

1-9 Dividing Decimals

Math Understandings

• The quotient for the division of one whole number by another may result in a whole number or in a terminating or a repeating decimal.
• If you multiply both the dividend and the divisor by the same number, the quotient remains the same.

A **terminating decimal** is a decimal that stops, or terminates. A **repeating decimal** repeats the same digit or group of digits without stopping, and is indicated by a bar over the repeating digit(s).

Examples: $6 \div 3 = 2$ whole number quotient
         $6 \div 4 = 1.5$ terminating decimal quotient
$6 \div 18 = 0.33 \ldots$ or $0.\overline{3}$ repeating decimal quotient

To divide a decimal by a decimal, multiply both the dividend and the divisor by the same number so that the divisor is a whole number.

1-10 Order of Operations

Math Understandings

• Mathematicians have agreed upon a sequence for performing arithmetic operations, called the order of operations, so that any mathematical expression will always have the same value.

An **expression** is a mathematical phrase containing numbers and operation symbols. A partial **order of operations** follows.

Order of Operations

1. Do all operations within parentheses first.
2. Multiply and divide in order from left to right.
3. Add and subtract in order from left to right.

Additional Professional Development Opportunities

Chapter 1 Math Background notes:
pp. 5, 10, 14, 20, 26, 31, 36, 40, 44, 49

Additional resources available from SkyLight Professional Development:

On-site courses, workshops, summer institutes. Online courses and chat rooms. Videocassettes and books. Visit www.skylightedu.com.

Ongoing Assessment and Intervention

The *Prentice Hall Mathematics* program provides many options for assessment in the Student Edition, Teacher's Edition, and teaching resources. From these options you may choose instructional materials that are appropriate for your students and that support your district's curriculum requirements.

Daily Assessment

 Instant Check System™ in Chapter 1

Allows students to check their own learning before, during, and after each lesson.

Diagnosing Readiness before the chapter (p. 4)

Check Skills You'll Need exercises in each lesson (pp. 5, 9, 13, 19, 25, 30, 35, 40, 43, 48)

Check Understanding questions with each Example (pp. 5, 6, 9, 10, 13, 14, 19, 20, 25, 26, 27, 31, 35, 36, 37, 40, 41, 43, 44, 45, 49)

Checkpoint Quiz (pp. 17, 39)

Formal Assessment

Assessment in the Student Text and in Additional Resources

Assess student progress throughout the Course 1 textbook and with blackline masters and CD-ROM.

Student Edition
- Chapter 1 Review, with Vocabulary, Skills, and Concepts Review, pp. 54–55
- Chapter 1 Test, p. 56

Assessment Resources
- Checkpoint Quizzes 1 & 2
- Chapter Test, forms A & B
- Chapter Alternative Assessment
Spanish versions available.

 **Computer Test Generator CD-ROM**
- Instant Chapter Tests™—pre-made tests with items that vary every time you print.
- Online Testing allows you to give tests online and receive progress reports.
- Prepare students by making tests based on standardized test objectives.

Algebra Readiness Tests
- Includes Basic Skills Tests and Concept-Readiness Tests.
- Assess understanding of skills and concepts needed for success in algebra.

Intervention

 Skills Intervention Kit

Online Intervention
Integrated within the iText, this online intervention system includes diagnostic tests and prescribed remediation, plus reports to track student mastery.

A *complete* system for the student who is struggling with course-level work

Eight intervention units cover core skills and allow you to:
- **Diagnose** students' gaps in basic skills
- **Prescribe** an individualized course of study
- **Monitor** student progress

Includes print workbooks, tutorial CD-ROM, teacher editions, progress folders, and more. *Available in Spanish.*

How to Use with Chapter 1

1-1	Whole Numbers, Skills 1, 3
1-2	Decimals, Skill 1
1-3	Decimals, Skill 3
1-4	Decimals, Skills 4–5, 11, 19
1-5	Decimals, Skills 6–7
1-6	Decimals, Skill 8
1-7	Decimals, Skills 9, 12
1-8	Decimals, Skills 10, 17
1-9	Decimals, Skills 15, 21
1-10	Pre–Algebra Basics, Skills 9, 12

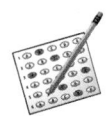

Standardized Test Preparation

The *Prentice Hall Mathematics* program integrates preparation for high-stakes standardized tests in every lesson of the Student Edition and continues this support in the Prentice Hall Assessment System.

Test Prep

In Student Text, Chapter 1

Teaches students strategies and gives them practice with all the test item formats they will encounter on high-stakes tests.

Test Prep exercises in each lesson (pp. 7, 12, 17, 23, 29, 33, 39, 42, 47, 51)

Test-Taking Strategies (p. 53: Writing Gridded Responses)

Test Prep (p. 57: Reading Comprehension)

A three-step approach to preparing students for high stakes, national, and state exams.

1 Diagnose & Prescribe

Content Diagnostic Tests
- Diagnose strengths and weaknesses with ongoing benchmark tests.
- Prescribe individualized reteaching opportunities.

2 Review & Reteach

Skills and Concepts Review
- Provides reteaching worksheets with instruction and practice for each skill.
- Includes course prerequisite skills.

3 Practice & Assess

Standardized Test Preparation
- Features practice for national standardized exams.
- Includes practice tests for NAEP, SAT10, ITBS, and Terra Nova.

Test-Taking Strategies with Transparencies
- Support the Test-Taking Strategies pages in the Student Edition.
- Provide a transparency and a worksheet for each strategy.

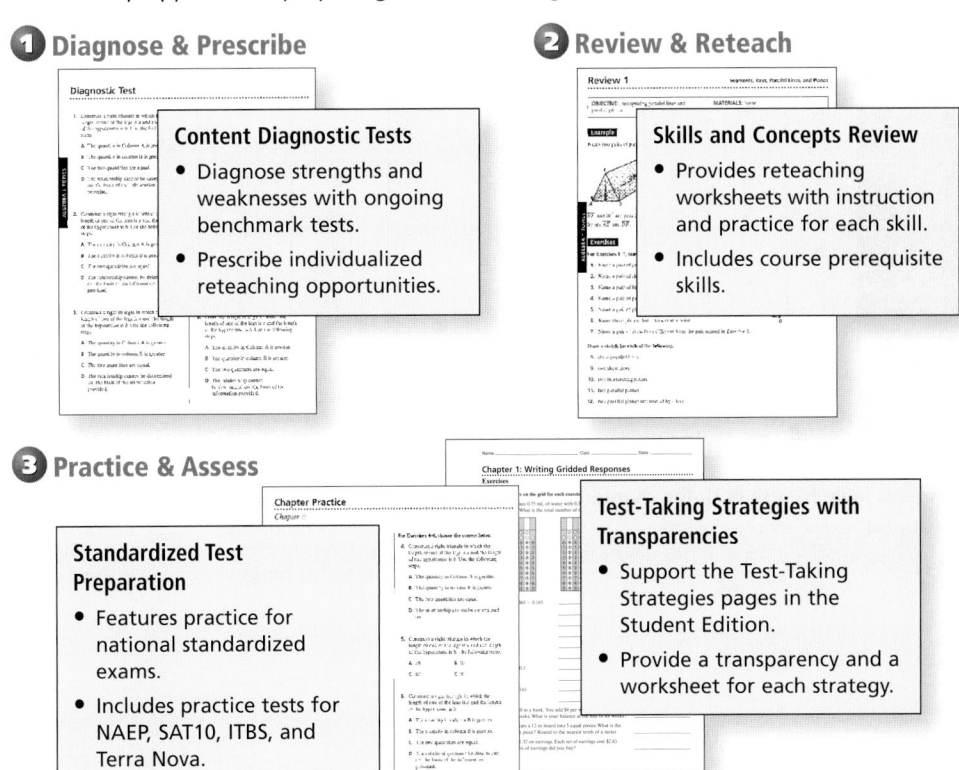

Correlation to Standardized Tests

Lesson		NAEP	Terra Nova				Local Test
			CAT6	CTBS	ITBS	SAT10	
1-1	Understanding Whole Numbers	N1a	■	■	■	■	
1-2	Reading and Writing Decimals	N1a	■				
1-3	Comparing and Ordering Decimals	N1i, N1j		■			
1-4	Estimating With Decimals	N2b	■	■	■	■	
1-5	Adding and Subtracting Decimals	N3a	■	■	■	■	
1-6	Problem Solving: Using a Problem-Solving Plan		■	■			
1-7	Multiplying Decimals	N3a	■	■	■	■	
1-8	Multiplying and Dividing by 10, 100, and 1,000	N3a, N3d	■	■	■	■	
1-9	Dividing Decimals	N3a	■	■	■	■	
1-10	Order of Operations	N3a	■	■	■	■	

NAEP National Assessment of Educational Progress
CAT6/Terra Nova California Achievement Test, 6th Ed.

CTBS/Terra Nova Comprehensive Test of Basic Skills
ITBS Iowa Test of Basic Skills, Form M.

SAT10 Stanford Achievement Test, 10th Ed.

Program Resources

	Resources in Grab & Go™ Files				Resources for Reaching All Students				Spanish Resources			Presentation Assistant Plus! Transparencies					Prentice Hall Presentation Pro CD-ROM
	Practice	Reteach	Enrich	Checkpt Quiz	Reading & Math Literacy	Technology Activities	Hands-On Activities	Guided Problem Solving	Practice	Reading & Math Literacy	Checkpt Quiz	Skills Check	Problem of the Day	Additional Examples	Answers to Exercises	Lesson Quiz	
1-1	■	■	■		■			■	■	■		■	■	■	■	■	■
1-2	■	■	■			■		■	■			■	■	■	■	■	■
1-3	■	■	■	■	■	■		■	■			■	■	■	■	■	■
1-4	■	■	■					■	■			■	■	■	■	■	■
1-5	■	■	■				■	■	■			■	■	■	■	■	■
1-6	■	■	■					■	■			■	■	■	■	■	■
1-7	■	■	■	■	■			■	■		■	■	■	■	■	■	■
1-8	■	■	■					■	■			■	■	■	■	■	■
1-9	■	■	■			■		■	■			■	■	■	■	■	■
1-10	■	■	■			■		■	■			■	■	■	■	■	■
For the Chapter	Chapter Projects, Chapter Tests, Alternative Assessment, Cumulative Review, Cumulative Assessment				**On web site only:** Home Activities, Interdisciplinary Activities, Algebra Readiness Puzzles				Spanish Chapter Tests, Alternative Assessment, Cumulative Review, Cumulative Assessment			Classroom Aid Transparencies					

Also available for use with the chapter:

PRENTICE HALL ASSESSMENT SYSTEM *See page 2F.*

- Practice Workbook
- Solution Key
- MathNotes folder

- For teacher support and access to student Web materials, use the Web Code aak-5500.
- For additional online and technology resources, *see below.*

Technology

iTEXT Online and on CD-ROM

Complete Interactive Student Text online and on CD-ROM—with instant feedback assessment, tutorial help, dynamic activities, instructional and real-world videos, audio, and additional practice.

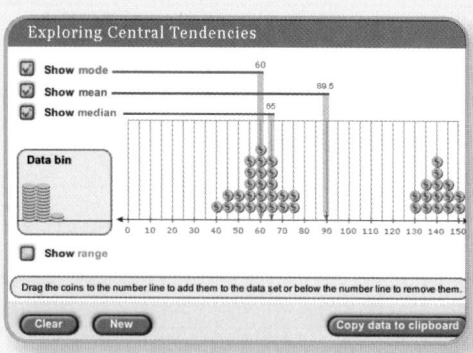

www.PHSchool.com For Students

Use Web codes for easy access to online activities, chapter projects, self-grading lesson quizzes, chapter tests, vocabulary quizzes, updated data sources, graphing calculator procedures, and more.

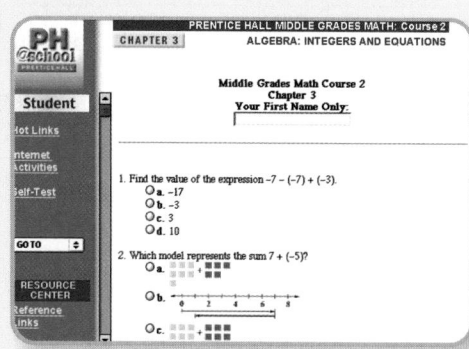

PH SuccessNet For Teachers

Online lesson planning with built-in state correlations, all the teaching resources, complete reference library, your own calendar and Teacher Web page, professional development, and more.

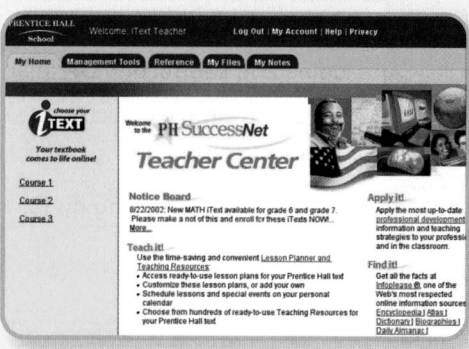

Presentation Assistant Plus!

The *Prentice Hall Presentation Assistant Plus!* provides you with the material you need to teach a lesson from beginning to end. Two easy-to-use formats—Transparencies and PowerPoint®—allow you to present a lesson the way you are most comfortable.

Transparencies

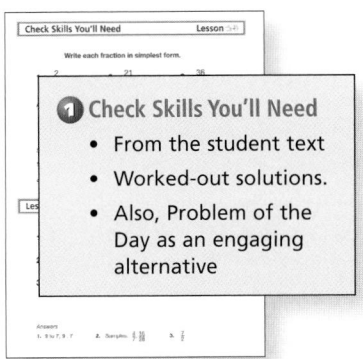

1 Check Skills You'll Need
- From the student text
- Worked-out solutions.
- Also, Problem of the Day as an engaging alternative

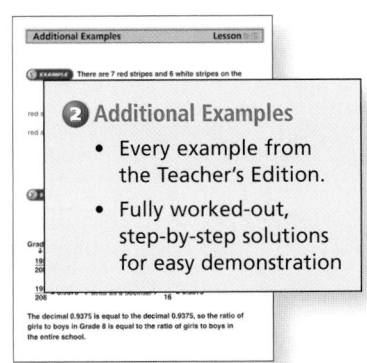

2 Additional Examples
- Every example from the Teacher's Edition.
- Fully worked-out, step-by-step solutions for easy demonstration

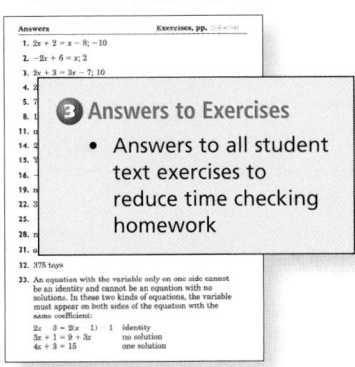

3 Answers to Exercises
- Answers to all student text exercises to reduce time checking homework

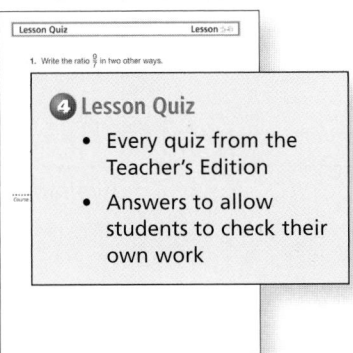

4 Lesson Quiz
- Every quiz from the Teacher's Edition
- Answers to allow students to check their own work

PowerPoint Throughout the Teacher's Edition, this symbol indicates material that is available in the Presentation Assistant Plus!

PowerPoint Prentice Hall Presentation Pro CD-ROM

- Includes all Transparencies.
- Conveniently organized by lesson so you can easily **1** Introduce, **2** Teach, **3** Check Homework, and **4** Assess each lesson.
- Animated examples allow step-by-step instruction at your own pace.
- Easy to edit so you can create custom presentations.

Teaching Chapter 1 Using Presentation Assistant Plus!

	1 Introduce	**2 Teach**	**3 Check Homework**	**4 Assess**
	Check Skills You'll Need	Additional Examples	Student Edition Answers	Lesson Quiz
1-1	p. 1	pp. 1	✔	p. 1
1-2	p. 2	p. 2	✔	p. 2
1-3	p. 3	pp. 3–5	✔	p. 3
1-4	p. 4	pp. 6–7	✔	p. 4
1-5	p. 5	pp. 8–12	✔	p. 5
1-6	p. 6	p. 13	✔	p. 6
1-7	p. 7	pp. 14–15	✔	p. 7
1-8	p. 8	p. 16	✔	p. 8
1-9	p. 9	pp. 17–19	✔	p. 10
1-10	p. 11	p. 20	✔	p. 11

Prentice Hall Presentation Pro

CD-ROM with dynamic PowerPoint® presentations for every lesson. Helps you introduce and develop concepts, check homework, and assess progress. Part of Presentation Assistant Plus! *(See above.)*

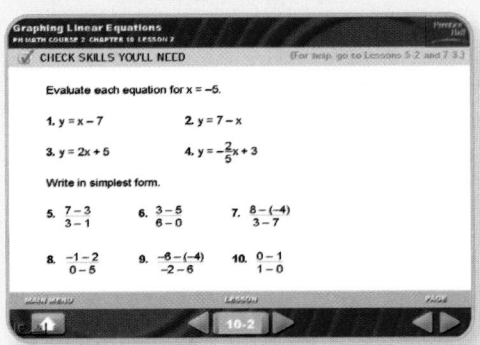

Computer Test Generator

CD-ROM to create practice sheets and tests for course objectives and standardized tests. Includes Instant Chapter Tests™, online testing, and student reports. Part of the PH Assessment System. *(See page 2F.)*

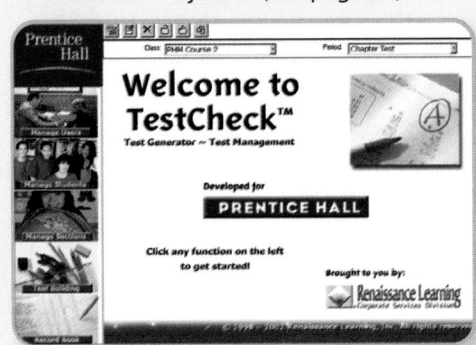

Resource Pro® with Planning Express®

CD-ROM with a lesson planning tool that allows you to import state and local objectives. Includes electronic versions of all the teaching resources.

Chapter Resources

Reading and Math Support

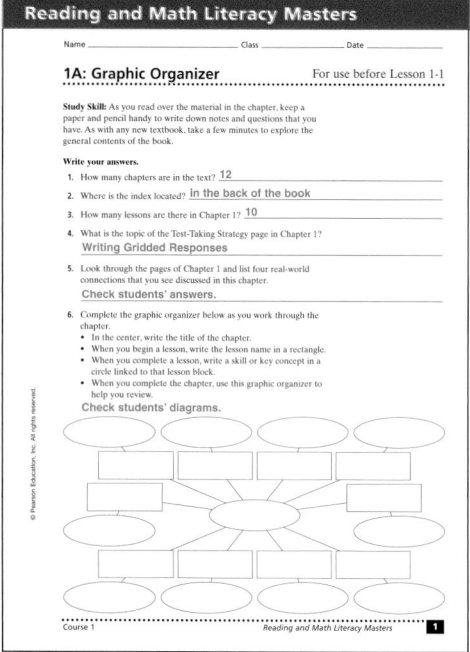

Available in Spanish

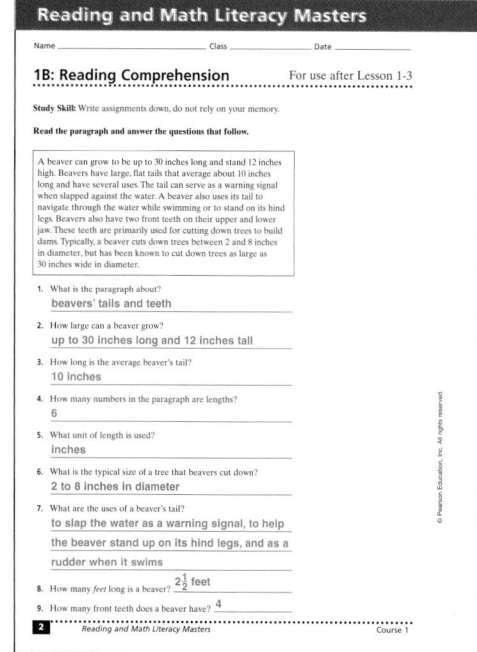

Available in Spanish

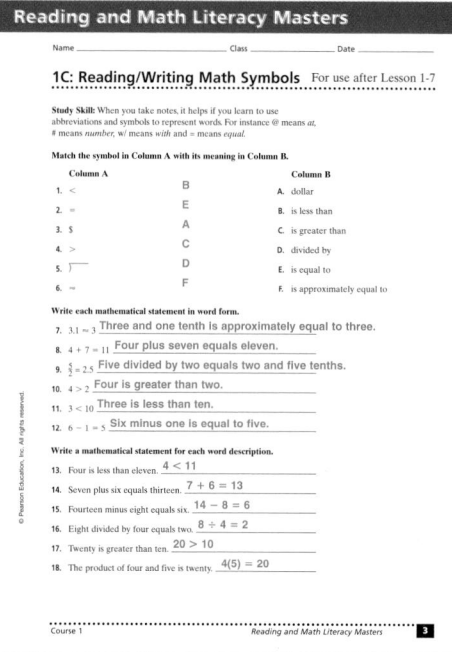

Available in Spanish

Problem Solving

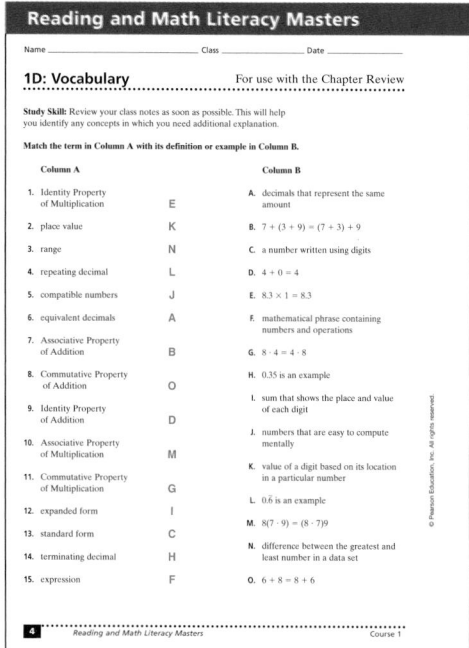

Available in Spanish

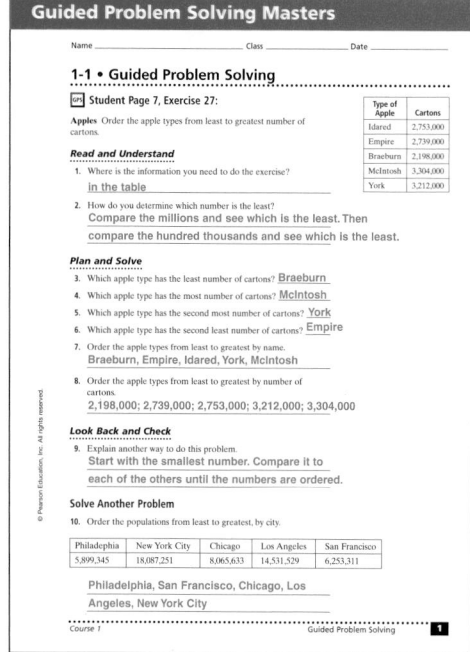

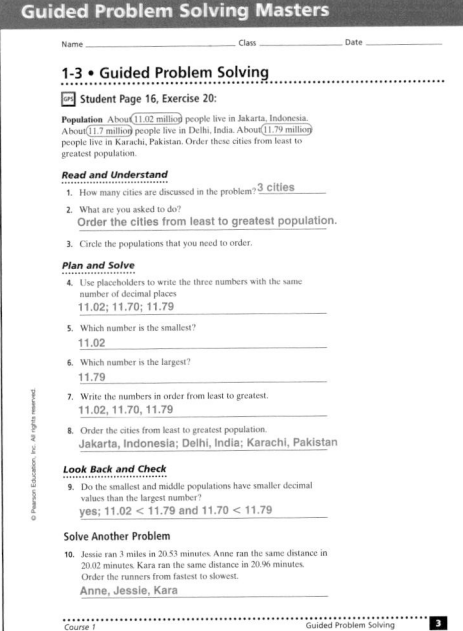

Name _____ Class _____ Date _____

1-3 • Guided Problem Solving

GPS Student Page 16, Exercise 20:

Population About 11.02 million people live in Jakarta, Indonesia. About 11.7 million people live in Karachi, Pakistan. About 11.79 million people live in Delhi, India. Order these cities from least to greatest population.

Read and Understand

1. How many cities are discussed in the problem? 3 cities

2. What are you asked to do?
   Order the cities from least to greatest population.

3. Circle the populations that you need to order.

Plan and Solve

4. Use placeholders to write the three numbers with the same number of decimal places.
   11.02; 11.70; 11.79

5. Which number is the smallest?
   11.02

6. Which number is the largest?
   11.79

7. Write the numbers in order from least to greatest.
   11.02, 11.70, 11.79

8. Order the cities from least to greatest population.
   Jakarta, Indonesia; Delhi, India; Karachi, Pakistan

Look Back and Check

9. Do the smallest and middle populations have smaller decimal values than the largest number?
   yes; 11.02 < 11.79 and 11.70 < 11.79

Solve Another Problem

10. Jessie ran 3 miles in 20.53 minutes. Anne ran the same distance in 20.02 minutes. Kara ran the same distance in 20.96 minutes. Order the runners from fastest to slowest.
    Anne, Jessie, Kara

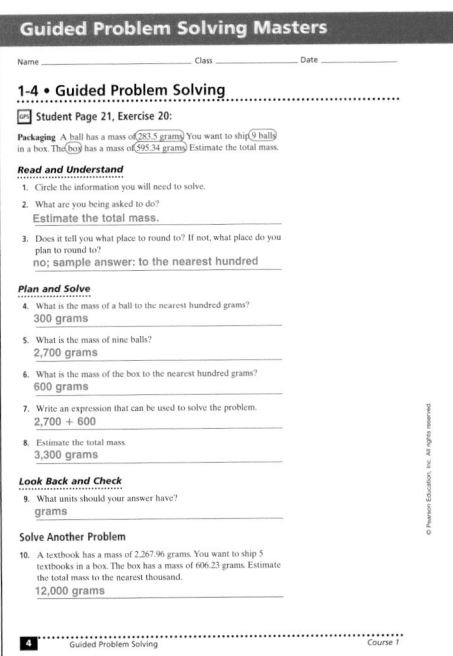

Name _____ Class _____ Date _____

1-4 • Guided Problem Solving

GPS Student Page 21, Exercise 20:

Packaging A ball has a mass of 283.5 grams. You want to ship 9 balls in a box. The box has a mass of 595.34 grams. Estimate the total mass.

Read and Understand

1. Circle the information you will need to solve.

2. What are you being asked to do?
   Estimate the total mass.

3. Does it tell you what place to round to? If not, what place do you plan to round to?
   no; sample answer: to the nearest hundred

Plan and Solve

4. What is the mass of a ball to the nearest hundred grams?
   300 grams

5. What is the mass of nine balls?
   2,700 grams

6. What is the mass of the box to the nearest hundred grams?
   600 grams

7. Write an expression that can be used to solve the problem.
   2,700 + 600

8. Estimate the total mass.
   3,300 grams

Look Back and Check

9. What units should your answer have?
   grams

Solve Another Problem

10. A textbook has a mass of 2,267.96 grams. You want to ship 5 textbooks in a box. The box has a mass of 606.23 grams. Estimate the total mass to the nearest thousand.
    12,000 grams

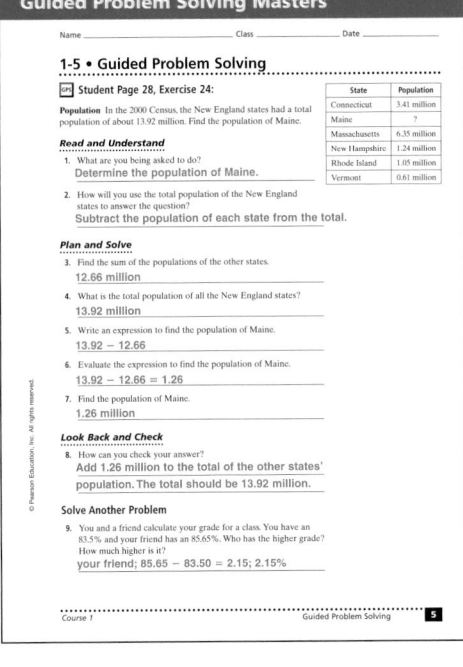

Name _____ Class _____ Date _____

1-5 • Guided Problem Solving

GPS Student Page 28, Exercise 24:

Population In the 2000 Census, the New England states had a total population of about 13.92 million. Find the population of Maine.

State	Population
Connecticut	3.41 million
Maine	?
Massachusetts	6.35 million
New Hampshire	1.24 million
Rhode Island	1.05 million
Vermont	0.61 million

Read and Understand

1. What are you being asked to do?
   Determine the population of Maine.

2. How will you use the total population of the New England states to answer the question?
   Subtract the population of each state from the total.

Plan and Solve

3. Find the sum of the populations of the other states.
   12.66 million

4. What is the total population of all the New England states?
   13.92 million

5. Write an expression to find the population of Maine.
   13.92 − 12.66

6. Evaluate the expression to find the population of Maine.
   13.92 − 12.66 = 1.26

7. Find the population of Maine.
   1.26 million

Look Back and Check

8. How can you check your answer?
   Add 1.26 million to the total of the other states' population. The total should be 13.92 million.

Solve Another Problem

9. You and a friend calculate your grade for a class. You have an 83.5% and your friend has an 85.65%. Who has the higher grade? How much higher is it?
   your friend; 85.65 − 83.50 = 2.15; 2.15%

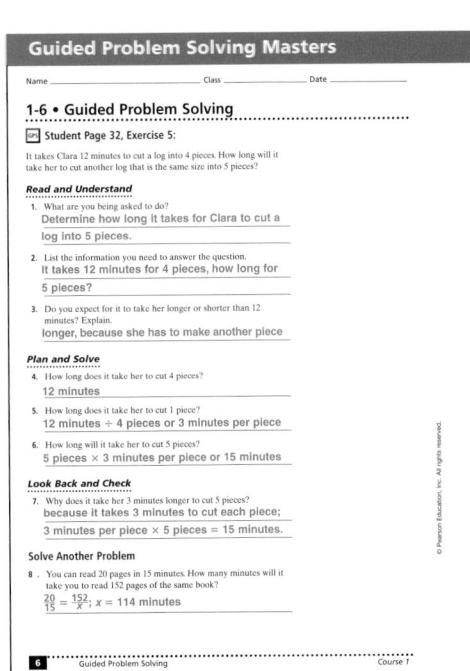

Name _____ Class _____ Date _____

1-6 • Guided Problem Solving

GPS Student Page 32, Exercise 5:

It takes Clara 12 minutes to cut a log into 4 pieces. How long will it take her to cut another log that is the same size into 5 pieces?

Read and Understand

1. What are you being asked to do?
   Determine how long it takes for Clara to cut a log into 5 pieces.

2. List the information you need to answer the question.
   It takes 12 minutes for 4 pieces, how long for 5 pieces?

3. Do you expect for it to take her longer or shorter than 12 minutes? Explain.
   longer, because she has to make another piece

Plan and Solve

4. How long does it take her to cut 4 pieces?
   12 minutes

5. How long does it take her to cut 1 piece?
   12 minutes ÷ 4 pieces or 3 minutes per piece

6. How long will it take her to cut 5 pieces?
   5 pieces × 3 minutes per piece or 15 minutes

Look Back and Check

7. Why does it take her 3 minutes longer to cut 5 pieces?
   because it takes 3 minutes to cut each piece; 3 minutes per piece × 5 pieces = 15 minutes.

Solve Another Problem

8. You can read 20 pages in 15 minutes. How many minutes will it take you to read 152 pages of the same book?
   $\frac{20}{15} = \frac{152}{x}$; $x = 114$ minutes

Name _____ Class _____ Date _____

1-7 • Guided Problem Solving

GPS Student Page 38, Exercise 44:

Nutrition There is 0.2 gram of calcium in 1 serving of cheddar cheese. How much calcium is in 3.25 servings of cheddar cheese?

Read and Understand

1. What is being compared in the exercise?
   the amount of calcium in one serving and the amount of calcium in 3.25 servings of cheddar cheese

2. What are you being asked to do?
   determine the amount of calcium in 3.25 servings

3. Will you multiply or divide to determine the answer? Explain.
   multiply, because you know the amount of calcium in one serving and want to know how much is in 3.25 servings

Plan and Solve

4. How much calcium is in one serving? 0.2 gram

5. How many servings do you want?
   3.25 servings

6. Write an expression to answer the exercise.
   0.2 × 3.25

7. How many grams of calcium are in 3.25 servings of cheddar cheese?
   0.65 gram

Look Back and Check

8. Should there be more or less than 0.2 gram of calcium in 3.25 servings of cheddar cheese? Explain.
   more; 3.25 servings is more than one serving

Solve Another Problem

9. There are 0.5 gram of fat in one serving of a breakfast cereal. How many grams of fat are in 4.25 servings?
   0.5 × 4.25 or 2.125 grams

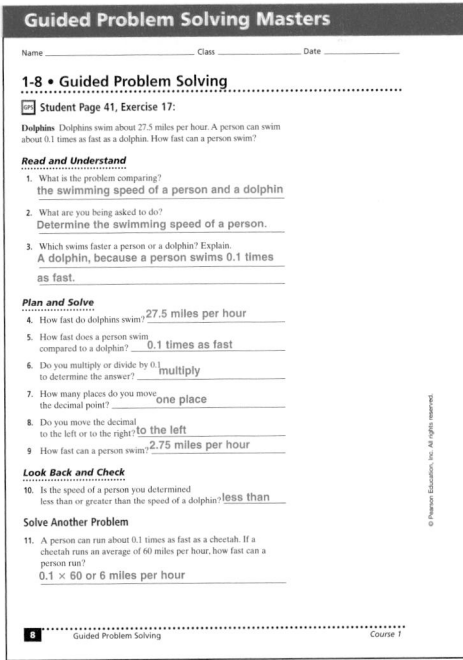

Name _____ Class _____ Date _____

1-8 • Guided Problem Solving

GPS Student Page 41, Exercise 17:

Dolphins Dolphins swim about 27.5 miles per hour. A person can swim about 0.1 times as fast as a dolphin. How fast can a person swim?

Read and Understand

1. What is the problem comparing?
   the swimming speed of a person and a dolphin

2. What are you being asked to do?
   Determine the swimming speed of a person.

3. Which swims faster a person or a dolphin? Explain.
   A dolphin, because a person swims 0.1 times as fast.

Plan and Solve

4. How fast do dolphins swim? 27.5 miles per hour

5. How fast does a person swim compared to a dolphin? 0.1 times as fast

6. Do you multiply or divide by 0.1 to determine the answer? multiply

7. How many places do you move the decimal point? one place

8. Do you move the decimal to the left or to the right? to the left

9. How fast can a person swim? 2.75 miles per hour

Look Back and Check

10. Is the speed of a person you determined less than or greater than the speed of a dolphin? less than

Solve Another Problem

11. A person can run about 0.1 times as fast as a cheetah. If a cheetah runs an average of 60 miles per hour, how fast can a person run?
    0.1 × 60 or 6 miles per hour

Guided Problem Solving Masters

Name _____ Class _____ Date _____

1-9 • Guided Problem Solving

GPS Student Page 46, Exercise 38:

School Supplies A stack of paper measures 0.9 centimeter thick. Each piece of paper is 0.01 centimeter thick.

a. How many pieces of paper are in the stack?

b. Could each of 25 students get three pieces of paper?

Read and Understand

1. Circle the information you will need to solve.

2. What are you asked to do in part *a*?
   Find how many pieces of paper are in the stack.

3. What are you asked to do in part *b*?
   Determine if there is enough paper for each of
   25 students to get three pieces of paper.

Plan and Solve

4. How thick is one piece of paper? 0.01 centimeter

5. How thick is the stack of paper? 0.9 centimeter

6. Do you multiply or divide to answer part a? divide

7. Write an expression to answer part a. 0.9 ÷ 0.01

8. How many pieces of paper are in the stack? 90 pieces of paper

9. How many pieces of paper are needed for each of 25 students to get three pieces of paper?
   25 × 3 or 75 pieces of paper.

10. Is there enough paper? 75 < 90; yes

Look Back and Check

11. Why is the number of pieces of paper 100 times more than the height of the stack of paper?
    Sample answer: because 90 = 100 × 0.9

Solve Another Problem

12. A stack of baseball cards measures 5.4 centimeter thick. Each baseball card is 0.1 centimeter thick. How many baseball cards are in the stack?
    5.4 ÷ 0.1 = 54; 54 baseball cards

Course 1   Guided Problem Solving   **9**

Guided Problem Solving Masters

Name _____ Class _____ Date _____

1-10 • Guided Problem Solving

GPS Student Page 50, Exercise 28:

Coins There are 312 coins of the same type in two stacks. One stack of coins is 15 inches tall. The other stack is 9 inches tall. Find the thickness of one coin to the nearest thousandth of an inch.

Read and Understand

1. List the information you need to solve the problem.
   312 coins total, one stack 15 inches tall,
   another stack 9 inches tall

2. What are you being asked to do?
   Find the thickness of one coin to the nearest
   hundredth of an inch.

Plan and Solve

3. How tall are the two stacks combined? 24 inches tall

4. How tall are 312 coins? 24 inches tall

5. How can you determine the thickness of one coin?
   Divide.

6. How thick is one coin?
   24 inches ÷ 312 coins or 0.077 inches

Look Back and Check

7. Multiply the thickness you determined in Exercise 6 by 312. Does this answer match the total thickness of all 312 coins?
   0.077 inches per coin × 312 coins or
   24 inches; yes

Solve Another Problem

8. There are 500 compact discs of the same type in two stacks. One stack is 7 inches tall. The other stack is 13 inches tall. Find the thickness of one compact disc to the nearest hundredth of an inch.
   (7 + 13) ÷ 500 = 0.04; 0.04 inches

10   Guided Problem Solving   Course 1

Hands-On Activities

Name _____ Class _____ Date _____

Activity 2: Snap Cube Decimals

Materials needed: paper, snap cubes

Work with a partner.

Each cube has the value 0.01.

1. a. Snap 10 cubes together. On a separate sheet of paper, express this row as a decimal.
   b. How many snap cubes do you need to show one tenth?
   c. Make 3 rows of 10 cubes each. Express all 3 rows as a decimal.
   d. How many snap cubes do you need to show 3 tenths?
   e. Combine 7 single cubes with your 3 rows. Express them as a decimal.
   f. How many snap cubes do you need to show 37 hundredths?

2. a. Use snap cubes to show each addend in the equation:
      0.45 + 0.29 = ?
   b. Combine the rows and cubes for both numbers.
   c. Make more rows from the combined cubes, if you can. How many did you make?
   d. Find the sum.

3. a. Have each partner make a decimal model using cubes and rows. Express each model as a decimal.
   b. Use the models to add the two decimals together.
   c. Repeat three times.

4. a. Use snap cubes to show the decimal 0.36.
   b. To take 0.07 away from 0.36, how many cubes will you remove?
   c. Remove the cubes to find the difference. If you remove cubes from a row, separate all of the cubes in that row into single cubes. Write the new number of rows and cubes.

5. a. Have your partner make a decimal model using cubes and rows.
   b. Express the model as a decimal.
   c. Write a subtraction problem in which a decimal amount is subtracted from the model.
   d. Have your partner use the model to subtract.

2   Activity 2   Courses 1–3 Hands-On Activities

Hands-On Activities

Name _____ Class _____ Date _____

Activity 4: Decimal Pocket Chart

Materials needed: 12″ × 18″ construction paper, glue, scissors, eight 3″ × 5″ note cards

Work with a partner.

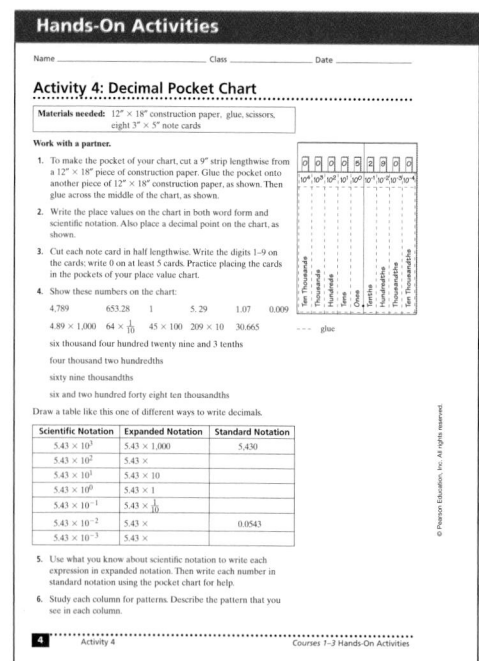

1. To make the pocket of your chart, cut a 9″ strip lengthwise from a 12″ × 18″ piece of construction paper. Glue the pocket onto another piece of 12″ × 18″ construction paper, as shown. Then glue across the middle of the chart, as shown.

2. Write the place values on the chart in both word form and scientific notation. Also place a decimal point on the chart, as shown.

3. Cut each note card in half lengthwise. Write the digits 1–9 on the cards; write 0 on at least 5 cards. Practice placing the cards in the pockets of your place value chart.

4. Show these numbers on the chart:

   4,789   653.28   1   5.29   1.07   0.009

   4.89 × 1,000   64 × $\frac{1}{10}$ 45 × 100   209 × 10   30.665

   six thousand four hundred twenty nine and 3 tenths

   four thousand two hundredths

   sixty nine thousandths

   six and two hundred forty eight ten thousandths

Draw a table like this one of different ways to write decimals.

Scientific Notation	Expanded Notation	Standard Notation
5.43×10^3	$5.43 \times 1,000$	5,430
5.43×10^2	5.43 ×	
5.43×10^1	5.43 × 10	
5.43×10^0	5.43 × 1	
5.43×10^{-1}	5.43 × $\frac{1}{10}$	
5.43×10^{-2}	5.43 ×	0.0543
5.43×10^{-3}	5.43 ×	

5. Use what you know about scientific notation to write each expression in expanded notation. Then write each number in standard notation using the pocket chart for help.

6. Study each column for patterns. Describe the pattern that you see in each column.

4   Activity 4   Courses 1–3 Hands-On Activities

Technology Activities

Name _____ Class _____ Date _____

Comparing and Ordering Decimals   Activity 1

Use your scientific calculator to do this activity.

Example 1: Compare 0.3 and 0.09.

① To compare 0.3 and 0.09, begin with the following key sequence:
   Enter .3, press ⊟, enter .09, press ⊒

② Look at the result. Since the answer is +.21, 0.3 > 0.09.

Example 2: Compare 5.12 and 5.099.

① Subtract 5.099 from 5.12.

② Look at the result. The answer is +.021, so 5.12 > 5.099.

Example 3: Compare 1.011 and 1.101.
1.011 − 1.101 = −.09, so 1.011 < 1.101.

Example 4: Order 1.001, 1.101, 1.010, 1.100, and 1.011 from smallest to largest.

① Find the *smallest* decimal. Subtract it from the other numbers to make sure it is the smallest number in the list. If your first choice is not the smallest number, choose a different number and repeat the subtractions.

② Write the *smallest* number first in your list. Repeat these steps to find the next smallest number. Complete the list.
   1.001, 1.010, 1.011, 1.100, 1.101

Exercises

Use <, >, or = to complete each statement. Use your calculator to help you.

1. 0.5 ☐ 0.02   2. 3.034 ☐ 3.340   3. 7.60 ☐ 7.06

4. 1.3 ☐ 1.30   5. 1.15 ☐ 1.015   6. 3.123 ☐ 3.321

7. 4.56 ☐ 4.067   8. 2.15 ☐ 2.51   9. 5.34 ☐ 5.43

Order the decimals from least to greatest. Use your calculator to help you.

10. 9.306, 9.360, 10.006, 9.036, 10.603

11. 2.47, 7.42, 2.07, 1.74, 4.74

12. The Frogs team collected $15.90 for a project. The Snails team collected $15.09. Which team collected the most money for the project?

Technology Activities   Activity 1   **1**

Technology Activities

Name _____ Class _____ Date _____

Exploring Order of Operations   Activity 3

Use your scientific calculator to do this activity.

Example

a. Calculate (7 × 4) + 3. Then calculate 7 × (4 + 3). Compare the results.

   ① To find (7 × 4) + 3, use the following key sequence:
      Press ⬛, enter 7, press ⨯, enter 4, press ⬛, press ⊞, enter 3, press ⊒. Write the result.

   ② Clear and calculate 7 × (4 + 3). Write the result.

   ③ Compare the results. The first expression gives a result of 31; the second gives 49.

b. Calculate the same expression without any grouping symbols: 7 × 4 + 3. Write the result.

   The result is 31, because the calculator multiplies before adding.

Exercises

1. a. Calculate 8 + 4 × 3. Which operation did the calculator do first?
   b. Insert parentheses in the expression so that the calculator gives the same result as when there are no parentheses.

2. Insert parentheses in the following expression so that your calculator gives an answer of 10.
   32 − 6 + 5 × 2

3. Insert parentheses in the following expression so that your calculator gives an answer of 62.
   32 − 6 + 5 × 2

4. Explain the difference between your answers to Exercises 2 and 3. Why are the results different even though the numbers are the same in both expressions?

5. Use your calculator to evaluate the expression
   2 + 3 × 4 − (5 − 3) × 2.

Insert parentheses so that the following statements are true. Use your calculator to check your answers.

6. 3 × 2 + 5 = 21

7. 3 + 5 × 6 + 12 ÷ 6 = 50

8. 3 + 5 × 6 + 12 ÷ 6 = 24

Technology Activities   Activity 3   **3**

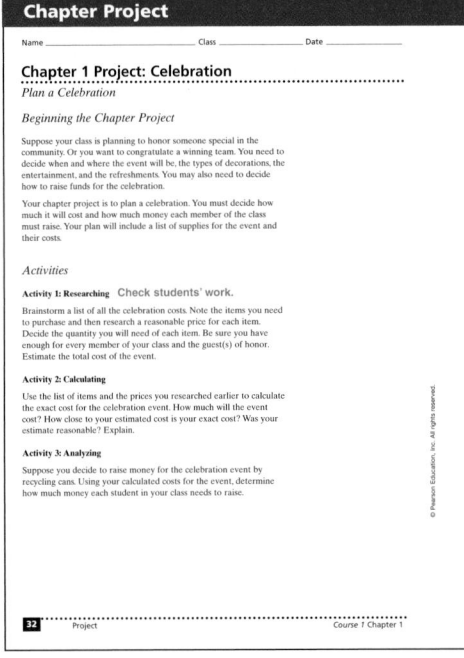

Name _____ Class _____ Date _____

Chapter 1 Project: Celebration
Plan a Celebration

Beginning the Chapter Project

Suppose your class is planning to honor someone special in the community. Or you want to congratulate a winning team. You need to decide when and where the event will be, the types of decorations, the entertainment, and the refreshments. You may also need to decide how to raise funds for the celebration.

Your chapter project is to plan a celebration. You must decide how much it will cost and how much money each member of the class must raise. Your plan will include a list of supplies for the event and their costs.

Activities

Activity 1: Researching Check students' work.

Brainstorm a list of all the celebration costs. Note the items you need to purchase and then research a reasonable price for each item. Decide the quantity you will need of each item. Be sure you have enough for every member of your class and the guest(s) of honor. Estimate the total cost of the event.

Activity 2: Calculating

Use the list of items and the prices you researched earlier to calculate the exact cost for the celebration event. How much will the event cost? How close to your estimated cost is your exact cost? Was your estimate reasonable? Explain.

Activity 3: Analyzing

Suppose you decide to raise money for the celebration event by recycling cans. Using your calculated costs for the event, determine how much money each student in your class needs to raise.

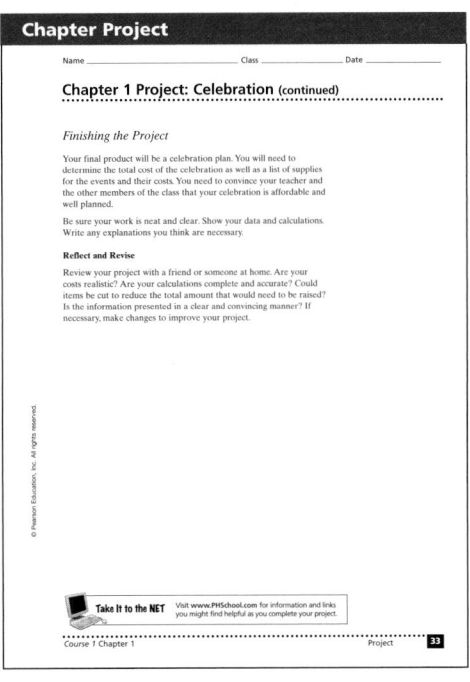

Name _____ Class _____ Date _____

Chapter 1 Project: Celebration (continued)

Finishing the Project

Your final product will be a celebration plan. You will need to determine the total cost of the celebration as well as a list of supplies for the events and their costs. You need to convince your teacher and the other members of the class that your celebration is affordable and well planned.

Be sure your work is neat and clear. Show your data and calculations. Write any explanations you think are necessary.

Reflect and Revise

Review your project with a friend or someone at home. Are your costs realistic? Are your calculations complete and accurate? Could items be cut to reduce the total amount that would need to be raised? Is the information presented in a clear and convincing manner? If necessary, make changes to improve your project.

Take It to the NET Visit www.PHSchool.com for information and links you might find helpful as you complete your project.

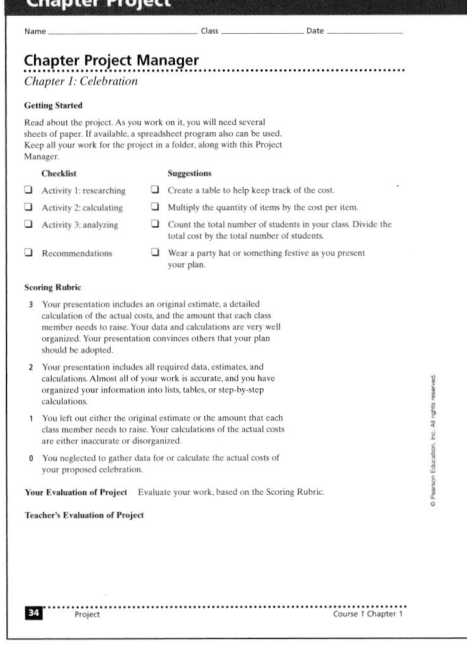

Name _____ Class _____ Date _____

Chapter Project Manager
Chapter 1: Celebration

Getting Started

Read about the project. As you work on it, you will need several sheets of paper. If available, a spreadsheet program also can be used. Keep all your work for the project in a folder, along with this Project Manager.

Checklist	Suggestions
☐ Activity 1: researching	☐ Create a table to help keep track of the cost.
☐ Activity 2: calculating	☐ Multiply the quantity of items by the cost per item.
☐ Activity 3: analyzing	☐ Count the total number of students in your class. Divide the total cost by the total number of students.
☐ Recommendations	☐ Wear a party hat or something festive as you present your plan.

Scoring Rubric

3 Your presentation includes an original estimate, a detailed calculation of the actual costs, and the amount that each class member needs to raise. Your data and calculations are very well organized. Your presentation convinces others that your plan should be adopted.

2 Your presentation includes all required data, estimates, and calculations. Almost all of your work is accurate, and you have organized your information into lists, tables, or step-by-step calculations.

1 You left out either the original estimate or the amount that each class member needs to raise. Your calculations of the actual costs are either inaccurate or disorganized.

0 You neglected to gather data for or calculate the actual costs of your proposed celebration.

Your Evaluation of Project Evaluate your work, based on the Scoring Rubric.

Teacher's Evaluation of Project

Transparencies

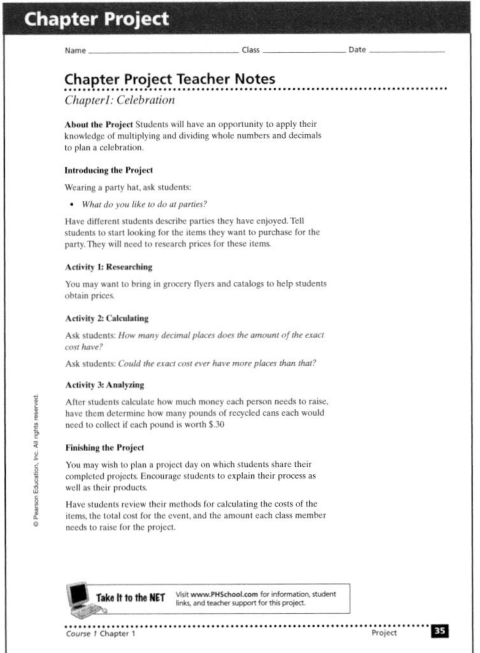

Name _____ Class _____ Date _____

Chapter Project Teacher Notes
Chapter 1: Celebration

About the Project Students will have an opportunity to apply their knowledge of multiplying and dividing whole numbers and decimals to plan a celebration.

Introducing the Project

Wearing a party hat, ask students:

• *What do you like to do at parties?*

Have different students describe parties they have enjoyed. Tell students to start looking for the items they want to purchase for the party. They will need to research prices for these items.

Activity 1: Researching

You may want to bring in grocery flyers and catalogs to help students obtain prices.

Activity 2: Calculating

Ask students: *How many decimal places does the amount of the exact cost have?*

Ask students: *Could the exact cost ever have more places than that?*

Activity 3: Analyzing

After students calculate how much money each person needs to raise, have them determine how many pounds of recycled cans each would need to collect if each pound is worth $.30.

Finishing the Project

You may wish to plan a project day on which students share their completed projects. Encourage students to explain their process as well as their products.

Have students review their methods for calculating the costs of the items, the total cost for the event, and the amount each class member needs to raise for the project.

Take It to the NET Visit www.PHSchool.com for information, student links, and teacher support for this project.

Problem of the Day Lesson 1-1

A pizza has 8 equal slices. You put only mushrooms on $\frac{1}{2}$ of them, and only sausage on $\frac{3}{8}$ of them. How many slices are left without a topping?

Answer

1 slice

Problem of the Day Lesson 1-2

If 300 cheeseburgers are ordered for lunch on a field trip and one out of every five must have mustard on it, how many will have mustard on them?

Answer

60

Problem of the Day Lesson 1-3

Write the decimal for two hundred six hundred-thousandths.

Answer

0.00206

Problem of the Day Lesson 1-4

A 12-in. submarine sandwich is divided into 6 slices, and a second 12-in. sandwich is divided into 8 slices. Which sandwich has the larger slices?

Answer

the sandwich with 6 slices

Problem of the Day Lesson 1-5

Find the pattern and write the next three numbers in the sequence.

$$\frac{1}{2}, \frac{1}{4}, \frac{1}{8}, \frac{1}{16}$$

Answer

$$\frac{1}{32}, \frac{1}{64}, \frac{1}{128}$$

Problem of the Day Lesson 1-6

What are the values of 9 in 9.0349?

Answer

ones place and ten-thousandths place

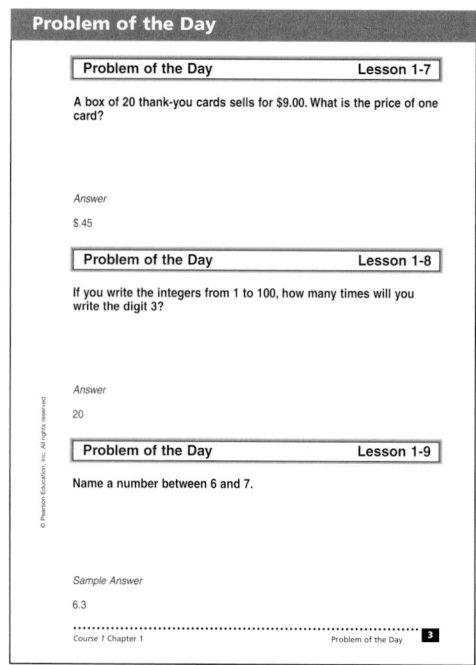

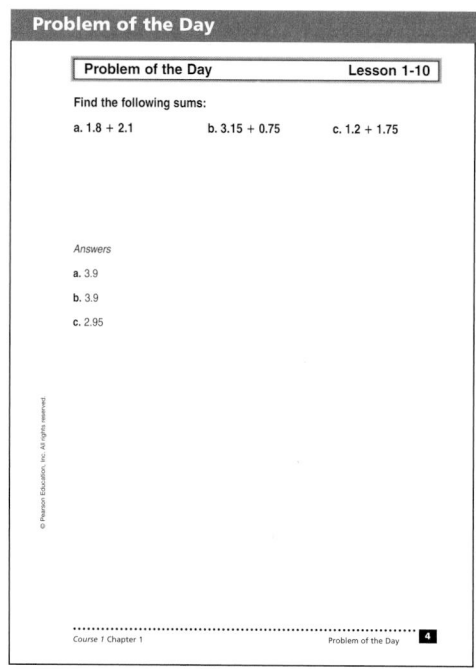

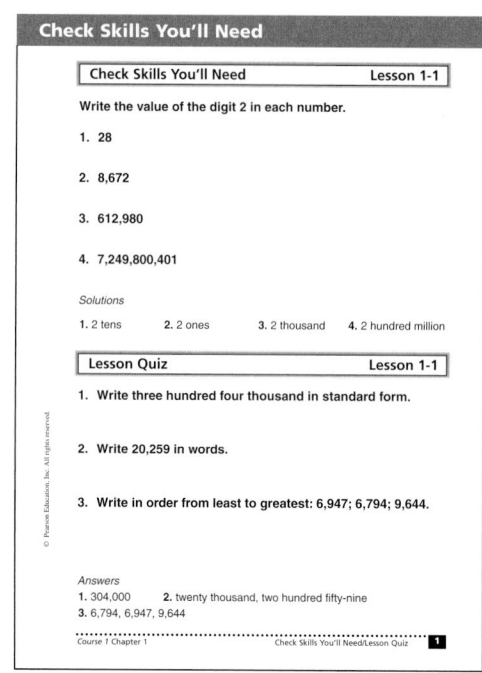

Sample page; see p. G for complete list.

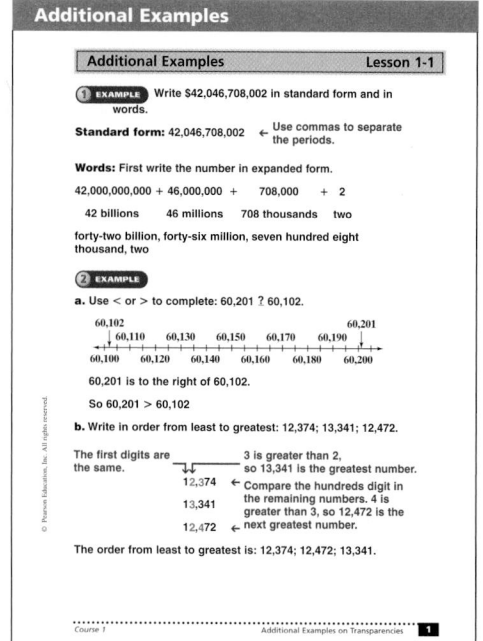

Sample page; see p. G for complete list.

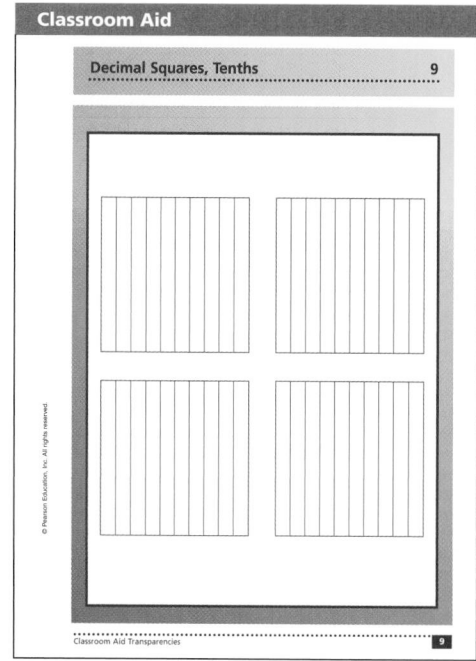

Sample page; see p. G for complete list.

Assessment

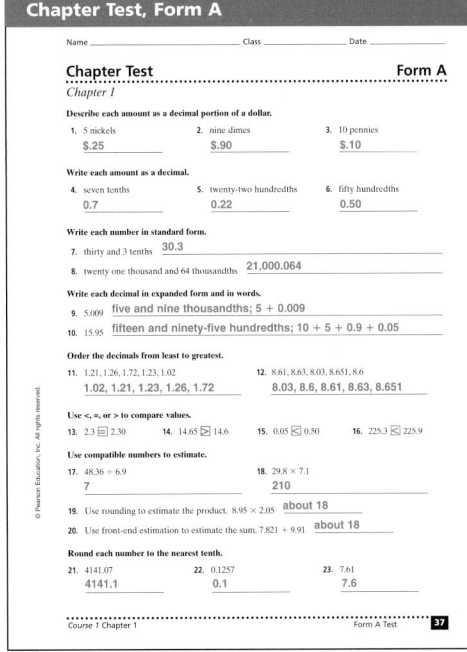

Sample page; see p. G for complete list.   *Available in Spanish*   *Available in Spanish*

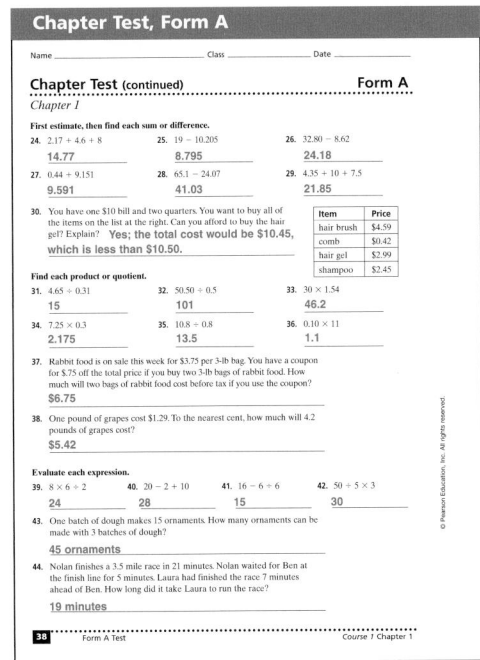
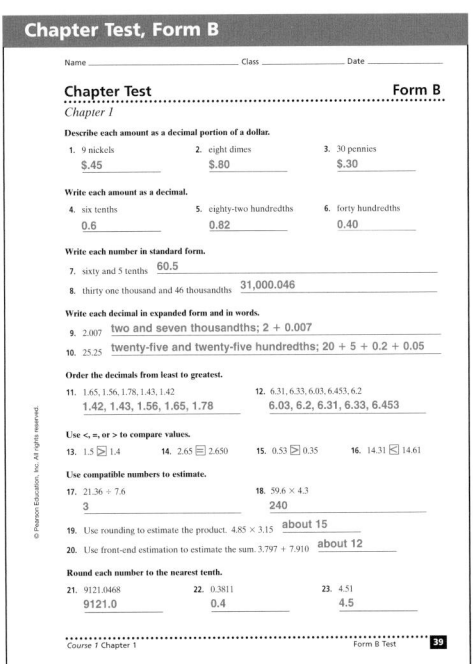
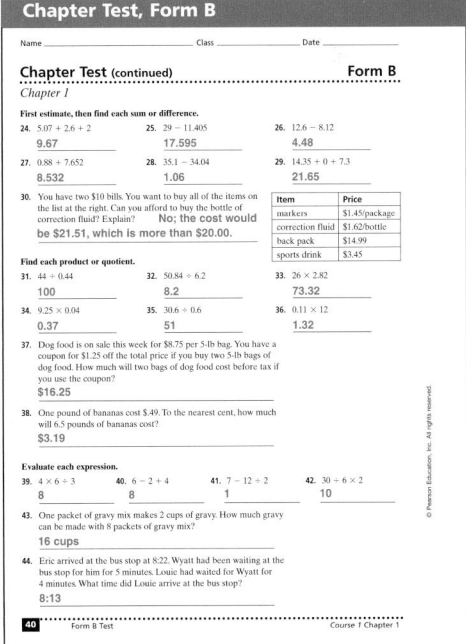

Available in Spanish   *Available in Spanish*   *Available in Spanish*

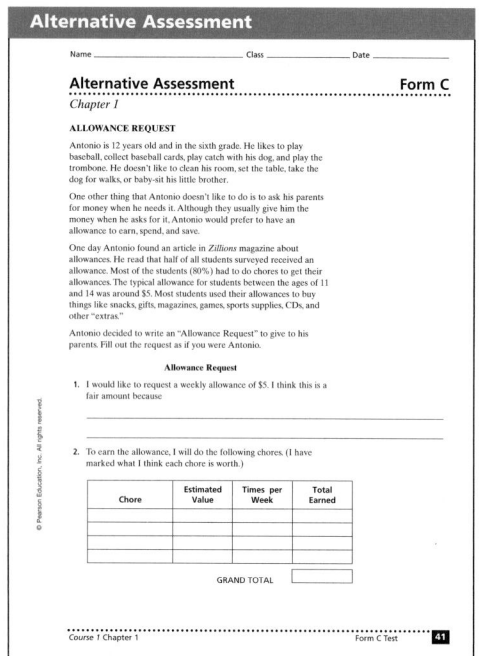

Available in Spanish

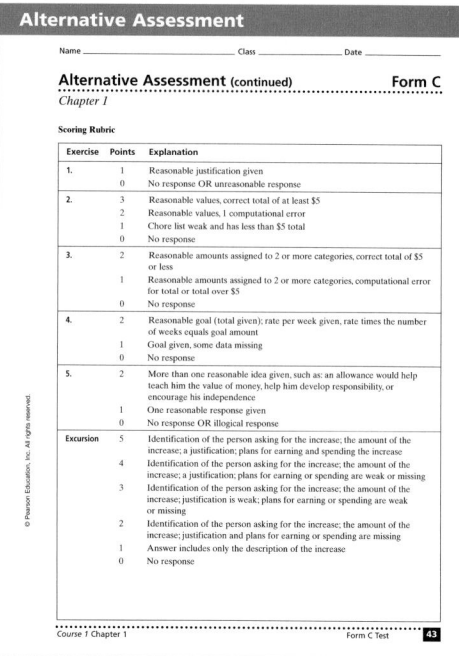

Available in Spanish

Available in Spanish

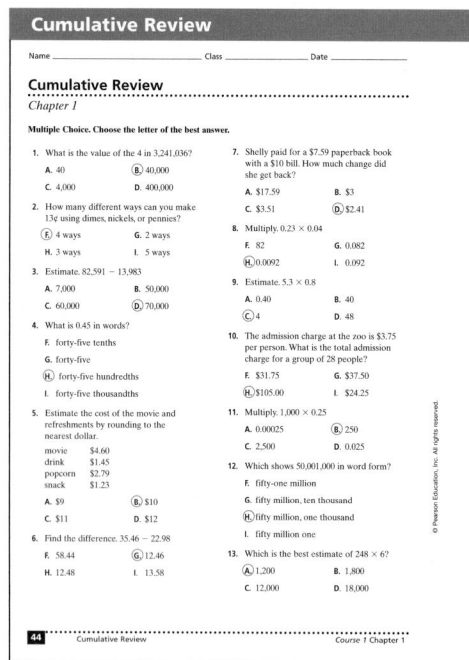

Available in Spanish

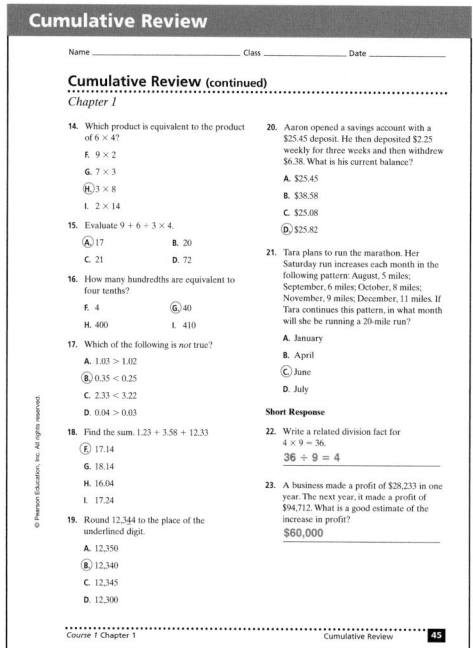

Available in Spanish

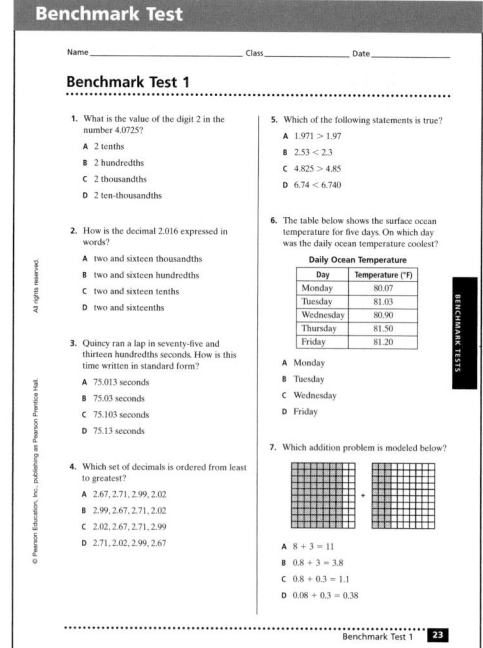

On PH Website

Test-Taking Strategies transparency
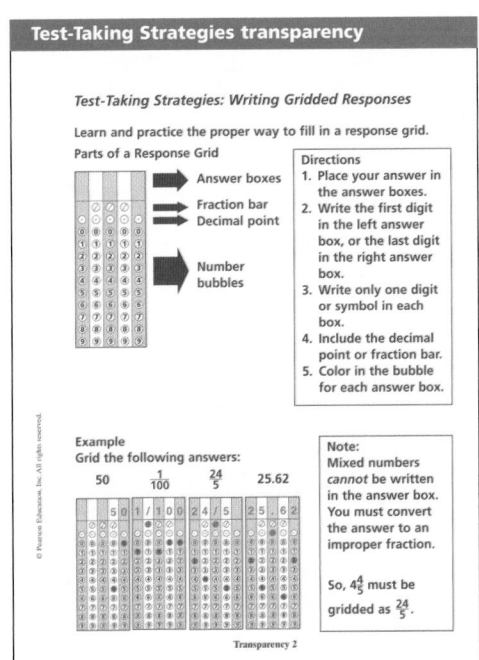

Test-Taking Strategies worksheet
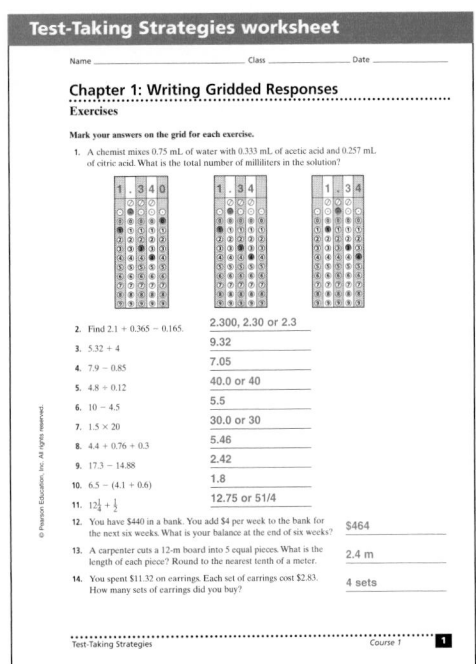

Home Activities
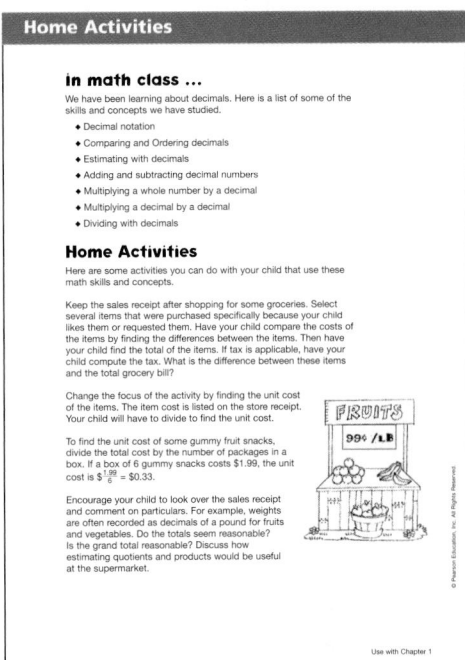

Available in Spanish;
Web Code: aak-5500

Interdisciplinary Activities
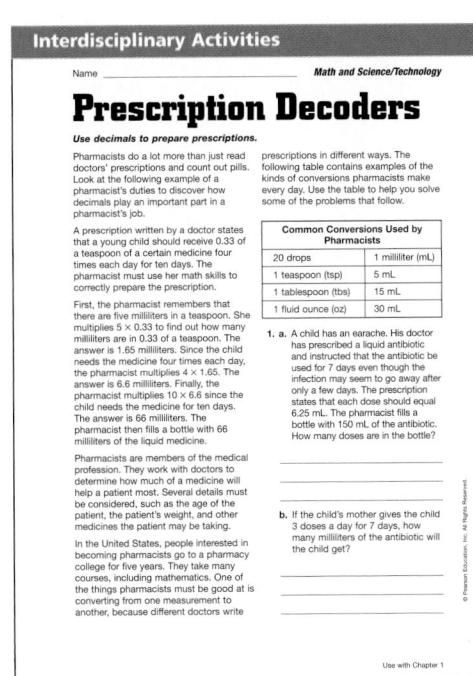

Available in Spanish;
Web Code: aak-5500

Interdisciplinary Activities

Available in Spanish;
Web Code: aak-5500

Algebra Readiness Puzzles
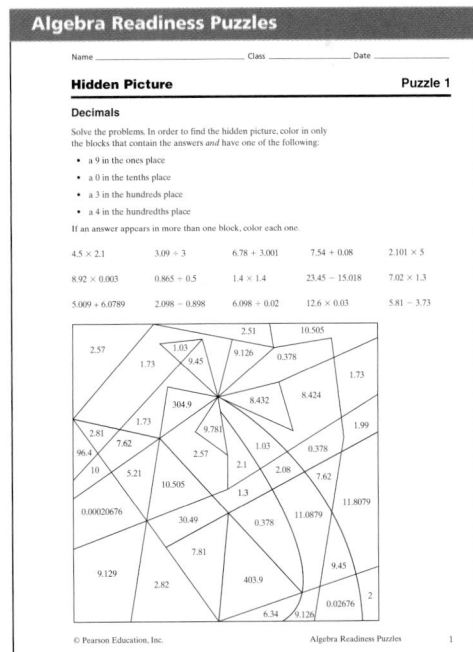

Web Code: aak-5500

CHAPTER 1

Decimals

Chapter 1 Overview

In this chapter students investigate and work with decimals. They compare and order decimals and add, subtract, multiply, and divide decimals. They explore and use patterns to multiply and divide decimals by powers of 10.

 **Reading Math**
- Reading Your Textbook, p. 18
- **Vocabulary:** A complete list, plus exercises, in the Chapter Review, p. 54
- **Illustrated Glossary:** Examples for each vocabulary term, plus definitions in English and Spanish, on p. 669

 **Test-Taking Strategies**
Writing Gridded Responses, p. 53

Real-World Problem Solving
- **Strategies:** Using a Problem Solving Plan, pp. 30–33
- **Real-World Snapshots:** That's an Order!, pp. 58–59
- **Chapter Project:** Celebration, p. 636

 **www.PHSchool.com**
Internet support includes:
- Self-grading Vocabulary and Chapter 1 Tests
- Activity Masters
- Chapter Project support
- Chapter Planner
- Ch. 1 Resources

Plus **iTEXT**

CHAPTER 1

2

Decimals

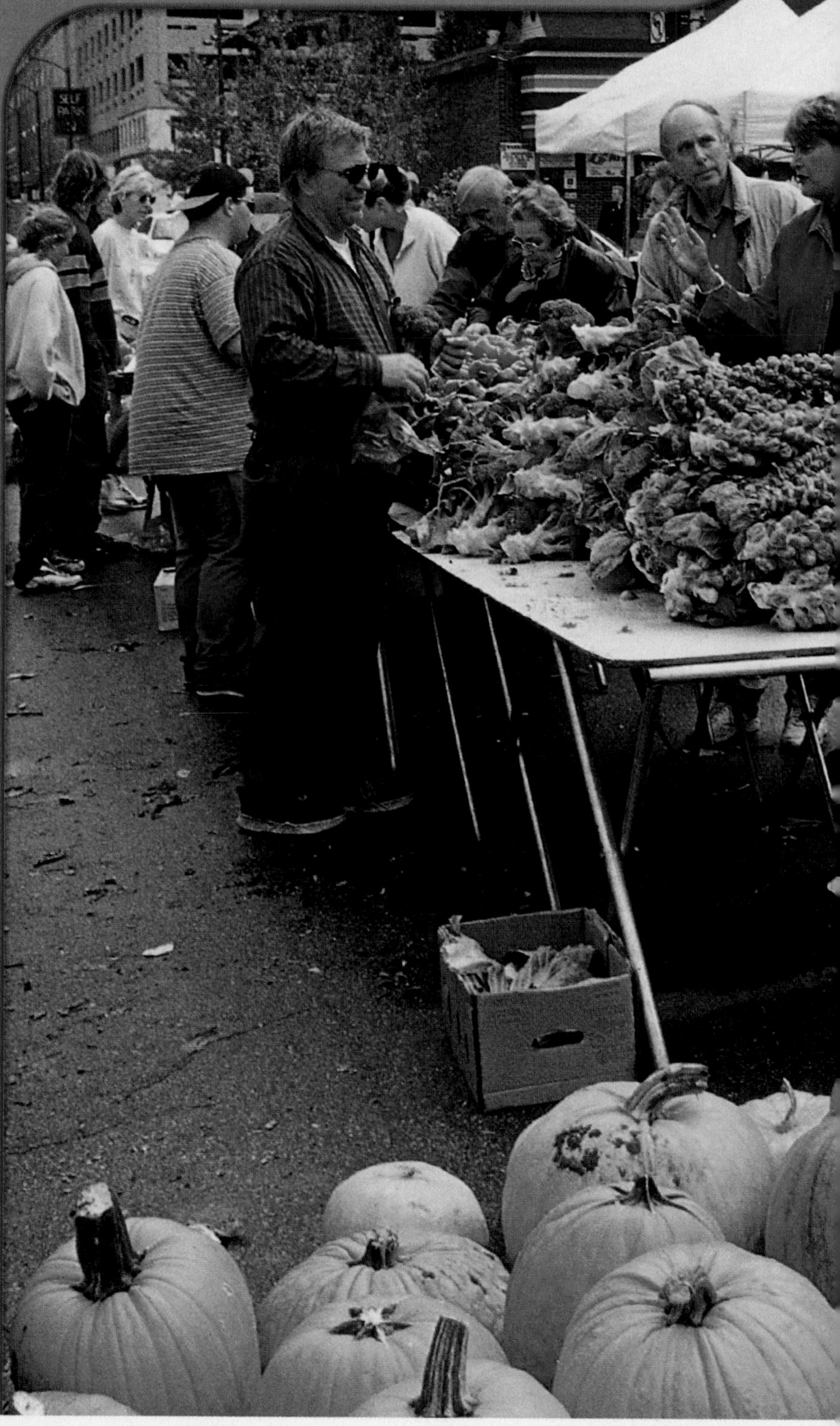

Activating Prior Knowledge
In this chapter students build on and extend their knowledge of whole numbers and whole-number properties and operations to understand and compute with decimals. Ask questions such as:
- *Use the order of operations to simplify: 4 + 8 × 2.* **20**
- *What is the missing number in this sequence: 1, 10, 100, ____, 10,000, 100,000, . . . ?* **1,000**

DK Real-World Snapshots
The data here will be used throughout the chapter. Have a volunteer read the opening passage, and then focus students on the Egyptian and Roman numerals in the chart and ask:
- *How could you express the number 12 using Roman numerals?* **XII**
- *How might you express the number 12 using Egyptian numerals?* **Sample: ∩ I I**

DK Real-World Snapshots

In today's markets, we pay for goods using dollars and coins. Our money, like our number system, is based on decimals. Other cultures, past and present, have used different symbols to represent numbers.

Data File Number Symbols

Arabic	Egyptian	Roman
0	No symbol	No symbol
1	I	I
2	II	II
3	III	III
4	IIII	IV
5	IIIII	V
6	IIIIII	VI

Arabic	Egyptian	Roman
7	IIIIIII	VII
8	IIIIIIII	VIII
9	IIIIIIIII	IX
10	∩	X
100	ℚ	C
1,000	ℊ	M
10,000	)	X̄

You will use the data above in this chapter:

- p. 7 Lesson 1-1
- p. 16 Lesson 1-3
- p. 28 Lesson 1-5

DK **Real-World Snapshots** On pages 58 and 59, you will solve problems involving order forms.

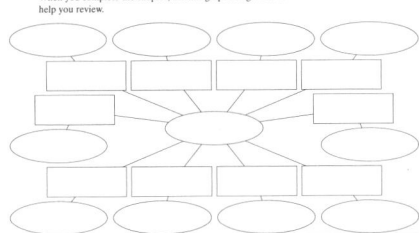

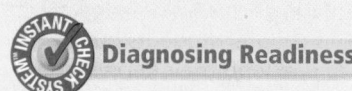
Diagnosing Readiness

Students will find answers to these exercises in the back of their textbooks.

Prescribing Intervention
For intervention, direct students to:

Rounding to the Nearest Ten
Skills Handbook: Rounding Whole Numbers, p. 655.

Adding and Subtracting Whole Numbers
Skills Handbook: Adding Whole Numbers, Subtracting Whole Numbers, pp. 656–657.

Multiplying Whole Numbers
Skills Handbook: Multiplying Whole Numbers, p. 658–659.

Dividing Whole Numbers
Skills Handbook: Dividing Whole Numbers, pp. 659–660.

Chapter 1 Preview

Where You've Been

● In a previous course, you added, subtracted, multiplied, and divided with whole numbers. You also estimated with whole numbers.

Where You're Going

● In Chapter 1, you will add, subtract, multiply, divide, compare, order, and estimate with decimals.

● Applying what you learn, you will perform operations with decimals in the correct order. You will compare decimals so you can find a nonfiction book in a library.

The Dewey Decimal System for nonfiction books assigns each book a number based on its topic.

 Instant self-check online and on CD-ROM

Diagnosing Readiness

 For help, go to the Skills Handbook.

Rounding to the Nearest Ten (Skills Handbook page 655)

Round each number to the nearest ten.

1. 312 310   **2.** 7,525 7,530   **3.** 38 40

4. 55 60   **5.** 699 700   **6.** 1,989 1,990

Adding and Subtracting Whole Numbers (Skills Handbook pages 656 and 657)

Add or subtract.

7. 59 + 116 175   **8.** 182 − 37 145   **9.** 8,745 + 5,447 14,192

10. 4,823 − 1,796 3,027   **11.** 9,004 + 996 10,000   **12.** 2,049 − 657 1,392

Multiplying Whole Numbers (Skills Handbook page 658)

Multiply.

13. 9 × 83 747   **14.** 64 × 71 4,544   **15.** 437 × 100 43,700

16. 25 × 1,000 25,000   **17.** 33 × 14 462   **18.** 232 × 8 1,856

Dividing Whole Numbers (Skills Handbook pages 659 and 660)

Divide.

19. 50 ÷ 10 5   **20.** 85 ÷ 5 17   **21.** 1,944 ÷ 27 72

22. 256 ÷ 8 32   **23.** 2,132 ÷ 164 13   **24.** 1,241 ÷ 17 73

Check Understanding

1. twenty-six billion, two hundred thirty-six million, eight hundred forty-six thousand, eighty dollars

1-1 Understanding Whole Numbers

What You'll Learn

OBJECTIVE 1 To write and compare whole numbers

. . . And Why

To compare amounts, as in Exercise 27

 Check Skills You'll Need

 For help, go to Skills Handbook p. 654.

Write the value of the digit 2 in each number.

1. 28 **2 tens**
2. 8,672 **2 ones**
3. 612,980 **2 thousand**
4. 7,249,800,401 **2 hundred million**

New Vocabulary
• standard form • expanded form

OBJECTIVE 1

 Interactive lesson includes instant self-check, tutorials, and activities.

Writing and Comparing Whole Numbers

To work with decimals, you need to understand the *place value* of whole numbers. The **standard form** of a number uses digits and place value. The *place* of the digit 5 in 254 is tens. The *value* of 5 is 5 tens, or 50. A sum that shows the place and value of each digit of a number is its **expanded form**.

Trillions Period			Billions Period			Millions Period			Thousands Period			Ones Period		
Hundreds	Tens	Ones	Hundreds	Tens	Ones	Hundreds	Tens	Ones	Hundreds	Tens	Ones	Hundreds	Tens	Ones
		2	6	2	3	6	8	4	6	0	8	0	0	0

Real-World Connection

The Sears Tower in Chicago is 1,454 feet tall without its antenna towers.

1 EXAMPLE Writing a Whole Number in Words  Real World

Buildings The number in the chart above is the number of pennies you would need to build a stack of pennies as tall as the Sears Tower. Write the number in standard form and in words.

Standard form: 2,623,684,608,000 ← Use commas to separate the periods.

Words: First write the number in expanded form.

2,000,000,000,000 + 623,000,000,000 + 684,000,000 + 608,000

2 trillions   623 billions   684 millions   608 thousands

two trillion, six hundred twenty-three billion, six hundred eighty-four million, six hundred eight thousand

 Check Understanding 1 Write the value of $26,236,846,080 in words. See margin.

 Ongoing Assessment and Intervention

Before the Lesson
Diagnose prerequisite skills using:
• Check Skills You'll Need

During the Lesson
Monitor progress using:
• Check Understanding
• Additional Examples
• Test Prep

After the Lesson
Assess knowledge using:
• Lesson Quiz
• Computer Test Generator CD

1-1

1. Plan

Lesson Preview

 PowerPoint

 Check Skills You'll Need

Place Value of Whole Numbers
Skills Handbook: Place Value of Whole Numbers, p. 654.

Lesson Resources

Teaching Support includes:
Practice, Reteaching, Enrichment
Assessment, Reading & Literacy,
Activities, Transparencies,
Technology, CD-ROMs, Spanish,
and More

See pp. 2G–2H for a complete list of resources for this lesson.

www.PHSchool.com
• Teacher Web Code: aak-5500
• Algebra Readiness Puzzles 42

Plus TEXT

2. Teach

Professional Development

Math Background

The *expanded form* of a number is a sum of the values of each digit. For example, the *standard form* number 1,275 can be written in expanded form as
1,000 + 200 + 70 + 5. In words, the number 1,275 is read as "one thousand, two hundred seventy-five." All three forms of a number represent equivalent values.

PowerPoint

 **Additional Examples**

1 Write $42,046,708,002 in standard form and in words. **42,046,708,002; forty-two billion, forty-six million, seven hundred eight thousand, two**

2 a. Use < or > to complete: 60,201 ■ 60,102. **>**

  b. Write in order from least to greatest: 12,374; 13,341; 12,472. **12,374, 12,472, 13,341**

5

- *What is the expanded form of a number?* the sum that shows the place value of each digit
- *How do you compare whole numbers?* Compare digits starting with the greater place value; or use a number line.

3. Practice

Assignment Guide

 **Objective 1**
  Ⓐ Ⓑ **Core** 1–32
  Ⓒ **Extension** 33

Test Prep 34–36
Mixed Review 37–40

Error Prevention!

Exercises 1–5 Encourage students to use a place-value chart.

4. Assess

 **Lesson Quiz 1-1**

1. Write three hundred four thousand in standard form.
   304,000

2. Write 20,259 in words.
   twenty thousand, two hundred fifty-nine

3. Write in order from least to greatest: 6,947; 6,794; 9,644. **6,794, 6,947, 9,644**

Alternative Assessment

Each student in a pair writes two whole numbers greater than 1,000. Partners exchange papers and write each other's numbers in expanded form and in words.

Test Prep

Resources
For additional practice with a variety of test item formats:
- Test Prep, p. 57
- Test-Taking Strategies, p. 53
- Test-Taking Strategies With Transparencies

You can use place value to compare and order whole numbers. You can also use a number line to compare whole numbers. The numbers on a number line are in order from least to greatest.

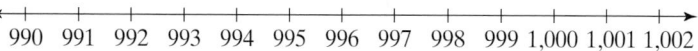

② EXAMPLE Comparing and Ordering Whole Numbers

a. Use < or > to complete: 995 ▦ 998.

995 is to the left of 998 on the number line above.

So, 995 < 998.

b. Write in order from least to greatest: 12,875; 12,675; 12,695.
Compare the digits starting with the highest place values.

The first two digits are the same. → 12,875 8 is greater than 6, so 12,875 is the greatest number.
12,675 ← Compare the tens digit in the remaining numbers.
12,695 9 is greater than 7, so 12,695 is the next greatest number.

The order from least to greatest is: 12,675; 12,695; 12,875.

Need Help?
To compare numbers, use these symbols.
< is read "is less than."
= is read "is equal to."
> is read "is greater than."

✔ **Check Understanding** ② **a.** Use < or > to complete: 129,631 ≤ 142,832.
b. Write in order from least to greatest: 9,897; 9,987; 9,789.
9,789; 9,897; 9,987

EXERCISES

❓ For more practice, see *Extra Practice*.

Ⓐ **Practice by Example**

Write each number in standard form and in words. 1–3. See margin.

Example 1
(page 5)

1. 20 + 5
2. 3,000 + 200
3. 500,000 + 8,000 + 300 + 10

4. 8 hundred 90
   890; eight hundred ninety
5. 7 trillion, 2 million, 31 thousand
   7,000,002,031,000; seven trillion, two million, and thirty-one thousand

Example 2
(page 6)

Use < or > to complete each statement.

6. 366 $\overset{>}{▦}$ 36
7. 54,001 $\overset{<}{▦}$ 54,901
8. 8,801 $\overset{>}{▦}$ 810

9. 84,123 $\overset{>}{▦}$ 9,996
10. 29,286 $\overset{<}{▦}$ 29,826
11. 31,010 $\overset{>}{▦}$ 30,101

Write in order from least to greatest. 12–13. See left.

12. 20,403; 20,304; 23,404; 23,040
13. 54,172; 51,472; 57,142; 51,572

12. 20,304; 20,403; 23,040; 23,404

13. 51,472; 51,572; 54,172; 57,142

14. 7,910; 7,890; 7,901
    7,890; 7,901; 7,910
15. 17,444; 18,242; 17,671; 17,414
    17,414; 17,444; 17,671; 18,242

👥 Reaching All Students

| **Below Level** Create a page of "empty" place-value charts similar to the one shown above Example 1. Guide students to accurately identify the starting place and not to skip zeros as they fill in the charts. | **Advanced Learners** In meters, the Sears Tower in Example 1 is 443.2 m. *How might the number of pennies corresponding to its height change if the tower is measured in meters instead of feet?* no change | **Error Prevention** See note on page 6. |

B Apply Your Skills

Write the value of the digit 4 in each number.

16. 468 400

17. 645,017 40,000

18. 146,215,020 40,000,000

19. 105,034,863 4,000

20. 542 40

21. 1,394 4

22. 418,920 400,000

23. 781,409 400

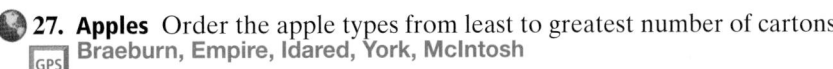

Data File, p. 3 The ancient Egyptians did not use a place-value system for their numbers. Instead, they used hieroglyphs to represent numerals.

24. What number is represented at the right? 687

25. Write 82 and 1,059 using hieroglyphs. **See back of book.**

26. Open-Ended Write a 5-digit number. Then write it using hieroglyphs. **See back of book.**

Type of Apple	Cartons
Idared	2,753,000
Empire	2,739,000
Braeburn	2,198,000
McIntosh	3,304,000
York	3,212,000

Source: U.S. Apple Association

27. Apples Order the apple types from least to greatest number of cartons. Braeburn, Empire, Idared, York, McIntosh

Use < or > to make each sentence true.

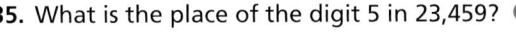

28. 60,789 < 60,798 < 62,532

29. 24,891 > 18,000 > 12,501

30. 42,101 > 42,077 > 41,963

31. 10,455 < 11,400 < 11,483

C Challenge

32. Writing in Math Describe two methods of comparing whole numbers. **See margin.**

33. Research How many zeros does the number one *quadrillion* have? How many zeros does the number one *quintillion* have? fifteen; eighteen

---

Test Prep

Multiple Choice

34. What is the value of the digit 2 in 524,065? **D**
A. two   B. twenty   C. two thousand   D. twenty thousand

35. What is the place of the digit 5 in 23,459? **G**
F. ones   G. tens   H. hundreds   I. thousands

Take It to the NET
Online lesson quiz at
www.PHSchool.com
Web Code: aaa-0101

36. Which number is NOT greater than 16,374? **C**
A. 16,734   B. 17,437   C. 16,347   D. 16,743

Mixed Review

Skills Handbook p. 656

Add.

37. 375 + 15 390

38. 120 + 6 126

39. 1,820 + 309 2,129

40. 2,617 + 1,904 4,521

1-1 Understanding Whole Numbers **7**

---

1. 25; twenty-five

2. 3,200; three thousand, two hundred

3. 508,310; five hundred eight thousand, three hundred ten

32. Answers may vary. Sample: First method: compare the digits starting with the highest place values. Second method: attempt to subtract one from the other.

 Use the Guided Problem Solving worksheet with Exercise 27.

Exploring Decimal Models

Students use grid models to represent decimals and equivalent decimals.
In Lesson 1-2, students learn to write decimals in words, standard form, and expanded form.

Optional Materials

• graph paper or blank grid models

Teaching Notes

Because monetary values are familiar to students, they provide a good place to begin when working with decimal models. One dollar can represent ten dimes (tenths) or 100 pennies (hundredths).

1 EXAMPLE Tactile Learners

Have students make the models shown in the example. If blank grids are unavailable, you may wish to provide graph paper for students to mark off 10 × 10 grids. Ask: *What decimal does the unshaded portion of your hundredths-grid represent?* 0.87

2 EXAMPLE Inclusion

Students can use dimes and pennies to verify their answers. Tell them that a completely shaded grid model represents $1. Ask:
• *What monetary value do both the grid models represent?* 50 cents ($.50 or 50¢)
• *How does each model show 50¢?* 5 of 10 equal-sized rectangles are shaded, representing 5 dimes; 50 of 100 equal-sized squares are shaded, representing 50 pennies.

Exercises

Have students work independently on the exercises.

8

Exploring Decimal Models

For Use With Lesson 1-2

You can use grid models to represent decimals. If you divide a square into 10 equal parts, each part is *one tenth* of the square.

Tenths Model

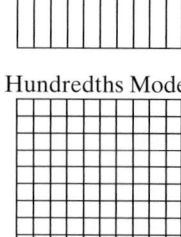

Hundredths Model

1 EXAMPLE **Modeling Decimals**

Write a decimal for the model below in words and in numerals.

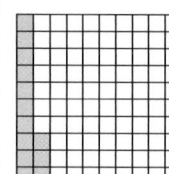

There are 100 squares.
Thirteen squares are shaded.

Words   thirteen hundredths

Numerals   0.13

2 EXAMPLE **Modeling Equal Decimals**

Find the number of hundredths that is equal to five tenths.

Draw a model. Shade five tenths, or 0.5.

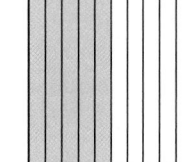

five tenths = 0.5

Divide the model into hundredths. Fifty squares are shaded.

fifty hundredths = 0.50

0.50 is equal to 0.5.

EXERCISES

Write a decimal for each model.

1. 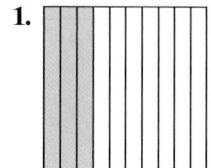 0.3

2. 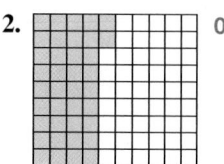 0.42

3. 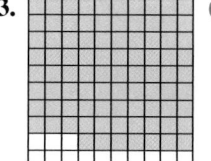 0.87

Write a decimal that is equal to each value.   4–10. Answers may vary. Samples are given.

4. sixty hundredths 0.60

5. forty hundredths 0.4

6. eight hundredths 0.08

7. 0.2 0.20

8. 0.9 0.90

9. 0.7 0.70

10. 0.40 0.4

8   **Investigation**   Exploring Decimal Models

1a. 3 + 0.1 + 0.04 + 0.001 + 0.0006

b. 0.8 + 0.06 + 0.005

c. 30 + 7 + 0.5

d. No; the zero in 6.207 is covered when you write "+0.007."

Reading and Writing Decimals

What You'll Learn

OBJECTIVE 1 To read and write decimals

. . . And Why

To read scores in sports, as in Example 3

 Check Skills You'll Need

Write each whole number in words.

1. 28 twenty-eight

2. 8,672 eight thousand, six hundred seventy-two

3. 612,980 six hundred twelve thousand, nine hundred eighty

4. 58,026,113 fifty-eight million, twenty-six thousand, one hundred thirteen

 For help, go to Lesson 1-1.

iTEXT Interactive lesson includes instant self-check, tutorials, and activities.

OBJECTIVE 1

Reading and Writing Decimals

Reading Math

To show that a number is between 0 and 1, a 0 is usually placed to the left of the decimal point.

You can extend the place-value chart in Lesson 1-1 to include values for decimal places. You can also write decimals in standard form and in expanded form.

Standard Form		Expanded Form		
0.75	=	0.7	+	0.05
seventy-five hundredths		seven tenths		five hundredths

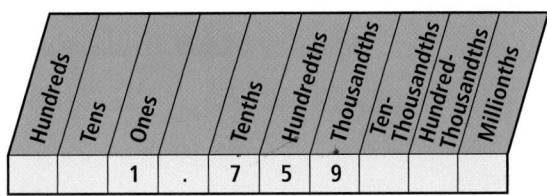

1 EXAMPLE Writing a Decimal in Expanded Form  Real World

Fuel The price of a gallon of gasoline is \$1.759. Write 1.759 from the chart above in expanded form.

	one	seven tenths	five hundredths	nine thousandths
1.759 =	1 +	0.7 +	0.05 +	0.009

 **Check Understanding** 1 Write each number in expanded form. 1a–d. See margin.

a. 3.1416   b. 0.865   c. 37.5

d. **Reasoning** Do you need to include 0.00 in the expanded form of 6.207? Explain.

Lesson Preview

 PowerPoint

 Check Skills You'll Need

Writing a Whole Number in Words
Lesson 1-1: Example 1. Extra Practice, p. 642.

Lesson Resources

Teaching Resources
Practice, Reteaching, Enrichment

Reaching All Students
Practice Workbook 1-2
Spanish Practice Workbook 1-2
Guided Problem Solving 1-2
Hands-On Activities 1, 4

Presentation Assistant Plus!
Transparencies
• Check Skills You'll Need 1-2
• Problem of the Day 1-2
• Additional Examples 1-2
• Student Edition Answers 1-2
• Lesson Quiz 1-2
PH Presentation Pro CD-ROM 1-2

PRENTICE HALL ASSESSMENT SYSTEM

Computer Test Generator CD

 **Technology**
Resource Pro® CD-ROM
Computer Test Generator CD
PH Presentation Pro CD-ROM

 **www.PHSchool.com**
Student Site
• Teacher Web Code: aak-5500
• Self-grading Lesson Quiz

PH SuccessNet Teacher Center Professional Development
• Lesson Planner
• Resources

Plus **iTEXT**

Ongoing Assessment and Intervention

Before the Lesson
Diagnose prerequisite skills using:
• Check Skills You'll Need

During the Lesson
Monitor progress using:
• Check Understanding
• Additional Examples
• Test Prep

After the Lesson
Assess knowledge using:
• Lesson Quiz
• Computer Test Generator CD

9

2. Teach

Math Background

The number 341 is read as "three hundred forty-one." The decimal 3.41 is read as "three and forty-one hundredths." When writing decimals as word expressions, "and" is used to represent the decimal point in decimals greater than 1. So "and" is not used in whole numbers or decimals less than 1.

Teaching Notes

① EXAMPLE Inclusion

Students might be confused because they are not accustomed to seeing monetary values with numbers in the thousandths place. Point out that the price of gasoline is rounded to the nearest hundredth, or cent. A customer buying one gallon of gas at $1.459 per gallon pays $1.46.

② EXAMPLE Error Prevention

Because students are accustomed to saying "dot com" and "point," they may try using this language when reading and writing decimals (e.g., "20 dot 408"). Provide a visual cue by rewriting the three numbers in Check Understanding 2a–c on the board and replacing each decimal with the word *and*.

PowerPoint
Additional Examples

① Write 608.0459 in expanded form. **600 + 8 + 0.04 + 0.005 + 0.0009**

② Write 1.0936 in words. **one and nine hundred thirty-six ten thousandths**

③ There are four thousand five hundred thirty-six ten thousandths kilograms in one pound. Write this number in standard form. **0.4536**

Closure

When writing a number in words, when do you use "and"? Use "and" for the decimal point with numbers greater than 1.

10

When you read a decimal that is greater than 1, read the decimal point as "and." Be careful to read "and" for the decimal point only.

② EXAMPLE Writing a Decimal in Words

Write 20.0408 in words.

$$20.0408 \quad \leftarrow \text{Four decimal places indicate ten-thousandths.}$$

twenty and four hundred eight ten-thousandths

✔ **Check Understanding** ② Write each decimal in words. **2a–c. See back of book.**

   a. 16,702.3   **b.** 1,670.234   **c.** 1.67023

③ EXAMPLE Writing a Decimal in Standard Form

Sports In the 2000 Olympic Games, the United States men's gymnastics team did not win a medal. Their score was one and thirty-six thousandths points too low. Write this number in standard form.

1	← Write the whole number part.
1.	← Place the decimal point.
1.■■■	← Thousandths is 3 places to the right of the decimal point.
1.■ 3 6	← Place 36 to the far right.
1.036	← Insert a zero for tenths.

9.587

Real-World 🌐 Connection

Blaine Wilson scored nine and five hundred eighty-seven thousandths on the pommel horse.

✔ **Check Understanding** ③ **a.** Refer to the photo caption. Write Blaine Wilson's score in standard form.

   b. Number Sense In Blaine Wilson's score, which has the greater value, the 5 or the 7? Explain. **the 5, since 0.5 > 0.007**

EXERCISES

❓ For more practice, see *Extra Practice*.

Ⓐ Practice by Example

Write each decimal in expanded form. **1–8. See margin.**

Example 1 (page 9)

1. 530.34	**2.** 3.004	**3.** 0.23	**4.** 7.5
5. 433.0005	**6.** 1.28	**7.** 93.68	**8.** 130.6

Example 2 (page 10)

Write each decimal in words. **9–12. See margin. 13–16. See back of book.**

9. 2.3	**10.** 6.02	**11.** 9.5	**12.** 0.006
13. 2.061	**14.** 3.0008	**15.** 0.40	**16.** 50.6003

10   Chapter 1   Decimals

👥 Reaching All Students

Below Level Have students write decimals in expanded form before writing them in words. For Example 2, students would first write 20.0408 as 20 + 0.04 + 0.0008.	**Advanced Learners** Have students create a chart with three headings— *expanded form, standard form,* and *words.* Have them use selected numbers from Exercises 1–28 to complete the chart.	**Inclusion** See note on page 10. **Diversity** See note on page 11.

Example 3
(page 10)

Write each decimal in standard form in Exercises 17–20.

17. forty and nine thousandths
40.009

18. six hundred and four millionths
600.000004

🌐 **19. Biology** The diameter of a white blood cell measures twelve ten-thousandths of a centimeter. 0.0012

🌐 **20. Running** A marathon race is twenty-six and two tenths miles long.
26.2

21–24. See back of book.

B Apply Your Skills

Write each number in expanded form and in words.

21. 8.2   **22.** 91.91   **23.** 91.091   **24.** 1,000,650.02

🌐 **Money** Write each amount as a decimal part of $1.00 in standard form.

25. two dimes
0.20

26. five pennies
0.05

27. one quarter
0.25

28. seven nickels
0.35

29. The value of each 2 is 10 times greater than the value of the 2 to its right.

29. <u>Writing in Math</u> Describe how the value represented by each "2" in the number 2,222.22 changes as you move from right to left. **See left.**

30. Data Analysis According to the bar graph, sales for Company A were $0.7 million. As a whole number, this value is written $700,000. Write each amount.

30b. $900,000

a. Company B sales as a decimal **$0.9 million**
b. Company B sales as a whole number
c. Company C sales as a decimal **$1.6 million**
d. Company C sales as a whole number
$1,600,000

Annual Sales

(bar graph: Dollars (millions) vs Company A, B, C)

Find the value of the digit 4 in each number.

31. 0.4   **4 tenths, or 0.4**   **32.** 42.3926   **4 tens, or 40**

33. 17.55643   **4 ten-thousandths, or 0.0004**   **34.** 34,567.89   **4 thousands, or 4,000**

🌐 **Money** A *mill* is a unit of money sometimes used by state governments. One mill is equal to one thousandth of a dollar ($0.001). Write each amount as part of a dollar.

35. 6 mills
$.006

36. 207 mills
$.207

37. 53 mills
$.053

38. 328 mills
$.328

🌐 **39. Heights** Artists use a ratio called the Golden Mean to describe a **GPS** person's height. Your height from the floor to your waist is usually six hundred eighteen thousandths of your total height. Write this number as a decimal. **0.618**

(vertical number line scale: 1, 0.75, ?, 0.5, 0.25, 0)

1-2   Reading and Writing Decimals   **11**

Assignment Guide

▼ Objective 1
   Ⓐ Ⓑ Core 1–39
   Ⓒ Extension 40–41

Test Prep 42–45
Mixed Review 46–48

Diversity
Exercise 20 Have volunteers describe their experiences of marathons or shorter road races.

Practice 1-2   Reading and Writing Decimals

Write each decimal in expanded form.

1. 213.23   Two hundred thirteen and twenty-three hundredths
2. 5.625   five and six hundred twenty-five thousandths
3. 19.01   nineteen and one hundredth
4. 7,430.25   seven thousand four hundred thirty and twenty-five hundredths
5. 81.8887   eighty-one and eight thousand eight hundred eighty-seven ten-thousandths
6. 3.70917   three and seventy thousand nine hundred seventeen hundred-thousandths

Write each decimal in words.

7. 12.873   twelve and eight hundred seventy-three thousandths
8. 8.0552   eight and five hundred fifty-two ten-thousandths
9. 0.00065   sixty-five hundred-thousandths

Write each decimal in standard form.

10. three tenths   0.3
11. fifty-two hundredths   0.52
12. eight tenths   0.8
13. two hundredths   0.02
14. seventy-nine hundredths   0.79
15. forty hundredths   0.40
16. six and five thousandths   6.005
17. nine hundred fifty-four ten-thousandths   0.0954
18. 20 + 0.01 + 0.003 + 0.0008   20.0138
19. 30 + 4 + 0.9 + 0.02   34.92
20. forty and eight hundredths   40.08
21. 200 + 10 + 0.04   210.04

What is the value of the digit 7 in each number?

22. 0.7   7 tenths
23. 4.00712   7 thousandths
24. 2.179   7 hundredths
25. 28,467.089   7 ones
26. 348.92971   7 ten-thousandths
27. 72.14   7 tens

Reteaching 1-2   Reading and Writing Decimals

- *Standard form:* 2.369
- To find the value of a digit, multiply the digit by its place value.
  9 stands for 9 × 0.001 or 0.009
- *Expanded form:*
  2.369 = 2 + 0.3 + 0.06 + 0.009

Ones	Tenths	Hundredths	Thousandths
2	3	6	9

2 and 369 thousandths

Write each decimal in expanded form.

1. 3.6   3 + 0.6
2. 4.72   4 + 0.7 + 0.02
3. 1.283   1 + 0.2 + 0.08 + 0.003
4. 21.5   20 + 1 + 0.5
5. 7.03   7 + 0.03
6. 15.308   10 + 5 + 0.3 + 0.008
7. 32.27   30 + 2 + 0.2 + 0.07
8. 6.475   6 + 0.4 + 0.07 + 0.005

Write each decimal in words.

9. 0.2   two tenths
10. 0.15   fifteen hundredths
11. 0.29   twenty-nine hundredths
12. 0.11   eleven hundredths
13. 0.60   sixty hundredths
14. 0.9   nine tenths
15. 0.50   fifty hundredths
16. 0.4   four tenths
17. 0.37   thirty-seven hundredths

Write each decimal in standard form.

18. seven tenths   0.7
19. one tenth   0.1
20. four hundredths   0.04
21. seven hundredths   0.07
22. twenty-two hundredths   0.22
23. forty-six hundredths   0.46
24. eighty hundredths   0.80
25. thirty hundredths   0.30
26. three hundredths   0.03

---

1. 500 + 30 + 0.3 + 0.04
2. 3 + 0.004
3. 0.2 + 0.03
4. 7 + 0.5
5. 400 + 30 + 3 + 0.0005
6. 1 + 0.2 + 0.08
7. 90 + 3 + 0.6 + 0.08
8. 100 + 30 + 0.6
9. two and three tenths
10. six and two hundredths
11. nine and five tenths
12. six thousandths

GPS Use the Guided Problem Solving worksheet with Exercise 39.

Lesson Quiz 1-2

1. Write 99.124 in expanded form. **90 + 9 + 0.1 + 0.02 + 0.004**

2. Write fifty-five and thirty-four thousandths in standard form. **55.034**

3. Write 500.04 in words. **five hundred and four hundredths**

4. Write 3,800.205 in words. **three thousand eight hundred and two hundred five thousandths**

Alternative Assessment

Each student in a pair writes three decimals greater than one. Partners exchange papers and write each other's decimals in expanded form and in words.

Test Prep

Resources

For additional practice with a variety of test item formats:
- Test-Prep, p. 57
- Test-Taking Strategies, p. 53
- Test-Taking Strategies With Transparencies

Exercise 42 Watch for students who confuse the digit 1 with the one's place value.

Enrichment 1-2   Reading and Writing Decimals
Decision Making

When you make a purchase, often you have a choice to give the clerk exact change or to receive change.

1. A cashier has only one-dollar bills, quarters, and dimes. List all the ways you could receive $2.50 in change.

$1.00	$.25	$.10	$1.00	$.25	$.10	$1.00	$.25	$0.10
2	2	0	1	2	10	0	8	5
2	0	5	1	0	15	0	4	15
1	6	0	0	10	0	0	0	25
1	4	5	0	2	20	0	6	10

2. Which of the combinations from Question 1 will provide you with the fewest coins? Which will provide you with the greatest number of coins?
2 one-dollar bills and 2 quarters; 25 dimes

3. If you had a choice, why might you want as many coins as possible returned as part of your change?
Sample answer: You need change for vending machines, bus fare, or video games.

4. If you had a choice, why might you pay for a purchase with exact change?
Sample answer: You don't want to carry coins in your pocket.

5. If you were to get change for a ten-dollar bill today, what would be the best combination of bills and coins for you? Explain.
Sample answer: One five-dollar bill, four one-dollar bills, and four quarters to have change to buy juice from the vending machine and pay back a friend.

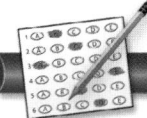 **C Challenge**

40. Extend the place value chart on page 9 to the right.
  a. Write 0.000001 in words. **one millionth**
  b. Write 0.0000001 in words. **one ten-millionth**
  c. Critical Thinking What place is to the right of millionths? Explain. **Ten-millionths; this amount is one tenth of one millionth.**

41. Stretch Your Thinking A three-digit whole number's last digit is three times its first digit. Its first digit is two times its second digit. What is the number? **216**

Test Prep

Multiple Choice

42. What is the value of the digit 1 in 94.107? **C**
  A. ten   **B.** one   **C.** one tenth   **D.** one hundredth

43. What is the place of the digit 3 in 14.038? **I**
  F. tens   **G.** ones   **H.** tenths   **I.** hundredths

Take It to the NET
Online lesson quiz at **www.PHSchool.com**
Web Code: aaa-0102

44. What is forty thousandths in standard form? **C**
  A. 40,000   **B.** 40   **C.** 0.040   **D.** 0.0040

45. What is one hundred and seven thousandths in standard form? **G**
  F. 107,000   **G.** 100.007   **H.** 100.0007   **I.** 0.107

Mixed Review

Lesson 1-1

Use < or > to complete each statement.

46. 98,410 $\overset{>}{\blacksquare}$ 98,140   **47.** 40,000 $\overset{<}{\blacksquare}$ 300,009   **48.** 478,296 $\overset{>}{\blacksquare}$ 478,269

Math at Work

 **Accountant**

Accountants use mathematics to prepare and analyze financial reports, tax returns, and budgets. They help individuals and companies track financial history and plan for future growth. Accountants' reports help people make good business decisions.

Take It to the NET For more information about accounting, go to **www.PHSchool.com**.
Web Code: aab-2031

Check Understanding

1.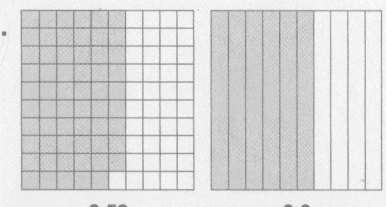

     0.6 is greater.

0.59   0.6

1-3 Comparing and Ordering Decimals

What You'll Learn

...And Why

To compare bodies of water, as in Example 4

✓ Check Skills You'll Need

❓ For help, go to Lesson 1-1.

 Use < or > to complete each statement.

1. 430 ■ 340   2. 2,005 ■ 205

3. 80,020 ■ 8,020   4. 473 ■ 347

5. **Number Sense** Two whole numbers have the same number of digits. To compare them, do you begin with the digits on the left or on the right? **digits on the left**

 OBJECTIVE 1 Comparing Decimals Using Models

📕**TEXT** Interactive lesson includes instant self-check, tutorials, and activities.

You can use grid models and number lines to compare and order decimals.

1 EXAMPLE Using Models to Compare Decimals

Draw models for 0.4 and 0.36. Which number is greater?

Use a tenths grid for 0.4.
Use a hundredths grid for 0.36.

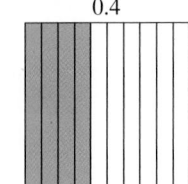 0.4
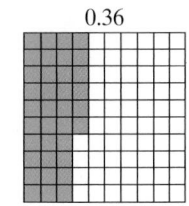 0.36

A greater area is shaded for 0.4 than for 0.36, so 0.4 is greater than 0.36.

✓ Check Understanding ① Draw models for 0.59 and 0.6. Which number is greater? **See margin.**

2 EXAMPLE Ordering Decimals on a Number Line

Order the decimals 2.4, 2.3, 2.17, and 2.43 on a number line.

All the numbers are between 2 and 2.5. Make a number line showing tenths. Then mark the hundredths. Graph the points.

✓ Check Understanding ② Order the decimals 1.76, 1.87, 1.09, 1.91, 1.67, and 1.3 on a number line. **See back of book.**

Ongoing Assessment and Intervention

Before the Lesson	During the Lesson	After the Lesson
Diagnose prerequisite skills using:	Monitor progress using:	Assess knowledge using:
• Check Skills You'll Need	• Check Understanding • Additional Examples • Test Prep	• Lesson Quiz • Computer Test Generator CD • Chapter Checkpoint 1 (p. 17)

Lesson Preview

 ✓ **Check Skills You'll Need** PowerPoint
Comparing Whole Numbers
Lesson 1-1: Example 2: Extra Practice p. 642.

Lesson Resources

Optional Materials
• graph paper

📁 **Teaching Resources**
Practice, Reteaching, Enrichment
Checkpoint Quiz 1

👥 **Reaching All Students**
Practice Workbook 1-3
Spanish Practice Workbook 1-3
Reading and Math Literacy 1B
Spanish Reading and Math Literacy 1B
Spanish Checkpoint Quiz 1
Guided Problem Solving 1-3
Technology Activities 1

⏰ **Presentation Assistant Plus!**
Transparencies
• Check Skills You'll Need 1-3
• Problem of the Day 1-3
• Additional Examples 1-3
• Student Edition Answers 1-3
• Lesson Quiz 1-3
• Classroom Aid 7, 9–10
PH Presentation Pro CD-ROM 1-3

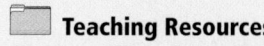 **PRENTICE HALL ASSESSMENT SYSTEM**
Checkpoint Quiz 1
Computer Test Generator CD

💻 **Technology**
Resource Pro® CD-ROM
Computer Test Generator CD
PH Presentation Pro CD-ROM

💻 **www.PHSchool.com**
Student Site
• Teacher Web Code: aak-5500
• Self-grading Lesson Quiz

PH SuccessNet Teacher Center
• Lesson Planner
• Resources

Plus 📕**TEXT**

2. Teach

Math Background

The number 0.6, or 6 tenths, is equivalent to 0.60, or 60 hundredths. Place values are used to compare decimal numbers, similar to how they are used to compare whole numbers. For example, 0.56 is less than 0.6 because 56 hundredths is less than 60 hundredths.

Teaching Notes

1 EXAMPLE Teaching Tip

Ask: *How much greater is 0.4 than 0.36?* 0.04

2 EXAMPLE Tactile Learners

Have students make number lines on their own paper. Then have them write 2.4, 2.3, 2.17, and 2.43 on slips of paper and move them on the number line until they have them ordered correctly.

Teaching Tip

Write these decimals on the board:

  0.76 0.08 0.79 0.85 0.71

Then ask:
- *Which of these numbers would appear on a number line between 0.7 and 0.8?*
  0.76, 0.79, 0.71
- *In what order should these three numbers appear?*
  0.71, 0.76, 0.79

3 EXAMPLE Inclusion

Remind students of the meanings of < (less than), = (equal), and > (greater than). Use 6 > 5 and 5 < 6 to show how the larger side of the symbol is on the side of the greater number.

4 EXAMPLE Technology Tip

You can use a computer program to order decimals automatically by using the *sort* feature. The decimals can be arranged in ascending or descending order.

3d. Answers may vary. Sample: Compare the digits starting with the highest place values. The ones and tenths digits are the same. The hundredths digit in 1.697 is greater than the hundredths digit in 1.679. So, 1.697 > 1.679.

You can use place value to compare two decimals, just as you do to compare whole numbers.

3 EXAMPLE   Comparing Two Decimals

Use <, =, or > to complete the statement 3.18 ■ 3.8.

Write a zero at the end of 3.8 so each number has the same number of decimal places.   3.18
    3.80

Compare the digits starting with the highest place values.   The ones digits are the same. → 3.18   The tenths digits are different. 1 is less than 8.
    3.80

Since the 1 tenth in 3.18 < the 8 tenths in 3.8, 3.18 < 3.8.

✓ **Check Understanding** 3 Use <, =, or > to complete each statement.

a. 2.37 ■ 2.7   **b.** 0.56 > 0.543   **c.** 1.650 = 1.65

d. Reasoning Explain how you can use place value to compare 1.679 and 1.697. **See margin.**

4 EXAMPLE   Ordering Decimals  Real World

Earth Science Order these bodies of water from least salty to most salty.

Salt per Liter in Major Bodies of Water

Body of Water	Arctic Ocean	Dead Sea	Caspian Sea	Black Sea
Salt per Liter	0.032 kg	0.28 kg	0.013 kg	0.018 kg

SOURCE: Natural Wonders of the World

Write a zero at the end of 0.28. Then compare the digits starting with the highest place values..

┌ 2 is the greatest tenths digit, so 0.280 is the greatest decimal.

0.032   0.032 ← 3 is the greatest hundredths digit, so 0.032 is the second greatest decimal.
0.280   0.280
0.013   0.013
0.018   0.018 ← 8 is the greatest thousandths digit, so 0.018 is the third greatest decimal.

The decimals from least to greatest are 0.013, 0.018, 0.032, and 0.28.

The bodies of water from least to most salty are the Caspian Sea, the Black Sea, the Arctic Ocean, and the Dead Sea.

Real-World Connection

People float easily in the salty water of the Dead Sea, which lies between Israel and Jordan.

✓ **Check Understanding** 4 Order each set of decimals from least to greatest.

a. 2.6, 2.76, 2.076   **b.** 3.059, 3.64, 3.46
  2.076, 2.6, 2.76   3.059, 3.46, 3.64

👥 Reaching All Students

Below Level Have students compare decimals that can be represented by dollars and cents, such as $5.10 and $1.05.

Advanced Learners Provide additional sets of decimals for students to order. Some decimals can be equivalent. For instance: 2.24, 2.2049, 2.19, 2.4200, 2.4, 2.190, 2.2409, 2.42, and 2.2046.

English Learners See note on page 16. **Inclusion** See note on page 14.

More Than One Way

Nutrition Use the table at the right. Order the foods by sodium content from least to greatest.

Food	Sodium
half a bagel	0.19 g
1 corn tortilla	0.04 g
3 pieces of Melba toast	0.12 g
5 crackers	0.195 g
1 slice of wheat bread	0.132 g

Elena's Method

I can use place value and mental math to order the decimals.

$$0.19 \quad 0.04 \quad 0.12 \quad 0.195 \quad 0.132$$

First, I compare the tenths place in all the numbers. $0 < 1$, so 0.04 is the least number.

Next, I compare the hundredths place in the remaining numbers. $2 < 3 < 9$, so $0.12 < 0.13 < 0.19$.

Finally, I compare 0.19 and 0.195. Since $0.19 = 0.190$ and $0 < 5$, $0.19 < 0.195$.

The correct order is $0.04, 0.12, 0.132, 0.19,$ and 0.195. The foods from least to greatest sodium content are corn tortilla, Melba toast, wheat bread, bagel, and crackers.

Leon's Method

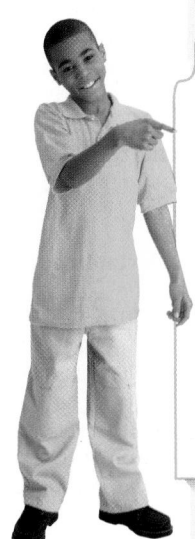

I can order the decimals by graphing them on a number line.

I see that all the numbers are between 0 and 0.2. I'll make a number line marked in hundredths.

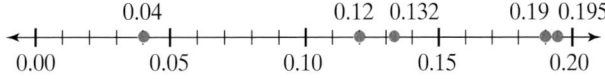

The decimals from least to greatest are $0.04, 0.12, 0.132, 0.19,$ and 0.195. The foods from least to greatest sodium content are corn tortilla, Melba toast, wheat bread, bagel, and crackers.

Choose a Method

Order the values 0.964, 0.26, 0.576, 0.059, 0.9, 0.96, and 0.264 from least to greatest. Describe your method and explain why you chose it.
0.059, 0.26, 0.264, 0.576, 0.9, 0.96, 0.964; Check students' methods.

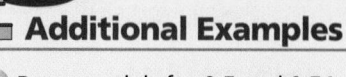
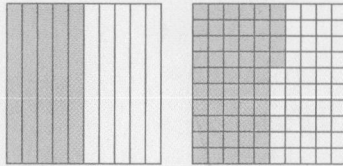

Additional Examples

1. Draw models for 0.5 and 0.54. Which number is larger?

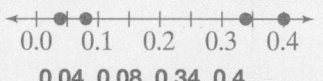

0.54 > 0.5

2. Order the decimals 0.34, 0.04, 0.08, and 0.4 on a number line.

0.0 0.1 0.2 0.3 0.4

0.04, 0.08, 0.34, 0.4

3. Use <, =, or > to complete each statement.

   a. 0.1 ■ 0.10 =

   b. 0.28 ■ 0.82 <

   c. 0.6 ■ 0.06 >

4. Order 0.8, 0.084, 0.48, and 0.84 from least to greatest.
0.084, 0.48, 0.8, 0.84

Closure

- Give three different methods for ordering decimals. **place value, a number line, and decimal models**
- Explain place value to compare two decimals. **Sample: Annex zeros so that each number has the same number of decimal places. Then compare the decimal values as if they were whole numbers.**

3. Practice

Assignment Guide

1 Objective 1
Ⓐ Ⓑ Core 1–7, 25
Ⓒ Extension 27

2 Objective 2
Ⓐ Ⓑ Core 8–24, 26
Ⓒ Extension 28–29

Test Prep 30–32
Mixed Review 33–38

English Learners
Exercise 20 Let students know that the word *about* refers to an estimate.

Practice 1-3 — Comparing and Ordering Decimals

Use <, =, or > to complete each statement.
1. 0.62 ⊡ 0.618   2. 9.8 ⊡ 9.80   3. 1.006 ⊡ 1.02   4. 41.3 ⊡ 41.03
5. 2.01 ⊡ 2.011   6. 1.400 ⊡ 1.40   7. 5.079 ⊡ 5.08   8. 12.96 ⊡ 12.967
9. 15.8 ⊡ 15.800   10. 7.98 ⊡ 7.89   11. 8.02 ⊡ 8.020   12. 5.693 ⊡ 5.299

Order each set of decimals on a number line.
13. 0.2, 0.6, 0.5   14. 0.26, 0.3, 0.5, 0.59, 0.7

15. Three points are graphed on the number line below. Write statements comparing 0.3 to 0.5 and 0.5 to 0.7.
0.3 < 0.5 and 0.7 > 0.5

16. Draw a number line. Use 10 tick marks. Label the first tick 0.6 and the tenth tick 0.7. Graph 0.67 and 0.675.   Check students' work.
a. Which is greater, 0.67 or 0.675?   0.675
b. How does the number line show which number is greater?
Numbers on a number line are greater as you move to the right.

17. Models for three decimals are shown below.
a. Write the decimal that each model represents.
0.73; 0.84; 0.12
b. Order the decimals from least to greatest.
0.12; 0.73; 0.84

Reteaching 1-3 — Comparing and Ordering Decimals

Use >, <, or = to show how 4.092 and 4.089 compare.
① Write the numbers on grid paper with the decimal points lined up.
② Compare digits in the greatest place. Move to the right until you find digits that are not the same.
4 ones = 4 ones
0 tenths = 0 tenths
9 hundreths > 8 hundreths
So, 4.092 > 4.089.
To order numbers from least to greatest:
① Write the numbers on grid paper (decimal points lined up) and compare.
② Then arrange the numbers from least to greatest.
4.089, 4.09, 4.092

Use <, =, or > to complete each statement.
1. 0.01 ⊡ 0.15   2. 0.25 ⊡ 0.21   3. 0.30 ⊡ 0.26
4. 0.10 ⊡ 0.12   5. 0.35 ⊡ 0.34   6. 0.1 ⊡ 0.4
7. 34.4 ⊡ 34.40   8. 0.207 ⊡ 0.27   9. 0.08 ⊡ 0.40
10. 0.32 ⊡ 0.309   11. 6.12 ⊡ 6.099   12. 0.990 ⊡ 0.99
13. 2.36 ⊡ 2.036   14. 0.05 ⊡ 0.15   15. 1.19 ⊡ 1.91

Use place value to order the decimals from least to greatest.
16. 3.46, 3.64, 3.59   17. 22.97, 21.79, 22.86   18. 43, 43.22, 43.022
3.46, 3.59, 3.64   21.79, 22.86, 22.97   43, 43.022, 43.22
19. 10.02, 10.2, 1.02   20. 1.09, 1.9, 1.1   21. 7.54, 75.4, 7.4
1.02, 10.02, 10.2   1.09, 1.1, 1.9   7.4, 7.54, 75.4

Order each set of numbers on a number line.
22. 0.67, 0.7, 0.6   23. 0.03, 0.29, 0.019   24. 8.36, 8.01, 8.1

16

EXERCISES

For more practice, see *Extra Practice*.

Ⓐ **Practice by Example**

Example 1 (page 13)
Draw models for each pair of decimals. Which number is greater?
1–3. See back of book.
1. 0.4 and 0.5   2. 0.35 and 0.53   3. 0.2 and 0.02

Example 2 (page 13)
Order each set of decimals on a number line. 4–7. See margin.
4. 0.7, 0.2, 0.35, 0.75   5. 2.1, 2.53, 2.3, 2.5
6. 6.4, 6.04, 7.6, 6.59, 7.2   7. 0.49, 0.34, 0.4, 0.3, 0.38

Example 3 (page 14)
Use <, =, or > to complete each statement.
8. 0.76 < 0.78   9. 1.42 > 1.4   10. 2.30 = 2.3
11. 0.3 > 0.27   12. 5.7 = 5.70   13. 0.048 < 0.408

Example 4 (page 14)
Order each set of decimals from least to greatest.
14. 0.5, 0.7, 0.65
0.5, 0.65, 0.7
15. 17.1, 17.7, 13.7
13.7, 17.1, 17.7
16. 0.503, 0.53, 0.529
0.503, 0.529, 0.53
17. 9.2, 9.02, 9.209, 9.024
9.02, 9.024, 9.2, 9.209

Ⓑ **Apply Your Skills**
18. 1.79, 2.19, 1.991, 2.185, 1.979
1.79, 1.979, 1.991, 2.185, 2.19
19. 5.5506, 5.5660, 5.561, 5.58, 5.665
5.5506, 5.561, 5.5660, 5.58, 5.665

20. **Population** About 11.02 million people live in Jakarta, Indonesia. About 11.7 million people live in Delhi, India. About 11.79 million people live in Karachi, Pakistan. Order the cities from least to greatest population. **Jakarta, Delhi, Karachi**

21. **Open-Ended** Write six numbers between 2.2 and 2.222. Order them from least to greatest. **Answers may vary. Sample: 2.21, 2.211, 2.212, 2.213, 2.214, 2.215**

Select all the values on the right that will make each statement true.

22. $4.18 < \blacksquare < 4.25$ 4.25, 4.17, 4.27, 4.2025, 4.319, 4.198
4.198, 4.2025
23. $0.57 < \blacksquare < 0.67$ 0.6595, 0.5025, 0.6701, 0.6095, 0.62, 0.567
0.6595, 0.6095, 0.62

24. **Olympics** The United States won the women's 100-meter run in all the years listed at the left. Order the times from least to greatest. **See margin.**

25. **Writing in Math** Alia ran the 100-yard dash in 11.88 seconds. Patty ran it in 11.9 seconds. Who ran faster? Explain how you know.
Alia; 11.88 < 11.9

26. **Data File, p. 3** Write $\overline{\text{XMCXIV}}$ and $\overline{\text{XMCXVI}}$ as Arabic numerals (standard form). Compare the Roman numerals using <, =, or >.
11,114; 11,116; $\overline{\text{XMCXIV}} < \overline{\text{XMCXVI}}$

Year	Time (seconds)
1984	10.97
1988	10.54
1992	10.82
1996	10.94
2000	10.75

Source: *The World Almanac*

16   Chapter 1 Decimals

GPS Use the Guided Problem Solving worksheet with Exercise 20.

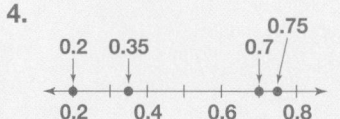
4.

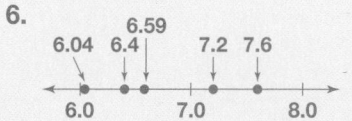
6.

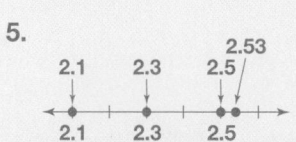
5.

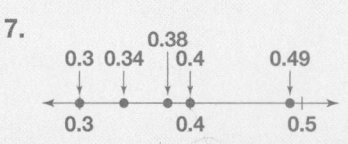
7.

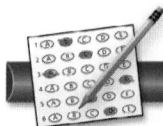 **Challenge**

27. Estimation Estimate the decimals represented by points A, B, and C.

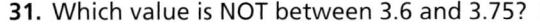

A: 0.25; B: 0.77; C: 1.05

709.52 952 370.973 031.02

398.9 944 398.2

28. Libraries The Dewey Decimal System assigns a number to every nonfiction book. These seven books are arranged in the correct order from left to right. Match each label to its book by ordering the labels from least to greatest. 031.02, 370.973, 398.2, 398.9, 709.52, 944, 952

29. Stretch Your Thinking During a scavenger hunt, Team A found 8 more items than Team B. Team C found twice as many items as Team B. Together, the three teams found a total of 72 items. How many items did Team A find? 24 items

 Test Prep

Multiple Choice

30. Which statement is NOT true about the decimals 0.2, 0.4, and 0.6? C
  A. $0.2 < 0.4$ and $0.4 < 0.6$
  B. $0.2 < 0.4$ and $0.6 > 0.2$
  C. $0.2 < 0.6$ and $0.6 < 0.4$
  D. $0.4 < 0.6$ and $0.6 > 0.2$

31. Which value is NOT between 3.6 and 3.75? I
  F. 3.62   **G.** 3.647   **H.** 3.7   **I.** 3.8

 Take It to the NET
Online lesson quiz at
www.PHSchool.com
Web Code: aaa-0103

32. Which value is greater than 0.72 and less than 1.29? B
  A. 0.7   **B.** 0.999   **C.** 1.3   **D.** 1.9

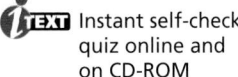 **Mixed Review**

Skills Handbook p. 657

Subtract.

33. $152 - 27$
  125
34. $34{,}567 - 488$
  34,079
35. $13{,}789 - 3{,}653$
  10,136
36. $91 - 62$
  29
37. $836 - 459$
  377
38. $4{,}071 - 2{,}190$
  1,881

Checkpoint Quiz 1   **Lessons 1-1 through 1-3**

iTEXT Instant self-check quiz online and on CD-ROM

1. Write 6,080,000,000,405.31 in words.
  six trillion, eighty billion, four hundred five and thirty-one hundredths
2. Write 12.035 in expanded form. $10 + 2 + 0.03 + 0.005$

3. Write the number four hundred and seven tenths in standard form.
  400.7
4. Use <, =, or > to complete the statement 1.082 ■ 1.28. <

5. Order the numbers 9, 8.7, 9.31, 8.0, and 8.05 from least to greatest.
  8.0, 8.05, 8.7, 9, 9.31

1-3 Comparing and Ordering Decimals **17**

24. 10.54, 10.75, 10.82, 10.94, 10.97

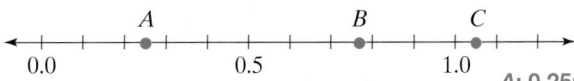 **4. Assess**

 **PowerPoint Lesson Quiz 1-3**

Order from least to greatest.

1. 0.54, 0.511, 0.5, 0.55
  0.5, 0.511, 0.54, 0.55

2. 2.79, 2.7, 2.708, 2.77
  2.7, 2.708, 2.77, 2.79

✔ Chapter Checkpoint

To check understanding of Lessons 1-1 to 1-3:

Checkpoint Quiz 1 (p. 17)

📁 **Teaching Resources**
Checkpoint Quiz 1 (also in *Prentice Hall Assessment System*)

Reaching All Students
Reading and Math Literacy 1B

Spanish versions available

Test Prep

Resources
For additional practice with a variety of test item formats:
• Test-Prep, p. 57
• Test-Taking Strategies, p. 53
• Test-Taking Strategies With Transparencies

Alternative Assessment

Partners write several one- or two-place decimals on small slips of paper and then jumble the slips. They randomly pick two slips of paper, model each decimal by shading a decimal grid, and then compare the decimals. Students should write their comparisons using <, =, or >.

17

Reading Your Textbook

Careful reading is very important for success in mathematics. You can help your students spot and use the many helpful clues the lessons in this text provide. This feature introduces, describes, and explores these useful elements.

Teaching Notes

Teaching Tip

Inform students that their textbook has been designed to guide them through the lessons in a systematic, logical way. Then have a volunteer read aloud the three general hints given. Ask: *What does it mean to "read with pencil and paper"?* Sample: to work independently, step-by-step through the examples given in the exposition of each lesson

Inclusion

To help students focus on key parts of lessons, have them (1) bracket sections with fingers as they read, (2) mask all but the portions of the page they are reading, or (3) make use of self-stick notes to highlight key sections, or to remind them of questions to ask or parts to reread.

Exercises

Work through the exercises together, discussing the text's recurring features. Direct students to notice the helpful icons, the highlighting colors, and the different kinds of print used. Invite students to flip through their texts to see consistencies in lesson formats and these design elements.

Ask pairs of students to come up with a list of steps to follow when approaching a new lesson in the text. Have pairs share their strategies with the class.

Here are some reading tips to keep in mind as you read this textbook.

- Read carefully. Even little words make a difference in mathematics. Read the graphs, diagrams, and symbols that go with the text. These items contain important mathematical information.

- Learn new vocabulary. Make your own list of new words. Include a definition and example for each word.

- Read with pencil and paper. You should work the steps of each example as you read.

This textbook has many features that can help you learn math. Answer the questions below to learn about some of these features.

EXERCISES

Each lesson begins with What You'll Learn, Check Skills You'll Need, and New Vocabulary features. Find these items for Lesson 1-4 on page 19. 1–3. See margin.

1. a. What are the two objectives in Lesson 1-4?
    b. Look through the lesson. On what page does each objective start?

2. a. What skills do you need to have before you start the lesson?
    b. Where in your book can you look for help with these skills?

3. What new vocabulary words are introduced in this lesson?

Find the three examples presented in Lesson 1-4, beginning on page 19.

4. Which example shows how to use front-end estimation? Example 3

5. Which example shows how to round in estimating a product? Example 1

6. Which example shows how to use compatible numbers? Example 2

Find the exercises for Lesson 1-4, beginning on page 21.

7. To the left of Exercises 1–7 on page 21, you see "**Example 1 (page 19).**" How could this information help you work these exercises?

Answers may vary. Sample: Following the steps in Example 1 can help you solve Exercises 1–7.

1a. to estimate by rounding and using compatible numbers; to use front-end estimation

b. The first objective starts on page 19; the second objective starts on page 20.

2a. You need to know how to round to the nearest ten and the nearest thousand.

b. You can go to your Skills Handbook, page 655.

3. compatible numbers, front-end estimation

Estimating With Decimals

What You'll Learn

 OBJECTIVE 1 To estimate by rounding and using compatible numbers

 OBJECTIVE 2 To use front-end estimation

. . . And Why

To estimate total costs, as in Example 3

 **Check Skills You'll Need**   **?** For help, go to Skills Handbook p. 655.

Round each number to the nearest ten.

1. 45 50
2. 65,328 65,330
3. 132,798 132,800

Round each number to the nearest thousand.

4. 30,910,067 30,910,000
5. 5,555 6,000
6. 15,345,357 15,345,000

New Vocabulary
- compatible numbers
- front-end estimation

iTEXT Interactive lesson includes instant self-check, tutorials, and activities.

OBJECTIVE 1

Estimating by Rounding and Using Compatible Numbers

? Need Help?
For help with rounding numbers, go to Skills Handbook page 655.

Rounding decimals is similar to rounding whole numbers. You know that 32 rounds down to 30, and 35 and 39 round up to 40.

	Round down:	Round up:	Round up:
Value < 5, so round down to nearest tenth. →	0.32	0.35	0.39	← **Value ≥ 5, so round up to nearest tenth.**
	↓	↓	↓
	0.3	0.4	0.4

1 EXAMPLE   **Estimate by Rounding**

Estimate. First round each decimal to the nearest whole number.

a.
$$\begin{array}{r} 10.93 \\ + 3.25 \end{array} \rightarrow \begin{array}{r} 11 \\ + 3 \\ \hline 14 \end{array}$$

So, $10.93 + 3.25 \approx 14$.   ← **The symbol ≈ means "is approximately equal to."**

b.
$$\begin{array}{r} 15.3 \\ \times 2.6 \end{array} \rightarrow \begin{array}{r} 15 \\ \times 3 \\ \hline 45 \end{array}$$

So, $15.3 \times 2.6 \approx 45$.

✓ **Check Understanding** **1** Estimate by first rounding to the nearest whole number.

a. 1.16×32.06
about 32

b. $5.05 - 1.9$
about 3

c. $18.75 + 93.346$
about 112

1-4 Estimating With Decimals   **19**

Lesson Preview

PowerPoint

✓ **Check Skills You'll Need**
Rounding Whole Numbers
Skills Handbook: Rounding Whole Numbers, p. 655.

Lesson Resources

Teaching Resources
Practice, Reteaching, Enrichment

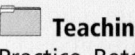 **Reaching All Students**
Practice Workbook 1-4
Spanish Practice Workbook 1-4
Guided Problem Solving 1-4

Presentation Assistant Plus!
Transparencies
- Check Skills You'll Need 1-4
- Problem of the Day 1-4
- Additional Examples 1-4
- Student Edition Answers 1-4
- Lesson Quiz 1-4
PH Presentation Pro CD-ROM 1-4

PRENTICE HALL ASSESSMENT SYSTEM

Computer Test Generator CD

 Technology
Resource Pro® CD-ROM
Computer Test Generator CD
PH Presentation Pro CD-ROM

 www.PHSchool.com
Student Site
- Teacher Web Code: aak-5500
- Algebra Readiness Puzzles 50
- Self-grading Lesson Quiz

PH SuccessNet Teacher Center
- Lesson Planner
- Resources

Plus **iTEXT**

 **Ongoing Assessment and Intervention**

Before the Lesson	**During the Lesson**	**After the Lesson**
Diagnose prerequisite skills using:	Monitor progress using:	Assess knowledge using:
• Check Skills You'll Need	• Check Understanding	• Lesson Quiz
	• Additional Examples	• Computer Test Generator CD
	• Test Prep	

Professional Development

Math Background

Whole numbers are rounded to the nearest 10, 100, and 1,000. Decimals can also be rounded to tenths, hundredths, thousandths, and so on. You can round decimals to estimate sums, differences, and products.

Two common estimation strategies are *front-end estimation* and *compatible numbers*. Front-end estimation is helpful when you add and subtract numbers. Compatible numbers are mostly used when you estimate products and quotients.

Teaching Notes

① EXAMPLE Error Prevention

In Check Understanding 1c, students may be confused when rounding a decimal with a digit in the thousandths place to the nearest whole number because of the "extra" digit that is not involved in the estimation. Emphasize that students should look at the number in the place to the right of the ones digit, the tenths place.

② EXAMPLE Inclusion

Before students estimate with compatible numbers, spend some time practicing how to identify compatible numbers. Emphasize the relationship between the numbers in basic division facts and in basic multiplication facts. Give students pairs of numbers and ask them whether or not those numbers are compatible. Encourage them to explain why or why not. Examples: 5, 3 (no); 6, 2 (yes; 6 is divisible by 2); 25, 4 (no); 30, 10 (yes; the numbers are easy to multiply or divide); 9, 3 (yes; divisibility); 17, 5 (no)

③ EXAMPLE Visual Learners

Help students focus on the "front end" and "back end" digits by completing the estimation in steps. Students can use self-stick notes to cover the parts of the numbers they aren't "using" in their estimation.

Compatible numbers are numbers that are easy to compute mentally. They are particularly useful for estimating products and quotients.

② EXAMPLE   Estimating With Compatible Numbers

a. Estimate 5.21 × 78.03.

$$5.21 \times 78.03$$
$$5 \times 80 = 400 \quad \leftarrow \text{Use compatible numbers such as 5 and 80.}$$

$$5.21 \times 78.03 \approx 400$$

b. Estimate 29.56 ÷ 4.13.

2a. because 28 is divisible by 4

$$29.56 \div 4.13$$
$$28 \div 4 = 7 \quad \leftarrow \text{Use compatible numbers such as 28 and 4.}$$

$$29.56 \div 4.13 \approx 7$$

See left.

✔ **Check Understanding** ② **a. Number Sense** In part (b), why are 28 and 4 compatible numbers?
b. Use compatible numbers to estimate 302.1 − 48.79. **about 250**

OBJECTIVE

2 Using Front-End Estimation

To use **front-end estimation,** you add the "front-end digits," estimate the sum of the remaining digits, and adjust the estimate as necessary.

Popcorn
Small $3.98
Medium $6.49
Large $9.08
Junior $3.47

③ EXAMPLE   Using Front-End Estimation   Real World

Food Use front-end estimation to estimate the total cost of one of each size of popcorn.

Step 1 Add the front-end digits, the dollars.

```
  $3.98
   6.49
   9.08
+  3.47
  $21
```

Step 2 Look at the cents and adjust the estimate.

```
  $3.98  →  about $1
   6.49 ⎫
   9.08 ⎬  about $1
+  3.47 ⎭
  $21      about $2
```

The total cost is about $21 + $2, or $23.

 Check Understanding ③ **a.** Use front-end estimation to estimate the total cost of one small popcorn and two large popcorns. **about $22**

3b. About $6; front-end estimation always involves the cents, so the estimates are higher and less likely to leave you short of money.

b. Reasoning Find an estimate for the total cost of two junior popcorns by rounding to the nearest whole number. Why is front-end estimation a good method when money is involved?

20   Chapter 1   Decimals

👥 Reaching All Students

| **Below Level** Some students are confused by "unnecessary" digits. Have them circle the digit immediately to the right of the desired rounding place. Students can then cross out all other digits to the right of it. | **Advanced Learners** Have students estimate each sum to the nearest tenth.
 35.026 + 3.502 + 0.3502 **38.9**
 123.4 + 12.34 + 1.234 **136.9** | **Inclusion** See notes on page 20.
 Visual Learners See note on page 20. |

Investigation: Finding an Exact or Estimated Answer

Most problems require an exact answer. Others need only an estimate for the answer. Decide whether each situation needs an exact or estimated answer. Explain your reasoning. **1–5. See margin.**

1. the record attendance at a college football game

2. amount of money you plan on spending when shopping

3. amount of money a store cashier earns each hour

4. the time it takes you to get to school

5. **Reasoning** Describe two situations, one that needs only an estimate and one that needs an exact answer. Explain why.

For more practice, see *Extra Practice*.

EXERCISES

A Practice by Example

Estimate by first rounding to the nearest whole number.

Example 1
(page 19)

1. 35.61
    + 0.816
    about 37

2. 10.581
    − 1.203
    about 10

3. 16.91
    × 2.25
    about 34

4. 15.3
    × 2.6
    about 45

5. 15.8 + 38.095
    about 54

6. 6.501 − 3.999
    about 3

7. 0.95 × 22.8
    about 23

Example 2
(page 20)

Use compatible numbers to estimate. Exercise 8 has been started for you.

8. 46.4 ÷ 4.75 → 45 ÷ 5 = ? about 9

9. 392 + 193
    about 600

10. 653 − 295 about 350

11. 27 × 9.98 about 270

12. 36.4 ÷ 6.2
    about 6

13. 73.25 ÷ 9.43 about 8

14. 23.3 × 4.2 about 100

15. 30.9 ÷ 5.1
    about 6

Example 3
(page 20)

Use front-end estimation to estimate each sum to the nearest dollar.

16. $4.89
    + $3.97
    about $9

17. $6.15
    + $8.86
    about $15

18. $14.65
    $27.29
    + $63.85
    about $106

19. $16.81
    $19.94
    + $11.49
    about $48

B Apply Your Skills

20. **Packaging** A ball has a mass of 283.5 grams. You want to ship 9 balls
    [GPS] in a box. The box has a mass of 595.34 grams. Estimate the total mass.
    about 3,300 grams

21. Estimate the total of 3.894 and 5.2. about 9

Investigation (Optional)
Have students work in pairs to find real-world examples of both exact and estimated data in newspapers, magazines, or articles from the Internet. Have them cut and place them on two large poster boards labeled *Exact Data* and *Estimated Data*.

PowerPoint
Additional Examples

1. Estimate by first rounding to the nearest whole number.
   a. 15.66 + 4.1 about 20
   b. 8.43 × 6.73 about 56

2. Use compatible numbers to estimate.
   a. 28.75 ÷ 9.2 about 3
   b. 2.97 × 96.5 about 300
   c. 147.3 − 96.99 about 50

3. A lemonade costs $1.79, sodas cost $1.29, and water costs $1.49. Use front-end estimation to estimate the total cost of one of each drink. about $4.50

Closure

- *When is front-end estimation appropriate to use?* when you estimate the sum or difference of numbers
- *When should you use compatible numbers to estimate?* when you estimate products and quotients

---

Investigation

1–5. Answers may vary. Samples are given.

1. Exact answer; an estimate is not a reliable way of knowing if a record is set.

2. Estimated answer; you can adjust your spending based on the amount you bring.

3. Exact answer; estimating could cause the cashier to make less or more than deserved.

4. Estimated answer; the time may vary, but an overestimate will ensure you get to school on time.

5. You only need to estimate the number of people who will attend a school dance, so you can determine an entry fee that will cover your cost. You need an exact measurement when you are cutting boards to build a birdhouse.

3. Practice

Assignment Guide

1 **Objective 1**
Ⓐ Ⓑ Core 1–15, 20–39, 42–46
Ⓒ Extension 47

2 **Objective 2**
Ⓐ Ⓑ Core 16–19, 40–41
Ⓒ Extension 48

Test Prep 49–52
Mixed Review 53–59

Error Prevention!

Exercises 16–19 Students may simply ignore the cents.

One Serving	Sugar Content
Orange Juice	0.886 oz
Granola bar	0.273 oz
Grapes	0.529 oz
Milk	0.413 oz
Yogurt	0.98 oz

 **Nutrition** Use the chart. Estimate to the nearest tenth of an ounce.

22. About how much sugar is in a serving of orange juice plus a granola bar? **about 1.2 oz**

23. If you ate one of every item in the chart, about how much sugar would you have eaten? **about 3.1 oz**

24. About how much more sugar is in a serving of yogurt than in a serving of milk? **about 0.6 oz**

25. About how much sugar is in the last three items combined? **about 1.9 oz**

Round each number to the place of the underlined digit.

26. 1.366 **1.4**   **27.** 72.418 **70**   **28.** 5.1251 **5.13**   **29.** 2.3196 **2.320**

30. 306.042 **310**   **31.** 10.901 **11**   **32.** 0.345 **0.35**   **33.** 14.9 **10**

Estimate each answer by rounding each number to the nearest whole number or by using compatible numbers.   **34–39. Answers may vary. Samples are given.**

34. 4.29 + 8.89
about 13

35. 11.42 − 7.201
about 4

36. 55.1 ÷ 8.6
about 7

37. 134.8 − 51.95
about 83

38. 8.56 × 9.863
about 80

39. 23.56 + 33.51
about 58

40. Writing in Math The cost for three copies of a book is $38.85. Estimate the cost for one book. Do you think your estimate is higher or lower than the book's actual cost? Explain. **See margin.**

41b. Compatible numbers make the division easy to compute mentally.

**Real-World Connection**
The largest paper money ever printed was the Chinese kwan note, which was used in the fourteenth century.

41. Savings Suppose you saved $443.75 in one year.
a. Estimate how much you saved each week. **about $9**
b. Reasoning Explain why you chose the method you used in part (a). **See left.**

42. Money This Chinese kwan note is 92.8 centimeters long. The United States dollar bill is 15.6 centimeters long. About how many times as long as a dollar bill is the kwan note? **about 6 times**

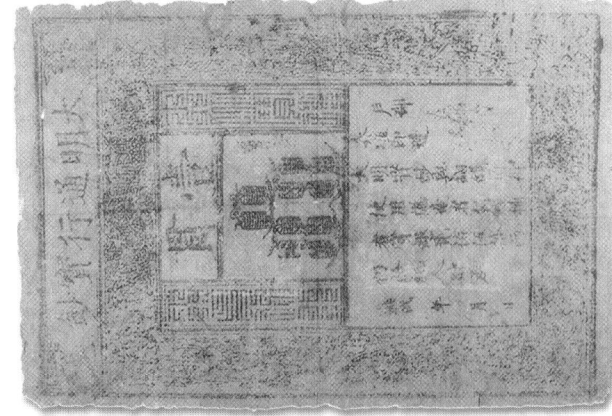

Practice 1-4

Estimating With Decimals

Estimate by first rounding to the nearest whole number.

1. 0.97 × 13.21 — 13
2. 11.9 × 4.76 — 60
3. 14.7 × 2.2 — 30
4. 18.95 × 0.76 — 19
5. 28.02 × 1.94 — 56
6. 11.93 × 1.63 — 24
7. 43.75 × 3.17 — 132
8. 5.02 × 3.16 — 15
9. 9.04 × 8.71 — 81

Use compatible numbers to estimate. Estimates may vary.

10. 38.9 ÷ 19.7 — 800
11. 18.47 ÷ 5.96 — 3
12. 208 + 196 — 400
13. 603 − 204 — 400
14. 76.3 ÷ 15.1 — 5
15. 93 − 77 — 10
16. 49.1 ÷ 15.6 — 3
17. 95 + 611 — 700
18. 18.6 ÷ 2.8 — 6

Use front-end estimation to estimate each sum to the nearest dollar.

19. $2.59 + $3.76 + $2.41 — $9
20. $8.19 + $2.46 + $3.57 — $14
21. $3.61 + $2.17 + $5.84 — $12
22. $9.14 + $8.72 + $5.63 — $24

Round each decimal to the place of the underlined digit.

23. 1.109 — 1.11
24. 2.357 — 2.4
25. 4.8772 — 4.877
26. 5.8045 — 5.80

Tim went shopping and spent $31.79 at each of 3 stores.

27. Use compatible numbers to estimate how much Tim spent altogether.
about $90

28. Use rounding to estimate how much Tim spent.
about $96

29. Which estimate is closer to the amount Tim actually spent? the rounded estimate

30. A politician wants to know how many people are in your county or town. Do you think the politician wants to know the exact number of people, or will an estimate be acceptable?
estimated number

Reteaching 1-4

Estimating with Decimals

To *round* $76.38 to the nearest dollar:
① Find the rounding place. $76.38
② Look at the digit to the right. $76.38
③ If that digit is less than 5, leave the digit in the rounding place as is. If the digit is 5 or greater, round up.
$76.38 rounds to $76.

You can use rounding to estimate a sum.
3.76 + 0.85 + 4.09
Round each number to the ones place.
3.76 → 4
0.85 → 1
4.09 → 4
Then add.   9
The sum is about 9.

You can estimate decimal products, quotients, sums, and differences by using *compatible numbers*.

Example 1 Estimate the product 9.47 × 3.81

9.47 → 10
×3.81 → × 4
        40
Change to compatible numbers—numbers that are easy to multiply.

The product is about 40.

Example 2 Estimate the quotient 23.96 ÷ 4.78.

23.96 ÷ 4.78
24 ÷ 4 = 6
Change to compatible numbers—numbers that are easy to divide.

The quotient is about 6.

Round each decimal to the nearest hundredth.

1. 1.679 — 1.68
2. 4.981 — 4.98
3. 12.602 — 12.60
4. 32.9744 — 32.97
5. 0.159 — 0.16
6. 2.008 — 2.01

Round each decimal to the nearest tenth.

7. 6.457 — 6.5
8. 15.0886 — 15.1
9. 0.1235 — 0.1
10. 1.036 — 1.0
11. 25.671 — 25.7
12. 6.390 — 6.4

Estimate each sum or difference. Estimates may vary.

13. $2.98 + $7.22 — $10
14. $5.33 + $2.91 — $8
15. $10.02 − $6.89 — $3
16. $15.84 + $37.12 — $53

Use compatible numbers to estimate. Accept reasonable estimates.

17. 7.21 ÷ 3 — about 2
18. 31.74 ÷ 5 — about 6
19. 522 + 81 — about 600
20. 908 − 445 — about 450
21. 477 + 78 — about 600
22. 73 + 229 — about 300

GPS Use the Guided Problem Solving worksheet with Exercise 20.

40. Answers may vary.
Sample: about $13; higher, because the total was rounded up to $39

Use "clustering" to estimate each sum. For example, the numbers 4.8, 5.2, and 4.9 cluster around the whole number 5. You can estimate their sum by multiplying 3 and 5 for a total of 15.

43. 5.879 + 6.3 + 5.6 + 6.09
about 24

44. $7.99 + $8.14 + $7.85
about $24

45. 2.6 + 3.3 + 2.8 + 2.91 + 3.14
about 15

46. $39.81 + $42 + $38.06
about $120

 **Challenge**

47. Open-Ended A number rounded to the nearest tenth is 10.6. Rounded to the nearest hundredth, it is 10.65. What could the number be?
Answers may vary. Sample: 10.646

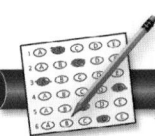

Need Help?
4 cups = 1 quart
4 quarts = 1 gallon

48. Writing in Math Your class is bringing apple juice to the fall school party. You know that 268 people are invited. You think that each person will drink one cup of juice. Explain the steps you would take to estimate how many gallons of apple juice your class should buy.
See margin.

Test Prep

Multiple Choice

49. Between which two numbers is the quotient 18.7 ÷ 5? **B**
   A. 2 and 3   **B.** 3 and 4   **C.** 4 and 5   **D.** 5 and 6

50. Which sum has an estimate of $22? **G**
   F. $4.22 + $10.85 + $8.97   **G.** $2.80 + $13.75 + $4.66
   H. $6.05 + $7.86 + $10.22   **I.** $15.32 + $9.63 + $.45

51. Tom has $20 to spend. He wants to buy a book for $7.29, film for $12.95, a marker for $3.95, and a magazine for $6.25. He can buy some items and have less than $1.00 left. Which items could he buy? **B**
   A. book, marker, and magazine   **B.** film and magazine
   C. book and film   **D.** film and marker

Take It to the NET
Online lesson quiz at
www.PHSchool.com
Web Code: aaa-0104

52. Yvonne earns $38.25 in one week by baby-sitting. She earns $4.75 per hour. Estimate the number of hours she works. **F**
   F. 8   **G.** 33.5   **H.** 43   **I.** 200

Mixed Review

Lesson 1-3

Use <, =, or > to complete each statement.

53. 0.112 < 0.121   **54.** 0.0009 < 0.001   **55.** 0.9985 > 0.998

Lesson 1-2

Write each decimal in standard form.

56. seven and eight tenths 7.8   **57.** twenty-three hundredths 0.23

58. two hundred eight and one tenth 208.1   **59.** thirty-eight ten-thousandths 0.0038

1-4 Estimating With Decimals   **23**

48. Answers may vary. Sample: First, I would determine the number of cups in a gallon: 1 × 4 × 4 = 16 cups; then I would estimate 268 ÷ 16 using the compatible numbers 300 and 15.

So, our class should buy 300 ÷ 15, or 20 gallons.

 **Lesson Quiz 1-4**

Estimate by first rounding to the nearest whole number.

1. 24.35 − 6.8 about 17

2. 14.9 × 6.355 about 90

Use compatible numbers to estimate.

3. 38.56 ÷ 9.73 about 4

4. 4.71 × 19.71 about 100

Alternative Assessment

Provide students with several empty food containers on which you have written prices. Have students work in small groups to round the prices of the items. Students can select a group of these items and add the rounded prices to estimate their cost.

Test Prep

Resources
For additional practice with a variety of test item formats:
• Test-Prep, p. 57
• Test-Taking Strategies, p. 53
• Test-Taking Strategies With Transparencies

Enrichment 1-4   Estimating With Decimals
Critical Thinking

Use all ten digits only once to make the number described in each problem. Notice that each number has 3 decimal places. Do not use 0 in either the millions or the thousandths places.

[?][?][?],[?][?][?],[?][?][?].[?][?][?]

1. the greatest number 9,876,543.201
2. the least number 1,023,456.789
3. when rounded to the nearest tenth, the greatest number that rounds to 5 tenths 9,876,432.501
4. when rounded to the nearest tenth, the least number that rounds to 5 tenths 1,023,567.489
5. when rounded to the nearest whole number, the least odd number 1,023,456.789
6. when rounded to the nearest whole number, the greatest odd number 9,876,543.201
7. when rounded to the nearest whole number, the greatest even number 9,876,542.301
8. when rounded to the nearest whole number, the least even number 1,023,457.689
9. the greatest number less than 5 million 4,987,653.201
10. the least number greater than 8 million 8,012,345.679
11. the number closest to 2 million 6 hundred thousand 2,601,234.789
12. Write a number with a 3 in the millions place whose sum of the first four digits equals the sum of the last four digits. Then write another number that does not use the same three digits in the decimal places.
Sample answers: 3,476,501.928; 3,824,659.701

23

Investigation

Using Models

Students create and shade in 10 x 10 grids to model addition and subtraction of decimals in tenths and hundredths.

Optional Materials

- graph paper or blank grid models
- base-ten blocks
- Classroom Aid 9–10

Teaching Notes

1 EXAMPLE Teaching Tip

Model the additions on a hundredths-grid on an overhead projector as students work along with you at their seats. You may wish to provide graph paper on which students can mark off 10 x 10 grids. Ask: *What number does a completely shaded hundredths-grid represent?* 1

2 EXAMPLE Visual Learners

Ask: *Look at the model for 1.4 − 0.6. How would you model the subtraction 1.4 − 0.65?* Sample: Make two hundredths-grids; shade all 10 columns on one and 4 columns on the other to show 1.4; cross out or color out 6 columns and 5 small squares.

Alternative Method

Students can model the examples using base-ten blocks. For addition, model each decimal and put the blocks together. For subtraction, model the first decimal and remove the model of the second decimal. This approach is well suited for tactile learners.

Exercises

Have students work in small groups on the exercises. Have one student read an exercise aloud while the others write it down. Remind students to write a decimal point when they hear the word "and" in each number.

24

You can use models to add or subtract two decimals.

1 EXAMPLE Modeling Decimal Sums

Draw a model to find each sum.

a. 0.4 + 0.03

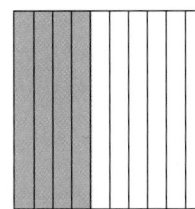 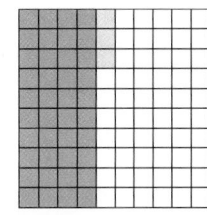

Draw a tenths grid and shade four tenths.

Divide the grid into hundredths. Shade three more hundredths.

43 hundredths of the grid are shaded, so 0.4 + 0.03 = 0.43.

b. 0.9 + 0.5

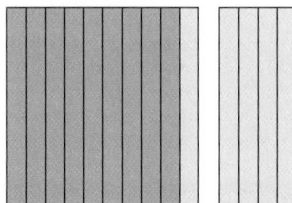

Draw a tenths grid and shade nine tenths. Shade five more tenths. To do this, you need to draw another grid.

The total amount shaded is 14 tenths.
0.9 + 0.5 = 14 tenths = 10 tenths and 4 tenths
= 1 and 4 tenths = 1.4

2 EXAMPLE Modeling Decimal Differences

Draw a model to find the difference 1.4 − 0.6.

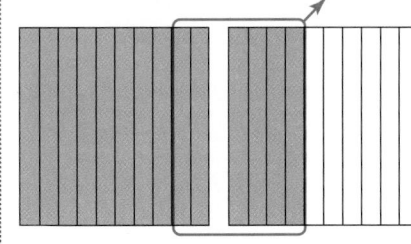

← Remove six tenths from fourteen tenths. Eight tenths remain.

1.4 − 0.6 = 0.8

EXERCISES

Draw a model on grid paper to find each sum or difference. 1–3. See margin. 4–8. See back of book.

1. 0.1 + 0.8	**2.** 0.41 + 0.59	**3.** 0.06 + 0.55	**4.** 0.8 + 0.34
5. 1.5 − 1.2	**6.** 1.2 − 0.7	**7.** 0.88 − 0.57	**8.** 1.54 − 0.72

1. 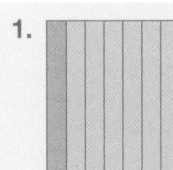 0.9

2. 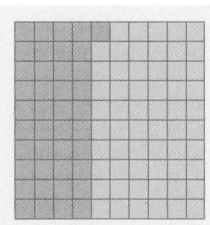 1.0

3. 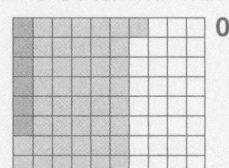 0.61

1-5 Adding and Subtracting Decimals

What You'll Learn

 OBJECTIVE 1 To add decimals

 OBJECTIVE 2 To subtract decimals

...And Why

To find basketball sizes, as in Example 3

 **Check Skills You'll Need**

For help, go to Lesson 1-4.

Round each decimal to the nearest whole number.

1. 8.7 9
2. 9.5 10
3. 4.94 5
4. 0.92 1
5. 2.982 3
6. 3.090 3

New Vocabulary

- Commutative Property of Addition
- Associative Property of Addition
- Identity Property of Addition

 Interactive lesson includes instant self-check, tutorials, and activities.

OBJECTIVE

1 Adding Decimals

If you estimate before adding, you can tell if your sum is reasonable.

> **1 EXAMPLE** **Finding Decimal Sums**
>
> Find the sum 3.026 + 4.7 + 1.38.
>
> **Estimate** $3.026 + 4.7 + 1.38 \approx 3 + 5 + 1$, or 9
>
> Add. 3.026 ← Line up the decimal points.
>   4.700 ← Write zeros so that all decimals have the same
>   + 1.380   number of digits to the right of the decimal point.
>   9.106
>
> **Check for Reasonableness** The sum 9.106 is reasonable since it is close to 9.

 Check Understanding ① First estimate and then find the sum 0.84 + 2.0 + 3.32. **about 6; 6.16**

Reading Math

Parentheses ( ) indicate operations that should be done first.

Key Concepts **Properties of Addition**

Commutative Property of Addition
Changing the order of the addends does not change the sum.
$$3.6 + 7 = 7 + 3.6$$

Associative Property of Addition
Changing the grouping of the addends does not change the sum.
$$(3.6 + 7) + 3 = 3.6 + (7 + 3)$$

Identity Property of Addition
The sum of 0 and any number is that number.
$$3.6 + 0 = 0 + 3.6 = 3.6$$

1-5 Adding and Subtracting Decimals **25**

1-5

1. Plan

Lesson Preview

 **PowerPoint**

 **Check Skills You'll Need**

Rounding Decimals
Lesson 1-4: Examples 1–2. Extra Practice p. 642.

Lesson Resources

Teaching Resources
Practice, Reteaching, Enrichment

Reaching All Students
Practice Workbook 1-5
Spanish Practice Workbook 1-5
Guided Problem Solving 1-5
Hands-On Activities 2

Presentation Assistant Plus!
Transparencies
- Check Skills You'll Need 1-5
- Problem of the Day 1-5
- Additional Examples 1-5
- Student Edition Answers 1-5
- Lesson Quiz 1-5
- Classroom Aid 2, 10
PH Presentation Pro CD-ROM 1-5

 PRENTICE HALL ASSESSMENT SYSTEM

Computer Test Generator CD

 Technology
Resource Pro® CD-ROM
Computer Test Generator CD
PH Presentation Pro CD-ROM

www.PHSchool.com
Student Site
- Data Update
- Teacher Web Code: aak-5500
- Self-grading Lesson Quiz

PH SuccessNet Teacher Center
- Lesson Planner
- Resources

Plus

Ongoing Assessment and Intervention

Before the Lesson	**During the Lesson**	**After the Lesson**
Diagnose prerequisite skills using:	Monitor progress using:	Assess knowledge using:
• Check Skills You'll Need	• Check Understanding	• Lesson Quiz
	• Additional Examples	• Computer Test Generator CD
	• Test Prep	

2. Teach

Professional Development

Math Background

The first step in adding and subtracting decimals is to line up the decimal points. Then the digits with the same place value are added or subtracted. When subtracting, you may need to annex zeros as placeholders and rename digits. For instance, $2.1 - 0.3$ involves renaming 2.1 as 1 and 11 tenths. $11 - 3$ results in 8 tenths, so $2.1 - 0.3$ is 1.8.

This lesson introduces the basic properties of addition: the Commutative, Associative, and Identity Properties of Addition.

Teaching Notes

English Learners

Use plain language to explain the properties of addition. Focus on the way the properties are used rather than on the names of the properties. For example, say: "$3.6 + 7 = 10.6$, and $7 + 3.6 = 10.6$. So, in addition the order of the numbers does not matter. The answer is the same."

② EXAMPLE Teaching Tip

Students may wonder why the expression $58 + 13.9$ in parentheses is not added. In this situation, the parentheses indicate what grouping is done first. The different groupings indicated by parentheses do not change the result. This is the fundamental concept behind the Associative Property of Addition.

③ EXAMPLE Error Prevention

In Check Understanding 3b–c, encourage students to first annex zeros in the first number so that both numbers have the same number of decimal places. Remind students that annexing zeros to the end of a decimal number does not change the value of the number. You may also want to have students place a dollar sign before each number so students can think in terms of money.

You can *simplify* an expression by replacing it with the simplest name for its value. So to simplify $4 + 5$, you write 9 for its value.

② EXAMPLE Using the Properties of Addition

Mental Math Use mental math to find the sum $42 + 13.9 + 58$.

What you think

42 and 58 are easy to add. Adding 42 and 58 gives you 100. Adding 100 and 13.9 gives you 113.9. So, $42 + 13.9 + 58 = 113.9$.

Why it works

$$42 + 13.9 + 58 = 42 + 58 + 13.9 \quad \leftarrow \text{Commutative Property of Addition}$$
$$= (42 + 58) + 13.9 \quad \leftarrow \text{Associative Property of Addition}$$
$$= 100 + 13.9 \quad \leftarrow \text{Add inside the parentheses.}$$
$$= 113.9 \quad \leftarrow \text{Simplify.}$$

✔ **Check Understanding** ② **Mental Math** Use mental math to find each sum.

   a. $8.9 + 0 + 5.0$ **b.** $74 + 19 + 1$ **c.** $5.92 + 0.4 + 3.08$
       13.9   94   9.4

OBJECTIVE

2 Subtracting Decimals

③ EXAMPLE Estimating and Finding a Difference  Real World

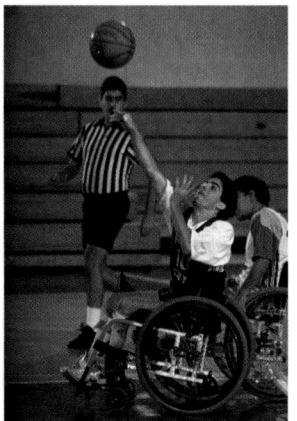

Sports According to the International Basketball Federation, the official distance around a basketball can be no more than 78.0 centimeters. The distance can also be no less than 74.9 centimeters. What is the difference between these distances?

Estimate $78.0 - 74.9 \approx 78 - 75$, or 3

Subtract.
$$\begin{array}{r} \overset{7\ 10}{7\,8.0} \quad \leftarrow \text{Rename 8 as 7 and 10 tenths.} \\ -\,7\,4.9 \quad \leftarrow \text{Subtract 74.9} \\ \hline 3.1 \quad \leftarrow \text{Simplify.} \end{array}$$

The difference between the distances is 3.1 centimeters.

Check for Reasonableness The difference 3.1 is reasonable since it is close to 3.

✔ **Check Understanding** ③ First estimate and then find each difference. **3b–c. See left.**

   a. $2.7 - 0.9$ about 2;1.8   **b.** $14.5 - 6.97$ **c.** $0.4 - 0.13$
3b. about 8; 7.53   **d. Reasoning** Use what you know about place value to explain why you
c. about 0.3; 0.27   should line up the decimal points before adding or subtracting.
               Answers may vary. Sample: Aligning the decimal points aligns all the
               places correctly.

26   **Chapter 1** Decimals

🎓 Reaching All Students

| Below Level Focus on the need to line up the decimal points by having students perform basic additions like the following:

$0.2 + 0.05$ 0.25 $0.25 + 3$ 3.25
$0.01 + 0.3 + 6$ 6.31 | Advanced Learners Have students find each sum.

$0.345 + 0.543$ 0.888
$2.468 + 8.642$ 11.11
$98.76 + 67.89$ 166.65 | English Learners
See note on page 26.
Diversity
See note on page 28. |

④ EXAMPLE **Subtracting Decimals From Whole Numbers**

Find the difference 50 − 7.86.

Estimate 50 − 7.86 ≈ 50 − 8, or 42

Subtract.

Write a decimal point and two zeros.	Rename 50 as 49 and 10 tenths.	Rename 10 tenths as 9 tenths and 10 hundredths.
5 0 . 0 0 − 7 . 8 6	⁴⁹ ¹⁰ 5̶0̶ . 0̶ 0 − 7 . 8 6	⁹ ⁴⁹ ¹⁰̶ ¹⁰ 5̶0̶ . 0̶ 0̶ − 7 . 8 6 ————— 4 2 . 1 4

Check for Reasonableness The difference 42.14 is reasonable since it is close to 42.

✔ Check Understanding ④ First estimate and then find each difference.
   a. 98 − 6.8
      about 91; 91.2
   b. 40 − 8.32
      about 32; 31.68
   c. 82 − 4.916
      about 77; 77.084

EXERCISES

❓ For more practice, see *Extra Practice*.

Ⓐ Practice by Example   **First estimate and then find each sum.**

Example 1
(page 25)
   1. 0.6 + 3.4
      about 4; 4
   2. 6.2 + 0.444
      about 6; 6.644
   3. 8.001 + 0.77
      about 9; 8.771
   4. 7 + 11.436 + 3.08
      about 21; 21.516
   5. 0.445 + 8.99 + 3
      about 12; 12.435
   6. 0.33 + 1.11 + 3.2
      about 4; 4.64

Example 2
(page 26)   **Use mental math to find each sum.**

   7. 0 + 5.7 + 4
      9.7
   8. 1.060 + 0 + 2.705
      3.765
   9. 8.37 + 1.4 + 2.6
      12.37
   10. 3.21 + 4.33 + 1.67
      9.21
   11. 18 + 6.354 + 102
      126.354
   12. 7.81 + 5.23 + 0.19
      13.23

Examples 3, 4
(pages 26, 27)   **First estimate and then find each difference.**

   13. 22.2 − 4.3
      about 18; 17.9
   14. 8.91 − 6.08
      about 3; 2.83
   15. 9.45 − 3.76
      about 5; 5.69
   16. 9.1 − 6.05
      about 3; 3.05
   17. 0.8 − 0.126
      about 1; 0.674
   18. 4 − 1.29
      about 3; 2.71
   19. 60 − 2.037
      about 58; 57.963
   20. 9 − 0.45
      about 9; 8.55

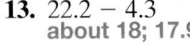
60 m 70 m 80 m
76.80 m
74.08 m
⬤ Men's record
⬤ Women's record

21. Data Analysis Use the graph at the left. How much greater is the women's world-record discus throw than the men's? **2.72 m**

🌐 **22. Bicycles** At one store, an 18-speed bicycle costs $174.99. At another store, the same bicycle costs $222.98. What is the difference in prices?
   $47.99

1-5 Adding and Subtracting Decimals   **27**

▣ Additional Examples

① First estimate and then find the sum 6.8 + 4.65 + 2.125. estimate: 14; sum: 13.575

② Use mental math to find each sum.
   a. 25 + 18 + 7 50
   b. 8.5 + 0.65 + 1.5 10.65
   c. 2.34 + 6.42 + 5.66 14.42

③ Professional ice hockey rinks can be from 25.9 m to 30.0 m wide. What is the difference between these widths? 4.1 m

④ First estimate and then find each difference.
   a. 16 − 8.79 7; 7.21
   b. 9 − 2.45 7; 6.55
   c. 11 − 6.15 5; 4.85

Closure

• *How do you add or subtract decimals?* Sample: Align the decimal points; annex zeros so that all decimals have the same number of digits to the right of the decimal point; then add or subtract as you do with whole numbers.

• *How do you use mental math to find sums?* Sample: Apply the Commutative Property of Addition and the Associative Property of Addition to simplify a sum.

3. Practice

Assignment Guide

1 Objective 1
- Ⓐ Ⓑ Core 1–12, 26–41
- Ⓒ Extension 42–43, 45

2 Objective 2
- Ⓐ Ⓑ Core 13–25
- Ⓒ Extension 44, 46

Test Prep 47–50
Mixed Review 51–55

Diversity
Exercises 42–43 Discuss how clothing sizes are marked, e.g., XXL for double extra large.

Real-World 🌐 Connection

Careers Every 10 years, census takers try to count every person in the United States.

Ⓑ **Apply Your Skills**

23. Money Jonah had $340.87 in his checking account. He withdrew $52 and wrote a check for $18.72. Find the new balance. **$270.15**

24. Population In the 2000 Census, the New England states had a total population of about 13.92 million. Find the population of Maine. **1.26 million**

25. Choose a Method A hot-dog vendor receives $20 for a $5.25 purchase. Is the vendor most likely to use estimation, mental math, paper and pencil, or a calculator to determine the amount of change? Why? **Answers may vary. Sample: mental math because it is quicker**

State	Population
Connecticut	3.41 million
Maine	■
Massachusetts	6.35 million
New Hampshire	1.24 million
Rhode Island	1.05 million
Vermont	0.61 million

SOURCE: U.S. Census Bureau.
Go to www.PHSchool.com for a data update.
Web Code: aag-2041

Use <, =, or > to complete each statement.

26. $0.041 + 0.009 \;\boxed{<}\; 0.5$

27. $0.315 + 0.14 + 0.05 \;\boxed{>}\; 0.5$

28. $6{,}869.583 + 1{,}504.222 \;\boxed{>}\; 8{,}373.8$

29. $97{,}655.5 - 89{,}281.7 \;\boxed{=}\; 8{,}373.8$

Find each missing number. Name the property of addition that you used.

30. $6.37 + ■ + 2.43 = 6.37 + 2.43$
0; Ident. Prop. of Add.

31. $0.43 + ■ = 0.43$
0; Ident. Prop. of Add.

32. $(2.1 + 0.3) + 4 = 2.1 + (■ + 4)$
0.3; Assoc. Prop. of Add.

33. $■ + 8.9 = 8.9 + 7.5$
7.5; Comm. Prop. of Add.

34. $(6 + 1.1) + ■ = 6 + (1.1 + 5.9)$
5.9; Assoc. Prop. of Add.

35. $6.4 + 3.1 = ■ + 6.4$
3.1; Comm. Prop. of Add.

36. $(5.6 + 0.4) + 0.1 = (0.4 + 5.6) + ■$
0.1; Comm. Prop. of Add.

Data Analysis **Refer to the data at the left.**

37. Add the numbers in the table. What does this sum represent?
1; total U.S. energy supply

38. Writing in Math What part of all the energy is produced from oil and coal? Is it more than half? Explain.   **0.63; yes; half is 0.5 and 0.63 > 0.5.**

39. Estimation Which natural resource produces an amount of energy approximately $\frac{1}{3}$ that of nuclear power?   **Hydroelectric**

40. Modeling Make a hundredths model showing the part of all energy produced by each natural resource.   **See margin.**

41a–b. See margin.

41. Data File, p. 3 Your friend drew the hieroglyph below to show that a pharaoh had 3,290 cattle.
a. Is he correct? Explain.
b. How would you correctly write 3,290 as a hieroglyph?

U.S. Energy Supply by Source

Oil	0.40
Coal	0.23
Gas	0.23
Nuclear	0.09
Hydroelectric	0.03
Other	0.02

SOURCE: Energy Information Administration

Practice 1-5

Adding and Subtracting Decimals

First estimate. Then find each sum or difference.

1. $0.6 + 5.8$ **6.4**	2. $2.1 + 3.4$ **5.5**	3. $3.4 - 0.972$ **2.428**	4. $3.1 - 2.076$ **1.024**
5. $8.13 - 2.716$ **5.414**	6. $5.91 + 2.38$ **8.29**	7. $3.086 + 6.152$ **9.238**	8. $4.7 - 1.9$ **2.8**
9. $9.3 - 3.9$ **5.4**	10. $5.2 - 1.86$ **3.34**	11. $15.98 + 26.37$ **42.35**	12. $9.27 + 15.006$ **24.276**
13. $5.9 - 2.803$ **3.097**	14. $15.7 - 8.923$ **6.777**	15. $4.19 - 2.016$ **2.174**	16. $14.75 - 6.9264$ **7.8236**
17. $5.1 + 4.83 + 9.002$ **18.932**	18. $3 + 4.02 + 8.6$ **15.62**	19. $4.7 + 5.26 + 8.931$ **18.891**	

Use mental math to find each sum.

20. $12 + 0.25 + 4.75$ **17**	21. $18.5 + 0.25 + 0.25$ **19**	22. $17 + 23 + 10.6$ **50.6**
23. $11.3 + 5.7$ **17**	24. $5 + 6.2 + 4.05$ **15.25**	25. $50.6 + 10.4 + 20$ **81**
26. $2.1 + 0.6 + 0.3$ **3**	27. $14.3 + 16$ **30.3**	28. $4.9 + 0.6 + 4$ **9.5**

Use the table at the right for Exercises 29–31.

29. Find the sum of the decimals given in the chart. What is the meaning of this sum?
1; it includes all workers who are paid on an hourly basis.

30. What part of the hourly work force is ages 25–44?
0.29 + 0.24 = 0.53

31. Which three age groups combined represent about one-fourth of the hourly work force?
16–19, 20–24, and 65 & over; or 20–24, 55–64, and 65 & over

Ages of Workers Earning Hourly Pay

Age of Workers	Part of Work Force
16–19	0.08
20–24	0.15
25–34	0.29
35–44	0.24
45–54	0.14
55–64	0.08
65 & over	0.02

Reteaching 1-5

Adding and Subtracting Decimals

Add $3.25 + 12.6 + 18.93$.

First estimate.
$3.25 \rightarrow 3$
$12.6 \rightarrow 13$
$+ 18.93 \rightarrow 19$
$\overline{\qquad 35}$

Then follow these steps.

① Line up the decimal points. Write in any needed zeros.
```
  3.25
 12.60
+18.93
```

② Add as you would add whole numbers. Regroup when needed.
```
  ¹¹
  3.25
 12.60
+18.93
 34.78
```

③ Place the decimal point.
```
  3.25
 12.60
+18.93
 34.78  ← Compare to your estimate.
```

To subtract decimals, follow similar steps. Work from right to left and regroup when needed. Place the decimal point to complete the subtraction.

First estimate and then find each sum.

1. $0.9 + 6.7$ Estimate **1 + 7 = 8** Sum **7.6**	2. $3.1 + 9.4$ Estimate **3 + 9 = 12** Sum **12.5**	3. $4.88 + 8.19$ Estimate **5 + 8 = 13** Sum **13.07**

Use mental math to find each sum.

4. $14.05 + 9.75$ **23.8**	5. $6 + 0.22 + 0.78$ **7**	6. $9.104 + 5.01 + 7.99$ **22.104**

First estimate and then find each difference.

7. $8.5 - 4.2$ Estimate **9 − 4 = 5** Difference **4.3**	8. $7.2 - 3.05$ Estimate **7 − 3 = 4** Difference **4.15**	9. $5.07 - 2.8$ Estimate **5 − 3 = 2** Difference **2.27**
10. $6.347 - 2.986$ **3; 3.361**	11. $14.2 - 9.86$ **4; 4.34**	12. $13.45 - 5.001$ **8; 8.449**
13. $22.7 - 12.06$ **11; 10.64**	14. $16.1 - 10.88$ **5; 5.22**	15. $1.79 - 0.879$ **1; 0.911**

GPS Use the Guided Problem Solving worksheet with Exercise 24.

40.

Coal Gas
Oil
Nuclear
Other Hydroelectric

41a. No; the value of the number he drew is 32,009

b.
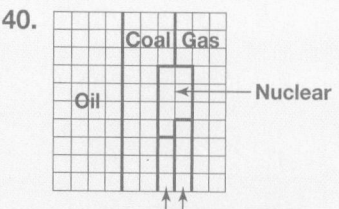

T-Shirts and Sweatshirts For Sale

Adult T-shirt   Adult Sweatshirt
(M-XL) $15.00   (M-XL) $29.50
(XXL) $17.95   (XXL) $29.95

Child's   Child's
T-shirt   Sweatshirt
$12.50 $16.95

Data Analysis **When you order clothes, you usually pay a shipping charge. Use the information in the charts.**

Shipping Charges

Order Amount	Charge
Under $25.00	$3.95
$25.00 – $39.99	$4.95
$40.00 – $49.99	$5.95
$50.00 – $74.99	$6.95
$75.00 – $99.99	$7.95
$100.00 and over	$8.95

42. a. A customer orders one adult sweatshirt (size XXL) and three child's T-shirts. What is the amount of the order? **$67.45**

b. Find the shipping charge and the total. **$6.95; $74.40**

43. A customer orders one adult T-shirt (size M) and one adult sweatshirt (size XL). Find the total cost, including the shipping charge. **$50.45**

Use <, =, or > to complete each statement.

44. 8,863.0024 − 486.2024 $\overset{>}{\blacksquare}$ 8,373.8

45. 2,562.031 + 4,792.019 $\overset{=}{\blacksquare}$ 7,354.05

46. **Stretch Your Thinking** Complete the number square at the right. The sum for each row, column, and diagonal should be 1.47.

0.76	0.13 ▦	0.58
0.31	0.49 ▦	0.67 ▦
0.40 ▦	0.85 ▦	0.22 ▦

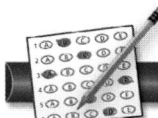

Test Prep

Multiple Choice

47. Which statement is NOT true? **C**
A. 10.3 = 10.30
B. 8.39 > 7.98
C. 4.9 < 4.889
D. 5.09 < 5.1

48. Which statement represents the Commutative Property of Addition? **G**
F. 1 + 7 = 8
G. 2 + 9 = 9 + 2
H. 3 + 6 = 4 + 5
I. 10 + 0 = 10

49. At a baseball game, you order nachos for $4.75 and two drinks for $3.25 each. You pay with a $20 bill. How much change will you get? **B**
A. $8.00   B. $8.75   C. $11.25   D. $12.00

50. Replacing the box with which number will make 0.22 + 0.▮8 > 0.5 true? **I**
F. 0   G. 1   H. 2   I. 3

Take It to the NET
Online lesson quiz at
www.PHSchool.com
Web Code: aaa-0105

Mixed Review

Lesson 1-4 **Round each number to the place of the underlined digit.**

51. 2̲0,567   52. 0.132̲9   53. 0.0̲93   54. 5.61̲84   55. 6,45̲6

21,000   0.133   0.1   5.62   6,460

---

4. Assess

 PowerPoint **Lesson Quiz 1-5**

Find each sum or difference.

1. 3.6 + 42.09 + 64 **109.69**

2. 100 − 21.75 **78.25**

3. 1.293 + 50.38 + 257.4 **309.073**

4. 52.7 − 7.002 **45.698**

Alternative Assessment

Each student in a pair writes a horizontal decimal addition and subtraction exercise. Partners exchange exercises and rewrite them vertically on graph paper to help them to align the decimals by place value. Students then find the sum or difference for each exercise.

Test Prep

Resources
For additional practice with a variety of test item formats:
• Test-Prep, p. 57
• Test-Taking Strategies, p. 53
• Test-Taking Strategies With Transparencies

Enrichment 1-5   Adding and Subtracting Decimals
Decision Making

Alyshia and Tamara went to the Neighborhood Cafe for lunch. They each chose one of the lunch specials, a beverage, and a dessert from the list printed on the menu board.

Lunch Specials		Desserts	
Lettuce Salad	$5.25	Carrot Cake	$1.50
Nature Salad	$4.75	Apple Pie	$2.25
Club Sandwich	$4.75		
Mushroom Burger	$4.50	**Beverages**	
Vegetable Burger	$3.75	Orange Juice	$1.25
		Bottled Water	$1.00

1. Tamara has $7 to spend for lunch. If she wants a special, a beverage, and a dessert, what items could she choose for her lunch? **Sample answers: vegetable burger, carrot cake, bottled water; vegetable burger, carrot cake, orange juice; vegetable burger, apple pie, bottled water; mushroom burger, carrot cake, bottled water**

2. Alyshia has $10 to spend for lunch. If she wants a special, a beverage, and a dessert, what items could she choose for her lunch? **any combination of a special, drink, and dessert**

3. Together, Tamara and Alyshia have $17. They want to leave a $3 tip for the waitress. How will this affect what they can order? How will each girl's order change from the selections above? **Sample answers: If they share equally, each girl will have $7 to spend after deducting the tip and can choose from the options in Question 1.**

4. Eight students are going to the Neighborhood Cafe to celebrate the end of the semester. Each student orders a special, a beverage, and a dessert. About how much will the eight lunches cost? How did you decide on that amount? **About $64 since a special costs about $5, a dessert costs about $2, and a drink costs about $1 for a total of $8 per meal. 8 × $8 = $64 for 8 students.**

29

1-6 Using a Problem-Solving Plan

Lesson Preview

✔ **Check Skills You'll Need**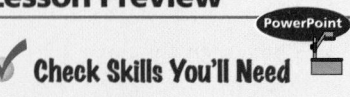

Subtracting Whole Numbers
Skills Handbook: Subtracting Whole Numbers, p. 657.

Lesson Resources

📁 **Teaching Resources**
Practice, Reteaching, Enrichment

👥 **Reaching All Students**
Practice Workbook 1-6
Spanish Practice Workbook 1-6
Guided Problem Solving 1-6

🕐 **Presentation Assistant Plus!**
Transparencies
• Check Skills You'll Need 1-6
• Problem of the Day 1-6
• Additional Examples 1-6
• Student Edition Answers 1-6
• Lesson Quiz 1-6
PH Presentation Pro CD-ROM 1-6

ASSESSMENT SYSTEM
Computer Test Generator CD

💻 **Technology**
Resource Pro® CD-ROM
Computer Test Generator CD
PH Presentation Pro CD-ROM

💻 **www.PHSchool.com**
Student Site
• Teacher Web Code: aak-5500
• Self-grading Lesson Quiz

PH SuccessNet Teacher Center
• Lesson Planner
• Resources

 Plus 🖹TEXT

What You'll Learn

OBJECTIVE 1 To use a plan to solve problems

. . . And Why

To have an organized way to solve problems, as in Example 1

✔ Check Skills You'll Need

❓ For help, go to Lesson 1–5.

Find each sum or difference.

1. $2.1 + 4.7$ **6.8**
2. $10.28 + 3.89$ **14.17**
3. $18.4 + 5.6$ **24**
4. $12.36 - 10.25$ **2.11**
5. $1.77 - 0.53$ **1.24**
6. $6.4 - 2.07$ **4.33**

OBJECTIVE 1

 Interactive lesson includes instant self-check, tutorials, and activities.

Using a Plan to Solve Problems

Some problems require good problem-solving skills. A problem-solving plan like the one below can help you solve more challenging problems.

> **Key Concepts**   **A Problem-Solving Plan**
> 1. Read and understand the problem.
> 2. Plan how to solve the problem, then solve it.
> 3. Look back and check to see if your answer makes sense.

---

1 EXAMPLE   Real-World 🌐 Problem Solving

Olympic Race Skeleton competitors slide headfirst down an ice track on a metal sled. The winner has the fastest total time in two heats, or runs.

At the 2002 Winter Olympics, Tristan Gale won the women's skeleton event. How much faster was Gale's total time than Parsley's?

Women's Skeleton Results

Name	Heat 1 Time (seconds)	Heat 2 Time (seconds)
Tristan Gale	52.26	52.85
Lea Ann Parsley	52.27	52.94
Alex Coomber	52.48	52.89

Ongoing Assessment and Intervention

Before the Lesson
Diagnose prerequisite skills using:
• Check Skills You'll Need

During the Lesson
Monitor progress using:
• Check Understanding
• Additional Examples
• Test Prep

After the Lesson
Assess knowledge using:
• Lesson Quiz
• Computer Test Generator CD

Read and Understand Determine what you know and what you need to find out.

> Read the problem again. Ask yourself, "What information is given? What information is missing? What am I being asked to find?"

You are asked to find how much faster Gale's total time was than Parsley's. You know the times of each heat for each person.

Plan and Solve Choose a strategy.

> As you learn problem-solving strategies throughout this book, you will decide which one is best for the problem you are trying to solve.

First, find the total time for each competitor mentioned. Extend the table.

Women's Skeleton Results

Name	Heat 1 Time (seconds)	Heat 2 Time (seconds)	Total Time (seconds)
Tristan Gale	52.26	52.85	▢
Lea Ann Parsley	52.27	52.94	▢

To find each competitor's total time, you add.
Gale's total time: 52.26 + 52.85 = 105.11 seconds
Parsley's total time: 52.27 + 52.94 = 105.21 seconds

To compare the total times, you subtract.
105.21 − 105.11 = 0.10 second

Gale's total time was 0.10 second faster than Parsley's total time.

Look Back and Check Think about how you solved the problem.

> Look back at your work and compare it with the information and question in the problem. Ask yourself, "Is my answer reasonable? Did I check my work?"

You can compare the times in each heat. Gale's time in the first heat was 0.01 second faster. In the second heat her time was 0.09 second faster. So, the answer, 0.10 second, for the total time is reasonable and checks.

✓ **Check Understanding** ① How much faster was Parsley's total time than Coomber's? **0.16 s**

1-6 Using a Problem-Solving Plan **31**

Real-World Connection
Tristan Gale won the gold medal in the first women's skeleton event in Olympic history.

2. Teach

Math Background
There are many ways to go about solving problems. In this program, students are introduced to a three-step Problem-Solving Plan: Read and Understand, Plan and Solve, and Look Back and Check. Rather than having students haphazardly approach the task of problem solving, this three-step plan gives them an organized procedure to follow for a wide range of problems.

Teaching Notes

Teaching Tip
Have students brainstorm strategies that they can use to solve real-world problems such as *Make a Table*. Write up their ideas on poster board and display them in the room for students' reference.

Data Analysis Connection
Point out that problem-solving strategies are used to solve many types of problems, mathematical and non-mathematical. Ask students to suggest real-world problems that might need to be analyzed by scientists, mathematicians, professional athletes and coaches, or other professionals.

Additional Examples
① 46 students and 3 teachers go to camp each day on a bus. The bus has 32 seats, and each seat holds 2 people. If every seat is used, how many seats will have two people?
17 seats

Closure
• *What are the three steps of the Problem-Solving Plan?* Read and understand the problem; plan how to solve the problem and solve it; look back and check if your answer is reasonable.

👫 Reaching All Students

Below Level Give students decimal addition and subtraction exercises in a horizontal format and have them first rewrite them with the decimal points aligned.
6.29 + 0.22 **6.51** 88.91 − 67.80 **21.11**

Advanced Learners Have students write an addition or a subtraction word problem using these lengths: 6.07 cm, 7.5 cm, and 2.6 cm. Challenge classmates to solve the problems.

Error Prevention See note on page 32.

31

? For more practice, see *Extra Practice*.

Assignment Guide

1 Objective 1
Ⓐ Ⓑ **Core** 1–9
Ⓒ **Extension** 10–11

Test Prep 12–15
Mixed Review 16–24

Error Prevention!

Exercise 1 Students may read the problem quickly and think that not enough information is provided.

Ⓐ **Practice by Example**

Example 1
(page 30)

Need Help?
- Reread the problem.
- Identify the key facts and details.
- Tell the problem in your own words.
- Try a different strategy.
- Check your work.

Use a problem-solving plan to solve each problem.

1. Entertainment Three friends go to a baseball game. Each has a hot dog, a bag of roasted peanuts, and a soda. They spend a total of $78 on food and tickets. How much does each person spend? **$26**

2. Shopping Granola bars cost $2.79 per box. A coupon in last Sunday's paper will save you $.45 on two boxes. How much will two boxes of granola bars cost before tax if you use the coupon? **$5.13**

3. Sasha arrived at the bowling alley at 6:37. Ellen and Rosa had been waiting for her for 8 minutes. Ellen had waited for Rosa for 4 minutes. What time did Ellen arrive at the bowling alley? **6:25**

4. A scientist used a cylinder as a vase for a rose. Each day, 14 mL of water evaporated. The water level originally read 100 mL. How much water remained after 4 days? **44 mL**

Ⓑ **Apply Your Skills**

Strategies

Draw a Diagram
Make a Graph
Make an Organized List
Make a Table and Look for a Pattern
Simulate a Problem
Solve a Simpler Problem
Try, Check, and Revise
Use Logical Reasoning
Work Backward
Write an Equation

Choose a strategy to solve each problem.

5. It takes Clara 12 minutes to cut a log into 4 pieces. How long will it take her to cut another log that is the same size into 5 pieces? **16 min**
GPS

6. Fundraising Chris, Ted, Tim, and Jerry biked in a 10-mile charity race. Tim was last in 39 minutes 6.5 seconds. Ted finished 2 minutes 0.3 second ahead of Tim. Jerry finished 47.8 seconds ahead of Ted. Chris finished 1 minute 57.4 seconds ahead of Jerry. What was Chris's time? **34 min 21 s**

7. Elections The candidates for sixth-grade president are Sheresa, Robert, and Bethany. The candidates for secretary are Tim, Ling, Dennis, and Annie. How many different teams of president and secretary are there? **12 teams**

8. A dog trainer has a bag of 70 dog treats. He gives 8 treats each day. How many whole days will the treats last? How many treats can he give on the last day? **8 days; 6 treats**

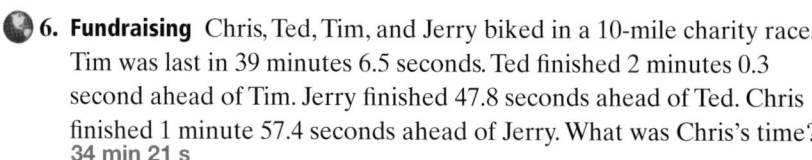

Practice 1-6   Using a Problem-Solving Plan

Use a problem-solving plan to solve each problem.

1. Philip won a cash prize in a spelling bee. He gave half of his money to his brother. Then he spent $22.50 on a new sweater and put the rest, $56.25, into his savings account. How much money did Philip win?
$157.50

2. Gabe, Raul, and Josh competed in a swimming race. Gabe finished in 32.01 seconds, Raul finished in 31.84 seconds and Josh finished in 31.92 seconds. Who came in first, second, and third?
Raul, Josh, and Gabe

3. You bought three CDs at the same price. Based on rounding, your estimate of the total cost was $30 before tax. If you rounded to the nearest dollar, what is the maximum price for each CD? What is the minimum price?
maximum price $10.49; minimum price $9.50

Choose a strategy to solve each problem.

4. Sherrill, Jennifer, Sandy, and Richard competed in a long-jump contest. Jennifer won the contest with a distance of 19.25 meters. Sandy jumped 8.65 meters less than Jennifer. Richard jumped 3.9 meters farther than Sandy but 2.75 meters less than Sherrill. How many meters did Sherrill jump?
17.25 meters

5. In January, Jeff bought three rabbits. By February, the rabbit population had doubled. By March, Jeff noticed that the population of the rabbits had doubled again. How many rabbits will Jeff have by May?
48 rabbits

6. Agatha made a five-digit number with 0, 3, 5, 8, and 9. The number is bigger than 39 and smaller than 53. The thousandths digit is 3 times the tenths digit. What number did Agatha make?
50.389

7. A family of four wants to take the least expensive form of transportation on their vacation. Roundtrip train tickets cost $95.50 per person, roundtrip airline tickets cost $195 per person—buy one get one free—and roundtrip bus tickets cost $64.50 per person plus overnight hotel costs of $162.50. Which form of transportation is the least expensive?
the train

Reteaching 1-6   Using a Problem-Solving Plan

Lincoln Middle School needs new smoke alarms. The school has $415 to spend. Alarms with escape lights cost $18, and alarms with a false-alarm silencer cost $11. The school wants 4 times as many escape-light alarms as silencer alarms. How many of each kind can the school purchase?

Read and Understand What facts are needed to solve the problem? *You need the costs of the alarms, $18 and $11; the amount to be spent, $415; and the fact that 4 times as many escape-light alarms as silencer alarms will be bought.*

Plan and Solve You can try values and check them to solve this problem. *Try:* Buy 12 escape-light alarms and 3 silencer alarms.

Check: 12 × $18 = $216
       3 × $11 = $ 33
       Add: $249

$249 is a lot less than the $415 that the school has to spend. Continue with different values until you solve the problem.

Buy 20 escape-light alarms and 5 silencer alarms.

       20 × $18 = $360
        5 × $11 = $ 55
       Add: $415

Look Back and Check Check to see whether your answer agrees with the information in the problem. *Is the total amount spent $415, or slightly less? Are there 4 times as many escape-light alarms as silencer alarms?*

Choose a strategy to solve each problem.

1. Tina needs batteries. AA batteries cost $3 per pack. D batteries cost $4 per pack. If she has $26 to spend and buys 3 times as many packs of AA batteries as D batteries, how many packs of each does she buy?
6 packs of AA, 2 packs of D

2. Ian needs cassette tapes for his recorder. One package of 3 tapes sells for $5. Another pack of 2 costs $4. If Ian has $19 and buys 11 cassettes, how many packs of each kind does he buy?
three $5 packs and one $4 pack

3. Hyugen has $50 to spend on CDs. New ones cost $9 and used cost $7. He wants to buy more new CDs than used. How many of each can he buy?
4 new CDs and 2 used CDs

4. Frank has $41 to spend on computer disks. A pack of 10 ES brand costs $13 and a pack of 11 CW brand costs $14. How many packs of each can he buy if he spends all his money?
1 ES brand and 2 CW brand

GPS   Use the Guided Problem Solving worksheet with Exercise 5.

9–11. See margin.

9. Jasmine paints a wooden block on the top and on four sides. She cuts it along the lines as shown.

   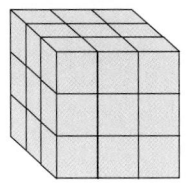

   a. How many cuts does Jasmine make?

   b. Into how many pieces does she cut the block?

   c. **Writing in Math** How many of the pieces do not have any paint on them? Explain how you know.

 **C** Challenge

10. Each competitor for men's halfpipe snowboarding is judged on two runs. The *greater* of the two scores determines the winner. How would the ranking have changed if the *total* score of both runs were used?

2002 Winter Olympics

Competitor	Scores in Points	
	Run 1	Run 2
Powers (USA)	46.1	32.0
Kass (USA)	42.5	41.5
Thomas (USA)	33.2	42.1
Kratter (Italy)	34.9	42.0
Nakai (Japan)	38.3	40.7
Czeschin (USA)	40.6	40.5

SOURCE: U.S. Ski Team

11. **Stretch Your Thinking** Turn the triangle "upside-down" by sliding one circle at a time to a new location so that it touches 2 other circles. How many moves did you make? (The fewest moves is 3.)

Test Prep

Multiple Choice

12. Which value completes the statement $54 = 3 \times \blacksquare$? **A**
    A. 18   **B.** 51   **C.** 57   **D.** 162

13. In 9 minutes, it will be 11:06. What time is it now? **I**
    F. 2:06   **G.** 11:15   **H.** 10:97   **I.** 10:57

14. The difference $8.7 - 0.368$ is closest to which value? **A**
    A. 8.3   **B.** 8.4   **C.** 8.7   **D.** 9

Take It to the NET
Online lesson quiz at
www.PHSchool.com
Web Code: aaa-0106

15. Which value completes the statement $3.15 + \blacksquare < 5$? **H**
    F. 1.95   **G.** 1.85   **H.** 1.84   **I.** 2.85

Mixed Review

Lesson 1-5   **Add or subtract.**

16. $0.8 + 0.5$
    1.3

17. $2.59 - 0.83$
    1.76

18. $0.56 + 0.9$
    0.65

19. $1.8 - 0.09$
    1.71

Lesson 1-2   **Write the place value of the digit 3 in each number.**

24. ten-thousandths

20. 108.39
    tenths

21. 38.22
    tens

22. 0.523
    thousandths

23. 345.650
    hundreds

24. 0.0293
    See left.

9a. 6 cuts

b. 27 pieces

c. 2 pieces; there is one side of the wooden block initially without paint. 8 pieces of that side have painted sides;

1 does not. There is also a piece in the center that doesn't get painted.

10. Kass, Czeschin, Nakai, Powers, Kratter, Thomas

11. Answers may vary. Sample given:

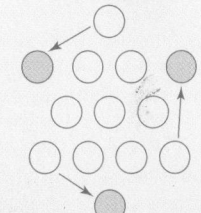

 **Lesson Quiz 1-6**

Use the problem-solving plan.

1. Carmen scored 26 points in a basketball game. Each field goal basket is worth 2 points. Each free throw is worth 1 point. If Carmen made nine baskets, how many free throws did she score? **8 free throws**

Alternative Assessment

Have students work in pairs or small groups. Each student writes a word problem similar to the Example in this lesson. Students exchange papers and solve each other's problem. Students share with the class how they used the problem-solving plan to find a solution.

Test Prep

Resources

For additional practice with a variety of test item formats:
• Test-Prep, p. 57
• Test-Taking Strategies, p. 53
• Test-Taking Strategies With Transparencies

Enrichment 1-6   Use a Problem-Solving Plan
Critical Thinking

At Monroe Middle School, there are 79 students in three sixth-grade history classes. The largest class has 28 students.

1. The school wants each history class to have the same number of students. Can the students be divided so that all the classes will be the same size? Explain.
   No; $79 \div 3 \approx 26.3$. You can't have 0.3 students.

2. Kaitlynn and Stephen are not in the history class with 28 students. If they are in different classes, can their classes be the same size? Explain.
   No; the other two classes have a total of 51 students. They cannot be divided evenly into two groups.

3. The students in the history classes are also in music classes. There are three music classes, and the largest class has 28 students. Kaitlynn and Stephen are in different music classes. They know that their classes are the same size. How many students are in each class?
   Two classes have 28 students, the other has 23.

4. Stephen's friends, Kyle and Lexann, move to his neighborhood. They both decide to take a music class. If each class can have any number of students, can the music students be divided so that each class will be the same size?
   Yes, each class will have 27 students.

5. Before Kyle and Lexann joined, each of three math classes had the same students as the three history classes. The school wants to place Kyle and Lexann so that the math classes will be as close to the same size as possible.
   a. Without reassigning any other students, to which math class(es) should the school assign Kyle and Lexann? Explain.
      the class with 23 students; the classes will then have 28, 28, and 25 students
   b. How many more students would need to join a math class for the classes to be equal?
      3 students

Modeling Multiplication of Decimals

Students create and shade in grids to model multiplication of a whole number and a decimal. Then they find the product of two decimals.

Optional Materials

- graph paper or blank grid models
- Classroom Aid 2, 9–10

Teaching Notes

Have students use graph paper and mark off two hundredths-grids. Elicit from them that each 10 x 10 region represents 1 whole. Then work through the first example on the board or on the overhead projector while students work at their seats.

1 EXAMPLE Teaching Tip

For an additional example, guide students to model the product 3×0.16 using a hundredths-grid. Here's one way to do it: shade three sets of 0.16 on the 10 x 10 grid, using a different color marker each time. Count the small squares. **48** The model shows three groups of 16 hundredths each.

2 EXAMPLE Visual Learners

You may find it useful to have students work with different styles, rather than different colors, to show multiplication by tenths. For example, if students mark the squares for 4 tenths with [////] and those for 5 tenths with [\\\\], the overlapped squares will be crisscrossed and easy to spot.

Alternative Method

Students can also explore multiplication using place-value models. They can use one hundred squares to represent ones, ten strips to represent tenths, and ones squares for hundredths.

Investigation — Modeling Multiplication of Decimals

For Use With Lesson 1-7

A model can help you understand how to multiply decimals.

1 EXAMPLE   Multiplying a Whole Number by a Decimal    Real World

Coin Collecting A collector buys two 1942 Mercury dimes. Each coin costs $.92. Draw a model to find the total cost.

You want to find $0.92 + 0.92$, or 2×0.92.

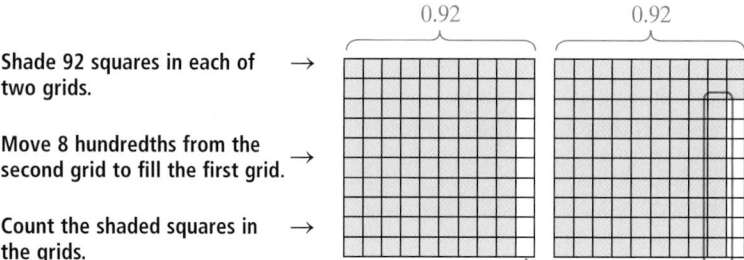

Shade 92 squares in each of two grids. →

Move 8 hundredths from the second grid to fill the first grid. →

Count the shaded squares in the grids. →

Move 8 squares.

The shaded area is 1 whole and 84 hundredths, or 1.84.
The total cost is $1.84.

Real-World Connection

Miss Liberty's wings look like the Roman god Mercury. So, the coin was called the "Mercury" dime.

2 EXAMPLE   Multiplying Decimals

Draw a model to find the product 0.5×0.4.

Shade 4 *columns* → of a grid to represent 0.4.

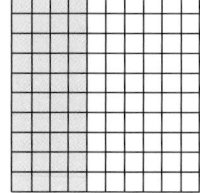

Shade 5 *rows* to → represent 0.5. Use a different color or style.

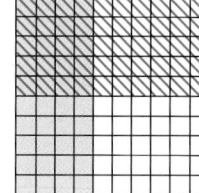

The shadings overlap in 20 squares, representing 20 hundredths, or 0.20.
So, $0.5 \times 0.4 = 0.20$.

EXERCISES

Draw a model on grid paper to find each product.   1–2. See back of book. 3–5. See margin.

1. 3×0.9 **2.** 2×0.61 **3.** 0.8×0.5 **4.** 0.7×0.2 **5.** 0.1×0.6

Investigation

3.
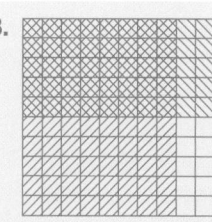
0.40

4.
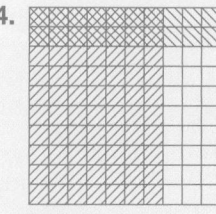
0.14

5.
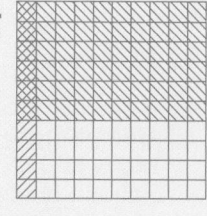
0.06

1-7 Multiplying Decimals

What You'll Learn

OBJECTIVE 1 To multiply decimals

OBJECTIVE 2 To use the properties of multiplication

. . . And Why

To predict tree growth, as in Example 3

 Check Skills You'll Need

For help, go to Skills Handbook, p. 658.

Multiply.

1. 7×21 **2.** 68×12 **3.** 41×527 **4.** $2{,}117 \times 20$
147   816   21,607   42,340

New Vocabulary

- Commutative Property of Multiplication
- Associative Property of Multiplication
- Identity Property of Multiplication

iTEXT Interactive lesson includes instant self-check, tutorials, and activities.

 OBJECTIVE 1

Multiplying Decimals

The model below shows how to find 0.5×1.5. You are finding half of 1.5.

Shade 1.5 grids.   **Shade 0.5 of each grid.**

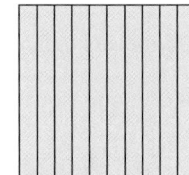 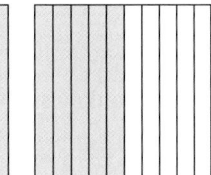   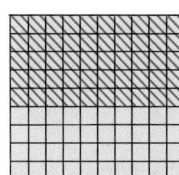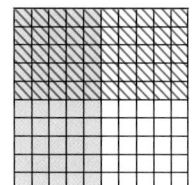

The shadings overlap in 75 squares, or 75 hundredths. So, $0.5 \times 1.5 = 0.75$.

The model also illustrates a pattern. You can add the number of decimal places in the factors to find the number of decimal places in the product.

> **Reading Math**
>
> *Factors* are numbers that are multiplied.

① EXAMPLE   **Multiplying a Whole Number by a Decimal**

Find the product 0.47×8.

$$
\begin{array}{rl}
0.47 & \leftarrow \quad \textbf{2 decimal places} \\
\underline{\times \quad 8} & \leftarrow + \textbf{ 0 decimal places} \\
3.76 & \leftarrow \quad \textbf{2 decimal places}
\end{array}
$$

 Check Understanding ① Find each product.   **a.** 6×0.13 **b.** 4.37×5
                                                  0.78   21.85

You can indicate multiplication in these three ways: 0.5×1.5, $0.5 \cdot 1.5$, and $0.5(1.5)$.

Lesson Preview

PowerPoint

 Check Skills You'll Need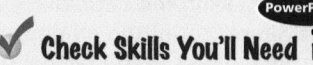

Multiplying Whole Numbers
Skills Handbook: Multiplying Whole Numbers, p. 658.

Lesson Resources

Teaching Resources
Practice, Reteaching, Enrichment
Checkpoint Quiz 2

Reaching All Students
Practice Workbook 1-7
Spanish Practice Workbook 1-7
Spanish Checkpoint Quiz 2
Guided Problem Solving 1-7
Hands-On Activities 3

Presentation Assistant Plus!
Transparencies
- Check Skills You'll Need 1-7
- Problem of the Day 1-7
- Additional Examples 1-7
- Student Edition Answers 1-7
- Lesson Quiz 1-7
- Classroom Aid 2, 10
PH Presentation Pro CD-ROM 1-7

PRENTICE HALL ASSESSMENT SYSTEM

Checkpoint Quiz 2
Computer Test Generator CD

 Technology
Resource Pro® CD-ROM
Computer Test Generator CD
PH Presentation Pro CD-ROM

www.PHSchool.com
Student Site
- Teacher Web Code: aak-5500
- Self-grading Lesson Quiz

PH SuccessNet Teacher Center
- Lesson Planner
- Resources

Plus

Ongoing Assessment and Intervention

Before the Lesson
Diagnose prerequisite skills using:
- Check Skills You'll Need

During the Lesson
Monitor progress using:
- Check Understanding
- Additional Examples
- Test Prep

After the Lesson
Assess knowledge using:
- Lesson Quiz
- Computer Test Generator CD
- Chapter Checkpoint 2 (p. 39)

Math Background

Multiplying decimals is similar to multiplying whole numbers except for the extra step of correctly placing the decimal point. Simply count the number of decimal places in the factors being multiplied. Then place the decimal point so that the number of decimal places in the product is the same as the total number in the factors. So, 2 × 1.5 results in 3.0, 0.2 × 1.5 results in 0.30, and 0.2 × 0.15 results in 0.030.

This lesson introduces the properties of multiplication that are closely related to the properties of addition introduced in Lesson 1-5. The Commutative Property of Multiplication states that 3 · 5 and 5 · 3 result in the same product. Similarly, the Associative Property of Multiplication states that (2 · 7) · 4 is the same product as 2 · (7 · 4).

Teaching Notes

① EXAMPLE Number Sense

Encourage students to estimate before multiplying. Ask:
- *What is a convenient number to round 0.47 to?* 0.5
- *What is 0.5 times 8?* 4
- *Does the answer 3.76 appear reasonable?* Yes; 3.76 is close to 4. Also, the answer should be less than 4 because 0.47 is less than 0.5.

Inclusion

Review the three ways to indicate the same multiplication as shown under Example 1. Ask: *What are three ways you can write 0.4 times 0.5?* 0.4 · 0.5; 0.4 × 0.5; 0.4(0.5) or (0.4)0.5

② EXAMPLE Alternative Method

Show students that they can perform simple decimal multiplications mentally. Ask:
- *What is the product of 3 × 7?* 21
- *How would the product change if you found 0.3 × 0.7 instead of 3 × 7?* The product would have a decimal point two places from the right, or 0.21.

36

---

② EXAMPLE Multiplying Decimals

Find the product 0.3 · 0.7.

$$
\begin{array}{rl}
0.3 & \leftarrow \textbf{1 decimal place} \\
\times\, 0.7 & \leftarrow +\textbf{1 decimal place} \\
\hline
0.21 & \leftarrow \textbf{2 decimal places}
\end{array}
$$

 Check Understanding ② Find each product. **a.** 0.3(0.2) 0.06 **b.** 0.9 · 0.14 0.126

c. Number Sense In parts (a) and (b), both factors are less than 1. How does the answer in each part compare to its factors? It is less than either factor.

③ EXAMPLE Real-World 🌐 Problem Solving

Growth Prediction A eucalyptus tree grows about 5.45 meters in one year. At that rate of growth, how much will the tree grow in 3.5 years?

Estimate 3.5 × 5.45 ≈ 4 × 5, or 20

Multiply.

$$
\begin{array}{r}
5.45 \quad \leftarrow \textbf{2 decimal places} \\
\times\, 3.5 \quad \leftarrow \textbf{1 decimal place} \\
\hline
2725 \\
+1635 \\
\hline
19.075 \quad \leftarrow \textbf{3 decimal places}
\end{array}
$$

The tree will grow about 19.075 meters in 3.5 years.

Check for Reasonableness 19.075 is reasonable since it is close to 20.

Real-World 🌐 Connection

The leaves and flowers of eucalyptus trees are the main diet of koala bears.

 Check Understanding ③ Find each product. **a.** 2.4 × 3.11 7.464 **b.** 15.1(3.84) 57.984

OBJECTIVE

2 Using the Properties of Multiplication

Key Concepts	Properties of Multiplication

Commutative Property of Multiplication

Changing the order of the factors does not change the product.
$$4.7 \times 5 = 5 \times 4.7$$

Associative Property of Multiplication

Changing the grouping of the factors does not change the product.
$$(4.7 \times 5) \times 2 = 4.7 \times (5 \times 2)$$

Identity Property of Multiplication

The product of 1 and any number is that number.
$$4.7 \times 1 = 1 \times 4.7 = 4.7$$

 Reaching All Students

Below Level Review the number of decimal places with various decimals such as these.	Advanced Learners Have students work on decimal multiplications with three factors such as these.	English Learners See note on page 37. Inclusion See note on page 36.
0.51 2 3.4 1 8 0 0.02 2 25 0 9.06 2	2.5 · 3.75 · 4.1 38.4375 88.3 · 6.2 · 5.4 2,956.284	

The properties of multiplication can also help you do math mentally. These properties let you change the order of multiplication.

4 EXAMPLE Using the Properties of Multiplication  Real World

Mental Math A customer buys 4 bags of corn. Each bag contains 8 ears of corn that cost $.25 per ear. Use mental math to find $4 \times (8 \times \$.25)$.

What you think

$.25 and 4 are easy to multiply. Multiplying $.25 and 4 gives $1. Multiplying $1 and 8 gives $8. So, $4 \times (8 \times \$.25) = \$8$.

Why it works

$4 \times (8 \times \$.25) = 4 \times (\$.25 \times 8)$ ← Commutative Property of Multiplication

$= (4 \times \$.25) \times 8$ ← Associative Property of Multiplication

$= \$1 \times 8$ ← Multiply inside the parentheses.

$= \$8$ ← Identity Property of Multiplication

Real-World Connection

Some people use mental math when making change.

✔ **Check Understanding** ④ Use mental math to find each product.

a. $2(5 \times 2.3)$
23

b. $3.1 \times 1 \times 100$
310

c. $500 \times 0.333(2)$
333

EXERCISES

❓ For more practice, see *Extra Practice*.

Ⓐ **Practice by Example**

Find each product. Exercises 1 and 9 have been started for you.

Example 1
(page 35)

1. 0.018 **0.072**
  × 4
  ―――
  72

2. 1.9 **17.1**
  × 9

3. 31 **173.6**
  × 5.6

4. 39 **2.34**
  × 0.06

5. 358(0.7)
250.6

6. 0.12(47)
5.64

7. 53 · 0.04
2.12

8. 0.28 · 92
25.76

Example 2
(page 36)

9. 0.2 **0.14**
  × 0.7
  ―――
  14

10. 0.8 **0.32**
  × 0.4

11. 0.3 **0.15**
  × 0.5

12. 0.7 **0.63**
  × 0.9

13. 0.12(0.96)
0.1152

14. 0.06(0.18)
0.0108

15. 0.486 · 0.9
0.4374

16. 0.03 · 0.574
0.01722

Example 3
(page 36)

17. 4.5(230)
1,035

18. 1.7 × 3.702
6.2934

19. 3.2 · 4.5
14.4

20. 8.1 · 1.3
10.53

21. 3.3(420)
1,386

22. 3.2 · 15.5
49.6

23. 4.25 · 6.18
26.265

24. 1.2 × 2.065
2.478

25. One pound of tomatoes costs $1.29. To the nearest cent, how much would 2.75 pounds of tomatoes cost? $3.55

③ EXAMPLE Error Prevention

When placing the decimal point in the product, students may incorrectly count decimal places from before the decimal point instead of after. For instance, in Example 3 they might write 190.75 instead of 19.075.

④ EXAMPLE English Learners

Use plain language to relate the properties of multiplication to the corresponding properties of addition. For example, "The Commutative Properties state that changing the order of addends or factors does not change the sum or product. This means $4 + 5 = 5 + 4$, and $4 \times 5 = 5 \times 4$. The Associative Properties state that changing the grouping of addends or factors does not change the sum or product. This means $(5 + 3) + 7 = 5 + (3 + 7)$ and $(2 \times 5) \times 3 = 2 \times (5 \times 3)$."

PowerPoint

📊 **Additional Examples**

① Find the product 2.73×4.
10.92

② Find the product 0.6×0.42.
0.252

③ Cameron can read 196 words in a minute. Robert reads 1.6 times as fast. How many words can Robert read in a minute? 313.6, or about 314 words

④ Use mental math to find each product.

a. $5(0.3) \times 20$ **30**

b. $0.25(1.5 \cdot 4)$ **1.5**

Closure

• *How do you multiply decimals?* Sample: Multiply decimals the same way you multiply whole numbers. Then count the number of decimal places in the factors, count off that many places in the product, and place the decimal point.

• *How do you use mental math to find products?* Sample: Use the Associative Property of Multiplication to change the grouping of factors, or use the Commutative Property of Multiplication to change the order of factors.

Assignment Guide

1 Objective 1
Ⓐ Ⓑ Core 1–25, 36–39, 44–46, 48
Ⓒ Extension 52–54

2 Objective 2
Ⓐ Ⓑ Core 26–35, 40–43, 47, 49–51
Ⓒ Extension 55

Test Prep 56–58
Mixed Review 59–61

Example 4
(page 37)

Use mental math to find each product.

26. $5 \times 0.47 \times 2$ **4.7**   **27.** $0.7 \times 1 \times 4$ **2.8**   **28.** $25 \cdot 1.3 \cdot 40$ **1,300**

29. $(20) \cdot (1.9)(5)$ **190**   **30.** $6.8 \cdot 25 \cdot 4$ **680**   **31.** $9.5 \cdot 1 \cdot 100$ **950**

32. $4 \times 0.2 \times 1,000$
800
33. $(0.02) \cdot (33)(50)$
33
34. $5 \times 6.83 \times 0.2$
6.83

35. Money What is the value in dollars of 25 rolls of nickels if there are 40 nickels in each roll? **$50.00**

Ⓑ Apply Your Skills

Find each product.

36. 522 **261**   **37.** 22.76 **68.28** **38.** 0.15 **0.0465** **39.** 8.42
   $\times\ 0.5$ $\times\ \ \ 3$ $\times 0.31$ $\times\ 6.7$
                                             56.414

Choose a Method Find each product. Tell whether you would use mental math, paper and pencil, or a calculator. **40–43. See margin.**

40. 16×2.5 **41.** $0.8 \cdot 0.008$ **42.** $60(0.5)$ **43.** $56.37 \cdot 5.29$

44. Nutrition There is 0.2 gram of calcium in 1 serving of cheddar cheese. **GPS** How much calcium is in 3.25 servings of cheddar cheese? **0.65 g**

45. Automobiles The average fuel rates for 2000 are at the left. How much farther could a car travel on 13 gallons of gas than an SUV? **58.5 mi**

46. Writing in Math Explain how multiplying 0.3×0.4 is like multiplying 3×4. How is it different? **See margin.**

47. Astronomy Mercury is about 36 million miles from the sun. Jupiter is about 13.43 times that distance. About how far is Jupiter from the sun? **483.48 million mi**

48. Which product does *not* equal 49.12? **D**
   A. 15.35×3.2 **B.** 12.8×3.8375 **C.** 16×3.07 **D.** 35.15×2.5

Error Analysis Estimate to tell if each calculator answer is correct. If incorrect, explain the error. **49–51. See margin.**

49. $0.937 \cdot 24.78$ **50.** $4.52 \cdot 0.615$ **51.** $43.45 \cdot 0.2162$
   232.1886   *2.7798*   *43.6662*

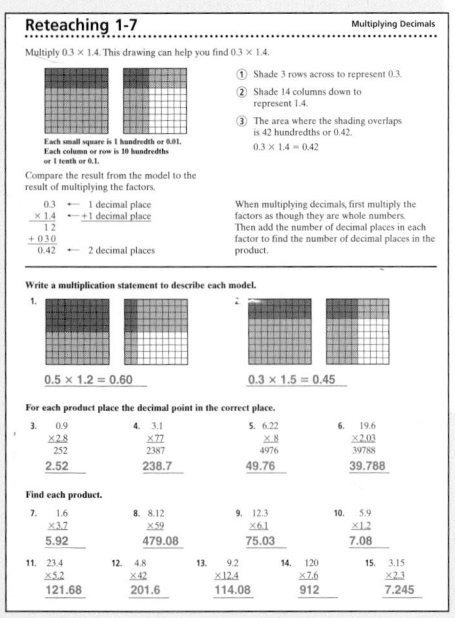

Passenger cars:
22.0 miles per gallon

Sport utility
vehicles (SUV):
17.5 miles per gallon

Ⓒ Challenge

Algebra Find the value that makes each statement true.

52. $\blacksquare \div 0.2 = 0.7$ **53.** $\blacksquare \div 0.03 = 0.5$ **54.** $\blacksquare \div 1.6 = 0.04$
0.14   **0.015**   **0.064**

55. Stretch Your Thinking Find the least whole number greater than 1,000 whose digits are all different. What is its units digit? **1,023; 3**

GPS Use the Guided Problem Solving worksheet with Exercise 44.

40–43. Methods may vary. Samples are given.
  40. 40; paper and pencil
  41. 0.0064; mental math
  42. 30; mental math
  43. 298.1973; calculator

46. Answers may vary. Sample: In both cases, you multiply 3 by 4; with 0.3×0.4, you need to show two decimal places.

Practice 1-7   Multiplying Decimals

Place the decimal point in each product.
1. $4.3 \times 2.9 = 1247$ 2. $0.279 \times 53 = 14787$ 3. $4.09 \times 3.96 = 161964$
   12.47   14.787   16.1964
4. $5.90 \times 6.3 = 3717$ 5. $0.74 \times 83 = 6142$ 6. $2.06 \times 15.9 = 32754$
   37.17   61.42   32.754

Find each product.
7. 43.59×0.1 8. 246×0.01 9. 726×0.1
   4.359   2.46   72.6
10. 5.342   11. 0.19   12. 6.4
   $\times\ \ 13$ $\times\ 0.05$ $\times\ 0.09$
   69.446   0.0095   0.576
13. 240   14. 43.79   15. 0.72
   $\times\ 0.02$ $\times\ \ \ 42$ $\times\ 0.43$
   4.8   1,839.18   0.3096

Write a multiplication statement you could use for each situation.
16. A pen costs $.59. How much would a dozen pens cost?
   $12 \times \$.59 = \$7.08$
17. A mint costs $.02. How much would a roll of 10 mints cost?
   $10 \times \$.02 = \$.20$
18. A bottle of juice has a deposit of $.10 on the bottle. How much deposit money would there be on 8 bottles?
   $8 \times \$.10 = \$.80$
19. An orange costs $.09. How much would 2 dozen oranges cost?
   $\$.09 \times 24 = \$2.16$

Find each product. Tell whether you would use mental math, paper and pencil, or a calculator.
20. $19(0.35)$ 21. 30×0.1 22. 22.62×1.08
   paper and pencil   mental math   calculator
   6.65   3   24.4296

Reteaching 1-7   Multiplying Decimals

Multiply 0.3×1.4. This drawing can help you find 0.3×1.4.

① Shade 3 rows across to represent 0.3.
② Shade 14 columns down to represent 1.4.
③ The area where the shading overlaps is 42 hundredths or 0.42.
   $0.3 \times 1.4 = 0.42$

Each small square is 1 hundredth or 0.01.
Each column or row is 10 hundredths or 1 tenth or 0.1.

Compare the result from the model to the result of multiplying the factors.

   0.3 ← 1 decimal place
$\times 1.4$ ← +1 decimal place
   1 2
$+ 0.3 0$
   0.42 ← 2 decimal places

When multiplying decimals, first multiply the factors as though they were whole numbers. Then add the number of decimal places in each factor to find the number of decimal places in the product.

Write a multiplication statement to describe each model.
1.   2.
   $0.5 \times 1.2 = 0.60$ $0.3 \times 1.5 = 0.45$

For each product place the decimal point in the correct place.
3. 0.9   4. 3.1   5. 6.22   6. 19.6
   $\times 2.8$ $\times 77$ $\times\ 8$ $\times 2.03$
   252   2387   4976   39788
   2.52   238.7   49.76   39.788

Find each product.
7. 1.6   8. 8.12   9. 12.3   10. 5.9
   $\times 3.7$ $\times 59$ $\times 6.1$ $\times 1.2$
   5.92   479.08   75.03   7.08
11. 23.4   12. 4.8   13. 9.2   14. 120   15. 3.15
   $\times 5.2$ $\times 42$ $\times 12.4$ $\times 7.6$ $\times 2.3$
   121.68   201.6   114.08   912   7.245

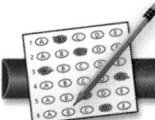
Reading Comprehension   Read the passage and answer the questions below.

Calories Burned	
Activity	**Calories/Minute/ Pound**
Dancing	0.05
Jumping rope	0.07
Running	0.10
Playing softball	0.04

Calorie Counter

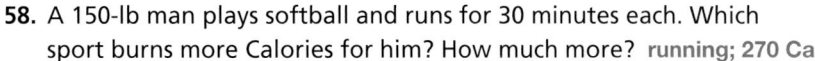

The energy in food and the energy your body uses are measured in Calories. Not all foods have the same number of Calories. Not all activities use the same number of Calories. Your weight is also a factor. The number of Calories you burn is equal to:

$$\text{Your weight} \times \text{Minutes of activity} \times \text{Calories burned per minute per pound}$$

56. Jim weighs 100 pounds. He jumps rope for 15 minutes and runs for 20 minutes. How many Calories does he burn?   **305 Cal**

57. Tara weighs 80 pounds and dances for 1 hour 50 minutes. How many Calories does she burn?   **440 Cal**

Take It to the NET
Online lesson quiz at
www.PHSchool.com
Web Code: aaa-0107

58. A 150-lb man plays softball and runs for 30 minutes each. Which sport burns more Calories for him? How much more?   **running; 270 Cal**

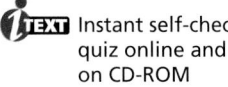 **Mixed Review**

Lesson 1-3   Use <, =, or > to complete each statement.

59. 6.225 ▦ 6.25   **60.** 0.156 ▦ 0.15   **61.** 17.34 ▦ 17.051
    <   >   >

 Checkpoint Quiz 2   **Lessons 1-4 through 1-7**

iTEXT Instant self-check quiz online and on CD-ROM

Estimate each answer.

1. $37.1 - 7.83$ **2.** 4.9×12.2 **3.** $7.94 + 5.29 + 2.08$ **4.** $68.4 \div 8.72$
    29   60   15   8

10. Answers may vary. Sample:
  $8 \cdot 13.1 \cdot 0.5$
    $= 8 \cdot 0.5 \cdot 13.1$
  Comm. Prop. of Mult.
    $= (8 \cdot 0.5) \cdot 13.1$
  Assoc. Prop. of Mult.
    $= 4 \cdot 13.1$
    $= 52.4$
  Assoc. Prop. of Mult.;
  $8(0.5) = 4$ and
  $4(13.1) = 52.4$

Find each sum, difference, or product.

5. $1.25 + 6.07$ **6.** $9.06 - 0.8$ **7.** 5.2×6.3 **8.** $1.7 - 0.28$
    7.32   8.26   32.76   1.42

9. Jo made 7 pounds of cookies. She gave 3.25 pounds to her friends and 0.7 pound each to her three brothers. How much did she have left?
    1.65 lb

10. Reasoning   Use properties to justify that $8 \cdot 13.1 \cdot 0.5 = 52.4$.
    See left.

49. Incorrect; the decimal point should move left one place.

50. correct

51. Incorrect; addition was used instead of multiplication.

Alternative Assessment

Each student in a pair writes two or three exercises involving decimal multiplication, as in Exercises 1–24. Partners exchange papers. Each partner records the number of decimal places that should occur in the product. Then partners work together to do the multiplication and discuss the results.

---

4. Assess

 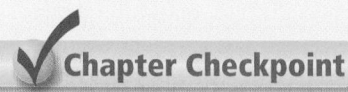 **Lesson Quiz 1-7**

1. Find 0.51×56.   28.56

2. Find $0.07(3.92)$.   0.2744

3. Find $7.29(5.08)$.   37.0332

4. Use mental math to find $0.2(7.3 \times 5)$.   7.3

 Chapter Checkpoint

To check understanding of Lessons 1-4 to 1-7:

Checkpoint Quiz 2 (p. 39)

 Teaching Resources
Checkpoint Quiz 2 (also in *Prentice Hall Assessment System*)

Reaching All Students
Reading and Math Literacy 1C

Spanish versions available

Test Prep

Resources
For additional practice with a variety of test item formats:
• Test-Prep, p. 57
• Test-Taking Strategies, p. 53
• Test-Taking Strategies With Transparencies

Enrichment 1-7   Multiplying Decimals

Decision Making

Suppose you need to buy fabric to make costumes for the school play. The budget is $16 for each costume. You need 12 costumes made from brown fabric. Each brown costume needs 3.25 yards of fabric. You need 8 costumes made from red fabric. Each red costume needs 3.5 yards of fabric.

You have gotten prices from two stores.

Store A: Brown fabric is $4.25 per yard. Red fabric is $4.75 per yard. On any purchase over $40, you will receive a $10 coupon for your next purchase. This store is 5 miles from school.

Store B: Both fabrics are $4.50 per yard. This store is walking distance from school.

1. What is the maximum budget for the fabric? $320.00

2. Complete the following tables to find the cost at each store.

Store A	Yards per costume	Cost per yard	Cost per costume	Number of costumes	Total cost
Red	3.5	$4.75	$16.625	8	$133.00
Brown	3.25	$4.25	$13.8125	12	$165.75
Both					$298.75

Store B	Yards per costume	Cost per yard	Cost per costume	Number of costumes	Total cost
Red	3.5	$4.50	$15.75	8	$126.00
Brown	3.25	$4.50	$14.625	12	$175.50
Both					$301.50

3. At which store would you buy the fabric for the costumes? Explain your thinking.
Sample answer: Store B because the difference in cost is small and the store is close to the school. The coupon is not useful unless more fabric will be needed.

Multiplying and Dividing Decimals by 10, 100, and 1,000

1. Plan

Lesson Preview

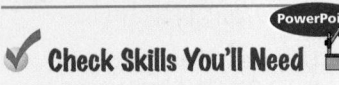 **Check Skills You'll Need**

Multiplying and Dividing Whole Numbers
Skills Handbook: Multiplying Whole Numbers, p. 658. Skills Handbook: Dividing Whole Numbers, p. 660.

Lesson Resources

Teaching Support includes:
Practice, Reteaching, Enrichment Assessment, Reading & Literacy, Activities, Transparencies, Technology, CD-ROMs, Spanish, and More

See pp. 2G–2H for a complete list of resources for this lesson.

 www.PHSchool.com
• Teacher Web Code: aak-5500

Plus

2. Teach

Math Background

You can mentally multiply or divide decimals by 10, 100, or 1,000, by moving the decimal point right for multiplication and left for division, annexing zeros as needed.

PowerPoint

Additional Examples

1 Use mental math to find each product.

a. 1,000(5.67) 5,670

b. 6.01 · 10 60.1

2 Use mental math to find each quotient.

a. 7.15 ÷ 10 0.715

b. 267.95 ÷ 1,000 0.26795

1 EXAMPLE Error Prevention

Show students how annexing zeros provides "placeholders."

40

What You'll Learn

OBJECTIVE 1 To multiply and divide decimals by 10, 100, and 1,000

. . . And Why

To use mental math to divide, as in Example 2

✓ Check Skills You'll Need

? For help, go to Skills Handbook p. 659.

Multiply or divide.

1. 10×36 360

2. 100×36 3,600

3. $1,000 \times 36$ 36,000

4. $4,700 \div 10$ 470

5. $4,700 \div 100$ 47

6. $4,700 \div 1,000$ 4.7

OBJECTIVE 1

iTEXT Interactive lesson includes instant self-check, tutorials, and activities.

Multiplying and Dividing by 10, 100, and 1,000

Investigation: Multiplying by 10, 100, and 1,000

1. Multiply.

a. $2.6 \times 10 = \blacksquare$ 26

$2.6 \times 100 = \blacksquare$ 260

$2.6 \times 1,000 = \blacksquare$ 2,600

b. $0.45 \times 10 = \blacksquare$ 4.5

$0.45 \times 100 = \blacksquare$ 45

$0.45 \times 1,000 = \blacksquare$ 450

2. Patterns What pattern do you notice in the products? (*Hint:* Think about the direction the decimal point moves and the number of decimal places in the answer.) See left.

2. The number of places the decimal moves to the right is the same as the number of zeroes in 10, 100, or 1,000.

There are shortcuts for multiplying decimals by 10, 100, and 1,000. You can use these shortcuts to multiply mentally.

1 EXAMPLE Multiplying by 10, 100, or 1,000

Use mental math to find each product.

a. $0.875 \times 100 = 0.87.5$
$= 87.5$
← To multiply a decimal by 100, move the decimal point 2 places to the right.

b. $0.41 \times 1,000 = 0.410.$
$= 410$
← To multiply a decimal by 1,000, move the decimal point 3 places to the right.

✓ **Check Understanding** **1** Use mental math to find each product.

a. $100(3.42)$
342

b. 0.235×10
2.35

c. $55.2 \cdot 1,000$
55,200

Ongoing Assessment and Intervention

Before the Lesson	During the Lesson	After the Lesson
Diagnose prerequisite skills using:	**Monitor progress using:**	**Assess knowledge using:**
• Check Skills You'll Need	• Check Understanding • Additional Examples • Test Prep	• Lesson Quiz • Computer Test Generator CD

To divide a number by 10, 100, or 1,000, you can move the decimal point to the left. You may need to insert zeros.

Dividing by 10 moves the point 1 place to the left.	$5{,}700 \div 10 = 570$ $570 \div 10 = 57$ $57 \div 10 = 5.7$	$5{,}700 \div 100 = 57$ $570 \div 100 = 5.7$ $57 \div 100 = 0.57$	**Dividing by 100** moves the point 2 places to the left.

Test-Prep Tip
You can sometimes do mental math faster than you can use a calculator.

② **EXAMPLE**   Dividing by 10, 100, or 1,000

Use mental math to find the quotient $43 \div 1{,}000$.

$43 \div 1{,}000 = .043. = 0.043$ ← To divide by 1,000, move the decimal point 3 places to the left.

✓ **Check Understanding** ② Use mental math to find each quotient.
 a. $534.2 \div 100$ **5.342** **b.** $0.235 \div 10$ **0.0235** **c.** $55.2 \div 1{,}000$ **0.0552**
 d. Number Sense Write a rule to divide by 10,000. Find $7.3 \div 10{,}000$.
 Sample: To divide by 10,000, move the decimal point in the dividend four places to the left; 0.00073.

EXERCISES

❓ For more practice, see *Extra Practice*.

Ⓐ **Practice by Example**   **Use mental math to find each product.**

Example 1
(page 40)
 1. 6.2×10 **62**   **2.** $100 \cdot 2.57$ **257**   **3.** $10(9.25)$ **92.5**
 4. 100×1.6 **160**   **5.** $1{,}000(4.3)$ **4,300**   **6.** $1{,}000 \cdot 0.89$ **890**

Example 2
(page 41)   **Use mental math to find each quotient.**
 7. $122.9 \div 10$ **12.29**   **8.** $1.37 \div 10$ **0.137**   **9.** $161.7 \div 100$ **1.617**
 10. $1.5 \div 100$ **0.015**   **11.** $2{,}048.8 \div 1{,}000$ **2.0488**   **12.** $8.17 \div 1{,}000$ **0.00817**

Ⓑ **Apply Your Skills**   **Use <, =, or > to complete each statement.**
 13. $0.92 \cdot 100 \;\boxed{<}\; 9.2 \cdot 1{,}000$ **14.** $2.5(0.56 \cdot 4) \;\boxed{=}\; 0.56 \cdot 10$
 15. $0.99 \div 100 \;\boxed{<}\; 9.9 \div 10$ **16.** $88 \div 100 \;\boxed{>}\; 8.8 \div 100$

🌐 **17. Dolphins** Dolphins swim about 27.5 miles per hour. A person can swim about 0.1 times as fast as a dolphin. How fast can a person swim? **about 2.75 mi/h**

🌐 **18. Packaging** Pencils come in packages of 10 each. Packages are packed 20 to a box, and boxes are packed 500 to a carton. How many pencils are in a carton? **100,000 pencils**

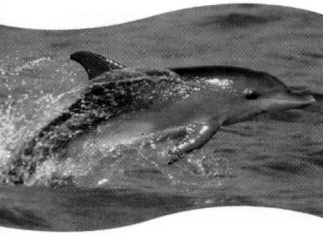

👥 **Reaching All Students**

| **Below Level** Review multiplying whole numbers by 10, 100, and 1,000 with simple exercises like these.
 4×10 **40** $55 \times 1{,}000$ **55,000**
 17×100 **1,700** 39×100 **3,900** | **Advanced Learners** Have students simplify the following.
 $(3.7 \div 4) \cdot 20$ **18.5**
 $(21 \div 1.1) \cdot 4.4$ **84**
 $22.4(9.4 \div 11.2)$ **18.8** | **Error Prevention** See note on page 40. |

Closure

How can you use mental math to multiply or divide decimals by 10, 100, or 1,000? Sample: Move the decimal point to the right for multiplication, or left for division, one place for each zero at the end of 10, 100, or 1,000, annexing or inserting zeros as needed.

3. Practice

Assignment Guide

▼ **① Objective 1**
 Ⓐ Ⓑ Core 1–24
 Ⓒ Extension 25–26

Test Prep 27–30
Mixed Review 31–36

4. Assess

 PowerPoint Lesson Quiz 1-8

Use mental math to find each product or quotient.
 1. $67 \div 1{,}000$ **0.067**
 2. $0.08 \cdot 100$ **8**
 3. 10×7.357 **73.57**
 4. $459.65 \div 100$ **4.5965**

Alternative Assessment

One student in a pair writes a decimal. The other chooses to multiply it or divide it by 10, 100, or 1,000. The first partner then mentally multiplies or divides. The second partner checks the computation. Partners alternate roles and continue as time permits.

Test Prep

Resources
For additional practice with a variety of test item formats:
• Test-Prep, p. 57
• Test-Taking Strategies, p. 53
• Test-Taking Strategies With Transparencies

41

True or False? If false, give an example to support your answer.

19. False; 300 ÷ 100 ≠ 300 × 0.1.

19. Dividing by 100 is the same as multiplying by 0.1. See left.

20. Multiplying by 0.001 is the same as dividing by 1,000. true

21. Changing the order of the factors does not change the product. true

22. Any decimal multiplied by 1 is equal to the original decimal. true

23. **Writing in Math** 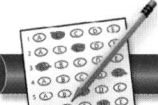 Use mental math to find 0.8 ÷ 100. Explain your method. **See margin.**

24. Multiply. 24a–e. See margin.
   a. 572 × 0.1   b. 572 × 0.01   c. 572 × 0.001   d. 572 × 0.0001
   e. **Patterns** What pattern do you notice in your answers to parts (a)–(d)?

C Challenge

25. Find each answer. 25a–f. See margin.
   a. 52 × 10   b. 52 ÷ 10   c. 52 × 0.1   d. 52 ÷ 0.1
   e. **Reasoning** Explain how you solved part (d).
   f. Complete: Dividing by 0.1 is the same as multiplying by ▨.

26. **Stretch Your Thinking** Six days after the day before yesterday is Monday. What day is today? **Thursday**

Test Prep

Multiple Choice

27. Which quotient is greatest? **C**
    A. 8.31 ÷ 10   B. 83.1 ÷ 100   C. 83.1 ÷ 10   D. 831 ÷ 1,000

28. Which value is NOT greater than 1? **F**
    F. 0.035 × 10   G. 9.8 × 10   H. 67.3 ÷ 10   I. 452 ÷ 10

29. Ten mice weigh 106.7 grams. About how much does one mouse weigh? **C**
    A. 1,067 grams   B. 106.7 grams   C. 10.67 grams   D. 1.067 grams

Take It to the NET
Online lesson quiz at
www.PHSchool.com
Web Code: aaa-0108

30. Replacing the box with which value will make ▨ ÷ 10 > 7.19 × 10 true? **I**
    F. 0.72   G. 7.2   H. 72   I. 720

Mixed Review

Lesson 1-4

Estimate using rounding or compatible numbers. 31–36. Answers may vary. Samples are given.

31. 90.88 ÷ 11.2 9

32. 6.7 × 4.1 28

33. 26.50 × 4 100

34. 37.6 ÷ 3.8 10

35. 86.2 × 43.9 2

36. 15.2 ÷ 8.3 2

GPS Use the Guided Problem Solving worksheet with Exercise 17.

23. 0.008; Answers may vary. Sample: I moved the decimal point in 0.8 two places to the left.

24a. 57.2   b. 5.72   c. 0.572   d. 0.0572
e. Answers may vary. Sample: The number of places after the decimal is the same before and after you multiply.

25a. 520   b. 5.2   c. 5.2   d. 520
e. I moved the decimal point one place to the right.
f. 10

1-9 Dividing Decimals

What You'll Learn

 OBJECTIVE 1 To divide decimals by whole numbers

 OBJECTIVE 2 To divide decimals by decimals

...And Why

To find the cost per person, as in Example 1

✔ Check Skills You'll Need

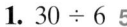

❓ For help, go to Skills Handbook p. 660.

Divide.

1. $30 \div 6$ **5**   2. $96 \div 3$ **32**   3. $1{,}212 \div 12$ **101**   4. $729 \div 27$ **27**

Tell whether each quotient has a remainder.

5. $89 \div 8$ **yes**   6. $35 \div 7$ **no**   7. $98 \div 10$ **yes**   8. $833 \div 4$ **yes**

New Vocabulary
• terminating decimal • repeating decimal

Lesson Preview

 ✔ **Check Skills You'll Need**

Dividing Whole Numbers
Skills Handbook: Dividing Whole Numbers, p. 660. Skills Handbook: Zeros in Quotients, p. 661.

Lesson Resources

Optional Materials
• graph paper

 Teaching Resources
Practice, Reteaching, Enrichment

Reaching All Students
Practice Workbook 1-9
Spanish Practice Workbook 1-9
Guided Problem Solving 1-9
Technology Activities 2

 **Presentation Assistant Plus!**
Transparencies
• Check Skills You'll Need 1-9
• Problem of the Day 1-9
• Additional Examples 1-9
• Student Edition Answers 1-9
• Lesson Quiz 1-9
• Classroom Aid 2, 9–10
PH Presentation Pro CD-ROM 1-9

PRENTICE HALL ASSESSMENT SYSTEM

Computer Test Generator CD

 Technology
Resource Pro® CD-ROM
Computer Test Generator CD
PH Presentation Pro CD-ROM

 www.PHSchool.com
Student Site
• Teacher Web Code: aak-5500
• Algebra Readiness Puzzles 1
• Self-grading Lesson Quiz

PH SuccessNet Teacher Center
• Lesson Planner
• Resources

Plus **iTEXT**

OBJECTIVE 1

Dividing Decimals by Whole Numbers

Dividing decimals is similar to dividing whole numbers.

 EXAMPLE **Dividing by a Whole Number**  **Real World**

Reading Math
You can rewrite $15 \div 3$ as follows:

$$\begin{array}{r} 5 \leftarrow \text{Quotient} \\ 3\overline{)15} \leftarrow \text{Dividend} \\ \uparrow \\ \text{Divisor} \end{array}$$

Entertainment Transportation and tickets to an amusement park cost $364.20 for 12 friends. How much will each person pay?

Since you are looking for the size of equal groups, you need to divide.

Estimate $364.20 \div 12 \approx 360 \div 12$, or 30

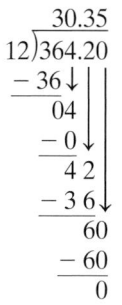

$$\begin{array}{r} 30.35 \\ 12\overline{)364.20} \\ -36\downarrow \\ \hline 04 \\ -0\downarrow \\ \hline 4\,2 \\ -3\,6\downarrow \\ \hline 60 \\ -60 \\ \hline 0 \end{array}$$

← Divide as with whole numbers. Place the decimal point in the quotient above the decimal point in the dividend.

Each person will pay $30.35 for the transportation and ticket.

● **Check for Reasonableness** 30.35 is reasonable since it is close to 30.

✔ **Check Understanding** ① Find each quotient.
 a. $9.12 \div 6$ **1.52**   b. $8\overline{)385.6}$ **48.2**   c. $12\overline{)1.728}$ **0.144**

 **INSTANT CHECK SYSTEM**
Ongoing Assessment and Intervention

Before the Lesson
Diagnose prerequisite skills using:
• Check Skills You'll Need

During the Lesson
Monitor progress using:
• Check Understanding
• Additional Examples
• Test Prep

After the Lesson
Assess knowledge using:
• Lesson Quiz
• Computer Test Generator CD

2. Teach

Math Background

Long division with decimals is similar to long division with whole numbers with an additional step: multiply both the divisor and dividend by a power of 10 to obtain a whole number divisor. Division by decimals between 0 and 1 gives a quotient greater than the original dividend, confusing some students.

If the division results in a remainder of 0, the decimal is called a *terminating decimal*. If the division does not end and produces a repeating pattern of nonzero remainders, the decimal is called a *repeating decimal*.

Teaching Notes

① EXAMPLE Diversity

Not all students may be familiar with amusement parks. Ask volunteers to describe their experiences at amusement parks or theme parks.

Visual Learners

Students sometimes have difficulty translating a division from the horizontal form to the "division house" form. Suggest that they make a display like the one below in their notebooks.

$$\text{dividend} \div \text{divisor} = \text{quotient}$$
$$\text{divisor}\overline{)\text{dividend}}^{\text{quotient}}$$

② EXAMPLE Error Prevention

Students may try to "find" repeating decimals by continuing to annex zeros to the dividend. Remind them that once they have a remainder of 0 in their long division, the decimal has terminated.

English Learners

The word *terminating* means "ending." Encourage students to think of other words that have the root *term*, such as *term*, *exterminate*, and *terminal*. Point out that math words may contain roots with which they are familiar.

44

A **terminating decimal** is a decimal that stops, or terminates. Examples are 0.5 and 1.25. A **repeating decimal** repeats the same digit or group of digits. A bar is drawn over the digits that repeat. You write $1.\overline{27}$ for $1.2727\ldots$

② EXAMPLE   Finding a Decimal Quotient

Find each quotient. Identify each as a terminating or repeating decimal.

a. $62 \div 8$

$$\begin{array}{r} 7.75 \\ 8\overline{)62.00} \\ -56 \\ \hline 60 \\ -56 \\ \hline 40 \\ -40 \\ \hline 0 \end{array}$$ ← Insert zeros when needed.

Since 7.75 ends, 7.75 is a terminating decimal.

b. $5 \div 6$

$$\begin{array}{r} 0.833\ldots \\ 6\overline{)5.000} \\ -48 \\ \hline 20 \\ -18 \\ \hline 20 \\ -18 \\ \hline 2 \end{array}$$ ← Insert zeros when needed.

← The subtraction $20 - 18$ will continue without end. So the digit 2 will keep repeating.

Since the 3 repeats, $0.8\overline{3}$ is a repeating decimal.

✔ **Check Understanding** ② Find each quotient. Identify each as a terminating or repeating decimal.

a. $2 \div 3$
$0.\overline{6}$; repeating

b. $2 \div 8$
0.25; terminating

c. $2 \div 11$
$0.\overline{18}$; repeating

OBJECTIVE

2 ▸ Dividing Decimals by Decimals

You can use a model to divide a decimal by a decimal.

③ EXAMPLE   Modeling Division by Tenths

Draw a model to find $0.8 \div 0.2$.

You want to know how many groups of 0.2 are in 0.8.

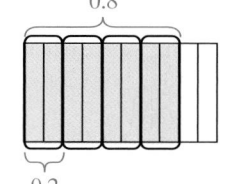

← Draw a model for 0.8.

← Circle groups of 0.2.

There are 4 groups of 0.2 in 0.8, so $0.8 \div 0.2 = 4$.

✔ **Check Understanding** ③ Draw a model to find each quotient. **3a–c. See margin.**

a. $0.8 \div 0.4$ **b.** $0.6 \div 0.2$ **c.** $0.9 \div 0.15$

d. Reasoning In the sentence $1.5 \div 0.75 = 2$, the divisor, 0.75, represents the size of each group. What does the quotient, 2, represent?
the number of groups

44   **Chapter 1** Decimals

👥 Reaching All Students

Below Level Have students perform whole number long divisions that result in decimals such as these.	Advanced Learners Have students divide the following and compare the quotients.	English Learners See note on page 44.
$30 \div 4$ **7.5** $32 \div 5$ **6.4** $75 \div 2$ **37.5** $36 \div 8$ **4.5**	$123 \div 0.45$ **$273.\overline{3}$** $123 \div 4.5$ **$27.\overline{3}$** $123 \div 45$ **$2.7\overline{3}$** $12.3 \div 45$ **$0.27\overline{3}$** $1.23 \div 45$ **$0.027\overline{3}$** $1.23 \div 4.5$ **$0.27\overline{3}$**	**Diversity** See notes on pages 44 and 45.

Study the pattern of quotients below.

	Dividend	÷	Divisor	=	Quotient
	0.8	÷	0.4	=	2
Multiply dividend and divisor by 10. →	8	÷	4	=	2
Multiply dividend and divisor by 100. →	80	÷	40	=	2

Note that if you multiply both the dividend and the divisor by the same number, the quotient remains the same.

> **Key Concepts**   **Dividing Decimals**
>
> To divide a decimal by a decimal, multiply both the dividend and the divisor by the same number so that the divisor is a whole number.

4 EXAMPLE   Dividing a Decimal by a Decimal    Real World

Recipes Alika uses 0.5 pound of strawberries in each smoothie. How many smoothies can Alika make with 2.25 pounds of strawberries?

$0.5\overline{)2.25}$

Since the divisor has one decimal place, multiply the dividend and divisor by 10 so that the divisor is a whole number.

$$\begin{array}{r} 4.5 \\ 5\overline{)22.5} \\ -20 \\ \hline 2\,5 \\ -2\,5 \\ \hline 0 \end{array}$$

← Now divide as with whole numbers. Place the decimal point in the quotient above the decimal point in the dividend.

Alika can make 4.5 smoothies.

✓ Check Understanding **4** Find each quotient.

a. $0.248 \div 0.04$ **6.2**   b. $0.08\overline{)8.64}$ **108**   c. $1.25\overline{)38.125}$ **30.5**

 **EXERCISES**   ❓ For more practice, see *Extra Practice.*

Ⓐ Practice by Example

Example 1 (page 43)

Find each quotient.

1. $328.25 \div 13$ **25.25**
2. $7\overline{)255.5}$ **36.5**
3. $237.6 \div 33$ **7.2**
4. $32\overline{)258.24}$ **8.07**
5. $84\overline{)26.46}$ **0.315**
6. $144.54 \div 6$ **24.09**
7. $27\overline{)99.36}$ **3.68**
8. $38.27 \div 43$ **0.89**

9. Four friends share a pizza that costs $12.72. How much does each friend owe for his or her share? **$3.18**

Check Understanding

3a.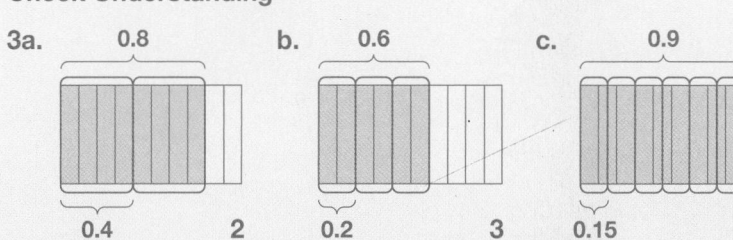
0.8   0.4   2
b. 0.6   0.2   3
c. 0.9   0.15   6

3 EXAMPLE Teaching Tip

Remind students that they can check division problems by multiplication. If $0.8 \div 0.2 = 4$, then 4×0.2 should equal 0.8.

4 EXAMPLE Diversity

Have student describe smoothies and what ingredients they prefer. Related fruit and yogurt beverages are enjoyed in many cultures and may create a lively discussion.

PowerPoint
Additional Examples

1. A class of 27 students held a picnic. They purchased food and drinks for the picnic for a total cost of $93.15. What was the price for each student's meal? **$3.45**

2. Find each quotient. Identify each as a terminating or repeating decimal.
   a. $6 \div 5$ **1.2; terminating**
   b. $9 \div 11$ **$0.\overline{81}$; repeating**

3. Draw a model to find the quotient $0.6 \div 0.05$. **12**

   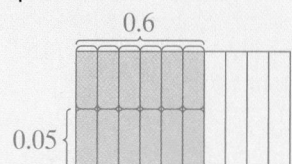
   0.6
   0.05

4. Find each quotient.
   a. $0.475 \div 0.05$ **9.5**
   b. $9.674 \div 0.7$ **13.82**
   c. $163.125 \div 2.9$ **56.25**

Closure

- *What is the difference between a terminating decimal and a repeating decimal? Give an example of each.* A terminating decimal, such as 2.5, stops, or terminates. A repeating decimal, such as $0.\overline{6}$, repeats the same digit or group of digits.

- *How do you divide a decimal by another decimal?* Sample: Multiply the dividend and divisor by the same number to make sure that the divisor is a whole number. Divide as with whole numbers, placing the decimal point in the quotient above the decimal point in the dividend.

3. Practice

Assignment Guide

Exercises 1–8 Watch for students who do not correctly "move" the decimal point up into the quotient.

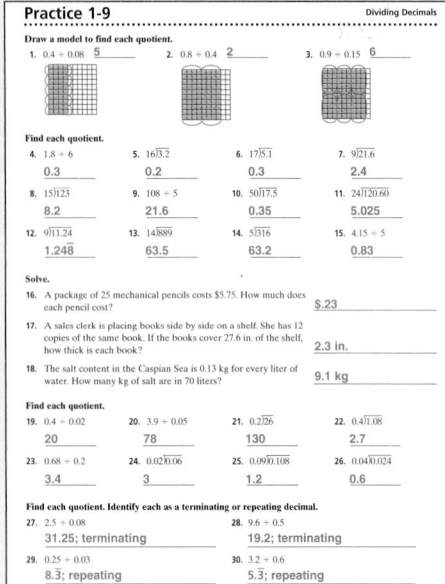

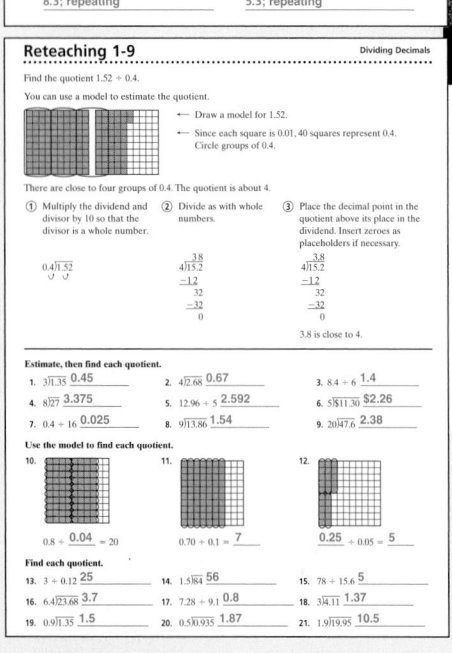

Example 2 (page 44)

10–17. See margin.

Find each quotient. Identify each as a terminating or repeating decimal.

10. $9 \div 4$ **11.** $6 \div 11$ **12.** $512 \div 80$ **13.** $19 \div 25$

14. $15 \div 33$ **15.** $3 \div 16$ **16.** $17 \div 20$ **17.** $17 \div 180$

Example 3 (page 44)

Draw a model to find each quotient. 18–21. See margin.

18. $0.6 \div 0.3$ **19.** $1.6 \div 0.8$ **20.** $0.9 \div 0.1$ **21.** $0.3 \div 0.15$

22. A pack of baseball cards costs $2.75. A friend tells you that each card costs $.25. Draw a model to find the number of cards in the pack. See back of book.

Example 4 (page 45)

Find each quotient.

23. $29.5 \div 0.4$ 73.75   **24.** $8.9\overline{)6.497}$ 0.73   **25.** $3.1\overline{)10.261}$ 3.31

26. $16.8 \div 2.4$ 7   **27.** $0.96\overline{)0.144}$ 0.15   **28.** $10.54 \div 0.17$ 62

B Apply Your Skills

Complete each equation.

29.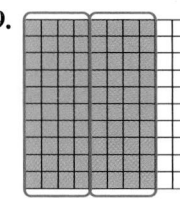

$\blacksquare \div 0.4 = 2$
0.8

30.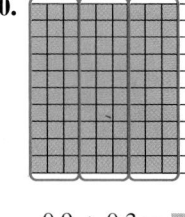

$0.9 \div 0.3 = \blacksquare$
3

31.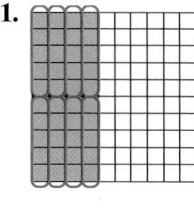

$0.4 \div \blacksquare = 8$
0.05

32. Bridges A bicyclist riding across the Great Seto Bridge can travel 500 meters in 1 minute. A person walking can travel 100 meters in 1 minute. How many minutes shorter is the bicycle trip than the walk? Use the caption at the left.   74.944 min

Find each quotient. Round each answer to the nearest hundredth.

33. $64.97 \div 3.2$ **34.** $10.126 \div 2.3$ **35.** $26.81 \div 3.3$ **36.** $5.637 \div 0.17$
   20.30   4.40   8.12   33.16

37. Museums Seventeen students each bought two posters at the museum shop. The total cost was $168.30. What was the price per poster? $4.95

38. School Supplies A stack of paper measures 0.9 centimeter thick. Each GPS piece of paper is 0.01 centimeter thick.
   a. How many pieces of paper are in the stack?   90 pieces
   b. Could each of 25 students get three pieces of paper?   yes

Real-World Connection

The Great Seto Bridge in Japan is six separate bridges with a total length of 9,368 meters.

GPS Use the Guided Problem Solving worksheet with Exercise 38.

10. 2.25; terminating

11. $0.\overline{54}$; repeating

12. 6.4; terminating

13. 0.76; terminating

14. $0.\overline{45}$; repeating

15. 0.1875; terminating

16. 0.85; terminating

17. $0.094\overline{4}$; repeating

18.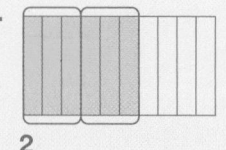

Find each quotient. Identify each as a terminating or repeating decimal.

40. 7.$\overline{714285}$; repeating
41. 0.2; terminating

39. $3.5 \div 0.7$
5; terminating

40. $7\overline{)54}$

41. $27\overline{)5.4}$

42. $36 \div 0.33$
109.$\overline{09}$; repeating

43. $0.59\overline{)0.0649}$
0.11; terminating

44. $1.5\overline{)4.48}$
2.98$\overline{6}$; repeating

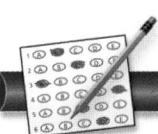 **Gas Mileage** Find the gas mileage. Round to the nearest tenth. To find the gas mileage of a vehicle in miles per gallon, divide the number of miles driven by the number of gallons of gas used.

45. A family car travels 367.9 miles on 12.5 gallons of gas. **29.4 mi/gal**

46. A hybrid car travels 414.3 miles on 6.6 gallons of gas. **62.8 mi/gal**

C Challenge

47. Divide the number of miles traveled by the gas mileage.

47. Reasoning Suppose you know a car's gas mileage and the number of miles the car traveled. How would you find the amount of gas used? **See left.**

48. Stretch Your Thinking All of the digits in a certain 4-digit whole number are different. The first digit, reading from the left, is twice the fourth digit. The second digit is twice the first digit. The last digit is twice the third digit. What is the number? **4,812**

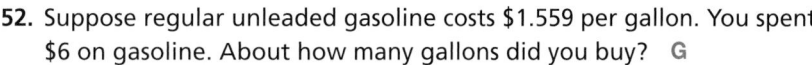 **Test Prep**

Multiple Choice

49. Which quotient is greatest? **D**
A. $0.075 \div 5$ B. $0.75 \div 10$ C. $0.625 \div 25$ D. $7.5 \div 10$

50. Which quotient is equivalent to three and eight-tenths divided by thirty-two thousandths? **H**
F. $0.032 \div 3.8$ G. $0.32 \div 3.8$ H. $3.8 \div 0.032$ I. $3.8 \div 0.32$

51. The quotient $1.35 \div 0.4$ is nearest which value? **B**
A. 0.3   B. 3   C. 30   D. 300

Take It to the NET
Online lesson quiz at
www.PHSchool.com
Web Code: aaa-0109

52. Suppose regular unleaded gasoline costs $1.559 per gallon. You spent $6 on gasoline. About how many gallons did you buy? **G**
F. 3 gallons   G. 4 gallons   H. 5 gallons   I. 6 gallons

Mixed Review

Lesson 1-7   **Find each product.**

53. 9.07×0.025
0.22675

54. 0.145×0.12
0.0174

55. $8.3 \cdot 5.6$
46.48

56. $15(0.87)$
13.05

57. $(1.013)5$
5.065

58. $3.0 \cdot 0.7$
2.1

1-9 Dividing Decimals   **47**

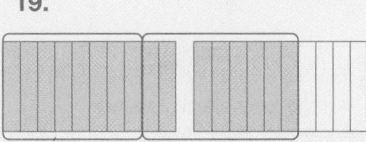

19.

2

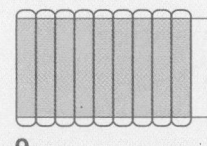

20.

9

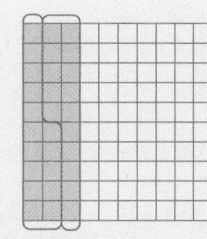

21.

2

 **Quiz 1-9**

Find each quotient.

1. $35.92 \div 8$ **4.49**

2. $6.045 \div 7.5$ **0.806**

Find each quotient. Identify each as a terminating or repeating decimal.

3. $14 \div 3$ **4.$\overline{6}$; repeating**

4. $15 \div 6$ **2.5; terminating**

Alternative Assessment

Each student in a pair writes a decimal. Then partners together write two division expressions with their decimals and perform each division. Partners should check their work using multiplication.

Test Prep

Resources
For additional practice with a variety of test item formats:
• Test-Prep, p. 57
• Test-Taking Strategies, p. 53
• Test-Taking Strategies With Transparencies

Enrichment 1-9   Dividing Decimals
Decision Making

Many food products are packaged in a variety of sizes. The list below gives the sizes and costs of fruit juice drinks at one store.

$1.92 single-serving multi-pack (serves 6) $1.12 one quart (serves 4)
$2.16 two quarts (serves 8) $3.52 one gallon (serves 16)

1. Choose two different sizes and give an advantage for buying each.
Sample answer: Single servings are
convenient to take in lunches; gallons are
better for a large group.

2. What is the cost per serving for each of the fruit juice packages? Which is the least expensive?
Single: $.32; quart: $.28; two quarts: $.27;
Gallon: $.22; a gallon is the least expensive.

3. Suppose you need to have 22 servings of the juice drink. Which size or sizes of containers would you buy? Explain your reasoning.
Sample answer: One gallon and two quarts is
the least expensive choice, although there
would be 2 servings left over.

4. Choose your favorite breakfast cereal. Go to the grocery store and record the number of ounces, the cost, and the number of servings for each size available. Then compute the cost per serving.

Size (in ounces)	Cost	Number of servings	Cost per serving

5. Which size is least expensive? **Check students' answers.**

6. Which size box of cereal would you prefer to buy? Explain your reasoning.
Check students' answers.

Lesson Preview

 Check Skills You'll Need

Comparing Two Decimals
Lesson 1-3: Example 3: Extra
Practice p. 642.

Lesson Resources

 Teaching Resources
Practice, Reteaching, Enrichment

Reaching All Students
Practice Workbook 1-10
Spanish Practice Workbook 1-10
Guided Problem Solving 1-10
Technology Activities 3

Presentation Assistant Plus!
Transparencies
• Check Skills You'll Need 1-10
• Problem of the Day 1-10
• Additional Examples 1-10
• Student Edition Answers 1-10
• Lesson Quiz 1-10
PH Presentation Pro CD-ROM 1-10

ASSESSMENT SYSTEM

Computer Test Generator CD

Technology
Resource Pro® CD-ROM
Computer Test Generator CD
PH Presentation Pro CD-ROM

 **www.PHSchool.com**
Student Site
• Teacher Web Code: aak-5500
• Algebra Readiness Puzzles 37
• Self-grading Lesson Quiz

PH SuccessNet Teacher Center
• Lesson Planner
• Resources

Plus **iTEXT**

Check Understanding

1d. I would add before
multiplying if the addition
of two numbers is done
within parentheses and
the multiplication is done
outside of the
parentheses.

What You'll Learn

OBJECTIVE 1 To use the order
of operations

...And Why

To find the total cost of a
purchase, as in Example 2

 Check Skills You'll Need   **?** For help, go to Lesson 1-3.

Use <, =, or > to complete each statement.

1. $25.005 \ \underline{=} \ 25.0050$ 2. $4.000 \ \underline{>} \ 3.999$ 3. $289.1 \ \underline{>} \ 289.001$

4. $1.382 \ \underline{>} \ 1.0385$ 5. $0.0107 \ \underline{<} \ 0.070$ 6. $9.0 \ \underline{<} \ 9.001$

New Vocabulary   • expression   • order of operations

iTEXT Interactive lesson includes instant self-check, tutorials, and activities.

OBJECTIVE 1   Using the Order of Operations

An **expression** is a mathematical phrase containing numbers and operation
symbols. The expression $18 + 11 \times 6$ contains two operations. You might
ask, "Which operation is performed first, the addition or the
multiplication?"

Diane's Work
(addition first)

$$18 + 11 \times 6 \stackrel{?}{=} (18 + 11) \times 6$$
$$\stackrel{?}{=} 29 \times 6$$
$$\stackrel{?}{=} 174 \qquad X$$

Dana's Work
(multiplication first)

$$18 + 11 \times 6 \stackrel{?}{=} 18 + (11 \times 6)$$
$$\stackrel{?}{=} 18 + 66$$
$$\stackrel{?}{=} 84 \qquad ✓$$

Real-World Connection
Even soccer equipment—
shoes with cleats, socks, shin
guards—needs to be put on
in a certain order.

Only one answer is correct. To make sure everyone gets the same value
for an expression, you use the **order of operations**.

Key Concepts   **Order of Operations**

1. Do all operations within parentheses first.

2. Multiply and divide in order from left to right.

3. Add and subtract in order from left to right.

Based on the order of operations, you multiply before you add.

$$18 + 11 \times 6 = 18 + 66$$
$$= 84$$

So Dana's answer is correct.

Ongoing Assessment and Intervention

Before the Lesson	During the Lesson	After the Lesson
Diagnose prerequisite skills using:	Monitor progress using:	Assess knowledge using:
• Check Skills You'll Need	• Check Understanding	• Lesson Quiz
	• Additional Examples	• Computer Test Generator CD
	• Test Prep	

1 EXAMPLE   Finding the Value of Expressions

Find the value of each expression.

a. $6 + 20.4 \div 2 = 6 + 10.2$ ← Divide 20.4 by 2.

$= 16.2$ ← Add.

b. $30 - (6 + 2) \times 3 = 30 - 8 \times 3$ ← Add 6 and 2 within the parentheses.

$= 30 - 24$ ← Multiply 8 and 3.

$= 6$ ← Subtract 24 from 30.

✔ **Check Understanding**  Find the value of each expression.
a. $17 - 4 \times 2.25$ **8**   **b.** $3.4 + 5 \times 2 - 1.7$ **11.7** **c.** $(6 + 18) \div 3 \times 2$ **16**
d. Reasoning Explain when you might add before multiplying. See margin.

2 EXAMPLE   Writing Expressions   🌐 Real World

Sales Receipts Suppose you buy the items shown in the store receipt at the left. Write an expression for the total cost, including the tax. Then find the value of the expression.

CRAWFORD'S

ITEMS ORDERED

JEANS	2@ $19.95 EACH
DISCOUNT	−$5.00
SHIRTS	3@ $15.99 EACH
TAX	$4.35
TOTAL	

Words	cost of jeans	−	discount	+	cost of shirts	+	tax

Expression	$2 \times \$19.95$	−	$\$5.00$	+	$3 \times \$15.99$	+	$\$4.35$
	$\$39.90$	−	$\$5.00$	+	$\$47.97$	+	$\$4.35$ ← Multiply.
			$\$34.90$	+	$\$47.97$	+	$\$4.35$ ← Subtract.
							$\$87.22$ ← Add.

The total cost, including tax, is $87.22.

✔ **Check Understanding** Find the value of $3 \times \$16.95 - \$10.00 + 4 \times \$1.50$. **$46.85**

EXERCISES

❓ For more practice, see *Extra Practice*.

A Practice by Example

Find the value of each expression.

Example 1 (page 49)

1. $6 - 2 + 4 \times 2$ **12**   **2.** $33 - (14 + 6)$ **13**   **3.** $6 \times (2 \times 5)$ **60**

4. $4 \times 3 + 20 \div 5$ **16**   **5.** $400 \div (44 - 24)$ **20**   **6.** $7 \times (4 + 6) \times 3$ **210**

7. $45 \div 4.5 + 6.2 \times 3$ **28.6**   **8.** $26 + 4.6 - 4 \times 2.4$ **21**

9. $14 - (7.6 + 5) \div 2$ **7.7**   **10.** $13 + 5.1 \times 12 - 4.2$ **70**

👫 Reaching All Students

Below Level Discuss with students the importance of parentheses in this set of exercises. $(8 + 3) \cdot (4 - 2)$ **22** $(8 + 3) \cdot 4 - 2$ **42** $8 + (3 \cdot 4) - 2$ **18** $8 + 3 \cdot (4 - 2)$ **14**	Advanced Learners Have students use 3 numbers, 2 operation signs, and 1 set of parentheses to write as many expressions as possible and simplify them. Sample: 12, 7, 2, +, − $12 - (2 + 7) = 3$, and so on	Inclusion See note on page 49. Visual Learners See note on page 49.

---

2. Teach

🔵 Professional Development

Math Background

The order of operations for expressions involving parentheses (grouping symbols) and the four basic operations are presented in this lesson. The order of operations is accepted worldwide. Without agreement, simple expressions such as $5 + 3 \cdot 2$ could have two different answers ($5 + 6 = 11$ or $8 \cdot 2 = 16$). The order of operations ensures that everyone obtains the same result, which in this expression is 11.

Teaching Notes

1 EXAMPLE Visual Learners

Some students might benefit from the following visual with arrows.

$30 - (6 + 2) \times 3$
↓
$30 - 8 \times 3$
↓
$30 - 24$
↓
6

Inclusion

Ask: *What do the parentheses in an expression indicate?*
Operations in parentheses need to be done first.

PowerPoint

Additional Examples

1 Find the value of each expression.
a. $(5.5 + 6.5) \div 6 \times 3$ **6**
b. $20 - 5 \times 8 \div 2$ **0**

2 Find the value of $\$3.50 + 8 \times \$.50 - 2 \times \$3.50$. **$.50**

Closure

• *What is an expression?*
a mathematical phrase that contains numbers and operation symbols

• *What is the order in which operations must be performed?*
Do all operations within parentheses; multiply and divide in order from left to right; add and subtract in order from left to right.

49

Assignment Guide

1 Objective 1
  Ⓐ Ⓑ Core 1–34
  Ⓒ Extension 35–39

Test Prep 40–43
Mixed Review 44–49

Error Prevention!

Exercises 20–25 Have students complete the operations on both sides before making a comparison.

Practice 1-10   Order of Operations

Which operation would you perform first in each expression?

1. $4 + 6 \times 9$ 2. $(7 - 5) \times 3$ 3. $14 + 2 \times 3$
   6×9 ___ $(7 - 5)$ ___ $14 \div 2$ ___

4. $18 - 5 + 3$ 5. $5 \times 2 + 6$ 6. $(9 + 14) - 8 \div 2$
   $18 - 5$ ___ 5×2 ___ $(9 + 14)$ ___

Find the value of each expression.

7. $8 - 3 \times 1 + 5$ 8. $(43 - 16) \times 5$ 9. $14 \times 6 \div 3$
   10 ___ 135 ___ 28 ___

10. $100 \div (63 - 43)$ 11. $9 \times (3 \times 5)$ 12. $7 \times (8 + 6)$
    5 ___ 135 ___ 98 ___

13. $15 - (5 + 7)$ 14. $(12 - 9) \times (6 + 1)$ 15. $(9 - 3) \times 2$
    3 ___ 21 ___ 12 ___

16. $8 - 3 \times 2 + 7$ 17. $(9 - 4) \times 6$ 18. $(35 - 5) \times 3$
    9 ___ 30 ___ 90 ___

Use <, =, or > to complete each statement.

19. $5 - 3 \times 1 \boxed{=} (5 - 3) \times 1$ 20. $(4 + 8) \times 3 \boxed{>} 4 + 8 \times 3$
21. $3 \times (8 - 2) \boxed{<} 3 \times 8 - 2$ 22. $(7 + 2) \times 4 \boxed{>} 7 + 2 \times 4$
23. $4 + (20 + 4) \boxed{>} (4 + 20) + 4$ 24. $42 - (35 + 4) \boxed{<} 42 - 35 + 4$
25. $(9 - 2) \times 3 \boxed{>} 9 - 2 \times 3$ 26. $55 + 10 - 7 \boxed{=} 55 + (10 - 7)$

Insert parentheses to make each statement true.

27. $6 + 7 \times 4 - 2 = 26$ 28. $14 - 5 + 3 = 3$
    $(6 + 7) \times (4 - 2) = 26$ $(14 - 5) \div 3 = 3$
29. $27 + 4 + 5 - 1 = 2$ 30. $6 \times 7 + 2 - 1 = 53$
    $27 + (4 + 5) - 1 = 2$ $6 \times (7 + 2) - 1 = 53$
31. Haircuts for boys cost $7. Haircuts for men cost $10. If 20 boys
    and 20 men went to the barber yesterday, how much did the
    barber earn?
    $(\$7 \times 20) + (\$10 \times 20) = \$340$

Reteaching 1-10   Order of Operations

To find the value of an expression follow the *order of operations*.

First, do all operations inside parentheses.
Next, multiply and divide from left to right.
Then, add and subtract from left to right.

Example 1 Find the value of $6 + (3 + 4) \times 2$.

① Work inside parentheses. → $(3 + 4) = 7$
                                $6 + 7 \times 2$
② Multiply next. → $7 \times 2 = 14$
                    $6 + 14$
③ Then, add.
       $6 + 14 = 20$

Example 2 Compare $10 - (6 \div 2) + 1$ and $(10 - 6) \div 2 + 1$.

First, find the value of each expression.   Then, use <, =, or > to compare.
$10 - (6 \div 2) + 1$ $(10 - 6) \div 2 + 1$ $8 > 3$
$10 -   3   + 1$ $4   \div 2 + 1$ So,
$7   + 1$ $2   + 1$ $10 - (6 \div 2) + 1 > (10 - 6) \div 2 + 1$.
   8 3

Find the value of each expression.

1. $3 + (4 + 1) \times 2$ 2. $24 \div (5 + 3) - 2$
   a. $4 + 1 = \underline{5}$ a. $5 + 3 = \underline{8}$
   b. $\underline{5} \times 2 = \underline{10}$ b. $24 \div \underline{8} = \underline{3}$
   c. $3 + \underline{10} = \underline{13}$ c. $\underline{3} - 2 = \underline{1}$
3. $2 + 6 \times 3 \div 3 = \underline{8}$ 4. $(6 + 2) \times 3 \div 4 = \underline{6}$
5. $7 + 5 \times 2 - 6 = \underline{11}$ 6. $12 \div 3 \times 5 - 6 = \underline{14}$

Use <, =, or > to complete each statement.

7. $9 + 3 \times 4 \boxed{=} 9 + (3 \times 4)$ 8. $(12 - 4) \times 3 \boxed{>} 12 - (4 \times 3)$
9. $6 + 3 + 4 \times 2 \boxed{=} (6 + 3) + 4 \times 2$ 10. $3 \times (12 - 5) + 2 \boxed{<} 3 \times 12 - (5 + 2)$
11. $15 - (12 + 3) \boxed{>} (15 - 12) + 3$ 12. $8 + 2 \times (9 - 7) \boxed{<} 8 + (2 \times 9) - 7$
13. $10 + (10 \div 5) \boxed{=} 10 + 10 \div 5$ 14. $20 - (2 \times 6) \boxed{<} (20 - 2) \times 6$

Example 2 (page 49)

Ⓑ **Apply Your Skills**

13. 10×3
14. $5 - 2$
15. $9 \div 3$

26. Subtract 5 from 7 to get 2; divide 8 by 4 and multiply by 6 to get 12; add 12 and 2 to get 14.

ENTRANCE

🌐 11. **Marbles** You buy 1 red rainbow marble at $.45 each, 3 bumblebee marbles at $.95 each, and 2 tricolored rainbows at $.65 each.
  a. Write an expression for the total cost of the marbles you buy.
  b. Find the total cost. **$4.60**
      11a. $1 \times \$.45 + 3 \times \$.95 + 2 \times \$.65$

🌐 12. **Jobs** You are paid $4.10 per hour to rake leaves. Your brother is paid $3.30 per hour.
      $3 \times \$4.10 + 2 \times \$3.30$
  a. Write an expression for how much the two of you will earn together if you work 3 hours and your brother works 2 hours.
  b. Find the total amount earned. **$18.90**

Which operation would you perform first in each expression?

13. $30 - 10 \times 3 \div 5$ 14. $63 \div 7 \times (5 - 2)$ 15. $12 - 9 \div 3 - 2$

Find the value of each expression.

16. $(63 - 48) \times 10$ **150**   17. $18 \div 6 - (5 - 4)$ **2**

18. $40 \times 0.1 - (9 - 6)$ **1**   19. $(0.1 + 0.9) \times 1 - 1$ **0**

Use <, =, or > to complete each statement.

20. $(3 + 6) \times 4 \boxed{>} 3 + 6 \times 4$ 21. $6 \times (8 - 2) \boxed{=} (8 - 2) \times 6$

22. $2 \times (15 - 3.5) \boxed{<} 2 \times 15 - 3.5$ 23. $62 - 37.3 + 8 \boxed{>} 62 - (37.3 + 8)$

24. $0.8 \div 2 \times 2 \boxed{>} 0.8 \div (2 \times 2)$ 25. $3.5 \times 10 \div 5 \boxed{=} 3.5 \times (10 \div 5)$

26. **Writing in Math** Explain the steps you would use to find the value of the expression $8 \div 4 \times 6 + (7 - 5)$. **See left.**

🌐 27. **Field Trip** A group of 11 boys and 9 girls go on a field trip to a Native American museum. The cost is $5 per person. Which expression does *not* show the total amount the group will pay? **C**
  A. $\$5 \times (11 + 9)$ **B.** $(\$5 \times 11) + (\$5 \times 9)$
  C. $\$5 \times 11 \times 9$ **D.** $\$5 \times 20$

🌐 28. **Coins** There are 312 coins of the same type in two stacks. One stack of
[GPS] coins is 15 inches tall. The other stack is 9 inches tall. Find the thickness of one coin to the nearest thousandth of an inch. **0.077 in.**

Reasoning Insert parentheses to make each statement true.

29. $11 - 7 \div 2 = 2$ 30. $1 + 2 \times 15 - 4 = 33$
    $(11 - 7) \div 2 = 2$ $(1 + 2) \times (15 - 4) = 33$
31. $7 - 2 \times 2 - 1 = 9$ 32. $5 \times 6 \div 2 + 1 = 10$
    $(7 - 2) \times 2 - 1 = 9$ $5 \times 6 \div (2 + 1) = 10$

50 Chapter 1 Decimals

[GPS] Use the Guided Problem Solving worksheet with Exercise 28.

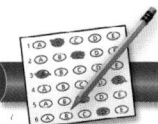

Nutrition **Use the chart below for Exercises 33 and 34.**

Food	Serving Size	Protein (grams)
Canned tuna	3 oz	24.4
Rye bread	1 slice	2.3
Cheese pizza	1 slice	7.8

33. How many grams of protein are in 4 sandwiches (2 slices of rye bread and 3 ounces of tuna each)? 116 g

34. **Estimation** About how many grams of protein are in a slice of pizza and a sandwich consisting of 2 slices of rye bread and 2 ounces of tuna? about 28 g

C Challenge

Insert operation symbols to make each statement true.

35. (6 ■ 9) ■ 4 ■ 6 = 10   +, ×, ÷

36. 15 ■ 3 ■ 2 = 10   −, −; or ÷, ×

37. (12 ■ 8) ■ (5 ■ 2) = 11   −, +, +

38. 14 ■ 7 ■ 2 ■ 3 = 7   ÷, +, +

39. **Algebra** In the expression (10 − ■) ÷ (▲ − 1), ■ and ▲ represent unknown values.

a. Find the value of the expression if ■ = 4 and ▲ = 3. 3

b. Find the value of the expression if ■ = 4 and ▲ = 4. 2

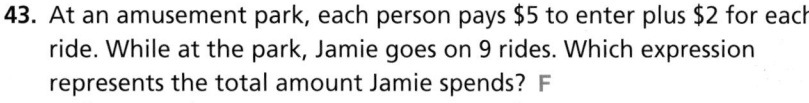

Test Prep

Multiple Choice

40. Find the value of the expression 36 ÷ 3 − 1 × 7. A

A. 5 **B.** 9 **C.** 77 **D.** 126

41. Find the value of the expression ($1.25 × 3) + ($3.50 ÷ 5). G

F. $3.05 **G.** $4.45 **H.** $4.50 **I.** $21.25

42. Which expression has a value of 0.40? C

A. (0.2 + 0.2) × (1 − 1) **B.** 2 × 0.1 + 0.1

C. 0.1 + (0.9 ÷ 3) **D.** 1.4 − 1 × 0.7

43. At an amusement park, each person pays $5 to enter plus $2 for each ride. While at the park, Jamie goes on 9 rides. Which expression represents the total amount Jamie spends? F

F. $5 + 9 × $2 **G.** ($5 + 9) × $2

H. ($5 × 9) + $2 **I.** $5 × 9 × $2

Take It to the NET
Online lesson quiz at **www.PHSchool.com**
Web Code: aaa-0110

Mixed Review

Lesson 1-8 **Use mental math to find each product or quotient.**

44. 1,000 × 0.035 35 **45.** 4(2.8 × 25) 280 **46.** 2 · 5.4 · 5 54

47. 0.462 ÷ 100 0.00462 **48.** 1.39 ÷ 1,000 0.00139 **49.** 25.6 ÷ 10 2.56

4. Assess

PowerPoint **Lesson Quiz 1-10**

Evaluate each expression.

1. 9 + 5 × 6 − 7 32
2. (12 − 8) × 10 ÷ 5 8
3. (4 × 6.2) + (4 × 8.5) 58.8
4. 200 − (99 ÷ 3) × 2.4 120.8

Alternative Assessment

Have students bring to class various empty food containers that show nutritional information. They can use the information about protein, carbohydrates, vitamins, and so forth to create word problems similar to Exercises 33 and 34. Students can challenge classmates to solve their problems.

Test Prep

Resources
For additional practice with a variety of test item formats:
- Test-Prep, p. 57
- Test-Taking Strategies, p. 53
- Test-Taking Strategies With Transparencies

Exercise 40 Before students begin, elicit the order of operations needed to evaluate the expression.

Enrichment 1-10 Order of Operations

Critical Thinking

Use the numbers and the operators given in each box to complete the equation. You may use the numbers and the operators only one time per equation.

1. 4 52 2 16 − ÷ 6
(16 ÷ 2) − 4 + 8 × 6 = 52
2. + 32 − 200 ÷
200 − 50 ÷ 10 + 15 = 32 + 178
3. × 0 + 6 10 − 4
10 × 2 + 0 = 3 + (4 × 6) − 7
4. 2 × ÷ 10 4 0 6 +
(2 + 6 + 9) × 0 ÷ 10 + 4 = 4
5. + 8 ÷ 70 10 1 2 − 3
(6 + 3) × (2 + 8) ÷ (10 − 1) = 70 ÷ 7
6. + 6 × 7 (2 12) 3
(2 ÷ 2 + 12) × 3 = 6 × 7 − 3
7. − 8 ÷ 5 100) 2 × 3
100 ÷ 2 ÷ 5 × 1 = (8 − 3) × 2
8. Make your own puzzle and trade with a classmate.
Check students' work.

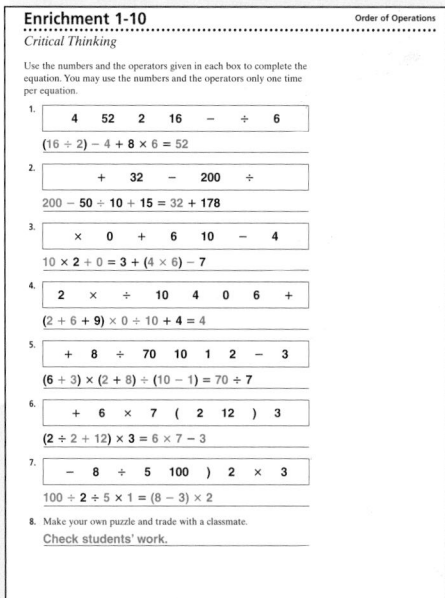

Technology

Exploring Order of Operations

Students learn keystroke sequences to use with simple calculators to preserve the order of operations when finding the value of numerical expressions.

Optional Materials

- simple or scientific calculators
- Classroom Aid 11

Teaching Notes

Begin by asking a volunteer to explain the order of operations. Write it on the board. Invite students to suggest acronyms that can help them to remember it, like PMDAS. Then have students determine whether or not they are working with a scientific calculator by entering the keystrokes for 18 + 6 ÷ 3 as shown in the text.

EXAMPLE Teaching Tip

If students are not using scientific calculators, ask a volunteer to explain how to modify the expression by inserting parentheses. Then have students enter the calculator keystrokes and find that value. As needed, provide an additional example that demands parentheses, like 24 − 2 × 5.
24 − (2 × 5) = 14

Teaching Tip

If your students are going to be working with scientific calculators, discuss the similarities and differences between features of simple calculators and scientific ones.

Error Prevention!

Students may press the wrong keys or press keys in the wrong order. Have students write the keystrokes they will use to evaluate the expressions in the exercises before they begin to work on them.

52

Technology   Exploring Order of Operations

For Use With Lesson 1-10

Some calculators use the order of operations in math and some do not. Check the value of 18 + 6 ÷ 3 on your calculator.

18 ➕ 6 ➗ 3 🟰

If the display is 20, your calculator follows the order of operations.

If the display is 8, your calculator has added first. You will have to enter expressions using the order of operations.

6 ➗ 3 ➕ 18 🟰

Some calculators have the parentheses keys ❨ and ❩. Use these when you want your calculator to do the operation in parentheses first.

EXAMPLE   **Using a Calculator**

Multiply 1.4 by the sum of 45.2 and 7.5.

Method 1 Use a calculator with ( ) keys.   1.4 ✖ ❨ 45.2 ➕ 7.5 ❩ 🟰 *73.78*   ← Put parentheses around 45.2 + 7.5 so addition will be completed first.

Method 2 Use a calculator without ( ) keys.   45.2 ➕ 7.5 🟰 *52.7*   ← Complete the addition first.
✖ 1.4 🟰 *73.78*   ← Then multiply your answer by 1.4.

EXERCISES

Write a calculator key sequence for each expression and give the value.
1–4. See margin.

1. Subtract 85.4 from 97.5. Then divide by 2.5.

2. Multiply 23.5 by 1.1. Then add 4.75.

3. Divide 7.28 by the sum of 0.14 and 1.86.

4. Divide the sum of 0.72 and 2.79 by 3.

Place parentheses, if needed, in each number sentence to make it true.

5. 4 × 8 − 1 = 28
4 × (8 − 1) = 28

6. 14 − 9 × 7 = 35
(14 − 9) × 7 = 35

7. 4.7 − 2.3 + 2.01 = 4.41
4.7 − 2.3 + 2.01 = 4.41

8. 14.9 − 2.6 + 8.3 = 4
14.9 − (2.6 + 8.3) = 4

9. 3.08 × 3.7 + 2.12 = 13.516
3.08 × 3.7 + 2.12 = 13.516

10. 6.5 + 3.2 × 7.1 = 68.87
(6.5 + 3.2) × 7.1 = 68.87

11. **Writing in Math** Suppose you use a calculator to divide 4.00 by 16. Is it necessary to enter all three digits in 4.00? Explain your answer.
No; the calculator automatically places the decimal point.

52   Technology   Exploring Order of Operations

1.   ❨ 97.5 ➖ 85.4 ❩ ➗ 2.5 🟰

2.   23.5 ✖ 1.1 ➕ 4.75 🟰

3.   7.28 ➗ ❨ 0.14 ➕ 1.86 ❩ 🟰

4.   ❨ 0.72 ➕ 2.79 ❩ ➗ 3 🟰

Test-Taking Strategies

Writing Gridded Responses

Writing Gridded Responses

This strategy provides students with examples that demonstrate how to correctly answer a gridded-response test question.

Resources

PRENTICE HALL
ASSESSMENT SYSTEM

Test-Taking Strategies With Transparencies
• Transparency 2
• Practice master, p. 1
• Blank sheet of grids, p. viii

Teaching Notes

Emphasize that fully completing a gridded-response test question involves two distinct parts: (1) writing the answer in the top row, one digit or symbol to a column, and (2) filling in the circle in each column that corresponds to the digit or symbol written at the top of that column.

Teaching Tip

Have volunteers explain how to fill in the correct responses. Show students that starting answers in any column works, as long as there are enough columns for all digits and symbols.

Some tests include gridded-response questions. When you find an answer, write the answer at the top of the grid and fill in the matching bubbles below.

EXAMPLE **Using the Answer Grid**

A fitness trail is 3.4 miles long. You walk 2.7 miles of the trail. How many miles farther must you walk to finish the trail?

3.4 miles − 2.7 miles = 0.7 mile

You can write the answer as 0.7, .7, or $\frac{7}{10}$. Here are the three ways to enter these answers. You do not include the label in a grid.

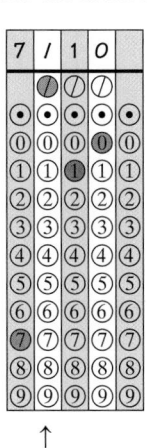

↑ Write a decimal point as part of the answer.   ↑   ↑ Write a slash with a fraction.

EXERCISES

Write what you would grid for each answer. If you have a grid, complete it.

1. 4.6 − 3
   1.6
2. 8 + 2.31
   10.31
3. 0.65 ÷ 5
   0.13
4. 0.75 × 0.02
   0.015
5. 2.2 × 5 − 11 + 6.6 ÷ 3
   2.2
6. 2.5 ÷ (0.5 × 5) × 1.525
   1.525

7. What decimal number does the model at the right represent? **0.5**

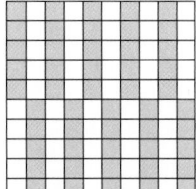

8. A diver received scores of 6.5, 5.5, 6.0, 6.5, and 6.0 in a diving competition. What is the total score? **30.5**

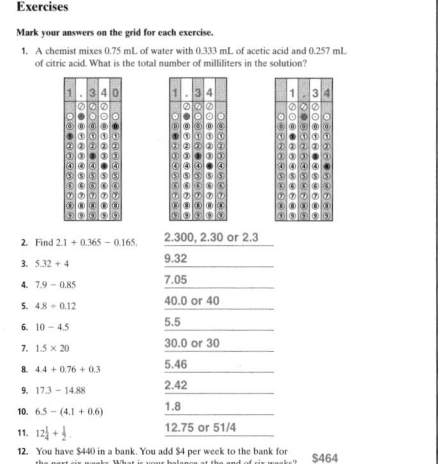

Test-Taking Strategies With Transparencies

Chapter 1: Writing Gridded Responses
Exercises

Mark your answers on the grid for each exercise.

1. A chemist mixes 0.75 mL of water with 0.333 mL of acetic acid and 0.257 mL of citric acid. What is the total number of milliliters in the solution?

2. Find 2.1 + 0.365 − 0.165.   **2.300, 2.30 or 2.3**
3. 5.32 + 4   **9.32**
4. 7.9 − 0.85   **7.05**
5. 4.8 ÷ 0.12   **40.0 or 40**
6. 10 − 4.5   **5.5**
7. 1.5 × 20   **30.0 or 30**
8. 4.4 + 0.76 + 0.3   **5.46**
9. 17.3 − 14.88   **2.42**
10. 6.5 − (4.1 + 0.6)   **1.8**
11. $12\frac{1}{4} ÷ \frac{1}{5}$ **12.75 or 51/4**
12. You have $440 in a bank. You add $4 per week to the bank for the next six weeks. What is your balance at the end of six weeks?   **$464**
13. A carpenter cuts a 12-m board into 5 equal pieces. What is the length of each piece? Round to the nearest tenth of a meter.   **2.4 m**
14. You spent $11.32 on earrings. Each set of earrings cost $2.83. How many sets of earrings did you buy?   **4 sets**

Resources

Student Edition
Extra Practice, Ch. 1, p. 642
English/Spanish Glossary, p. 669
Table of Symbols, p. 666

 Reaching All Students
Reading and Math Literacy 1D
Spanish Reading and Math
Literacy 1D

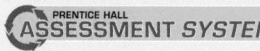 PRENTICE HALL
ASSESSMENT *SYSTEM*

Test Preparation
• Chapter 1 practice in test
formats

 www.PHSchool.com
Student Site
• Self-grading vocabulary test

PH SuccessNet Teacher Center
• Resources

Plus

Vocabulary

Associative Property of Addition (p. 25)	compatible numbers (p. 20)	order of operations (p. 48)
Associative Property of Multiplication (p. 36)	expanded form (p. 5)	repeating decimal (p. 44)
Commutative Property of Addition (p. 25)	expression (p. 48)	standard form (p. 5)
Commutative Property of Multiplication (p. 36)	front-end estimation (p. 20)	terminating decimal (p. 44)
	Identity Property of Addition (p. 25)	
	Identity Property of Multiplication (p. 36)	

 Reading Math:
Understanding
Vocabulary

Take It to the NET
Online vocabulary quiz
at www.PHSchool.com
Web Code: aaj-0151

Choose the correct vocabulary term to complete each sentence.

1. An example of the ? is $5 + 0 = 5$. **Identity Prop. of Add.**

2. $(4 + 7) \div 2$ is an example of a(n) ? . **expression**

3. 0.5830 is in ? . **standard form**

4. An example of a(n) ? is $157.\overline{3}$. **repeating decimal**

5. $5.3 + (6.8 + 8.1) = (5.3 + 6.8) + 8.1$ is an example of the ? . **Assoc. Prop. of Add**

Skills and Concepts

1-1, 1-2, and 1-3 Objectives

▼ To write and compare whole numbers

▼ To read and write decimals

▼ To compare decimals using models

▼ To use place value

You can write decimals in words, in **standard form,** or in **expanded form.** A decimal in expanded form shows the place and value of each digit. You can compare and order decimals using models, a number line, or place value.

Write each number in standard form.

6. six million, four thousand thirty **6,004,030**

7. six and forty-three thousandths **6.043**

Write each number in words and in expanded form. **8–11. See margin.**

8. 525.5   **9.** 5,000,025   **10.** 0.5255   **11.** 5.025

Use <, =, or > to complete each statement.

12. 4,406 $\overset{>}{\blacksquare}$ 640   **13.** 0.33 $\overset{<}{\blacksquare}$ 0.35   **14.** 1.838 $\overset{<}{\blacksquare}$ 1.839   **15.** 0.18 $\overset{>}{\blacksquare}$ 0.081

Order each set of decimals from least to greatest.

16. 0.52; 0.4; 0.14; 0.06
0.06; 0.14; 0.4; 0.52

17. 23; 23.2; 23.25; 23.03
23; 23.03; 23.2; 23.25

18. 9.4; 9.24; 9.04; 9.2
9.04; 9.2; 9.24; 9.4

8. five hundred twenty-five and five tenths; $500 + 20 + 5 + 0.5$

9. five million, twenty-five; $5,000,000 + 20 + 5$

10. five thousand, two hundred fifty-five ten-thousandths; $0.5 + 0.02 + 0.005 + 0.0005$

11. five and twenty-five thousandths; $5 + 0.02 + 0.005$

Spanish Reading and Math Literacy

Reading and Math Literacy

1D: Vocabulary — For use with the Chapter Review

Study Skill: Review your class notes as soon as possible. This will help to identify any concepts in which you need additional explanation.

Match the term in Column A with its definition in Column B.

Column A		Column B
1. Identity Property of Multiplication	E	A. decimals that represent the same amount
2. place value	K	B. $7 + (3 + 9) = (7 + 3) + 9$
3. range	N	C. a number written using digits
4. repeating decimal	L	D. $4 + 0 = 4$
5. compatible numbers	J	E. $8.3 \times 1 = 8.3$
6. equivalent decimals	A	F. mathematical phrase containing numbers and operations
7. Associative Property of Addition	B	G. $8 \cdot 4 = 4 \cdot 8$
8. Commutative Property of Addition	O	H. 0.35 is an example
9. Identity Property of Addition	D	I. sum that shows the place and value of each digit
10. Associative Property of Multiplication	M	J. numbers that are easy to compute mentally
11. Commutative Property of Multiplication	G	K. value of a digit based on its location in a particular number
12. expanded form	I	L. $0.\overline{6}$ is an example
13. standard form	C	M. $8(7 \cdot 9) = (8 \cdot 7)9$
14. terminating decimal	H	N. difference between the greatest and least number in a data set
15. expression	F	O. $6 + 8 = 8 + 6$

1-4 and 1-5 Objectives

▼ To estimate by rounding and using compatible numbers

▼ To use front-end estimation

▼ To add decimals

▼ To subtract decimals

To estimate, you can round each number or you can use **compatible numbers.** You can also use **front-end estimation** to estimate a sum.

Use rounding, front-end estimation, or compatible numbers to estimate each answer. 19–22. Answers may vary. Samples are given.

19. $337.4 + 20.08$
about 357

20. $1.741 - 0.81$
about 1

21. 3.21×1.04
about 3

22. $6.25 \div 1.25$
about 6

Find each sum or difference.

23. $1.6 + 1.8$
3.4

24. $0.96 - 0.79$
0.17

25. $4.12 - 0.253$
3.867

26. $2.01 + 5.39$
7.4

1-6 Objective

▼ To use a plan to solve problems

When solving a problem, be sure to *read and understand* the problem, *plan* how to solve it, *solve* the problem, and then *look back and check* to see if your answer makes sense.

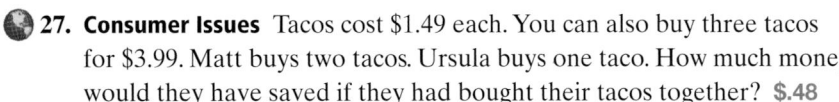 **27. Consumer Issues** Tacos cost $1.49 each. You can also buy three tacos for $3.99. Matt buys two tacos. Ursula buys one taco. How much money would they have saved if they had bought their tacos together? $.48

1-7, 1-8, and 1-9 Objectives

▼ To multiply decimals

▼ To use the properties of multiplication

▼ To multiply and divide decimals by 10, 100, and 1,000

▼ To divide decimals by whole numbers

▼ To divide decimals by decimals

When multiplying decimals, add the decimal places in the factors to place the decimal point in the product. When dividing decimals, multiply both the dividend and the divisor by the same number so that the divisor is a whole number.

You can use the **Commutative, Associative,** and **Identity Properties of Multiplication** to help you multiply mentally.

Find each product or quotient.

28. 1.2×29.5
35.4

29. $12.12 \div 6$
2.02

30. $38.4 \div 0.08$
480

31. $0.54 \cdot 17$
9.18

Use mental math to find each product or quotient.

32. $5 \times 34 \times 0.02$
3.4

33. $(0.3)(3)(1)$
0.9

34. $98.127 \div 100$
0.98127

1-10 Objective

▼ To use the order of operations

An **expression** is a mathematical phrase containing numbers and operation symbols. You use the **order of operations** to find the value of an expression.

Find the value of each expression.

35. $30 - 5 + 4 \times 3$
37

36. $6 - (27 - 9) \div 3$
0

37. $5.3 \times 8 + 4 \div 2$
44.4

Resources

Take It to the NET
Online chapter test at
www.PHSchool.com
Web Code: aaa-0152

Write each number in standard form.

1. two thousand twenty and twenty-five thousandths **2,020.025**

2. one million, four hundred nine thousand, eight hundred thirty-five **1,409,835**

Write each decimal in words and in expanded form. 3–5. See margin.

3. 623.7   **4.** 2.086   **5.** 89.123

6. **Writing in Math** Explain why thirteen hundredths are equivalent to one hundred thirty thousandths. **See margin.**

Use <, =, or > to complete each statement.

7. 32.12 ■ 32.42 **<**   **8.** 9.7 ■ 9.70 **=**

Order each set of decimals from least to greatest.

9. 8.1, 8.2, 8.08, 8.15, 8.03
8.03, 8.08, 8.1, 8.15, 8.2

10. 1.63, 1.064, 0.163, 1.036, 0.153
0.153, 0.163, 1.036, 1.064, 1.63

Use rounding, front-end estimation, or compatible numbers to estimate each answer.
11–16. Answers may vary. Samples are given.

11. 50.32 × 22.1
about 1,000
12. 4.63 × 50.491
about 250
13. 98.13 ÷ 24.27
about 4
14. 4.38 + 2.74 + 1.17
about 8
15. 1.01 + 2.89
about 4
16. 62.85 − 24.12
about 40

🌐 **17.** **DVDs** Five DVDs cost $74.85. Explain whether the best estimate for the cost of one DVD is greater than or less than $14.
Greater than $14; answers may vary.
Sample: 5 × $14 = $70, and $74.85 > $70.

First estimate, then find each sum or difference.

18. 3.89 + 15.3
about 19; 19.19
19. 4.6 − 2.07
about 3; 2.53
20. 41.2 − 19.8
about 20; 21.4
21. 53.7 + 28.6
about 80; 82.3

Use mental math to find each answer.
22–27. Answers may vary. Samples are given.
22. 8.29 + 0 + 0.71
9
23. 3.6 + (7.28 + 6.4)
17.28
24. 100 × 5.2
520
25. 25 × 6.7 × 4
670
26. 4.3 × 1 × 10
43
27. 83.11 ÷ 1,000
0.08311

🌐 **28.** **Working** Larry wants to work 2.75 hours each day from Monday through Wednesday. How many hours must he work on Thursday to work a total of 10 hours? **1.75 h**

Find each product or quotient.

29. 9.063 × 24
217.512
30. 0.36(1.5) **0.54**
31. 21.6 ÷ 0.06 **360**
32. 10 ÷ 3 **3.3̄**
33. 7 ÷ 0.14 **50**
34. 6.34 · 1.091 **6.91694**

🌐 **35.** **Pet Food** Zelda spent $6.24 on pet food. The food cost $.24 per cup. How many cups of pet food did Zelda purchase? **26 c**

🌐 **36.** **Money** What is the value of 18 rolls of quarters if there are 40 quarters in each roll?
$180.00

Find the value of each expression.

37. 16 ÷ (4 × 4) **1**   **38.** 8 − 4 ÷ 2 **6**

39. 5 + (3.3 − 1.6)
6.7
40. (9 − 1.2 × 3) ÷ 4
1.35

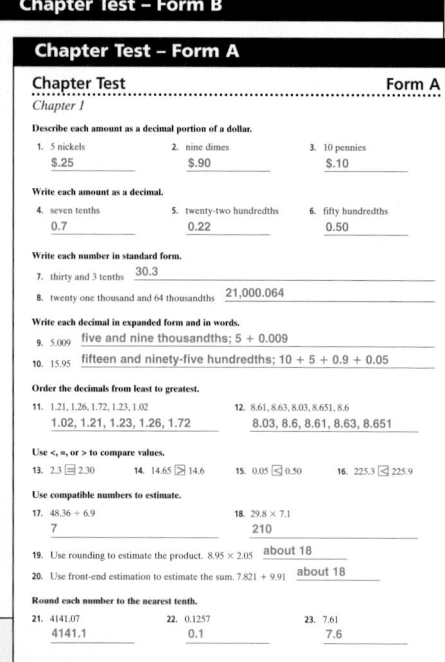
3. 600 + 20 + 3 + 0.7; six hundred twenty-three and seven tenths

4. 2 + 0.08 + 0.006; two and eighty-six thousandths

5. 80 + 9 + 0.1 + 0.02 + 0.003; eighty-nine and one hundred twenty-three thousandths

6. Each hundredth is equal to 10 thousandths, so 13 hundredths equals 13 × 10, or 130, thousandths.

Test Prep

 **Test Prep**

Students must be able to extract information from reading passages, answer multiple-choice questions, and construct responses in order to be successful in current state and national assessments.

Resources

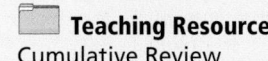 **Teaching Resources**
Cumulative Review

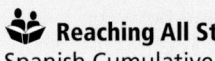 **Reaching All Students**
Spanish Cumulative Review

 PRENTICE HALL
ASSESSMENT SYSTEM

Test Preparation
• Ch. 1 standardized test prep

Assessment Resources
• Cumulative Review

Computer Test Generator CD
• Standardized test prep

 www.PHSchool.com
• Standardized test prep
• Resources

Plus

Reading Comprehension Read each passage below. Then answer the questions based on what you have read.

> **Rainfall** Hilo, Hawaii, usually receives 129.19 inches of rain each year. Compare that to Phoenix, Arizona, which receives 7.66 inches of rain a year. In Hilo, the wettest month is April, with 15.26 inches of rain, while its driest month is June with 6.2 inches of rain. Phoenix's wettest month is December with 1 inch, and its driest is May with 0.12 inch.

1. In Hilo, how many more inches of rain typically fall in April than in June? **B**
   A. 0.88 inch
   B. 9.06 inches
   C. 15.26 inches
   D. 21.46 inches

2. In July, Phoenix typically gets 0.83 inch of rain. About how many times as much rain falls in July as in May? **G**
   F. 6   G. 7   H. 8   I. 9

3. How many inches of rain does Hilo receive in a typical ten-year period? **A**
   A. 1,291.9 inches
   B. 76.60 inches
   C. 12.919 inches
   D. 0.766 inch

4. Hilo's yearly rainfall is about how many times the yearly rainfall in Phoenix? **I**
   F. 1,040 times
   G. 138 times
   H. 122 times
   I. 16 times

> **Coins** Did you know that some coins contain more pure metal than others? American Gold Eagle coins are 0.9166 gold and Canadian Maple Leaf coins are 0.9999 gold. American Silver Eagle coins are 0.999 silver while the American Platinum Eagle coins are 0.9995 platinum.

5. How might you write the purity of the American Silver Eagle coin in order to compare it with the other coins? **C**
   A. 0.99
   B. 0.0999
   C. 0.9990
   D. 0.9999

6. What portion of the American Gold Eagle coin is NOT gold? **H**
   F. 0.0004
   G. 0.0034
   H. 0.0834
   I. 0.0934

7. Which of the five coins mentioned contains the greatest portion of pure metal? **C**
   A. American Silver Eagle
   B. American Gold Eagle
   C. Canadian Maple Leaf
   D. American Platinum Eagle

8. How much gold is in an American Gold Eagle coin that weighs 0.1 ounce? **I**
   F. 9.166 ounces
   G. 0.9166 ounce
   H. 0.91660 ounce
   I. 0.09166 ounce

Cumulative Review

Cumulative Review
Chapter 1

Multiple Choice. Choose the letter of the best answer.

1. What is the value of the 4 in 3,241,036?
   A. 40
   B. 40,000
   C. 4,000
   D. 400,000

2. How many different ways can you make 13¢ using dimes, nickels, or pennies?
   F. 4 ways
   G. 2 ways
   H. 3 ways
   I. 5 ways

3. Estimate. 82,591 − 13,983
   A. 7,000
   B. 50,000
   C. 60,000
   D. 70,000

4. What is 0.45 in words?
   F. forty-five tenths
   G. forty-five
   H. forty-five hundredths
   I. forty-five thousandths

5. Estimate the cost of the movie and refreshments by rounding to the nearest dollar.
   movie $4.60
   drink $1.45
   popcorn $2.79
   snack $1.23
   A. $9
   B. $10
   C. $11
   D. $12

6. Find the difference. 35.46 − 22.98
   F. 58.44
   G. 12.46
   H. 12.48
   I. 13.58

7. Shelly paid for a $7.59 paperback book with a $10 bill. How much change did she get back?
   A. $17.59
   B. $3
   C. $3.51
   D. $2.41

8. Multiply. 0.23 × 0.04
   F. 82
   G. 0.082
   H. 0.0092
   I. 0.092

9. Estimate. 5.3 × 0.8
   A. 0.40
   B. 40
   C. 4
   D. 48

10. The admission charge at the zoo is $3.75 per person. What is the total admission charge for a group of 28 people?
    F. $31.75
    G. $37.50
    H. $105.00
    I. $24.25

11. Multiply. 1,000 × 0.25
    A. 0.00025
    B. 250
    C. 2,500
    D. 0.025

12. Which shows 50,001,000 in word form?
    F. fifty-one million
    G. fifty million, ten thousand
    H. fifty million, one thousand
    I. fifty million one

13. Which is the best estimate of 248 × 6?
    A. 1,200
    B. 1,800
    C. 12,000
    D. 18,000

That's an Order!

Students will use data from these two pages to answer the questions posed here in Put It All Together.

Activating Prior Knowledge

Have students discuss what they know about early forms of writing—what the marks looked like and how they were used. Explain that Mesopotamia describes the land between the Tigris River and Euphrates River that is now the modern-day country of Iraq.

Teaching Notes

Give students a moment to read the data about cuneiform and about the other early ways to tally data.

Language Arts Connection

Inform students that cuneiform (kyoo NEE uh form) is what the wedge-like symbols used by Sumerians (as early as 3500 B.C.) were later called. The term comes from the Latin word *cuneus*, or wedge. Discuss that as the cities in the region grew, people used cuneiform more and more. This use led to the need for scribes and schools that trained these scribes.

Math Connection

Refer students to the picture of the Napier's Rods shown. Inform them that John Napier invented latticed rods (called "bones") in 1617 as a way to multiply. Napier also invented *logarithms*. Invite your advanced students to learn about logarithms. Logarithms are the exponents that indicate the power to which a number is raised to produce a given number; the logarithm of 64 to base 8 is 2.

That's an Order!

Applying Decimals Ancient Mesopotamians bought and traded grain and other items. They developed a writing system to keep track of their goods and money. Today, we use order forms and receipts to purchase items and record the money we spend.

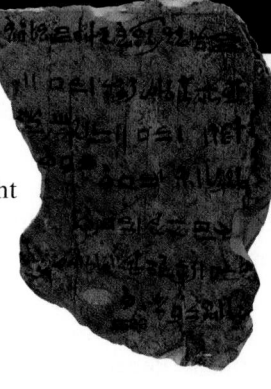

How Much for That Goat?

This piece of limestone shows part of a business deal including a goat worth one deben of copper, an Ancient Egyptian measure of metal. One deben equals 3 ounces.

Put It All Together

1. Find the five missing values in the sample order form. (*Hint:* Some missing values cannot be found without finding others first.)

2. **Open-Ended** Suppose you have a clothing budget of $500.

   a. **Research** Make a list of items you would like to purchase. Find their prices.

   b. Use an order form like the sample. Complete the Quantity, Description, and Unit Price columns for the items on your list. At least four of the values in the Quantity column should be greater than 1.

   c. Find the total for each row by multiplying the quantity by the unit price. Follow the directions on the order form to fill in the rest of the boxes. Make sure you stay within your budget!

   d. Copy your order form onto another sheet of paper. Leave some boxes blank as in the sample. Trade order forms with another student and find each other's missing values.

Sample Order Form

Quantity	Description	Unit Price	Total
■	20-gallon aquarium	$119.99	$119.99
1	Air pump	$14.95	$14.95
2	Water filter	■	$64.98
3	Tropical fish food	$7.49	$22.47
■	Gravel, one bag	$1.99	■
3	Driftwood decoration	$13.25	$39.75
Subtotal (Add the totals from above.)			■
6% Shipping (Multiply subtotal by 0.06.)			$16.44
Total (Add subtotal and shipping.)			$290.52

Tally Sticks

People have used notched sticks for tallying totals for thousands of years. Larger notches denote greater amounts.

Calculations and More

Handheld calculators, which once took the place of adding machines, perform many mathematical operations. This one can display graphs.

58

1. 1; $32.49; 6; $11.94; $274.08

2. Answers may vary. Sample:

   a. blue jeans, $39.99; tee-shirts, $5.49; winter coat, $117.29; socks, $2.99; sweatshirt, $36.89; winter hat, $14.99; running shoes, $56.79; shorts, $22; boots, $55.99

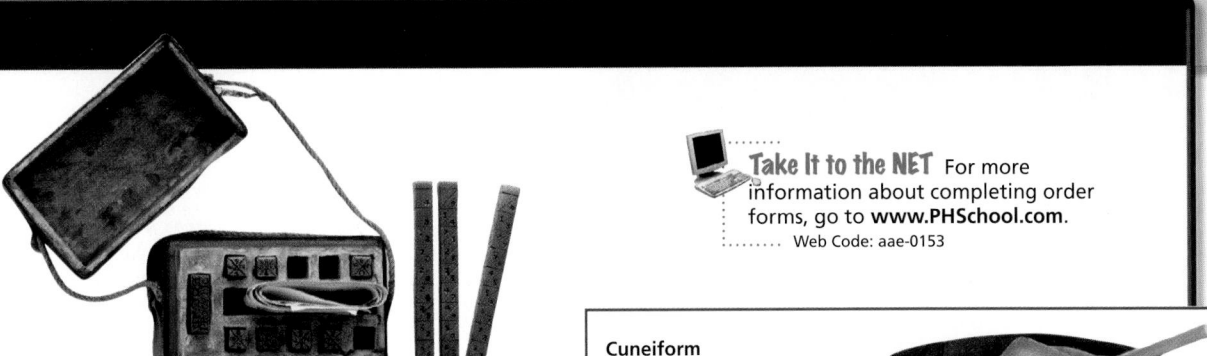

Napier's Rods

You can use Napier's rods to find products. The rods in the photo show multiples of 4, 7, and 9.

💻 **Take It to the NET** For more information about completing order forms, go to **www.PHSchool.com**.

Web Code: aae-0153

Cuneiform

Ancient Babylonians wrote their numbers in cuneiform, printed with sticks and wedges in clay tablets. The Babylonian number system is sexagesimal, which means it is based on counting 60s. This system remains in our measures of time and angles.

Counting Sheep

The cuneiform characters on this clay tablet are a tally of sheep and goats from an area called Tello, in ancient Mesopotamia.

59

Put It All Together

Help students understand what information each column of the order form shows. For example, ask: *How do you find the unit price for an item?* Sample: Divide the total price by the quantity. Have students work in pairs to answer the questions.

Inclusion
Provide actual order forms or receipts for students to examine and discuss.

Exercise 1 Elicit from students that to find the number of gravel bags in this order, they will need to work backward. One way: First, find the total cost of the gravel by adding all the other known totals plus the amount of tax. Then subtract that total from $290.52. Once they have the gravel cost, they can divide by its unit price to find the quantity.

Geography Connection
Ask students to find Mesopotamia on a map of the ancient Middle East and on a map of the region as it looks today. Have them describe the changes they see.

b.   c.   d. Check students' work.

Quantity	Description	Unit	Total
2	Blue Jeans	$39.99	$79.98
4	Tee-shirts	$5.49	$21.96
1	Winter Coat	$117.29	$117.29
6	Socks, pair	$2.99	$17.94
3	Sweatshirt	$36.89	$110.67
1	Winter Hat	$14.99	$14.99
1	Running Shoes, pair	$56.79	$56.79
1	Shorts, pair	$22.00	$22.00
1	Boots, pair	$55.99	$55.99

CHAPTER 2

Patterns and Variables

Chapter at a Glance

2-1 Algebra
Describing a Pattern
pp. 63–67

Objectives
- ▼ Continuing a Number Pattern
- ② Writing a Rule for a Number Pattern

New Vocabulary
term, conjecture

Optional Materials
graph paper

NCTM Standards
1, 2, 3, 6, 7, 8, 9, 10

Local Standards

2-2 Algebra
Variables and Expressions
pp. 68–72

Objectives
- ▼ Using Variables
- ② Evaluating Algebraic Expressions

New Vocabulary
numerical expression, variable, algebraic expression, evaluate

Optional Materials
compass, algebra tiles

NCTM Standards
1, 3, 6, 7, 8, 9, 10

Local Standards

2-3 Algebra
Writing Algebraic Expressions
pp. 74–78

Objectives
- ▼ Relating Words to Algebraic Expressions
- ② Using Algebraic Expressions

NCTM Standards
1, 3, 6, 7, 8, 9, 10

Local Standards

✓ Checkpoint Quiz 1

2-4 Problem Solving
Make a Table and Look for a Pattern
pp. 80–82

Objectives
- ▼ Solving Problems by Making a Table to Find a Pattern

NCTM Standards
1, 2, 3, 6, 7, 8, 9, 10

Local Standards

2-5 Algebra
Using Number Sense to Solve One-Step Equations pp. 84–88

Objectives
- ▼ Using Mental Math to Solve Equations
- ② Estimating Solutions of Equations

New Vocabulary
equation, open sentence, solution

NCTM Standards
1, 2, 6, 7, 8, 9, 10

Local Standards

2-6 Algebra
Solving Addition and Subtraction Equations
pp. 90–94

Objectives
- ▼ Solving Equations by Subtracting
- ② Solving Equations by Addition

New Vocabulary
inverse operations, Subtraction Property of Equality, Addition Property of Equality

NCTM Standards
1, 2, 3, 6, 7, 8, 9, 10

Local Standards

2-7 Algebra
Solving Multiplication and Division Equations pp. 95–98

Objectives
- ▼ Solving Equations by Dividing
- ② Solving Equations by Multiplying

New Vocabulary
Division Property of Equality, Multiplication Property of Equality

NCTM Standards
1, 2, 3, 6, 7, 8, 9, 10

Local Standards

✓ Checkpoint Quiz 2

2-8
Exponents
pp. 99–103

Objectives
- ▼ Using Exponents
- ② Simplifying Expressions with Exponents

New Vocabulary
exponent, base, power

NCTM Standards
1, 3, 4, 6, 7, 8, 9, 10

Local Standards

2-9 Algebra
The Distributive Property
pp. 105–108

Objectives
- ▼ Using the Distributive Property

New Vocabulary
Distributive Property

Optional Materials
graph paper

NCTM Standards
1, 2, 3, 6, 7, 8, 9, 10

Local Standards

Reaching All Students

Additional Instructional Options in Chapter 2

Reading and Math Literacy

Reading Math

Reading Algebraic Expressions, p. 73

Reading Math hints, pp. 63, 84, 86, 100

Understanding Vocabulary, p. 110

Writing in Math

Writing to Compare, p. 83

Daily Writing Practice, pp. 66, 71, 77, 81, 87, 93, 97, 102, 103, 107, 112

Writing Short Responses, p. 109

Above Level

C Challenge exercises

pp. 67, 72, 77, 82, 88, 94, 98, 103, 107

Extension

Using Formulas, p. 79

Scientific Notation, p. 104

Hands-On and Technology

Investigations

Recognizing and Extending Patterns, p. 63

Patterns and Algebraic Expressions, p. 68

Using Models to Solve Equations, p. 89

Making Area Models, p. 105

Activities and Projects

Real-World Snapshots

Applying Patterns pp. 114–115

Chapter Project

Stepping Stones, p. 636

Test Prep

Daily Test Prep

pp. 67, 72, 78, 82, 88, 94, 98, 103, 108

Test-Taking Strategies

Writing Short Responses, p. 109

Test Prep

Cumulative Review (Chapters 1–2), p. 113

Chapter Assessment

Checkpoint Quiz

pp. 78, 98

Chapter Review

pp. 110–111

Chapter Test

p. 112

Pacing Options

This chart suggests pacing only for the core lessons and their parts. It is provided as a possible guide. It will help you determine how much time you have in your schedule to cover the additional features and assessment, as described at the left.

Day	Traditional 45-minute class periods	Block 90-minute class periods
1	2-1 ▽ ▽	2-1 ▽ ▽
		2-2 ▽
2	2-2 ▽	2-2 ▽
		2-3 ▽ ▽
3	2-2 ▽	2-4 ▽
		2-5 ▽
4	2-3 ▽	2-5 ▽
		2-6 ▽
5	2-3 ▽	2-6 ▽
		2-7 ▽
6	2-4 ▽	2-7 ▽
		2-8 ▽
7	2-5 ▽	2-8 ▽
		2-9 ▽
8	2-5 ▽	
9	2-6 ▽	
10	2-6 ▽	
11	2-7 ▽	
12	2-7 ▽	
13	2-8 ▽	
14	2-8 ▽	
15	2-9 ▽	

NCTM STANDARDS 2000

1	Number and Operations	6	Problem Solving
2	Algebra	7	Reasoning and Proof
3	Geometry	8	Communication
4	Measurement	9	Connections
5	Data Analysis and Probability	10	Representation

Math Background

Skills Trace

BEFORE Chapter 2
Grade 5 presented basic algebraic expressions and equations.

DURING Chapter 2
Course 1 extends the study of algebra to solving one-step equations and evaluating algebraic expressions.

AFTER Chapter 2
Throughout this course students write and solve algebraic equations.

2-1 Describing a Pattern

Math Understandings
- When you continue a pattern, or find the next term in a pattern, you assume that the pattern will continue in the same way.
- You can define or describe a number pattern by giving the first term and a rule that describes how you get from one term to the next.
- You can create and continue patterns of many different types and forms.

Each number in a number pattern is called a **term.** The three dots after the last number tell you that the pattern continues beyond the given terms. A **conjecture** is a prediction about what may happen. You can make a conjecture about how a pattern will continue.

Example: Write a rule for each number pattern.

4, 7, 10, 13, 16, . . .   1, 2, 4, 8, 16, 32, . . .
Start with 4 and add 3.   Start with 1 and multiply by 2.

2-2 Variables and Expressions

Math Understandings
- An algebraic expression differs from an open sentence or equation in that it has no equal sign.
- The value of an algebraic expression can vary depending on the value of the variable.
- Within a single problem, the value of the variable remains the same.

A **numerical expression** is a mathematical phrase with only numbers and operation symbols ($+$, $-$, $\times$, $\div$). A **variable** is a symbol that represents one or more numbers. A mathematical expression with one or more variables is an **algebraic expression.** You can model algebraic expressions using algebra tiles. The smallest tile represents 1. The next smallest tile has a width of 1 and an unknown length to represent x (or another variable).

$5x + 3$    ←5 green tiles represent $5x$, and three yellow tiles represent 3.

2-3 Writing Algebraic Expressions

Math Understandings
- In order to write a word phrase as an algebraic expression, you translate the words into numbers and operational symbols.

Some examples of key words and their corresponding mathematical operations follow.

Operation	Key Words
Addition	sum, add, plus, increased by, more than
Subtraction	difference, subtract, minus, decreased by, less than
Multiplication	product, multiplied by, times
Division	quotient, divided by

2-4 Make a Table and Look for a Pattern

You can make a table to help you look for a pattern. Then you can use the pattern to solve a problem.

2-5 Using Number Sense to Solve One-Step Equations

Math Understandings

- Until you replace the variable in an open sentence with a number value, the open sentence is neither true nor false.
- All open sentences are equations, but not all equations are open sentences.
- You can estimate solutions to equations using mental math.

An **equation** is a mathematical sentence that has an equal sign. An equation with one or more variables is an **open sentence**. A **solution** of an equation is a value of the variable that makes the equation true.

2-6 / 2-7 Solving Addition and Subtraction Equations Solving Multiplication and Division Equations

Math Understandings

- To solve an equation, use the mathematical properties to get the variable alone on one side of the equation.

PROPERTIES OF EQUALITY	
Arithmetic	Algebra
Addition Property of Equality	
$2 \cdot 3 = 6$, so $2 \cdot 3 + 4 = 6 + 4$.	If $a = b$, then $a + c = b + c$.
Subtraction Property of Equality	
$2 \cdot 3 = 6$, so $2 \cdot 3 - 4 = 6 - 4$.	If $a = b$, then $a - c = b - c$.
Multiplication Property of Equality	
$6 \div 2 = 3$, so $(6 \div 2) \times 2 = 3 \times 2$.	If $a = b$, then $a \cdot c = b \cdot c$.
Division Property of Equality	
$4 \times 2 = 8$, so $4 \times 2 \div 2 = 8 \div 2$.	If $a = b$ and $c \neq 0$, then $a \div c = b \div c$.

Operations that undo each other, such as addition and subtraction or multiplication and division, are **inverse operations**.

2-8 Exponents

Math Understandings

- When you write a base with an exponent, you are using a mathematical operation that indicates repeated multiplication.

An exponent tells you how many times a number, or base, is used as a factor.

$$5 \times 5 \times 5 \times 5 = 5^4$$

exponent
base

A number expressed using an exponent is called a **power**. The order of operations can be extended to include exponents.

Order of Operations
1. Do all operations within parentheses first.
2. Do all work with exponents.
3. Multiply and divide in order from left to right.
4. Add and subtract in order from left to right.

2-9 The Distributive Property

Math Understandings

- You use the Distributive Property to evaluate expressions that have a number multiplied by a sum or difference.
- The Distributive Property can be written and used in several different forms.

The **Distributive Property** shows how multiplication affects an addition or subtraction.

$$8 \times (4 + 6) = (8 \times 4) + (8 \times 6) \quad (6 - 2) \times 7 = (6 \times 7) - (2 \times 7)$$

Additional Professional Development Opportunities

Chapter 2 Math Background notes:
pp. 64, 69, 75, 80, 85, 91, 96, 100, 106

Additional resources available from SkyLight Professional Development:

On-site courses, workshops, summer institutes. Online courses and chat rooms. Videocassettes and books. Visit www.skylightedu.com.

Ongoing Assessment and Intervention

The *Prentice Hall Mathematics* program provides many options for assessment in the Student Edition, Teacher's Edition, and teaching resources. From these options you may choose instructional materials that are appropriate for your students and that support your district's curriculum requirements.

Daily Assessment

 Instant Check System™ in Chapter 2

Allows students to check their own learning before, during, and after each lesson.

Diagnosing Readiness before the chapter (p. 62)

Check Skills You'll Need exercises in each lesson (pp. 63, 68, 74, 80, 84, 90, 95, 99, 105)

Check Understanding questions with each Example (pp. 64, 65, 69, 70, 74, 75, 76, 80, 84, 85, 90, 91, 92, 95, 96, 99, 100, 101, 106)

Checkpoint Quiz (pp. 78, 98)

Formal Assessment

Assessment in the Student Text and in Additional Resources

Assess student progress throughout the Course 1 textbook and with blackline masters and CD-ROM.

Student Edition
- Chapter 2 Review, with Vocabulary, Skills, and Concepts Review, pp. 110–111
- Chapter 2 Test, p. 112

Assessment Resources
- Checkpoint Quizzes 1 & 2
- Chapter Test, forms A & B
- Chapter Alternative Assessment

Spanish versions available.

 Computer Test Generator CD-ROM
- Instant Chapter Tests™—pre-made tests with items that vary every time you print.
- Online Testing allows you to give tests online and receive progress reports.
- Prepare students by making tests based on standardized test objectives.

Algebra Readiness Tests
- Includes Basic Skills Tests and Concept-Readiness Tests.
- Assess understanding of skills and concepts needed for success in algebra.

Intervention

 Skills Intervention Kit

Online Intervention
Integrated within the iText, this online intervention system includes diagnostic tests and prescribed remediation, plus reports to track student mastery.

A *complete* system for the student who is struggling with course-level work

Eight intervention units cover core skills and allow you to:
- **Diagnose** students' gaps in basic skills
- **Prescribe** an individualized course of study
- **Monitor** student progress

Includes print workbooks, tutorial CD-ROM, teacher editions, progress folders, and more. *Available in Spanish.*

How to Use with Chapter 2

2-2	Pre-Algebra Basics, Skill 11
2-3	Pre-Algebra Basics, Skill 10
2-5	Pre-Algebra Basics, Skill 13
2-6	Pre-Algebra Basics, Skill 13
2-7	Pre-Algebra Basics, Skill 13
2-8	Pre-Algebra Basics, Skill 20

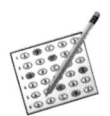

Standardized Test Preparation

The *Prentice Hall Mathematics* program integrates preparation for high-stakes standardized tests in every lesson of the Student Edition and continues this support in the Prentice Hall Assessment System.

Test Prep

In Student Text, Chapter 2

Teaches students strategies and gives them practice with all the test item formats they will encounter on high-stakes tests.

Test Prep exercises in each lesson (pp. 67, 72, 78, 82, 88, 94, 98, 103, 108)

Test-Taking Strategies (p. 109: Writing Short Responses)

Test Prep Cumulative Review (Chapters 1–2), p. 113

A three-step approach to preparing students for high stakes, national, and state exams.

1 Diagnose & Prescribe

Content Diagnostic Tests
- Diagnose strengths and weaknesses with ongoing benchmark tests.
- Prescribe individualized reteaching opportunities.

2 Review & Reteach

Skills and Concepts Review
- Provides reteaching worksheets with instruction and practice for each skill.
- Includes course prerequisite skills.

3 Practice & Assess

Standardized Test Preparation
- Features practice for national standardized exams.
- Includes practice tests for NAEP, SAT10, ITBS, and Terra Nova.

Test-Taking Strategies with Transparencies
- Support the Test-Taking Strategies pages in the Student Edition.
- Provide a transparency and a worksheet for each strategy.

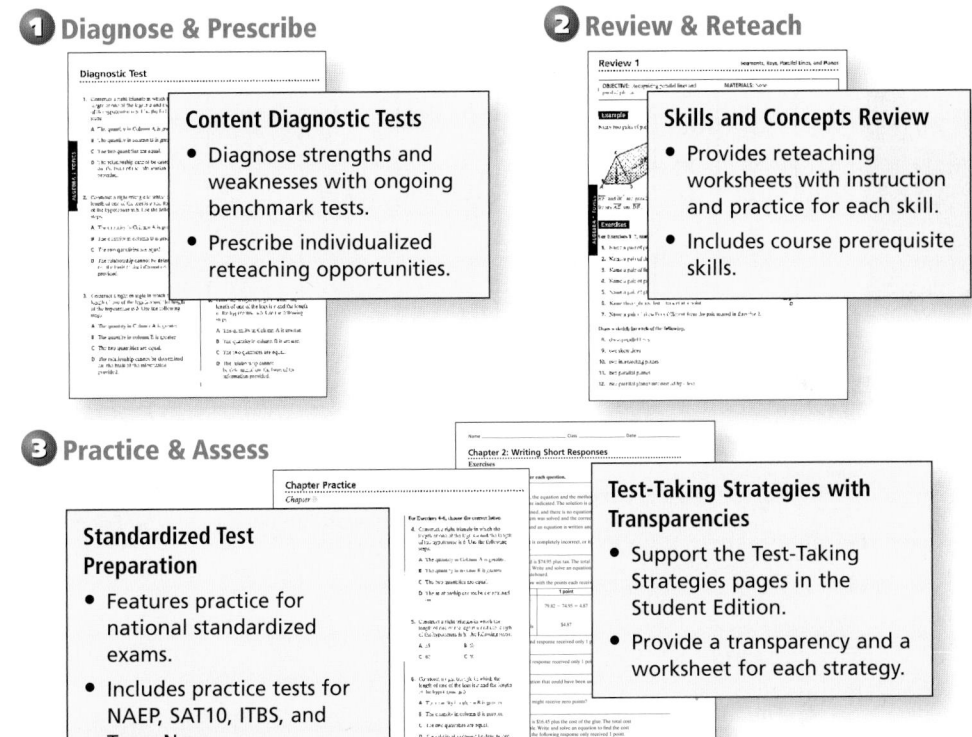

Correlation to Standardized Tests

Lesson		NAEP	Terra Nova CAT6	CTBS	ITBS	SAT10	Local Test
2-1	Describing a Pattern	A1a	■	■	■	■	
2-2	Variables and Expressions	A3a, A3b		■	■	■	
2-3	Writing Algebraic Expressions	A3a, A3b		■	■	■	
2-4	P. S.: Make a Table and Look for a Pattern	A1a	■				
2-5	Using Number Sense to Solve One-Step Equations	A4a		■		■	
2-6	Solving Addition and Subtraction Equations	A4a				■	■
2-7	Solving Multiplication and Division Equations	A4a				■	■
2-8	Exponents	N1d, N3a				■	
2-9	The Distributive Property	N3a				■	

NAEP National Assessment of Educational Progress
CAT6/Terra Nova California Achievement Test, 6th Ed.

CTBS/Terra Nova Comprehensive Test of Basic Skills
ITBS Iowa Test of Basic Skills, Form M.

SAT10 Stanford Achievement Test, 10th Ed.

Program Resources

	Resources in Grab & Go™ Files				Resources for Reaching All Students				Spanish Resources			Presentation Assistant Plus! Transparencies					Prentice Hall Presentation Pro CD-ROM
	Practice	Reteach	Enrich	Checkpt Quiz	Reading & Math Literacy	Technology Activities	Hands-On Activities	Guided Problem Solving	Practice	Reading & Math Literacy	Checkpt Quiz	Skills Check	Problem of the Day	Additional Examples	Answers to Exercises	Lesson Quiz	
2-1	■	■	■		■			■	■	■		■	■	■	■	■	■
2-2	■	■	■			■		■	■			■	■	■	■	■	■
2-3	■	■	■	■	■			■	■	■	■	■	■	■	■	■	■
2-4	■	■	■					■	■			■	■	■	■	■	■
2-5	■	■	■					■	■			■	■	■	■	■	■
2-6	■	■	■				■	■	■			■	■	■	■	■	■
2-7	■	■	■	■			■	■	■	■	■	■	■	■	■	■	■
2-8	■	■	■			■		■	■			■	■	■	■	■	■
2-9	■	■	■				■	■	■			■	■	■	■	■	■
For the Chapter	Chapter Projects, Chapter Tests, Alternative Assessment, Cumulative Review, Cumulative Assessment				On web site only: Home Activities, Interdisciplinary Activities, Algebra Readiness Puzzles				Spanish Chapter Tests, Alternative Assessment, Cumulative Review, Cumulative Assessment			Classroom Aid Transparencies					

Also available for use with the chapter:

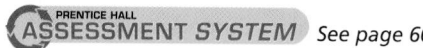 *See page 60F.*

- Practice Workbook
- Solution Key
- MathNotes folder

- For teacher support and access to student Web materials, use the Web Code aak-5500.
- For additional online and technology resources, *see below.*

Technology

iTEXT Online and on CD-ROM

Complete Interactive Student Text online and on CD-ROM—with instant feedback assessment, tutorial help, dynamic activities, instructional and real-world videos, audio, and additional practice.

www.PHSchool.com For Students

Use Web codes for easy access to online activities, chapter projects, self-grading lesson quizzes, chapter tests, vocabulary quizzes, updated data sources, graphing calculator procedures, and more.

PH SuccessNet For Teachers

Online lesson planning with built-in state correlations, all the teaching resources, complete reference library, your own calendar and Teacher Web page, professional development, and more.

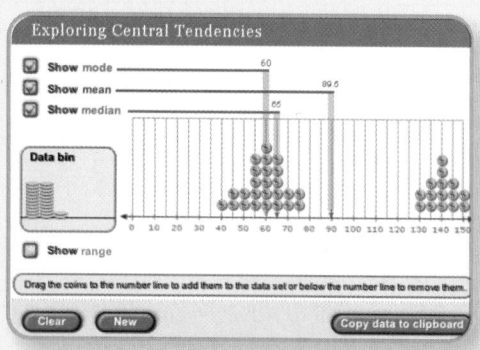

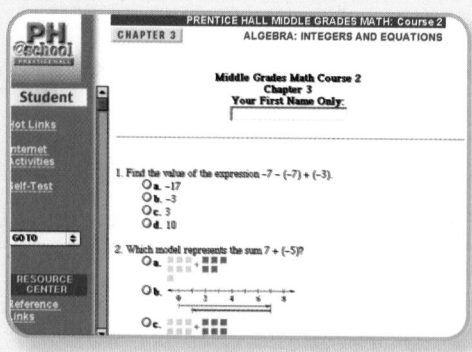

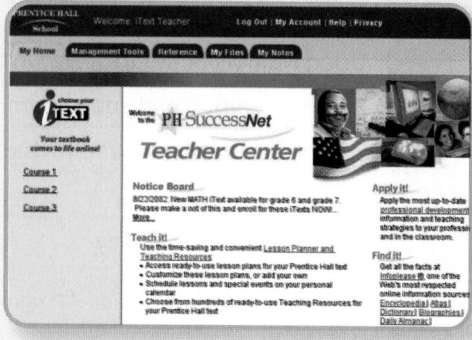

Presentation Assistant Plus!

The *Prentice Hall Presentation Assistant Plus!* provides you with the material you need to teach a lesson from beginning to end. Two easy-to-use formats—Transparencies and PowerPoint®—allow you to present a lesson the way you are most comfortable.

 ## Transparencies

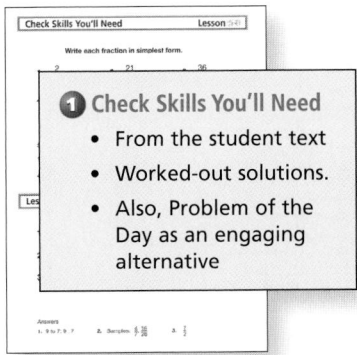

❶ **Check Skills You'll Need**
- From the student text
- Worked-out solutions.
- Also, Problem of the Day as an engaging alternative

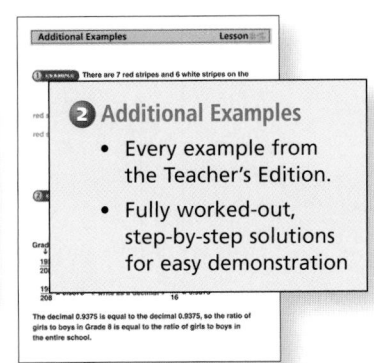

❷ **Additional Examples**
- Every example from the Teacher's Edition.
- Fully worked-out, step-by-step solutions for easy demonstration

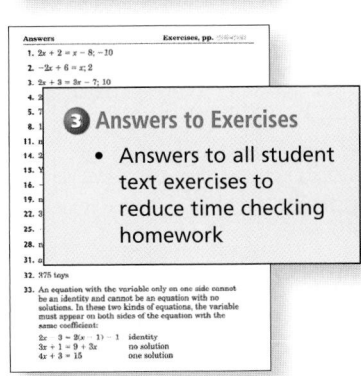

❸ **Answers to Exercises**
- Answers to all student text exercises to reduce time checking homework

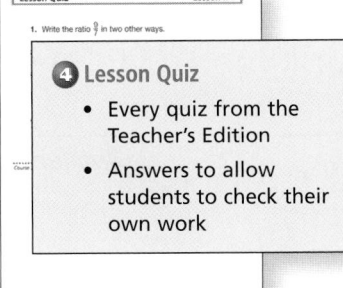

❹ **Lesson Quiz**
- Every quiz from the Teacher's Edition
- Answers to allow students to check their own work

 **PowerPoint** Throughout the Teacher's Edition, this symbol indicates material that is available in the Presentation Assistant Plus!

PowerPoint Prentice Hall Presentation Pro CD-ROM

- Includes all Transparencies.
- Conveniently organized by lesson so you can easily ❶Introduce, ❷Teach, ❸Check Homework, and ❹Assess each lesson.
- Animated examples allow step-by-step instruction at your own pace.
- Easy to edit so you can create custom presentations.

Teaching Chapter 2 Using Presentation Assistant Plus!

	❶ Introduce	❷ Teach	❸ Check Homework	❹ Assess
	Check Skills You'll Need	Additional Examples	Student Edition Answers	Lesson Quiz
2-1	p. 12	p. 21	✔	p. 12
2-2	p. 13	p. 22	✔	p. 13
2-3	p. 14	pp. 23–24	✔	p. 14
2-4	p. 15	p. 25	✔	p. 15
2-5	p. 16	pp. 26–27	✔	p. 16
2-6	p. 17	pp. 28–29	✔	p. 17
2-7	p. 18	pp. 30–31	✔	p. 18
2-8	p. 19	p. 32	✔	p. 19
2-9	p. 20	p. 33	✔	p. 20

 ### Prentice Hall Presentation Pro

CD-ROM with dynamic PowerPoint® presentations for every lesson. Helps you introduce and develop concepts, check homework, and assess progress. Part of Presentation Assistant Plus! *(See above.)*

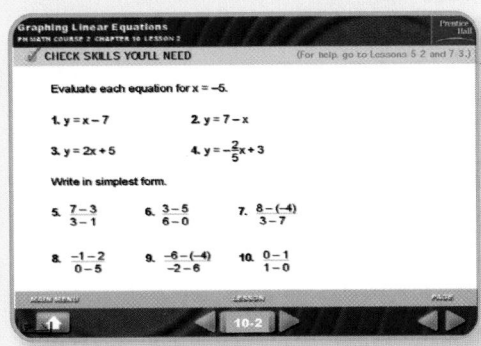

 ### Computer Test Generator

CD-ROM to create practice sheets and tests for course objectives and standardized tests. Includes Instant Chapter Tests™, online testing, and student reports. Part of the PH Assessment System. *(See page 60F.)*

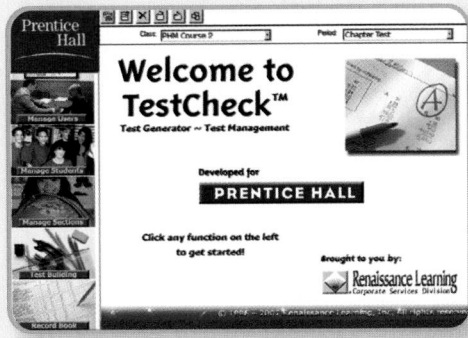

 ### Resource Pro® with Planning Express®

CD-ROM with a lesson planning tool that allows you to import state and local objectives. Includes electronic versions of all the teaching resources.

Chapter Resources

Reading and Math Support

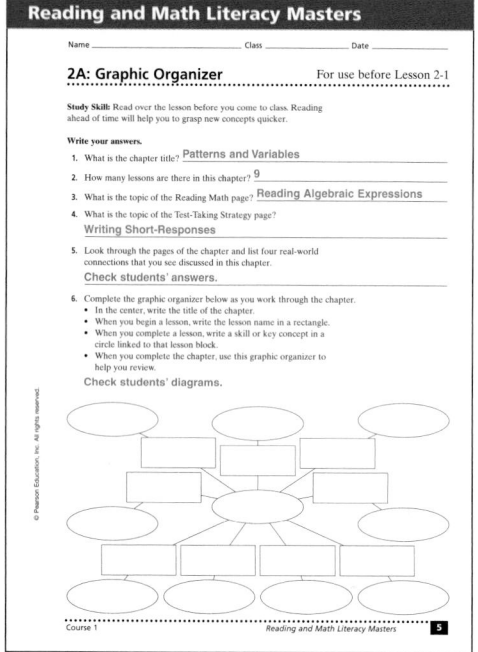

Available in Spanish

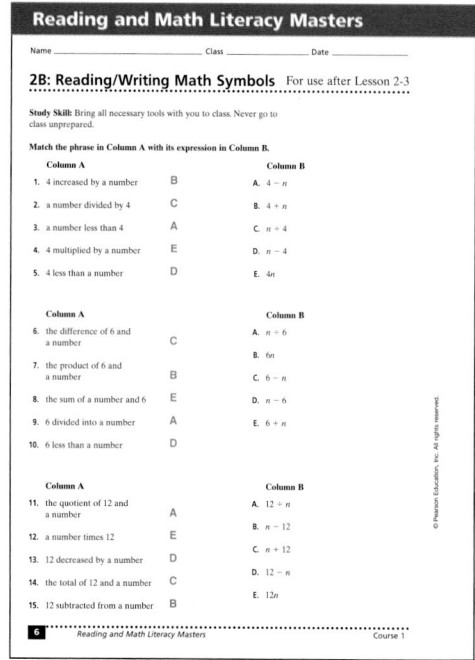

Available in Spanish

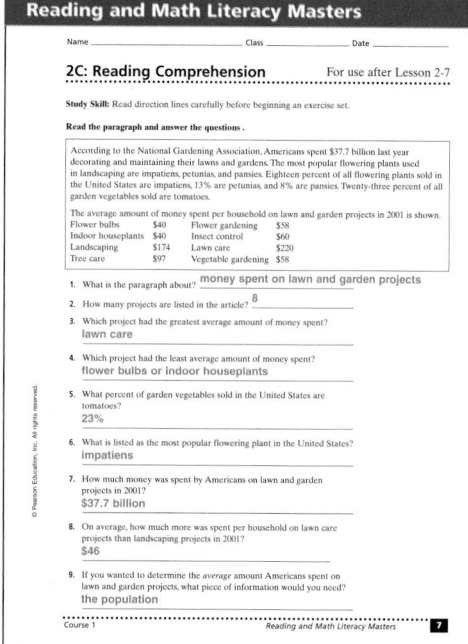

Available in Spanish

Problem Solving

Reading and Math Literacy Masters

Name _____ Class _____ Date _____

2D: Vocabulary   For use with the Chapter Review

Study Skill: Follow directions carefully.

Complete the crossword puzzle. For help, use the glossary in your textbook.

```
            A S S O C I A T I V E
            O          C
  D I S T R I B U T I V E P R O P E R T Y
  N     E     T     A     O     M     A
  V     R     I     R     W     M     N
  E     M     O     I     E     U     G
  R     E     N     A     R     T     E
  S           A     B           A
  E X P O N E N T    L           T
  O           L      E           I
  P           E                  V
  E Q U A T I O N   E X P R E S S I O N
  R                              E
  A
  T R E E D I A G R A M
  I
  C O N J E C T U R E
  O
  N
  S
```

ACROSS

1. $12(3 + 9) = 12(9 + 3)$ is an example of this property
4. $7(4 + 3) = 7(4) + 7(3)$ is an example of this property.
10. shows how many times a number is used as a factor
11. mathematical sentence that contains an equal sign
12. mathematical phrase containing numbers and operation
13. organized list of possible combinations
14. predicts how a pattern may continue

DOWN

2. number that makes an equation true
3. $100 + 32 = 32 + 100$ is an example of this property
5. operations that undo one another
6. each number in a number pattern
7. a symbol that stands for an unknown number
8. number expressed using an exponent
9. difference between the highest and lowest number in a data set

Available in Spanish

Guided Problem Solving Masters

Name _____ Class _____ Date _____

2-1 • Guided Problem Solving

GPS Student Page 66, Exercise 26:

Business A dry cleaner charges $5.00 to clean one item. He offers to clean a second item for $4.50, and a third item for $4.00.

a. If he continues to subtract $.50 for each additional item, how much will it cost to clean six items?

b. If the pattern continues, which item will be cleaned for free?

Read and Understand

1. What are you being asked to do in part a?
   Find how much it will cost to clean six items.

2. What are you being asked to do in part b?
   Use the pattern to determine which item is free.

3. What problem solving strategy will best solve this problem?
   finding the pattern

Plan and Solve

4. What is the cost of the 4th item? $3.50
5. What is the cost of the 5th item? $3.00
6. What is the cost of the 6th item? $2.50
7. Write and evaluate an expression for the cost of six items.
   $5.00 + $4.50 + $4.00 + $3.50 + $3.00 + $2.50 = $22.50
8. What is the cost of the 7th, 8th, 9th, and 10th items?
   $2.00, $1.50, $1.00, $.50
9. Which item will be cleaned for free? the eleventh item

Look Back and Check

10. Can you think of another way to solve the problem? Explain.
    Yes; you could write a rule for the pattern.

Solve Another Problem

11. Susie is trying to increase the distance she runs. The first week she ran $\frac{1}{2}$ mi, the second week she ran $\frac{3}{4}$ mi, the third week she ran 1 mile. How far will she run during the sixth week?
    $1\frac{3}{4}$ mi

Guided Problem Solving Masters

Name _____ Class _____ Date _____

2-2 • Guided Problem Solving

GPS Student Page 71, Exercise 30:

Bricklayer's Formula The formula $N = 7 \times \ell \times h$ gives the number of bricks needed for a wall of length ℓ feet and height h feet. How many bricks are needed for a wall with length 22 feet and height 30 feet?

Read and Understand

1. What are you being asked to do?
   Find the number of bricks needed for a wall that is 22 feet long and 30 feet high.

2. What does N represent?
   the number of bricks needed

Plan and Solve

3. What is the formula for the number of bricks?
   $N = 7 \times \ell \times h$
4. What do you replace ℓ and w with? 22 and 30
5. Replace ℓ and w with the values. $N = 7 \times 22 \times 30$
6. Simplify the expression. $N = 4,620$
7. How many bricks are needed? 4,620 bricks

Look Back and Check

8. How can you check your answer? Use your method to see if your answer is correct.
   Divide your answer by 7 and see if the answer is 22 × 30, or 660. 4,620 ÷ 7 = 660, so the answer checks.

Solve Another Problem

9. The sum of the interior angles of a polygon can be found using the formula $S = (N - 2) \times 180°$, where N is the number of sides of the polygon. What is the sum of the interior angles of a polygon with 8 sides?
   $S = (8 - 2) \times 180°; S = 6 \times 180°; S = 1,080°$

Name _____ Class _____ Date _____

2-3 • Guided Problem Solving

GPS Student Page 77, Exercise 22:

Zoo On Saturday, admission to the zoo costs $3 per person. The Sengs have a coupon for a discount of $5 off for a family. There are *p* people in the Seng family. Write an expression for how much the Sengs pay for admission to the zoo if they use the coupon.

Read and Understand

1. What are you being asked to do?
   Write an expression for how much the Sengs
   pay for admission to the zoo if they use the
   coupon.

2. What does the variable represent in the expression?
   the number of people in the Seng family

3. Circle the information you will need to solve the problem.

Plan and Solve

4. How much does admission to the zoo cost for each person?
   $3

5. Write an expression for the cost of the tickets if there are *p* people in the Seng family.
   3*p*

6. Write an expression for the cost of the tickets if there are *p* people in the Seng family and they use the $5 coupon.
   3*p* − 5

Look Back and Check

7. Could you write the expression another way? Explain.
   yes; −5 × 3*p*

Solve Another Problem

8. Each room in Anna's house needs 4 outlet covers. Write an expression that describes the total number of outlet covers Anna bought if she still needs 2 outlet covers.
   4*r* − 2

Name _____ Class _____ Date _____

2-4 • Guided Problem Solving

GPS Student Page 81, Exercise 7:

Band Tia, Lewis, and Jill play trombone. Wendi, Pali, and Nigel play baritone. How many different pairs of a trombone player and a baritone player are there?

Read and Understand

1. What are you being asked to do?
   Find the number of possible different pairs.

2. What problem solving strategy will best solve this problem?
   create an organized list

Plan and Solve

3. If Tia is the trombone player, how many pairs are possible?
   3 pairs

4. If Lewis is the trombone player, how many pairs are possible?
   3 pairs

5. If Jill is the trombone player, how many pairs are possible?
   3 pairs

6. How do you find the total pairs possible?
   Add the possible pairs for each trombone player.

7. How many total pairs are there? 9 pairs

Look Back and Check

8. What other strategy could you use to solve this problem? Do you get same answer?
   draw a diagram; yes, 9 pairs

Solve Another Problem

9. This year Leo can choose three of his classes. For his language he can choose Spanish, French, or Latin. For his art class he can choose drawing, ceramics, or photo shop. For his science he can choose either physical science or chemistry. How many different combinations are there for Leo's schedule?
   18 different combinations

Name _____ Class _____ Date _____

2-5 • Guided Problem Solving

GPS Student Page 87, Exercise 29:

Pollution When burned, 18 gallons of gasoline produce about 360 pounds of carbon dioxide. Solve the equation $18n = 360$ to find how much carbon dioxide 1 gallon produces.

Read and Understand

1. What are you being asked to do?
   Find the amount of carbon dioxide produced
   by burning 1 gallon of gasoline.

2. How can mental math help you to solve this problem?
   You can use your knowledge of compatible
   numbers to determine the answer.

Plan and Solve

3. What does the equation, $18n = 360$, mean?
   18 times what number is 360?

4. What is $360 \div 18$? 20

5. How many times more carbon dioxide is produced compared to the amount of gasoline?
   20 times

6. For 1 gallon of gasoline, how much carbon dioxide is produced?
   20 lb

Look Back and Check

7. Why is the amount of carbon dioxide 20 times more than the amount of gasoline?
   360 ÷ 18 = 20; this ratio should be the same
   for any amount of gasoline.

Solve Another Problem

8. At a school, there are 72 teachers for 1,872 students. If all the teachers have the same amount of students, use the equation, $72n = 1,872$ to find how many students 1 teacher has.
   $n = 1,872 \div 72$; each teacher has 26 students.

Name _____ Class _____ Date _____

2-6 • Guided Problem Solving

GPS Student Page 93, Exercise 30:

You buy a poster and a framing kit. The total cost is $18.95. You have $7.05 left in your wallet. Write and solve an equation to find how much money was in your wallet before these purchases.

Read and Understand

1. What are you being asked to do?
   Find how much money was in your wallet
   before you made any purchases.

2. What will the variable represent in the equation?
   the amount of money in your wallet before the
   purchases

3. Circle the information you will need to solve.

Plan and Solve

4. How much did you pay for the poster and framing kit? $18.95

5. Write an expression for the amount in your wallet minus the amount you paid for the poster and the framing kit. Choose any variable for the amount in your wallet. *m* − 18.95

6. How much money was left in your wallet after the purchase?
   $7.05

7. Write an equation comparing the amounts in Steps 5 and 6.
   m − 18.95 = 7.05

8. What do you do to both sides of the equation to isolate the variable?
   add 18.95

9. Solve the equation.
   m = 26.00

10. How much money was in your wallet before these purchases? $26.00

Look Back and Check

11. Explain how you can check your answer. Then check your answer. 26 − 18.95 = 7.05; the answer checks

Solve Another Problem

12. Jim has saved $78. This is $23 more than his sister has saved. Write and solve an equation to find how much money his sister has saved?
    78 = 23 + *s*; *s* = $55

Name _____ Class _____ Date _____

2-7 • Guided Problem Solving

GPS Student Page 97, Exercise 30:

Biology An adult female elephant's height is about 5.5 times the length of her hind footprint. Use an equation to find the approximate height of an adult female elephant whose hind footprint is 1.5 feet long.

Read and Understand

1. What are you being asked to do?
   Write and solve an equation to find the height
   of an adult female elephant whose hind
   footprint is 1.5 feet long.

2. Circle the information you will need to solve.

3. The word set 5.5 *times* tells you to perform what operation?
   It tells you to multiply.

Plan and Solve

4. What is the length of the hind footprint of this particular adult female elephant? 1.5 feet

5. Write an expression to represent the phrase, 5.5 *times the length of the hind footprint.* 5.5 × 1.5

6. Write an equation for the height of the elephant. *h* = 5.5 × 1.5

7. What is the height of the elephant? 8.25 feet

Look Back and Check

8. Explain how you can check your answer. Does your answer check?
   Divide the answer by 5.5 and see if the result
   is 1.5; the answer checks.

Solve Another Problem

9. Angela makes 1.75 times the amount of money that Janet makes. If Janet makes $38,200, how much does Angela make? Write and solve an equation.
   1.75 × 38,200 = $66,850

Name _____ Class _____ Date _____

2-8 • Guided Problem Solving

GPS Student Page 102, Exercise 40:

Biology Suppose a single-celled animal splits in two after one hour. Each new cell also splits in two after one hour. How many cells will there be after eight hours? Write your answer using an exponent.

Read and Understand

1. What are you being asked to do?
   Find how many cells there will be after
   8 hours.

2. Explain what it means to write a number with an exponent.
   It means the number is the product of a
   number multiplied by itself more than 2 times.

Plan and Solve

3. How many cells are there after 3 hours?
   Write the number using an exponent. 2^3 cells

4. How many cells are there after 4 hours?
   Write the number using an exponent. 2^4 cells

5. How many cells are there after 6 hours?
   Write the number using an exponent. 2^6 cells

6. How many cells are there after 8 hours?
   Write the number using an exponent. 2^8 cells

Look Back and Check

7. Why is the exponent 8?
   because the cell doubled eight times

Solve Another Problem

8. An organism divides into 3 different organisms after the first hour. Each of those 3 organisms divide into 3 different organisms after the second hour. If this pattern continues, how many organisms are there after 4 hours? Write the number using an exponent.
   3^4 organisms

Activities and Projects

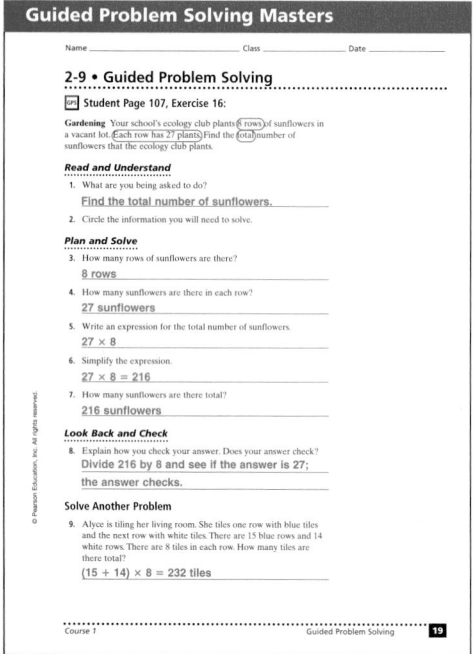

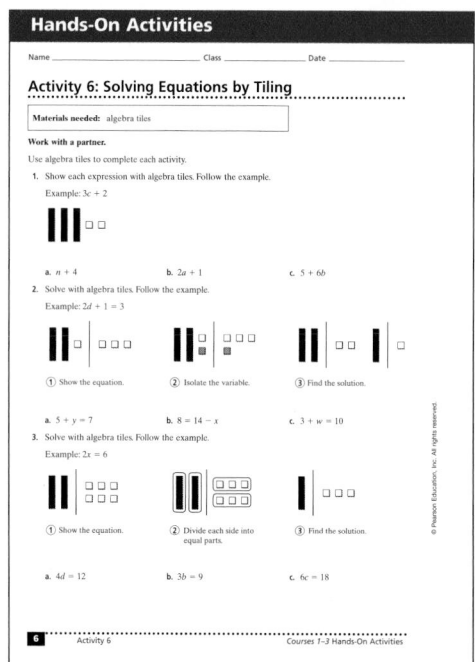

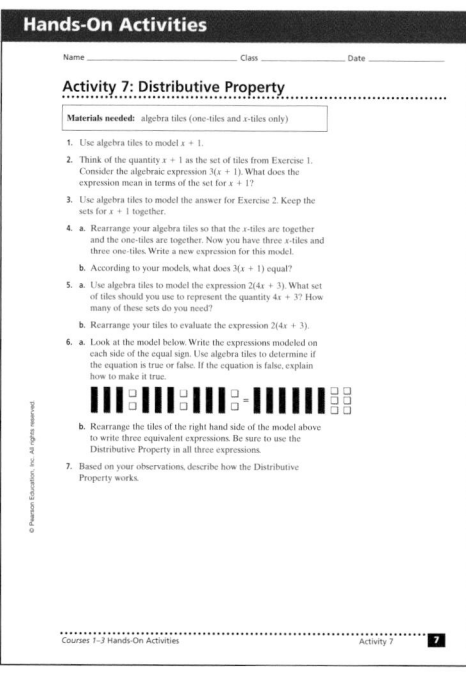

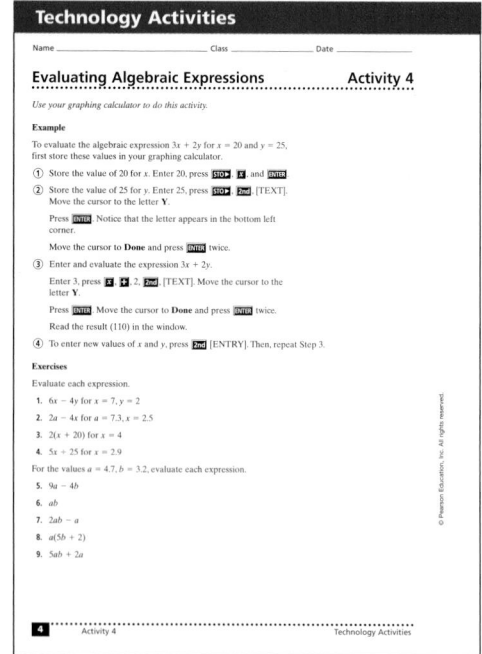

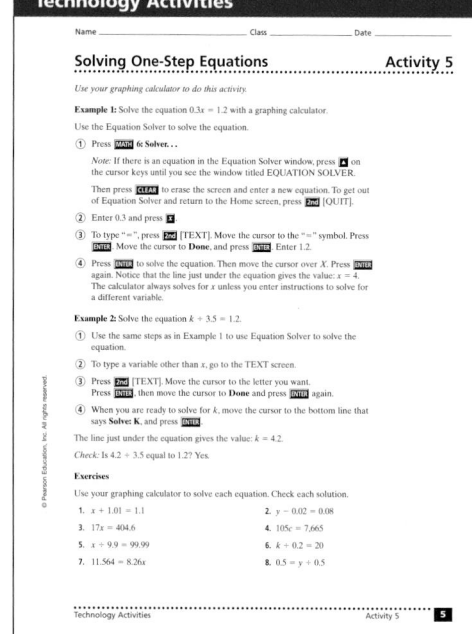

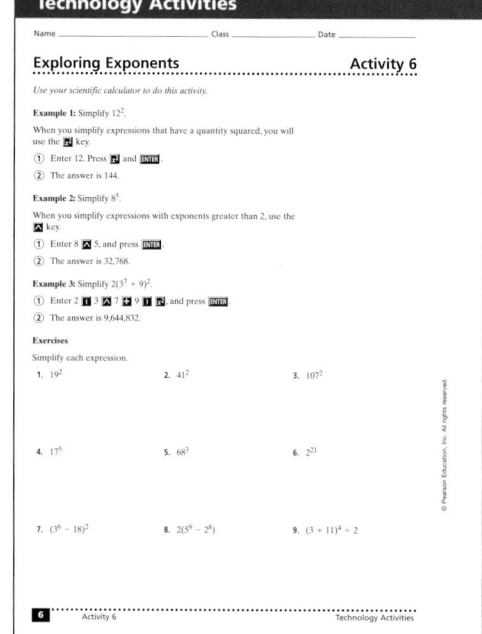

Chapter 2 Project: Stepping Stones

Building a Fort

Beginning the Chapter Project

Think about a historic building, such as one of the ancient pyramids or the Eiffel Tower. How many pieces of stone do you think were needed for the bottom of a pyramid compared to a layer near the top? Many building use mathematical patterns in their design.

For this project, you will build a model of a simple fort. You will record the amount of materials needed for each layer. You will look for patterns and write equations to describe the patterns.

Activities

Activity 1: Modeling Check students' work.

Start by planning a foundation for a fort like the one shown here. You can choose the shape and size of your foundation, but use no more than 30 objects. Suppose each object is worth $.01. Find the value of your foundation layer. Now add your first layer of the walls by stacking an object on top of each of the objects along the outer edge. What is the value of your fort with one layer in the wall?

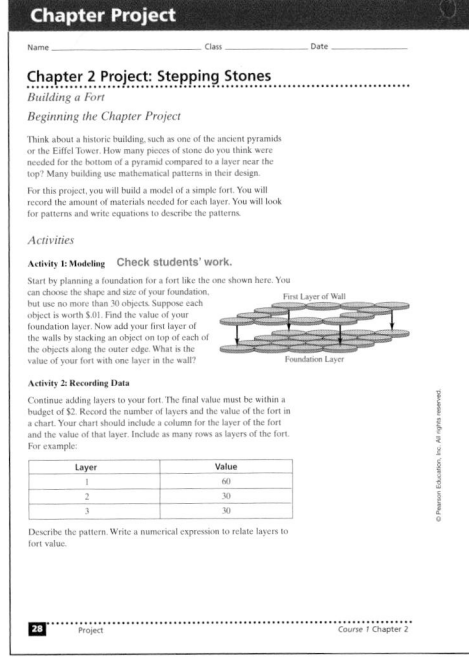

First Layer of Wall

Foundation Layer

Activity 2: Recording Data

Continue adding layers to your fort. The final value must be within a budget of $2. Record the number of layers and the value of the fort in a chart. Your chart should include a column for the layer of the fort and the value of that layer. Include as many rows as layers of the fort. For example:

Layer	Value
1	60
2	30
3	30

Describe the pattern. Write a numerical expression to relate layers to fort value.

Chapter 2 Project: Stepping Stones (continued)

Activity 3: Calculating

Write a sentence to describe how to calculate the value of the walls of your fort if you know the number of layers. Then write an equation to find the value of the fort.

Finishing the Project

Your final product will be a visual presentation of your fort, including a report with a diagram, a table, and calculations. You need to convince your teacher and the other members of the class that your fort is appropriate and within budget.

Be sure your work is neat and clear. Show your data and calculations. Write any explanations you think are necessary.

Reflect and Revise

Ask a classmate to review your project with you.
Is your fort a reasonable size and shape?
Is it within the $2 budget?
Are your numerical expression and equation correct?
If necessary, revise your project before presenting it to the class.

Extending the Project

Research some famous French forts, such as Fort Beauséjour. Draw a sketch of each fort that you study and provide the dimensions. Classify the shape of the fort and provide an explanation as to why that shape was used.

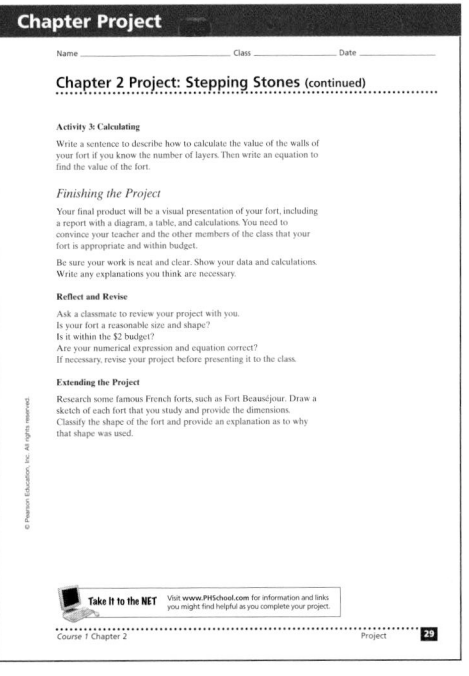

Take It to the NET Visit www.PHSchool.com for information and links you might find helpful as you complete your project.

Chapter Project Manager

Chapter 2: Stepping Stones

Getting Started

Read about the project. As you work on it, you will need several sheets of paper. If available, a spreadsheet program also can be used. Keep all your work for the project in a folder, along with this Project Manager.

Checklist	Suggestions
☐ Activity 1: modeling	☐ Check the value of one layer of the fort because this is the first number in your pattern.
☐ Activity 2: recording data	☐ Count the number of layers in your fort to determine the number of rows needed for the chart.
☐ Activity 3: calculating	☐ The expression you write should be true for all values in the chart.
☐ Recommendations	☐ Use pictures of actual forts or to add interest to your display.

Scoring Rubric

3 Your data is accurate and complete. Your numerical expressions and equation accurately and clearly describe the reasons for the pattern in the data. Your data, equations, diagrams, and explanations are all organized to give a clear and interesting picture of the pattern you discovered.

2 Your data may be missing some key elements. Your numerical expression and equation correctly describe the pattern, and the total value is within the $2 budget. Your work is complete and neat.

1 Much of the data is incorrect or incomplete. Your data tables, numerical expressions, and equations are complete, buy there are some errors in the equations or data.

0 Major elements of the project are incomplete or missing. Diagrams, data tables, numerical expressions, or equations are not complete.

Your Evaluation of Project Evaluate your work, based on the Scoring Rubric.

Teacher's Evaluation of Project

Transparencies

Chapter Project Teacher Notes

Chapter 2: Stepping Stones

About the Project

Students will have an opportunity to apply their knowledge of patterns and equations to building a fort.

Introducing the Project

Have students practice designing a fort using cubes. Ask students:

- *If your foundation is rectangular, what are all the combinations of foundation lengths and widths that use exactly 30 cubes?*

- *Have students imagine building a wall of cubes on the perimeter of each of these rectangular foundations. Which of these combinations makes a fort with walls and an interior room?*

Activity 1: Modeling

Have students compare the foundation of their fort with a real foundation.

Activity 2: Recording Data

Challenge students to describe the pattern with a word phrase. Then have them write the phrase as a variable expression.

Activity 3: Calculating

To prompt students, ask: *How many layers have the same number of coins? How can you show this in a mathematical expression?*

Finishing the Project

You may wish to plan a project day on which students share their completed projects. Encourage students to explain their process as well as their products.

- Have students review their methods for building their forts, making their charts, and calculating the value of each layer.

- Ask students to share any insight they gained when completing the project, such as the relationship between amount and cost.

Take It to the NET Visit www.PHSchool.com for information, student links, and teacher support for this project.

Problem of the Day	Lesson 2-7

Determine a rule for a pattern. Make the pattern using a set of three drawings using squares. Have the first drawing for the pattern be one square. Use your rule for your pattern to determine how to make drawings two and three.

Check students' work.

Problem of the Day	Lesson 2-8

Shaun told two students a number. They each told three other students who each told two other students. How many students, including Shaun, know Shaun's number?

Answer

21

Problem of the Day	Lesson 2-9

Jake paid $92.40 for 11 yards of fabric. How much did the fabric cost per yard?

Answer

$8.40

Problem of the Day	Lesson 2-4

Use this data to answer the following questions:

June   13 years, 10 months
Kari   15 years, 5 months
Steve   15 years, 9 months

a. Who is the oldest?   b. How much older is Kari than June?

Answers

a. Steve   b. 1 year 7 months

Problem of the Day	Lesson 2-5

Write the next three multiples for each sequence.

a. 3, 6, 9, . . .   b. 12, 24, 36, . . .   c. 14, 28, 42, . . .

Answers

a. 12, 15, 18
b. 48, 60, 72
c. 56, 70, 84

Problem of the Day	Lesson 2-6

Estimate the following:

a. 19.055 − 4.41

b. 12.89 − 5.24

c. 4.63 + 7.71

Answers

a. 15   b. 8   c. 13

Problem of the Day — Lesson 2-1

There are 3 feet in 1 yard and 12 inches in 1 foot. Express 3 yards and 1 foot in inches.

Answer

120 inches

Problem of the Day — Lesson 2-2

Find the product of the numbers in each line.

a. 1, 2　　　b. 1, 2, 3　　　c. 1, 2, 3, 4

Answers

a. 2　　　b. 6　　　c. 24

Problem of the Day — Lesson 2-3

Erica had a piece of red licorice 15 inches long. She cut it into 10 equal pieces. How long is each piece?

Answer

$1\frac{1}{2}$ inches

Check Skills You'll Need — Lesson 2-1

Order each set of decimals from least to greatest.

1. 0.105, 0.0105, 10.5　　　2. 3.331, 3.1, 3.31

3. 9.06, 9.6, 9.09　　　4. 20.06, 26.0, 0.602

5. 100.1, 101.0, 100.01　　　6. 0.99, 0.4, 0.35

Solutions

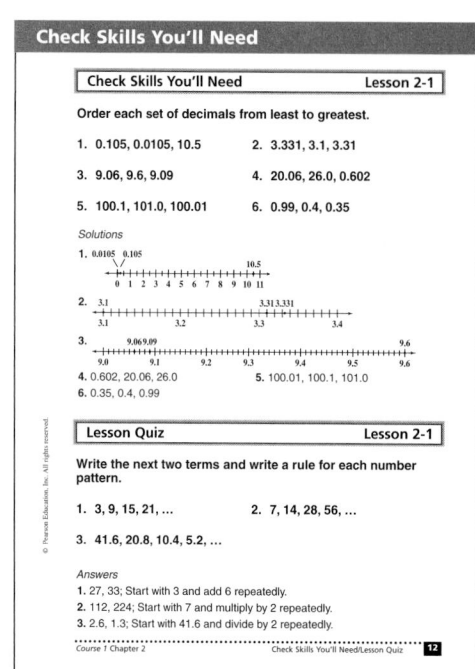

4. 0.602, 20.06, 26.0　　　5. 100.01, 100.1, 101.0

6. 0.35, 0.4, 0.99

Lesson Quiz — Lesson 2-1

Write the next two terms and write a rule for each number pattern.

1. 3, 9, 15, 21, …　　　2. 7, 14, 28, 56, …

3. 41.6, 20.8, 10.4, 5.2, …

Answers

1. 27, 33; Start with 3 and add 6 repeatedly.
2. 112, 224; Start with 7 and multiply by 2 repeatedly.
3. 2.6, 1.3; Start with 41.6 and divide by 2 repeatedly.

Sample page; see p. G for complete list.

Additional Examples — Lesson 2-1

1 EXAMPLE Write the next two terms in this number pattern.

5, 12, 19, 26, …

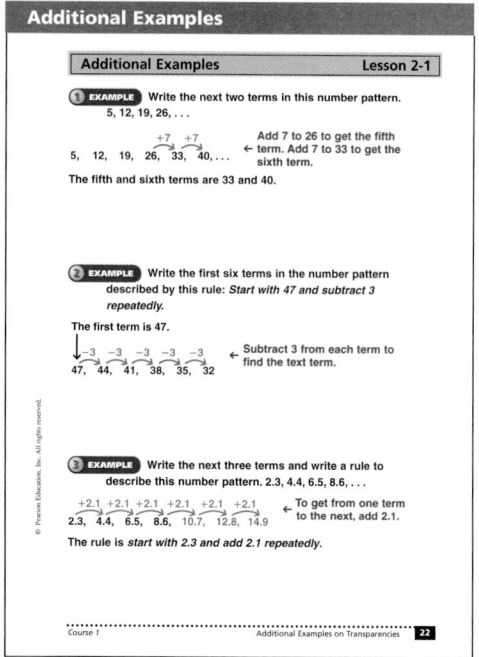

Add 7 to 26 to get the fifth term. Add 7 to 33 to get the sixth term.

The fifth and sixth terms are 33 and 40.

2 EXAMPLE Write the first six terms in the number pattern described by this rule: *Start with 47 and subtract 3 repeatedly.*

The first term is 47.

47, 44, 41, 38, 35, 32

Subtract 3 from each term to find the next term.

3 EXAMPLE Write the next three terms and write a rule to describe this number pattern. 2.3, 4.4, 6.5, 8.6, …

2.3, 4.4, 6.5, 8.6, 10.7, 12.8, 14.9

To get from one term to the next, add 2.1.

The rule is *start with 2.3 and add 2.1 repeatedly.*

Sample page; see p. G for complete list.

Algebra Tiles — 37

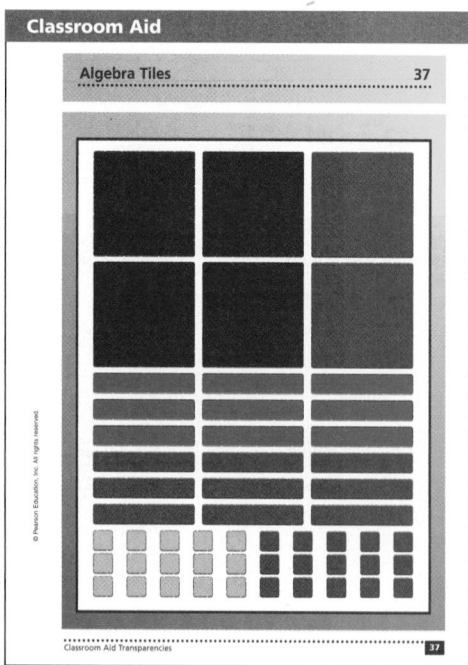

Answers for Lesson *On Your Own* Exercises

1. Sample: 1 : 4, 1 to 4, $\frac{1}{4}$
2. Sample: 24 to 25, 24 : 25, $\frac{24}{25}$
3. 12 to 4, $\frac{12}{4}$
4. 8 : 10, $\frac{8}{10}$
5. 5 to 4, 5 : 4
6. 13 to 8, $\frac{13}{8}$
7. 21 to 28, $\frac{21}{28}$
8. 8 to 18, 8 : 18
9. B
10a. 7 : 15, 7 to 15, $\frac{7}{15}$
　b. 7 : 8, 7 to 8, $\frac{7}{8}$
11a. 23 : 19, 23 to 19, $\frac{23}{19}$
　b. 19 : 42, 19 to 42, $\frac{19}{42}$
12. No; the new ratio is 16 : 11.
13. 0.9　　14. 3.6　　15. 2.7　　16. 0.7
17. 0.5　　18. 1.0
19a. 225 : 3, 455 : 7
　b. 75, 65
　c. Answers may vary. Sample: Train A travels 75 mi/h while Train B travels 65 mi/h
20a. $\frac{13}{18}$
　b. $\frac{169}{324}$
　c. The ratio of areas is the square of the ratio of sides.
21–26. Answers may vary. Samples are given.
21. 13 : 27, 78 : 162
22. 6 to 22, 3 to 11
23. $\frac{106}{50}$, $\frac{53}{25}$
24. $\frac{7}{1}$, $\frac{14}{2}$
25. $\frac{9}{18}$, $\frac{3}{6}$
26. 2 : 12, 3 : 18
27. 5 : 2
28. 1 to 9
29. $\frac{1}{50}$
30. 4 to 1
31. 1 : 2
32. $\frac{1}{3}$
33. 25 to 1
34a. 101 and 107
　b. 7 : 12
35a. 8 : 4
　b. 10 qt antifreeze, 5 qt water

Sample page; see p. G for complete list.

Check Skills You'll Need — Lesson 2-2

Find the value of each expression.

1. $40 - 16 \div 2$　　　2. $3 \times 5 + 12 \div 3$

3. $7 \times (9.5 - 3.2)$　　　4. $48 \div (5.8 + 6.2)$

Solutions

1. $40 - 16 \div 2 = 40 - 8$
　　$= 32$
2. $3 \times 5 + 12 \div 3 = 15 + 4$
　　$= 19$
3. $7 \times (9.5 - 3.2) = 7 \times 6.3$
　　$= 44.1$
4. $48 \div (5.8 + 6.2) = 48 \div 12$
　　$= 4$

Lesson Quiz — Lesson 2-2

Evaluate each expression for $n = 9$.

1. $n + 15$　　2. $4n - 10$　　3. $3(6 + n)$　　4. $2n \div 3$

Answers

1. 24　　2. 26　　3. 45　　4. 6

Sample page; see p. G for complete list.

Assessment

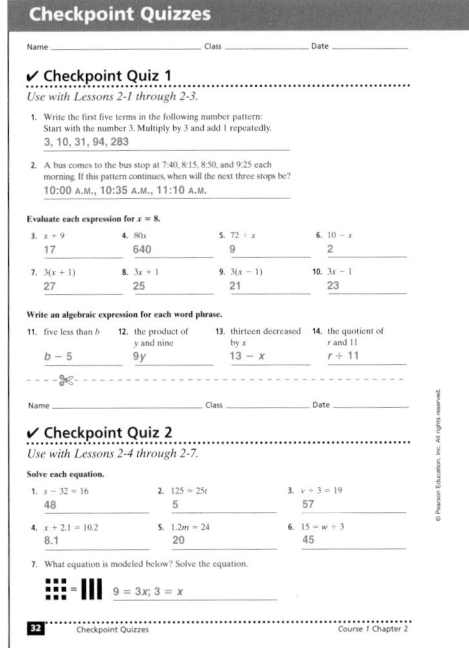

Checkpoint Quizzes

Name _____ Class _____ Date _____

✔ Checkpoint Quiz 1

Use with Lessons 2-1 through 2-3.

1. Write the first five terms in the following number pattern:
Start with the number 3. Multiply by 3 and add 1 repeatedly.
3, 10, 31, 94, 283

2. A bus comes to the bus stop at 7:40, 8:15, 8:50, and 9:25 each morning. If this pattern continues, when will the next three stops be?
10:00 A.M., 10:35 A.M., 11:10 A.M.

Evaluate each expression for $x = 8$.

3. $x + 9$ — **17**
4. $80x$ — **640**
5. $72 \div x$ — **9**
6. $10 - x$ — **2**
7. $3(x + 1)$ — **27**
8. $3x + 1$ — **25**
9. $3(x - 1)$ — **21**
10. $3x - 1$ — **23**

Write an algebraic expression for each word phrase.

11. five less than b — **$b - 5$**
12. the product of y and nine — **$9y$**
13. thirteen decreased by x — **$13 - x$**
14. the quotient of r and 11 — **$r \div 11$**

Name _____ Class _____ Date _____

✔ Checkpoint Quiz 2

Use with Lessons 2-4 through 2-7.

Solve each equation.

1. $s - 32 = 16$ — **48**
2. $125 = 25t$ — **5**
3. $v + 3 = 19$ — **57**
4. $x + 2.1 = 10.2$ — **8.1**
5. $1.2m = 24$ — **20**
6. $15 = w + 3$ — **45**

7. What equation is modeled below? Solve the equation.
$9 = 3x; 3 = x$

32 Checkpoint Quizzes — Course 1 Chapter 2

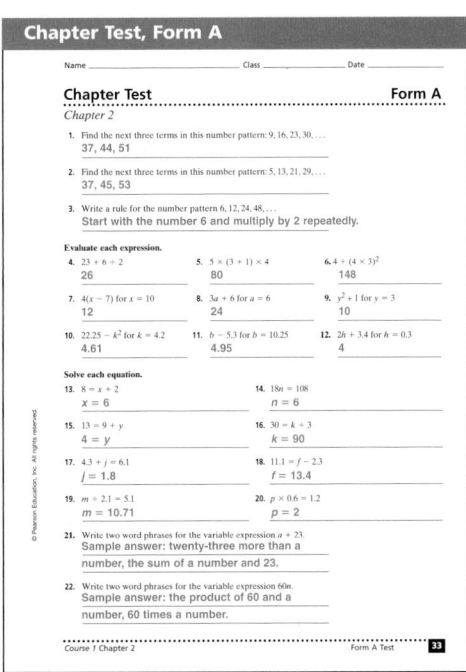

Chapter Test, Form A

Name _____ Class _____ Date _____

Chapter Test — Form A
Chapter 2

1. Find the next three terms in this number pattern: 9, 16, 23, 30, . . .
37, 44, 51

2. Find the next three terms in this number pattern: 5, 13, 21, 29, . . .
37, 45, 53

3. Write a rule for the number pattern 6, 12, 24, 48, . . .
Start with the number 6 and multiply by 2 repeatedly.

Evaluate each expression.

4. $23 \div 6 + 2$ — **26**
5. $5 \times (3 + 1) \times 4$ — **80**
6. $4 + (4 \times 3)^2$ — **148**
7. $4(x - 7)$ for $x = 10$ — **12**
8. $3a + 6$ for $a = 6$ — **24**
9. $y^2 + 1$ for $y = 3$ — **10**
10. $22.25 - k^2$ for $k = 4.2$ — **4.61**
11. $b - 5.3$ for $b = 10.25$ — **4.95**
12. $2h + 3.4$ for $h = 0.3$ — **4**

Solve each equation.

13. $8 = x + 2$ — **$x = 6$**
14. $18n = 108$ — **$n = 6$**
15. $13 = 9 + y$ — **$4 = y$**
16. $30 = k + 3$ — **$k = 90$**
17. $4.3 + j = 6.1$ — **$j = 1.8$**
18. $11.1 = f - 2.3$ — **$f = 13.4$**
19. $m \div 2.1 = 5.1$ — **$m = 10.71$**
20. $p \times 0.6 = 1.2$ — **$p = 2$**

21. Write two word phrases for the variable expression $a + 23$.
Sample answer: twenty-three more than a number, the sum of a number and 23.

22. Write two word phrases for the variable expression 60n.
Sample answer: the product of 60 and a number, 60 times a number.

Course 1 Chapter 2 — Form A Test 33

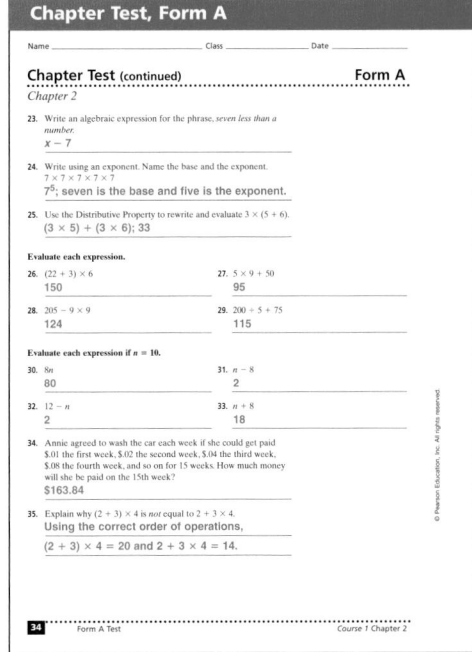

Chapter Test, Form A

Name _____ Class _____ Date _____

Chapter Test (continued) — Form A
Chapter 2

23. Write an algebraic expression for the phrase, *seven less than a number.*
$x - 7$

24. Write using an exponent. Name the base and the exponent.
$7 \times 7 \times 7 \times 7 \times 7$
7^5; seven is the base and five is the exponent.

25. Use the Distributive Property to rewrite and evaluate $3 \times (5 + 6)$.
$(3 \times 5) + (3 \times 6); 33$

Evaluate each expression.

26. $(22 + 3) \times 6$ — **150**
27. $5 \times 9 + 50$ — **95**
28. $205 - 9 \times 9$ — **124**
29. $200 \div 5 + 75$ — **115**

Evaluate each expression if $n = 10$.

30. $8n$ — **80**
31. $n - 8$ — **2**
32. $12 - n$ — **2**
33. $n + 8$ — **18**

34. Annie agreed to wash the car each week if she could get paid $.01 the first week, $.02 the second week, $.04 the third week, $.08 the fourth week, and so on for 15 weeks. How much money will she be paid on the 15th week?
$163.84

35. Explain why $(2 + 3) \times 4$ is *not* equal to $2 + 3 \times 4$.
Using the correct order of operations, $(2 + 3) \times 4 = 20$ and $2 + 3 \times 4 = 14$.

34 Form A Test — Course 1 Chapter 2

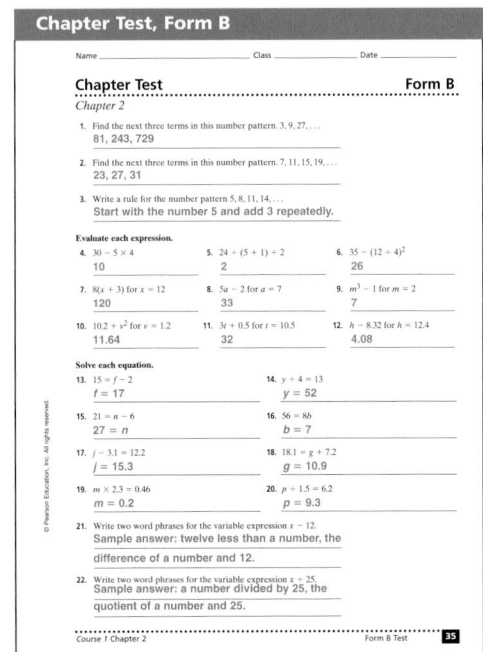

Chapter Test, Form B

Name _____ Class _____ Date _____

Chapter Test — Form B
Chapter 2

1. Find the next three terms in this number pattern: 3, 9, 27, . . .
81, 243, 729

2. Find the next three terms in this number pattern: 7, 11, 15, 19, . . .
23, 27, 31

3. Write a rule for the number pattern 5, 8, 11, 14, . . .
Start with the number 5 and add 3 repeatedly.

Evaluate each expression.

4. $30 - 5 \times 4$ — **10**
5. $24 \div (5 + 1) \div 2$ — **2**
6. $35 - (12 \div 4)^2$ — **26**
7. $8(x + 3)$ for $x = 12$ — **120**
8. $5a - 2$ for $a = 7$ — **33**
9. $m^3 - 1$ for $m = 2$ — **7**
10. $10.2 + v^2$ for $v = 1.2$ — **11.64**
11. $3x + 0.5$ for $t = 10.5$ — **32**
12. $h - 8.32$ for $h = 12.4$ — **4.08**

Solve each equation.

13. $15 = f - 2$ — **$f = 17$**
14. $y \div 4 = 13$ — **$y = 52$**
15. $21 = n - 6$ — **$27 = n$**
16. $56 = 8b$ — **$b = 7$**
17. $j - 3.1 = 12.2$ — **$j = 15.3$**
18. $18.1 = g + 7.2$ — **$g = 10.9$**
19. $m \times 2.3 = 0.46$ — **$m = 0.2$**
20. $p + 1.5 = 6.2$ — **$p = 9.3$**

21. Write two word phrases for the variable expression $x - 12$.
Sample answer: twelve less than a number, the difference of a number and 12.

22. Write two word phrases for the variable expression $x + 25$.
Sample answer: a number divided by 25, the quotient of a number and 25.

Course 1 Chapter 2 — Form B Test 35

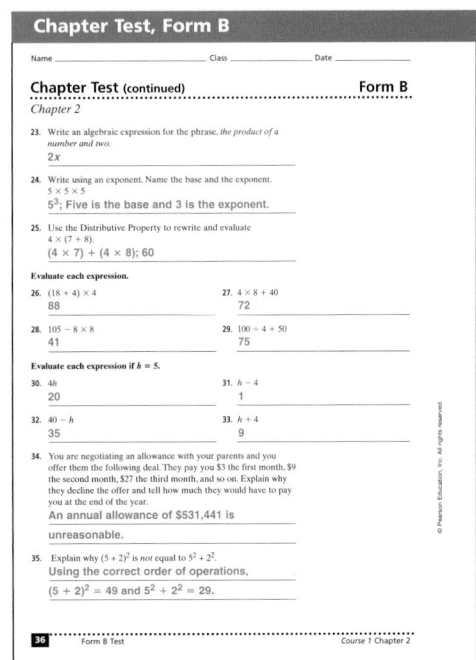

Chapter Test, Form B

Name _____ Class _____ Date _____

Chapter Test (continued) — Form B
Chapter 2

23. Write an algebraic expression for the phrase, *the product of a number and two.*
$2x$

24. Write using an exponent. Name the base and the exponent.
$5 \times 5 \times 5$
5^3; Five is the base and 3 is the exponent.

25. Use the Distributive Property to rewrite and evaluate $4 \times (7 + 8)$.
$(4 \times 7) + (4 \times 8); 60$

Evaluate each expression.

26. $(18 + 4) \times 4$ — **88**
27. $4 \times 8 + 40$ — **72**
28. $105 - 8 \times 8$ — **41**
29. $100 \div 4 + 50$ — **75**

Evaluate each expression if $h = 5$.

30. $4h$ — **20**
31. $h - 4$ — **1**
32. $40 - h$ — **35**
33. $h + 4$ — **9**

34. You are negotiating an allowance with your parents and you offer them the following deal. They pay you $3 the first month, $9 the second month, $27 the third month, and so on. Explain why they decline the offer and tell how much they would have to pay you at the end of the year.
An annual allowance of $531,441 is unreasonable.

35. Explain why $(5 + 2)^2$ is *not* equal to $5^2 + 2^2$.
Using the correct order of operations, $(5 + 2)^2 = 49$ and $5^2 + 2^2 = 29$.

36 Form B Test — Course 1 Chapter 2

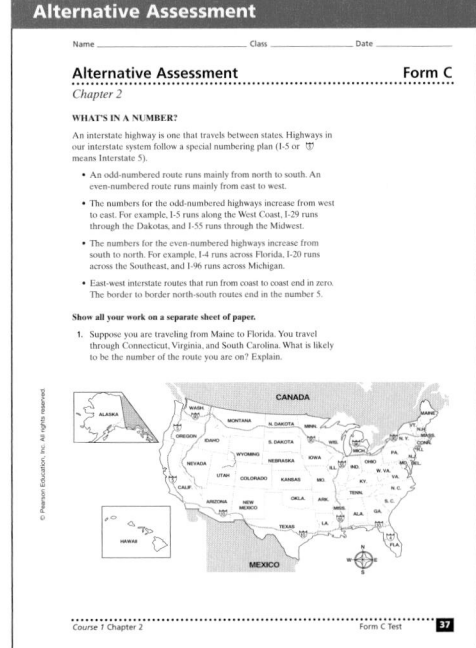

Alternative Assessment

Name _____ Class _____ Date _____

Alternative Assessment — Form C
Chapter 2

WHAT'S IN A NUMBER?

An interstate highway is one that travels between states. Highways in our interstate system follow a special numbering plan (I-5 or Ⓘ⑤ means Interstate 5).

- An odd-numbered route runs mainly from north to south. An even-numbered route runs mainly from east to west.
- The numbers for the odd-numbered highways increase from west to east. For example, I-5 runs along the West Coast, I-29 runs through the Dakotas, and I-55 runs through the Midwest.
- The numbers for the even-numbered highways increase from south to north. For example, I-4 runs across Florida, I-20 runs across the Southeast, and I-96 runs across Michigan.
- East-west interstate routes that run from coast to coast end in zero. The border to border north-south routes end in the number 5.

Show all your work on a separate sheet of paper.

1. Suppose you are traveling from Maine to Florida. You travel through Connecticut, Virginia, and South Carolina. What is likely to be the number of the route you are on? Explain.

Course 1 Chapter 2 — Form C Test 37

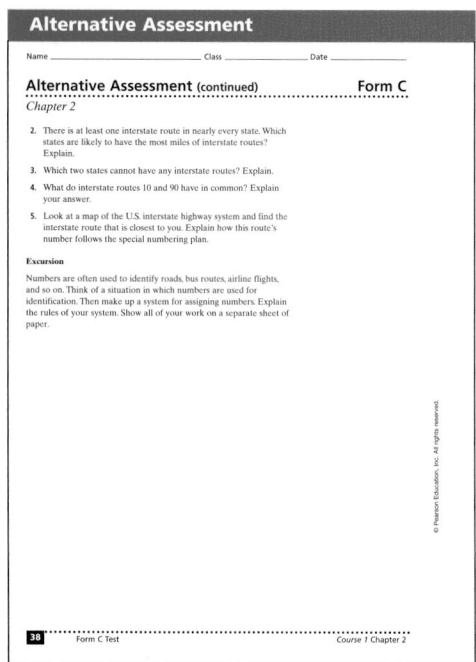

Name _____ Class _____ Date _____

Alternative Assessment (continued) Form C
Chapter 2

2. There is at least one interstate route in nearly every state. Which states are likely to have the most miles of interstate routes? Explain.

3. Which two states cannot have any interstate routes? Explain.

4. What do interstate routes 10 and 90 have in common? Explain your answer.

5. Look at a map of the U.S. interstate highway system and find the interstate route that is closest to you. Explain how this route's number follows the special numbering plan.

Excursion

Numbers are often used to identify roads, bus routes, airline flights, and so on. Think of a situation in which numbers are used for identification. Then make up a system for assigning numbers. Explain the rules of your system. Show all of your work on a separate sheet of paper.

Available in Spanish

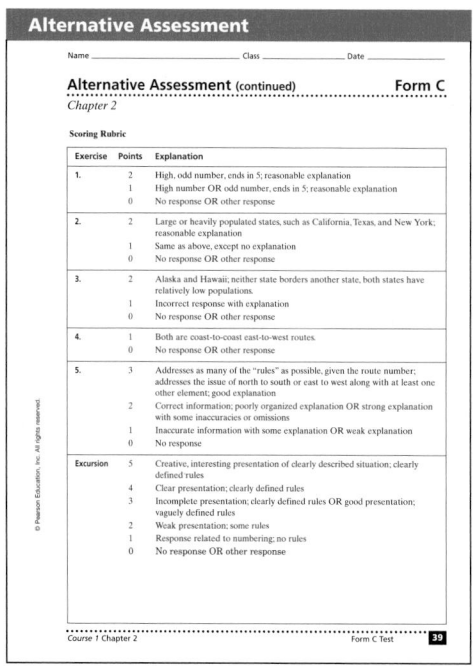

Name _____ Class _____ Date _____

Alternative Assessment (continued) Form C
Chapter 2

Scoring Rubric

Exercise	Points	Explanation
1.	2	High, odd number, ends in 5; reasonable explanation
	1	High number OR odd number, ends in 5; reasonable explanation
	0	No response OR other response
2.	2	Large or heavily populated states, such as California, Texas, and New York; reasonable explanation
	1	Same as above, except no explanation
	0	No response OR other response
3.	2	Alaska and Hawaii; neither state borders another state, both states have relatively low populations.
	1	Incorrect response with explanation
	0	No response OR other response
4.	1	Both are coast-to-coast east-to-west routes.
	0	No response OR other response
5.	3	Addresses as many of the "rules" as possible, given the route number; addresses the issue of north to south or east to west along with at least one other element; good explanation
	2	Correct information; poorly organized explanation OR strong explanation with some inaccuracies or omissions
	1	Inaccurate information with some explanation OR weak explanation
	0	No response
Excursion	5	Creative, interesting presentation of clearly described situation; clearly defined rules
	4	Clear presentation; clearly defined rules
	3	Incomplete presentation; clearly defined rules OR good presentation; vaguely defined rules
	2	Weak presentation; some rules
	1	Response related to numbering; no rules
	0	No response OR other response

Available in Spanish

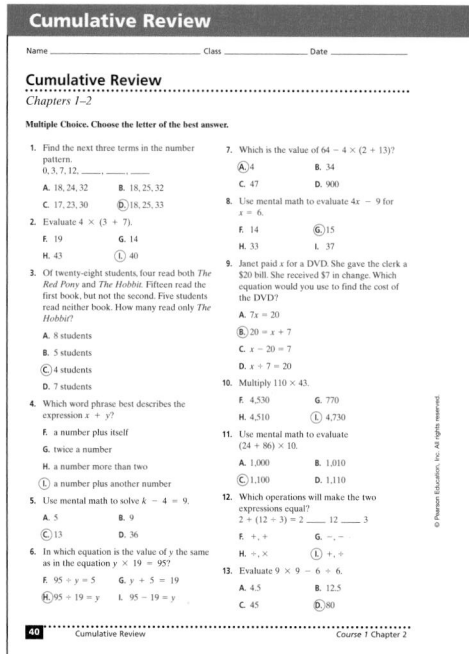

Name _____ Class _____ Date _____

Cumulative Review
Chapters 1–2

Multiple Choice. Choose the letter of the best answer.

1. Find the next three terms in the number pattern.
   0, 3, 7, 12, ____, ____, ____
   - A. 18, 24, 32
   - B. 18, 25, 32
   - C. 17, 23, 30
   - (D.) 18, 25, 33

2. Evaluate $4 \times (3 + 7)$.
   - F. 19
   - G. 14
   - H. 43
   - (I.) 40

3. Of twenty-eight students, four read both *The Red Pony* and *The Hobbit*. Fifteen read the first book, but not the second. Five students read neither book. How many read only *The Hobbit*?
   - A. 8 students
   - B. 5 students
   - (C.) 4 students
   - D. 7 students

4. Which word phrase best describes the expression $x + y$?
   - F. a number plus itself
   - G. twice a number
   - H. a number more than two
   - (I.) a number plus another number

5. Use mental math to solve $k - 4 = 9$.
   - A. 5
   - B. 9
   - (C.) 13
   - D. 36

6. In which equation is the value of *y* the same as in the equation $y \times 19 = 95$?
   - F. $95 \div y = 5$
   - G. $y + 5 = 19$
   - (H.) $95 \div 19 = y$
   - I. $95 - 19 = y$

7. Which is the value of $64 - 4 \times (2 + 13)$?
   - (A.) 4
   - B. 34
   - C. 47
   - D. 900

8. Use mental math to evaluate $4x - 9$ for $x = 6$.
   - F. 14
   - (G.) 15
   - H. 33
   - I. 37

9. Janet paid *x* for a DVD. She gave the clerk a $20 bill. She received $7 in change. Which equation would you use to find the cost of the DVD?
   - A. $7x = 20$
   - (B.) $20 = x + 7$
   - C. $x - 20 = 7$
   - D. $x + 7 = 20$

10. Multiply 110×43.
    - F. 4,530
    - G. 770
    - H. 4,510
    - (I.) 4,730

11. Use mental math to evaluate $(24 + 86) \times 10$.
    - A. 1,000
    - B. 1,010
    - (C.) 1,100
    - D. 1,110

12. Which operations will make the two expressions equal?
    $2 + (12 \div 3) = 2 \_\_\_ 12 \_\_\_ 3$
    - F. $+, +$
    - G. $-, -$
    - H. $\div, \times$
    - (I.) $+, +$

13. Evaluate $9 \times 9 - 6 \div 6$.
    - A. 4.5
    - B. 12.5
    - C. 45
    - (D.) 80

Available in Spanish

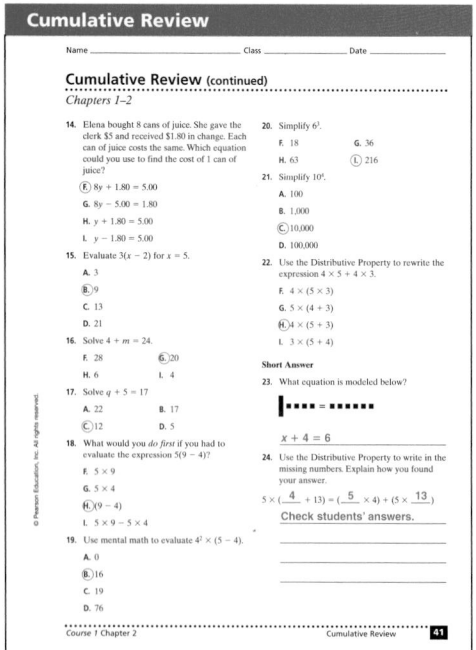

Name _____ Class _____ Date _____

Cumulative Review (continued)
Chapters 1–2

14. Elena bought 8 cans of juice. She gave the clerk $5 and received $1.80 in change. Each can of juice costs the same. Which equation could you use to find the cost of 1 can of juice?
    - (F.) $8y + 1.80 = 5.00$
    - G. $8y - 5.00 = 1.80$
    - H. $y + 1.80 = 5.00$
    - I. $y - 1.80 = 5.00$

15. Evaluate $3(x - 2)$ for $x = 5$.
    - A. 3
    - (B.) 9
    - C. 13
    - D. 21

16. Solve $4 + m = 24$.
    - F. 28
    - (G.) 20
    - H. 6
    - I. 4

17. Solve $q + 5 = 17$.
    - A. 22
    - B. 17
    - (C.) 12
    - D. 5

18. What would you *do first* if you had to evaluate the expression $5(9 - 4)$?
    - F. 5×9
    - G. 5×4
    - (H.) $(9 - 4)$
    - I. $5 \times 9 - 5 \times 4$

19. Use mental math to evaluate $4^2 \times (5 - 4)$.
    - A. 0
    - (B.) 16
    - C. 19
    - D. 76

20. Simplify 6^2.
    - F. 18
    - G. 36
    - H. 63
    - (I.) 216

21. Simplify 10^4.
    - A. 100
    - B. 1,000
    - (C.) 10,000
    - D. 100,000

22. Use the Distributive Property to rewrite the expression $4 \times 5 + 4 \times 3$.
    - F. $4 \times (5 \times 3)$
    - G. $5 \times (4 + 3)$
    - (H.) $4 \times (5 + 3)$
    - I. $3 \times (5 + 4)$

Short Answer

23. What equation is modeled below?

    ▮ ■■■■■■■

    $x + 4 = 6$

24. Use the Distributive Property to write in the missing numbers. Explain how you found your answer.

    $5 \times (\underline{4} + 13) = (\underline{5} \times 4) + (5 \times \underline{13})$

    Check students' answers.
    _____
    _____
    _____

Available in Spanish

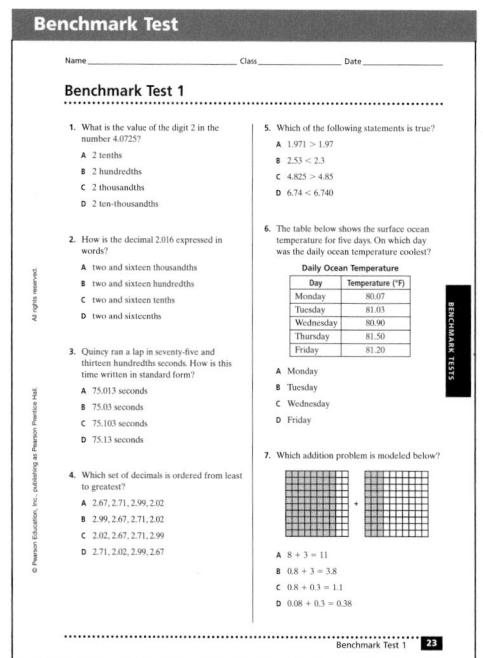

Name _____ Class _____ Date _____

Benchmark Test 1

1. What is the value of the digit 2 in the number 4.0725?
   - A 2 tenths
   - B 2 hundredths
   - C 2 thousandths
   - D 2 ten-thousandths

2. How is the decimal 2.016 expressed in words?
   - A two and sixteen thousandths
   - B two and sixteen hundredths
   - C two and sixteen tenths
   - D two and sixteenths

3. Quincy ran a lap in seventy-five and thirteen hundredths seconds. How is this time written in standard form?
   - A 75.013 seconds
   - B 75.03 seconds
   - C 75.103 seconds
   - D 75.13 seconds

4. Which set of decimals is ordered from least to greatest?
   - A 2.67, 2.71, 2.99, 2.02
   - B 2.99, 2.67, 2.71, 2.02
   - C 2.02, 2.67, 2.71, 2.99
   - D 2.71, 2.02, 2.99, 2.67

5. Which of the following statements is true?
   - A $1.971 > 1.97$
   - B $2.53 < 2.3$
   - C $4.825 > 4.85$
   - D $6.74 < 6.740$

6. The table below shows the surface ocean temperature for five days. On which day was the daily ocean temperature coolest?

   Daily Ocean Temperature

Day	Temperature (°F)
Monday	80.07
Tuesday	81.03
Wednesday	80.90
Thursday	81.50
Friday	81.20

   - A Monday
   - B Tuesday
   - C Wednesday
   - D Friday

7. Which addition problem is modeled below?

   - A $8 + 3 = 11$
   - B $0.8 + 3 = 3.8$
   - C $0.8 + 0.3 = 1.1$
   - D $0.08 + 0.3 = 0.38$

BENCHMARK TESTS

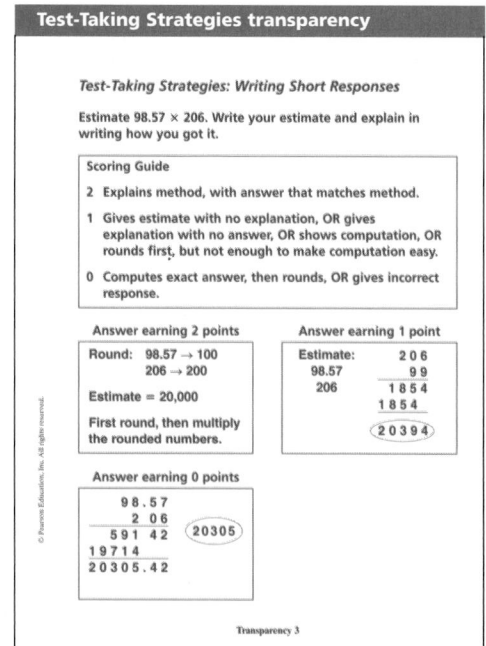

Test-Taking Strategies: Writing Short Responses

Estimate 98.57×206. Write your estimate and explain in writing how you got it.

Scoring Guide

2 Explains method, with answer that matches method.

1 Gives estimate with no explanation, OR gives explanation with no answer, OR shows computation, OR rounds first, but not enough to make computation easy.

0 Computes exact answer, then rounds, OR gives incorrect response.

Answer earning 2 points

Round: $98.57 \rightarrow 100$
$206 \rightarrow 200$

Estimate = 20,000

First round, then multiply the rounded numbers.

Answer earning 1 point

Estimate:
```
  2 0 6
 ×  9 9
 1 8 5 4
1 8 5 4
2 0 3 9 4
```
(20394)

Answer earning 0 points
```
  9 8.5 7
×   2  0 6
 5 9 1 4 2    (20305)
1 9 7 1 4
2 0 3 0 5.4 2
```

Transparency 3

On PH Website

Test-Taking Strategies worksheet

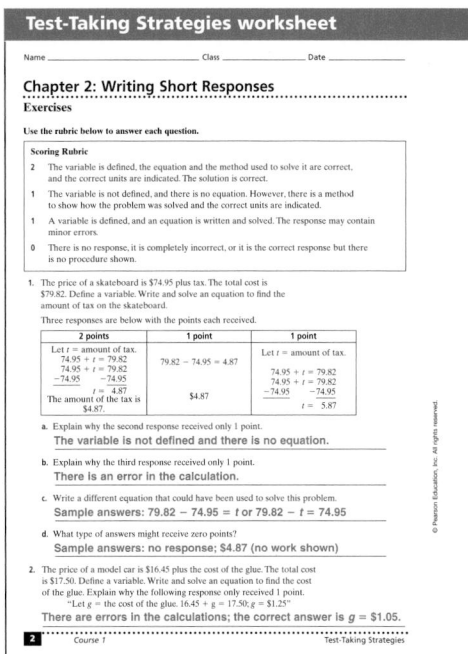

Name ____________ Class ____________ Date ____________

Chapter 2: Writing Short Responses

Exercises

Use the rubric below to answer each question.

Scoring Rubric

2 The variable is defined, the equation and the method used to solve it are correct, and the correct units are indicated. The solution is correct.

1 The variable is not defined, and there is no equation. However, there is a method to show how the problem was solved and the correct units are indicated.

1 A variable is defined, and an equation is written and solved. The response may contain minor errors.

0 There is no response, it is completely incorrect, or it is the correct response but there is no procedure shown.

1. The price of a skateboard is \$74.95 plus tax. The total cost is \$79.82. Define a variable. Write and solve an equation to find the amount of tax on the skateboard.

   Three responses are below with the points each received.

2 points	1 point	1 point
Let t = amount of tax. $74.95 + t = 79.82$ $74.95 + t = 79.82$ $-74.95 \quad -74.95$ $t = 4.87$ The amount of the tax is \$4.87.	$79.82 - 74.95 = 4.87$ \$4.87	Let t = amount of tax. $74.95 + t = 79.82$ $74.95 + t = 79.82$ $-74.95 \quad -74.95$ $t = 5.87$

   a. Explain why the second response received only 1 point.
   The variable is not defined and there is no equation.

   b. Explain why the third response received only 1 point.
   There is an error in the calculation.

   c. Write a different equation that could have been used to solve this problem.
   Sample answers: $79.82 - 74.95 = t$ or $79.82 - t = 74.95$

   d. What type of answers might receive zero points?
   Sample answers: no response; \$4.87 (no work shown)

2. The price of a model car is \$16.45 plus the cost of the glue. The total cost is \$17.50. Define a variable. Write and solve an equation to find the cost of the glue. Explain why the following response only received 1 point.
   "Let g = the cost of the glue. $16.45 + g = 17.50$; $g = \$1.25$"
   There are errors in the calculations; the correct answer is $g = \$1.05$.

2 Course 1 Test-Taking Strategies

Home Activities

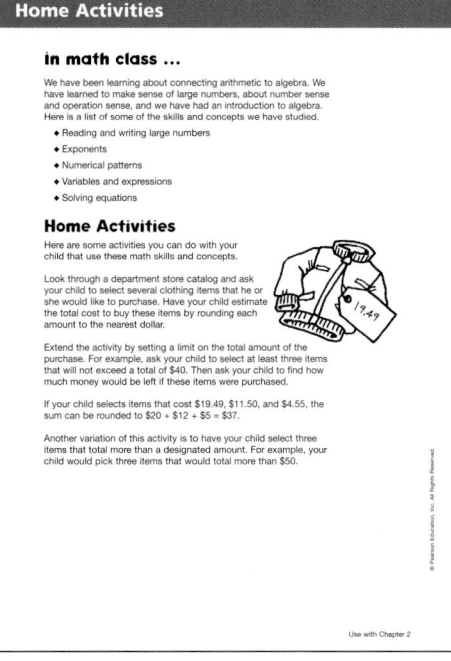

in math class ...

We have been learning about connecting arithmetic to algebra. We have learned to make sense of large numbers, about number sense and operation sense, and we have had an introduction to algebra. Here is a list of some of the skills and concepts we have studied.

- Reading and writing large numbers
- Exponents
- Numerical patterns
- Variables and expressions
- Solving equations

Home Activities

Here are some activities you can do with your child that use these math skills and concepts.

Look through a department store catalog and ask your child to select several clothing items that he or she would like to purchase. Have your child estimate the total cost to buy these items by rounding each amount to the nearest dollar.

Extend the activity by setting a limit on the total amount of the purchase. For example, ask your child to select at least three items that will not exceed a total of \$40. Then ask your child to find how much money would be left if these items were purchased.

If your child selects items that cost \$19.49, \$11.50, and \$4.55, the sum can be rounded to \$20 + \$12 + \$5 = \$37.

Another variation of this activity is to have your child select three items that total more than a designated amount. For example, your child would pick three items that would total more than \$50.

Use with Chapter 2

Available in Spanish;
Web Code: aak-5500

Interdisciplinary Activities

Name ____________ ***Math and Science/Technology***

Gearing Up to Dive Down

Use introductory algebra to explore SCUBA diving.

Oceanography is the study of the world's oceans. The scientists who specialize in this work are called oceanographers. Oceanographers explore many things in the oceans. For example, they trace the paths and temperatures of huge rivers in the ocean, which are called currents. They study waves and the salts that are dissolved in ocean water. They study how the oceans formed and how their bottoms are still changing, and they study the millions of different living things—animals, plants, and even tiny microorganisms—that live and interact in the ocean.

Some oceanographers explore the oceans from ships on the surface. Others go down thousands of feet in small submarines. Those who study the first few hundred feet of the ocean use a special device that frees them to swim with the fishes. That device was invented by two scientists in 1943, one of whom is Frenchman Jacques Cousteau, the most famous oceanographer in the world. His partner was another Frenchman, Emile Gagnon. The device they invented was SCUBA, which stands for self-contained underwater breathing apparatus.

Cousteau and Gagnon's invention consists of one, two, or three cylinders, or tanks, which divers carry on their backs. The cylinders contain a supply of compressed air which divers breathe through a special mouthpiece called a regulator. The regulator keeps the air flowing smoothly and comfortably as the diver moves from one depth to another. It does this by delivering the air at the same pressure as the surrounding water. The pressure of the water is caused by its weight. The deeper the water, the greater the pressure. For a diver to breathe under water, the pressure of the air coming out of the mouthpiece must equal the pressure of the water. So you can appreciate the importance of a regulator.

Before undersea explorers can make a dive, they must consider the amount of air in their tanks, the depth of their dive, and how active they will be. All of these factors determine how long a diver can stay under the water.

Scuba divers carry a limited supply of compressed air in one or more tanks strapped to their backs. Before entering the water, scuba divers must calculate how long their air supply will last so they do not run out of air while deep underwater.

Use with Chapter 2

Available in Spanish;
Web Code: aak-5500

Interdisciplinary Activities

Name ____________ ***Math and Science/Technology***

1. Divers know how much air is in their tanks before they put them on. They also know that if they are very active in the water, they will use up more air than if they are less active. The following two expressions describe this situation.

   First expression
   Amount of air = 2 full tanks
   Depth = 50 feet
   Activity = swimming
   Time till air runs out = 60 minutes

   Second expression
   Amount of air = 2 full tanks
   Depth = 50 feet
   Activity = floating
   Time till air runs out = 90 minutes

   What is the variable in the expressions?

2. a. Using scuba gear, some divers reach a depth of 400 feet or more. However, the farther down divers go, the greater the water pressure that is exerted on them. The water pressure, in turn, affects the rate at which air is used by the diver. The greater the depth, the faster the air will be used up. What is the variable in these expressions?

   b. A diver dives to an unknown number of feet. (Let d represent the unknown number of feet.) Then, she doubles her depth. Then she triples her depth, and finally, she quadruples her depth. Write expressions to represent each stage of the diver's plunge.

3. Write an equation for each situation:

   a. A diver dives 49 feet, then f feet, and then 68 feet. He descends a total of 150 feet.

   b. A diver dives 247 feet and then comes back up t feet to 112 feet.

4. Why is it important that divers be able to calculate mathematical equations before they begin their dives?

5. Why was Cousteau and Gagnon's invention of scuba equipment a breakthrough in undersea exploration technology?

6. At sea level, the gases we breathe—mainly nitrogen and oxygen—are either harmless or beneficial to us. But deep in the water, these gases can be deadly. Do some research to find out the conditions under which nitrogen and oxygen can be dangerous to a diver's health. Describe how those dangers can be avoided.

7. Do some research on new developments in diving technology Create a display of your findings by mounting and labeling drawings or photographs.

Use withChapter2

Available in Spanish;
Web Code: aak-5500

Algebra Readiness Puzzles

Name ____________ Class ____________ Date ____________

Compatible Numbers and Break Apart — Puzzle 43

You can use **compatible numbers** to do calculations mentally. Compatible numbers are pairs of numbers that "go together" so that calculation is easy.

These pairs of addends "go together" to make 100.

$50 + 50 \qquad 25 + 75 \qquad 60 + 40$

These pairs of factors also make 100.

$2 \times 50 \qquad 4 \times 25 \qquad 5 \times 20$

You can break apart numbers to make mental calculations easier.

$4 \times 31 \rightarrow (4 \times \mathbf{30}) + (4 \times \mathbf{1})$
$\downarrow \qquad \downarrow$
$120 + 4 = 124$

$4 \times 31 = 124$

$3 \times 48 \rightarrow (3 \times \mathbf{50}) - (3 \times \mathbf{2})$
$\downarrow \qquad \downarrow$
$150 - 6 = 144$

$3 \times 48 = 144$

Fill in the missing compatible numbers.

1. $2 +$ ______ $= 10$ **2.** ______ $+ 3 = 10$ **3.** $2 \times$ ______ $= 10$

4. $70 +$ ______ $= 100$ **5.** $10 \times$ ______ $= 100$ **6.** ______ $+ 90 = 100$

7. $20 +$ ______ $= 100$ **8.** ______ $+ 300 = 1{,}000$ **9.** $250 +$ ______ $= 1{,}000$

Use compatible numbers to find each sum or product mentally.

10. $2 \times 9 \times 5$ ______ **11.** $7 \times 2 \times 50$ ______ **12.** $75 + 36 + 25$ ______

13. $80 + 50 + 20$ ______ **14.** $70 + 250 + 250$ ______ **15.** $500 \times 21 \times 2$ ______

Break apart the numbers to find each product mentally.

16. 5×23 ______ **17.** 7×39 ______ **18.** 2×225 ______

19. 6×108 ______ **20.** 425×2 ______ **21.** 3×195 ______

 Algebra Readiness Puzzles 43

Web Code: aak-5500

Algebra Readiness Puzzles

Name ____________ Class ____________ Date ____________

Math Manners — Puzzle 60

Because of his First-Place entry in the Mathematics Fair, young Ver E. Bright was to be awarded the key to the city by the mayor. Ver asked his math teacher what he should say upon receiving the award. Instead of answering directly, his teacher handed him a sheet of problems and said, "Translate each situation into an algebraic expression. One of the expressions will give you the answer you seek."
Help Ver out. Write the algebraic expression for each problem. Then make a check next to the answer that he needs.

- ☐ $3 - x$ → I do not deserve this.
- ☐ $t - 5$ → Mathematics is its own reward.
- ☐ $10q$ → Thank you.
- ☐ $4x$ → I am *so* grateful for this!
- ☐ $2n - 3$ → Many years of hard work have earned this.
- ☐ $t \div 42$ → My teachers deserve this award, not I.
- ☐ $\frac{2}{y}$ → This award confirms my belief in the power of diligent study.

1. Rachel's dog had puppies. Rachel has sold 3 of them. Let n be the number of puppies Rachel has now. Write an expression that tells the original number of puppies.

2. Jake ran 5 more miles this week than he ran last week. Let t be the number of miles he ran last week. Write an expression that tells how many miles he ran this week.

3. Mr. Stellar hired 3 students to deliver advertising fliers. He paid each student the same amount. Let x be the total amount the students earned. Write an expression that tells how much 1 student earned.

4. There are 42 members of the Drama Club. Let t be the amount of money each earned for the spring trip. Write an expression that tells the total amount the club raised.

5. The Rocket Club is 7 years old. It now has 10 times its original membership. Let q be the original number of club members. Write an expression that tells the number of members now.

6. Wes is 4 years older than his sister. Let x be his sister's age. Write an expression that tells how old Wes is.

7. A radio is on sale for half price. Let y be its original price. Write an expression that tells its sale price.

60 Algebra Readiness Puzzles

Web Code: aak-5500

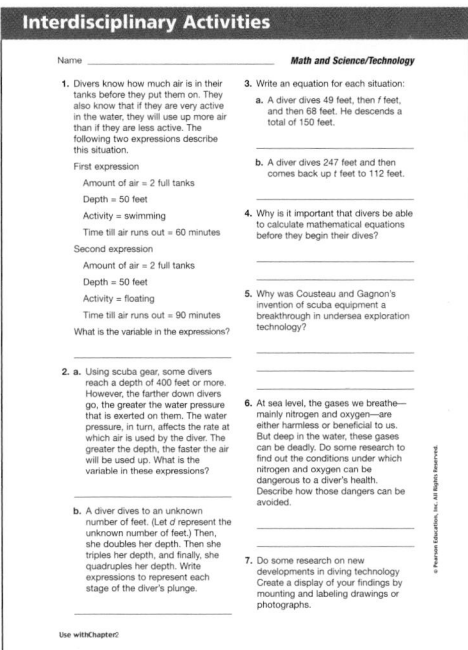

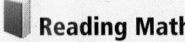

CHAPTER 2

Patterns and Variables

Chapter 2 Overview

In this chapter students use algebraic concepts and properties of numbers to investigate patterns, to write and use expressions, and to write and solve one-step equations involving addition, subtraction, multiplication, or division.

Reading Math
- Reading Algebraic Expressions, p. 73
- **Vocabulary:** A complete list, plus exercises, in the Chapter Review, p. 110
- **Illustrated Glossary:** Examples for each vocabulary term, plus definitions in English and Spanish, on p. 669

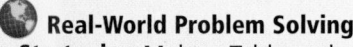

Test-Taking Strategies
Writing Short Responses, p. 109

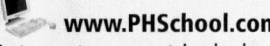

Real-World Problem Solving
- **Strategies:** Make a Table and Look for a Pattern, pp. 80–82
- **Real-World Snapshots:** It's About Time, pp. 114–115
- **Chapter Project:** Stepping Stones, p. 636

www.PHSchool.com
Internet support includes:
- Self-grading Vocabulary and Chapter 2 Tests
- Activity Masters
- Chapter Project support
- Chapter Planner
- Ch. 2 Resources

Plus **iTEXT**

CHAPTER 2

Lessons

Key Vocabulary

- algebraic expression (p. 69)
- base (p. 99)
- Distributive Property (p. 105)
- exponent (p. 99)
- inverse operations (p. 90)
- numerical expression (p. 68)
- power (p. 100)
- Properties of Equality (pp. 90, 91, 95, 96)
- term (p. 63)
- variable (p. 69)

60

Patterns and Variables

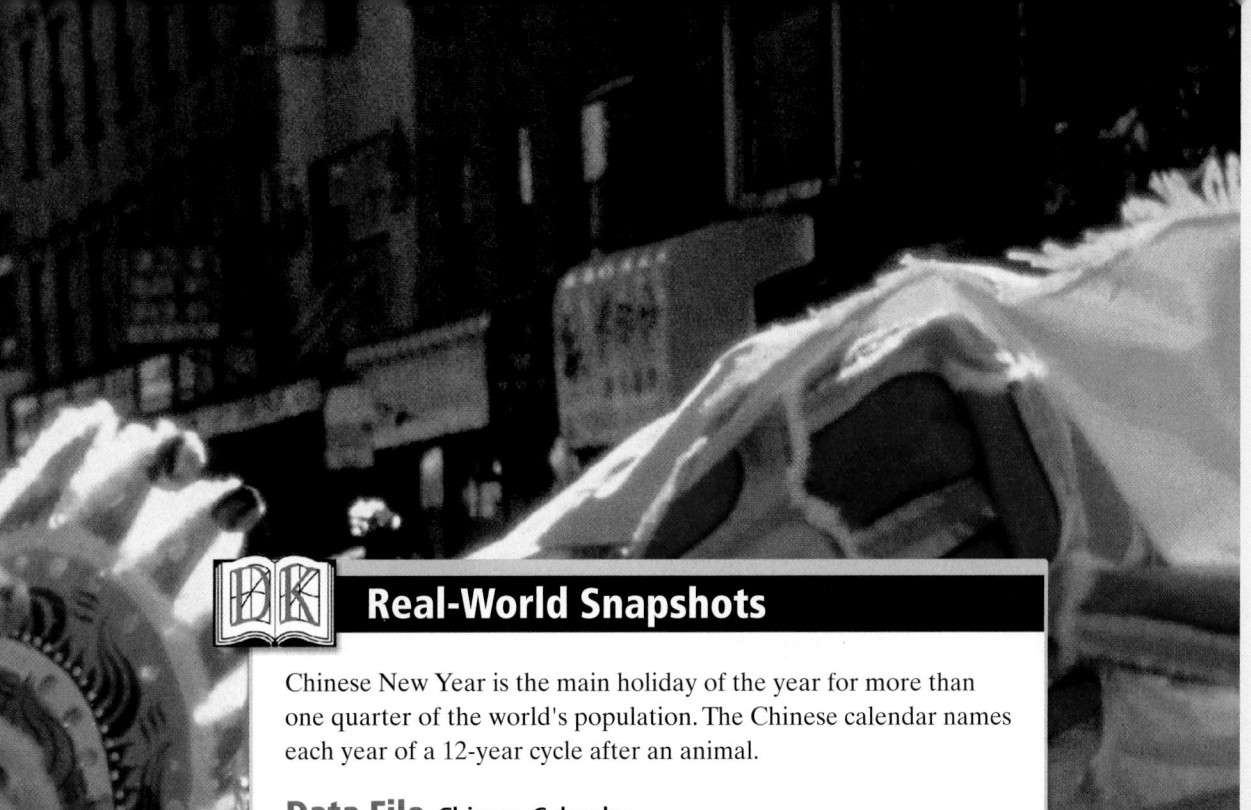

Real-World Snapshots

Chinese New Year is the main holiday of the year for more than one quarter of the world's population. The Chinese calendar names each year of a 12-year cycle after an animal.

Data File Chinese Calendar

Chinese Year	Animal	Gregorian Calendar
4694	Rat	February 19, 1996
4695	Ox	February 7, 1997
4696	Tiger	January 28, 1998
4697	Hare/Rabbit	February 16, 1999
4698	Dragon	February 5, 2000
4699	Snake	January 24, 2001
4700	Horse	February 12, 2002
4701	Ram/Sheep	February 1, 2003
4702	Monkey	January 22, 2004
4703	Rooster	February 9, 2005
4704	Dog	January 29, 2006
4705	Boar	February 18, 2007

You will use the data above in this chapter:
- p. 71   Lesson 2-2
- p. 93   Lesson 2-6

 Real-World Snapshots On pages 114 and 115, you will solve problems involving patterns in the solar system.

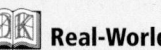
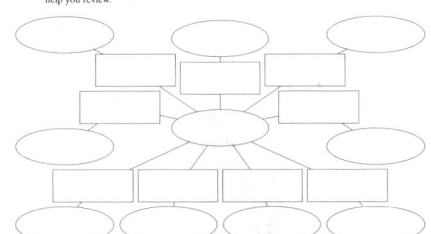

Diagnosing Readiness

Students will find answers to these exercises in the back of their textbooks.

Prescribing Intervention
For intervention, direct students to:

Estimating With Decimals
Lesson 1-4: Example 1. Extra Practice, p. 642.

Adding and Subtracting Decimals
Lesson 1-5: Examples 1, 4. Extra Practice, p. 642.

Using Mental Math to Multiply and Divide Decimals
Lesson 1-8: Examples 1–2. Extra Practice, p. 642.

Using the Order of Operations
Lesson 1-10: Example 1. Extra Practice, p. 642.

Chapter 2 Preview

Where You've Been

- In Chapter 1, you learned to compare, order, and estimate with decimals. You used the order of operations to compute with decimals.

Where You're Going

- In Chapter 2, you will learn how to use algebraic expressions to describe words and patterns.

- You will solve one-step equations.

- Applying what you learn, you will continue patterns, such as those found in a sunflower's rings.

The number of seeds in a sunflower's ring are part of the pattern 1, 1, 2, 3, 5, 8, . . .

 Instant self-check online and on CD-ROM

Diagnosing Readiness    **? For help, go to the lesson in green.**

Estimating With Decimals (Lesson 1-4)

Estimate by first rounding to the nearest whole number.

1. 5.26×9.8 about 50   **2.** $3.71 + 2.86$ about 7   **3.** $57.35 - 4.92$ about 52

Adding and Subtracting Decimals (Lesson 1-5)

First estimate then find each sum or difference.

4. $36.05 + 6.1$ about 42; 42.15 **5.** $36 - 26.5$ about 9; 9.5   **6.** $0.05 + 5.05$ about 5; 5.1

Using Mental Math to Multiply and Divide Decimals (Lesson 1-8)

Find each product or quotient.

7. $3.79 \times 5 \times 20$ 379   **8.** $1,000 \times 3.04$ 3,040   **9.** $157 \div 100$ 1.57

Using the Order of Operations (Lesson 1-10)

Find the value of each expression.

10. $3 \times 8 + 2.5$ 26.5   **11.** $36 + 6 \div 2$ 39   **12.** $48.2 - 6.2 \times 5$ 17.2

Check Skills You'll Need

1. 0.0105, 0.105, 10.5

2. 3.1, 3.31, 3.331

3. 9.06, 9.09, 9.6

4. 0.602, 20.06, 26.0

5. 100.01, 100.1, 101.0

6. 0.35, 0.4, 0.99

Investigation

1.

2-1 Describing a Pattern

What You'll Learn

OBJECTIVE 1 To continue a number pattern

OBJECTIVE 2 To write a rule for a number pattern

. . . And Why

To find the number of tiles in a pattern, as in Example 1

✓ **Check Skills You'll Need**

❓ For help, go to Lesson 1-3.

Order each set of decimals from least to greatest. 1–6. See margin.

1. 0.105, 0.0105, 10.5

2. 3.331, 3.1, 3.31

3. 9.06, 9.6, 9.09

4. 20.06, 26.0, 0.602

5. 100.1, 101.0, 100.01

6. 0.99, 0.4, 0.35

New Vocabulary • term • conjecture

 **Interactive lesson includes instant self-check, tutorials, and activities.**

OBJECTIVE 1

Continuing a Number Pattern

Investigation: Recognizing and Extending Patterns

The first three designs in a pattern are shown at the right.

1. Continue the pattern. Sketch the fourth and fifth designs on grid paper. **See margin.**

4th
9 + 13

2. How many squares are in the fourth design? The fifth design?
13 squares; 17 squares

3. Copy and complete the table.

Design Number	1	2	3	4	5	6	7
Number of Squares	1	5					

9   13   17   21   25

4. Answers may vary. Sample: Multiply (10 − 1), or 9, by 4, and then add 1.

4. Reasoning Describe how you will find the tenth design in the pattern.

Reading Math

Read the three dots in the pattern 1, 4, 7, 10, . . . as "and so on."

The numbers 1, 4, 7, 10, . . . form a number pattern. Each number in the pattern is a **term.** For example, the third term in this pattern is 7.

The three dots after the number 10 tell you that the pattern continues beyond what is shown.

2-1 Describing a Pattern **63**

63

Math Background

Patterns are the cornerstone of mathematics. In fact, mathematics has been described as "the search for pattern." In this lesson, students learn to recognize, extend, and describe addition/subtraction patterns and multiplication/division patterns.

In an addition/subtraction pattern, each term is derived from the one before it by consistently adding or subtracting the same amount. Formally, this type of pattern is called an *arithmetic sequence*.

In a multiplication/division pattern, each term is derived from the one before it by consistently multiplying or dividing by the same amount. Patterns of this type are called *geometric sequences*.

Teaching Notes

English Learners
When students hear the word *pattern*, they might think of a *repeating pattern*, the type of pattern they see on rugs, quilts, and other decorative items; Help students understand that the word *pattern* here refers to a rule that is repeated again and again.

Investigation (Optional)
Lead students to see the following relationships:
• Each design in the geometric pattern has four more squares than the preceding design.
• Each term in the number pattern is four greater than the term that precedes it.

1 EXAMPLE Teaching Tip

After discussing Example 1, ask: *How would the pattern be different if the first term were 2?* Each term would increase by 1; the pattern would be 2, 5, 8, 11, 14, ...

A **conjecture** is a prediction about what may happen. You can use the terms you know to make a conjecture about how a pattern will continue.

1 EXAMPLE Finding Number Patterns  Real World

Decorating Jacob is creating a pattern of colored tiles for a wall in his bathroom. The first four designs are shown below. How many squares will be in the fifth and sixth designs?

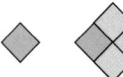 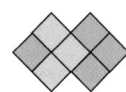 

Count the squares in each design. There are 1, 4, 7, and 10 squares. Notice that each design has three more squares than the one before it.

$$1, \quad 4, \quad 7, \quad \overset{+3}{\underset{}{10}}, \quad \overset{+3}{\underset{}{13}}, \quad 16, \ldots \quad \leftarrow \begin{array}{l} \text{Add 3 to 10 to get the fifth term.} \\ \text{Add 3 to 13 to get the sixth term.} \end{array}$$

So, the fifth and sixth designs will have 13 and 16 squares.

✓ **Check Understanding** ① Write the next two terms in each number pattern.

1a. 41, 51   **a.** 1, 11, 21, 31, . . .   **b.** 56, 48, 40, 32, . . .   **c.** 29, 36, 43, 50, . . .
1b. 24, 16   **d. Reasoning** In Example 1, the eighth design will go all the way
1c. 57, 64   across Jacob's bathroom wall. How many tiles will be in the eighth design? 22 tiles

OBJECTIVE

2 Writing a Rule for a Number Pattern

One way you can describe a number pattern is to give the first term and the rule. A rule is an explanation of how you go from one term to the next.

2 EXAMPLE Writing Number Patterns From Rules

Write the first six terms in the number pattern described by this rule: *Start with 1 and multiply by 2 repeatedly.*

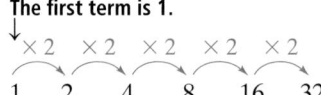

The first term is 1.

$$\overset{\times 2}{\underset{}{1}}, \quad \overset{\times 2}{\underset{}{2}}, \quad \overset{\times 2}{\underset{}{4}}, \quad \overset{\times 2}{\underset{}{8}}, \quad \overset{\times 2}{\underset{}{16}}, \quad 32 \quad \leftarrow \begin{array}{l} \text{Multiply each term by} \\ \text{2 to find the next term.} \end{array}$$

✓ **Check Understanding** ② Write the first six terms in each number pattern.
a. Start with 90 and subtract 15 repeatedly. 90, 75, 60, 45, 30, 15
b. Start with 1 and multiply by 3 repeatedly.' 1, 3, 9, 27, 81, 243
c. Start with 17 and add 19 repeatedly. 17, 36, 55, 74, 93, 112

👫 Reaching All Students

Below Level Have students practice skip-counting by 2, by 3, by 4, and so on. 2, 4, 6, 8, 10, . . . ; 3, 6, 9, 12, 15, . . . ; 4, 8, 12, 16, 20, . . . ; and so on	Advanced Learners Have students create original geometric patterns that represent number patterns, such as the designs in the Investigation and in Example 1.	English Learners See note on page 64. Inclusion See note on page 65.

3 EXAMPLE Writing a Rule

Patterns Write the next three terms in each pattern. Then write a rule for the pattern.

a. 53, 49, 45, 41, . . .

$$\overset{-4\ -4\ -4\ -4\ -4\ -4}{53,\ \ 49,\ \ 45,\ \ 41,\ \ 37,\ \ 33,\ \ 29}$$ ← To get from one term to the next, subtract 4.

The rule is *start with 53 and subtract 4 repeatedly.*

b. 1.5, 4.5, 13.5, 40.5, . . .

$$\overset{\times 3\ \ \times 3\ \ \times 3\ \ \times 3\ \ \times 3\ \ \times 3}{1.5,\ \ 4.5,\ \ 13.5,\ \ 40.5,\ \ 121.5,\ 364.5,\ 1,093.5}$$ ← To get from one term to the next, multiply by 3.

The rule is *start with 1.5 and multiply by 3 repeatedly.*

✔ **Check Understanding** **3** Write the next three terms and write a rule to describe each number pattern. **See margin.**

a. 1, 7, 49, 343, . . .　　**b.** 10.0, 8.8, 7.6, . . .　　**c.** 256, 128, 64, . . .

EXERCISES

🔖 For more practice, see *Extra Practice.*

A Practice by Example

Write the next two terms in each number pattern.

Example 1
(page 64)

1. 2, 6, 10, 14, . . . **18, 22**　　　**2.** 99, 88, 77, 66, . . . **55, 44**

3. 1, 3, 9, 27, . . . **81, 243**　　　**4.** 1, 1.4, 1.8, 2.2, . . . **2.6, 3.0**

Example 2
(page 64)

Write the first six terms in each number pattern.

5. Start with 7 and add 4 repeatedly. **7, 11, 15, 19, 23, 27, . . .**

6. Start with 512 and divide by 2 repeatedly. **512, 256, 128, 64, 32, 16**

Example 3
(page 65)

Write the next three terms and write a rule for each number pattern.
7–10. See margin.

7. 1, 5, 25, 125, . . .　　　　　　**8.** 2, 10, 50, 250, . . .

9. 6,000,000; 600,000; 60,000; . . .　　**10.** $2.85, $5.70, $8.55, . . .

Departures

Red Train	Blue Train
12:51 P.M.	12:17 P.M.
1:51 P.M.	1:02 P.M.
2:51 P.M.	1:47 P.M.
3:51 P.M.	2:32 P.M.

🌐 **11. Schedules** The schedule shows the departure times for two trains. Predict the remaining departure times before 6 P.M. for each train.

　a. The Blue Train.　　　　　**b.** The Red Train.
　　4:51, 5:51　　　　　　　　　　**3:17, 4:02, 4:47, 5:32**

Check Understanding

3a. 2,401, 16,807, 117,649; the first term is 1; multiply each term by 7 to get the next term.

b. 6.4, 5.2, 4; the first term is 10.0; subtract 1.2 from a term to get the next term.

c. 32, 16, 8; the first term is 256; divide each term by 2 to get the next term.

Exercises

7. 625; 3,125; 15,625; the first term is 1; multiply a term by 5 to get the next term.

8. 1,250; 6,250; 31,250; the first term is 2; multiply a term by 5 to get the next term.

9. 6,000; 600, 60; the first term is 6,000,000, divide a term by 10 to get the next term.

After discussing Example 2, ask: *How would the pattern be different if the first term were 2?* It is the same pattern, but without the term 1; the pattern would be 2, 4, 8, 16, 32, ...

3 EXAMPLE Inclusion

Stress the importance of identifying the two parts of the rule: the first term, and the explanation of how you go from one term to the next. Ask: *When you write the rule for the pattern in part a, why is it not enough to say, "Subtract 4 from a term to get the next term."?* Sample: That sentence by itself could describe a different pattern, such as 20, 16, 12, 8, ...

PowerPoint
Additional Examples

1 Write the next two terms in this number pattern.
5, 12, 19, 26, . . . **33, 40**

2 Write the first six terms in the number pattern described by this rule: *Start with 47 and subtract 3 repeatedly.* **47, 44, 41, 38, 35, 32**

3 Write the next three terms and write a rule to describe this number pattern.
2.3, 4.4, 6.5, 8.6, . . . **10.7, 12.8, 14.9; rule: Start with 2.3 and add 2.1 repeatedly.**

Closure

- *What is a number pattern?* Sample: a set of numbers in which each number is related to the next number by a rule
- *What is a term of a pattern?* one of the numbers in the pattern
- *How do you describe a number pattern?* Give the first term and the rule.

10. $11.40, $14.25, $17.10; the first term is $2.85; add $2.85 to a term to get the next term.

Assignment Guide

1 Objective 1
Ⓐ Ⓑ Core 1–4, 12–24
Ⓒ Extension 31

2 Objective 2
Ⓐ Ⓑ Core 5–11, 25–29
Ⓒ Extension 30

Test Prep 32–36
Mixed Review 37–42

Error Prevention!

Exercises 1–10 Have students softly repeat the operation they use for each successive term.

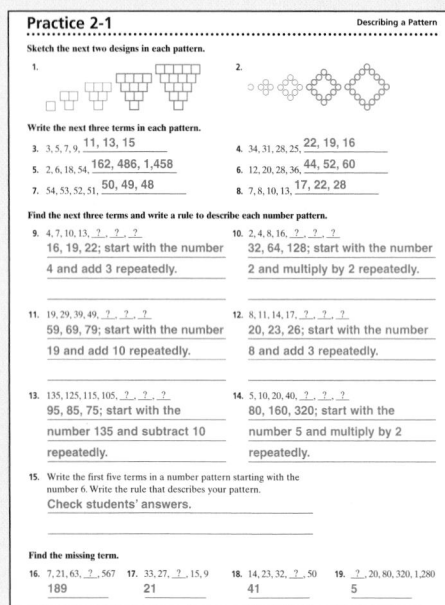

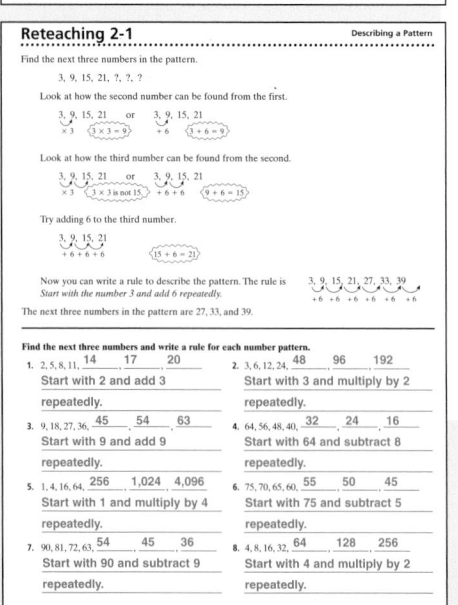

Ⓑ Apply Your Skills

Write the fifth term of each number pattern.

12. 1, 8, 64, 512, . . . **4,096**
13. 18, 15, 12, 9, . . . **6**

14. 0, 17, 34, 51, . . . **68**
15. 0.12, 1.2, 12, 120, . . . **1,200**

16. 2, 8, 14, 20, . . . **26**
17. 100, 89, 78, 67, . . . **56**

18. Astronomy Edmond Halley (1656–1742) first saw the comet named for him in 1682. He correctly predicted that it would return about every 76 years. **1986**
   a. Based on Halley's calculations, when did the comet last appear?
   b. When is the comet expected to return next? About how old will you be when that happens? **2062; check students' work.**
   c. Number Sense Did Halley see the comet a second time? Explain.
   No. The next appearance after 1682 was 1758, 16 years after his death.

Find the missing term.

19. 7, 21, 63, ■, 567   **189**
20. 352, ■, 88, 44, 22, 11   **176**

21. ■, 180, 144, 108   **216**
22. 1, 0.2, 0.04, ■, 0.0016   **0.008**

23. 1.2, 2.4, ■, 9.6, 19.2   **4.8**
24. ■, 91, 83, 75   **99**

Real-World Connection

Astronomers use patterns to predict the paths of comets.

25. Answers may vary. Sample: 480, 240, 120, 60, 30... ; divide by 2

25. Writing in Math Write a number pattern and its rule.

26. Business A dry cleaner charges $5.00 to clean one item. He offers to clean a second item for $4.50, and a third item for $4.00.
   a. If he continues to subtract $.50 for each additional item, how much will it cost to clean six items? **$22.50**
   b. If the pattern continues, which item will be cleaned for free?
   the 11ᵗʰ item

27. Computers The Difference Engine is a computer designed by Charles Babbage (1791–1871). If you feed it a list of numbers, it will look for a pattern and continue the list, if possible. Why do you think the computer was given this name? **The computer looked at the difference between terms in a list to compute a pattern.**

Geometry Draw the next design in each pattern.

Practice 2-1
Describing a Pattern

Sketch the next two designs in each pattern.

1.
2.

Write the next three terms in each pattern.

3. 3, 5, 7, 9, _11, 13, 15_
4. 34, 31, 28, 25, _22, 19, 16_
5. 2, 6, 18, 54, _162, 486, 1,458_
6. 12, 20, 28, 36, _44, 52, 60_
7. 54, 53, 52, 51, _50, 49, 48_
8. 7, 8, 10, 13, _17, 22, 28_

Find the next three terms and write a rule to describe each number pattern.

9. 4, 7, 10, 13, _?_, _?_, _?_
   16, 19, 22; start with the number 4 and add 3 repeatedly.
10. 2, 4, 8, 16, _?_, _?_, _?_
   32, 64, 128; start with the number 2 and multiply by 2 repeatedly.

11. 19, 29, 39, 49, _?_, _?_, _?_
   59, 69, 79; start with the number 19 and add 10 repeatedly.
12. 8, 11, 14, 17, _?_, _?_, _?_
   20, 23, 26; start with the number 8 and add 3 repeatedly.

13. 135, 125, 115, 105, _?_, _?_, _?_
   95, 85, 75; start with the number 135 and subtract 10 repeatedly.
14. 5, 10, 20, 40, _?_, _?_, _?_
   80, 160, 320; start with the number 5 and multiply by 2 repeatedly.

15. Write the first five terms in a number pattern starting with the number 6. Write the rule that describes your pattern.
   Check students' answers.

Find the missing term.

16. 7, 21, 63, _?_, 567   189
17. 33, 27, _?_, 15, 9   21
18. 14, 23, 32, _?_, 50   41
19. _?_, 20, 80, 320, 1,280   5

Reteaching 2-1
Describing a Pattern

Find the next three numbers in the pattern.

   3, 9, 15, 21, ?, ?, ?

Look at how the second number can be found from the first.

   3, 9, 15, 21   or   3, 9, 15, 21
   × 3 (3 × 3 = 9)   + 6 (3 + 6 = 9)

Look at how the third number can be found from the second.

   3, 9, 15, 21   or   3, 9, 15, 21
   × 3 (3 × 3 is not 15)   + 6 + 6 (9 + 6 = 15)

Try adding 6 to the third number.

   3, 9, 15, 21
   + 6 + 6 + 6   (15 + 6 = 21)

Now you can write a rule to describe the pattern. The rule is
Start with the number 3 and add 6 repeatedly.
The next three numbers in the pattern are 27, 33, and 39.
   3, 9, 15, 21, 27, 33, 39
   +6 +6 +6 +6 +6 +6

Find the next three numbers and write a rule for each number pattern.

1. 2, 5, 8, 11, _14_ _17_ _20_
   Start with 2 and add 3 repeatedly.
2. 3, 6, 12, 24, _48_ _96_ _192_
   Start with 3 and multiply by 2 repeatedly.

3. 9, 18, 27, 36, _45_ _54_ _63_
   Start with 9 and add 9 repeatedly.
4. 64, 56, 48, 40, _32_ _24_ _16_
   Start with 64 and subtract 8 repeatedly.

5. 1, 4, 16, 64, _256_ _1,024_ _4,096_
   Start with 1 and multiply by 4 repeatedly.
6. 75, 70, 65, 60, _55_ _50_ _45_
   Start with 75 and subtract 5 repeatedly.

7. 90, 81, 72, 63, _54_ _45_ _36_
   Start with 90 and subtract 9 repeatedly.
8. 4, 8, 16, 32, _64_ _128_ _256_
   Start with 4 and multiply by 2 repeatedly.

28.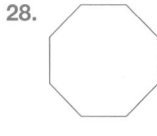
29.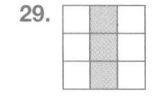

28.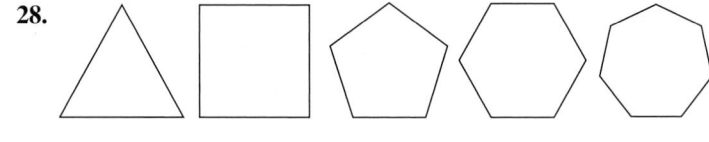

29.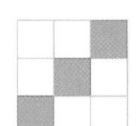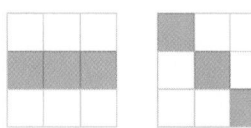

 Use the Guided Problem Solving worksheet with Exercise 26.

 **Challenge**

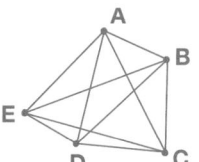

A
B
E
D C

30. The number pattern below is called a Fibonacci sequence. Write a rule to describe this number pattern. **See margin.**

1, 1, 2, 3, 5, 8, 13, 21, 34, 55, . . .

31. Stretch Your Thinking How many different straight lines can you draw through any two of the points at the right? **10 lines**

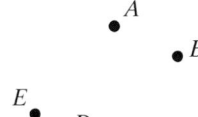

A
B
E
D
C

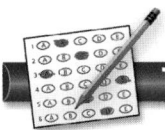

Test Prep

Reading Comprehension   **Read the article below and answer Exercises 32 and 33.**

Leap Year

It takes about 365.24 days for Earth to orbit the sun. Four years of 365.24 days is about three years with 365 days each, plus a fourth year with 366 days. This fourth year is known as a "leap year."

In a leap year, February has 29 days. A leap year is any year that can be divided by 4, except century years, such as 1500. Only century years that can be divided evenly by 400, such as 1600, are leap years.

32. Which years between 2007 and 2030 will be leap years?
2008, 2012, 2016, 2020, 2024, 2028

33. Will 2100 be a leap year? Explain. **No; 2100 is not divisible by 400.**

Multiple Choice

34. What is the value of the missing term? 102, 94, 86, ■, 70, 62, 54.
  A. 76 **B.** 78 **C.** 79 **D.** 80

35. What is the fifth term in the number pattern? 1; 20; 400; 8,000; . . .
  F. 8,400 **G.** 16,000 **H.** 80,000 **I.** 160,000

36. What is the fifth term in the number pattern? 3, 7, 11, 15, . . . **D**
  A. 16 **B.** 17 **C.** 18 **D.** 19

Take It to the NET
Online lesson quiz at
www.PHSchool.com
Web Code: aaa-0201

Mixed Review

Lesson 1-5   **First estimate then find each sum or difference.**

37. 15.1 − 11.9
  about 3; 3.2
38. 1.10 − 0.04
  about 1; 1.06
39. 50.2 − 0.99
  about 49; 49.21
40. 17.2 − 4.5
  about 12; 12.7
41. 2.005 + 2.307
  about 4.5; 4.312
42. 8.01 + 1.7 + 1.09
  about 11; 10.8

2-1 Describing a Pattern **67**

30. The first term is 1; the second term is 1; add the two previous terms to get the next term.

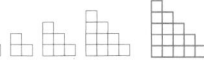
67

2-2

Variables and Expressions

Lesson Preview

 Check Skills You'll Need

Using the Order of Operations
Lesson 1-10: Example 1. Extra
Practice p. 642.

Lesson Resources

Optional Materials
• compass
• algebra tiles

 Teaching Resources
Practice, Reteaching, Enrichment

 Reaching All Students
Practice Workbook 2-2
Spanish Practice Workbook 2-2
Guided Problem Solving 2-2
Technology Activities 4

 Presentation Assistant Plus!
Transparencies
• Check Skills You'll Need 2-2
• Problem of the Day 2-2
• Additional Examples 2-2
• Student Edition Answers 2-2
• Lesson Quiz 2–2
• Classroom Aid 37
PH Presentation Pro CD-ROM 2-2

 PRENTICE HALL
ASSESSMENT SYSTEM

Computer Test Generator CD

 Technology
Resource Pro® CD-ROM
Computer Test Generator CD
PH Presentation Pro CD-ROM

 www.PHSchool.com
Student Site
• Teacher Web Code: aak-5500
• Algebra Readiness Puzzles 65
• Self-grading Lesson Quiz

PH SuccessNet Teacher Center
• Lesson Planner
• Resources

Plus

What You'll Learn

 OBJECTIVE 1 To use variables

 OBJECTIVE 2 To evaluate algebraic expressions

. . . And Why

To describe earnings, as in Example 3

 Check Skills You'll Need

? For help, go to Lesson 1-10.

Find the value of each expression.

1. $40 - 16 \div 2$ **32**
2. $3 \times 5 + 12 \div 3$ **19**
3. $7 \times (9.5 - 3.2)$ **44.1**
4. $48 \div (5.8 + 6.2)$ **4**

New Vocabulary
• numerical expression
• variable
• algebraic expression
• evaluate

iTEXT Interactive lesson includes instant self-check, tutorials, and activities.

OBJECTIVE 1 Using Variables

Investigation: Patterns and Algebraic Expressions

1. In each diagram, segments already join point *A* to the points next to it on the circle. Copy each diagram. Join *A* to the other points.

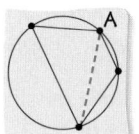 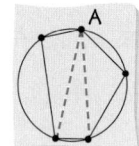 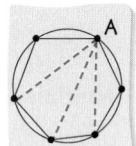

2. Copy and complete the table using your drawings from part 1.

Number of points on circle	4	5	6
Number of segments drawn to other points	▥ **1**	▥ **2**	▥ **3**

3. **a.** Extend your table to include 7 points and 8 points on a circle.
   b. How many segments would you draw for *n* points on a circle?

   3a. **4; 5**

   b. $n - 3$

A **numerical expression** is a mathematical phrase with only numbers and operation symbols $(+, -, \times, \div)$. The following expressions are numerical expressions.

$$8 + 5 - 2 \qquad 25 \times 4 - 9^2 \times 13 \qquad (7 - 6 \div 3) \times 12$$

Ongoing Assessment and Intervention

INSTANT CHECK ANALYSIS

Before the Lesson	During the Lesson	After the Lesson
Diagnose prerequisite skills using:	Monitor progress using:	Assess knowledge using:
• Check Skills You'll Need	• Check Understanding • Additional Examples • Test Prep	• Lesson Quiz • Computer Test Generator CD

Need Help?
The expression 5*d* means "5 times a number *d*."

The following mathematical expressions have symbols that represent unknown numbers.

$$n + 2 \qquad 5d \qquad 7b - 2 \qquad 12x \div 3$$

In the expressions above, *n*, *d*, *b*, and *x* are variables. A **variable** is a symbol that represents one or more numbers. A mathematical expression with one or more variables is an **algebraic expression.**

You can model algebraic expressions using algebra tiles.

A yellow tile ☐ represents 1.

▌ A green tile represents a variable.

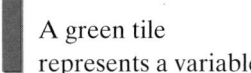 **From Expressions to Algebra Tiles**

Model the expression 5*x* + 3 with algebra tiles.

 ← 5 green tiles represent 5*x*, and 3 yellow tiles represent 3.

✓ **Check Understanding** ① Draw algebra tiles to model each expression. a–c. See back of book.

a. 3*x* b. *x* + 2 c. 4*x* + 3

OBJECTIVE

2 Evaluating Algebraic Expressions

The first screen of a video game usually asks, "How many players?" The number of players is a variable. The game software uses your entry to set up the game.

Similarly, to **evaluate** an algebraic expression, you replace each variable with a number. Use the order of operations to simplify the expression.

 **Evaluating Algebraic Expressions**

Evaluate 2*x* − 8 for *x* = 11.

$2x - 8 = 2(11) - 8$ ← Replace *x* with 11.
$\qquad\quad = 22 - 8$ ← Multiply 2 and 11.
$\qquad\quad = 14$ ← Subtract 8 from 22.

✓ **Check Understanding** ② Evaluate each expression for *x* = 7.

a. 3*x* + 15 36 b. 5*x* ÷ 7 5 c. 56 − 4*x* 28

d. **Reasoning** Explain how you used the order of operations to evaluate the expression in part (c). *x* was replaced by 7; 7 was multiplied by 4; 28 was subtracted from 56.

2-2 Variables and Expressions **69**

👥 **Reaching All Students**

| **Below Level** Show students several arrangements of algebra tiles that represent algebraic expressions. Have them write the expression each arrangement represents. | **Advanced Learners** Write four algebraic expressions involving the variable *z* whose value is 9 when *z* is replaced by 3. Samples: *z* + 6; 12 − *z*; 3*z*; 27 ÷ *z* | **English Learners** See note on page 69. **Visual Learners** See note on page 70. |

---

2. Teach

 Professional Development

Math Background

Numerical expressions are meaningful combinations of numbers and operation signs. Familiar additions, subtractions, multiplications, and divisions, such as 5 + 7, 8 − 3, 3 × 5, and 36 ÷ 4, are all examples of numerical expressions.

A *variable* is a letter or other symbol that is a placeholder for an unknown number. An expression that contains at least one variable is called an *algebraic expression*. When each variable in an algebraic expression is replaced by a number, the result is a numerical expression whose value can be calculated. This process is called *evaluating the algebraic expression*.

Teaching Notes

Investigation (Optional)
When answering Question 4, students might initially give a response such as, "Whatever *n* is, subtract 3 to get the number of segments." Ask questions that lead them toward writing the algebraic expression *n* − 3. For instance, *Is there a way to say that by using symbols and not words?*

English Learners
Stress the relationship between the word *variable* and the word *vary*. Discuss everyday quantities that vary. For instance: *The price of a CD might vary from store to store.* Point out that, in a similar way, the number a variable represents might vary from situation to situation.

PowerPoint
🖳 **Additional Examples**

① Draw algebra tiles to model the expression 2*x* + 3.

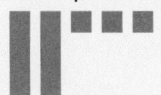

② Evaluate 8*x* + 2 for *x* = 3. 26

69

PowerPoint
Additional Examples

Closure

③ **EXAMPLE**  Real-World Problem Solving

Fundraising The history club sells magazine subscriptions to earn money for a trip to the state capitol. For each subscription, the club earns $3. The expression $3s$ represents the amount of money the club earns. Complete the table for the given number of subscriptions.

Number of Subscriptions	Dollars Club Earns
s	$3s$
15	■ 45
40	■ 120
65	■ 195

Substitute each number of subscriptions for s.

$\leftarrow 3 \times 15 = 45$
$\leftarrow 3 \times 40 = 120$
$\leftarrow 3 \times 65 = 195$

 **Check Understanding** ③ How much will the club earn if they sell 85 subscriptions? $255

More Than One Way

Jessica and Luis want to make a long-distance call. The call costs 10 cents, plus 4.5 cents for each minute. How much will an 8-minute call cost?

Jessica's Method

To find the cost of the call, I can use the algebraic expression $10 + 4.5m$, with m representing the number of minutes. Then I will evaluate the expression for $m = 8$.

$10 + 4.5m = 10 + 4.5(8)$ $\leftarrow$ Replace m with 8.

$= 10 + 36$ $\leftarrow$ Multiply 4.5 and 8.

$= 46$ $\leftarrow$ Add 10 and 36.

The telephone call will cost 46 cents.

Luis's Method

If one minute costs 4.5 cents, then a two-minute call will cost 9 cents, a four-minute call will cost 18 cents, and an eight-minute call will cost 36 cents. I need to add the 10 cents. So the total cost is $36 + 10$, or 46 cents.

Choose a Method

Another long-distance plan charges 5 cents per call, plus 4 cents for each minute. Find how much a 10-minute call costs with this plan. Explain why you chose the method you used.
45 cents; check students' methods.

1.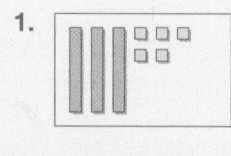

2.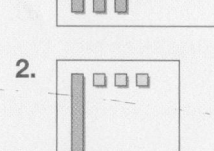

3.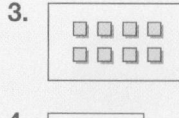

4.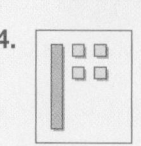

5.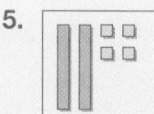

6.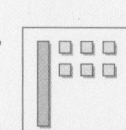

A Practice by Example

Draw algebra tiles to model each expression. 1–8. See margin.

Example 1
(page 69)

1. $3x + 5$ **2.** $c + 3$ **3.** 8 **4.** $z + 4$

5. $4 + 2x$ **6.** $a + 6$ **7.** $c + c + c$ **8.** $3m + 2$

Example 2
(page 69)

Evaluate each expression for $x = 8$.

9. $x + 12$ 20   **10.** $80 \div x$ 10   **11.** $2x - 3$ 13   **12.** $2(x - 3)$ 10

13. $10 + 2x$ 26   **14.** $12x$ 96   **15.** $42(x - 7)$ 42   **16.** $2x \div 4$ 4

Example 3
(page 70)

17. Rentals The rental fee for a bicycle is \$5, plus \$2 for each hour h the bike is rented. The expression for the total cost is $5 + 2h$. Copy and complete the table for the given number of hours.

Hour	Rental Fee
h	$5 + 2h$
1	■ 7
2	■ 9
3	■ 11

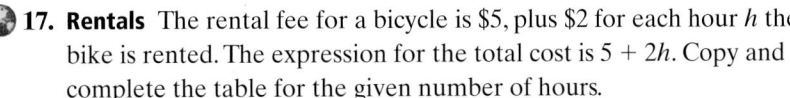

B Apply Your Skills

Evaluate each expression.

18. $24 \div d$ for $d = 3$ 8   **19.** $p + 8$ for $p = 6$ 14

20. $3r - 2$ for $r = 65$ 193   **21.** $8b - 12$ for $b = 2.1$ 4.8

22. $n \div 10$ for $n = 30$ 3   **23.** $n \div 10$ for $n = 17$ 1.7

24. $3(2c)$ for $c = 3$ 18   **25.** $18 - 3y$ for $y = 2.5$ 10.5

26. $75s$ for $s = 5$ 375   **27.** $5x - y$ for $x = 12, y = 14$ 46

28. Writing in Math How are numerical and algebraic expressions different? Give examples. **A numerical expression contains only numbers while an algebraic expression will also include variables.**

29. Data File, p. 61 Write an expression for finding the Year of the Dog in the Gregorian calendar starting with the year 2006. **2006 + 12x**

30. Bricklayer's Formula The formula $N = 7 \times \ell \times h$ gives the number of bricks needed for a wall of length ℓ feet and height h feet. How many bricks are needed for a wall with length 22 feet and height 30 feet? **4,620 bricks**

GPS

2-2 Variables and Expressions **71**

7.

8.

GPS Use the Guided Problem Solving worksheet with Exercise 30.

Assignment Guide

1 Objective 1
   A **B** Core 1–8, 29
   C Extension 40

2 Objective 2
   A **B** Core 9–28, 30–33
   C Extension 34–39

Test Prep 41–43
Mixed Review 44–49

Error Prevention!

Exercise 14 Students might substitute 8 for x in $12x$ but calculate $12 + 8$.

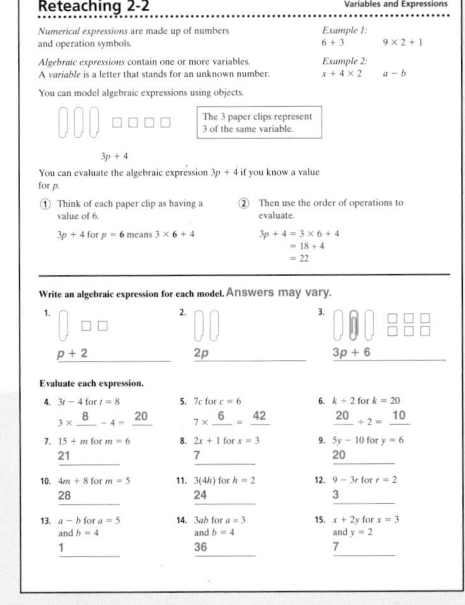

Evaluate each expression for n = 9.

1. n + 15 24

2. 4n − 10 26

3. 3(6 + n) 45

4. 2n ÷ 3 6

Alternative Assessment

Students work in pairs to write one-step algebraic expressions, such as x + 4 or 4x, for each of the four operations. Together, partners use number sense to decide on a value for the variable in each expression and then evaluate the expression. When students show proficiency in evaluating simple expressions, vary the activity by having them write and evaluate expressions such as 4x − 3 and 5x ÷ 4.

Test Prep

Resources

For additional practice with a variety of test item formats:
- Test-Prep, p. 113
- Test-Taking Strategies, p. 109
- Test-Taking Strategies With Transparencies

Copy and complete each table.

31.

x	x + 6
1	7
4	■10
7	■13

32.

x	7x
2	■14
4	■28
6	■42

33.

x	100 − x
20	■80
35	■65
50	■50

C Challenge

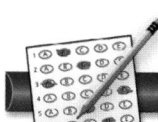

Evaluate each expression.

34. x + y for x = 12 and y = 37 49

35. 2r + st for r = 7, s = 30, and t = 5 164

36. 4m + n for m = 1.5 and n = 2.2 8.2

37. 2ab for a = 35 and b = 3 210

38. 11t − 6v for t = 9 and v = 4 75

39. 2x + 3y for x = 3 and y = 4 18

40. Stretch Your Thinking A class attended a school fair. For one activity, each of the 25 students in the class got one throw. When the ball hit the target, the class got 12 points toward prizes. They lost 8 points for each miss. The class started with a score of 0 and ended with a score of 0. How many hits and how many misses did the class have?
10 hits; 15 misses

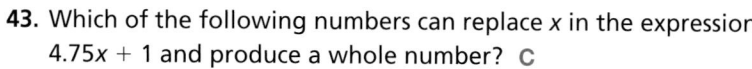

Test Prep

Multiple Choice

41. What is the value of 3p + 6 when p = 7? C
   A. 7   **B.** 21   **C.** 27   **D.** 45

42. Which number pattern can be described by the rule *start with 1 and multiply by 4 repeatedly*? I
   F. 1, 3, 5, 7, . . .   **G.** 1, 2, 4, 7, . . .   **H.** 1, 5, 9, 13, . . .   **I.** 1, 4, 16, 64, . . .

43. Which of the following numbers can replace x in the expression 4.75x + 1 and produce a whole number? C
   A. 2   **B.** 3   **C.** 4   **D.** 5

Mixed Review

Lesson 2-1   **Algebra** Write the next two terms in each number pattern.

44. 32, 35, 38, 41, . . .   **45.** 729, 243, 81, 27, . . .   **46.** 101, 97, 93, 89, . . .
   44, 47   9, 3   85, 81

Lesson 1-7   **Find each product.**

47. 2.43 × 12   **48.** 4.05 × 1.5   **49.** 37.4 × 0.001
   29.16   6.075   0.0374

■ **Reading Math**

Reading Algebraic Expressions

Students need to be able to read and understand algebraic expressions, including those that do not contain operational symbols. This lesson emphasizes the value of reading expressions aloud to help comprehend their meaning.

Teaching Notes

Auditory Learners
Read aloud the expressions with n and 3 and have students repeat them softly to themselves. You may wish to introduce other ways to say the expressions without changing meanings. For example, $3 - n$ can be read "three minus some number, n."

EXAMPLE Teaching Tip

Build upon your students' understanding of variables and expressions as you discuss the meanings of the expressions in parts a–c. Say aloud additional expressions that a volunteer can write on the board while other students write them at their seats.

Error Prevention!

In part c of the Example, the comma is essential because the phrase "t divided by 4 plus 1" could mean $\frac{t}{4 + 1}$ instead of $\frac{t}{4} + 1$.

Exercises

Have students work independently on the Exercises.

To read or evaluate an algebraic expression, you must identify the operations. Sometimes, numbers or variables are placed next to each other without an operation symbol between them.

Expression	Meaning
$3\frac{1}{2}$	You read $3\frac{1}{2}$ as "three and one half." The word *and* translates to addition. So, $3\frac{1}{2}$ means "3 plus $\frac{1}{2}$."
$3n$	In $3n$, multiplication is an unwritten operation. $3n$ means "3 times n."
$\frac{18}{a}$	The fraction bar represents division, so $\frac{18}{a}$ means "18 divided by a."

Sometimes, a slight change in words can greatly affect what an expression or inequality means and how to write it.

$n < 3$ means "n is less than 3."

$3 - n$ means "n less than 3" or "3 minus n."

$n - 3$ means "n less 3" or "n minus 3."

EXAMPLE **Reading Expressions**

Read each of the following.

Expression	How to read the expression
a. $7c$	"seven times c"
b. $x > 6.3$	"x is greater than six and three tenths."
c. $\frac{t}{4} + 1$	"t divided by four, plus one"

EXERCISES

1. Write an algebraic expression for the sum of n and 2. **$n + 2$**

2. **Reasoning** Is "5 less than 11" the same as "5 less 11"? Explain.
   No; "5 less than 11" is written "$11 - 5$," but "5 less 11" is written "$5 - 11$."

Write each of the following in words as you would read it. **3–10. See margin.**

3. $d + 7x$ **4.** $3 \cdot d$ **5.** $6 < z$ **6.** $\frac{a}{9}$

7. $y - 6z$ **8.** $8 < 5w$ **9.** $12 \div r$ **10.** $5\frac{1}{2} - b$

3–10. Answers may vary. Sample answers are given.

3. d increased by the product of seven and x

4. three multiplied by d

5. Six is less than z.

6. a divided by nine

7. y decreased by the product of six and z

8. Eight is less than 5 multiplied by w.

9. twelve divided by r

10. five and one-half minus b

1. Plan

Lesson Preview

 Check Skills You'll Need
Evaluating Algebraic Expressions
Lesson 2-2: Example 2. Extra Practice p. 643.

Lesson Resources

 Teaching Resources
Practice, Reteaching, Enrichment
Checkpoint Quiz 1

Reaching All Students
Practice Workbook 2-3
Spanish Practice Workbook 2-3
Reading and Math Literacy 2B
Spanish Reading and Math
  Literacy 2B
Spanish Checkpoint Quiz 1
Guided Problem Solving 2-3

Presentation Assistant Plus!
Transparencies
• Check Skills You'll Need 2-3
• Problem of the Day 2-3
• Additional Examples 2-3
• Student Edition Answers 2-3
• Lesson Quiz 2-3
PH Presentation Pro CD-ROM 2-3

ASSESSMENT SYSTEM

Checkpoint Quiz 1
Computer Test Generator CD

 Technology
Resource Pro® CD-ROM
Computer Test Generator CD
PH Presentation Pro CD-ROM

 www.PHSchool.com
Student Site
• Teacher Web Code: aak-5500
• Algebra Readiness Puzzles 60
• Self-grading Lesson Quiz

PH SuccessNet Teacher Center
• Lesson Planner
• Resources

Plus

74

What You'll Learn

OBJECTIVE 1
To write algebraic expressions

OBJECTIVE 2
To use algebraic expressions

. . . And Why

To describe total cost, as in Example 2

 Check Skills You'll Need   For help, go to Lesson 2-2.

Evaluate each expression for $a = 7$.

1. $a + 3$ 10
2. $a - 6$ 1
3. $2a + 1$ 15
4. $7a - 19$ 30
5. $6 \cdot (a + 1)$ 48
6. $2 + (2a - 5)$ 11

OBJECTIVE 1   Interactive lesson includes instant self-check, tutorials, and activities.

Relating Words to Algebraic Expressions

You can write a word phrase as an algebraic expression.

Operation	Word Phrase	Algebraic Expression
addition	a number plus 45 the sum of a number and 45 45 more than a number	$m + 45$
subtraction	a number minus 6 the difference of a number and 6 6 subtracted from a number	$p - 6$
multiplication	4 times a number the product of 4 and a number	$4k$
division	the quotient of a number and 25 a number divided by 25	$\dfrac{z}{25}$

1 EXAMPLE   **From Words to Expressions**

Write an expression for each word phrase.
a. 2 more than x b. the product of 7 and k

    $x + 2$ $7 \cdot k$, or $7k$

 **Check Understanding** ① Write an expression for each word phrase.
a. five divided by y b. six times z c. m increased by 3.4
   $5 \div y$ $6z$ $m + 3.4$

74   Chapter 2   Patterns and Variables

Ongoing Assessment and Intervention

Before the Lesson
Diagnose prerequisite skills using:
• Check Skills You'll Need

During the Lesson
Monitor progress using:
• Check Understanding
• Additional Examples
• Test Prep

After the Lesson
Assess knowledge using:
• Lesson Quiz
• Computer Test Generator CD
• Chapter Checkpoint 1 (p. 78)

Drawing a diagram can help you write an algebraic expression for a real-world situation.

2 EXAMPLE <u>Real-World</u> <u>Problem Solving</u>

Bowling When Tai goes bowling on Saturday afternoons, he bowls three games. Shoe rental for the day is $1.75. Use g for the cost of one game. Write an algebraic expression for the total Tai pays when he bowls.

Total Cost			
g	g	g	1.75

Write the cost of 3 games as $3g$.

The total cost is $3g + 1.75$.

✔ **Check Understanding** ② At the end of a space flight, an astronaut's height can temporarily be 2 inches greater than normal. Write an algebraic expression that describes an astronaut's height h after a flight. $h + 2$

OBJECTIVE

2 Using Algebraic Expressions

You can use an algebraic expression to describe the relationship of data in a table.

3 EXAMPLE **From Patterns to Expressions**

Write an expression to describe the relationship of the data in the table.

n	▪
1	14
2	15
3	16

$1 + 13 = 14$
$2 + 13 = 15$
$3 + 13 = 16$

Adding 13 to each number in the first column gives you the number in the second column.

The expression $n + 13$ describes the pattern.

3. Answers may vary. Samples are given.

✔ **Check Understanding** ③ Write an expression to describe the relationship of the data in each table.

a.

n	▪
2	1
6	3
9	4.5

$n \div 2$

b.

n	▪
2	6
5	9
7	11

$n + 4$

Sometimes you will need to decide on what variable to use and state what it represents in a real-world situation.

---

2. Teach

Math Background

Professional Development

An English phrase is a collection of words that form a cohesive unit, but the unit is less than a complete sentence. In a sense, expressions are the phrases of mathematics. That is, an expression is a collection of numbers, variables, and operation symbols that form a cohesive unit, but these units are less than a complete mathematical sentence.

Teaching Notes

① EXAMPLE **Visual Learners**

Use arrows to connect the corresponding words and symbols.

2	more than	x
↓	↓	↓
2	+	x

$x + 2$

Error Prevention!

For Check Understanding 1b, students might write $6 \times z$. Point out that the $\times$ symbol can be misread as the variable x, and so it is generally avoided in algebraic expressions. Preferred forms include $6z$, or $6 \cdot z$.

PowerPoint

Additional Examples

① Write an expression for each word phrase.

  a. 8 less than r $r - 8$

  b. the quotient when y is divided by 12 $y \div 12$

② A newspaper advertisement reads, "Buy 3 T-shirts of the same kind, take $5 off the total price." Let t represent the cost of one T-shirt. Write an algebraic expression that describes the situation. $3t - 5$

③ Write an expression to describe the relationship of the data in the table. $3n$

n	1	4	5
▪	3	12	15

75

Test-Prep Tip

When choosing a variable, use a letter that reminds you what the variable stands for.

4 EXAMPLE **Real-World Problem Solving**

Age Brandon is 5 years older than his sister Ruth. Write an expression using Brandon's age to describe Ruth's age.

Let b = Brandon's age. ← You don't know Brandon's age, so choose a variable to represent it.

Since Brandon is older than Ruth, Ruth's age is 5 years *less* than Brandon's age. So, Ruth's age is $b - 5$.

✓ **Check Understanding** 4 **a.** Brandon is 28 years younger than his father. Write an expression using Brandon's age to describe his father's age. **b + 28**

b. If Brandon is 13, how old is his father? **41**

EXERCISES

? For more practice, see *Extra Practice*.

Ⓐ **Practice by Example**

Write an expression for each word phrase.

Example 1
(page 74)

1. 34 less than k **k − 34** **2.** 4 plus e **4 + e** **3.** d more than 50 **50 + d**

4. 23 times q **23q** **5.** 7 decreased by b **7 − b** **6.** b divided by 3 **b ÷ 3**

Example 2
(page 75)

Write an expression for each situation.

7. Boating A paddle boat rents for $10 plus $8 per hour. How much does it cost to rent a paddle boat for h hours? **10 + 8h**

8. You buy one 10-pack of juice boxes. Each juice box contains j ounces. How many ounces of juice did you buy? **10j**

Example 3
(page 75)

Write an expression to describe the relationship of the data in each table.

9.

n	■
10	7
12	9
15	12

$n - 3$

10.

n	■
1	7
2	14
3	21

$7n$

11.

n	■
3	5
4.5	6.5
7	9

$n + 2$

Example 4
(page 76)

12. a. Jobs Jon and his two brothers make money by doing yardwork for neighbors. The boys split the money equally. Write an expression that describes how much money each boy makes in one day.

b. If they get $36 for yardwork, how much does each boy receive?

12a. $m ÷ 3$ **b.** $12

13. a. A bike shop has been in business 20 years longer than a skateboard store across the street. The bike shop is y years old. Write an expression for the number of years the skateboard store has been in business. $y - 20$

b. If the bike shop is 27 years old, how old is the skateboard store? **7 years**

Assignment Guide

1 **Objective 1**
Ⓐ Ⓑ Core 1–8, 18–22
Ⓒ Extension 23

2 **Objective 2**
Ⓐ Ⓑ Core 9–17,
Ⓒ Extension 24

Test Prep 25–28
Mixed Review 29–34

Ⓑ **Apply Your Skills**   **Write an expression to describe the relationship of the data in each table.**

14. $n \div 6$

n	■
42	7
54	9
72	12

15. $11n$

n	■
1	11
2	22
3	33

16. $n - 7$

n	■
30	23
45	38
52	45

17. a. Cooking The largest pan of lasagna weighed 3,477 pounds. The length of the pan was ten times its width. Write an algebraic expression for the length of the pan of lasagna in terms of its width w. **10w**

b. The lasagna measured 7 feet wide. Evaluate the expression to find the length of the pan of lasagna. **70 feet**

Diversity
Exercise 7 Have a student explain what a paddle boat is.

Real-World 🌐 Connection

A regular-size pan of lasagna weighs about 3 pounds.

Write an expression for each word phrase.

18. 5 less than the quotient of m and n $m \div n - 5$

19. 12 greater than the product of 3 and j $3j + 12$

20. Buying Paint Customers in a paint store use the chart at the right to decide how many gallons of paint they need. Write an expression that relates the painted area A in square feet to the number of gallons of paint. $A \div 400 =$ **gallons of paint needed.**

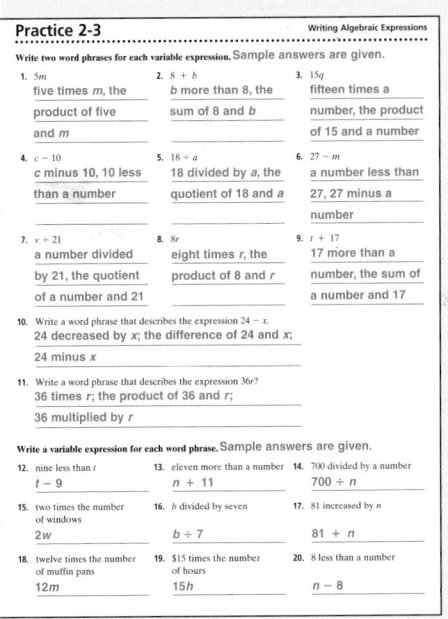

Area sq. ft.	Gallons
400	1
800	2
2,000	5
3,200	8

21. Answers may vary. Sample: Your grandfather is 50 years older than you. The expression $y + 50$ relates his age to yours.

21. Writing in Math Describe a situation you could model with $y + 50$.

22. Zoo On Saturday, admission to the zoo costs \$3 per person. The Sengs [GPS] have a coupon for a discount of \$5 off for a family. There are p people in the Seng family. Write an expression for how much the Sengs pay for admission to the zoo if they use the coupon. $3p - 5$

Ⓒ **Challenge**

23. A store that personalizes T-shirts charges \$20 for a shirt plus \$.75 for each letter. Write an algebraic expression for the total cost of a shirt using n letters. $20 + .75n$

24. Stretch Your Thinking The 4-digit number 2,■ ■ 5 is a product of a number and itself. What are the two missing digits? *(0 2)*

[GPS] Use the Guided Problem Solving worksheet with Exercise 22.

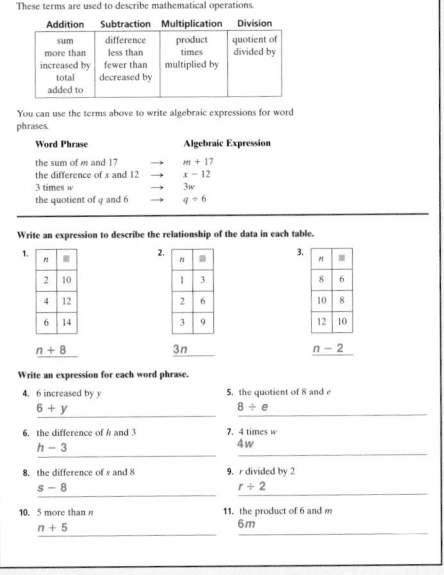

Practice 2-3   Writing Algebraic Expressions

Write two word phrases for each variable expression. Sample answers are given.

1. $5m$ — five times m, the product of five and m
2. $8 + b$ — b more than 8, the sum of 8 and b
3. $15q$ — fifteen times a number, the product of 15 and a number
4. $c - 10$ — c minus 10, 10 less than a number
5. $18 \div a$ — 18 divided by a, the quotient of 18 and a
6. $27 - m$ — a number less than 27, 27 minus a number
7. $v \div 21$ — a number divided by 21, the quotient of a number and 21
8. $8r$ — eight times r, the product of 8 and r
9. $t + 17$ — 17 more than a number, the sum of a number and 17

10. Write a word phrase that describes the expression $24 - x$. — 24 decreased by x; the difference of 24 and x; 24 minus x
11. Write a word phrase that describes the expression $36r$? — 36 times r; the product of 36 and r; 36 multiplied by r

Write a variable expression for each word phrase. Sample answers are given.

12. nine less than t — $t - 9$
13. eleven more than a number — $n + 11$
14. 700 divided by a number — $700 \div n$
15. two times the number of windows — $2w$
16. b divided by seven — $b \div 7$
17. 81 increased by n — $81 + n$
18. twelve times the number of muffin pans — $12m$
19. \$15 times the number of hours — $15h$
20. 8 less than a number — $n - 8$

Reteaching 2-3   Writing Algebraic Expressions

These terms are used to describe mathematical operations.

Addition	Subtraction	Multiplication	Division
sum	difference	product	quotient of
more than	less than	times	divided by
increased by	fewer than	multiplied by	
total	decreased by		
added to			

You can use the terms above to write algebraic expressions for word phrases.

Word Phrase		Algebraic Expression
the sum of m and 17	→	$m + 17$
the difference of x and 12	→	$x - 12$
3 times w	→	$3w$
the quotient of q and 6	→	$q \div 6$

Write an expression to describe the relationship of the data in each table.

1. $n + 8$

n	■
2	10
4	12
6	14

2. $3n$

n	■
1	3
2	6
3	9

3. $n - 2$

n	■
8	6
10	8
12	10

Write an expression for each word phrase.

4. 6 increased by y — $6 + y$
5. the quotient of 8 and e — $8 \div e$
6. the difference of h and 3 — $h - 3$
7. 4 times w — $4w$
8. the difference of s and 8 — $s - 8$
9. r divided by 2 — $r \div 2$
10. 5 more than n — $n + 5$
11. the product of 6 and m — $6m$

77

4. Assess

Lesson Quiz 2-3

Write an expression for each word phrase.

1. a increased by 7 $a + 7$

2. 6 less than c $c - 6$

3. 16 cups costs c dollars. Write an expression for the cost of one cup. $\frac{c}{16}$

Chapter Checkpoint

To check understanding of Lessons 2-1 to 2-3:

Checkpoint Quiz 1 (p. 78)

  Teaching Resources
Checkpoint Quiz 1 (also in *Prentice Hall Assessment System*)

👥 **Reaching All Students**
Reading and Math Literacy 2B

Spanish versions available.

Alternative Assessment

Each student in a pair writes three word phrases similar to those in Exercises 1–6. Partners exchange papers and write the algebraic expression for each word phrase.

78

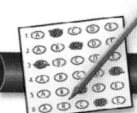
Multiple Choice

25. Which of the following describes the expression uv? **D**
  A. the difference of u and v
  B. the total of u and v
  C. u divided by v
  D. the product of u and v

26. Which of the following does NOT describe the expression $x - 36$? **G**
  F. x minus 36
  G. x less than 36
  H. 36 subtracted from x
  I. 36 less than x

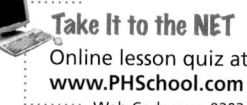

Take It to the NET
Online lesson quiz at
www.PHSchool.com
Web Code: aaa-0203

27. In what order should operations be performed in the expression $36 \times 7 - 12 \div 2 + 3$? **D**
  A. $\times - \div +$ **B.** $- + \times \div$ **C.** $\div \times + -$ **D.** $\times \div - +$

28. If you know the dimensions of a piece of property, which operation will be most useful in finding the perimeter of the property? **F**
  F. addition **G.** subtraction **H.** multiplication **I.** division

Mixed Review

Lesson 1-5 **Find each sum.**

29. $4.432 + 1.009$ 5.441
30. $2.005 + 12.5$ **14.505**
31. $2.449 + 0.7$ 3.149

Lesson 1-4 **Estimate each product by first rounding to the nearest whole number.**

32. 2.25×13.76 about 28
33. 38.1×9.87 about 380
34. 15.23×3.47 about 45

Checkpoint Quiz 1   Lessons 2-1 through 2-3

 Instant self-check quiz online and on CD-ROM

1. 1,296; 7,776; 46,656; the first term is 1; multiply a term by 6 to get the next term.

2. 225, 210, 195; the first term is 285; subtract 15 from a term to get the next term.

3. 0.005, 0.0005, 0.00005; the first term is 50; divide a term by 10 to get the next term.

Write the next three terms and write a rule for each pattern. **1–3. See left.**

1. $1, 6, 36, 216, \ldots$ **2.** $285, 270, 255, 240, \ldots$ **3.** $50, 5, 0.5, 0.05, \ldots$

Evaluate each expression for $x = 7$.

4. $8x$ 56 **5.** $3 \cdot (x - 4)$ 9 **6.** $3x \div 2$ 10.5

Write an expression for each word phrase.

7. d less than 17
  $17 - d$
8. a times e ae
9. 14 divided by q
  $14 \div q$

10. a. Each guest receives five party favors. Write an expression that describes the total number of party favors Mrs. Jones bought if three favors are left. $5g + 3$
  b. If there were 12 guests, how many favors did Mrs. Jones buy? 63

Test Prep

Resources
For additional practice with a variety of test item formats:
• Test-Prep, p. 113
• Test-Taking Strategies, p. 109
• Test-Taking Strategies With Transparencies

Using Formulas

A formula is an equation that shows a relationship between quantities that are represented by variables.

 **EXAMPLE**

The formula $d = rt$ relates distance d, rate r, and time t. How far will you travel if you drive with an average speed (rate) of 52 miles per hour for 3 hours?

$d = rt$ ← Write the formula.

$d = 52 \cdot 3$ ← Substitute 52 for r and 3 for t.

$d = 156$ ← Multiply.

You will travel 156 miles.

2 EXAMPLE

The formula $F = \frac{n}{4} + 37$ relates the number of chirps a cricket makes in one minute n to the approximate outside temperature in Fahrenheit F. Estimate the temperature when a cricket chirps 88 times in one minute.

$F = \frac{n}{4} + 37$ ← Write the formula.

$F = \frac{88}{4} + 37$ ← Substitute 88 for n.

$F = 22 + 37$ ← Divide.

$F = 59$ ← Add.

The temperature is about 59°F.

EXERCISES

1. Use the formula in Example 2 to estimate the temperature outside if a cricket chirps 104 times in one minute. **about 63° F**

2. A plane flies at a speed of about 325 miles per hour. Use the formula $d = rt$ to find how far it travels in 4 hours. **about 1,300 miles**

Use the formula $P = 2\ell + 2w$, to find the perimeter of each rectangle.

3.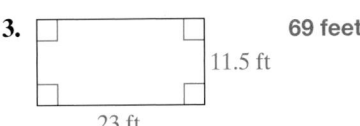
69 feet
11.5 ft
23 ft

4.
9.2 in.
39.9 in.
98.2 inches

Using Formulas

In this extension of Lesson 2-3, students use their understanding of algebraic expressions to evaluate formulas.

Teaching Notes

English Learners
Some students may be unclear about the meaning of *formula* in mathematics. Emphasize that in math a formula is an equation. Discuss other meanings of formula, such as food for infants, a recipe, or a set of symbols for a chemical compound.

1 EXAMPLE Teaching Tip

Remind students that a variable in a mathematical formula, or any equation, represents quantities that vary. For example, the formula $d = rt$ can represent many different combinations of distance, speed, and time. This fact is what makes a formula so useful.

Inclusion
Explain that to use a formula, you need to substitute values for the variables. Then have students examine Example 1 and ask:
- *How many variables are in the formula* d = rt? **three**
- *How many values are given and what are they?* **Two; 52 miles per hour is the rate, r, and 3 hours is the time, t.**
- *What do you find by substituting the given values?* **the distance d in miles**

Then have students examine Example 2 and ask:
- *How many variables are in the formula* F = $\frac{n}{4}$ + 37? **two**
- *How many values are given and what are they?* **One; 88 chirps in one minute is the number of chirps, n.**
- *What do you find by substituting the given values?* **the outside temperature F in degrees Fahrenheit**

Error Prevention!

Elicit from students that the answers to both Examples 1 and 2 are real-world measurements that require specific units.

1. Plan

Lesson Preview

✓ **Check Skills You'll Need**

Finding Number Patterns
Lesson 2-1: Example 1. Extra
Practice p. 643.

Lesson Resources

Teaching Support includes:
Practice, Reteaching, Enrichment
Assessment, Reading & Literacy,
Activities, Transparencies,
Technology, CD-ROMs, Spanish,
and More

*See pp. 60G–60H for a complete
list of resources for this lesson.*

www.PHSchool.com
• Teacher Web Code: aak-5500

Plus

2. Teach

Math Background

Look for a pattern often
"partners" with other problem-
solving strategies. In this lesson,
the partner is *make a table*.

Teaching Notes

Tactile Learners
Give students several blank
2-in.-by-3-in. cards. Have them
label the 2-in. sides "2 seats"
and the 3-in. sides "3 seats."
Students use the cards to form
the rectangle chains and calculate
the number of available seats.

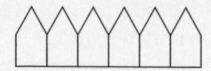
Additional Examples

1 Each side of a five-sided table
seats two people. Find the
number of available seats in
this chain of 6 tables. **40 seats**

2-4

Make a Table and Look for a Pattern

What You'll Learn

OBJECTIVE 1 To solve problems by making a table to find a pattern

... And Why

To organize information, as in Example 1

✓ **Check Skills You'll Need**

❓ For help, go to Lesson 2-1.

Write the next three terms in each number pattern.

1. 1, 4, 16, 64, . . .
256; 1,024; 4,096

2. 7, 14, 21, 28, . . .
35, 42, 49

3. 7, 14, 28, 56, . . .
112, 224, 448

4. 88, 79, 70, 61, . . .
52, 43, 34

5. 1.7, 2.8, 3.9, 5.0, . . .
6.1, 7.2, 8.3

6. 80, 40, 20, 10, . . .
5; 2.5; 1.25

OBJECTIVE 1

 Interactive lesson includes instant self-check, tutorials, and activities.

Solving Problems by Making a Table to Find a Pattern

When to Use This Strategy You can make a table to help you look for a pattern. Then you can use the pattern to solve a problem.

1 EXAMPLE Make a Table to Find a Pattern

A rectangular table seats two people on each end and three on each side. How many seats are available if you push the ends of five tables together?

Read and Understand There are five rectangular tables. Each table seats two people on each end and three on a side.

Plan and Solve To find the number of seats when five tables are pushed together, start by finding the number of seats when there are fewer tables.

1 table → 10 seats   2 tables → 16 seats   3 tables → 22 seats

Number of Tables	1	2	3	4	5
Number of Seats	10	16	22	28	34

Extend the pattern by adding 6 seats for each new table.

There will be 34 seats available.

Look Back and Check Five tables pushed together seat 5×6, or 30, people on the sides and 2 people on each end, or $30 + 2 + 2 = 34$.

✓ **Check Understanding** 1 **Number Sense** Is the number of available seats for 20 tables pushed together twice the number of seats for ten tables pushed together? Explain. **See above left.**

1. No; for 10 tables, there are 64 seats, but for 20 tables there are 124 seats (not 128).

Ongoing Assessment and Intervention

Before the Lesson
Diagnose prerequisite skills using:
• Check Skills You'll Need

During the Lesson
Monitor progress using:
• Check Understanding
• Additional Examples
• Test Prep

After the Lesson
Assess knowledge using:
• Lesson Quiz
• Computer Test Generator CD

Closure

How do you use patterns and tables to solve a problem? Sample: Make a table of data from a set of related problems and look for a pattern.

A Practice by Example

Example 1
(page 80)

Solve each problem by making a table and looking for a pattern.

1. Suppose a rectangular table seats four people on each side and three on each end. How many seats are available if the ends of seven tables are pushed together? **62 seats**

Need Help?
- Reread the problem.
- Identify the key facts and details.
- Tell the problem in your own words.
- Try a different strategy.
- Check your work.

2. **Savings** A high school student has started a new job. He plans to save $1 the first week, $2 the second week, $4 the third week, and $8 the fourth week. If this pattern of savings could continue, how much would he save the tenth week? **$512**

3. **a.** Fence posts are 10 feet apart. How many fence posts are required for a straight fence that is 100 feet long? **11 fence posts**
   b. What if the fence is circular? **10 fence posts**

4. **Geometry** A figure made from seven identical trapezoids is shown. Find the perimeter of the figure. **44.5**

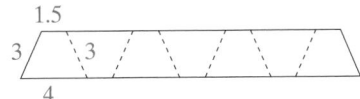

B Apply Your Skills

Choose a strategy to solve the problem.

Strategies

Draw a Diagram
Make a Graph
Make an Organized List
Make a Table and
  Look for a Pattern
Simulate a Problem
Solve a Simpler Problem
Try, Check, and Revise
Use Logical Reasoning
Work Backward
Write an Equation

5. **Cars** A car dealer sells at least 3 cars a day. On Monday morning there are 50 cars on the lot. By Friday evening of that week, what is the greatest number of cars the dealer can expect to have left? **35 cars**

6. **Jobs** Sanjay earns $13.00 each week from his paper route. He earns $.15 for each daily paper and $.35 for each Sunday paper he delivers. He delivers twice as many daily papers as Sunday papers. How many of each type does he deliver each week? **40 daily papers, 20 Sunday papers**

7. **Band** Tia, Lewis, and Jill play trombone. Wendi, Pali, and Nigel play baritone. How many different pairs of a trombone player and a baritone player are there? **9 pairs**

8. **Writing in Math** Your younger brother is pulling his sled up a hill. Each minute he moves forward 20 feet but also slides back 3 feet. Describe how you can determine the time he needs to pull his sled 130 feet forward.

8. Answers may vary. Sample: Make a table that shows how far he has gone (after going forward and slipping back) after 1 minute, 2 minutes, 3 minutes, and so on. Look for a pattern.

3. Practice

Assignment Guide

▼ **Objective 1**
  A B Core 1–10
  C Extension 11–12

Test Prep 13–16
Mixed Review 17–28

Error Prevention!

Exercise 1 To help students understand the problem situation, encourage them to first draw a diagram.

4. Assess

PowerPoint Lesson Quiz 2-4

1. Six people are in a room. Each person will shake hands once with each of the others in the room. How many handshakes will take place?
   15 handshakes

Alternative Assessment

Have students solve Example 1 by pushing together the sides with three people. Ask: *How many seats are available if five tables are used?* 26 *How many seats are added with each new table?* 4

Test Prep

Resources
For additional practice with a variety of test item formats:
- Test-Prep, p. 113
- Test-Taking Strategies, p. 109
- Test-Taking Strategies With Transparencies

👫 **Reaching All Students**

| **Below Level** Review the meaning of perimeter. Have students find the perimeters of several rectangles given the length and width. Use plain language to relate perimeter to the number of seats on each side of a table. | **Advanced Learners** Find the perimeter of this block of 25 rectangles. Each rectangle has length 3 meters and width 2 meters. **50 meters** | **Tactile Learners** See note on page 80. **Error Prevention** See note on page 81. |

Practice 2-4 Problem-Solving Strategy: Make a Table and Look for a Pattern

Solve the problem by making a table and looking for a pattern.

1. A radio station held a contest to give away concert tickets. On the first day, the first caller won. On the second day, the second caller won. On the third day, the fourth caller won. On the fourth day, the seventh caller won. Assuming that this pattern continued, did the thirtieth caller win?
   no

2. Three drawings are shown. What would the next three look like?
   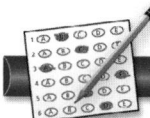

Chose a strategy to solve the problem.

3. Find two numbers with a product of 72 and a sum of 17.
   9 and 8

4. Juana is one year younger than her husband, Leo. The product of their ages is 650. How old are each?
   Juana, 25; Leo, 26

5. A carpenter charges a basic fee of $25, plus $22 per hour. How much will she charge Ms. Lin if she works for 18 hours?
   $421

6. The product of two numbers is 442. The sum of the two numbers is 43. Find the two numbers.
   26 and 17

7. There are 42 students who signed up for youth camp and 56 students who signed up for family camp. There are 15 students who are signed up for both camps. What is the total number of students who are signed up for camp?
   83 students

8. Marquetta charged the Lees a basic fee of $35, plus $25 per hour for repairing their washing machine. What did the Lees pay if it took Marquetta 2.5 hours to finish the job?
   $97.50

Reteaching 2-4 Problem Solving: Make a Table and Look for a Pattern

Stony Hollow School District has a softball playoff each spring for its 8 schools. Each school plays 1 game against every other school. The winner is the school with the greatest number of victories. How many playoff games are played in all?

Read and Understand What does the problem ask you to find? *You need to find the total number of playoff games.*
How many times will one school play any other school? *1 time*

Plan and Solve How can you simplify the problem? *Draw a diagram for a few schools. Look for a pattern.*

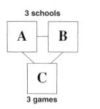 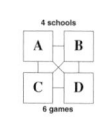

Make a table. Use the pattern you discovered to extend the table to 8 schools.

28 games must be played.

Look Back and Check Does the pattern make sense? *Yes. Each school added to the table plays each of the other schools once. So the number of games added is 1 less than the total number of schools.*

Number of Schools	Number of Games	
2	1	+2
3	3	+3
4	6	+4
5	10	+5
6	15	+6
7	21	+7
8	28	

Solve each problem by making a table and looking for a pattern.

1. School C won the Stony Hollow School District softball tournament. How many games did School C play in all?
   7 games

2. If the Stony Hollow School District had 10 schools, how many playoff games would there be in all?
   45 games

3. Each umpire is paid $25 per game. There are 2 umpires for each game. What is the total amount paid to umpires for an 8-team playoff?
   $1,400

4. Suppose one team wins all of its games. Why is it impossible for there to be a tie for the championship?
   Every other team has lost at least one game.

Enrichment 2-4 Problem-Solving Strategy: Make a Table and Look for a Pattern

Decision Making

Suppose you were offered these opportunities. Which choice would you make? Explain why you would make each choice. Show an equation, number pattern, or other mathematical explanation to support your decision.

1. Which would you rather receive? Why?
   a. One penny the first day, two pennies the second, four pennies the third, eight pennies the fourth, and so on for 30 days.
   b. One dollar each day for one month.
   Sample answer: Option a, which has a much greater balance; Option a, 0.01 + 0.02 + 0.04 + . . . = 10,737,418.23; Option b, $1 + $1 + $1 + . . . = 30.

2. Suppose you were paying money to a friend. Would that change your answer to Question 1? Why or why not?
   Sample answer: Yes; option b would be better because less money would be paid out.

3. Suppose you win a sweepstakes that pays money for thirty days. You have a choice of the two options below. The first day you are given $1. Which options would you choose? Why?
   a. The amount you receive is doubled every two days.
   b. The amount you receive is tripled every four days.
   Sample answer: Option a, which has the greater balance; Option a pattern: 1, 1, 2, 2, 4, 4, . . . ; winnings equal $65,534. Option b pattern: 1, 1, 1, 1, 3, 3, 3, 3, 9, 9, 9, 9, . . . ; winnings equal $8,746.

4. The table shows a graphic designer's fees to design magazine covers. Copy and complete the table.

Time (h)	1.5	2	2.5	3
Fees ($)	52.50	70.00	87.50	105.00

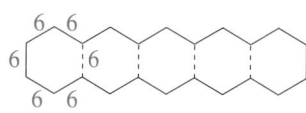

9. **Geometry** This figure is made from a chain of five identical hexagons. All sides are 6 inches. Find the perimeter of the figure. **132 in.**

10. **Sports** At the beginning of a singles badminton tournament, 24 players are paired. At the end of each match, the loser is eliminated. How many matches must be played to determine the winner of the tournament?
    23 matches

C Challenge

11. There are many ways to add any of the numbers 3, 5, 7, 9, 11, and 12 to get a sum of 20. Numbers may be repeated. One way to get a sum of 20 is 9 + 5 + 3 + 3. Find four other ways. **See margin.**

12. **Stretch Your Thinking** The sum of three consecutive odd numbers is 387. Find the numbers. **127, 129, and 131**

Test Prep

Multiple Choice

13. What is the value of $8x - 6$ when $x = 4$? **B**
    A. 16   B. 26   C. 32   D. 38

Take It to the NET
Online lesson quiz at
www.PHSchool.com
Web Code: aaa-0204

14. What is the value of $5n + 2$ when $n = 9$? **H**
    F. 43   G. 45   H. 47   I. 55

15. For which value of a does $7a - 2$ equal 40? **B**
    A. 4   B. 6   C. 10   D. 11

16. Which expression represents x decreased by 4? **F**
    F. $x - 4$ G. 4   H. $\frac{x}{4}$ I. $4 - x$

Mixed Review

Lesson 2-3 **Algebra** Write an expression for each word phrase.

17. 12 times c **12c**
18. 9 multiplied by d **9d**
19. n more than 4.5 **4.5 + n**
20. 6.8 less than g **g − 6.8**
21. r less than 13 **13 − r**
22. 8.1 decreased by y **8.1 − y**

Lesson 2-2 **Algebra** Evaluate each expression for $x = 6$.

23. $2x - 9$ **3**
24. $x + 15$ **21**
25. $4 \cdot (x + 2)$ **32**
26. $52.7 - 3x$ **34.7**
27. $4x + 3$ **27**
28. $5x - (x + 2)$ **22**

82 Chapter 2 Patterns and Variables

 GPS Use the Guided Problem Solving worksheet with Exercise 7.

11. Answers may vary.
    Sample:
    3 + 5 + 12 = 20;
    3 + 3 + 3 + 11 = 20;
    3 + 5 + 5 + 7 = 20;
    3 + 3 + 3 + 3 + 3 + 5 = 20

Writing in Math

Writing to Compare

When you are asked to compare two methods or concepts, you should
a. Describe each concept. Try to include diagrams to illustrate your descriptions.
b. State any similarities and differences between the two concepts.

 **EXAMPLE**

Compare the following two rules for patterns.

i. Start with 1 and add 2 repeatedly.
ii. Start with the first term. Multiply the term number by 2, and subtract 1 to get the value of the term.

a. Describe each rule.
   - The first rule begins with 1; you find the next term by adding 2.
     The pattern is 1, 3, 5, 7, 9, . . .
   - In the second rule, the first term is $1 \times 2 - 1 = 1$; the next term is $2 \times 2 - 1 = 3$, and so on.
     The pattern is 1, 3, 5, 7, 9, . . .

b. State any similarities or differences.
   - Both rules result in the same pattern: 1, 3, 5, 7, 9, . . .
   - The first rule uses the *previous term* to get the next term. The second rule uses the *term number* to get the new term.
   - The first rule uses addition; the second rule uses multiplication and subtraction.

EXERCISES

1–3. See margin.

1. Compare the following two rules for number patterns.

   i. Start with 1 and add 4 repeatedly.
   ii. Multiply the term number by 4, and then subtract 3 to get the term.

2. Compare the following two rules for number patterns.

   i. Multiply the term number by itself.
   ii. Start with 1. Find the next term by adding 3, and next by adding 5, and so on.

3. Compare "simplifying an expression" and "evaluating an expression."

1a. In the first rule, the pattern begins with 1; you find the next term by adding 4.

The pattern is 1, 5, 9, 13, 17, 21, . . .

In the second rule, the first term is $1 \times 4 - 3 = 1$; the next term is $2 \times 4 - 3 = 5$, and so on.

The pattern is 1, 5, 9, 13, 17, and 21, . . .

b. Similarities and Differences: Both rules result in the same pattern: 1, 5, 9, 13, 17, 21, . . .

The first rule uses the previous term to get the next term. The second

---

Writing in Math

Writing to Compare

Students need to be able to write coherently when formulating and sharing their mathematical ideas and methods. This feature introduces them to the kind of expository writing in which they compare or contrast two things to point out or explain their similarities and differences.

Teaching Notes

Discuss the importance of being able to communicate mathematical ideas confidently and effectively. Then have students identify the two "steps" involved in comparing two methods or concepts presented before the Example. **Sample: First describe each concept. Then state any similarities and differences.**

English Learners
As needed, review the vocabulary *term* and *rule*. Each number in the number pattern is a term. A rule is an explanation of how you begin and go from one term to the next.

EXAMPLE Teaching Tip

Examine with students the response presented for the two number patterns. Guide students to see that the similarities and differences have been clearly identified and explained.

Exercises
Have students work independently on the exercises. Then have them share their written comparisons within small groups. Ask students to adjust their responses based upon the group discussion. Guide them to look for ways to make their reasoning more explicit and concise.

rule uses the term number to get the new term.

The first rule uses addition. The second rule uses multiplication and subtraction.

2a–3b. See back of book.

83

2-5

1. Plan

Lesson Preview

 Check Skills You'll Need

Estimating by Rounding
Lesson 1-4: Example 1. Extra
Practice p. 642.

Lesson Resources

 Teaching Resources
Practice, Reteaching, Enrichment

 Reaching All Students
Practice Workbook 2-5
Spanish Practice Workbook 2-5
Guided Problem Solving 2-5

 Presentation Assistant Plus!
Transparencies
• Check Skills You'll Need 2-5
• Problem of the Day 2-5
• Additional Examples 2-5
• Student Edition Answers 2-5
• Lesson Quiz 2-5
PH Presentation Pro CD-ROM 2-5

ASSESSMENT SYSTEM

Computer Test Generator CD

 Technology
Resource Pro® CD-ROM
Computer Test Generator CD
PH Presentation Pro CD-ROM

www.PHSchool.com
Student Site
• Teacher Web Code: aak-5500
• Self-grading Lesson Quiz

PH SuccessNet Teacher Center
• Lesson Planner
• Resources

Plus

2-5

Using Number Sense to Solve One-Step Equations

Algebra

What You'll Learn

 OBJECTIVE 1
To use mental math to solve equations

 OBJECTIVE 2
To estimate solutions of equations

. . . And Why

To solve problems using mental math, as in Example 2

Check Skills You'll Need

? For help, go to Lesson 1-4.

Estimate by first rounding to the nearest whole number.

1. $5.3 + 1.07$ about 6
2. $6.1 - 2.4$ about 4
3. $8 - 6.3$ about 2
4. $12.04 + 3.6$ about 16
5. $24 + 0.085$ about 24
6. $4.5 - 0.106$ about 5

New Vocabulary   • equation   • open sentence   • solution

OBJECTIVE 1

 iTEXT Interactive lesson includes instant self-check, tutorials, and activities.

Using Mental Math to Solve Equations

An **equation** is a mathematical sentence that has an equal sign, =.
An equation is like a balanced scale. To be in balance, a scale must have
weights with the same total on each side. A true equation has equal values
on each side of the equal sign.

$$8 + 4 = 3 \times 4$$

If each side of the equation does not have the same value, the equation is
false. Use ≠ to indicate that an equation is false.

1 EXAMPLE   **Deciding If an Equation Is True or False**

Is the equation $6 + 13 = 18$ true or false?

$6 + 13 \overset{?}{=} 18$ ← Write the equation.
$\qquad 19$ ← Add $6 + 13$.
$\quad 19 \neq 18$ ← Compare.

The equation is false.

Reading Math

Read "$1 \overset{?}{=} 2$" as "Does 1 equal 2?" Read "$1 \neq 2$" as "1 does not equal 2."

 **Check Understanding**  Tell whether each equation is true or false.

a. $7 \times 9 = 63$ true
b. $4 + 5 = 45$ false
c. $70 - 39 = 41$ false

84   Chapter 2   Patterns and Variables

Ongoing Assessment and Intervention

Before the Lesson
Diagnose prerequisite skills using:
• Check Skills You'll Need

During the Lesson
Monitor progress using:
• Check Understanding
• Additional Examples
• Test Prep

After the Lesson
Assess knowledge using:
• Lesson Quiz
• Computer Test Generator CD

An equation with one or more variables is an **open sentence.** A **solution** of an equation is the value of the variable that makes the equation true. For example, $x - 15 = 12$ is an open sentence. Since $27 - 15 = 12$, the value 27 is the solution of $x - 15 = 12$.

You can use mental math to find the solution of some equations.

② EXAMPLE   Using Mental Math

Baseball Cards How many baseball cards do you need to add to the 14 cards you already own to have a total of 25 cards? Solve the equation $n + 14 = 25$, which models this situation.

What you think

$11 + 14 = 25$, so the solution is 11.

● You need 11 more cards.

✔ **Check Understanding** ② **Mental Math** Use mental math to solve each equation.

    a. $17 - x = 8$ **9**   **b.** $w \div 4 = 20$ **80**   **c.** $4.7 + c = 5.9$ **1.2**

OBJECTIVE

2 ⟩ Estimating Solutions of Equations

③ EXAMPLE   Estimating Solutions

Estimation Estimate the solution of each equation.

a. $n - 3.85 = 12.33$

    Round 3.85 and 12.33 to the nearest whole number

    $3.85 \approx 4$ $12.33 \approx 12$

    Estimate the solution of $n - 3.85 = 12.33$ by solving $n - 4 = 12$.

    Since $16 - 4 = 12$, the solution of $n - 3.85 = 12.33$ is about 16.

b. $12n = 105$

    Use compatible numbers: 12 divides 108 without a remainder and 108 is close to 105. Solve $12n = 108$ to estimate the solution of $12n = 105$.

        $12n = 108$

      $12 \cdot 9 = 108$

    The solution of $12n = 105$ is about 9.

✔ **Check Understanding** ③ **Estimation** Estimate the solution of each equation.

    a. $y - 6.14 = 23.08$ **b.** $8.2x = 49.3$ **c.** $d - 3.8 = 14.1$
       about 29   about 6   about 18

👥 Reaching All Students

Below Level Help students distinguish between an equation and an expression. An expression does not contain an equal sign. Emphasize that both equations and expressions may or may not have a variable.	**Advanced Learners** Have students use number sense or models to solve these equations.
	
	  $3r + 1 = 16$ **5**
	  $2m + 4 = 3m$ **4**
		Inclusion
		See note on page 85.
		Error Prevention
		See note on page 87.

---

2. Teach

Math Background

An *equation* is a mathematical sentence that contains an equal sign. If both *sides* of an equation are numerical expressions, then you can characterize the equation as true or false. If one side is an algebraic expression, then the equation is an *open sentence*; that is, it is neither true nor false. You determine whether a number is a *solution* to such an equation by evaluating the algebraic expression when that number replaces the variable. If the resulting statement is true, the number is a solution.

Teaching Notes

① EXAMPLE Teaching Tip

Point out that the equal sign with a question mark above ($\overset{?}{=}$) indicates that you do not yet know whether the equation is true or false.

② EXAMPLE Inclusion

Some students may not know what to do to begin. Encourage them to substitute a value for the variable and see if the result is true by using mental math.

🖥 Additional Examples

① Is the equation $24 - 16 = 8$ true or false? true

② Use mental math to solve each equation.

    a. $y - 7 = 15$ **22**

    b. $d \div 9 = 6$ **54**

③ Estimate the solution of each equation.

    a. $r \div 3 = 67$ about 210

    b. $b - 29.23 = 41.06$ about 70

Closure

- *What is an equation?* a mathematical sentence that contains an equal sign
- *What is a solution to an equation?* When an equation contains a variable, a solution is a value of the variable that makes the equation true.

85

Assignment Guide

 **Objective 1**

Ⓐ Ⓑ **Core** 1–15, 22–29, 31–34, 39

Ⓒ **Extension** 47

 **Objective 2**

Ⓐ Ⓑ **Core** 16–21, 30, 35–38, 40

Ⓒ **Extension** 41–46

Test Prep 48–53

Mixed Review 54–59

Practice 2-5   Using Number Sense to Solve One-Step Equations

Tell whether each equation is true or false.

1. $11 + 7 = 18$ true
2. $14 = 9 + 6$ false
3. $8 \times 7 = 42$ false

4. $3 + 1 + 4 = 7 + 1$ true
5. $8 \times 13 = 13 \times (6 + 2)$ true
6. $81 \div 7 = 9$ false

7. $31 + 4 = 41 + 3$ false
8. $3 \times (2 + 1) = 2 \times (3 + 1)$ false
9. $1 \times 63 = 1$ false

Use mental math to solve each equation.

10. $t + 19 = 47$ 28
11. $v + 14 = 76$ 62
12. $94 = y + 32$ 62
13. $86 = a + 29$ 57

14. $w - 53 = 76$ 129
15. $53 = z - 19$ 72
16. $112 = x - 74$ 186
17. $49 = c + 7$ 343

18. $b \div 24 = 4$ 96
19. $117 = 69 + a$ 48
20. $e - 84 = 79$ 163
21. $62 = g - 27$ 89

Estimate the solution of each equation.

22. $6d = 75$ 12
23. $7m = 24$ 3
24. $10 + x = 43$ 30

25. $a \div 6 = 21$ 120
26. $70 - t = 18$ 50
27. $9b = 42$ 5

28. $60 \div p = 16$ 3
29. $5n = 121$ 25
30. $24 = 49 \div w$ 2

Tell whether the given number is a solution of the equation.

31. $3x + 2x = 10; 2$ yes
32. $9y - 4y = 25; 3$ no
33. $6 \cdot 3n = 54; 18$ no

34. The winners of a slam dunk basketball competition receive t-shirts. The coach pays $50.40 for the entire team, and each t-shirt costs $4.20. Solve the equation $(4.20)n = 50.40$ to find the number of team members.   12 team members

---

Reteaching 2-5   Using Number Sense to Solve One-Step Equations

One way to solve some equations is to use mental math.

Example 1: Find the solution to the equation. $a + 5 = 10$

What you think:
If I add 5 to 5, the sum is 10.
$5 + 5 = 10$
So, $a = 5$.

Example 2: Find the solution to the equation. $y - 9 = 15$

What you think:
If I subtract 9 from 24, the difference is 15.
$24 - 9 = 15$
So, $y = 24$.

Example 3: Find the solution to the equation. $w \div 5 = 100$

What you think:
$w \div 5$ means w divided by 5.
I know that $500 \div 5 = 100$.
$500 \div 5 = 100$
So, $w = 500$.

Example 4: Find the solution to the equation. $4w = 24$

What you think:
$4w$ means 4 times w.
I know that $4 \cdot 6 = 24$.
So, $w = 6$.

Use mental math to solve each equation.

1. $4q = 12$ $q = 3$
2. $3w = 15$ $w = 5$

3. $h + 7 = 16$ $h = 9$
4. $h + 2 = 8$ $h = 6$

5. $h \div 3 = 12$ $h = 36$
6. $m + 2 = 10$ $m = 20$

7. $y - 8 = 12$ $y = 20$
8. $w - 5 = 8$ $w = 13$

Tell whether each equation is true or false.

9. $100 \div 8 = 25$ false
10. $18 + 25 = 43$ true
11. $1,100 - 200 = 900$ true

12. $16 \times 4 = 32$ false
13. $18 = 9 \div 2$ false
14. $32 = 16 + 16$ true

15. $77 + 12 = 99$ false
16. $2 \times 9 = 81$ false

📖 **Reading Math**

Algebraic is pronounced "al juh BRAY ik."

Many open sentences are true for only one solution. There are some open sentences that are true for every value you use for the variable. The algebraic equations that illustrate the number properties below are true for all values of a, b, and c.

> **Key Concepts**   **Number Properties**
>
> **Identity Properties**
>
> The sum of 0 and any number is that number.
>
> **Algebra** $0 + a = a$ **Arithmetic** $0 + 9 = 9$
>
> The product of 1 and any number is that number.
>
> **Algebra** $1 \cdot a = a$ **Arithmetic** $1 \cdot 9 = 9$
>
> **Commutative Properties**
>
> Changing the order of addends or factors does not change the sum or the product.
>
> **Algebra** $a + b = b + a$ $a \cdot b = b \cdot a$
>
> **Arithmetic** $9 + 6 = 6 + 9$ $9 \cdot 6 = 6 \cdot 9$
>
> **Associative Properties**
>
> Changing the grouping of numbers does not change the sum or the product.
>
> **Algebra** $a + (b + c) = (a + b) + c$ $a(bc) = (ab)c$
>
> **Arithmetic** $9 + (6 + 4) = (9 + 6) + 4$ $9 \cdot (6 \cdot 4) = (9 \cdot 6) \cdot 4$

EXERCISES

❓ For more practice, see *Extra Practice*.

Ⓐ **Practice by Example**   **Tell whether each equation is true or false.**

Example 1 (page 84)

1. $3 + 50 = 80$ false
2. $4 \times 7 = 28$ true
3. $25 = 35 + 10$ false

4. $0 \times 5.7 = 5.7$ false
5. $54 \div 9 = 7$ false
6. $3 + 4 + 6 = 3 + 10$ true

Example 2 (page 85)

Mental Math   **Use mental math to solve each equation.**

7. $x + 5 = 7$ 2
8. $4x = 32$ 8
9. $25 = 25 - x$ 0
10. $x + 2 = 6.3$ 4.3

11. $g \div 4 = 2$ 8
12. $p - 6 = 25$ 31
13. $x + 14 = 23$ 9
14. $1.2 = a + 0.2$ 1

🌐 **15. Sports** A hockey team spends $75 on chin straps. Each strap costs $5. Solve the equation $5n = 75$ to find how many straps the team buys.   15 straps

86   **Chapter 2**   Patterns and Variables

GPS   Use the Guided Problem Solving worksheet with Exercise 29.

Example 3
(page 85)

Estimation **Estimate the solution of each equation.**
16–21. Answers may vary. Samples are given.

16. $6d = 75$
about 12

17. $k + 9.3 = 28.4$
about 19

18. $p \div 4 = 7.99$
about 32

19. $420 = 63n$
about 7

20. $b - 2.33 = 6.8$
about 9

21. $w + 12.8 = 68.7$
about 56

B **Apply Your Skills**

Tell whether each equation is true or false.

22. $0 + 3a = 3a$ **true**

23. $1 \cdot 3a = 3a$ **true**

24. $3 \cdot 5 + x = 8 + x$
false

Tell whether the given number is a solution of the equation.

25. $3x + 2x = 10;\ 2$
yes

26. $120n = 40;\ 30$
no

27. $b + b = 22;\ 2$
no

 28. Shopping Suppose you spent $20 for a shirt. You also bought a jacket, but you cannot find the sales receipt. You know that the total amount you spent was $75. Solve the equation $20 + j = 75$ to find how much you spent on the jacket. **$55**

29. Pollution When burned, 18 gallons of gasoline produce about
GPS 360 pounds of carbon dioxide. Solve the equation $18n = 360$ to find how much carbon dioxide 1 gallon produces. **20 lb**

30. Answers may vary. Sample: After riding the school bus for 7.5 miles, Sarah walks 1.2 miles to her house. What is the distance from Sarah's house to her school?

30. Writing in Math Write a real-world problem that could be modeled by the equation $x - 7.5 = 1.2$.

Reasoning **Tell whether each equation is true or false. Explain.**
31–34. See margin for explanations.

31. $x + 1 = x$ **false**

32. $3 + x = 1 + 2 + x$ **true**

33. $98n = (100 - 2)n$ **true**

34. $8 + x = x + 8$ **true**

Tell which choice, 100, 500, or 1,000, is the best estimate of the solution.

35. $4{,}272 = 53x$
100

36. $n - 109.15 = 326.5$
500

37. $m \div 47 = 8.89$
500

38. You have 1.5 pounds of pecans, a pounds of almonds, and 2.7 pounds of peanuts. You have 6 pounds of nuts altogether. To find how many pounds of almonds you have, solve the equation $1.5 + a + 2.7 = 6$, which models this situation. **1.8 lb**

39. Error Analysis Your friend claims that the equation $2x = 3x$ is always false. Do you agree with your friend? Explain. **No; $2x = 3x$ is true if $x = 0$.**

40. Writing in Math Explain how to estimate the solution of the equation $s - 4.87 = 32.42$. **Answers may vary. Sample: Use front-end estimation to estimate $32.42 + 4.8$ as about 37.**

Error Prevention!

Exercises 7–8 Students might identify the solution as the number at the right of the equal sign in the original equation. Remind them that a solution is a value of the variable that makes the equation true. It replaces the variable in the original equation.

Exercise 9 Some students may think the variable has to be on the left side.

Exercises 25, 27 Make sure students understand that the variable must be replaced by the same number each time it occurs in the equation.

Geometry Connection
Exercise 47 Students might think that, since the figures at the lower left and lower right are squares, they are not rectangles. Remind them that a rectangle is a four-sided polygon with four right angles. Since a square has four right angles, a square is a type of rectangle.

31. 1 more than a number can never be equal to the number.

34. The order of the addends does not matter.

32. $1 + 2 + x$ simplifies to $3 + x$. $3 + x = 3 + x$.

33. $(100 - 2)$ simplifies to 98. $98n = 98n$

 **Lesson Quiz 2-5**

Tell whether each equation is true or false.

1. $3 + 29 = 32$ true

2. $3 + 4 = 4 + 3 - 1$ false

Estimate the solution of each equation.

3. $c - 5.65 = 38.25$ about 44

4. $8.3z = 57.4$ about 7

Use mental math to solve each equation.

5. $g \div 6 = 8$ $g = 48$

6. $h + 20 = 30$ $h = 10$

Alternative Assessment

Each student in a pair writes four equations that contain only numbers. Partners trade papers and identify whether each of the other's equations are true or false.

Test Prep

Resources

For additional practice with a variety of test item formats:
- Test-Prep, p. 113
- Test-Taking Strategies, p. 109
- Test-Taking Strategies With Transparencies

Enrichment 2-5 Using Number Sense to Solve One-Step Equations
Critical Thinking

A marathon runner runs 26 miles to complete a race. A marathoner ran a race in the following segments:
- 50 minutes for the first 10 miles
- 48 minutes for the next 8 miles
- 28 minutes for the next 4 miles
- 20 minutes for the final 4 miles

What was the runner's speed for each segment?

1. To calculate the speed for each race segment, what kind of equation will you set up, a multiplication equation or a division equation? Explain.
   Sample answer: A division equation; divide the number of miles by the time to get the speed for each segment.

2. Write an equation you can use to find the time for each race segment. Make sure you define all variables.
   Sample answer: $s = d \div t$, where d = miles for each segment, s = speed, and t = time for each segment.

3. Use your equation from Exercise 2 to complete the table for each race segment. Round your answers to the nearest hundredth.

Number of miles	Time per segment	Miles per minute
10	50 minutes	0.20
8	48 minutes	0.17
4	28 minutes	0.14
4	20 minutes	0.20

4. Find the total time, in minutes, it took the runner to run the entire race. **146 minutes**

5. Another marathon runner ran the 26-mile race at a constant speed. The runner finished the race in 2.85 hours. How can you find the runner's time in minutes?
   Multiply 2.85 by 60.

6. Calculate the runner's speed in Exercise 5 to the nearest hundredth.
   about 0.15 miles per minute

7. Who finished the race first, the runner with a varied speed or the runner with a constant speed?
   the runner with the varied speed

88

C Challenge **Number Sense Without solving the equations, tell if each solution is less than, greater than, or equal to 10.**

41. $x + 0.6 = 15$
greater than

42. $999 = x + 990$
less than

43. $10x = 15$
less than

44. $1 = 0.1x$
equal to

45. $x + 32 = 40$
less than

46. $5x = 50$
equal to

47. Stretch Your Thinking How many different rectangles are in the figure at the right? **10**

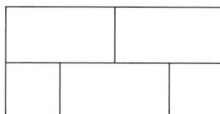

Test Prep

Multiple Choice

48. What is the solution of $n + 62 = 100$? **C**
A. 100　　　B. 62　　　C. 38　　　D. 26

49. What is the solution of $18 = 54 - x$? **H**
F. 72　　　G. 54　　　H. 36　　　I. 18

50. What is the solution of $60 \div n = 4$? **B**
A. 12　　　B. 15　　　C. 64　　　D. 240

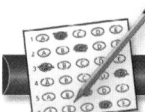 **Take It to the NET**
Online lesson quiz at
www.PHSchool.com
Web Code: aaa-0205

51. What is the solution of $5f = 140$? **G**
F. 5　　　G. 28　　　H. 140　　　I. 700

52. What is the solution of $c \div 4 = 12$? **C**
A. 3　　　B. 8　　　C. 48　　　D. 124

53. Which equation has the solution 22? **G**
F. $2(44) = s$　　　G. $2s = 44$　　　H. $2 \div s = 44$　　　I. $2 = 44s$

Mixed Review

Lesson 2-1　**Algebra** **Write the next three terms in each number pattern.**

54. $100, 97, 94, 91, \ldots$ **88, 85, 82**

55. $4, 12, 36, 108, \ldots$
324, 972, 2,916

56. **Algebra** Write the first six terms in the pattern. *Start with 3.2 and multiply by 5 repeatedly.* **3.2; 16; 80; 400; 2,000; 10,000**

Lesson 1-10　**Find the value of each expression.**

57. $7 \times 8 + 4$
60

58. $2.2 + 3.1 \times 7$
23.9

59. $9.6 \div 2.4 \times 4$
16

Investigation

1.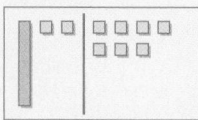

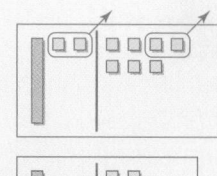

2.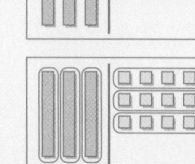

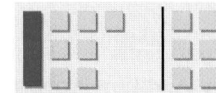

Using Models to Solve Equations

Models can help you understand the steps you need to follow to solve equations.

1 EXAMPLE Solving Equations by Subtracting

Solve $x + 7 = 15$.

$x + 7 = 15$ ← Model the equation.

$\begin{array}{rr} x + 7 = & 15 \\ -7 & -7 \end{array}$ ← Remove 7 tiles from each side.

$x \quad = \quad 8$ ← Find the solution.

2 EXAMPLE Solving Equations by Dividing

Solve $4x = 12$.

$4x = 12$ ← Model the equation.

$4x \div 4 = 12 \div 4$ ← Divide each side of the equation into 4 equal parts.

$x = 3$ ← Find the solution.

EXERCISES

Solve each equation by drawing or using tiles. 1–6. See margin for tiles.

1. $x + 2 = 7$ 5

2. $3g = 12$ 4

3. $a + 9 = 12$ 3

4. $5c = 35$ 7

5. $8 = n + 5$ 3

6. $7m = 21$ 3

Investigation   Using Models to Solve Equations   **89**

3.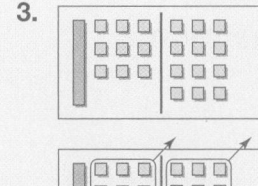

4–6. See back of book.

○ Investigation

Using Models to Solve Equations

This investigation shows students how to use algebra tiles to model and solve one-step equations.

Optional Materials

- algebra tiles
- Classroom Aid 37

Resources

Student Manipulatives Kit

Teaching Notes

Students were introduced to algebra tiles in Lesson 2-2 to model algebraic expressions. You may want to review the distinction between an *x*-tile and a unit tile.

1 EXAMPLE Visual Learners

Have students examine the models and ask:
- *What is different about the model for an equation and the models for an expression?* The vertical bar that divides the tiles into two groups or expressions.
- *What does the vertical bar correspond to in the algebra equation* $x + 7 = 15$? the equal sign, =

2 EXAMPLE Teaching Tip

Have students examine the models and ask:
- *Why are the x-tiles and unit tiles divided into 4 equal groups?* Sample: The expression 4x describes 4 groups of x.
- *Why is there only one x-tile and one unit tile in the final model?* Sample: The model illustrates x = 3, which is one of the 4 equal parts.

Inclusion

Students with impaired coordination might have difficulty manipulating or drawing the algebra tiles. Have students work in pairs or small groups to complete the exercises.

2-6

2-6

Solving Addition and Subtraction Equations

Lesson Preview

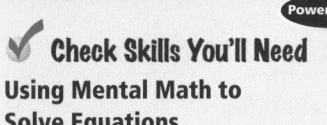

✓ **Check Skills You'll Need** 🖥 PowerPoint

Using Mental Math to Solve Equations
Lesson 2-5: Example 2. Extra Practice p. 643.

Lesson Resources

📁 **Teaching Resources**
Practice, Reteaching, Enrichment

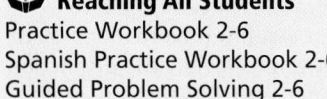 **Reaching All Students**
Practice Workbook 2-6
Spanish Practice Workbook 2-6
Guided Problem Solving 2-6
Hands-On Activities 6

⏰ **Presentation Assistant Plus!**
Transparencies
• Check Skills You'll Need 2-6
• Problem of the Day 2-6
• Additional Examples 2-6
• Student Edition Answers 2-6
• Lesson Quiz 2-6
• Classroom Aid 8, 37
PH Presentation Pro CD-ROM 2-6

ASSESSMENT SYSTEM PRENTICE HALL

Computer Test Generator CD

💻 **Technology**
Resource Pro® CD-ROM
Computer Test Generator CD
PH Presentation Pro CD-ROM

💻 **www.PHSchool.com**
Student Site
• Teacher Web Code: aak-5500
• Algebra Readiness Puzzles 71
• Self-grading Lesson Quiz

PH SuccessNet Teacher Center
• Lesson Planner
• Resources

Plus 🅸TEXT

What You'll Learn

 OBJECTIVE 1 To solve equations by subtracting

 OBJECTIVE 2 To solve equations by adding

. . . And Why

To solve problems involving weights, as in Example 2

✓ Check Skills You'll Need

❓ For help, go to Lesson 2-5.

Use mental math to solve each equation.

1. $3x = 27$ **9**
2. $4 = 5 - t$ **1**
3. $x + 4 = 74$ **70**
4. $6 \div y = 3$ **2**
5. $p \div 3 = 3$ **9**
6. $7x = 21$ **3**

New Vocabulary

• inverse operations • Subtraction Property of Equality • Addition Property of Equality

---

OBJECTIVE 1   Interactive lesson includes instant self-check, tutorials, and activities.

Solving Equations by Subtracting

In the equation $x + 4 = 38$, 4 is added to the variable. You undo adding 4 by subtracting 4. Operations that *undo* each other, such as addition and subtraction, are **inverse operations.**

> **Key Concepts** **Subtraction Property of Equality**
>
> If you subtract the same value from each side of an equation, the two sides remain equal.
>
> | **Arithmetic** | **Algebra** |
> |---|---|
> | $2 \cdot 3 = 6$, so $2 \cdot 3 - 4 = 6 - 4$. | If $a = b$, then $a - c = b - c$. |

1 EXAMPLE **Solving Equations by Subtracting**

Solve $x + 4 = 38$.

Get x alone on one side of the equation.

$$\begin{array}{rl} x + 4 = & 38 \\ \underline{-4 \quad -4} & \quad \leftarrow \text{Subtract 4 from each side to undo the addition and get } x \text{ by itself.} \\ x = & 34 \quad \leftarrow \text{Simplify.} \end{array}$$

Check $x + 4 = 38$ ← Check your solution in the original equation.

$34 + 4 \overset{?}{=} 38$ ← Substitute 34 for x.

$38 = 38$ ✓

✓ **Check Understanding** ① Solve $w + 4.3 = 9.1$. Check the solution. **4.8**

⚡ **Ongoing Assessment and Intervention**

Before the Lesson	**During the Lesson**	**After the Lesson**
Diagnose prerequisite skills using:	Monitor progress using:	Assess knowledge using:
• Check Skills You'll Need	• Check Understanding	• Lesson Quiz
	• Additional Examples	• Computer Test Generator CD
	• Test Prep	

When you solve real-world problems using equations, drawing a diagram first may help you. The model at the right indicates that the whole = part + part.

Whole	
Part	Part

 **2 EXAMPLE** <u>Real-World</u> <u>Problem Solving</u>

Cats When a kitten was brought home from the animal shelter, it weighed 15 ounces. After two years, the kitten had grown into a cat weighing 120 ounces. How many ounces did the cat gain?

Weight after 2 years	
Original weight	Ounces gained

Let g = the ounces gained.

120	
15	g

The equation $15 + g = 120$ models this situation.

$$15 + g = 120$$

$$
\begin{array}{rcl}
15 + g &=& 120 \\
-15 && -15 \quad \leftarrow \text{Subtract 15 from each side to undo the addition.} \\
\hline
g &=& 105 \quad \leftarrow \text{Simplify.}
\end{array}
$$

The cat gained 105 ounces.

 **Check Understanding** **2** A cat has gained 1.8 pounds since its checkup a year ago. It now weighs 11.6 pounds. How much did it weigh at its checkup last year? **9.8 lb**

OBJECTIVE

2 **Solving Equations by Adding**

Just as you can subtract the same amount from each side of an equation, you can add the same amount to each side of an equation.

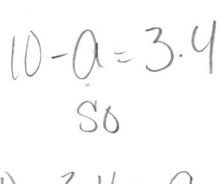
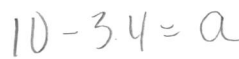
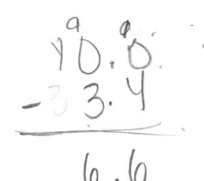

Key Concepts **Addition Property of Equality**

If you add the same value to each side of an equation the two sides remain equal.

Arithmetic	Algebra
$2 \cdot 3 = 6$, so $2 \cdot 3 + 4 = 6 + 4$.	If $a = b$, then $a + c = b + c$.

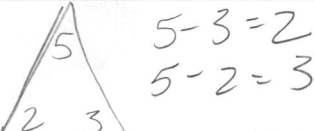
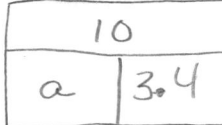

2-6 Solving Addition and Subtraction Equations **91**

Reaching All Students

| **Below Level** Give students several addition/subtraction exercises like these to illustrate inverse operations.

32 + 6 **38**   28 − 7 **21**
38 − 6 **32**   21 + 7 **28** | **Advanced Learners** Exactly one of these equations has a solution. Which equation is it, and what is the solution? $n + n = 2$; **1**

$n + 2 = n$ $n − 2 = n$
$n + n = 2$ $n − n = 2$ | **Diversity**
See note on page 91.
Alternative Method
See notes on pages 91 and 92. |

---

2. Teach

Professional Development

Math Background

In Lesson 2-5 students solved equations using number sense. This method is useful in solving relatively simple equations. In this lesson, students will begin to look at algebraic methods that can be used to solve equations. At the heart of these algebraic methods is the concept of *inverse operations*: Addition and subtraction "undo" each other; and multiplication and division "undo" each other.

Teaching Notes

Error Prevention!

Stress the importance of checking a proposed solution by substituting it for the variable *in the original equation*.

1 EXAMPLE Alternative Method

Some students are better able to visualize the process of subtracting the same number from each side when the subtraction is performed vertically.

$$
\begin{array}{rcl}
x + 4 &=& 38 \\
-4 &=& -4 \\
\hline
x &=& 34
\end{array}
$$

2 EXAMPLE Diversity

Ask a volunteer to explain what an animal shelter is and how individuals can adopt a pet.

Error Prevention!

In Check Understanding 2, students may obtain the incorrect solution 13.4 because of careless reading. Suggest that students translate the words into an equation before trying to solve the problem.

PowerPoint

Additional Examples

1 Solve $h + 9 = 14$. **5**

2 Today Anna discovered that she is 4 in. taller than she was last year at this time. Anna's height today is 51 in. What was Anna's height last year at this time? **47 in.**

91

3 EXAMPLE Alternative Method

Parallel the alternative method suggested for Example 1 by showing students how to perform the addition vertically.

$$
\begin{aligned}
c - 12 &= 43 \\
+ 12 &= +12 \\
\hline
c &= 55
\end{aligned}
$$

4 EXAMPLE Teaching Tip

Stress the importance of always indicating what quantity the variable represents.

**PowerPoint
Additional Examples**

3 Solve $p - 22.3 = 5.08$.
27.38

4 The sale price of a CD is $11.49. This is $3.50 less than the regular price of the CD. What is the regular price of the CD? $14.99

Closure

• *What are inverse operations?* operations that undo each other, such as addition and subtraction
• *How do you use subtraction to solve an equation?* Sample: For an equation like $y + 4 = 20$, subtract 4 from each side to undo the addition; then simplify to get $y = 16$.
• *How do you use addition to solve an equation?* Sample: For an equation like $m - 9 = 17$, add 9 to each side to undo the subtraction; then simplify to get $m = 26$.

When you have an equation with a number subtracted on one side, add that number to each side of the equation to solve the equations.

3 EXAMPLE Solving Equations by Adding

Solve $c - 12 = 43$.

$c - 12 + 12 = 43 + 12$ ← Add 12 to undo the subtraction.

$c = 55$ ← Simplify.

✓ **Check Understanding** **3** Solve each equation.

a. $n - 53 = 28$ **81** **b.** $x - 43 = 12$ **55** **c.** $k - 6.4 = 0$ **6.4**

Another way to model a real-world situation is to start by stating the problem as simply as you can. Then write an equation from your statement.

4 EXAMPLE Real-World Problem Solving

Savings Susan saved $87.11. Susan's savings are $9.62 less than Dorinne's savings. How much has Dorinne saved?

| Words | Susan's savings | are | $9.62 | less than | Dorinne's savings |

Let d = Dorinne's savings.

| Equation | $87.11 | = | d | − | $9.62 |

$d - 9.62 = 87.11$ ← Write the equation.

$+ 9.62 \quad + 9.62$ ← Add 9.62 to each side to undo the subtraction.

$d = 96.73$ ← Simplify.

Dorinne has saved $96.73.

✓ **Check Understanding** **4** The temperature dropped 9°F between 7 P.M. and midnight. It was 54°F at midnight. Write and solve an equation to find the temperature at 7 P.M.
t = temperature at 7:00 P.M.
$t - 9 = 54$; 63°F

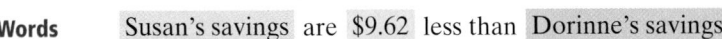

EXERCISES

 For more practice, see *Extra Practice*.

A Practice by Example

Solve each equation. Then check the solution.

Example 1
(page 90)

1. $x + 46 = 72$ **26** **2.** $d + 5 = 53$ **48** **3.** $y + 12 = 64$ **52**

4. $n + 17 = 56$ **39** **5.** $m + 1.3 = 2.8$ **1.5** **6.** $n + 4.5 = 10.8$ **6.3**

7. $k + 8 = 15$ **7** **8.** $2.7 + g = 8.2$ **5.5** **9.** $2.6 = 1.9 + g$ **0.7**

92 Chapter 2 Patterns and Variables

Example 2
(page 91)

10. s = number of minutes a sea otter can hold its breath; $s + 10 = 15$; $s = 5$

11. s = sale price of the jeans; $s + 4.99 = 29.97$; $s = \$24.98$

Write and solve an equation. Then check the solution.

 10. **Biology** A hippopotamus can hold its breath for about 15 minutes. A sea otter can hold its breath about 10 minutes less than a hippopotamus. How long can a sea otter hold its breath?

11. **Sale** Jeans that were on sale last week now cost \$29.97. The savings were \$4.99. What was the sale price of the jeans?

Example 3
(page 92)

Solve each equation.

12. $x - 16 = 72$ 88

13. $x - 5.7 = 5.7$ 11.4

14. $n - 2 = 18$ 20

15. $d - 8 = 40$ 48

16. $y - 12 = 23$ 35

17. $k - 56 = 107$ 163

18. $5.8 = n - 0.35$ 6.15

19. $0.6 = h - 2.9$ 3.5

20. $q - 8 = 154$ 162

Example 4
(page 92)

21. **Biology** The height of the female giraffe in one zoo is 14.1 feet. The female is 3.2 feet shorter than the male giraffe. Write and solve an equation to find the male's height. m = height of male giraffe; $m - 3.2 = 14.1$; 17.3 feet

 **Apply Your Skills**

Solve each equation.

10.18
22. $y + 13.82 = 24$

8.2
23. $1.5 + x = 9.7$

10
24. $p - 1.23 = 8.77$

25. $0.4 + g = 1.9$
1.5

26. $n - 10.5 = 11.7$
22.2

27. $11.4 = h + 5.9$
5.5

29. No; using estimation, about 60 + about 30 = about 90, and 90 is not at all close to 31.8.

28. **Writing in Math** Write a real-world problem that can be solved by writing an equation that contains a variable. Then solve the equation. Check students' work.

29. **Estimation** Use estimation to check whether 59.4 is a reasonable solution for the equation $x + 27.6 = 31.8$. Explain your answer. **See left.**

30. You buy a poster and a framing kit. The total cost is \$18.95. You have [GPS] \$7.05 left in your wallet. Write and solve an equation to find how much money was in your wallet before these purchases.
$m - 18.95 = 7.05$; $m = \$26$

31. **National Seashores** The area of Cape Canaveral National Seashore in Florida is approximately 57,627 acres. The area of Cape Cod National Seashore in Massachusetts is approximately 14,101 acres smaller. Write and solve an equation to find the approximate area of Cape Cod National Seashore. **Let c = approximate area of Cape Cod National Seashore; $c + 14,101 = 57,627$; 43,526 acres**

32. **a.** **Data File, p. 61** Write and solve an equation to find the last Year of the Monkey prior to 2004. **32a–b. See margin.**

b. Write and solve an equation to find the next Year of the Dragon.

32a. Equations may vary. Sample: let m = last Year of the Monkey prior to 2004; $2004 - 12 = m$ $m = 1992$

b. Let d = the next Year of the Dragon $d = 2000 + 12$ $d = 2012$

 Use the Guided Problem Solving worksheet with Exercise 30.

---

3. Practice

Assignment Guide

1 **Objective 1**
Ⓐ Ⓑ **Core** 1–11, 29–31
Ⓒ **Extension** 35

2 **Objective 2**
Ⓐ Ⓑ **Core** 12–28, 32
Ⓒ **Extension** 33–34

Test Prep 36–40
Mixed Review 41–45

Error Prevention!

Exercises 1–9 Watch for students who try to add or subtract on only one side of the equal sign.

Practice 2-6 Solving Addition and Subtraction Equations

13.4

Solve each equation. Then check each solution.

1. $h + 3.6 = 8.6$
$h = $ 5

2. $b - 7 = 12.3$
$b = $ 19.3

3. $9 + t = 12.4$
$t = $ 3.4

4. $10 - a = 3.4$
$a = $ 6.6

5. $r + 2.2 = 5.7$
$r = $ 3.5

6. $n - 6.2 = 11.4$
$n = $ 17.6

7. $8 + j = 15.34$
$j = $ 7.34

8. $14.3 - g = 6.3$
$g = $ 8

9. $m + 7.3 = 9.1$
$m = $ 1.8

10. $d - 10.3 = 1.8$
$d = $ 12.1

11. $8.3 + f = 10.5$
$f = $ 4.2

12. $3.9 - c = 3.1$
$c = $ 0.8

13. $q + \$18.30 = \$20$
$q = $ \$1.70

14. $k - 5.1 = 2.9$
$k = $ 8

15. $3.89 + x = 5.2$
$x = $ 1.31

16. $18.4 - u = 9.6$
$u = $ 8.8

17. $e + 2.7 = 10$
$e = $ 7.3

18. $r - 7.5 = 3.1$
$r = $ 10.6

19. $5.62 + p = 5.99$
$p = $ 0.37

20. $8.3 - y = 2.7$
$y = $ 5.6

Write and solve an equation. Then check each solution.

21. The top three best-selling albums of all time are Michael Jackson's *Thriller* (24 million copies), Fleetwood Mac's *Rumours* (17 million copies), and Boston's *Boston* (b million copies). The three albums sold a combined total of 56 million copies. How many million copies of *Boston* were sold?
$24 + 17 + b = 56$; $b = 15$ million copies

22. Yesterday, Stephanie spent \$38.72 on new shoes and \$23.19 on computer software. When she was finished, she had \$31.18. How much money did she have before she went shopping?
$m - \$38.72 - \$23.19 = \$31.18$; $m = \$93.09$

23. The owner of a used music store bought a compact disc for \$4.70 and sold it for \$9.45. Write and solve an equation to find the profit.
$\$4.70 + p = \$9.45$; $p = \$4.75$

Solve each equation.

24. $x - 10 = 89$ 99
25. $n + 14 = 73$ 59
26. $15 - y = 14$ 1
27. $38 + b = 42$ 4
28. $x - 7 = 77$ 84
29. $a + 22 = 120$ 98
30. $42 - z = 16$ 26
31. $19 + m = 19$ 0
32. $d - 6 = 52$ 58

Reteaching 2-6 Solving Addition and Subtraction Equations

Addition Equations	**Subtraction Equations**
There are 4 more than needed to fill the x box.	$r - 3 = 9$
$x + 4 = 11$	To *solve* this equation, find the value of r. Since 3 is subtracted from r, add 3 to both sides. $r - 3 = 9$ $r - 3 + 3 = 9 + 3$ $r = 12$
To *solve* this equation, find the value of x that makes the scales balance. Since 4 is added to x, subtract 4 from both sides. $x + 4 = 11$ $x + 4 - 4 = 11 - 4$ $x = 7$ The *solution* to the equation is $x = 7$.	The *solution* to the equation is $r = 12$.

Solve each equation.

1. $a + 15 = 31$
$a + 15 - 15 = 31 - 15$
$a = 16$

2. $5 = x - 20$
$5 + 20 = x - 20 + 20$
$25 = x$

3. $19 + t = 51$
32

4. $p - 11 = 12$
23

5. $60 = n + 30$
30

6. $71 = b - 29$
100

7. $86 + m = 107$
21

8. $w + 349 = 761$
412

9. $50 - y = 30$
20

10. $d - 125 = 75$
200

11. A car dealer purchased a car for \$2,000 and then sold it for \$3,200. Write and solve an equation to find the profit.
$\$2,000 + p = \$3,200$; $p = \$1,200$

Alternative Assessment

Provide small groups of students with a balance scale, centimeter cubes, and several addition and subtraction equations that deal with whole numbers. Have students model the equations on the balance. For example, for the equation $x + 9 = 25$, have them place 9 cubes on one pan and 25 on the other. Then have them take away enough cubes from 25 so that the pans balance. Ask students to record the solution to each equation.

Test Prep

Resources
For additional practice with a variety of test item formats:
• Test-Prep, p. 113
• Test-Taking Strategies, p. 109
• Test-Taking Strategies With Transparencies

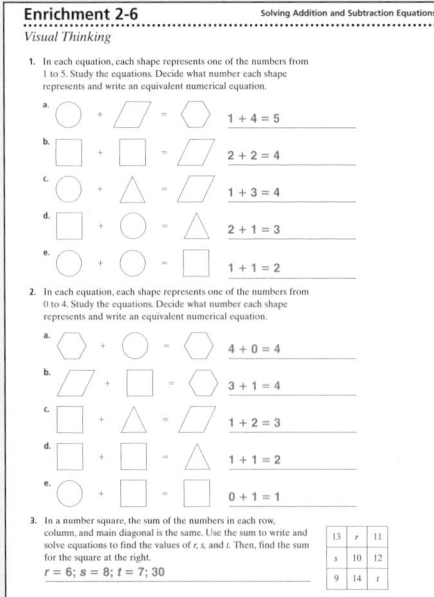

94

C Challenge

The earliest known number square, the *lo-shu,* was written on a tortoise shell. It may have looked like this drawing.

33. **Error Analysis** Sonja says the solution to $y - 1,214 = 31,214$ is 30,000. What is her error? **She subtracted 1,214 from 31,214 when she should have added.**

34. **Number Squares** In a number square, the sum of the numbers in each row, column, and main diagonal is the same. **34a–b. See margin.**
    a. Find the sum for the square at the right.
    b. Use the sum to write and solve equations to find the values of a, b, and c.

a	7	2
1	5	b
8	c	4

35. **Stretch Your Thinking** A large stepping stone in a garden weighs five times as much as a brick. Together, one brick and one stepping stone weigh 30 pounds. Find the weight of the stepping stone.
    25 pounds

Test Prep

Multiple Choice

36. Which of the following operations would you use to get the variable in $x + 6 = 27$ alone on one side of the equation? **B**
    A. Add 6 to both sides.   B. Subtract 6 from both sides.
    C. Add 27 to both sides.   D. Subtract 27 from both sides.

37. What is the solution of $x - 42 = 17$? **I**
    F. 25   G. 35   H. 49   I. 59

38. What is the solution of $n + 16 = 85$? **D**
    A. 86   B. 83   C. 73   D. 69

39. What is the solution of $z - 2.71 = 5$? **I**
    F. 2.29   G. 2.76   H. 3.21   I. 7.71

40. What is the solution of $86.04 = 57.2 + y$? **D**
    A. 143.24   B. 29.24   C. 29.2   D. 28.84

Mixed Review

Lesson 2-1   41. **Algebra** Write the first five terms in the number pattern *start with 37 and add 3 repeatedly.* **37; 40; 43; 46; 49**

Lesson 1-10   **Find the value of each expression.**

42. $24 \div 4 - 2 \times 3$ **0**   43. $24 \div 3 - 2 \times 4$ **0**

44. $24 \div (3 - 2) \times 4$ **96**   45. $(24 \div 3 - 2) \times 4$ **24**

94   **Chapter 2** Patterns and Variables

34a. 15; the sum of the diagonal numbers $8 + 5 + 2 = 15$.

b. $a + 1 + 8 = 15$; $a = 6$
$2 + b + 4 = 15$; $b = 9$
$7 + 5 + c = 15$; $c = 3$

2-7 Solving Multiplication and Division Equations

What You'll Learn

OBJECTIVE 1 To solve equations by dividing

OBJECTIVE 2 To solve equations by multiplying

. . . And Why

To split costs equally, as in Example 2

 Check Skills You'll Need

❓ For help, go to Lesson 1-4.

Use compatible numbers to estimate each product or quotient.

1. 7.3×1.07 **7**
2. $6.1 \div 1.1$ **6**
3. 8×2.3 **16**
4. $12.04 \div 3.8$ **3**
5. $24 \div 3.085$ **8**
6. 16.1×1.89 **32**

New Vocabulary
- Division Property of Equality
- Multiplication Property of Equality

OBJECTIVE

1 Solving Equations by Dividing

📱 **TEXT** Interactive lesson includes instant self-check, tutorials, and activities.

You can use the Division Property of Equality to solve equations involving multiplication.

> **Key Concepts**   **Division Property of Equality**
>
> If you divide each side of an equation by the same nonzero number, the two sides remain equal.
>
> | **Arithmetic** | **Algebra** |
> |---|---|
> | $4 \times 2 = 8$, | If $a = b$ and $c \neq 0$, |
> | so $4 \times 2 \div 2 = 8 \div 2$. | then $a \div c = b \div c$. |

❓ **Need Help?**
Recall that $4n$ means 4 times n. So $4n \div 4 = n$.

1 EXAMPLE   **Solving Equations by Dividing**

Solve $4n = 68$.

$4n \div 4 = 68 \div 4$ ← Divide each side by 4 to undo the multiplication and get n alone on one side.

$n = 17$ ← Simplify.

Check $4n = 68$ ← Check your solution in the original equation.

$4 \times 17 \overset{?}{=} 68$ ← Replace n with 17.

$68 = 68$ ✓

✔ **Check Understanding** ① Solve each equation. Then check the solution.
a. $9x = 36$ **4**
b. $10y = 27$ **2.7**
c. $0.8p = 32$ **40**

2-7 Solving Multiplication and Division Equations **95**

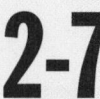
2-7

1. Plan

Lesson Preview

 Check Skills You'll Need   **PowerPoint**

Estimating With Compatible Numbers
Lesson 1-4: Example 2. Extra Practice p. 642.

Lesson Resources

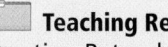

📁 **Teaching Resources**
Practice, Reteaching, Enrichment
Checkpoint Quiz 2

👥 **Reaching All Students**
Practice Workbook 2-7
Spanish Practice Workbook 2-7
Reading and Math Literacy 2C
Spanish Reading and Math Literacy 2C
Spanish Checkpoint Quiz 2
Guided Problem Solving 2-7
Technology Activities 5
Hands-On Activities 6

⏱ **Presentation Assistant Plus!**
Transparencies
- Check Skills You'll Need 2-7
- Problem of the Day 2-7
- Additional Examples 2-7
- Student Edition Answers 2-7
- Lesson Quiz 2-7
- Classroom Aid 8, 37
PH Presentation Pro CD-ROM 2-7

PRENTICE HALL ASSESSMENT SYSTEM

Checkpoint Quiz 2
Computer Test Generator CD

💻 **Technology**
Resource Pro® CD-ROM
Computer Test Generator CD
PH Presentation Pro CD-ROM

💻 **www.PHSchool.com**
Student Site
- Teacher Web Code: aak-5500
- Algebra Readiness Puzzles 72
- Self-grading Lesson Quiz

PH SuccessNet Teacher Center
- Lesson Planner
- Resources

Plus 📱 **TEXT**

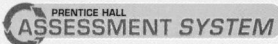
Ongoing Assessment and Intervention

Before the Lesson
Diagnose prerequisite skills using:
- Check Skills You'll Need

During the Lesson
Monitor progress using:
- Check Understanding
- Additional Examples
- Test Prep

After the Lesson
Assess knowledge using:
- Lesson Quiz
- Computer Test Generator CD
- Chapter Checkpoint 2 (p. 98)

Math Background

Just as addition and subtraction are a pair of inverse operations, so too are multiplication and division. Students should note the principle that ties together the four properties of equality: If you perform the same operation on each side of an equation, the solution of the resulting equation is the same as the solution of the original equation. Students should also be aware of the restriction to the Division Property of Equality; that is, you cannot divide the sides of an equation by zero.

Teaching Notes

① EXAMPLE Visual Learners

Present the following solution:

$$4x = 68$$
$$x \cdot 4 = 68$$
$$x \cdot 4 \div 4 = 68 \div 4$$
$$x = 17$$

Error Prevention!

Some students might apply the Division Property of Equality correctly but use the wrong number as the dividend. Suggest that they use this visual aid.

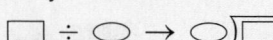

Additional Examples

① Solve $6x = 144$. **24**

② The cost of a pay-per-view concert on television is $39.95. Five friends decide to watch the concert together and split the cost equally. What amount will each friend pay? **$7.99**

③ Solve $x \div 6.3 = 9$. **56.7**

Closure

• *How do you use division to solve an equation?* Divide each side of an equation by the same nonzero number; then simplify.
• *How do you use multiplication to solve an equation?* Multiply each side of an equation by the same number; then simplify.

96

---

② EXAMPLE Real-World 🌐 Problem Solving

Buying in Bulk A package of blank CDs costs $38.88, including tax. Six friends share the CDs and split the cost equally. How much does each friend pay?

Use a diagram to help write an equation.

Let c = each person's share of the cost of the package of CDs. The equation $6c = 38.88$ models this situation.

$38.88					
c	c	c	c	c	c

$$6c = 38.88 \qquad \leftarrow \text{Write the equation.}$$
$$6c \div 6 = 38.88 \div 6 \qquad \leftarrow \text{Divide each side by 6 to undo the multiplication.}$$
$$c = 6.48 \qquad \leftarrow \text{Simplify.}$$

Each friend's share is $6.48.

✓ **Check Understanding** ② The Pep Club sells greeting cards for a fundraiser. It receives $.35 profit for each card it sells. The club's total profit is $302.75. Write and solve an equation to find the number of greeting cards the Pep Club sells.
Equations may vary. Sample: $.35c = 302.75$; 865 cards

OBJECTIVE

2 Solving Equations by Multiplying

You can use the Multiplication Property of Equality to solve equations involving division.

Key Concepts **Multiplication Property of Equality**

If you multiply each side of an equation by the same number, the two sides remain equal.

Arithmetic	**Algebra**
$6 \div 2 = 3$,	If $a = b$, then $a \cdot c = b \cdot c$.
so $(6 \div 2) \times 2 = 3 \times 2$.	

③ EXAMPLE Solving Equations by Multiplying

Solve $y \div 6.4 = 8$.

$$y \div 6.4 \times 6.4 = 8 \times 6.4 \qquad \leftarrow \text{Multiply by 6.4 to undo the division and get } y \text{ alone.}$$
$$y = 51.2 \qquad \leftarrow \text{Simplify.}$$

✓ **Check Understanding** ③ Solve each equation. Then check the solution.
a. $n \div 5 = 40$ **200**   **b.** $w \div 1.5 = 10$ **15**   **c.** $z \div 0.2 = 7.9$ **1.58**

👥 **Reaching All Students**

| **Below Level** Give students several multiplication/division exercises like these to illustrate inverse operations.

6×9 54 $88 \div 4$ 22
$54 \div 9$ 6 22×4 88 | **Advanced Learners** Explain how to use the properties of equality to solve $4z + 1.5 = 6.3$. Subtract 1.5 from each side to get $4z = 4.8$. Then divide each side by 4 to get $z = 1.2$. | **Visual Learners** See note on page 96.

Error Prevention See note on page 96. |

3. Practice

Practice by Example

Example 1
(page 95)

Example 2
(page 96)

Example 3
(page 96)

Solve each equation. Then check the solution.

1. $5a = 100$ **20**
2. $8k = 76$ **9.5**
3. $7n = 11.9$ **1.7**
4. $25h = 450$ **18**
5. $0.4x = 1$ **2.5**
6. $75 = 15c$ **5**
7. $16j = 80$ **5**
8. $2.5g = 17.5$ **7**
9. $10y = 5$ **0.5**

Write and solve an equation for each situation. Then check the solution.

10. Each shelf in a store can hold 24 videos. The store has a total of 8,616 videos. How many shelves are needed for the videos?
359 shelves

 11. **Geography** The area of the Pacific Ocean is about 64,000,000 square miles. This area is about twice the area of the Atlantic Ocean. Find the approximate area of the Atlantic Ocean. **32,000,000 square miles**

Solve each equation. Then check the solution.

12. $q \div 6 = 4$ **24**
13. $a \div 7 = 63$ **441**
14. $n \div 2.5 = 3$ **7.5**
15. $y \div 43 = 1,204$ **51,772**
16. $10 = k \div 20$ **200**
17. $12 = r \div 9$ **108**
18. $n \div 4 = 0.6$ **2.4**
19. $t \div 0.3 = 1.4$ **0.42**
20. $b \div 11 = 87$ **957**

Apply Your Skills

21. **Videos** A video store charges the same price to rent any movie. The store collected a total of $80.73 for the daily rentals shown in the line plot. Write and solve an equation to find the rental charge for one movie.
$2.99 per video

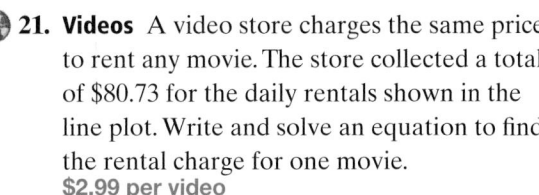

22. <u>Writing in Math</u> Explain what you would do to solve the equation $z \div 48 = 6$.
Multiply each side of the equation by 48 to undo the division.

Solve each equation. Then check the solution.

23. $y \div 1.6 = 0.256$ **0.4096**
24. $13 = 65x$ **0.2**
25. $30 = p \div 30$ **900**
26. $5.6k = 19.152$ **3.42**
27. $0.02g = 6$ **300**
28. $h \div 2.4 = 15$ **36**

29. **Error Analysis** Your soccer team scored 41 goals this season. Explain what is wrong with a teammate's claim that he scored half the goals.
See margin.

 **Real-World Connection**

After about six months, a baby elephant is too large to stand under its mother.

30. **Biology** An adult female elephant's height is about 5.5 times the length of her hind footprint. Use an equation to find the approximate height of an adult female elephant whose hind footprint is 1.5 feet long.
about 8.25 feet

29. The teammate could not have scored half the goals because half of 41 is 20.5. It is impossible to score half of a goal.

 Use the Guided Problem Solving worksheet with Exercise 30.

Assignment Guide

1 **Objective 1**
 Ⓐ Ⓑ Core 1–11, 21, 29
 Ⓒ Extension 32

2 **Objective 2**
 Ⓐ Ⓑ Core 12–20, 22–28, 30
 Ⓒ Extension 31

Test Prep 33–39
Mixed Review 40–43

Error Prevention!

Exercise 21 Remind students that each X represents one movie rental.

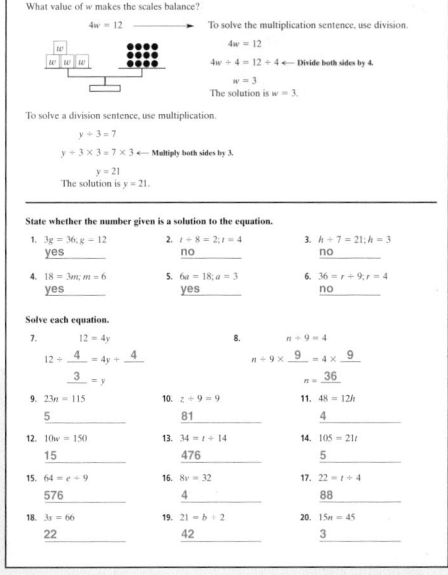

Solve each equation.

1. $6x = 156$ **26**

2. $y \div 11 = 15$ **165**

3. $3w = 13.5$ **4.5**

4. $z \div 2.7 = 9$ **24.3**

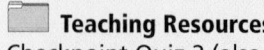

✔ Chapter Checkpoint

To check understanding of
Lessons 2-4 to 2-7:

Checkpoint Quiz 2 (p. 98)

📁 **Teaching Resources**
Checkpoint Quiz 2 (also in
Prentice Hall Assessment System)

👥 **Reaching All Students**
Reading and Math Literacy 2C

Spanish versions available.

Alternative Assessment

Provide pairs of students with red
pencils. Each partner writes a
multiplication and a division
equation. Partners exchange
papers and solve each other's
equations, using the red pencils
to write the inverse operations.

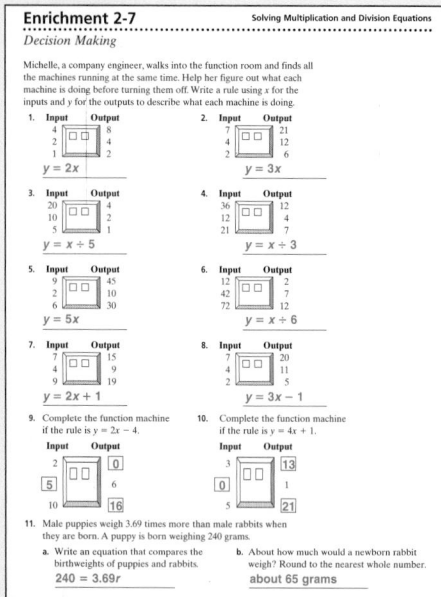

---

31. Measurement One of the world's largest oil tankers, the *Jahre Viking*, is so long that if 3.5 similar tankers were placed end-to-end, they would measure about 1 mile long. Find the length, in feet, of the *Jahre Viking*. (*Hint*: 1 mile = 5,280 feet) **about 1,508.6 feet**

32. Stretch Your Thinking The single-digit numbers in the following expressions have been replaced with the symbols ⊙, △, and □. Each symbol represents the same number in all three expressions. Find what number each symbol represents. **⊙ = 5; △ = 6; □ = 9**

$$□ - △ = 3 \qquad ⊙ + △ + □ = 20 \qquad ⊙ \times △ = 30$$

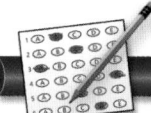 ## Test Prep

Gridded Response

What is the solution of each equation?

33. $15x = 135$ **9**   **34.** $y \div 15 = 1.5$ **22.5**   **35.** $4x = 2.8$ **0.7**

36. $1.5 = q \div 3.06$ **4.59**   **37.** $n \div 3.5 = 2$ **7**   **38.** $8.4 = 0.14k$ **60**

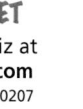
Take It to the NET
Online lesson quiz at
www.PHSchool.com
Web Code: aaa-0207

39. About 0.95 of the weight of a watermelon is water. What is the weight in pounds of the water in a 13-pound watermelon? **12.35**

Mixed Review

Lesson 1-3 Use <, =, or > to complete each statement.

40. 6 $\boxed{>}$ 1.6

41. 3.4 $\boxed{=}$ 3.40

42. 8.05 $\boxed{>}$ 5.08

Lesson 1-2 **43.** Write the decimal eighteen hundredths in standard form. **0.18**

✔ Checkpoint Quiz 2 Lessons 2-4 through 2-7

 Instant self-check
quiz online and
on CD-ROM

Solve each equation.

1. $5x = 65$ **13**   **2.** $n - 3.2 = 15$ **18.2**   **3.** $z + 6 = 8.2$ **2.2**

4. $k \div 4 = 3.6$ **14.4**   **5.** $14 = 3.2 + y$ **10.8**   **6.** $28 = 1.4a$ **20**

7. $x - 4.8 = 3.6$ **8.4**   **8.** $23 = 16 + y$ **7**   **9.** $48 = 9.6a$ **5**

10. You pay for refreshments at a movie theater with a $10 bill. The refreshments cost $5.73. Use an equation to find how much change you should receive. **x = change received; $x + 5.73 = 10.00$; $4.27**

Test Prep

Resources
A sheet of blank grids is available in the *Test-Taking Strategies With Transparencies* booklet. Give copies of this sheet to students so they can practice filling in grids.

For additional practice with a variety of test item formats:
• Test-Prep, p. 113
• Test-Taking Strategies, p. 109
• Test-Taking Strategies With Transparencies

2-8 Exponents

What You'll Learn

 OBJECTIVE 1 To use exponents

 OBJECTIVE 2 To simplify expressions with exponents

. . . And Why

To use exponents to write a product, as in Example 1

2-8

1. Plan

✓ Check Skills You'll Need

? For help, go to Lesson 1-10.

Find the value of each expression.

1. $3 \times 3 + 4 \times 4$ **25**

2. $1 \times 3 - 1 \times 3$ **0**

3. $3.2 \times 4.5 + 4.8$ **19.2**

4. $10 \times 10 \times 10 \times 10$ **10,000**

5. $1 \times 1 \times 1$ **1**

6. $1 + 1 \times 2 - 1$ **2**

New Vocabulary
• **exponent** • **base** • **power**

 iTEXT Interactive lesson includes instant self-check, tutorials, and activities.

OBJECTIVE 1 — Using Exponents

You can write 625 as a product of factors.

$$625 = \underbrace{5 \times 5 \times 5 \times 5}_{\text{factors}}$$

Reading Math
You read 5^4 as "5 to the fourth power."

The number 5 is used as a factor four times. You can indicate repeated multiplication of the same number by using an exponent. An **exponent** tells you how many times a number, or **base,** is used as a factor.

$$5 \times 5 \times 5 \times 5 = 5^4 \quad \leftarrow \text{exponent}$$
$$\uparrow \text{base}$$

1 EXAMPLE Using Exponents

Write $3 \times 3 \times 3 \times 3$ using an exponent. Name the base and the exponent.

$3 \times 3 \times 3 \times 3 = 3^4$ ← 3^4 means that 3 is used as a factor 4 times.

The base is 3 and the exponent is 4.

1a–c. See left.

✓ Check Understanding

1 Write each expression using an exponent. Name the base and the exponent.

a. 3.94×3.94 **b.** $7 \times 7 \times 7 \times 7$ **c.** $x \cdot x \cdot x$

1a. 3.94^2; 3.94; 2

b. 7^4; 7; 4

c. x^3; x; 3

d. Number Sense Does 5^4 have the same value as 5×4? Explain.
No; 5^4 means $5 \times 5 \times 5 \times 5$, which is 625. 5×4 is 20.

The area of the square is 3×3, or 3^2. You read 3^2 as "three squared."

The volume of the cube is $4 \times 4 \times 4$, or 4^3. You read 4^3 as "four cubed."

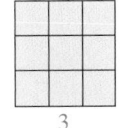
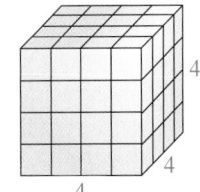

2-8 Exponents   **99**

Lesson Preview

 **PowerPoint**

✓ Check Skills You'll Need
Applying the Order of Operations
Lesson 1-10: Example 1. Extra Practice p. 642.

Lesson Resources

📁 **Teaching Resources**
Practice, Reteaching, Enrichment

👥 **Reaching All Students**
Practice Workbook 2-8
Spanish Practice Workbook 2-8
Guided Problem Solving 2-8
Technology Activities 6

⏰ **Presentation Assistant Plus!**
Transparencies
• Check Skills You'll Need 2-8
• Problem of the Day 2-8
• Additional Examples 2-8
• Student Edition Answers 2-8
• Lesson Quiz 2-1
• Classroom Aid 11
PH Presentation Pro CD-ROM 2-8

 **ASSESSMENT SYSTEM**

Computer Test Generator CD

 **Technology**
Resource Pro® CD-ROM
Computer Test Generator CD
PH Presentation Pro CD-ROM

💻 **www.PHSchool.com**
Student Site
• Teacher Web Code: aak-5500
• Self-grading Lesson Quiz

PH SuccessNet Teacher Center
• Lesson Planner
• Resources

 *Plus* **iTEXT**

⚡ Ongoing Assessment and Intervention

Before the Lesson	During the Lesson	After the Lesson
Diagnose prerequisite skills using:	Monitor progress using:	Assess knowledge using:
• Check Skills You'll Need	• Check Understanding	• Lesson Quiz
	• Additional Examples	• Computer Test Generator CD
	• Test Prep	

2. Teach

Math Background

Many real-world situations give rise to calculations involving one number used as a factor several times. Exponents are a mathematical "shorthand" for indicating such calculations:

$$\underbrace{a \times a \times a \times \cdots \times a}_{n \text{ factors}} = a^n$$

In the expression a^n, a is the *base* and n is the *exponent*. When a is a nonzero number, the value of a^0 is defined to be 1. (For example, $5^0 = 1$; $9^0 = 1$; $25^0 = 1$)

In Lesson 1-10, students studied the order of operations in relation to grouping symbols and the four basic operations. This lesson completes the development of the order of operations by establishing the position of exponents in the sequence: parentheses; exponents; multiplication and division in order from left to right; addition and subtraction in order from left to right.

Teaching Notes

1 EXAMPLE Inclusion

Some students with visual impairments might find it difficult to distinguish exponents from bases. For instance, they might see the expression 3^4 as 34. Suggest that these students align the edge of a ruler with the bottom of the expression and look for that part of the expression that does not touch the ruler. This will be the exponent.

Tactile Learners

When discussing the square and cube that appear after Example 1, have students make models of the figures using small square tiles and cubes.

3 EXAMPLE Technology Tip

You might need to help students locate the x^y or $\wedge$ key on their calculators.

100

Reading Math

You read 10^{100} as "ten to the hundredth power." 10^{100} is called a *googol*.

2a. $5 \times 10^4 + 5 \times 10^3 + 6 \times 10^2 + 0 \times 10^1 + 7 \times 1$

b. $3 \times 10^5 + 8 \times 10^4 + 0 \times 10^3 + 2 \times 10^2 + 5 \times 10^1 + 4 \times 1$

A **power** is a number that can be expressed using an exponent. You read 10^5 as "ten to the fifth power." Powers of 10 are used to name the place-value positions in our number system. You can use powers of 10 to write numbers in expanded form.

2 EXAMPLE Writing in Expanded Form

Write the number 9,572 in expanded form using powers of 10.

$$9{,}572 = 9{,}000 + 500 + 70 + 2$$
$$= 9 \times 1{,}000 + 5 \times 100 + 7 \times 10 + 2 \times 1$$
$$= 9 \times 10^3 + 5 \times 10^2 + 7 \times 10^1 + 2 \times 1$$

2a–b. See above left.

✓ **Check Understanding** 2 Write each number in expanded form using powers of 10.
  a. 55,607   b. 380,254

OBJECTIVE

2 Simplifying Expressions With Exponents

Some calculators have special keys to use with exponents. You can use the x^2 key to square a number. You can use the $\wedge$ key to evaluate any power.

3 EXAMPLE Simplifying Powers

Simplify each expression.

a. $2^5 = 2 \times 2 \times 2 \times 2 \times 2 = 32$ ← The base 2 is used as a factor 5 times.

b.  $4^3 = 4 \times 4 \times 4 = 64$ ← Use a calculator without an exponent key.

c.  $1.5^3 = 1.5 \wedge 3 = 3.375$ ← Use a calculator with an exponent key.

2 beads

2^5 beads

✓ **Check Understanding** 3 Simplify each expression.
  a. 10^5 100,000   b. 3^9 19,683   c. 1.1^3 1.331
  d. **Reasoning** Does 2^5 have the same value as 5^2? Explain.
     No; 2^5 means $2 \times 2 \times 2 \times 2 \times 2$ which is 32; 5^2 means 5×5, which is 25.

The order of operations can be extended to include exponents.

Key Concepts | **Order of Operations**

1. Do all operations within parentheses first.
2. **Do all work with exponents.**
3. Multiply and divide in order from left to right.
4. Add and subtract in order from left to right.

👥 **Reaching All Students**

Below Level Have students evaluate several pairs of powers like these.

2^3, 3^2 8; 9 5^2, 2^5 25; 32
3^4, 4^3 81; 64 7^3, 3^7 343; 2,187

Advanced Learners Fill in the boxes with whole numbers to make a true statement. Find as many answers as possible.

$\Box^{\Box} = 64$ 2^6, 4^3, 8^2, 64^1

Inclusion
See note on page 100.

Visual Learners
See note on page 101.

The phrase **P**lease **E**xcuse **M**y **D**ear **A**unt **S**ally can help you remember the order of operations.

P	**P**arentheses
E	**E**xponents
M, D	**M**ultiplication and **D**ivision in order from left to right
A, S	**A**ddition and **S**ubtraction in order from left to right

4 EXAMPLE **Simplifying Expressions**

Simplify the expression: $3 \times (7^2 + 18 \div 2)$.

$$3 \times (49 + 18 \div 2) \quad \leftarrow \text{Simplify } 7^2 \text{ in parentheses first.}$$
$$3 \times (49 + 9) \quad \leftarrow \text{In parentheses, simplify } 18 \div 2.$$
$$3 \times (58) \quad \leftarrow \text{In parentheses, add } 49 + 9.$$
$$174 \quad \leftarrow \text{Multiply 3 and 58.}$$

✔ **Check Understanding** **4** Simplify each expression.

a. $2^3 - 6 \div 3$ **6**   **b.** $1 + 11^2 - 20 \div 2$ **112** **c.** $5 + (2 + 1)^2$ **14**

EXERCISES

❓ For more practice, see *Extra Practice*.

A **Practice by Example** **Write each expression using an exponent. Name the base and exponent.**

Example 1 (page 99)

1. 3×3 3^2; 3; 2   **2.** $2 \times 2 \times 2$ 2^3; 2; 3   **3.** $9 \times 9 \times 9$ 9^3; 9; 3

4. 100×100 100^2; 100; 2 **5.** $12 \times 12 \times 12 \times 12$ 12^4; 12; 4   **6.** $8.1 \cdot 8.1$ 8.1^2; 8.1; 2

7. $1 \times 1 \times 1 \times 1 \times 1$ 1^5; 1; 5 **8.** 29 29^1; 29; 1   **9.** $n \cdot n \cdot n \cdot n \cdot n \cdot n$ n^6; n; 6

Example 2 (page 100)

Write each number in expanded form using powers of 10.

10–15. See margin.

10. 7,650   **11.** 83,792   **12.** 41,006

13. 60,251   **14.** 400,003   **15.** 7,892,510

Examples 3, 4 (pages 100, 101)

Simplify each expression. Exercise 16 has been started for you.

16. $14^2 = 14 \times 14 = $  196   **17.** 2^6 64   **18.** 3^5 243

19. 25^3 15,625   **20.** 2.5^3 15.625   **21.** 3^4 81

22. $4^2 + 5$ 21   **23.** $2^2 + 3^2$ 13   **24.** $(2 + 3)^2$ 25

25. $(3^2 - 1)^2$ 64   **26.** $5(5^2 - 9)$ 80   **27.** $(9 - 7)^3 \times 6$ 48

2-8 Exponents **101**

---

10. $7 \times 10^3 + 6 \times 10^2 + 5 \times 10^1 + 0 \times 1$

11. $8 \times 10^4 + 3 \times 10^3 + 7 \times 10^2 + 9 \times 10^1 + 2 \times 1$

12. $4 \times 10^4 + 1 \times 10^3 + 0 \times 10^2 + 0 \times 10^1 + 6 \times 1$

13. $6 \times 10^4 + 0 \times 10^3 + 2 \times 10^2 + 5 \times 10^1 + 1 \times 1$

14. $4 \times 10^5 + 0 \times 10^4 + 0 \times 10^3 + 0 \times 10^2 + 0 \times 10^1 + 3 \times 1$

15. $7 \times 10^6 + 8 \times 10^5 + 9 \times 10^4 + 2 \times 10^3 + 5 \times 10^2 + 1 \times 10^1 + 0 \times 1$

---

4 EXAMPLE **Visual Learners**

Students might find it helpful to begin their work by examining the entire expression and writing the appropriate letter from PEMDAS above each symbol.

$$\overset{\begin{matrix} & & & \text{P} \\ \text{M} & \text{E} & \text{A} & \text{D} \end{matrix}}{3 \times (7^2 \times 18 \div 2)}$$

PowerPoint

📀 **Additional Examples**

1 Write $5 \times 5 \times 5 \times 5$ using an exponent. Name the base and the exponent. 5^4; the base is 5 and the exponent is 4.

2 Write the number 82,306 in expanded form using powers of 10. $8 \times 10^4 + 2 \times 10^3 + 3 \times 10^2 + 0 \times 10^1 + 6 \times 1$

3 Simplify each expression.

   a. 6^3 216

   b. 3^5 243

   c. 2.7^4 53.1441

4 Simplify the expression: $24 - (8 - 1.2 \times 5)^2$. 20

Closure

- *How do you evaluate a base raised to an exponent?* Sample: Perform a multiplication in which the base is used as a factor the number of times indicated by the exponent.

- *What is the order of operations in an expression that includes exponents?* Sample: Do operations within parentheses first; do all work with exponents; multiply and divide in order from left to right; add and subtract in order from left to right

Assignment Guide

1 Objective 1
A B Core 1–15, 35–39, 42–47
C Extension 55

2 Objective 2
A B Core 16–34, 40–41, 48–54
C Extension 56

Test Prep 57–60
Mixed Review 61–69

Science Connection
Exercise 40 This pattern is called *exponential growth*.

Practice 2-8 Exponents

Write each expression using an exponent. Name the base and the exponent.

1. $3 \times 3 \times 3 \times 3$
3^4; 3 is the base,
4 is the exponent

2. $7 \times 7 \times 7 \times 7 \times 7 \times 7$
7^6; 7 is the base,
6 is the exponent

3. $9 \times 9 \times 9$
9^3; 9 is the base,
3 is the exponent

Write each number in expanded form using powers of 10.

4. 98,364
$9 \times 10^4 + 8 \times 10^3 +$
$3 \times 10^2 + 6 \times 10^1 +$
4×1

5. 20,351,401
$2 \times 10^7 + 3 \times 10^5 +$
$5 \times 10^4 + 1 \times 10^3 +$
$4 \times 10^2 + 1 \times 1$

6. 875,020
$8 \times 10^5 + 7 \times 10^4 +$
$5 \times 10^3 + 2 \times 10^1$

Simplify each expression.

7. 9^2 — 81
8. 6^4 — 1,296
9. 5^3 — 125
10. 7^3 — 343

11. $156 + (256 \div 8^2)$ — 160
12. $32 \div 64 + 2^3$ — 104
13. $53 + 64 \div 2^3$ — 61
14. $1,280 - 5 \times 6^2$ — 1,100

Find each answer to complete the puzzle.

ACROSS
1. $(3 \times 4)^2$
3. $60 \div (8 + 7) + 11$
4. $2^2 \times 5^2 + 106$
5. $4 + 7 \times 2^3$
6. $7^2 + 4$
9. $48 + 4 \times 5 - 2 \times 5$
10. $(4 + 3) \times (2 + 1)$
12. $12 \times (30 + 37)$
13. $5 \times (9 + 4) + 362 \div 2$
14. $29 \times 18 \div 9$

DOWN
1. $8 \times (5 + 4) \div 6$
2. $700 \times (2 + 4) + (17 - 7)$
3. $11 \times (18 - 3)$
5. $60 + (5 \times 4^3) + 2^2 \times 55$
7. $7^2 - 7 \times 2$
8. $(4^2 - 4) \times 10$
9. $2^4 \times 2^5$
11. $(3 + 2) \times (6^2 - 7)$
12. $3^4 + 405 + 81$

Reteaching 2-8 Exponents

An *exponent* tells how many times a number is used as a factor.

$3 \times 3 \times 3 \times 3$ shows the number 3 is used as a factor 4 times.

$3 \times 3 \times 3 \times 3$ can be written 3^4.

In 3^4, 3 is the *base* and 4 is the exponent.

Read 3^4 as "three to the fourth power."

• To *simplify* a power, first write it as a product.
$2^5 = 2 \times 2 \times 2 \times 2 \times 2 = 32$

• When you simplify expressions with exponents, do all operations inside parentheses first. Then simplify the powers.

Example: $30 - (2 + 3)^2 = 30 - 5^2$
$= 30 - 25$
$= 5$

Name the base and the exponent.

1. 3^6
base 3
exponent 6

2. 6^2
base 6
exponent 2

3. 8^4
base 8
exponent 4

Write each expression using an exponent. Name the base and the exponent.

4. $9 \times 9 \times 9$
9^3; 9; 3

5. $6 \times 6 \times 6 \times 6$
6^4; 6; 4

6. $1 \times 1 \times 1 \times 1 \times 1$
1^5; 1; 5

Simplify each expression.

7. 6^2 — 36
8. 3^5 — 243
9. 10^4 — 10,000

10. $4^2 + 5^2$ — 41
11. $2 \times 6 - 2^3$ — 4
12. $6^2 + 4^2$ — 52

13. $5 + 5^2 - 2$ — 28
14. $24 \div 4 + 2^4$ — 22
15. $9 + (40 \div 2^3)$ — 14

16. $(4^2 + 4) \div 5$ — 4
17. $10 \times (30 - 5^2)$ — 50
18. $12 + 18 \div 3^2$ — 14

Simplify each expression.

28. $37^3 + 1$ — 50,654
29. $(37 + 1)^3$ — 54,872
30. $(9 + 1)^2 - 1^3$ — 99

31. $15^2 - (1 + 13^2) + 5$ — 60
32. $(10 - 8)^4 \times 3.5$ — 56
33. $2 \times 3^2 \times 4^2$ — 288

34. The expressions do not have the same value. According to the order of operations, $2^2 \cdot 3^2 - 2^3 - 1$ simplifies to 27, but $2^2 \cdot (3^2 - 2^3) - 1$ simplifies to 3.

34. **Number Sense** Tell whether the expression $2^2 \cdot 3^2 - 2^3 - 1$ has the same value as the expression $2^2 \cdot (3^2 - 2^3) - 1$. Explain why or why not.

Find the missing exponent that makes each equation true.

35. $40 = 2^3 \times 5$
36. $45 = 5 \times 3^2$
37. $343 = 7^3$
38. $144 = 9 \cdot 4^2$

39a. 10,000; 10^5; 100,000

b. The exponent tells the number of 0s in standard form.

c. 10^7; 10,000,000; 10^8; 100,000,000

39. **Patterns** Copy the table at the right.
a. Fill in the missing values.
b. **Writing in Math** Explain how the number of zeros in the standard form of a power of 10 relates to the exponent.
c. Extend and complete the table for 10^7 and 10^8.

Power	Standard Form
10^1	10
10^2	100
10^3	1,000
10^4	■
■	■

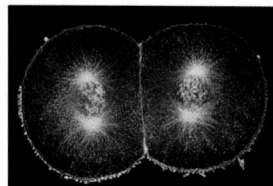

40. **Biology** Suppose a single-celled animal splits in two after one hour. Each new cell also splits in two after one hour. How many cells will there be after eight hours? Write your answer using an exponent.
2^8 cells

41. **Astronomy** The interior temperature of the sun is about 35,000,000°F. Write this number in expanded form using powers of 10.
$3 \times 10^7 + 5 \times 10^6$

42. **Science** Scientists estimate that Earth is approximately 15×10^9 years old. Write this number in standard form.
15,000,000,000

43. Copy and complete the table of cubes below.

n^3	1^3	2^3	3^3	4^3	5^3	6^3
Standard Form	1	8	■	■	■	■

27; 64; 125; 216

Write each product or quotient using an exponent.

44. $5^2 \times 5^3$ — 5^5
45. $2^4 \times 2^3$ — 2^7
46. $4^5 \div 4^2$ — 4^3
47. $10^6 \div 10^1$ — 10^5

Simplify each expression.

48. $(2 \times 3^3 + 1) \div 11$ — 5
49. $10^2 \times 4 \div 5$ — 80
50. $(4^2 - 1) \div 3 + 1$ — 6

51. $(1 + 6)^2 - (1^2 + 6^2)$ — 12
52. $100 - (1.8 + 5)^2$ — 53.76
53. $2.7(125 \div 5^2)$ — 13.5

 GPS

Use the Guided Problem Solving worksheet with Exercise 40.

54. Entertainment The size of the image of a motion picture is related to the distance of the projector from the screen.

Distance From Screen	Picture Size
1 unit	1 unit²
2 units	4 units²
3 units	9 units²
4 units	16 units²

  a.  **Writing in Math** Describe how the size of the image is related to the distance the projector is from the screen. **See margin.**

  b. Patterns A projector is 25 feet from a screen. How large will the image of the motion picture be? **625 square feet**

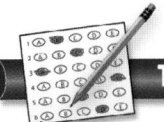 C Challenge

55. Patterns Copy the pattern at the right.
  a. Extend the pattern three more rows.
  b. Write the sum of each row using an exponent.
  c. What is the sum of the first 20 odd numbers?
  55a–c. **See margin.**

$$1 = 1$$
$$1 + 3 = 4$$
$$1 + 3 + 5 = 9$$
$$1 + 3 + 5 + 7 = 16$$

56. Stretch Your Thinking In the equations at the right, ■ represents a one-digit number and ✿ represents a two-digit number. What are the numbers?
  ■ = 8; ✿ = 14

$$22 - ■ = ✿$$
$$6 + ■ = ✿$$

Test Prep

Multiple Choice

57. Which expression is NOT equivalent to $3 \times 3 \times 3 \times 3$? **A**
  A. $(3 + 3)^2 \times 3 \times 3$
  B. $3^1 \times 3^3$
  C. $(3 + 3 + 3) \times 3^2$
  D. $3^2 \times (3 \times 3)$

58. What is the value of $2^3 \times 3^2$? **F**
  F. 72   **G.** 54   **H.** 48   **I.** 36

59. What is the value of $5 + 6^2 - 1$? **C**
  A. 16   **B.** 30   **C.** 40   **D.** 120

60. What is the value of $2 + (2^4 + 100) \div 2^2$? **H**
  F. 9   **G.** 11   **H.** 31   **I.** 32

Take It to the NET
Online lesson quiz at
www.PHSchool.com
Web Code: aaa-0208

Mixed Review

Lesson 1-7   **Find each product.**

61. 11.23×100 **1,123**
62. 7.005×10 **70.05**
63. $1,000 \times 0.88$ **880**

64. 1.25×4.5 **5.625**
65. 9.05×3.30 **29.865**
66. 11×0.18 **1.98**

Lesson 1-3   **Use <, =, or > to complete each statement.**

67. 10.0010 ■ 10.01
  $<$
68. 0.0991 ■ 0.00999
  $>$
69. 21.1 ■ 21.100
  $=$

2-8   Exponents   **103**

54a. The size of the image is the square of the distance of the projector to the screen.

55a. $1 + 3 + 5 + 7 + 9 = 25$
$1 + 3 + 5 + 7 + 9 + 11 = 36$
$1 + 3 + 5 + 7 + 9 + 11 + 13 = 49$

b. $1^2; 2^2; 3^2; 4^2; 5^2; 6^2$

c. 20^2 or 400.

4. Assess

 PowerPoint **Lesson Quiz 2-8**

Write each expression using an exponent.

1. 6×6 6^2 **2.** $8 \times 8 \times 8$ 8^3

Simplify each expression.

3. 5^4 625   **4.** 3.2^2 10.24

5. $2^3 + (10 - 5)$ 13

6. $3^2 \times (9 - 2) + 1$ 64

Alternative Assessment

Provide pairs of students with two sets of 1–9 digit cards. Pairs shuffle each set and place them facedown in separate stacks, designating one stack as the base and one as the exponent. Partners work together to turn over one card from each stack. They then evaluate the expression and record each base, exponent, and result.

Test Prep

Resources
For additional practice with a variety of test item formats:
• Test-Prep, p. 113
• Test-Taking Strategies, p. 109
• Test-Taking Strategies With Transparencies

Enrichment 2-8   Exponents
Patterns in Numbers

You have learned that repeated multiplication can be represented using exponents. You may discover some interesting patterns when working with these numbers.

The table at the right shows powers of 2 from 2^1 to 2^{10} in exponential and standard forms.

Powers of 2	Powers of 3
$2^1 = 2$	$3^1 = 3$
$2^2 = 4$	$3^2 = 9$
$2^3 = 8$	$3^3 = 27$
$2^4 = 16$	$3^4 = 81$
$2^5 = 32$	$3^5 = 243$
$2^6 = 64$	$3^6 = 729$
$2^7 = 128$	$3^7 = 2,187$
$2^8 = 256$	$3^8 = 6,561$
$2^9 = 512$	$3^9 = 19,683$
$2^{10} = 1,024$	$3^{10} = 59,049$

1. Describe the pattern in the table.
   Sample answer: Exponent increases by 1; value doubles; ones digits: 2, 4, 8, 6, 2, 4, 8, 6 . . .

2. Continue the pattern. Write the next three numbers in exponential and standard forms.
   2^{11}; 2,048
   2^{12}; 4,096
   2^{13}; 8,192

3. Complete the chart above to represent the powers of 3 from 3^1 through 3^{10}. What patterns do you see in these numbers?
   Sample answer: Exponent increases by 1; number in standard form triples; ones digits form pattern: 3, 9, 7, 1, 3, 9, 7, 1 . . .

4. Are the patterns the same for the powers of 2 and 3? Why or why not?
   Sample answer: Yes; exponent increases by 1; number in standard form increases by a factor equal to the base; ones digits form pattern.

5. The speed of light is about 3×10^5 km/sec. Write this speed in standard form.
   about 300,000 km/sec

103

Scientific Notation

This extension of Lesson 2-7 shows students how to use scientific notation to represent very large numbers.

Teaching Notes

Teaching Tip
Guide students to apply the following strategy to write numbers in scientific notation:
- To form the factor that is equal to or greater than 1 and less than 10, move the decimal point *left,* stopping just to the right of the front-end digit.
- To get the power of 10, count the number of decimal places you moved the decimal point.

Inclusion
Help students understand that when they multiply the factors of a number expressed in scientific notation, the product will be in *standard* form.

Additional Example
Tell students that light travels at a speed of about 186,000 miles per second and that a *light year* is the distance it travels in a year. Have them write in scientific notation the distance represented by 20 light years, using 365 days per year. 117,313,920,000,000 mi or 1.1731392×10^{14} mi

---

The distance from Earth to the sun is about 150,000,000 kilometers. You can write this number in *scientific notation.*

To write a number in scientific notation, write the number as a product of two factors. The first factor is a number equal to or greater than 1 but less than 10. The second factor is a power of 10.

1 EXAMPLE   Changing to Scientific Notation

Write 150,000,000 using scientific notation.

$$150{,}000{,}000. = 1.5 \times 10^{8}$$

Move the decimal point to the left, so that you have a factor greater than or equal to 1 and less than 10.

The exponent, 8, shows that you moved the decimal point 8 places.

2 EXAMPLE   Changing to Standard Form

The distance from Earth to the moon is approximately 3.844×10^{5} kilometers. Write 3.844×10^{5} in standard notation.

$$3.844 \times 10^{5} = 384{,}400.$$

Move the decimal point 5 places to the right. Use zeros to fill places as needed.

EXERCISES

Write each number in scientific notation.

1. 34,000 3.4×10^{4}
2. 165,000,000,000 1.65×10^{11}
3. 800,000 8×10^{5}
4. 310,210 3.1021×10^{5}

5. 22,030,000 2.203×10^{7}
6. 902,000,000 9.02×10^{8}
7. 4,000,500,000 4.0005×10^{9}
8. 3,045,250 3.04525×10^{6}

Write each number in standard form.

9. 3.05×10^{2} 305
10. 2×10^{11} 200,000,000,000
11. 9.037×10^{8} 903,700,000
12. 1×10^{9} 1,000,000,000

13. 6.5×10^{1} 65
14. 4.0201×10^{7} 40,201,000
15. 1.4×10^{5} 140,000
16. 7.3×10^{2} 730

17. The distance from our sun to the nearest star, Alpha Centauri, is about 42,000,000,000,000 kilometers. Write this distance in scientific notation. 4.2×10^{13} km

2-9 The Distributive Property

What You'll Learn

 OBJECTIVE 1 To use the Distributive Property

...And Why

To find a salary, as in Example 2

 Check Skills You'll Need

? For help, go to Lesson 1-5.

Use mental math to find each sum.

1. $1.5 + 8.4 + 3.5$ **13.4**
2. $4.4 + 7.3 + 5.6$ **17.3**
3. $8.1 + 5.3 + 9.9$ **23.3**
4. $6.5 + 3.7 + 6.3$ **16.5**

New Vocabulary   • Distributive Property

Lesson Preview

 PowerPoint

✔ **Check Skills You'll Need**
Using the Properties of Addition
Lesson 1-5: Example 2. Extra Practice p. 642.

Lesson Resources

Optional Materials
• graph paper

📁 **Teaching Resources**
Practice, Reteaching, Enrichment

👥 **Reaching All Students**
Practice Workbook 2-9
Spanish Practice Workbook 2-9
Guided Problem Solving 2-9
Hands-On Activities 7

⏱ **Presentation Assistant Plus!**
Transparencies
• Check Skills You'll Need 2-9
• Problem of the Day 2-9
• Additional Examples 2-9
• Student Edition Answers 2-9
• Lesson Quiz 2-9
• Classroom Aid 2
PH Presentation Pro CD-ROM 2-9

PRENTICE HALL ASSESSMENT SYSTEM

Computer Test Generator CD

💻 **Technology**
Resource Pro® CD-ROM
Computer Test Generator CD
PH Presentation Pro CD-ROM

💻 **www.PHSchool.com**
Student Site
• Teacher Web Code: aak-5500
• Algebra Readiness Puzzles 43
• Self-grading Lesson Quiz

PH SuccessNet Teacher Center
• Lesson Planner
• Resources

Plus

OBJECTIVE

1 Using the Distributive Property

iTEXT Interactive lesson includes instant self-check, tutorials, and activities.

 **Investigation:** Making Area Models

1. On graph paper, draw rectangles like those shown below.

```
 3 [          ]        3 [      ]
        7                    5
```
Check students' work.

2. **a.** Count the squares to find the area of each rectangle. **21; 15**
   b. What is the sum of the two areas? **36**

3. **a.** Cut out the rectangles. Arrange them so that the sides of length 3 touch. What are the length and width of the new rectangle? **length: 12; width: 3**
   b. Count the squares to find the area of the new rectangle. **36**

4. What do you notice about the results of Questions 2(b) and 3(b)?
   They are the same.

The **Distributive Property** shows how multiplication affects an addition or subtraction.

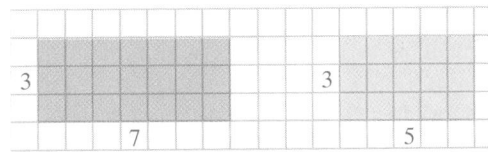

$$3 \times (7 + 5) = (3 \times 7) + (3 \times 5) \qquad 9 \times (5 - 2) = (9 \times 5) - (9 \times 2)$$
$$= \quad 21 \quad + \quad 15 \qquad\qquad\qquad = \quad 45 \quad - \quad 18$$
$$= \qquad 36 \qquad\qquad\qquad\qquad\qquad = \qquad 27$$

Ongoing Assessment and Intervention

Before the Lesson
Diagnose prerequisite skills using:
• Check Skills You'll Need

During the Lesson
Monitor progress using:
• Check Understanding
• Additional Examples
• Test Prep

After the Lesson
Assess knowledge using:
• Lesson Quiz
• Computer Test Generator CD

Math Background

The Distributive Property provides an important alternative when evaluating certain expressions. According to the order of operations, an expression like $3 \times (10 + 8)$ is evaluated by first performing the addition within parentheses, $10 + 8 = 18$, and then multiplying $3 \times 18 = 54$. By the Distributive Property, however, this expression is equivalent to $3 \times 10 + 3 \times 8$. So the value of $3 \times (10 + 8)$ can be found more easily by calculating $3 \times 10 = 30$ and $3 \times 8 = 24$, then performing the simple addition $30 + 24 = 54$.

Teaching Notes

Investigation (Optional)
The areas of the rectangles model a specific instance of the Distributive Property shown below.
$(3 \times 7) + (3 \times 5) = 3 \times (7 + 5)$

English Learners
Students might have difficulty with the term *distributive*. Ask: *What happens when a teacher distributes test papers to a class?* The teacher gives one test paper to each student in the class. Point out that, in a similar way, the number outside the parentheses "distributes" itself to each number inside the parentheses.

PowerPoint
Additional Examples

1. Use the Distributive Property to simplify 5×47. **235**

2. A student bought 4 tickets that cost $5.50. What was the total cost of the tickets? **$22**

Closure

Explain the Distributive Property. Sample: When a sum or difference inside parentheses is multiplied by a number outside the parentheses, you can multiply each number inside the parentheses by the number outside, then add or subtract as indicated.

106

Key Concepts — The Distributive Property

Arithmetic	Algebra
$8 \times (4 + 6) = (8 \times 4) + (8 \times 6)$	$a(b + c) = ab + ac$
$7 \times (6 - 2) = (7 \times 6) - (7 \times 2)$	$a(b - c) = ab - ac$

You can use the Distributive Property to multiply mentally. To simplify 4×29, you can think of 29 as $(20 + 9)$ or as $(30 - 1)$. Then multiply.

1 EXAMPLE Evaluating Expressions

Simplify 4×29.

What you think

Think of 29 as $30 - 1$. Then multiply by 4: $4 \times 30 = 120$ and $4 \times 1 = 4$. Now subtract the two products: $120 - 4 = 116$.

Why it works

$4 \times 29 = 4 \times (30 - 1)$ ← Write 29 as $30 - 1$.

$= (4 \times 30) - (4 \times 1)$ ← Use the Distributive Property.

$= 120 - 4$ ← Simplify within parentheses.

$= 116$ ← Subtract.

✔ **Check Understanding** ① Use the Distributive Property to simplify each expression.

a. 3×42
$3 \times (40 + 2) = (3 \times 40) + (3 \times 2) = 120 + 6 = 126$

b. 5×68
$5 \times (70 - 2) = (5 \times 70) - (5 \times 2) = 350 - 10 = 340$

You can use the Distributive Property to multiply a whole number and a decimal.

2 EXAMPLE Real-World Problem Solving

Salary A summer job as an assistant camp counselor pays $6.50 per hour. What is the salary for working 8 hours?

$8 \times 6.50 = 8(6.00 + 0.50)$ ← Write 6.50 as $6.00 + 0.50$.

$= (8 \times 6.00) + (8 \times 0.50)$ ← Use the Distributive Property.

$= 48.00 + 4.00$ ← Simplify within parentheses.

$= 52.00$ ← Add.

The salary for working 8 hours is $52.00.

✔ **Check Understanding** ② A local video store charges $2.80 for each day a rental is late. What are the late charges if a video is 5 days late? **$14**

Reaching All Students

Below Level Give students several exercises like these to practice mental computations.	Advanced Learners Justify whether this statement is true or false.	English Learners See note on page 106.
8×30 **240** 7×800 **5,600** $360 + 12$ **372** $350 - 7$ **343**	$a + (b \cdot c) = (a + b) \cdot (a + c)$ Sample: false; $2 + (3 \cdot 4) = 14$; $(2 + 3) \cdot (2 + 4) = 30$; so $2 + (3 \cdot 4) \neq (2 + 3) \cdot (2 + 4)$	**Error Prevention** See note on page 107.

❓ For more practice, see *Extra Practice*.

Ⓐ Practice by Example

Use the Distributive Property to simplify each expression. Exercises 1 and 2 have been started for you.

Example 1
(page 106)

1. $4 \times 18 = 4 \times (10 + 8) = (4 \times \boxed{10}) + (4 \times \boxed{8}) = \boxed{40} + \boxed{32} = \boxed{72}$

2. $4 \times 18 = 4 \times (20 - 2) = (4 \times \boxed{20}) - (4 \times \boxed{2}) = \boxed{80} - \boxed{8} = \boxed{72}$

3. 8×28 **4.** 5×63 **5.** 12×34

3–5. See margin.

Example 2
(page 106)

🌎 **6. Fundraising** Your class is selling Earth Day posters for $2.90 each. On the first day of sales, your class sold 8 posters. How much money did your class collect on the first day of sales? **$23.20**

7. A group of 6 students plan to go to a skating rink. The rink charges $4.50 per person. Find the total cost for the group. **$27.00**

Ⓑ Apply Your Skills

Use the Distributive Property to simplify each expression.

8. 7×83 **581**   **9.** 3×2.9 **8.7**   **10.** 9×48 **432**

11. 5×1.9 **9.5**   **12.** 6×99 **594**   **13.** 11×8.7 **95.7**

Real-World 🌎 Connection

Careers Auto mechanics use computers to help diagnose engine problems.

🌎 **14. Money** Mr. Garcia's company pays him 32.5 cents per mile for gasoline and car maintenance when he uses his car for company business. How much money does he receive for driving 40 miles on company business? **$13.00**

🌎 **15. Fundraising** There are 53 people walking in a fundraising event. Each participant walks 5 miles. How many total miles do the participants walk? **265 mi**

🌎 **16. Gardening** Your school's ecology club plants 8 rows of sunflowers in a vacant lot. Each row has 27 plants. Find the total number of sunflowers that the ecology club plants. **216 sunflowers**

17. Writing in Math Describe two ways to find the total area of the rectangle at the right. See back of book.

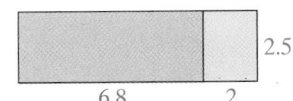

Ⓒ Challenge

Algebra **Copy and complete each equation.**

18. $4(7 - y) = (4 \cdot 7) - (4 \cdot \boxed{\ })$
$(4 \cdot 7) - (4 \cdot y) = 28 - 4y$

19. $9(a + b) = (\boxed{\ } \cdot a) + (9 \cdot \boxed{\ })$
$(9 \cdot a) + (9 \cdot b) = 9a + 9b$

20. Stretch Your Thinking Change two operations in the expression below so that the value of the expression is 35.

$5 + 5 + 5 + 5 + 5 + 5$

Answers may vary.
Sample:
$5 \times 5 - 5 + 5 + 5 + 5$

2-9 The Distributive Property   **107**

3. $8(20 + 8) = 8 \times 20 + 8 \times 8 = 160 + 64 = 224$

4. $5 \times (60 + 3) = 5 \times 60 + 5 \times 3 = 300 + 15 = 315$

5. $12 \times (30 + 4) = 12 \times 30 + 12 \times 4 = 360 + 48 = 408$

GPS Use the Guided Problem Solving worksheet with Exercise 16.

Assignment Guide

1 **Objective 1**
Ⓐ Ⓑ **Core** 1–17
Ⓒ **Extension** 18–20

Test Prep 21–23
Mixed Review 24–28

Error Prevention!

Exercises 3–5 Students may rewrite each expression correctly but forget to distribute the number outside the parentheses to the second number inside the parentheses. Have them draw arrows as a reminder.

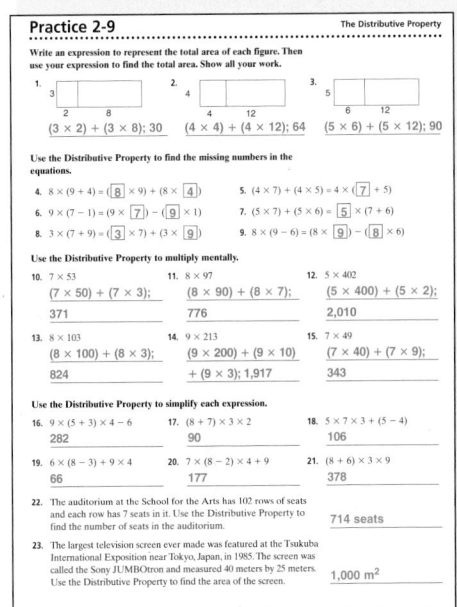

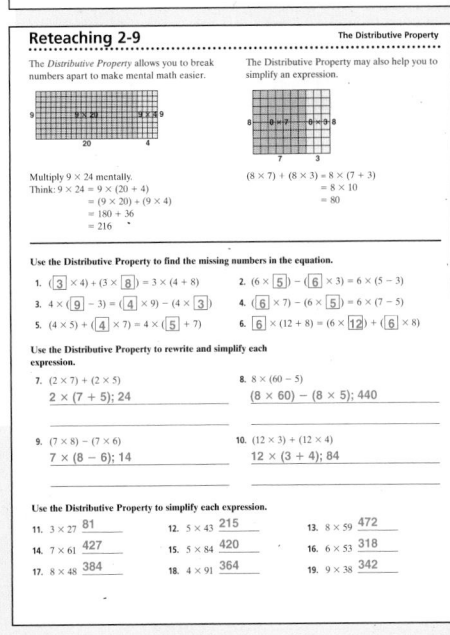

Lesson Quiz 2-9

1. Find the missing numbers in 5 × (70 + 8) = (■ × 70) + (5 × ■). **5; 8**

Rewrite each expression using the Distributive Property and then simplify. **Answers may vary. Samples are given.**

2. 3 × 24
(3 × 25) − (3 × 1) = 72

3. 7 × 43
(7 × 40) + (7 × 3) = 301

Alternative Assessment

Each student in a pair writes a multiplication problem similar to those in Exercises 3–5. Partners exchange papers and rewrite the expression using the Distributive Property. Students then simplify using mental math.

Test Prep

Resources

For additional practice with a variety of test item formats:
• Test-Prep, p. 113
• Test-Taking Strategies, p. 109
• Test-Taking Strategies With Transparencies

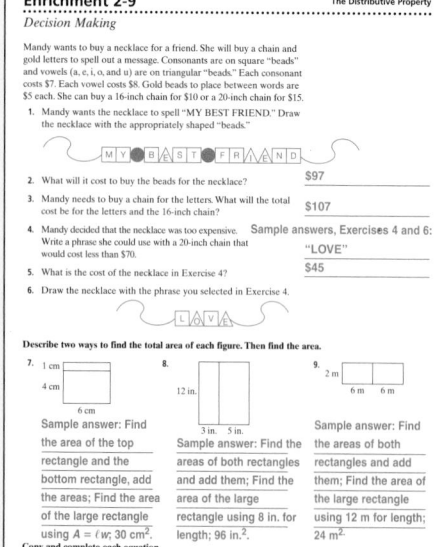

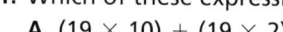

Test Prep

Multiple Choice

21. Which of these expressions is NOT equivalent to 19 × 12? **D**
   A. (19 × 10) + (19 × 2)   B. (10 × 12) + (9 × 12)
   C. (20 × 12) − (1 × 12)   D. (10 × 10) + (9 × 2)

22. A family is buying carpeting for two rooms. One room measures 15 feet by 17.5 feet and the other is 17.5 feet by 20 feet. Which expression gives the total square feet of carpet that the family is buying? **H**
   F. 35 × 35   G. 32.5 × 37.5   H. 17.5 × 35   I. 15 × 37.5

23. Which expression is NOT equivalent to the others? **B**
   A. (3 × 5) + (2 × 5)   B. 3 × (5 + 2)
   C. (3 + 2) × 5   D. (2 + 3) × 5

Take It to the NET
Online lesson quiz at
www.PHSchool.com
Web Code: aaa-0209

Mixed Review

Lesson 2-5   **Tell whether each equation is true or false.**

24. 5 × 3 = 8 **false**   25. 0 × 9.8 = 9.8 **false**   26. 1 × 6.7 = 6.7 **true**

Lesson 2-1   27. **(Algebra)** Write the next two terms in the following pattern.
1, 2, 4, 8, 16, . . .   **32, 64**

28. **Geometry** Draw the next two figures in the pattern. **See margin.**

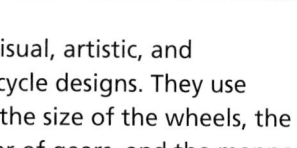

Math at Work   **Bicycle Designer**

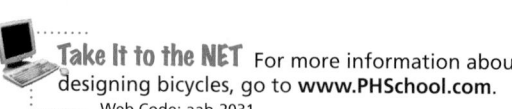

Bicycle designers combine visual, artistic, and mathematical skills to make bicycle designs. They use mathematical patterns to find the size of the wheels, the shape of the frame, the number of gears, and the manner in which these parts will work together.

Take It to the NET For more information about designing bicycles, go to **www.PHSchool.com**.
Web Code: aab-2031

108   Chapter 2   Patterns and Variables

28.

Short-response questions in this textbook are worth 2 points. To receive full credit, you must give the correct answer with units, if needed, and show your work or explain your reasoning.

EXAMPLE

Measurement Jenny stands on a scale. She weighs 104 pounds. Then she steps on the scale while holding her dog. Now the scale reads 121 pounds. Define a variable. Write and solve an equation to find the weight of the dog.

The problem asks you to define a variable, set up an equation, and solve the equation to find the weight of the dog. Below is a scoring guide that shows the number of points awarded for different answers.

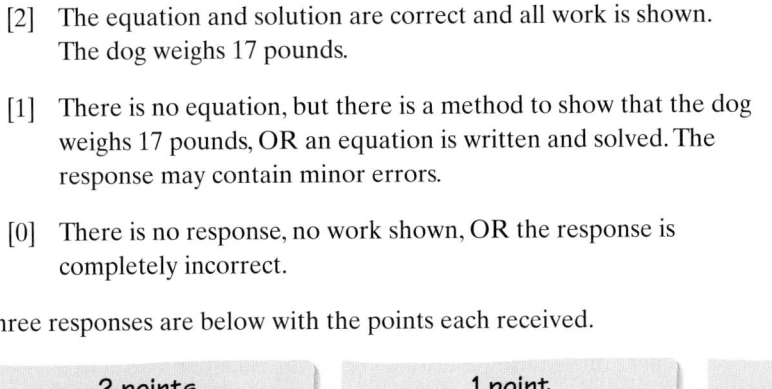

Scoring

[2]   The equation and solution are correct and all work is shown. The dog weighs 17 pounds.

[1]   There is no equation, but there is a method to show that the dog weighs 17 pounds, OR an equation is written and solved. The response may contain minor errors.

[0]   There is no response, no work shown, OR the response is completely incorrect.

Three responses are below with the points each received.

2 points	1 point	0 points
Let d = weight of dog. $104 + d = 121$ $104 + d - 104 = 121 - 104$ $d = 17$ The dog weighs 17 pounds.	$121 - 104 = 17$ 17 pounds	27 pounds

EXERCISES

Use Example 1 to answer each question.

  1–2. See margin.

1. Why did each response receive the indicated number of points?

2. Write a 2-point response for solving the equation $121 - d = 104$.

1–2. Answers may vary. Samples are given.

1. The 2-point response defined the variable, set up an equation, solved the equation, found the weight of dog; the 1-point response only showed a method and found the weight of dog;

2. Let d = weight of the dog.
   $121 - d = 104$
   $121 - d + d = 104 + d$
   $121 = 104 + d$
   $121 - 104 = 104 - 104 + d$
   $17 = d$
   The dog weighs 17 pounds.

Writing Short Responses

This strategy provides students with a scoring rubric and an example showing how to get full credit for answers to short-response questions.

Resources

PRENTICE HALL
ASSESSMENT SYSTEM

Test-Taking Strategies With Transparencies
• Transparency 3
• Practice master, p. 2

Teaching Notes

Stress the importance of answering short-response questions completely in order to get full credit.

EXAMPLE **Teaching Tip**

Have students read the problem carefully to identify each of the distinct parts of the answer. Then emphasize the importance of always breaking down a short-response question into its parts when approaching such a problem on a test.

Test-Taking Strategies With Transparencies

Chapter 2: Writing Short Responses

Exercises

Use the rubric below to answer each question.

Scoring Rubric

2	The variable is defined, the equation and the method used to solve it are correct, and the correct units are indicated. The solution is correct.
1	The variable is not defined, and there is no equation. However, there is a method to show how the problem was solved and the correct units are indicated.
1	A variable is defined, and an equation is written and solved. The response may contain minor errors.
0	There is no response, it is completely incorrect, or it is the correct response but there is no procedure shown.

1. The price of a skateboard is $74.95 plus tax. The total cost is $79.82. Define a variable. Write and solve an equation to find the amount of tax on the skateboard.

Three responses are below with the points each received.

2 points	1 point	1 point
Let t = amount of tax. $74.95 + t = 79.82$ $74.95 + t = 79.82$ $-74.95 \quad -74.95$ $t = 4.87$ The amount of the tax is $4.87.	$79.82 - 74.95 = 4.87$ $4.87	Let t = amount of tax. $74.95 + t = 79.82$ $74.95 + t = 79.82$ $-74.95 \quad -74.95$ $t = 5.87$

a. Explain why the second response received only 1 point.
   The variable is not defined and there is no equation.

b. Explain why the third response received only 1 point.
   There is an error in the calculation.

c. Write a different equation that could have been used to solve this problem.
   Sample answers: $79.82 - 74.95 = t$ or $79.82 - t = 74.95$

d. What type of answers might receive zero points?
   Sample answers: no response; $4.87 (no work shown)

2. The price of a model car is $16.45 plus the cost of the glue. The total cost is $17.50. Define a variable. Write and solve an equation to find the cost of the glue. Explain why the following response only received 1 point.
   "Let g = the cost of the glue. $16.45 + g = 17.50; g = 1.25"
   There are errors in the calculations; the correct answer is $g = \$1.05$.

109

Chapter Review

Resources

Student Edition
Extra Practice, Ch. 2, p. 643
English/Spanish Glossary, p. 669
Table of Symbols, p. 666

 Reaching All Students
Reading and Math Literacy 2D
Spanish Reading and Math
Literacy 2D

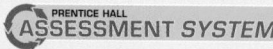
ASSESSMENT SYSTEM

Test Preparation
• Chapter 2 practice in test
formats

 www.PHSchool.com
Student Site
• Self-grading vocabulary test

PH SuccessNet Teacher Center
• Resources

Plus

Vocabulary

Addition Property of Equality (p. 91)	equation (p. 84)	power (p. 100)
algebraic expression (p. 69)	evaluate (p. 69)	solution (p. 85)
base (p. 99)	exponent (p. 99)	Subtraction Property of Equality (p. 90)
conjecture (p. 64)	inverse operations (p. 90)	term (p. 63)
Distributive Property (p. 105)	Multiplication Property of Equality (p. 96)	variable (p. 69)
Division Property of Equality (p. 95)	numerical expression (p. 68)	
	open sentence (p. 85)	

 Reading Math:
Understanding
Vocabulary

Take It to the NET
Online vocabulary quiz
at **www.PHSchool.com**
Web Code: aaj-0251

Fill in the blank.

1. Each number in a number pattern is called a(n) __?__. **term**

2. A(n) __?__ contains one or more variables. **algebraic expression OR equation**

3. In the expression 4^2, the factor 4 is called the __?__. **base**

4. A(n) __?__ is a symbol that stands for a number. **variable**

5. A(n) __?__ tells how many times to multiply a factor. **exponent**

Skills and Concepts

2-1 Objectives
▼ To continue a number pattern
▼ To write a rule for a number pattern

Each number in a number pattern is called a **term.** A **conjecture** predicts how a pattern may continue. You can describe a pattern with a rule.

Write the next three terms and write a rule for each number pattern.
6–8. See margin.

6. 2, 6, 18, 54, . . .   **7.** 7, 19, 31, 43, . . .   **8.** 7, 14, 28, 56, . . .

2-2 and 2-3 Objectives
▼ To use variables
▼ To evaluate algebraic expressions
▼ To write algebraic expressions
▼ To use algebraic expressions

A **numerical expression** contains only numbers and operation symbols. An **algebraic expression** contains at least one **variable.** To **evaluate** an algebraic expression, replace each variable with a number.

Evaluate each expression.

9. $48 \div x$ for $x = 6$ **8**   **10.** $c - 7$ for $c = 56$ **49**   **11.** $14b$ for $b = 3$ **42**

Write an expression for each word phrase.

12. x divided by 12   **13.** 2 times b **14.** h plus k
   $x \div 12$ 2b $h + k$

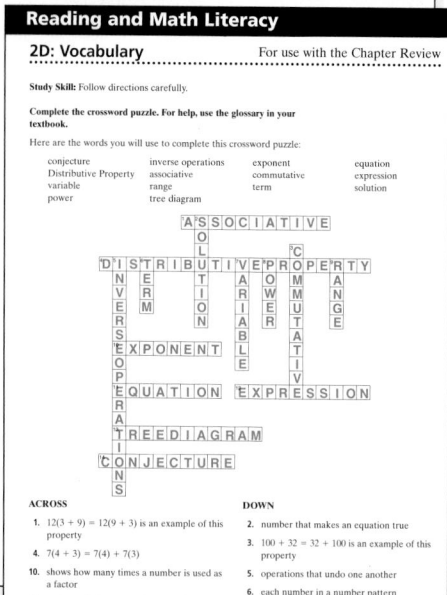

6. 162; 486; 1,458; the first term is 2; multiply a term by 3 to get the next term.

7. 55, 67, 79; the first term is 7; add 12 to a term to get the next term.

8. 112, 224, 448; the first term is 7; multiply a term by 2 to get the next term.

2-4 Objective

▼ To solve problems by making a table to find a pattern

To solve problems involving a progression of data, you can make a table that will help you organize information and find a pattern.

15. Swimming To train for a swim meet, Theresa plans to swim 4 laps each day in the first week, 8 laps each day in the second week, 12 laps each day in the third week, 16 laps each day in the fourth week, and so on. How many laps does she plan to swim each day in the seventh week? **28 laps**

2-5, 2-6, and 2-7 Objectives

▼ To use mental math to solve equations

▼ To estimate solutions of equations

▼ To solve equations by adding and subtracting

▼ To solve equations by multiplying and dividing

An **equation** is a mathematical sentence that contains an equal sign. An **open sentence** is an equation that contains one or more variables. The value of the variable that makes an equation true is a **solution.**

Tell whether each equation is true or false.

16. $15 + 25 = 30$
false

17. $21 \div 3 = 7$
true

18. $6 \times 4 = 28$
false

Mental Math Use mental math to solve each equation.

19. $x + 7 = 12$ **5**

20. $m + 13 = 21$ **8**

21. $4t = 32$ **8**

Solve each equation.

22. $r - 1,078 = 4,562$ 5,640

23. $m + 8 = 15$ **7**

24. $756 = p - 254$ 1,010

25. $78x = 4,368$ **56**

26. $t \div 4 = 32$ **128**

27. $d - 2.16 = 3.9$ 6.06

28. $5.6 + x = 7$ **1.4**

29. $4.5 = 5n$ **0.9**

30. $v \div 3.2 = 19$ **60.8**

2-8 Objectives

▼ To use exponents

▼ To simplify expressions with exponents

You can use an **exponent** to show how many times a number, or **base,** is used as a factor. A number expressed using an exponent is called a **power.**

Simplify each expression.

31. 2×4^3 **128**

32. $10^3 \div 5^2$ **40**

33. $3^2 + 2^3$ **17**

34. $(5^2 - 1) - 3^2$ 15

2-9 Objective

▼ To use the Distributive Property

You can use the **Distributive Property** to simplify an expression.

Use the Distributive Property to simplify each expression.

35. 7×28

36. 5×3.4

37. 11×57

35–37. See margin.

38. Shopping You go back-to-school shopping and buy five notebooks for $3.80 each. Find the total cost of the notebooks. **$19.00**

35. $7(20 + 8) = 140 + 56 = 196$

36. $5(3 + 0.4) = 15 + 2.0 = 17$

37. $(10 + 1)57 = 570 + 57 = 627$

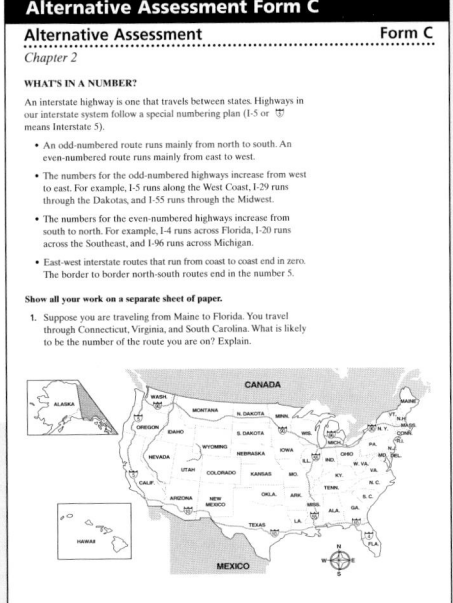

Alternative Assessment Form C

Alternative Assessment   Form C
Chapter 2

WHAT'S IN A NUMBER?

An interstate highway is one that travels between states. Highways in our interstate system follow a special numbering plan (I-5 or 🛣 means Interstate 5).

- An odd-numbered route runs mainly from north to south. An even-numbered route runs mainly from east to west.
- The numbers for the odd-numbered highways increase from west to east. For example, I-5 runs along the West Coast, I-29 runs through the Dakotas, and I-55 runs through the Midwest.
- The numbers for the even-numbered highways increase from south to north. For example, I-4 runs across Florida, I-20 runs across the Southeast, and I-96 runs across Michigan.
- East-west interstate routes that run from coast to coast end in zero. The border to border north-south routes end in the number 5.

Show all your work on a separate sheet of paper.

1. Suppose you are traveling from Maine to Florida. You travel through Connecticut, Virginia, and South Carolina. What is likely to be the number of the route you are on? Explain.

Resources

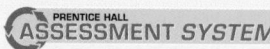

3. 22, 26, 30; the first term
is 6; add 4 to a term to
get the next term.

4. 4, 2, 1; the first term is
64; divide a term by 2 to
get the next term.

**Write the first six terms in each number
pattern described.**

1. Start with 10 then multiply by 2 repeatedly.
10, 20, 40, 80, 160, 320

2. Start with 50 then subtract by 4 repeatedly.
50, 46, 42, 38, 34, 30

**Write the next three terms and write a rule for
each number pattern.**

3. 6, 10, 14, 18, . . .   4. 64, 32, 16, 8, . . .

5. 78, 69, 60, 51, . . .   6. 4, 12, 36, 108, . . .
3–6. See margin.

Evaluate each expression for x = 12.

7. 500 + (x − 8)   8. 2x − 3   9. 8 + x ÷ 2
504   21   14

Write an algebraic expression for each model.

10. 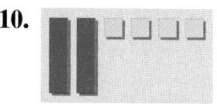   11.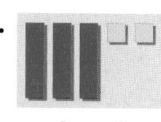

2x + 4   3x + 2

**Use algebra tiles or a drawing to model each
equation. Then solve.**

12. v + 3 = 8   13. 3g = 15
12–13. See margin.

Write an expression for each word phrase.

14. c more than 4   15. 8 less than 3d
4 + c   3d − 8

16. Gus is 8 years younger than his brother, Alex.
Alex is x years old. Write an algebraic
expression that describes how old Gus is.
x − 8

17. **Writing in Math** Write a word problem that
could be described by the expression d + 4.
Check students' work.

Tell whether each equation is true or false.

18. 6 + 7 × 3 = 39   19. 1.5 × (6 − 4) = 3
false   true

**Tell whether the given number is a solution to
the equation.**

20. x + 1.5 = 32; 17   21. h − 8 = 2; 28
no   no

Solve each equation.

22. n − 4 = 8.4 12.4   23. 25 + b = 138 113

24. k ÷ 12 = 3 36   25. 11t = 99 9

26. **Fundraising** The baseball team sold greeting
cards to raise money for uniforms. They
received $.40 profit for each card they sold.
Their total profit was $302. How many cards
did the team sell? 755 cards

27. **Patterns** Look at the pattern below. How
many squares will be in the sixth figure?

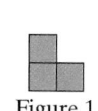   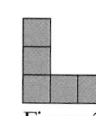   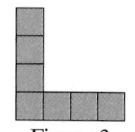

Figure 1   Figure 2   Figure 3
13 squares

**Write each expression using an exponent. Name
the base and the exponent.**

28. 10 × 10 × 10 × 10 10⁴; the base is 10 and
the exponent is 4.

29. p · p · p · p · p · p p⁶; the base is p and
the exponent is 6.

Simplify each expression.

30. 4³ − 1 63   31. 2 × 3² 18

32. 150 ÷ 5² 6   33. (9 × 4) − (8 − 6)⁴
20

---

5. 42, 33, 24; the first term
is 78; subtract 9 from a
term to get the next term.

6. 324; 972; 2,916; the first
term is 4; multiply a term
by 3 to get the next term.

12–13. Answers may vary.

Samples are given.

12.
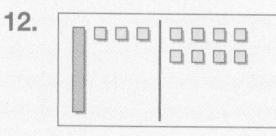
5

13.
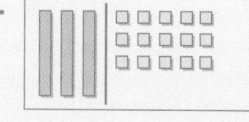
5

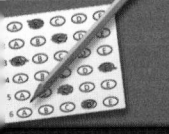

Test Prep

CUMULATIVE REVIEW
CHAPTERS 1–2

Multiple Choice

For Exercises 1–10, choose the correct letter.

1. What is the decimal for fifty-four hundredths? **B**
   A. 0.054   B. 0.54   C. 5.40   D. 54.00

2. Which inequality is NOT a true statement? **H**
   F. $0.04 > 0.01$ G. $0.014 < 0.02$
   H. $0.48 < 0.4798$ I. $29.6 > 29.06$

3. Which sentence represents the Commutative Property of Multiplication? **C**
   A. $5 \times 2 = 10$
   B. $5 \times (6 + 3) = 5 \times 9$
   C. $5 \times 9 = 9 \times 5$
   D. $(5 \times 6) \times 2 = 5 \times (6 \times 2)$

4. For 4 days, Akiko recorded the number of laps she jogged around a track. The numbers she recorded were 7, 11, 15, and 19. If she continues in the same pattern, how many laps will she jog on the sixth day? **I**
   F. 21   G. 23   H. 25   I. 27

5. Which word phrase does NOT describe the algebraic expression $b - 10$? **B**
   A. ten less than b B. b less than ten
   C. b less ten   D. b minus ten

6. Which expression has a value of 13? **H**
   F. $(3 + 2)^2$ G. $3 + (2)^2$
   H. $3^2 + 2^2$ I. $3^3 + 2^2$

7. Which operation would you use to get the variable in $x - 15 = 40$ alone on one side of the equation? **C**
   A. Subtract x from each side.
   B. Subtract 15 from each side.
   C. Add 15 to each side.
   D. Add 40 to each side.

8. What is the value of $2.5c + 2$ when $c = 6$? **G**
   F. 2.56   G. 17   H. 20   I. 256

9. Which expression is NOT equivalent to the others? **C**
   A. $13 \times (20 + 2)$
   B. $13 \times 20 + 13 \times 2$
   C. $(10 + 13) \times (10 + 12)$
   D. $22 \times (10 + 3)$

10. Apples cost $.38 each. You have $4.00. What is the greatest number of apples you can buy?
    F. 10   G. 9   H. 5   I. 11 **F**

Gridded Response

11. What is the solution of $x - 0.15 = 1.2$? **1.35**

12. Fresh cod sells for $4.86 per pound. You buy two pieces, which cost a total of $12.15. How many pounds of fish did you buy? **2.5**

13. A sheet of metal has a thickness of 0.004 inches. In inches, how many inches thick is a stack of 100 sheets? **0.4**

Short Response

14. a. Draw the fourth figure in the pattern.
    b. How many white squares will the sixth figure have?

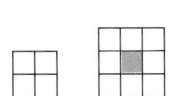 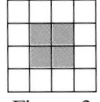

Figure 1   Figure 2   Figure 3
14a–b. See margin.

15. How many different sandwiches can you make from the choices of wheat bread, rye bread, or oatmeal bread with a filling of chicken, turkey, cheese, or peanut butter? Explain your method. **15. See back of book.**

Chapter 2   Test Prep   **113**

Item	1	2	3	4	5	6	7	8	9	10	11	12	13	14	15
Lesson	1-2	1-3	1-7	2-1	2-3	2-8	2-6	2-2	2-9	1-9	2-7	2-7	1-8	2-1	2-4

14. [2] a.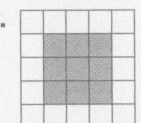

b. The sixth figure will have 7 small squares on each side. In the center,

the shaded part will have 5 small squares on each side. The number

Test Prep

Resources

Teaching Resources
Cumulative Review

Reaching All Students
Spanish Cumulative Review

Test Preparation
• Ch. 2 standardized test prep

Assessment Resources
• Cumulative Review

Computer Test Generator CD
• Standardized test prep

www.PHSchool.com
• Standardized test prep
• Resources

Plus

of white squares will be $7^2 - 5^2 = 49 - 25 = 24$ squares.

[1] Incorrect figure with correct number of white squares OR correct figure with incorrect number of white squares.

Cumulative Review
Cumulative Review
Chapters 1–2

Multiple Choice. Choose the letter of the best answer.

1. Find the next three terms in the number pattern.
   0, 3, 7, 12, ___, ___, ___
   A. 18, 24, 32   B. 18, 25, 32
   C. 17, 23, 30   D. 18, 25, 33

2. Evaluate $4 \times (3 + 7)$.
   F. 19   G. 14
   H. 43   I. 40

3. Of twenty-eight students, four read both *The Red Pony* and *The Hobbit*. Fifteen read the first book, but not the second. Five students read neither book. How many read only *The Hobbit*?
   A. 8 students
   B. 5 students
   C. 4 students
   D. 7 students

4. Which word phrase best describes the expression $x + y$?
   F. a number plus itself
   G. twice a number
   H. a number more than two
   I. a number plus another number

5. Use mental math to solve $k - 4 = 9$.
   A. 5   B. 9
   C. 13   D. 36

6. In which equation is the value of y the same as in the equation $y \times 19 = 95$?
   F. $95 \div y = 5$ G. $y + 5 = 19$
   H. $95 \div 19 = y$ I. $95 - 19 = y$

7. Which is the value of $64 - 4 \times (2 + 13)$?
   A. 4   B. 34
   C. 47   D. 900

8. Use mental math to evaluate $4x - 9$ for $x = 6$.
   F. 14   G. 15
   H. 33   I. 37

9. Janet paid x for a DVD. She gave the clerk a $20 bill. She received $7 in change. Which equation would you use to find the cost of the DVD?
   A. $7x = 20$
   B. $20 = x + 7$
   C. $x - 20 = 7$
   D. $x + 7 = 20$

10. Multiply 110×43.
    F. 4,530   G. 770
    H. 4,510   I. 4,730

11. Use mental math to evaluate $(24 + 86) \times 10$.
    A. 1,000   B. 1,010
    C. 1,100   D. 1,110

12. Which operations will make the two expressions equal?
    $2 + (12 \div 3) = 2 \underline{\quad} 12 \underline{\quad} 3$
    F. $+, \times$ G. $-, -$
    H. $-, \times$ I. $+, \div$

13. Evaluate $9 \times 9 - 6 \div 6$.
    A. 4.5   B. 12.5
    C. 45   D. 80

113

It's About Time

Students will use data from these two pages to answer the questions posed here in Put It All Together.

Activating Prior Knowledge

Elicit from students that the sun is the controlling body in our solar system of nine planets and their moons. Discuss that although the sun is a star of average size, it appears unusually large and bright because of its proximity to Earth. Point out that the sun is 400,000 times as bright as the full moon.

Teaching Notes

Have students examine and discuss the sketch of the solar system and the astronomy data presented.

English Learners

Discuss the terms *orbit* and *axis*. Call on volunteers to demonstrate the meaning of each.

Astronomy Connection

Pluto is the only planet not visible with good binoculars. Pluto was discovered at the Lowell Observatory in Flagstaff, Arizona.

History Connection

Have students investigate the history of sundials. Research questions might include:
- *When were the first sundials used?*
- *Who used them?*
- *What did they look like?*
- *How accurate were they as tools for measuring time?*

Have students report on their findings.

 **Real-World Snapshots**

It's About Time

Applying Patterns Our day, month, and year are all based on the motion of Earth and the moon. One day is 24 hours long because that's how long it takes Earth to rotate once about its axis. The moon takes one month to orbit Earth, and Earth takes one year to orbit the sun. If we lived on another planet, each of these measures would be different, and we would have different measurements of time.

Earth's Moon

The moon contains almost the same elements, minerals, and rocks as Earth, but it has no water and no atmosphere. The moon orbits Earth in 29 days, 12 hours, 44 minutes, and 3 seconds, on average.

The Last Planet

In 1930, U.S. astronomer Clyde Tombaugh discovered Pluto, the ninth planet in the solar system. During part of Pluto's year its orbit brings it closer to the sun than Neptune.

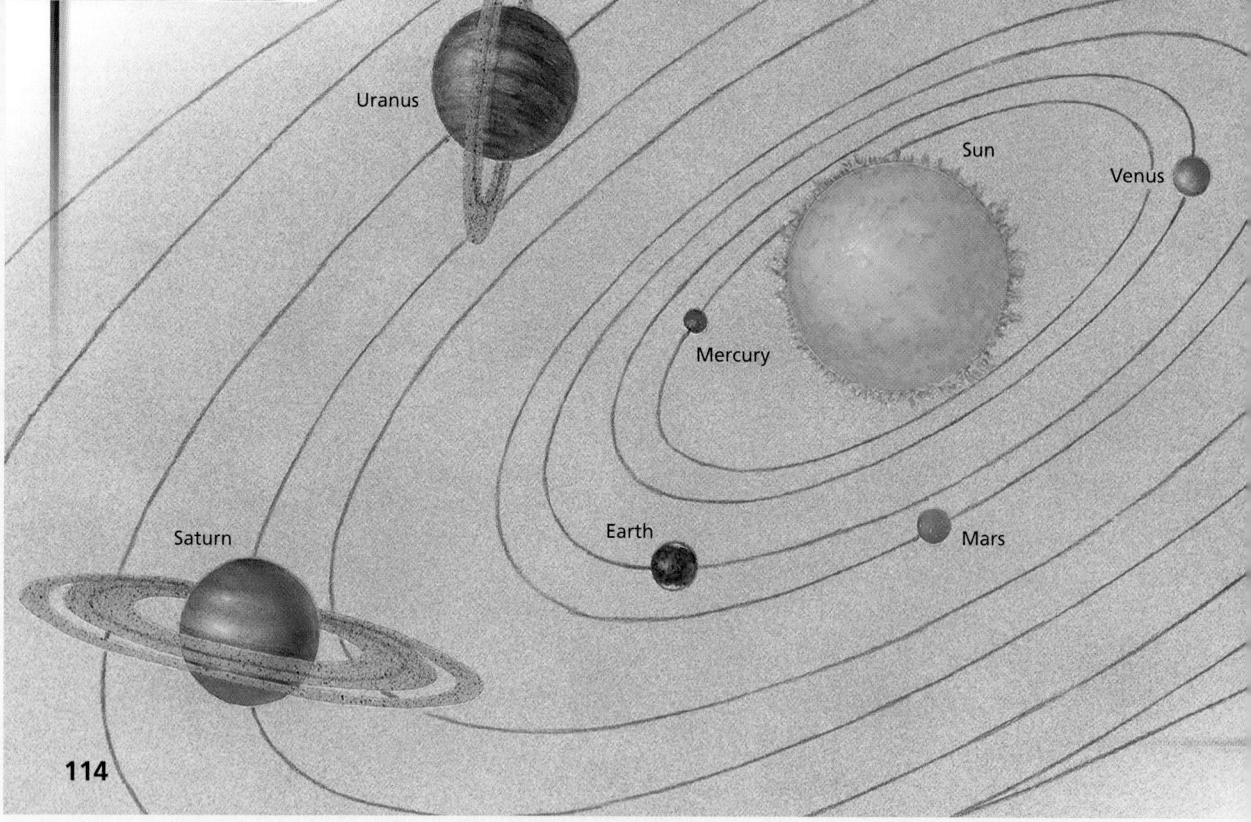

Pluto

Jupiter

Uranus

Sun

Venus

Mercury

Saturn

Earth

Mars

114

1a. **4 Mercury years**

b. **Check students' work.**

2a. **Answers may vary. Sample: about 7 birthdays. You would celebrate a birthday once every Jupiter year, which equals 4332.71/365.24, or 11.86 Earth years.**

b. **None. You could not celebrate a birthday after one year on Pluto, which equals 90,777.3/365.24, or about 249 Earth years.**

Measuring Time

The Jantar Mantar observatory, built between 1728 and 1734 in Jaipur, India, includes a giant sundial 27.5 meters high. You climb the steps to read the time, which is accurate to within a few seconds.

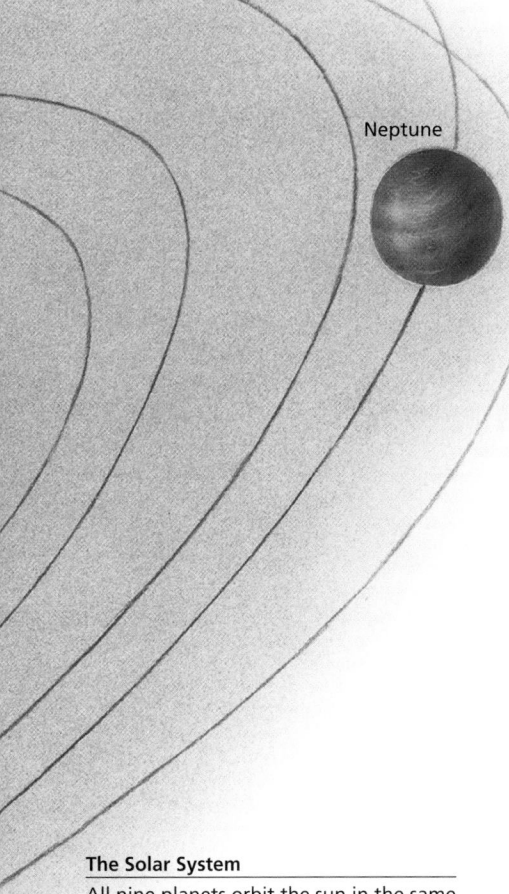

Neptune

The Solar System

All nine planets orbit the sun in the same direction (counterclockwise when viewed from above), and most spin around their axes in the direction, also.

Put It All Together

	Planet	Length of Day (Earth hours)	Length of Year (Earth days)
☿	Mercury	1,407.51	87.97
♀	Venus	5,832.61	224.7
⊕	Earth	23.93	365.24
♂	Mars	24.62	686.98
♃	Jupiter	9.93	4,332.71
♄	Saturn	10.23	10,759.3
♅	Uranus	17.23	30,684
♆	Neptune	16.11	60,188.3
♇	Pluto	153.29	90,777.3

SOURCE: *The Cambridge Planetary Handbook*

1. **a.** How many Mercury years are equivalent to one Earth year? (Give your answer to the nearest whole number.)
   b. If you lived on Mercury, how old would you now be in Mercury years?

2. **a.** If you lived on Jupiter, how many birthdays would you be likely to celebrate in your lifetime? Explain.
   b. How many birthdays would you celebrate if you lived on Pluto? Explain.

3. Mars has two moons, Phobos and Deimos. Phobos orbits the planet every 7.5 hours and Deimos every 30.25 hours.
   a. **Writing in Math** How might you define a "month" on Mars? Explain.
   b. **Reasoning** Do you think a Martian month would be a useful measure of time? Explain.

Take It to the NET For more information about planets, go to **www.PHSchool.com**.
Web Code: aae-0253

Put It All Together

Make sure students understand what determines a day, a month, and a year. Then have students work in pairs to answer the questions.

Inclusion
Help students read the table. Ask:
• *Which planets have shorter days than Earth?* Jupiter, Saturn, Uranus, Neptune
• *Which planets have shorter years than Earth?* Venus, Mercury
• *What can you say about the relationship between a planet's distance from the sun and the length of its year?* The further a planet is from the sun, the longer is its year.

Exercise 3 Students' answers to this question should show an understanding that a month is the amount of time it takes a moon to orbit a planet. Mars might have two different months or the orbit of one of its moons might be chosen as the defining month.

3a. Answers may vary. Sample: a month on Mars could be defined as the time that it takes one of its moons to orbit the planet. This is roughly the definition of one month on Earth.

b. No. Answers may vary. Sample: a Martian month is almost the same as a Martian day.

CHAPTER 3

Number Theory and Fractions

Chapter at a Glance

3-1
Divisibility and Mental Math
pp. 119–122

Objectives
▼ Using Divisibility Tests

New Vocabulary
divisible, even number, odd number

NCTM Standards
1, 6, 7, 8, 9, 10

Local Standards

3-2
Prime Numbers and Prime Factorization
pp. 123–126

Objectives
1 Finding Factors of a Number
2 Finding the Prime Factorization of a Number

New Vocabulary
factor, composite number, prime number, prime factorization

NCTM Standards
1, 3, 6, 7, 8, 9, 10

Local Standards

3-3
Greatest Common Factor
pp. 128–131

Objectives
▼ Finding the Greatest Common Factor

New Vocabulary
common factor, greatest common factor (GCF)

NCTM Standards
1, 3, 6, 7, 8, 9, 10

Local Standards

✔ Checkpoint Quiz 1

3-4
Equivalent Fractions
pp. 134–137

Objectives
1 Finding Equivalent Fractions
2 Writing Fractions in Simplest Form

New Vocabulary
equivalent fractions, simplest form

Optional Materials
fraction calculator

NCTM Standards
1, 3, 6, 7, 8, 9, 10

Local Standards

3-5
Mixed Numbers and Improper Fractions
pp. 139–142

Objectives
1 Writing Mixed Numbers as Improper Fractions
2 Writing Improper Fractions as Mixed Numbers

New Vocabulary
proper fraction, mixed number, improper fraction

NCTM Standards
1, 3, 6, 7, 8, 9, 10

Local Standards

3-6
Least Common Multiple
pp. 143–146

Objectives
▼ Finding the Least Common Multiple

New Vocabulary
common multiple, least common multiple (LCM)

NCTM Standards
1, 6, 7, 8, 9, 10

Local Standards

3-7
Comparing and Ordering Fractions
pp. 148–152

Objectives
1 Comparing Fractions
2 Ordering Fractions

New Vocabulary
least common denominator (LCD)

NCTM Standards
1, 4, 6, 7, 8, 9, 10

Local Standards

✔ Checkpoint Quiz 2

3-8
Fractions and Decimals
pp. 153–156

Objectives
1 Writing Decimals as Fractions
2 Writing Fractions as Decimals

NCTM Standards
1, 4, 6, 7, 8, 9, 10

Local Standards

3-9 Problem Solving
Try, Check, and Revise
pp. 157–160

Objectives
▼ Solving Problems by Trying, Checking, and Revising

NCTM Standards
1, 6, 7, 8, 9, 10

Local Standards

Reaching All Students

Additional Instructional Options in Chapter 3

Pacing Options

This chart suggests pacing only for the core lessons and their parts. It is provided as a possible guide. It will help you determine how much time you have in your schedule to cover the additional features and assessment, as described at the left.

Reading and Math Literacy

📘 Reading Math

Learning Vocabulary, p. 147

Reading Math hints, pp. 141, 153

Reading Comprehension, p. 165

Understanding Vocabulary, pp. 142, 162

✏️ Writing in Math

Writing Extended Responses, p. 161

Daily Writing Practice, pp. 121, 122, 125, 130, 136, 145, 151, 155, 159, 164

Above Level

🅒 Challenge exercises

pp. 122, 125, 130, 137, 142, 146, 151, 156, 159

⬤ Extension

The Sieve of Eratosthenes, p. 127

Hands-On and Technology

🔍 Investigations

Modeling Divisibility with Rectangles, p. 123

Modeling Fractions, p. 132

Comparing Numerators and Denominators, p. 139

Comparing Fractions, p. 148

💻 Technology

Simplifying Fractions, p. 138

Activities and Projects

📖 Real-World Snapshots

Applying Fractions pp. 166–167

📁 Chapter Project

Home Court Advantage, p. 637

Test Prep

📝 Daily Test Prep

pp. 122, 126, 131, 137, 142, 146, 152, 156, 160

📝 Test-Taking Strategies

Writing Extended Responses, p. 161

📝 Test Prep

Reading Comprehension, p. 165

Chapter Assessment

✔️ Checkpoint Quiz

pp. 131, 152

⬤ Chapter Review

pp. 162–163

⬤ Chapter Test

p. 164

Day	Traditional 45-minute class periods	Block 90-minute class periods
1	3-1 ▽	3-1 ▽ 3-2 ▽
2	3-2 ▽	3-2 ▽ 3-3 ▽
3	3-2 ▽	3-4 ▽ ▽ 3-5 ▽
4	3-3 ▽	3-5 ▽ 3-6 ▽
5	3-4 ▽	3-7 ▽ ▽
6	3-4 ▽	3-8 ▽ ▽
7	3-5 ▽	3-9 ▽
8	3-5 ▽	
9	3-6 ▽	
10	3-7 ▽	
11	3-7 ▽	
12	3-8 ▽	
13	3-8 ▽	
14	3-9 ▽	

NCTM STANDARDS 2000	
1 Number and Operations	6 Problem Solving
2 Algebra	7 Reasoning and Proof
3 Geometry	8 Communication
4 Measurement	9 Connections
5 Data Analysis and Probability	10 Representation

Math Background

Skills Trace

BEFORE Chapter 3
Grade 5 presented basic fraction concepts.

DURING Chapter 3
Course 1 extends fraction concepts and uses basic number theory to find prime factorizations, GCFs, LCMs, and LCDs.

AFTER Chapter 3
Throughout this course students use fraction concepts and basic number theory.

3-1 Divisibility and Mental Math

Math Understandings
- When you find one whole number that divides a second, you know that all the factors of that whole number also divide the second number.

One whole number is **divisible** by a second whole number if the remainder is 0 when the first number is divided by the second number.

Divisibility of Whole Numbers

A whole number is divisible by
- 2 if it ends in 0, 2, 4, 6, or 8.
- 3 if the sum of its digits is divisible by 3.
- 5 if it ends in 0 or 5.
- 9 if the sum of its digits is divisible by 9.
- 10 if it ends in 0.

An **even number** is any whole number that ends with a 0, 2, 4, 6, or 8. An **odd number** is a whole number that ends with a 1, 3, 5, 7, or 9.

Example: Test 3,471 for divisibility by 3.

$3 + 4 + 7 + 1 = 15$ and $15 \div 3 = 5$. So 3,471 is divisible by 3.

3-2 Prime Numbers and Prime Factorization

Math Understandings
- Every integer greater than one can be expressed as a product of prime factors in one and only one way, except for the order of the factors.
- Every whole number has at least two factors, one and itself.
- The whole numbers 0 and 1 are neither prime nor composite.

A **factor** is a whole number that divides a nonzero whole number with remainder 0. A **composite number** is a whole number greater than 1 with more than two factors. A **prime number** is a whole number with exactly two factors, 1 and the number itself. Writing a composite number as a product of prime numbers gives the **prime factorization** of the number.

3-3 Greatest Common Factor

Math Understandings
- Two or more whole numbers may have several common factors, but they have only one greatest common factor.

A factor that two or more numbers share is a **common factor**. The **greatest common factor (GCF)** of two or more numbers is the greatest factor shared by all the numbers. You can find the GCF for two numbers by listing all the factors, using a division ladder, or using factor trees.

3-4 Equivalent Fractions

Math Understandings
- A fraction is a number representing some part of a whole and may be written in the form $\frac{a}{b}$ where $b \neq 0$.

Equivalent fractions are fractions that name the same amount. A fraction is in **simplest form** when the only common factor of the numerator and denominator is 1. One way to write a fraction in simplest form is to divide both the numerator and denominator by their greatest common factor.

Example: $\frac{12}{16} = \frac{3 \cdot 4}{4 \cdot 4} = \frac{3}{4} \cdot \frac{4}{4} = \frac{3}{4} \cdot 1 = \frac{3}{4}$

3-5

Mixed Numbers and Improper Fractions

Math Understandings
- One number can be written in many different forms, all of which are equivalent.
- A fraction has a unique simplest form, which may be an improper fraction or mixed number.

Name	Description	Example
proper fraction	numerator less than its denominator	$\frac{1}{2}$
improper fraction	numerator is greater than or equal to its denominator	$\frac{5}{2}$
mixed number	shows the sum of a whole number and a proper fraction.	$2\frac{1}{2}$

Example: Change $5\frac{1}{6}$ to an improper fraction.
$$5\frac{1}{6} = \frac{5 \times 6 + 1}{6} = \frac{31}{6}$$

 3-6

Least Common Multiple

Math Understandings
- Two positive integers have an infinite number of common multiples but only one LCM.

A number that is a multiple of each of two or more numbers is a **common multiple**. The **least common multiple (LCM)** of two numbers is the least multiple that is common to both.

Example: Find the least common multiple of 4 and 6.
Multiples of 4: 4, 8, ⑫, 16, 20, ㉔
Multiples of 6: 6, ⑫, 18, ㉔
The least common multiple is 12.

 3-7

Comparing and Ordering Fractions

Math Understandings
- If the denominators of two fractions are the same, the fraction with the greater numerator is greater.
- If the numerators are the same, the fraction with the lesser denominator has the greater value.
- If the denominators of two fractions are different, rewrite the fractions with common denominators, then compare.

The **least common denominator (LCD)** of two or more fractions is the least common multiple (LCM) of their denominators.

 3-8

Fractions and Decimals

Math Understandings
- To write a decimal as a fraction, write the fraction as you would say the decimal and simplify.
- When you write fractions as decimals, the result may be a decimal that continuously repeats one digit or a set of digits.

A fraction indicates division. To write a fraction as a decimal, divide the numerator by the denominator.

Example: Compare $\frac{5}{6} = 6\overline{)5.000}^{\,.833} = 0.8\overline{3}$

 3-9

Try, Check, and Revise

You can use the *try, check, and revise* strategy when the solution to a problem involves several related numbers. First try to make a reasonable estimate of the solution; then check it, and revise, as necessary.

Additional Professional Development Opportunities

Chapter 3 Math Background notes:
pp. 120, 124, 129, 135, 140, 144, 149, 154, 158

 SkyLight Professional Development

Additional resources available from SkyLight Professional Development:

On-site courses, workshops, summer institutes. Online courses and chat rooms. Videocassettes and books. Visit www.skylightedu.com.

 Professional Development

Ongoing Assessment and Intervention

The *Prentice Hall Mathematics* program provides many options for assessment in the Student Edition, Teacher's Edition, and teaching resources. From these options you may choose instructional materials that are appropriate for your students and that support your district's curriculum requirements.

Daily Assessment

 Instant Check System™ in Chapter 3

Allows students to check their own learning before, during, and after each lesson.

Diagnosing Readiness before the chapter (p. 118)

Check Skills You'll Need exercises in each lesson (pp. 119, 123, 128, 134, 139, 143, 148, 153, 157)

Check Understanding questions with each Example (pp. 119, 120, 123, 124, 128, 129, 134, 135, 140, 143, 144, 149, 150, 153, 154, 158)

Checkpoint Quiz (pp. 131, 152)

Formal Assessment

Assessment in the Student Text and in Additional Resources

Assess student progress throughout the Course 1 textbook and with blackline masters and CD-ROM.

Student Edition
- Chapter 3 Review, with Vocabulary, Skills, and Concepts Review, pp. 162–163
- Chapter 3 Test, p. 164

Assessment Resources
- Checkpoint Quizzes 1 & 2
- Chapter Test, forms A & B
- Chapter Alternative Assessment

Spanish versions available.

 **Computer Test Generator CD-ROM**
- Instant Chapter Tests™—pre-made tests with items that vary every time you print.
- Online Testing allows you to give tests online and receive progress reports.
- Prepare students by making tests based on standardized test objectives.

Algebra Readiness Tests
- Includes Basic Skills Tests and Concept-Readiness Tests.
- Assess understanding of skills and concepts needed for success in algebra.

Intervention

 Skills Intervention Kit

 **Online Intervention**
Integrated within the iText, this online intervention system includes diagnostic tests and prescribed remediation, plus reports to track student mastery.

A *complete* system for the student who is struggling with course-level work

Eight intervention units cover core skills and allow you to:
- **Diagnose** students' gaps in basic skills
- **Prescribe** an individualized course of study
- **Monitor** student progress

Includes print workbooks, tutorial CD-ROM, teacher editions, progress folders, and more. *Available in Spanish.*

How to Use with Chapter 3

3-1	Number Theory and Fraction Concepts, Skill 1
3-2	Number Theory and Fraction Concepts, Skills 2–5
3-3	Number Theory and Fraction Concepts, Skill 6
3-4	Number Theory and Fraction Concepts, Skills 11–12
3-5	Number Theory and Fraction Concepts, Skills 14–15
3-6	Number Theory and Fraction Concepts, Skill 7
3-7	Number Theory and Fraction Concepts, Skill 16
3-8	Number Theory and Fraction Concepts, Skills 17–18

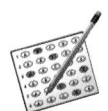

Standardized Test Preparation

The *Prentice Hall Mathematics* program integrates preparation for high-stakes standardized tests in every lesson of the Student Edition and continues this support in the Prentice Hall Assessment System.

Test Prep

In Student Text, Chapter 3

Teaches students strategies and gives them practice with all the test item formats they will encounter on high-stakes tests.

Test Prep exercises in each lesson (pp. 122, 126, 131, 137, 142, 146, 152, 156, 160)

Test-Taking Strategies (p. 161: Writing Extended Responses)

Test Prep (p. 165: Reading Comprehension)

A three-step approach to preparing students for high stakes, national, and state exams.

1 Diagnose & Prescribe

Content Diagnostic Tests
- Diagnose strengths and weaknesses with ongoing benchmark tests.
- Prescribe individualized reteaching opportunities.

2 Review & Reteach

Skills and Concepts Review
- Provides reteaching worksheets with instruction and practice for each skill.
- Includes course prerequisite skills.

3 Practice & Assess

Standardized Test Preparation
- Features practice for national standardized exams.
- Includes practice tests for NAEP, SAT10, ITBS, and Terra Nova.

Test-Taking Strategies with Transparencies
- Support the Test-Taking Strategies pages in the Student Edition.
- Provide a transparency and a worksheet for each strategy.

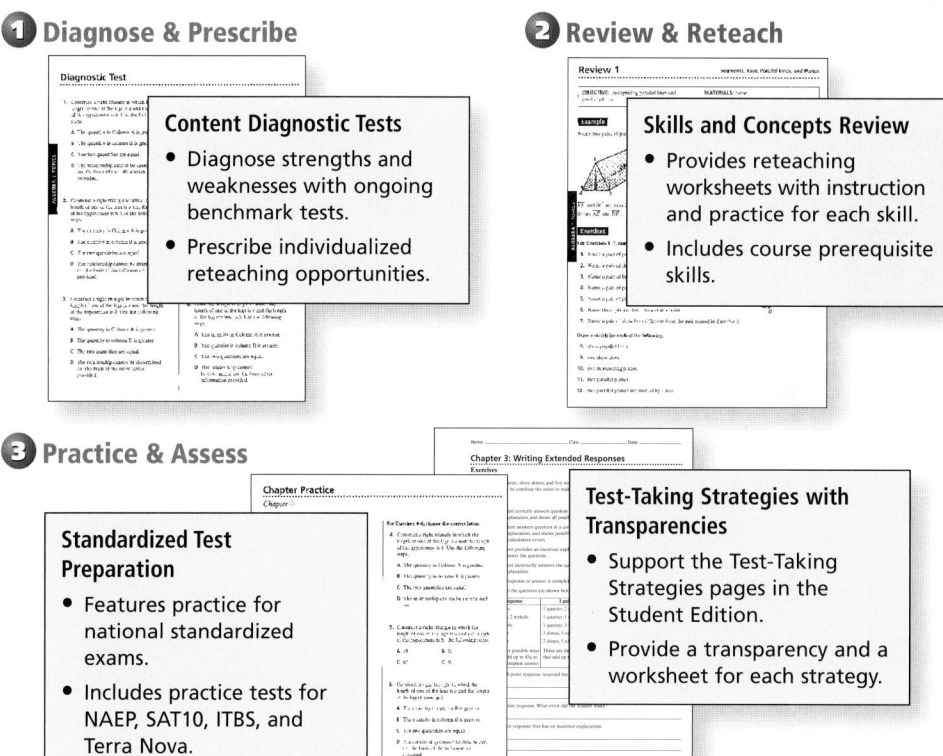

Correlation to Standardized Tests

Lesson		NAEP	Terra Nova				Local Test
			CAT6	CTBS	ITBS	SAT10	
3-1	Divisibility and Mental Math	N5d	■		■		
3-2	Prime Numbers and Prime Factorization	N5b	■			■	
3-3	Greatest Common Factor	N3a	■				
3-4	Equivalent Fractions	N3a	■	■	■	■	
3-5	Mixed Numbers and Improper Fractions	N3a	■			■	
3-6	Least Common Multiple	N3a	■				
3-7	Comparing and Ordering Fractions	N1e, N1j		■		■	
3-8	Fractions and Decimals		■	■	■	■	
3-9	Problem Solving: Try, Check, and Revise						

NAEP National Assessment of Educational Progress
CAT6/Terra Nova California Achievement Test, 6th Ed.
CTBS/Terra Nova Comprehensive Test of Basic Skills
ITBS Iowa Test of Basic Skills, Form M.
SAT10 Stanford Achievement Test, 10th Ed.

Program Resources

	Resources in Grab & Go™ Files				Resources for Reaching All Students				Spanish Resources			Presentation Assistant Plus! — Transparencies					Prentice Hall Presentation Pro CD-ROM
	Practice	Reteach	Enrich	Checkpt Quiz	Reading & Math Literacy	Technology Activities	Hands-On Activities	Guided Problem Solving	Practice	Reading & Math Literacy	Checkpt Quiz	Skills Check	Problem of the Day	Additional Examples	Answers to Exercises	Lesson Quiz	
3-1	■	■	■		■		■	■	■			■	■	■	■	■	■
3-2	■	■	■			■		■	■			■	■	■	■	■	■
3-3	■	■	■	■	■		■	■	■	■	■	■	■	■	■	■	■
3-4	■	■	■				■	■	■			■	■	■	■	■	■
3-5	■	■	■		■			■	■			■	■	■	■	■	■
3-6	■	■	■					■	■			■	■	■	■	■	■
3-7	■	■	■	■	■			■	■	■	■	■	■	■	■	■	■
3-8	■	■	■			■		■	■			■	■	■	■	■	■
3-9	■	■	■					■	■			■	■	■	■	■	■
For the Chapter	Chapter Projects, Chapter Tests, Alternative Assessment, Cumulative Review, Cumulative Assessment				**On web site only:** Home Activities, Interdisciplinary Activities, Algebra Readiness Puzzles				Spanish Chapter Tests, Alternative Assessment, Cumulative Review, Cumulative Assessment			Classroom Aid Transparencies					

Also available for use with the chapter:

 PRENTICE HALL ASSESSMENT *SYSTEM*   *See page 116F.*

- Practice Workbook
- Solution Key
- MathNotes folder

- For teacher support and access to student Web materials, use the Web Code aak-5500.
- For additional online and technology resources, *see below.*

 **Technology**

 **Online and on CD-ROM**

Complete Interactive Student Text online and on CD-ROM—with instant feedback assessment, tutorial help, dynamic activities, instructional and real-world videos, audio, and additional practice.

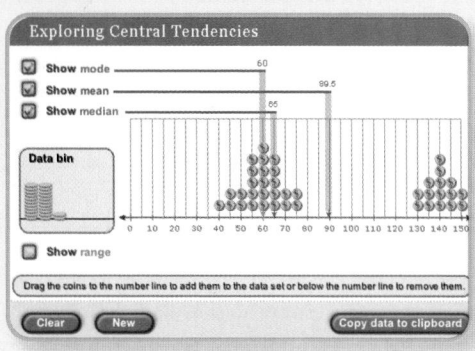

 www.PHSchool.com For Students

Use Web codes for easy access to online activities, chapter projects, self-grading lesson quizzes, chapter tests, vocabulary quizzes, updated data sources, graphing calculator procedures, and more.

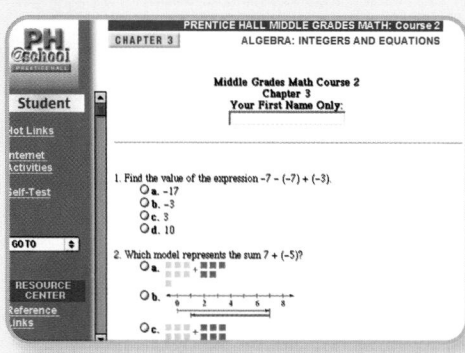

PH SuccessNet **For Teachers**

Online lesson planning with built-in state correlations, all the teaching resources, complete reference library, your own calendar and Teacher Web page, professional development, and more.

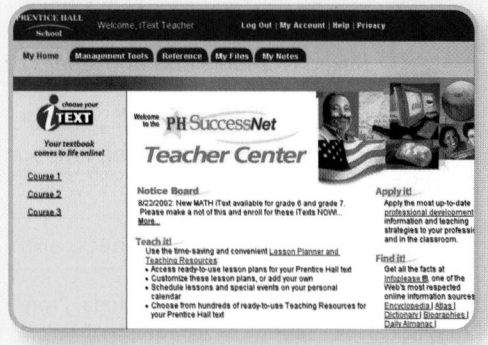

Presentation Assistant Plus!

The *Prentice Hall Presentation Assistant Plus!* provides you with the material you need to teach a lesson from beginning to end. Two easy-to-use formats—Transparencies and PowerPoint®—allow you to present a lesson the way you are most comfortable.

Transparencies

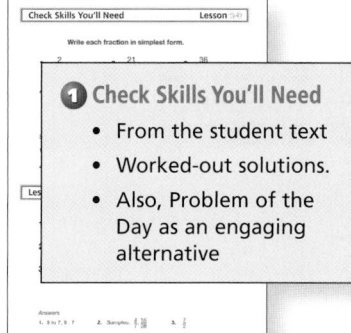

1 Check Skills You'll Need
- From the student text
- Worked-out solutions.
- Also, Problem of the Day as an engaging alternative

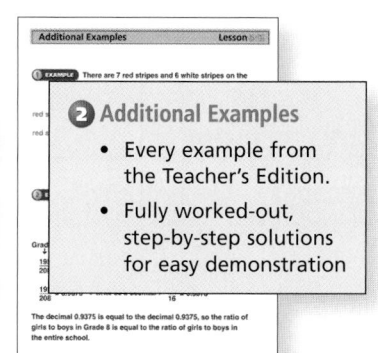

2 Additional Examples
- Every example from the Teacher's Edition.
- Fully worked-out, step-by-step solutions for easy demonstration

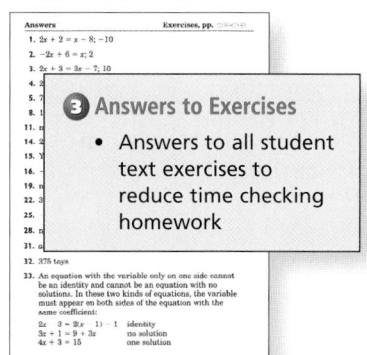

3 Answers to Exercises
- Answers to all student text exercises to reduce time checking homework

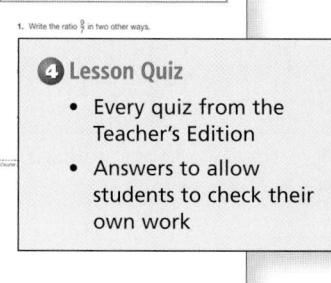

4 Lesson Quiz
- Every quiz from the Teacher's Edition
- Answers to allow students to check their own work

 **PowerPoint** Throughout the Teacher's Edition, this symbol indicates material that is available in the Presentation Assistant Plus!

PowerPoint **Prentice Hall Presentation Pro CD-ROM**

- Includes all Transparencies.
- Conveniently organized by lesson so you can easily **1** Introduce, **2** Teach, **3** Check Homework, and **4** Assess each lesson.
- Animated examples allow step-by-step instruction at your own pace.
- Easy to edit so you can create custom presentations.

Teaching Chapter 3 Using Presentation Assistant Plus!

	1 Introduce	**2 Teach**	**3 Check Homework**	**4 Assess**
	Check Skills You'll Need	Additional Examples	Student Edition Answers	Lesson Quiz
3-1	p. 21	p. 34	✔	p. 21
3-2	p. 22	pp. 35–36	✔	p. 22
3-3	p. 23	p. 37	✔	p. 23
3-4	p. 24	pp. 38–39	✔	p. 24
3-5	p. 25	p. 40	✔	p. 25
3-6	p. 26	p. 41	✔	p. 26
3-7	p. 27	pp. 42–43	✔	p. 27
3-8	p. 28	p. 44	✔	p. 28
3-9	p. 29	pp. 45–46	✔	p. 29

Prentice Hall Presentation Pro

CD-ROM with dynamic PowerPoint® presentations for every lesson. Helps you introduce and develop concepts, check homework, and assess progress. Part of Presentation Assistant Plus! *(See above.)*

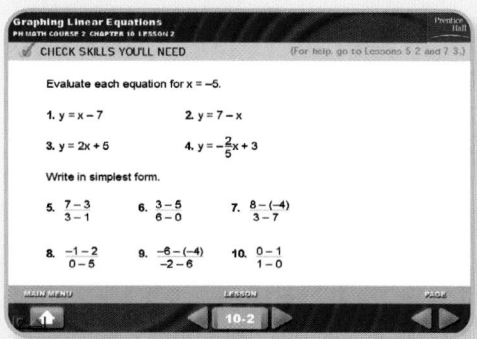

Computer Test Generator

CD-ROM to create practice sheets and tests for course objectives and standardized tests. Includes Instant Chapter Tests™, online testing, and student reports. Part of the PH Assessment System. *(See page 116F.)*

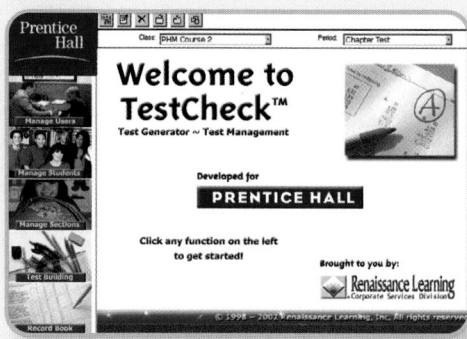

Resource Pro® with Planning Express®

CD-ROM with a lesson planning tool that allows you to import state and local objectives. Includes electronic versions of all the teaching resources.

Chapter Resources

Reading and Math Support

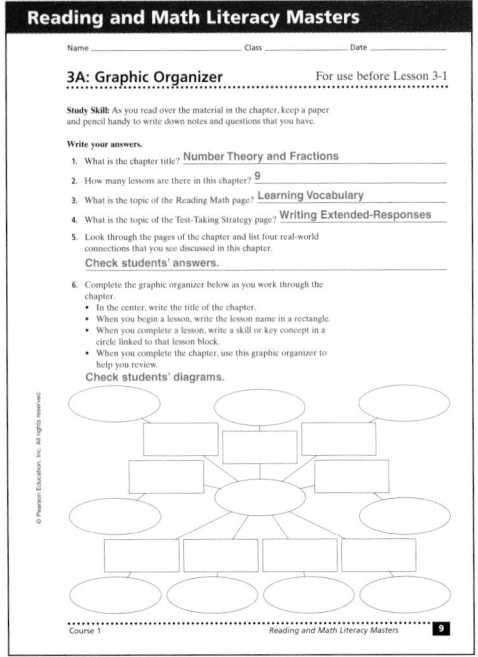

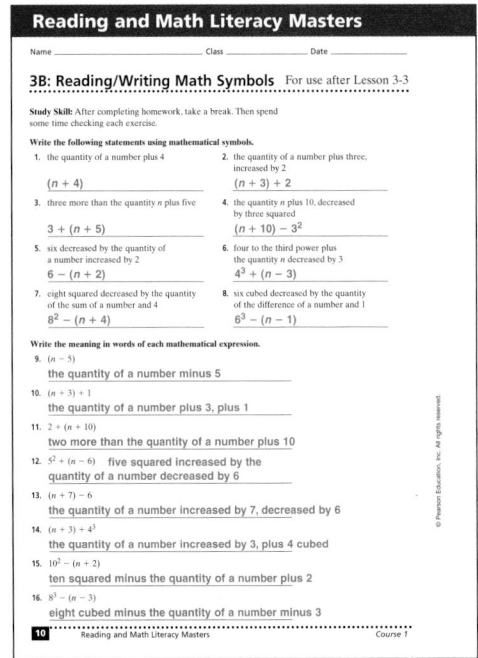

Problem Solving

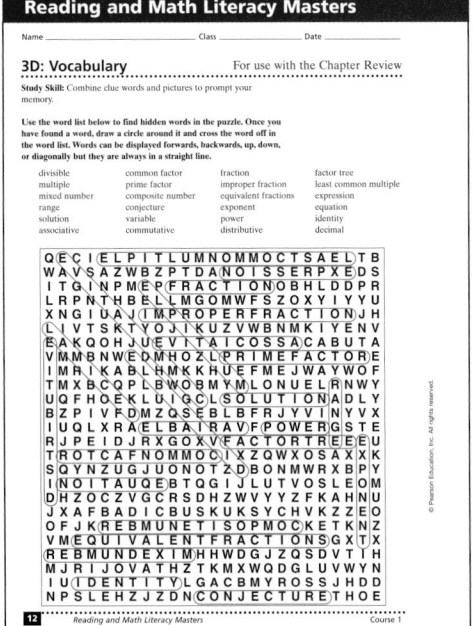

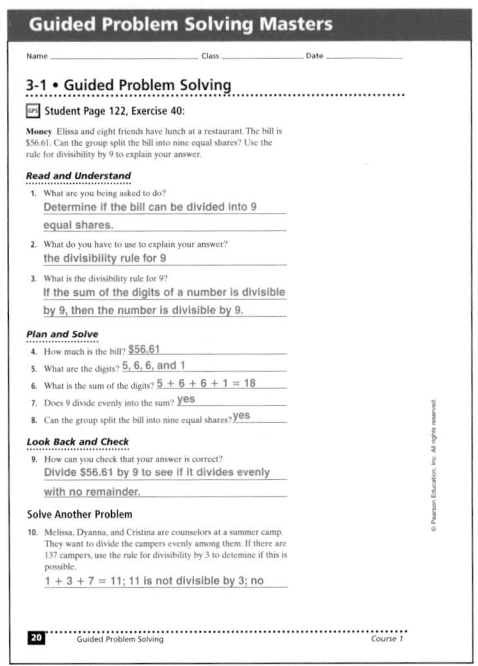

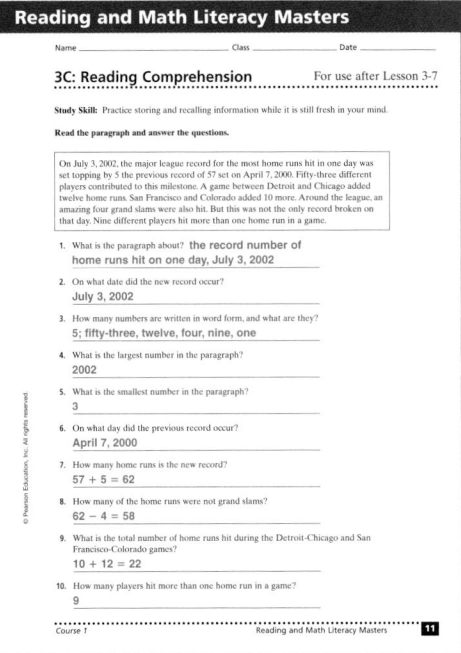

Guided Problem Solving Masters

Name _____ Class _____ Date _____

3-3 • Guided Problem Solving

GPS Student Page 130, Exercise 27:

Baseball Cards Three friends pool their money to buy baseball cards. Brand A has 8 cards in each pack, Brand B has 12 cards, and Brand C has 15 cards. If they want to split the cards equally, which two brands should they buy? Explain.

Read and Understand

1. What does *split the cards equally* mean?
   Each person gets the same number.

Plan and Solve

2. How many cards will they have if they buy Brand A and Brand B?
   20 cards

3. Is the number you found in Exercise 3, divisible by 3? Why or why not?
   No, 2 is not divisible by 3.

4. How many cards will they have if they buy Brand A and Brand C?
   23 cards

5. How many cards will they have if they buy Brand B and Brand C?
   27 cards

6. Which of the answers to Exercises 4 and 5 are divisible by 3? 27

7. Which two brands should they buy?
   Brands B and C

Look Back and Check

8. Explain your decision.
   Brand B and C have 27 cards, which is divisible by 3.

Solve Another Problem

9. Carrie is lining up 45 students in the drill team and 25 students in the color guard. She wants each row to have the same number of students in both groups. How many rows are there, and how many students are in each row?
   5 rows of 9 drill team students and 5 rows of 5
   color guard students

Guided Problem Solving Masters

Name _____ Class _____ Date _____

3-4 • Guided Problem Solving

GPS Student Page 136, Exercise 31:

Traffic Planning Two traffic engineers are writing about the average driving time between two towns. One engineer writes the time as 45, but the other writes it as $\frac{3}{4}$. What could explain the difference?

Read and Understand

1. What are you being asked to do?
   Explain why the engineers wrote the driving
   time differently.

2. What is the relationship between the two measurements?
   They are the same.

Plan and Solve

3. Name some units in which time can be measured.
   Sample answers: seconds, minutes, hours,
   days, weeks, months, years

4. What is a reasonable unit for the engineer who wrote 45?
   minutes

5. What is a reasonable unit for the engineer who wrote $\frac{3}{4}$?
   hours

6. What explains the difference?
   One engineer wrote the time in minutes and
   the other wrote it in hours.

Look Back and Check

7. Why did you choose those units?
   Sample answer: Time is more easily measured
   in minutes and hours in this situation.

Solve Another Problem

8. A scientist measured the time it took for a reaction to take place in $\frac{1}{4}$ hour. To use the results, he needs to write the numbers as minutes. How many minutes did it take for the reaction to take place?
   $60 \times \frac{1}{4} = 15$; 15 minutes

Guided Problem Solving Masters

Name _____ Class _____ Date _____

3-5 • Guided Problem Solving

GPS Student Page 141, Exercise 37:

Food A caterer plans to serve two slices of melon to each of 50 guests. She estimates getting 12 slices from each melon. Write the number of melons she will use as a mixed number. How many whole melons does she need?

Read and Understand

1. Circle the information you will need to solve.

2. What are you being asked to do?
   Write the number of melons as a mixed number;
   then find how many whole melons are needed.

Plan and Solve

3. How many slices does she need to feed 50 guests?
   $50 \text{ guests} \times 2 \frac{\text{slices}}{\text{guest}}$ or 100 slices

4. How many slices does she get from each melon?
   12 slices

5. What operation do you use to find the number of melons she needs?
   division

6. Write the number of melons she will use as a mixed number.
   $100 \text{ slices} \div 12 \frac{\text{slices}}{\text{melon}}$ or $8\frac{1}{3}$ melons

7. How many *whole* melons does she need?
   9 melons

Look Back and Check

8. Why does she need to know how many whole melons are needed?
   Parts of melons are not usually sold in bulk.

Solve Another Problem

9. Three hundred twenty-one students are going on a field trip. One bus can seat 48 students. Write the number of buses needed as a mixed number. How many whole buses are needed?
   $321 \text{ students} \div 48 \frac{\text{students}}{\text{bus}}$ or $3\frac{11}{16}$; 4 buses

---

Guided Problem Solving Masters

Name _____ Class _____ Date _____

3-6 • Guided Problem Solving

GPS Student Page 145, Exercise 17:

Business During a promotion, a music store gives a free CD to every fifteenth customer and a free DVD to every fortieth customer. Which customer will be the first to get both a free CD and a free DVD?

Read and Understand

1. Circle the information you will need to solve.

2. What are you being asked to do?
   Find which customer will be the first to get
   both a free CD and a free DVD.

Plan and Solve

3. Which customers will receive a free CD?
   The 15th, 30th, 45th, 60th, 75th, 90th, 105th,
   120th, 135th, 150th, etc.

4. Which customers will receive a free DVD?
   The 40th, 80th, 120th, 160th, 200th, etc.

5. Which customer will be the first to get both a free CD and a free DVD?
   the 120th customer

Look Back and Check

6. Explain how you can check your answer.
   Both 15 and 40 divide evenly into 120.

Solve Another Problem

7. Emanuel, Michelle, and Kim volunteer at the swimming pool. Emanuel works every 5 days. Michelle works every 6 days. Kim works every 15 days. They are working together today. How many days will it be until the next time they work together?
   Number of days until each volunteer works
   again: 5, 10, 15, 20, 25, 30; 6, 12, 18, 24, 30;
   15, 30; Number of days until they work
   together: 30 days

Guided Problem Solving Masters

Name _____ Class _____ Date _____

3-7 • Guided Problem Solving

GPS Student Page 151, Exercise 23:

Shopping Two sports drinks have the same price. The cherry-flavored drink is $12\frac{9}{20}$ ounces. The blueberry-flavored drink is $12\frac{7}{16}$ ounces. Assuming you like both flavors, which drink is the better buy?

Read and Understand

1. Circle the information you will need to solve.

2. What are you being asked to do?
   Determine which drink is the better buy.

3. Since both drinks are priced the same, what do you have to determine?
   which is bigger

Plan and Solve

4. What is the common denominator for $12\frac{9}{20}$ and $12\frac{7}{16}$? 80

5. Rewrite the fractional part of each mixed number with the common denominator. $\frac{36}{80}, \frac{35}{80}$

6. Which fraction is bigger? $\frac{36}{80}$

7. Which drink is the better buy? the $12\frac{9}{20}$-ounce drink

Look Back and Check

8. What is another way you could answer this question?
   Change both mixed numbers to decimals and
   then compare them.

Solve Another Problem

9. Mary, Ana, and Tim shared the driving on a trip. Mary drove $\frac{1}{4}$ of the distance. Ana drove $\frac{1}{8}$ of the distance. Did Mary or Ana drive more miles? Explain how you know.
   Ana drove more miles because $\frac{1}{4} > \frac{1}{8}$.

Guided Problem Solving Masters

Name _____ Class _____ Date _____

3-8 • Guided Problem Solving

GPS Student Page 155, Exercise 25:

Shopping You order $1\frac{1}{4}$ pounds of cheese at a deli. What decimal number should the digital scale show?

Read and Understand

1. What are you being asked to do?
   Rewrite the fraction $1\frac{1}{4}$ as a decimal.

2. How do you read $\frac{1}{4}$ as a division problem?
   one divided by four

Plan and Solve

3. How do you write 1 as a decimal?
   1.0

4. Divide 1 by 4.
   0.25

5. Write $1\frac{1}{4}$ as a decimal.
   $1.0 + 0.25 = 1.25$

6. What decimal number should the digital scale show?
   1.25 pounds

Look Back and Check

7. How can you check your answer?
   Write 1.25 as a fraction and see if it is the
   same as $1\frac{1}{4}$.

Solve Another Problem

8. A recipe calls for $3\frac{3}{4}$ pounds of flour. Your scale only measures in decimals. What will the scale read?
   3.75 pounds

Activities and Projects

Guided Problem Solving Masters

Name _____ Class _____ Date _____

3-9 • Guided Problem Solving

[GPS] **Student Page 159, Exercise 7:**

Trains leave Farmville for Lexinburg (every 40 minutes) The (first train) leaves at (5:00 A.M.) What is the departure time (closest) to (2:35 P.M.)

Read and Understand
1. Circle the information you will need to solve.

2. What are you being asked to do?
   Find the departure time closest to 12:35 P.M.

Plan and Solve
3. List the first 8 departure times.
   5:00, 5:40, 6:20, 7:00, 7:40, 8:20, 9:00, 9:40

4. What is the pattern?
   The odd hours have 2 departures, on the hour
   and forty minutes after the hour. The even
   hours have one departure at 20 minutes after
   the hour.

5. Is 12:00 P.M. an even or odd hour? **even**

6. How many departure times are there from
   12:00 P.M. – 1:00 P.M.? **2**

7. What are the departure times? **12:00 P.M. and 12:40 P.M.**

8. What is the departure time closest to 12:35 P.M.? **12:40 P.M.**

Look Back and Check
9. Explain another method to answer this question.
   List all of the departure times starting at 5:00 P.M.

Solve Another Problem
10. Buses leave for Downtown every 15 minutes. The first bus leaves at 7:15 A.M. What is the departure time closest to 10:25 A.M.?
    7:15, 7:30, 7:45, 8:00, 8:15, etc.; 10:30 A.M. is
    closest to 10:25.

Hands-On Activities

Name _____ Class _____ Date _____

Activity 9: Prime and Composite Numbers

Materials needed:	24″ × 24″ poster board, markers for making both thick and thin lines

Work in small groups of 3–4.

A number is divisible by	Rule
2	if it is an even number.
3	if the sum of its digits is divisible by 3.
5	if the number ends in 5 or 0.
9	if the sum of its digits is divisible by 9.
10	if the number ends in a 0.

1. Write the numbers 1–40 on the poster board in rows of 10 numbers each. Leave enough room around each number to make 3 circles around each number with a thin marker.

2. Test whether each number on the chart is divisible without a remainder by applying the rules in the chart.

3. Have group members take turns following the directions below to circle the numbers with their markers. If you need to circle a number more than once, make the second or third circle smaller or larger than the first. Circle the number with:

   Yellow if the number is exactly divisible by 2.
   Red if the number is exactly divisible by 3.
   Blue if the number is exactly divisible by 5.
   Purple if the number is exactly divisible by 9.
   Green if the number is exactly divisible by 10.

4. Use the poster to answer the questions:
   a. Name seven prime numbers.
   b. Which numbers on the chart show 3 factors?
   c. What patterns do you see?

Hands-On Activities

Name _____ Class _____ Date _____

Activity 10: Factors

Materials needed:	paper; red, blue, and black ink pens

Work in groups of three.

1. On a sheet of paper, create four grids with the numbers 1 through 50 like the one shown below. Draw three boxes beside each grid.

1	2	3	4	5	6	7	8	9	10
11	12	13	14	15	16	17	18	19	20
21	22	23	24	25	26	27	28	29	30
31	32	33	34	35	36	37	38	39	40
41	42	43	44	45	46	47	48	49	50

2. The player with the longest last name is Player 1, next longest is Player 2, and shortest is Player 3. If your last names are the same length, use your first names to determine players.

3. Player 3 calls out a number between 11 and 20 and writes the number in one of the boxes beside the first grid. Using a red pen, Player 1 marks out all of the factors of that number in the grid. For example, 14 has factors 1, 2, 7, and 14.

4. If Player 1 correctly marks out all of the factors of the number, he or she receives one point. If any factors were left out, Player 2 receives one point for each missing factor that he or she can identify. If Player 1 marks out any numbers that are not factors, Player 2 receives two points for each incorrect factor that he or she can identify. (Player 3 should help determine whether factors are correctly identified.) Keep a tally of your points.

5. Switch roles. Player 1 will call out a number between 11 and 20 and write the number in the second box beside the grid. Using a blue pen and the same grid, Player 2 will mark out all of the factors of the number. Player 3 will then try to identify any incorrect or missing factors. Use the same scoring method and record your points in your table.

6. Switch roles again, so Player 2 calls out a number between 11 and 20. Player 3 crosses out its factors using a black pen. Player 1 then tries to identify any missing or incorrect factors. Use the same scoring method and record your points.

7. Use a new grid for Round 2. Call out numbers between 21 and 30.

8. Complete Round 3 using numbers between 31 and 40. Complete Round 4 using numbers between 41 and 50. The player with the most points at the end of four rounds wins.

Hands-On Activities

Name _____ Class _____ Date _____

Activity 11: Fractions and Rulers

Materials needed:	ruler marked in eighths and sixteenths of an inch, metric ruler marked in mm and cm, calculator, small classroom objects

Work with a partner.

On a separate sheet of paper, list the objects in 2 columns as shown below. Measure the objects in each row. Then draw lines on your paper to match equivalent fractions between the two columns. Write the simplest form of the equivalent fractions on each line you draw.

Measure each object to an *eighth* of an inch.
Measure each object to a *sixteenth* of an inch.

1. lima bean   a. kernel of corn

2. string bean   b. coat button

3. kernel of rice   c. penny

4. grape   d. paper clip

5. spiral noodle (uncooked)   e. eraser

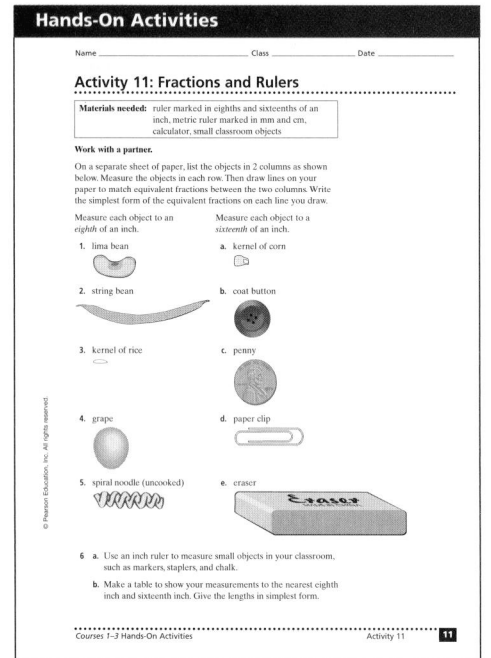

6. a. Use an inch ruler to measure small objects in your classroom, such as markers, staplers, and chalk.

   b. Make a table to show your measurements to the nearest eighth inch and sixteenth inch. Give the lengths in simplest form.

Technology Activities

Name _____ Class _____ Date _____

Testing Divisibility   Activity 7

Use your scientific calculator to do this activity.

Example 1: Is 91 prime or composite? If it is composite, write the prime factorization.

① First, use mental math and the divisibility rules to test whether 91 is divisible by 2, 3, 5, 9, or 10.

② Next, look for prime factors. To determine which prime factor to use to start checking, find the square root of 91. Press [2nd] [√] 91 [ENTER]. The square root is about 9.5.

③ Now use the Integer Divide feature of the calculator to see whether the next prime number less than 9.5, 7, is a factor. Enter 91 [2nd] [Int ÷] 7 [ENTER]. The quotient is 13 with a remainder of zero. Since the remainder is zero, 7 is a factor, and 91 is composite.

④ The quotient when 91 was divided by 7 was 13, which is also prime. Since the two factors are prime, then the prime factorization of 91 is 7 × 13.

Example 2: Is 97 prime or composite? If it is composite, write the prime factorization.

① Using mental math, you can find that 97 is not divisible by 2, 3, 5, 9, or 10.

② Next, look for prime factors. To determine which prime factor to start checking, find the square root of 97. Press [2nd] [√] 97 [ENTER]. The square root is about 9.8.

③ Now check to see whether the next prime number less than 9.8 is a factor. Enter 97 [2nd] [Int ÷] 7 [ENTER]. The quotient is 13 with a remainder of six. Since there is a remainder, 7 is not a factor of 97.

④ Now, check other prime numbers less than 9.5. Since you've already checked 5, 3, and 2 mentally and none was a factor, 97 is prime.

Exercises

Tell whether each number is prime. If it is composite, give the prime factorization.

1. 119   2. 127   3. 323

4. 551   5. 439   6. 667

Technology Activities

Name _____ Class _____ Date _____

Comparing Fractions and Decimals   Activity 8

Use your scientific calculator to do this activity.

Example 1: Write $\frac{7}{8}$ as a decimal.

① Enter 7 [÷] 8 [▶D]. The decimal 0.875 appears on the display. So, $\frac{7}{8}$ written as a decimal is 0.875.

Example 2: Write $2\frac{6}{11}$ as a decimal.

① Enter 2 [UNIT] 6 [/] 11 [▶D]. The decimal 2.545454545 appears on the display.

② Notice this is a repeating decimal. You can write $2\frac{6}{11}$ as a decimal is $2.\overline{54}$.

Example 3: Write 0.145 as a fraction in simplest form.

① Press [2nd] [FracMode]. Use the right arrow key to move to the right to select from the menu choices. When the underline appears under **Auto**, press [ENTER]. Once you do this step, you should not have to do it again, unless you see that the calculator is not simplifying fractions automatically.

② Enter 0.145 [▶F] [ENTER]. The calculator window shows $\frac{29}{200}$. So, 0.145 written as a fraction is $\frac{29}{200}$.

Example 4: Write 7.0125 as a mixed number in simplest form.

① Enter 7.0125 [2nd] [Ab/c ◄► n/c] [ENTER]. The calculator window shows 7u1/80. The u is a separator that shows that 7 is the unit part of the mixed number. This means that 7.0125 written as a mixed number is $7\frac{1}{80}$.

Exercises

Write each decimal as a fraction or mixed number. Write each fraction or mixed number as a decimal.

1. $\frac{4}{15}$ 2. 0.34   3. $\frac{15}{16}$

4. 0.822   5. $36\frac{8}{20}$ 6. $14\frac{5}{12}$

7. $97\frac{45}{50}$ 8. $236\frac{5}{8}$ 9. 734.0275

Chapter Project

Name _____ Class _____ Date _____

Chapter 3 Project: Home Court Advantage
Compare Basketball Statistics

Beginning the Chapter Project

In Malcolm's daydream, he is floating in the air on the way to a slam dunk. In reality, he is tossing pieces of paper into a wastebasket. He makes some shots, and he misses others.

Your project will be to record and compare baskets attempted and baskets made by the players on your own imaginary basketball team. You can shoot baskets with a real basketball on a real court, or you can toss pieces of paper into a wastebasket.

Activities

Activity 1: Recording   Check students' work.

You'll need five starters and two substitutes for your basketball team. Use the names of real players or make some up. If you use a ball of paper as a basketball, place your "foul line" about 10 ft from the trash can. Your first player should take 10 shots, your second player 9 shots, your third player 8 shots, and so on. Make a table to record the number of shots taken and the number of shots made by each player. For example:

Player's Name	Number of Shots Taken	Number of Shots Made
Player 1	10	
Player 2	9	
Player 3	8	
Player 4	7	
Player 5	6	
Substitute 1	5	
Substitute 2	4	

Activity 2: Calculating

Add a fourth column to your data table and write each player's shooting record as a fraction. Then compare and order the fractions. Rank your players from best to worst at foul shooting.

Chapter Project

Name _____ Class _____ Date _____

Chapter 3 Project: Home Court Advantage (continued)

Activity 3: Comparing

You now have another way to compare the records of your players. Convert the fractions in your table to decimals. Use the decimals to rank your players. Does the order agree with the order you got when you compared fractions?

Finishing the Project

Make a poster to present your table and rankings to your class. You may wish to decorate the poster by adding a team name and logo, using homemade sports cards for some of your players, or sketching a team uniform. You could even make a tape-recorded interview with your top foul shooter!

Be sure your work is neat and clear. Show your data and calculations. Write any explanations you think are necessary.

Reflect and Revise

Ask a classmate to review your project with you. Are your calculations correct? Do your rankings correspond to your calculations? Is your table clearly presented? If necessary, make changes to improve your poster.

Extending the Project

Research foul shot statistics of some basketball players at your school or of professional basketball players. How do the foul shooting records compare? Based on the records, create a news report of a game between your team and the players you researched or another imaginary team.

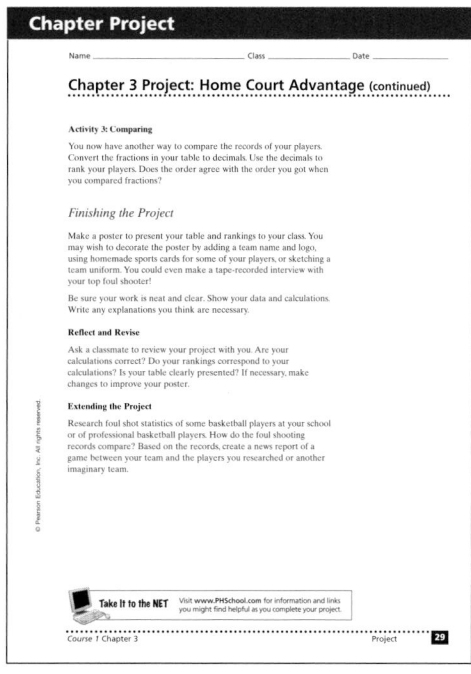
Take It to the NET Visit www.PHSchool.com for information and links you might find helpful as you complete your project.

Chapter Project

Name _____ Class _____ Date _____

Chapter Project Manager
Chapter 3: Home Court Advantage

Getting Started

Read about the project. As you work on it, you will need several sheets of paper. If available, a spreadsheet program also can be used. Keep all your work for the project in a folder, along with this Project Manager.

Checklist	Suggestions
☐ Activity 1: recording	☐ The number of players should determine the number of rows in your table.
☐ Activity 2: calculating	☐ Look at previous exercises to remember how to compare and order fractions.
☐ Activity 3: comparing	☐ Look at previous exercises to remember how to convert fractions to decimals.
☐ Recommendations	☐ Use large lettering on your poster so that other classmates can see it from a distance.

Scoring Rubric

3 Your data is accurate and complete. You've used both fractions and decimals to compare the shooting records of at least seven players. These seven players each make a different number of attempts so that your fractions have different denominators. All your information is accurate and is displayed in an attractive table that lists the players in order from best record to worst record.

2 Most of your comparisons are based on fractions with different denominators. Your fractions and decimals are almost all accurate. The shooting records are listed in order form best to worst in a neat table.

1 You didn't collect data for enough players, you didn't vary the denominator of your fractions, or you incorrectly compared the players' shooting records.

0 You only compared shooting records for a few players, or you left out the fractions, decimals, or table of comparisons.

Your Evaluation of Project Evaluate your work, based on the Scoring Rubric.

Teacher's Evaluation of Project

Chapter Project

Name _____ Class _____ Date _____

Chapter Project Teacher Notes
Chapter 3: Home Court Advantage

About the Project Students will have an opportunity to apply their knowledge of fractions to designing a game.

Introducing the Project

You may want to bring in games you have at home, including games from other countries. Or find games other students have created. Use the games to inspire creativity. Ask students:

- *What board games have you played?*
- *What made the games enjoyable?*
- *Did you use fractions in playing the games? How?*

Activity 1: Recording

Have students write the fraction of shots made for each player. For example, if the first player made 7 out of 10 shots, their fraction is $\frac{7}{10}$. Have students model each of the fractions.

Activity 2: Calculating

If students have already written the fraction of shots each player made, have them check over the work and then order the fractions. Then challenge them to write the shooting record as a different fraction, such as the fraction of shots missed. Have them order these fractions. Ask: *Do the two lists of fractions give you the same player ranking?*

Activity 3: Comparing

Have students also find the decimal to represent the fraction of baskets each player missed. Have them compare these decimals to rank the players again. Ask students:

- *Does this order agree with the other rankings?*
- *What would a greater decimal mean in this case?*

Finishing the Project

You may wish to plan a project day on which students share their completed projects. Encourage students to explain their process as well as their projects. After students share their projects, you may want to challenge them to find the best players in all the projects to form an all-star team.

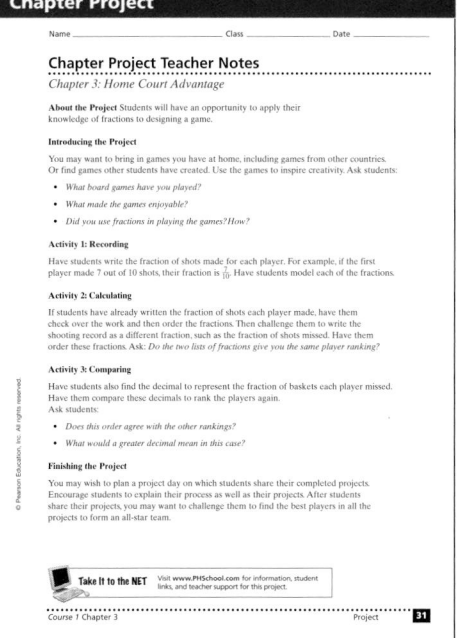
Take It to the NET Visit www.PHSchool.com for information, student links, and teacher support for this project.

Transparencies

Problem of the Day

Problem of the Day	Lesson 3-1

A six-pound bag of dog food sells for $2.70. Kay has three dogs. She bought three bags. How much did she pay for the dog food?

Answer

$8.10

Problem of the Day	Lesson 3-2

Write the next number in the sequence:

0.214, 0.234, 0.254, 0.274, . . .

Answer

0.294

Problem of the Day	Lesson 3-3

The largest crater on the moon is called Bailly. It covers an area of about 26,000 square miles. Write this area in scientific notation.

Answer

2.6×10^4 square miles

Problem of the Day

Problem of the Day	Lesson 3-4

What is the value of the 6 in 2.0346?

Answer

6 ten-thousandths

Problem of the Day	Lesson 3-5

Write the number 8 billion.

Answer

8,000,000,000

Problem of the Day	Lesson 3-6

Evaluate $\frac{48}{2 \times 4}$.

Answer

6

Problem of the Day — **Lesson 3-7**

The sum of two whole numbers each rounded to the nearest ten is 100. One number rounds to 80. What are the two largest whole numbers that these numbers can be?

Answer

84, 24

Problem of the Day — **Lesson 3-8**

What will be the 23rd position in this pattern?

♥ ♠ ✖ ▲ ♠ ♥ ♠ ✖ ▲ ✖

Answer

✖

Problem of the Day — **Lesson 3-9**

Find three numbers whose sum is 14 and whose product is 54.

Answer

2, 3, 9

Check Skills You'll Need — **Lesson 3-1**

Solve each equation. Then check the solution.

1. $10x = 490$
2. $5x = 205$
3. $2x = 83$

4. $725 = 5x$
5. $123 = 3x$
6. $0.6x = 30$

Solutions

1. $10x = 490$
$10x \div 10 = 490 \div 10$
$x = 49$
Check: $10 \times 49 \stackrel{?}{=} 490$
$490 = 490$

2. $5x = 205$
$5x \div 5 = 205 \div 5$
$x = 41$
Check: $5 \times 41 \stackrel{?}{=} 205$
$205 = 205$

3. $2x = 83$
$2x \div 2 = 83 \div 2$
$x = 41.5$
Check: $2 \times 41.5 \stackrel{?}{=} 83$
$83 = 83$

4. $725 = 5x$
$725 \div 5 = 5x \div 5$
$145 = x$
Check: $725 \stackrel{?}{=} 5 \times 145$
$725 = 725$

5. $123 = 3x$
$123 \div 3 = 3x \div 3$
$41 = x$
Check: $123 \stackrel{?}{=} 3 \times 41$
$123 = 123$

6. $0.6x = 30$
$0.6x \div 0.6 = 30 \div 0.6$
$x = 50$
Check: $0.6 \times 50 \stackrel{?}{=} 30$
$30 = 30$

Lesson Quiz — **Lesson 3-1**

Test each number for divisibility by 2, 3, 5, 9, and 10.

1. 18,520
2. 270
3. 5,625
4. 100,000

Answers

1. 2, 5, 10 **2.** 2, 3, 5, 9, 10 **3.** 3, 5, 9 **4.** 2, 5, 10

Sample page; see p. G for complete list.

Additional Examples — **Lesson 3-1**

1 EXAMPLE Is the first number divisible by the second? Use mental math.

a. 46 by 3
Think Since $3 \times 15 = 45$ and $3 \times 16 = 48$, 46 is not divisible by 3.

b. 63 by 7
Think Since $7 \times 9 = 63$, 63 is divisible by 7.

2 EXAMPLE Test each number for divisibility by 2, 5, or 10.

a. 580
580 ends with a 0. So it is divisible by 2, 5, and 10.

b. 3,042
3,042 ends with a 2. So, it is divisible by 2, but not by 5 or 10.

3 EXAMPLE Test 6,515 for divisibility by 3.

$6 + 5 + 1 + 5 = 17$ ← Find the sum of the digits in 6,515.

$17 \div 3$ has a remainder of 2. ← The sum is not divisible by 3.

So, 6,515 is not divisible by 3.

4 EXAMPLE A baker sells muffins in boxes that contain exactly 9 muffins each. Can the baker place 576 muffins in boxes of 9 with none left over?

If 576 is divisible by 9, then there will be no muffins left over.

$5 + 7 + 6 = 18$ ← Find the sum of the digits in 576.

$18 \div 9 = 2$ ← The sum is divisible by 9.

So, 576 is divisible by 9. There will be no muffins left over.

Sample page; see p. G for complete list.

Fraction Models, Halves, Thirds — 12

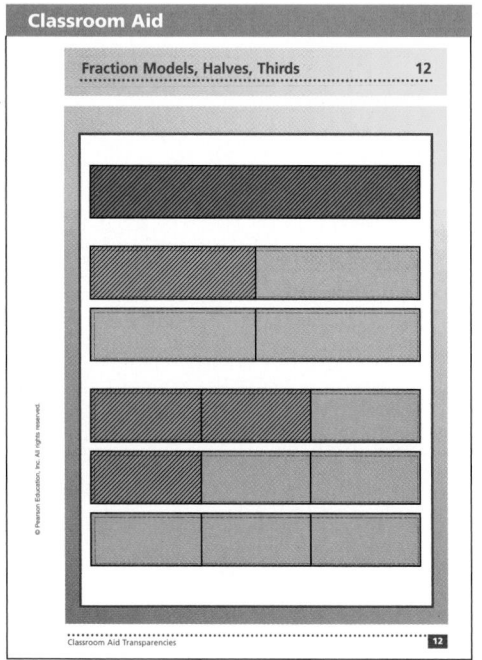

Answers for Lesson *On Your Own* Exercises

1. Sample: $1:4$, 1 to 4, $\frac{1}{4}$
2. Sample: 24 to 25, $24:25$, $\frac{24}{25}$
3. 12 to 4, $\frac{12}{4}$
4. $8:10$, $\frac{8}{10}$
5. 5 to 4, $5:4$
6. 13 to 8, $\frac{13}{8}$
7. 21 to 28, $\frac{21}{28}$
8. 8 to 18, $8:18$
9. B
10a. $7:15$, 7 to 15, $\frac{7}{15}$
   b. $7:8$, 7 to 8, $\frac{7}{8}$
11a. $23:19$, 23 to 19, $\frac{23}{19}$
   b. $19:42$, 19 to 42, $\frac{19}{42}$
12. No; the new ratio is $16:11$.
13. 0.9
14. 3.6
15. 2.7
16. 0.7
17. 0.5
18. 1.0
19a. $225:3$, $455:7$
   b. 75, 65
   c. Answers may vary. Sample: Train A travels 75 mi/h while Train B travels 65 mi/h
20a. $\frac{13}{18}$
   b. $\frac{169}{324}$
   c. The ratio of areas is the square of the ratio of sides.
21–26. Answers may vary. Samples are given.
21. $13:27$, $78:162$
22. 6 to 22, 3 to 11
23. $\frac{106}{50}$, $\frac{53}{25}$
24. $\frac{7}{1}$, $\frac{14}{2}$
25. $\frac{9}{18}$, $\frac{3}{6}$
26. $2:12$, $3:18$
27. $5:2$
28. 1 to 9
29. $\frac{1}{50}$
30. 4 to 1
31. $1:2$
32. $\frac{1}{3}$
33. 25 to 1
34a. 101 and 107
   b. $7:12$
35a. $8:4$
   b. 10 qt antifreeze, 5 qt water

Check Skills You'll Need — **Lesson 3-2**

Test each number for divisibility by 2, 3, 5, 9, or 10.

1. 990
2. 901
3. 695
4. 800
5. 2,080
6. 94,022

Solutions

1. 990 ends in 0, so it is divisible by 2, 5, and 10; $9 + 9 + 0 = 18$, so it is divisible by 3 and 9.
2. 901 ends in 1, so it is not divisible by 2, 5, or 10; $9 + 0 + 1 = 10$, so it is not divisible by 3 or 9.
3. 695 ends in 5, so it is divisible by 5, but not by 2 or 10; $6 + 9 + 5 = 20$, so it is not divisible by 3 or 9.
4. 800 ends in 0, so it is divisible by 2, 5, and 10; $8 + 0 + 0 = 8$, so it is not divisible by 3 or 9.
5. 2,080 ends in 0, so it is divisible by 2, 5, and 10; $2 + 0 + 8 + 0 = 10$, so it is not divisible by 3 or 9.
6. 94,022 ends in 2, so it is divisible by 2, but not by 5 or 10; $9 + 4 + 0 + 2 + 2 = 17$, so it is not divisible by 3 or 9.

Lesson Quiz — **Lesson 3-2**

Write the prime factorization for each number.

1. 36
2. 150
3. 99
4. 225

Answers

1. $2^2 \times 3^2$ **2.** $2 \times 3 \times 5^2$ **3.** $3^2 \times 11$ **4.** $3^2 \times 5^2$

Sample page; see p. G for complete list.

116M

Assessment

Checkpoint Quizzes

Name _____ Class _____ Date _____

✔ Checkpoint Quiz 1
Use with Lessons 3-1 through 3-3.

State whether each number is divisible by 2, 3, 5, 9, or 10.

1. 135 3, 5, 9   2. 1,006 2   3. 170 2, 5, 10

4. 459 3, 9   5. 2,730 2, 3, 5, 10   6. 2,431 none

Use a factor tree to find the prime factorization of each number.

7. 300 $2^2 \times 3 \times 5^2$ 8. 72 $2^3 \times 3^2$ 9. 68 $2^2 \times 17$

Find the GCF of each pair of numbers.

10. 15, 27 3   11. 125, 250 125   12. 132, 156 12

13. Make a list of factors to find all the common factors of 12 and 40. 2, 4

- - - ✂ - - -

Name _____ Class _____ Date _____

✔ Checkpoint Quiz 2
Use with Lessons 3-4 through 3-7.

1. You have four nickels and 8 dimes in your piggy bank. What fraction of the coins is dimes? Write your answer in simplest form.
$\frac{2}{3}$

2. If you have walked $\frac{3}{4}$ of 1 mile, what fraction of a mile do you have to walk to reach 1 mile?
$\frac{1}{4}$

3. Draw a number line from 0 to 1. Plot and label all the points less than 1 for fractions with a denominator of 5.
0 1/5 2/5 3/5 4/5 1

State whether each fraction is in simplest form. If not, write it in simplest form.

4. $\frac{13}{39}$ no; $\frac{1}{3}$ 5. $\frac{24}{32}$ no; $\frac{3}{4}$ 6. $\frac{36}{48}$ no; $\frac{1}{2}$ 7. $\frac{40}{48}$ no; $\frac{5}{6}$

8. Write a fraction equivalent to $\frac{4}{10}$ with a denominator of 5. $\frac{2}{5}$

9. How many $\frac{1}{8}$'s are in $1\frac{5}{8}$? 13

10. Write $\frac{9}{4}$ as a mixed number. $2\frac{1}{4}$

Available in Spanish

Chapter Test, Form A

Name _____ Class _____ Date _____

Chapter Test   Form A
Chapter 3

State whether each number is divisible by 2, 3, 5, 9, or 10.

1. 32,715   2. 5,265   3. 7,475   4. 840

3, 5, 9   3, 5, 9   5   2, 3, 5, 10

5. Find the digits between 0 and 9 that make 2▢,402 divisible by 3. 1, 4, 7

6. Which of these numbers is prime? 53; 65; 72; 365; 3,411 53

Find the prime factorization of each number using a factor tree.

7. 630   8. 64   9. 76

$2 \times 3 \times 3 \times 5 \times 7$ $2 \times 2 \times 2 \times 2 \times 2 \times 2$ $2 \times 2 \times 19$

10. 88   11. 525   12. 308

$2 \times 2 \times 2 \times 11$ $3 \times 5 \times 5 \times 7$ $2 \times 2 \times 7 \times 11$

Find the GCF for each set of numbers.

13. 65 and 195   14. 42 and 63   15. 24 and 60

65   21   12

Name the fraction modeled.

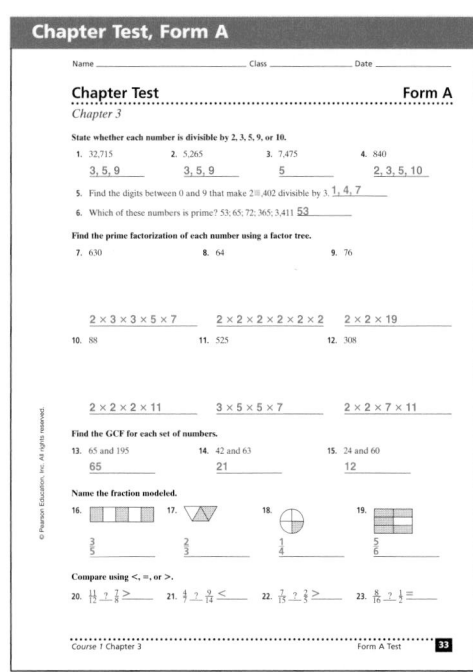

16. _____ 17. _____ 18. _____ 19. _____

$\frac{3}{5}$ $\frac{2}{3}$ $\frac{1}{4}$ $\frac{6}{10}$

Compare using <, =, or >.

20. $\frac{11}{12}$? $\frac{7}{8}$ >   21. $\frac{4}{7}$? $\frac{9}{14}$ <   22. $\frac{7}{15}$? $\frac{2}{5}$ >   23. $\frac{8}{16}$? $\frac{1}{2}$ =

Available in Spanish

Chapter Test, Form A

Name _____ Class _____ Date _____

Chapter Test (continued)   Form A
Chapter 3

Write each number in simplest form.

24. $\frac{65}{195}$ 25. $\frac{21}{81}$ 26. 0.52
$\frac{1}{3}$ $\frac{7}{27}$ $\frac{13}{25}$

Write each improper fraction as a mixed number. Write each mixed number as an improper fraction.

27. $\frac{42}{4}$ 28. $7\frac{4}{21}$ 29. $6\frac{4}{7}$
$10\frac{1}{2}$ $\frac{151}{21}$ $\frac{46}{7}$

Find the LCM for each set of numbers.

30. 8 and 10   31. 26 and 30   32. 6, 16, and 44
40   390   528

Write each fraction as a decimal.

33. $\frac{4}{9}$ 34. $\frac{2}{11}$ 35. $\frac{11}{12}$
$0.\overline{4}$ $0.\overline{18}$ $0.91\overline{6}$

Answer each question.

36. Miss Gold asked her class groups to make posters for the bulletin board. She told them to draw, color, or paste 42 stars on poster board. The only rule was that the stars had to be in equal groups and the number of stars in each group had to be prime. How many groups of stars might be on a poster, and how many stars are in each group?

Sample answer: Forty-two groups of one, twenty-one groups of two, fourteen groups of three, or six groups of seven.

37. How do you use the LCM to write two or more fractions with a common denominator?

Find the LCM of the denominators. This is the LCD of the two fractions. Multiply the numerators by a number that makes their denominators equal the LCD. Then the fractions will have a common denominator.

Available in Spanish

Chapter Test, Form B

Name _____ Class _____ Date _____

Chapter Test   Form B
Chapter 3

State whether each number is divisible by 2, 3, 5, 9, or 10.

1. 50,322   2. 4,520   3. 4,993   4. 270

2, 3   2, 5, 10   none   2, 3, 5, 9, 10

5. Find the digits between 0 and 9 that make 3▢,513 divisible by 9. 6

6. Which of these numbers is prime? 51; 67; 85; 483; 5,211 67

Find the prime factorization of each number using a factor tree.

7. 540   8. 56   9. 108

$2 \times 2 \times 3 \times 3 \times 3 \times 5$ $2 \times 2 \times 2 \times 7$ $2 \times 2 \times 3 \times 3 \times 3$

10. 48   11. 550   12. 882

$2 \times 2 \times 2 \times 2 \times 3$ $2 \times 5 \times 5 \times 11$ $2 \times 3 \times 3 \times 7 \times 7$

Find the GCF for each set of numbers.

13. 78 and 104   14. 324 and 90   15. 42 and 56

26   18   14

Name the fraction modeled.

16. _____ 17. _____ 18. _____ 19. _____

$\frac{4}{5}$ $\frac{1}{2}$ $\frac{1}{3}$ $\frac{2}{5}$

Compare using <, =, or >.

20. $\frac{17}{18}$? $\frac{7}{8}$ >   21. $\frac{5}{6}$? $\frac{7}{24}$ >   22. $\frac{7}{15}$? $\frac{4}{5}$ <   23. $\frac{8}{16}$? $\frac{5}{10}$ =

Available in Spanish

Chapter Test, Form B

Name _____ Class _____ Date _____

Chapter Test (continued)   Form B
Chapter 3

Write each number in simplest form.

24. $\frac{36}{60}$ 25. $\frac{27}{81}$ 26. 0.048
$\frac{3}{5}$ $\frac{1}{3}$ $\frac{6}{125}$

Write each improper fraction as a mixed number. Write each mixed number as an improper fraction.

27. $\frac{13}{4}$ 28. $2\frac{4}{7}$ 29. $7\frac{4}{7}$
$3\frac{1}{4}$ $\frac{18}{7}$ $7\frac{1}{7}$

Find the LCM for each set of numbers.

30. 15 and 25   31. 8 and 12   32. 12, 18, and 42
75   24   252

Write each fraction as a decimal.

33. $\frac{7}{9}$ 34. $\frac{13}{20}$ 35. $\frac{5}{6}$
$0.\overline{7}$ 0.65 $0.8\overline{3}$

Answer each question.

36. At the end of the day, Carly had $3.02 in change left in her purse. She had spent $3.56 for lunch and had given $2.10 to her brother. After school, she had bought an ice cream cone for $.58. How much money did she have at the beginning of the day?
$9.26

37. How can the GCF be used to write a fraction in simplest form?
Find the GCF of the numerator and denominator. Divide both the numerator and denominator by this GCF, and write the fraction in simplest form.

Available in Spanish

Alternative Assessment

Name _____ Class _____ Date _____

Alternative Assessment   Form C
Chapter 3

THE PERFECT BIRDHOUSE

Did you know that birds will not move into just any birdhouse? A bird wants a house that fits; most prefer houses that are just big enough for them to squeeze into.

The drawing below shows an entrance hole that is just the right size for a downy woodpecker. The table beside it lists the right size hole for some other kinds of birds.

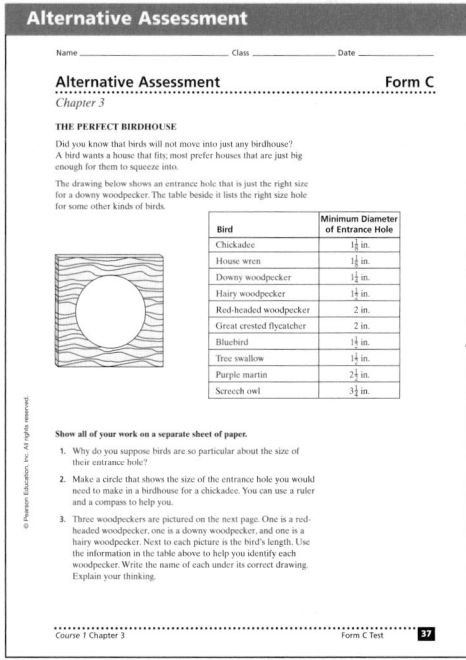

Bird	Minimum Diameter of Entrance Hole
Chickadee	$1\frac{1}{8}$ in.
House wren	$1\frac{1}{8}$ in.
Downy woodpecker	$1\frac{1}{4}$ in.
Hairy woodpecker	$1\frac{1}{2}$ in.
Red-headed woodpecker	2 in.
Great crested flycatcher	2 in.
Bluebird	$1\frac{1}{2}$ in.
Tree swallow	$1\frac{1}{2}$ in.
Purple martin	$2\frac{1}{4}$ in.
Screech owl	$3\frac{1}{2}$ in.

Show all of your work on a separate sheet of paper.

1. Why do you suppose birds are so particular about the size of their entrance hole?

2. Make a circle that shows the size of the entrance hole you would need to make in a birdhouse for a chickadee. You can use a ruler and a compass to help you.

3. Three woodpeckers are pictured on the next page. One is a red-headed woodpecker, one is a downy woodpecker, and one is a hairy woodpecker. Next to each picture is the bird's length. Use the information in the table above to help you identify each woodpecker. Write the name of each under its correct drawing. Explain your thinking.

Available in Spanish

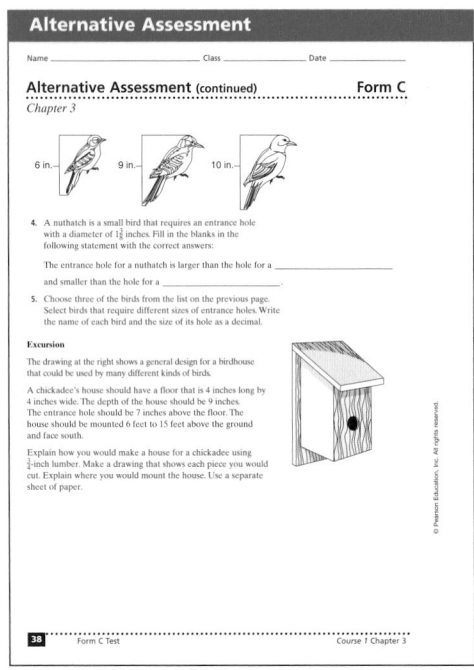

Available in Spanish

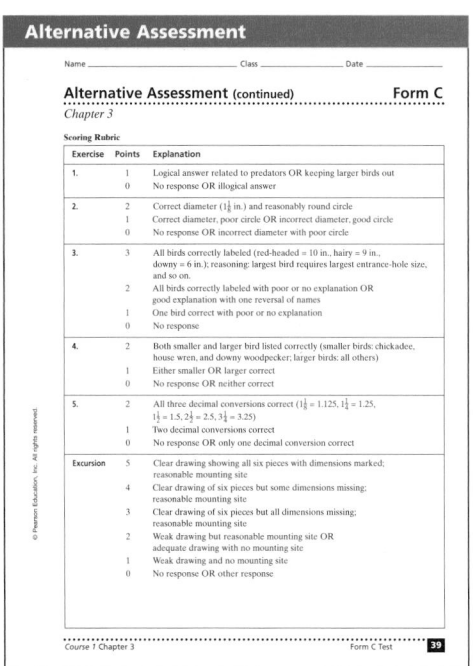

Available in Spanish

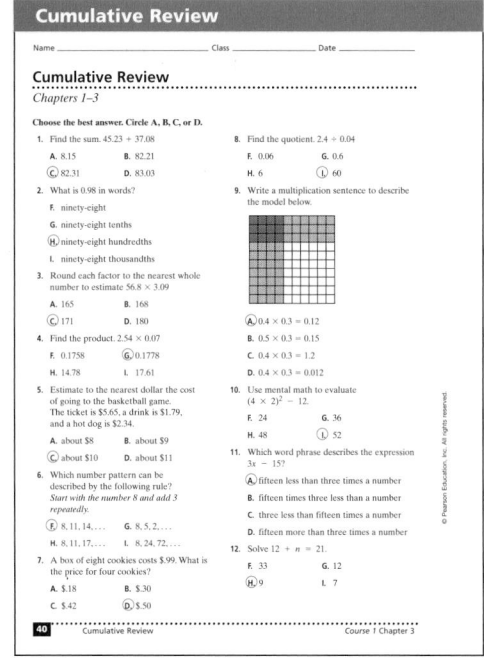

Available in Spanish

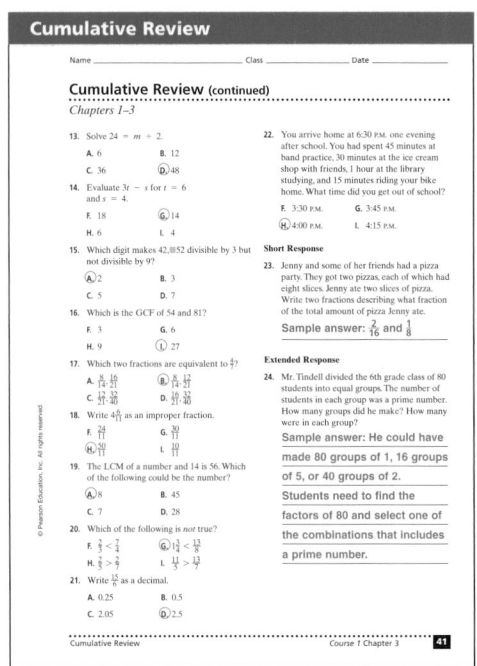

Available in Spanish

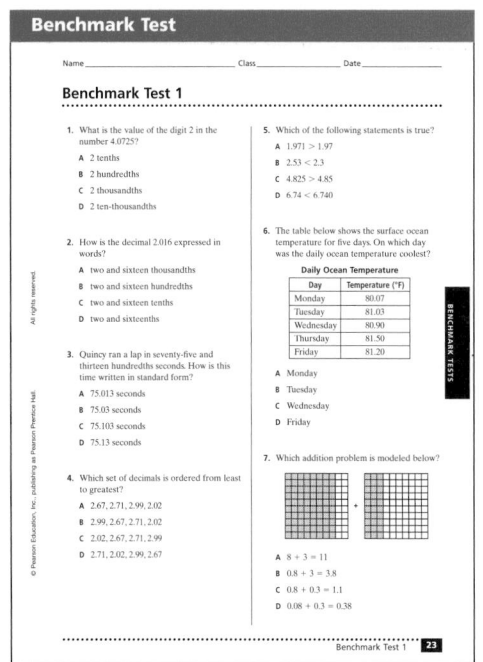

On PH Website

Name _____ Class _____ Date _____

Chapter 3: Writing Extended Responses
Exercises

David has one quarter, three dimes, and five nickels. How many different ways can he combine the coins to make 45¢?

Scoring Rubric

- **4 points:** Student correctly answers question in a complete sentence, provides an explanation, and shows all possible combinations.
- **3 points:** Student answers question in a complete sentence, provides an explanation, and shows possible combinations, but makes minor calculation errors.
- **2 point:** Student provides an incorrect explanation and does not completely answer the question.
- **1 point:** Student incorrectly answers the question and does not provide an explanation.
- **0 points:** No response or answer is completely incorrect.

Three responses to the question are shown below.

4 point response	3 point response	1 point response
1 quarter, 2 dimes	1 quarter, 2 dimes	1 quarter, 2 dimes
1 quarter, 1 dime, 2 nickels	1 quarter, 1 dime, 2 nickels	
1 quarter, 4 nickels	1 quarter, 3 nickels	1 quarter, 1 dime, 2 nickels
1 quarter, 3 nickels	3 dimes, 3 nickels	
3 dimes, 3 nickels	2 dimes, 5 nickels	1 quarter, 4 nickels
2 dimes, 5 nickels		2 dimes, 5 nickels
There are no other possible ways for the coins to add up to 45¢ so this must be the complete answer.	These are the only combinations that add up to 45¢.	

1. Tell why the 4-point response received the points it did.
   It shows all work and answers to both parts of the problem. The response includes an explanation of why this is the complete answer.

2. Read the 3-point response. What error did the student make?
   1 quarter + 3 nickels equals 40¢, not 45¢.

3. Write a 2-point response that has an incorrect explanation.
   Sample answer: 1 quarter and 2 dimes, 1 quarter and 4 nickels, 3 dimes and 3 nickels; all these add up to 45¢.

Test-Taking Strategies — Course 1 — **3**

---

in math class ...

We have been learning about patterns and number theory. Here is a list of some of the skills and concepts we have studied.

- Divisibility
- Prime factorization
- Understanding fractions
- Fractions in lowest terms
- Improper fractions and mixed numbers
- Converting fractions and decimals
- Comparing and ordering fractions

Home Activities

Here are some activities you can do with your child that use these math skills and concepts.

Use food items around the house to quiz your child on fractions. Allow your child to quiz you, too. Select a food such as fruit, and have your child describe a fraction of the group. For example, find the fraction of a bowl of fruit that is apples. Record the fraction in simplest form. Repeat the activity several times, each time recording the fraction in simplest form. After recording several fractions, your child can order the fractions from least to greatest.

The following table provides you with some common fractions equivalent to fractions in simplest form.

Fraction (simplest form)	Equivalent fractions

To order fractions, your child can find a common denominator and then order the fractions by comparing the numerators.

Vary the above game by playing a simplest form version and having a fraction race. In this version, the fraction must be named immediately in simplest form at the beginning. You can also include mixed numbers by looking for wholes and fractions.

Discuss methods and strategies for choosing fractions in the game. Did you try to stump each other with fractions with odd denominators or did you look for fractions that could be simplified to slow the other player down? Devise methods to play similar fraction games.

Use with Chapter 3

Available in Spanish;
Web Code: aak-5500

Name _____   *Math and Science/Technology*

Gardening By the Numbers
Use number theory to help with gardening.

There are many people who grow their own vegetables in "backyard" gardens. Even so, the majority of vegetables that we eat today are grown on farms. The people who grow these vegetables are professionals. They have studied *agriculture*, which is the science of farming. Through experimentation, they have learned what works best. Here are examples of things backyard gardeners have learned from professionals and from their own experiments.

- The soil in which vegetables are planted should be loose, so roots, air, and water can travel through it easily.
- The planting beds must be located where they will get the most sun. They need at least a half day of full sun each sunny day.
- Fertilizer should be placed on the bottom of each planting area. The planting mix is then placed on top of the fertilizer. This will prompt the roots to grow deep.
- The top inch of soil should be free of fertilizer. This will keep weed seedlings from growing quickly.
- Vegetables should be planted when the threat of frost has passed.
- Planted seeds or seedlings should be fertilized from time to time.
- Plants that will grow tall, such as tomatoes, must be able to attach themselves to tall posts, poles, stakes, or trellises.
- Plants should be watered regularly if not enough rain falls.

Backyard gardeners must also put their math skills to work. They must know how to make correct calculations when they divide their garden and arrange seeds and seedlings.

1. Though you can plant onion seeds or seedlings, it is better to buy little onions called onion sets because they are easier to plant and grow faster. If you want to share 81 onion sets with two other vegetable gardeners, explain why you can or cannot divide the sets evenly among the three of you?

   _____
   _____

2. Peter Chan is a well-known vegetable gardener. Chan likes to use raised vegetable beds in his garden. The planting area looks like a box. The border is filled with planting mix. Seeds or seedlings are then planted in the mix. Chan prefers the raised bed because it enables the gardener to grow the most vegetables in the smallest amount of space. Here are the reasons why: The dirt in a raised bed warms faster in the spring, since it is on top of the earth. That means that the gardener can start planting earlier in the spring. The dirt also drains better, so plants do not decay from being in too much water. Furthermore, if a raised bed is long and narrow, the gardener can work from the side of the bed and not step into it. That way, the plants are not trampled accidentally. Chan uses $3\frac{1}{2}$ by 14-foot raised beds.

Use with Chapter 3

Web Code: aak-5500

Name _____   *Math and Science/Technology*

a. How many feet of wood were needed as a border for one of Chan's beds?

_____

b. Chan uses wood that comes in ten-foot lengths. Does Chan have to cut any of the pieces of wood to build a border? Use a divisibility rule to explain your answer.

_____

c. How many lengths of wood must Chan buy for one border?

_____

3. Some vegetables are harvested shortly after they are planted. Radishes, for example, can be picked about a month after they are planted. Other plants, however, take much longer to grow. For instance, pumpkins may take the whole growing season.

   a. A gardener puts equal amounts of fertilizer on her three pumpkin patches. How many liters of fertilizer did she use: 79, 59, or 39? Explain your answer using a divisibility rule.

b. For how many weeks did the gardener fertilize her pumpkin seedlings?

_____

4. In Blake's garden, carrot seedlings have been planted two inches apart. Leek seedlings have been planted six inches apart. The carrot furrow and the leek furrow are beside each other. The first carrot and leek seedlings are next to each other. How many inches from the first carrot and leek seedlings will there be before the next pair of carrot/leek seedlings again end up side-by-side?

5. How would math skills, such as divisibility rules, help you if you decided to grow a backyard vegetable garden?

_____

6. Use the Internet to discover the growing season in your area and the kinds of vegetables that grow best in your climate. Then go to the library or call an agricultural agent to find out what kinds of plants are grown on farms in or around your area.

_____

Use with Chapter 3

Web Code: aak-5500

Name _____ Class _____ Date _____

Clue Me In   Puzzle 48

Holmes and Watson needed to find the combination to unlock a locker at Charing Cross Station. Here are the clues they had.

1. One number is the GCF of 12 and 15.

Factors of 12

Factors of 15

Common Factors

2. Another number is the GCF of 19 and 57.

3. The third number is the GCF of 27, 36, and 45.

To put the numbers in the proper order, Holmes and Watson had one more clue.

4. The first number is the square of the third.

Combination: _____ _____ _____

Write your own lock combination problem and clues to share with Holmes or a friend.

5. _____
   _____

48   Algebra Readiness Puzzles   © Pearson Education, Inc.

Web Code: aak-5500

Name _____ Class _____ Date _____

An Apple a Day   Puzzle 111

Choose a strategy to help you solve the problem below. Use the chart to help you.

Farmer Snarb had a wonderful idea. The apples in his orchard had to be harvested quickly. Farmer Snarb divided his apple pickers into two teams, the McIntoshes and the Granny Smiths. Each member of the team that picked the most apples would receive a $100 bonus.

At sunset, Farmer Snarb announced the winner—the McIntoshes! Each member of the team had picked two bushels of apples while members of the Granny Smiths had picked only one bushel each. In all, there were twenty-three apple pickers and altogether they picked 35 bushels of apples. How many apple pickers were on each team?

McIntoshes		Granny Smiths	
Pickers	Number of Bushels	Pickers	Number of Bushels
1	2	1	1

© Pearson Education, Inc.   Algebra Readiness Puzzles   111

Web Code: aak-5500

CHAPTER 3

Number Theory and Fractions

Chapter 3 Overview

In this chapter on fractions, students focus on several fraction concepts and properties in preparation for computing with fractions. They use the idea of divisibility and their mental math skills to investigate prime numbers and prime factorization. They work with the concepts of greatest common factor (GCF) and least common multiple (LCM) as they find equivalent fractions, simplify fractions, convert mixed numbers and improper fractions, and express fractions in simplest form.

 **Reading Math**
- Learning Vocabulary, p. 147
- **Vocabulary:** A complete list, plus exercises, in the Chapter Review, p. 162
- **Illustrated Glossary:** Examples for each vocabulary term, plus definitions in English and Spanish, on p. 669

 **Test-Taking Strategies**
Writing Extended Responses, p. 161

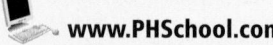 **Real-World Problem Solving**
- **Strategies:** Try, Check, and Revise, pp. 157–160
- **Real-World Snapshots:** Lifting With Levers, pp. 166–167
- **Chapter Project:** Home Court Advantage, p. 637

www.PHSchool.com
Internet support includes:
- Self-grading Vocabulary and Chapter 3 Tests
- Activity Masters
- Chapter Project support
- Chapter Planner
- Ch. 3 Resources

Plus **iTEXT**

CHAPTER 3

Number Theory and Fractions

Lessons

Key Vocabulary

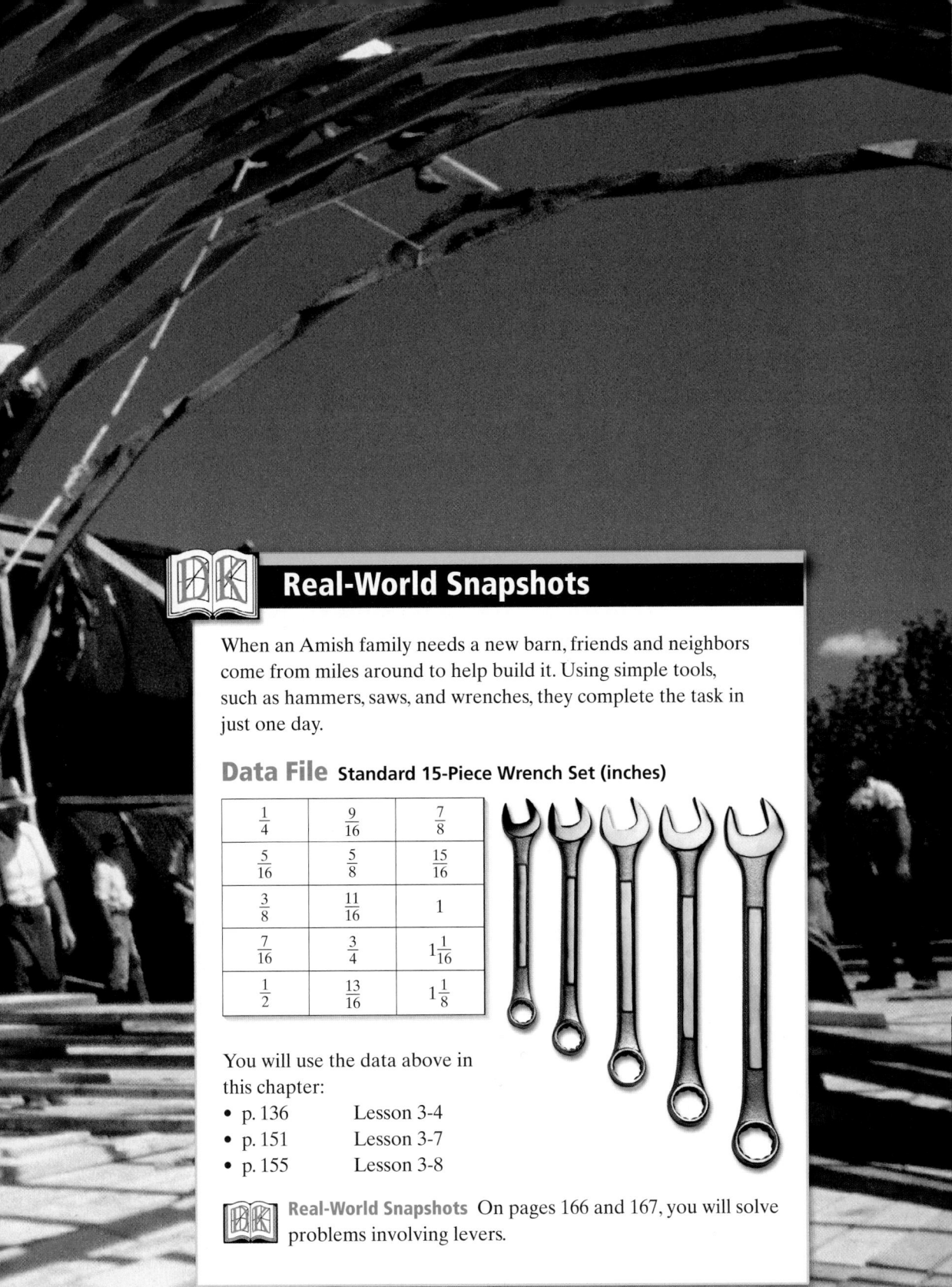

Real-World Snapshots

When an Amish family needs a new barn, friends and neighbors come from miles around to help build it. Using simple tools, such as hammers, saws, and wrenches, they complete the task in just one day.

Data File Standard 15-Piece Wrench Set (inches)

$\frac{1}{4}$	$\frac{9}{16}$	$\frac{7}{8}$
$\frac{5}{16}$	$\frac{5}{8}$	$\frac{15}{16}$
$\frac{3}{8}$	$\frac{11}{16}$	1
$\frac{7}{16}$	$\frac{3}{4}$	$1\frac{1}{16}$
$\frac{1}{2}$	$\frac{13}{16}$	$1\frac{1}{8}$

You will use the data above in this chapter:

- p. 136   Lesson 3-4
- p. 151   Lesson 3-7
- p. 155   Lesson 3-8

Real-World Snapshots On pages 166 and 167, you will solve problems involving levers.

Real-World Snapshots On pages 166 and 167, you will solve problems involving levers.

Teaching Notes

Activating Prior Knowledge
In this chapter students build on and extend their knowledge of number theory, of decimals, and of properties of fractions in order to simplify fractions, to find equivalent fractions, and to express fractions as decimals. Ask questions such as:

- *What do the following numbers have in common: 3, 11, 29, and 41?* Sample: each is odd; each is divisible only by itself and 1; each is prime.
- *What do these numbers have in common: 12, 18, 20, and 52?* Sample: each is an even number; each is a multiple of 2; each is divisible by 2.

Real-World Snapshots
The data here about inch wrench sizes will be used throughout the chapter. Have a volunteer read the opening paragraph. Focus students on the data in the chart and ask:

- *What do the fractions in the table represent?* Sample: The measures of 15 different-sized wrenches in inches.
- *How do the fractions appear to be ordered in the table?* Sample: The fractions increase from top to bottom and from left to right.

Reading and Math Literacy

3A: Graphic Organizer   For use before Lesson 3-1

Study Skill: As you read over the material in the chapter, keep a paper and pencil handy to write down notes and questions that you have.

Write your answers.

1. What is the chapter title? Number Theory and Fractions
2. How many lessons are there in this chapter? 10
3. What is the topic of the Reading Math page? Learning Vocabulary
4. What is the topic of the Test-Taking Strategy page? Extended-Response Questions
5. Look through the pages of the chapter and list four real-world connections that you see discussed in this chapter. Answers will vary.

6. Complete the graphic organizer below as you work through the chapter.
   - In the center, write the title of the chapter.
   - When you begin a lesson, write the lesson name in a rectangle.
   - When you complete a lesson, write a skill or key concept in a circle linked to that lesson block.
   - When you complete the chapter, use this graphic organizer to help you review.

Available in Spanish

117

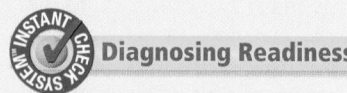

Diagnosing Readiness

Students will find answers to these exercises in the back of their textbooks.

Prescribing Intervention
For intervention, direct students to:

Reading and Writing Decimals
Lesson 1-2: Example 2. Extra Practice, p. 642.

Comparing and Ordering Decimals
Lesson 1-3: Example 4. Extra Practice, p. 642.

Dividing Decimals
Lesson 1-9: Examples 1–2, 4. Extra Practice, p. 642.

Exponents
Lesson 2-8: Example 1. Extra Practice, p. 643.

Chapter **3** Preview

Where You've Been

- In Chapter 2, you worked with patterns, variables, and algebraic expressions. You also learned to solve equations.

Where You're Going

- In Chapter 3, you will work with divisibility rules, prime numbers, factors, and fractions.

- You will compare and order fractions and write decimals as fractions and fractions as decimals.

- Applying what you learn, you will see how common factors and multiples are important in everyday functions such as time keeping.

Daily life for many people is divided into hours and minutes.

 Instant self-check online and on CD-ROM

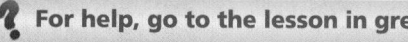

Diagnosing Readiness   ❓ **For help, go to the lesson in green.**

Reading and Writing Decimals (Lesson 1-2)

Write each decimal in words. **1–6. See margin.**

1. 0.4	**2.** 0.37	**3.** 1.8
4. 0.205	**5.** 20.88	**6.** 0.150

Comparing and Ordering Decimals (Lesson 1-3)

Order the decimals from least to greatest.

7. 4.2, 4.02, 4.21
   4.02, 4.2, 4.21

8. 0.3, 0.33, 0.033
   0.033, 0.3, 0.33

9. 6.032, 6.302, 6.203
   6.032, 6.203, 6.302

Dividing Decimals (Lesson 1-9)

Find each quotient.

10. $1.6 \div 2$ **0.8**	**11.** $3.85 \div 7$ **0.55**	**12.** $7.6 \div 0.4$ **19**
13. $290.4 \div 8$ **36.3**	**14.** $211.2 \div 1.6$ **132**	**15.** $583 \div 11$ **53**

Exponents (Lesson 2-8)

Write each expression using an exponent.

16. $3 \times 3 \times 3$ 3^3

17. 5×5 5^2

18. $2 \times 2 \times 2 \times 2 \times 2 \times 2$
   2^6

1. four tenths

2. thirty-seven hundredths

3. one and eight tenths

4. two hundred five thousandths

5. twenty and eighty-eight hundredths

6. one hundred fifty thousandths

Divisibility and Mental Math

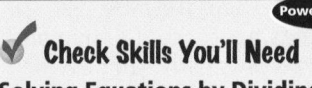
What You'll Learn

OBJECTIVE 1
To identify numbers divisible by 2, 3, 5, 9, or 10

. . . And Why

To form teams, as in Example 4

 Check Skills You'll Need   For help, go to Lesson 2-7.

Solve each equation. Then check the solution.

1. $10x = 490$ **49**
2. $5x = 205$ **41**
3. $2x = 83$ **41.5**
4. $725 = 5x$ **145**
5. $123 = 3x$ **41**
6. $0.6x = 30$ **50**

New Vocabulary   • divisible   • even number   • odd number

OBJECTIVE

1 **Using Divisibility Tests**

*i*TEXT Interactive lesson includes instant self-check, tutorials, and activities.

One whole number is **divisible** by a second whole number if the remainder is 0 when the first number is divided by the second number. For example, 84 is divisible by 4, since $84 \div 4 = 21$, with no remainder.

You can use multiplication facts to decide about divisibility.

Need Help?
For help with multiplying whole numbers, go to Skills Handbook page 658.

1 EXAMPLE   **Using Mental Math for Divisibility**

a. Is 56 divisible by 7?

Think Since $56 = 8 \times 7$, 56 is divisible by 7.

b. Is 56 divisible by 4?

Think Since $56 = 8 \times 7 = (4 \times 2) \times 7$, 56 is divisible by 4.

 **Check Understanding** **a.** Is 64 divisible by 6? **no**

b. Is 93 divisible by 3? **yes**

c. Number Sense Since 54 is divisible by 6, explain why 54 is also divisible by 2 and by 3. **$54 = 9 \times 6 = 9 \times (2 \times 3)$**

Divisibility tests can help you determine divisibility.

Key Concepts   **Divisibility of Whole Numbers**

A whole number is divisible by

• 2 if it ends in 0, 2, 4, 6, or 8.

• 3 if the sum of its digits is divisible by 3.

• 5 if it ends in 0 or 5.

• 9 if the sum of its digits is divisible by 9.

• 10 if it ends in 0.

Lesson Preview

 PowerPoint

✓ **Check Skills You'll Need**
Solving Equations by Dividing
Lesson 2-7: Example 1. Extra Practice p. 643.

Lesson Resources

Teaching Resources
Practice, Reteaching, Enrichment

Reaching All Students
Practice Workbook 3-1
Spanish Practice Workbook 3-1
Guided Problem Solving 3-1
Hands-On Activities 9, 10

 Presentation Assistant Plus!
Transparencies
• Check Skills You'll Need 3-1
• Problem of the Day 3-1
• Additional Examples 3-1
• Student Edition Answers 3-1
• Lesson Quiz 3-1
• Classroom Aid 11
PH Presentation Pro CD-ROM 3-1

PRENTICE HALL
ASSESSMENT SYSTEM

Computer Test Generator CD

 **Technology**
Resource Pro® CD-ROM
Computer Test Generator CD
PH Presentation Pro CD-ROM

www.PHSchool.com
Student Site
• Teacher Web Code: aak-5500
• Algebra Readiness Puzzles 3, 44
• Self-grading Lesson Quiz

PH SuccessNet Teacher Center
• Lesson Planner
• Resources

Plus *i*TEXT

 Ongoing Assessment and Intervention

Before the Lesson
Diagnose prerequisite skills using:
• Check Skills You'll Need

During the Lesson
Monitor progress using:
• Check Understanding
• Additional Examples
• Test Prep

After the Lesson
Assess knowledge using:
• Lesson Quiz
• Computer Test Generator CD

Math Background

The branch of mathematics that deals with the properties of the whole numbers is called *number theory*. Perhaps the most fundamental concern of number theory is *divisibility*. That is, when one whole number is divided by another, is there a remainder? In this lesson, students learn several methods for determining divisibility. These methods are often called *divisibility tests*.

Teaching Notes

English Learners

Help students understand that a *remainder* is the whole number that "remains" after one whole number is divided by another.

Error Prevention!

Students might believe that a number is divisible by 2, 5, or 10 if the sum of the digits is divisible by 2, 5, or 10. Stress that the sum-of-the-digits divisibility method applies only to 3 and 9.

PowerPoint
Additional Examples

1. Is the first number divisible by the second? Use mental math.

    a. 46 by 3 no

    b. 63 by 7 yes

2. Test each number for divisibility by 2, 5, or 10.

    a. 580 divisible by 2, 5, and 10

    b. 3,042 divisible by 2

3. Test 6,515 for divisibility by 3. not divisible by 3

4. A baker sells muffins in boxes that contain exactly 9 muffins each. Can the baker place 576 muffins in boxes of 9 with none left over? yes

Closure

Describe the tests for divisibility by 2, 5, and 10. Sample: If a number is even, it is divisible by 2; if a number ends in 5 or 0, it is divisible by 5; if a number ends in 0, it is divisible by 10.

2a. divisible by 2, 5, and 10

b. divisible by 5

c. divisible by none of these

d. divisible by 2

An **even number** is any whole number that ends with a 0, 2, 4, 6, or 8.
An **odd number** is a whole number that ends with a 1, 3, 5, 7, or 9.

2 EXAMPLE Divisibility by 2, 5, or 10

Test each number for divisibility by 2, 5, or 10.

a. 715

715 ends with a 5. So, it is divisible by 5, but not by 2 or 10.

b. 1,020

1,020 ends with a 0. So, it is divisible by 2, 5, and 10.

✓ **Check Understanding** 2 Test each number for divisibility by 2, 5, or 10. See above left.

a. 150   **b.** 325   **c.** 1,021   **d.** 2,112

3 EXAMPLE Divisibility by 3

Test 2,571 for divisibility by 3.

$2 + 5 + 7 + 1 = 15$ ← Find the sum of the digits in 2,571.

$15 \div 3 = 5$ ← The sum is divisible by 3.

So, 2,571 is divisible by 3.

✓ **Check Understanding** 3 Test each number for divisibility by 3.

a. 613 no   **b.** 1,770 yes   **c.** 882 yes

Real-World Connection
Softball became an Olympic medal sport for the first time at the Summer Games in 1996.

To test a number for divisibility by 9, you start by finding the sum of its digits—just as you did with 3.

4 EXAMPLE Divisibility by 9  Real World

Planning One of the activities at a company picnic is a softball tournament. Each team will have exactly 9 players. If 163 people have signed up to play, will everyone who has signed up have a spot on a 9-person team?

If 163 is divisible by 9, then everyone will have a spot on a team.

$1 + 6 + 3 = 10$ ← Find the sum of the digits in 163.

$10 \div 9$ has a remainder of 1. ← The sum is not divisible by 9.

So, 163 is not divisible by 9. Not everyone will have a spot on a team.

✓ **Check Understanding** 4 Test each number for divisibility by 9.

a. 225 yes   **b.** 1,655 no   **c.** 52,371 yes

d. Reasoning Explain why a number that is divisible by 9 must also be divisible by 3. If the sum of the digits is divisible by 9, the sum is divisible by 3 because 9 is divisible by 3.

120   **Chapter 3** Number Theory and Fractions

Reaching All Students

| **Below Level** Review remainders by giving students several pairs of divisions like these.

$35 \div 5$ 7 R0 $90 \div 6$ 15 R0
$36 \div 5$ 7 R1 $94 \div 6$ 15 R4 | **Advanced Learners** Find all the even numbers between 1,000 and 2,000 that are divisible by 5 and also by 9. 1,080; 1,170; 1,260; 1,350; 1,440; 1,530; 1,620; 1,710; 1,800; 1,890; 1,980 | **English Learners**
See note on page 120.
Inclusion
See note on page 121. |

EXERCISES

A Practice by Example

Example 1
(page 119)

Is the first number divisible by the second? Use mental math.

1. 48 by 4 yes

2. 46 by 4 no

3. 63 by 7 yes

4. 122 by 6 no

5. 42 by 6 yes

6. 88 by 11 yes

Example 2
(page 120)

Test each number for divisibility by 2, 5, or 10.

7. 48,960 2, 5, and 10

8. 2,385 5

9. 928 2

10. 672 2

11. 202,470 2, 5, and 10

12. 53,559 none

Example 3
(page 120)

Test each number for divisibility by 3.

13. 57 yes

14. 92 no

15. 171 yes

16. 962 no

17. 1,956 yes

18. 11,160 yes

Example 4
(page 120)

Test each number for divisibility by 9.

19. 1,187 no

20. 2,187 yes

21. 17,595 yes

22. 988 no

23. 6,283 no

24. 10,005 no

25. Planning A total of 114 people have signed up to play in a basketball tournament. There are 3 people on each team. Will everyone who has signed up have a spot on a 3-person team? Explain.
Yes; since 1 + 1 + 4 = 6 and 6 is divisible by 3, 114 is divisible by 3.

B Apply Your Skills

Test each number for divisibility by 2, 3, 5, 9, or 10.

26. 836 2

27. 837 3 and 9

28. 840 2, 3, 5, and 10

29. 842 2

30. 621 3 and 9

31. 1,086 2 and 3

32. 1,110 2, 3, 5, and 10

33. 5,555 5

34. Use a calculator to divide. If the answer is a whole number, then one number is divisible by the other.

34. Writing in Math Describe how you can use a calculator to tell if one number is divisible by another. See left.

Number Sense **Find the digit that makes each number divisible by 9.**

35. 9,0█5
    4

36. █7,302
    6

37. 2█6,555
    4

38. Which numbers between 150 and 200 are divisible by 9?
    153, 162, 171, 180, 189, and 198

 39. Time The number 60 is convenient for timekeeping because it can be easily divided by many numbers. Test 60 for divisibility by 2, 3, 4, 5, 6, 7, 8, 9, or 10. divisible by 2, 3, 4, 5, 6, and 10

GPS Use the Guided Problem Solving worksheet with Exercise 40.

Assignment Guide

▼ **1** Objective 1
  Ⓐ Ⓑ Core 1–42
  Ⓒ Extension 43, 44

Test Prep 45–48
Mixed Review 49–57

Inclusion
Exercise 34 Make sure students understand that the presence of digits, other than zero, to the right of the decimal point indicates there is a remainder.

Practice 3-1 Divisibility and Mental Math

Is the first number divisible by the second? Use mental math.

1. 475 by 5 yes
2. 5,296 by 3 no
3. 843 by 2 no
4. 76,780 by 10 yes
5. 456,790 by 5 yes
6. 3,460 by 2 yes
7. 4,197 by 3 yes
8. 100,005 by 10 no

Test each number for divisibility by 2, 3, 5, 9, or 10.

9. 126 2, 3, 9
10. 257 none
11. 430 2, 5, 10
12. 535 5
13. 745 5
14. 896 2
15. 729 3, 9
16. 945 3, 5, 9
17. 4,580 2, 5, 10
18. 6,331 none
19. 7,952 2
20. 8,000 2, 5, 10
21. 19,450 2, 5, 10
22. 21,789 3, 9
23. 43,785 3, 5, 9
24. 28,751 none

Find the digit that makes each number divisible by 9.

25. 54,78█3
26. 42.█5█97
27. 83,2█1█4
28. 53█6█,904

Name the numbers that are divisible by the numbers given.

29. numbers between 40 and 50, divisible by 3 and 5
    45
30. numbers between 10 and 20, divisible by 2, 3, and 9
    18
31. numbers between 380 and 410, divisible by 2, 5, and 10
    390, 400
32. numbers between 590 and 610, divisible by 2, 3, 5, and 10
    600
33. There are 159 students to be grouped into relay teams. Each team is to have the same number of students. Can each team have 3, 5, or 6 students?
    3 students

Reteaching 3-1 Divisibility and Mental Math

A number is **divisible** by a second number if the second number divides into the first with no remainder. Here are some rules.

Last Digit of a Number	The Number Is Divisible by	Examples
any	1	any number
0, 2, 4, 6, 8	2	10; 24; 32; 54; 106; 138
0, 5	5	10; 25; 70; 915; 1,250
0	10	10; 20; 90; 500; 4,300

The Sum of the Digits	The Number Is Divisible by	Examples	
is divisible by 3	3	843 → 8 + 4 + 3 = 15 and 15 ÷ 3 = 5	281 R0 3)843
is divisible by 9	9	2,898 → 2 + 8 + 9 + 8 = 27 and 27 ÷ 9 = 3	322 R0 9)2,898

Circle the numbers that are divisible by the number at the left.

1. 2   8   15   28   42   97   105   218
2. 5   14   10   25   18   975   1,005   2,340
3. 10   100   75   23   60   99   250   655
4. 3   51   73   12   82   93   153   274
5. 9   27   32   36   108   126   245   587

Use mental math to determine if the first number is divisible by the second.

6. 185; 5 yes
7. 76,870; 10 yes
8. 461; 1 yes
9. 456; 3 yes
10. 35,994; 2 yes
11. 6,791; 3 no
12. 12,866; 9 no
13. 151,002; 9 yes
14. 55,340; 5 yes
15. 6,888; 2 yes
16. 31,067; 5 no
17. 901,204; 3 no
18. 2,232; 3 yes
19. 45,812; 9 no
20. 3,090; 10 yes
21. 312; 9 no
22. 1,933; 3 no
23. 28,889; 2 no

Test each number for being divisible by 2, 5, or 10. Some numbers may be divisible by more than one number.

24. 800 2, 5, 10
25. 65 5
26. 1,010 2, 5, 10

Lesson Quiz 3-1

Test each number for divisibility by 2, 3, 5, 9, and 10.

1. 18,520 2, 5, 10

2. 270 2, 3, 5, 9, 10

3. 5,625 3, 5, 9

4. 100,000 2, 5, 10

Alternative Assessment

Have students work in pairs. Partners write a list of the whole numbers from 1 to 100. Using a colored pencil, they circle each digit in the ones place and write 2, 5, and/or 10 to the left of each number by which that number is divisible. Next, they write the sum of the digits of the numbers at the right. For each, they determine whether the number is divisible by 3 and/or 9, and use a second color to indicate whether this is so.

Test Prep

Resources

For additional practice with a variety of test item formats:
• Test-Prep, p. 165
• Test-Taking Strategies, p. 161
• Test-Taking Strategies With Transparencies

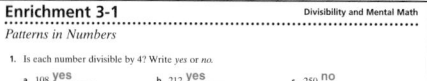

Enrichment 3-1   Divisibility and Mental Math

Patterns in Numbers

1. Is each number divisible by 4? Write *yes* or *no*.
   a. 108 yes   b. 212 yes   c. 250 no
   d. 316 yes   e. 625 no   f. 1,020 yes

2. List the numbers in Question 1 that were divisible by 4.
   108, 212, 316, 1,020

3. Choose one of the numbers that was divisible by 4. Change the hundreds digit. Write the new number. Is the number still divisible by 4? How do you know?
   Sample answer: Change 108 to 208. The new number is
   divisible by 4 since there is no remainder when divided by 4.

4. Look at the numbers formed by the last two digits in each of the numbers you listed in Question 2. What pattern do you see in these digits?
   The numbers increase by 4, and all are evenly
   divisible by 4.

5. Write a divisibility rule for dividing by 4.
   If the number formed by the last two digits of a given
   number is divisible by 4, then the number is divisible by 4.

6. Test your rule. Is each number divisible by 4? Write *yes* or *no*.
   a. 111 no   b. 128 yes   c. 296 yes
   d. 332 yes   e. 548 yes   f. 1,036 yes
   g. 3,456 yes   h. 65,728 yes i. 362,042 no

7. Kendra has 324 marbles. She wants to use them in a game with three friends.
   a. Can the group divide the marbles equally?
   yes
   b. Suppose she finds five more marbles. Can she divide all the marbles equally among four players? Use your rule to explain your answer.
   No; 29 is not divisible by 4.

122

40. Money Elissa and eight friends have lunch at a restaurant. The bill is $56.61. Can the group split the bill into nine equal shares? Use the rule for divisibility by 9 to explain your answer. **Yes; since 5 + 6 + 6 + 1 = 18 and 18 is divisible by 9, then 56.61 is divisible by 9.**

41. Patterns A number pattern begins 6, 12, 18, 24, . . .
   a. Write the next four numbers in the pattern. **30, 36, 42, 48**
   b. Which of the eight numbers are divisible by both 2 and 3? **All are divisible by 2 and 3.**
   c. **Writing in Math** Write a rule for divisibility by 6.
   See margin.

42. If a number is divisible by 2 and 5, is it divisible by 10? Explain. **See margin.**

C Challenge

43. (**Algebra**) Explain why the value of the expression $2n + 1$ is always an odd number. (Assume the variable n is a whole number.) **See margin.**

44. Stretch Your Thinking Write all the three-digit numbers containing a 1, 2, and 3. Which of these numbers are divisible by 4?
123, 132, 213, 231, 312, 321; 132 and 312

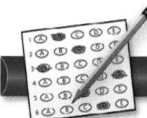

Test Prep

Multiple Choice

45. Which number is NOT divisible by 9? **C**
   A. 351   B. 657   C. 753   D. 855

Take It to the NET
Online lesson quiz at
www.PHSchool.com
Web Code: aaa-0301

46. Which number is NOT divisible by both 2 and 5? **G**
   F. 385,290   G. 621,765   H. 773,270   I. 817,020

47. Which number is divisible by both 2 and 3? **C**
   A. 1,323   B. 1,298   C. 1,230   D. 1,148

Short Response

48. Which two-digit numbers ending in 5 or 7 are divisible by 3? Explain how you can use the rule for divisibility by 3 to help find your answer. **See margin.**

Mixed Review

Lesson 2-6   (**Algebra**) Solve each equation.

49. $x - 10 = 35$ **45**   **50.** $y - 8 = 92$ **100**   **51.** $n - 6.2 = 10$ **16.2**

52. $a - 4.25 = 1.75$ **6**   **53.** $b - 0.06 = 1.4$ **1.46**   **54.** $c - 1.02 = 3.6$ **4.62**

Lesson 2-2   (**Algebra**) Evaluate each expression for $a = 1.5$.

55. $2(a - 1)$ **1**   **56.** $10a \div 3$ **5**   **57.** $1 + 7a$ **11.5**

41c. Any number that is divisible by both 2 and 3 is also divisible by 6.

42. Yes; 10 is divisible by 2 and 5, so any number divisible by both 2 and 5 will also be divisible by 10.

43. The product of 2 and any whole number will always be even. Since whole numbers alternate between even and odd, the sum of any even number and 1 will always be odd.

48. [2] 15, 27, 45, 57, 75, 87; list the two digit numbers that end with 5 or 7 and select the numbers whose digits have a sum divisible by 3.

[1] no work shown

3-2

Prime Numbers and Prime Factorization

What You'll Learn

 OBJECTIVE 1
To find factors of a number

 OBJECTIVE 2
To find the prime factorization

...And Why

To find formations for marching, as in Exercise 27

✓ **Check Skills You'll Need**   ❓ For help, go to Lesson 3-1.

Test each number for divisibility by 2, 3, 5, 9, or 10.

1. 990   2, 3, 5, 9, and 10   2. 901   none   3. 695   5

4. 800   2, 5, and 10   5. 2,080   2, 5, and 10   6. 94,022   2

New Vocabulary   • factor   • composite number   • prime number
   • prime factorization

Lesson Preview

✓ **Check Skills You'll Need**   PowerPoint
Divisibility by 2, 3, 5, 9, or 10
Lesson 3-1: Examples 2–4. Extra Practice p. 644.

Lesson Resources

Optional Materials
• graph paper

📁 **Teaching Resources**
Practice, Reteaching, Enrichment

👥 **Reaching All Students**
Practice Workbook 3-2
Spanish Practice Workbook 3-2
Guided Problem Solving 3-2
Technology Activities 7
Hands-On Activities 9–10

⏱ **Presentation Assistant Plus!**
Transparencies
• Check Skills You'll Need 3-2
• Problem of the Day 3-2
• Additional Examples 3-2
• Student Edition Answers 3-2
• Lesson Quiz 3-2
• Classroom Aid 2
PH Presentation Pro CD-ROM 3-2

PRENTICE HALL ASSESSMENT SYSTEM

Computer Test Generator CD

💻 **Technology**
Resource Pro® CD-ROM
Computer Test Generator CD
PH Presentation Pro CD-ROM

💻 **www.PHSchool.com**
Student Site
• Teacher Web Code: aak-5500
• Self-grading Lesson Quiz

PH SuccessNet Teacher Center
• Lesson Planner
• Resources

Plus *i*TEXT

 **OBJECTIVE 1**
Finding Factors of a Number

*i*TEXT Interactive lesson includes instant self-check, tutorials, and activities.

Investigation: Modeling Divisibility With Rectangles

1–3. See back of book.

1. Use graph paper. Draw as many different rectangles as you can by using exactly 12 squares of the grid at a time. What are the dimensions of each rectangle?

2. How many different rectangles can you draw using 24 squares? Using 25 squares? Using 7 squares?

3. Explain how the number of rectangles that you can draw relates to the divisibility of a number.

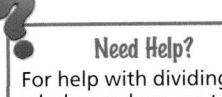 **Need Help?**
For help with dividing whole numbers, go to Skills Handbook page 660.

Rules for divisibility can help you find factors. A **factor** is a whole number that divides a nonzero whole number with remainder 0.

① **EXAMPLE**   Finding Factors

List all the factors of 20.

1×20 ← Write factor pairs. Start with 1.

$2 \times 10, 4 \times 5$ ← 2 and 4 are factors. Skip 3, since 20 is not divisible by 3.

5×4 ← Stop when you repeat factors.

The factors of 20 are 1, 2, 4, 5, 10, and 20.

✓ **Check Understanding** ① List all the factors of 42.   1, 2, 3, 6, 7, 14, 21, 42

Ongoing Assessment and Intervention

Before the Lesson
Diagnose prerequisite skills using:
• Check Skills You'll Need

During the Lesson
Monitor progress using:
• Check Understanding
• Additional Examples
• Test Prep

After the Lesson
Assess knowledge using:
• Lesson Quiz
• Computer Test Generator CD

Math Background

When one whole number is divisible by a second, the second number is said to be a *factor* of the first. If a whole number greater than 1 has exactly two factors, 1 and the number itself, it is called a *prime number*. If a whole number greater than 1 has more than two factors, it is called a *composite number*. Writing a whole number as a product of prime factors is called the *prime factorization* of the number. Every whole number greater than 1 has exactly one prime factorization.

Teaching Notes

Investigation (Optional)
For Question 2, make sure students understand that a rectangle 3 units across and 8 units tall is not different than a rectangle 8 units across and 3 units tall.

English Learners
Students might think *factor* refers to any number that is multiplied. Make sure they understand that the term factor is being used in a different sense in this lesson: When one whole number is divisible by another, the second number is a *factor* of the first.

PowerPoint
Additional Examples

1. List the factors of each number.

   a. 24 1, 2, 3, 4, 6, 8, 12, 24

   b. 35 1, 5, 7, 35

2. Tell whether each number is prime or composite. Explain.

   a. 61 61 is prime. There are only two factors: 1 and 61.

   b. 65 65 is composite. 5 is a factor of 65.

3. Find the prime factorization of 90. $2 \times 3^2 \times 5$

Closure

What is the prime factorization of a number? an expression that shows the number as a product of prime numbers

---

A **composite number** is a whole number greater than 1 with more than two factors. For example, 25 is composite since it has three factors: 1, 5, and 25.

A **prime number** is a whole number with exactly two factors, 1 and the number itself. The first ten prime numbers are 2, 3, 5, 7, 11, 13, 17, 19, 23, and 29. The whole numbers 0 and 1 are neither prime nor composite.

2a. composite; $39 = 3 \times 13$

b. Prime; it has only two factors, 1 and 47.

c. composite; $63 = 3 \times 21$ or $63 = 7 \times 9$

2 EXAMPLE Prime or Composite?

Tell whether each number is prime or composite. Explain.

a. 51

Composite; 51 is divisible by 3, so it has more than two factors.

b. 53

Prime; 53 has only two factors, 1 and 53.

✔ **Check Understanding** 2 Tell whether each number is prime or composite. Explain.

a. 39   b. 47   c. 63

See above left.

OBJECTIVE
2 Finding the Prime Factorization of a Number

Writing a composite number as a product of prime numbers gives the **prime factorization** of the number. You can use a *division ladder* or a *factor tree* to find the prime factorization of a composite number.

3 EXAMPLE Prime Factorization

Find the prime factorization of 84.

Method 1 Using a division ladder

$2\overline{)84}$ ← Divide 84 by the prime number 2. Work down.
$2\overline{)42}$ ← The result is 42. Since 42 is even, divide by 2 again.
$3\overline{)21}$ ← The result is 21. Divide by the prime number 3.
7 ← The prime factorization is $2 \times 2 \times 3 \times 7$.

Method 2 Using a factor tree

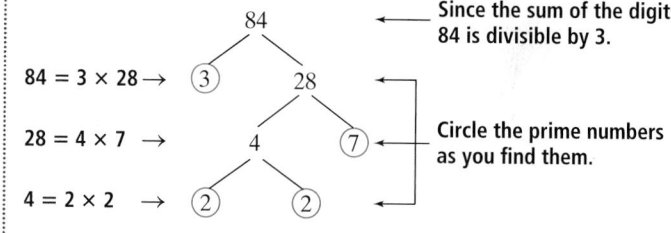

$84 = 3 \times 28 \rightarrow$

$28 = 4 \times 7 \rightarrow$

$4 = 2 \times 2 \rightarrow$

Since the sum of the digits of 84 is 12, 84 is divisible by 3.

Circle the prime numbers as you find them.

The prime factorization of 84 is $2^2 \times 3 \times 7$.

✔ **Check Understanding** 3 Find the prime factorization of each number.

a. 36 $2^2 \times 3^2$

b. 125 5^3

👥 Reaching All Students

Below Level Give students several missing-factor exercises like these.	Advanced Learners Find all the whole numbers less than 50 whose only prime factors are 2 or 3. 2, 3, 4, 6, 8, 9, 12, 16, 18, 24, 27, 32, 36, 48	English Learners See note on page 124. Error Prevention See note on page 125.
$34 = 2 \times \blacksquare$ 17 $57 = 3 \times \blacksquare$ 19 $65 = 5 \times \blacksquare$ 13 $161 = 7 \times \blacksquare$ 23 $66 = 2 \times 3 \times \blacksquare$ 11 $63 = 3 \times 3 \times \blacksquare$ 7		

A Practice by Example

List the factors of each number.

Example 1
(page 123)

1. 8 1, 2, 4, 8
2. 12 1, 2, 3, 4, 6, 12
3. 18 1, 2, 3, 6, 9, 18
4. 35 1, 5, 7, 35

5. 28 1, 2, 4, 7, 14, 28
6. 21 1, 3, 7, 21
7. 17 1, 17
8. 60 See margin.

Example 2
(page 124)

Tell whether each number is prime or composite. Explain.
9–16. See margin.

9. 55
10. 51
11. 83
12. 87

13. 19
14. 67
15. 57
16. 91

Example 3
(page 124)

Find the prime factorization of each number. 17–24. For factor trees, see back of book.

17. 32 2^5
18. 42 $2 \times 3 \times 7$
19. 75 $5^2 \times 3$
20. 400 $2^4 \times 5^2$

21. 15 3×5
22. 45 $3^2 \times 5$
23. 450 $2 \times 3^2 \times 5^2$
24. 10,000 $2^4 \times 5^4$

B Apply Your Skills

Calculator **Find the number with the given prime factorization.**

25. $7 \times 11 \times 13$ 1,001
26. $2^3 \times 5^2 \times 7 \times 11$ 15,400

27. Parades A group has 36 ceremonial guards. When they march, they form rows of equal numbers of guards. What numbers of rows can they make? How many guards will be in each row?
$1 \times 36; 2 \times 18; 3 \times 12; 4 \times 9; 6 \times 6$

Tell whether each number is prime or composite. For each composite number, find the prime factorization.

28. 216 comp.; $2^3 \times 3^3$
29. 135 comp.; $3^3 \times 5$
30. 47 prime
31. 210 comp.; $2 \times 3 \times 5 \times 7$

32. 432 comp.; $2^4 \times 3^3$
33. 73 prime
34. 765 comp.; $3^2 \times 5 \times 17$
35. 1,089 comp. $3^2 \times 11^2$

Real-World Connection

In England, the Queen's birthday is celebrated with a military parade.

36. Writing in Math Explain how you would use divisibility rules to make a factor tree for 864. Then find the prime factorization. See back of book.

C Challenge

37. **Algebra** Suppose p is a prime number greater than 2. Does $p + 1$ represent a prime or a composite number? Explain.
If $p > 2$ and prime, then p is odd. So $p + 1$ is even and always composite.

38. An *emirp* (*prime* spelled backward) is a number that is a *different* prime when its digits are reversed. The number 13 is the first emirp (13 and 31). Find the other emirps less than 100. 13, 31; 17, 71; 37, 73; 79, 97

39. Stretch Your Thinking Norma used a total of 192 digits to number the pages of her book, starting with page 1. How many pages are in Norma's book? 100 pages

---

8. 1, 2, 3, 4, 5, 6, 10, 12, 15, 20, 30, 60

9. composite; $55 = 5 \times 11$

10. composite; $51 = 3 \times 17$

11. Prime; the only factors are 1 and 83.

12. composite; $87 = 3 \times 29$

13. Prime; the only factors are 1 and 19.

14. Prime; the only factors are 1 and 67.

15. composite; $57 = 3 \times 19$

16. composite; $91 = 7 \times 13$

GPS Use the Guided Problem Solving worksheet with Exercise 27.

Error Prevention!

Exercises 17–24 Students who use factor trees may end with one or more composite numbers.

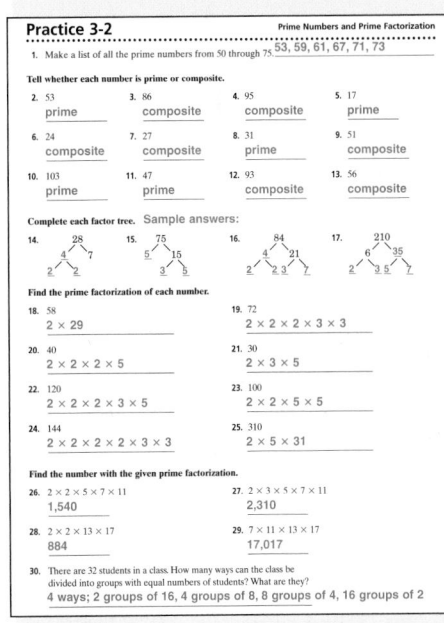

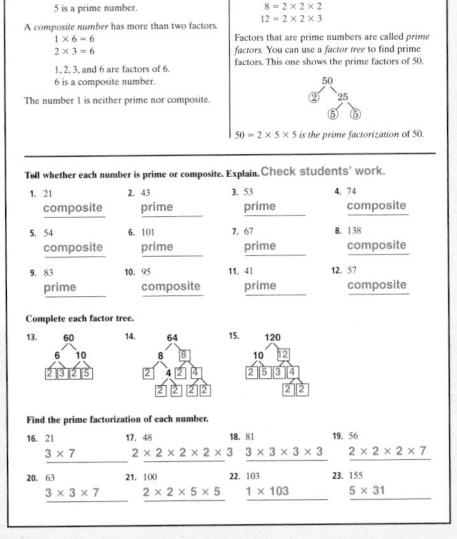

 **Lesson Quiz 3-2**

Write the prime factorization for each number.

1. 36 $2^2 \times 3^2$

2. 150 $2 \times 3 \times 5^2$

3. 99 $3^2 \times 11$

4. 225 $3^2 \times 5^2$

Alternative Assessment

Provide student pairs with several composite numbers such as 40, 72, 90, and 500. They are to find the prime factorization using factor trees. For 72, they might start with 8 · 9. One partner writes the factors for the first branch, 8, and the other writes the factors for the second branch, 9. Partners work together to write the prime factorization.

Test Prep

Resources

For additional practice with a variety of test item formats:
• Test-Prep, p. 165
• Test-Taking Strategies, p. 161
• Test-Taking Strategies With Transparencies

Enrichment 3-2 Prime Numbers and Prime Factorization
Critical Thinking

Goldbach's Conjecture

Christian Goldbach, an eighteenth-century Russian mathematician, believed that every even number greater than 4 could be written as the sum of two odd primes. For example $16 = 5 + 11$. He also believed that every even number greater than 4 could be written as the sum of three primes. For example, $16 = 2 + 3 + 11$, or $16 = 2 + 7 + 7$.

1. Complete the table. **Sample answers:**

Number	Sum of two odd primes	Sum of three primes
6	3 + 3	2 + 2 + 2
8	3 + 5	2 + 3 + 3
14	7 + 7	2 + 5 + 7
30	11 + 19	2 + 11 + 17
38	7 + 31	2 + 5 + 31
40	17 + 23	2 + 7 + 31
50	19 + 31	2 + 7 + 41
88	5 + 83	2 + 3 + 83
100	47 + 53	2 + 31 + 67
116	19 + 97	2 + 53 + 61
132	23 + 109	2 + 59 + 71
150	71 + 79	2 + 59 + 89
152	73 + 79	2 + 61 + 89

Write a composite number between 60 and 70 as the sum of:

2. two primes 23 + 41 = 64   3. three primes 2 + 31 + 31 = 64

Write a composite number between 135 and 150 as the sum of:

4. two primes 67 + 73 = 140   5. three primes 2 + 67 + 71 = 140

6. Suppose p is a prime number and $q = 42 + p$. Can you write q as the sum of three primes? Explain.
Yes; you can write 42 as the sum of two primes.

 **Test Prep**

Multiple Choice

40. What is the prime factorization of 48? **D**
   A. 12 · 4   **B.** 6 · 2^4 **C.** 3 · 2 · 2^2 **D.** 3 · 2^4

41. What number has the prime factorization $2^3 \times 3^2 \times 7$? **I**
   F. 252   **G.** 336   **H.** 378   **I.** 504

Short Response

Take It to the NET
Online lesson quiz at
www.PHSchool.com
Web Code: aaa-0302

42. Make a factor tree for 81. Write the prime factorization.
   See back of book.

43. a. Explain why $2^3 \times 5^2 \times 9 \times 11 \times 15$ is NOT a correct prime factorization.
   b. Give the correct prime factorization.
   a–b. See margin.

Mixed Review

Lesson 2-7 **Algebra** Solve each equation.

44. $x \div 3 = 12$ **36**   45. $x \div 10 = 5$ **50**   46. $30 = y \div 6$ **180**

Lesson 1-10 Use <, =, or > to complete each statement.

47. $(8 + 10) \div 2 \;\overset{>}{\blacksquare}\; 14 \div (2 + 5)$ 48. $4 + 12 \times 2 \;\overset{>}{\blacksquare}\; (6 + 10) \div 2$

49. $3.5 + 2.5 \times 2 \;\underset{<}{\blacksquare}\; 24 \div 4 + 3$ 50. $15 - 5 \div 5 \;\underset{=}{\blacksquare}\; 4 \times 7 \div 2$

Practice Game

Triple Prime Time

Getting Started

• Draw a 4-by-4 grid.
• Arrange the following numbers on your grid, one in each square.
   12, 18, 20, 28, 30, 42, 45, 50, 63, 66, 70, 75, 105, 110, 154, 165
• The host writes the prime numbers **2, 3, 5, 7,** and **11** on separate pieces of paper and puts them in a container.

How to Play

• The host draws a prime number, calls it out, and replaces it.
• Find a number on your grid for which the number called is a factor. Write the number called in that square.
• The host continues to draw slips and call numbers.
• When you record all three prime factors for a square, cross out the square. For example, you can cross out the square with 28 when you record 2, 2, and 7.
• The first player to cross out 4 squares in a row wins.

43. **[2]** This is not the correct prime factorization because the factors 9 and 15 are not prime.

$2^3 \times 3^3 \times 5^3 \times 11$

[1] The explanation is correct, but the prime factorization is not written out, OR the prime factorization is correct, but there is no explanation.

The Sieve of Eratosthenes

For Use With Lesson 3-2

The Sieve of Eratosthenes

This extension of Lesson 3-2 introduces a method for finding prime numbers.

Eratosthenes (circa 275–194 B.C.) was a Greek scientist. He found a method to identify prime numbers. This method is now known as the "Sieve of Eratosthenes."

Teaching Notes

Begin by asking students to define prime and composite numbers. Then have a volunteer read aloud the opening paragraph as the other students read it to themselves.

Activity

To make the sieve for numbers up to 40, follow these steps.

Step 1 Make a list of whole numbers from 1 to 40. Cross out 1, since it is not prime.

Step 2 Circle 2, the first prime number. Cross out every number divisible by 2, beginning with 4.

```
 X  ②  3  4  5  6  7  8  9  10
11  12  13  14  15  16  17  18  19  20
21  22  23  24  25  26  27  28  29  30
31  32  33  34  35  36  37  38  39  40
```

Step 3 The next unmarked number, 3, is prime. Circle it. Cross out every number divisible by 3, beginning with 6. (Some numbers will already be crossed out.)

```
 X  ②  ③  4  5  6  7  8  9  10
11  12  13  14  15  16  17  18  19  20
21  22  23  24  25  26  27  28  29  30
31  32  33  34  35  36  37  38  39  40
```

Have another volunteer, at the chalkboard or using an overhead projector, use the Sieve of Eratosthenes to find the prime numbers less than 30. As this student works, have all others do the activity at their seats. Guide them to list all the numbers from 2 through 30 consecutively.

Step 4 Circle the next unmarked number, 5. Cross out every number divisible by 5 that is greater than 5.

Step 5 Continue until all numbers have been circled or crossed out. The circled numbers are prime.

Teaching Tip

Challenge students to predict how many prime numbers there are between 100 and 200. Students can continue the Sieve to check their guesses. **21 primes: 101, 103, 107, 109, 113, 127, 131, 137, 139, 149, 151, 157, 163, 167, 173, 179, 181, 191, 193, 197, 199**

EXERCISES

1. a. Use the method of the Sieve of Eratosthenes to find the prime numbers between 2 and 100. List them. **2, 3, 5, 7, 11, 13, 17, 19, 23, 29, 31, 37, 41, 43, 47, 53, 59, 61, 67, 71, 73, 79, 83, 89, 97**

b. *Twin primes* are pairs of prime numbers that differ by 2. For example, 11 and 13 are twin primes. Identify all the twin primes less than 100. **3 and 5; 5 and 7; 11 and 13; 17 and 19; 29 and 31; 41 and 43; 59 and 61; 71 and 73**

2. Reasoning Explain why it is not necessary to cross out numbers divisible by 9. **All multiples of 9 are also multiples of 3. So when multiples of 3 are crossed out, multiples of 9 are crossed out.**

3. (**Algebra**) Many prime numbers have the form $6n + 1$, where n is a whole number. Two examples are $6(1) + 1 = 7$ and $6(2) + 1 = 13$. Evaluate $6n + 1$ for each value of n, and identify the result as prime or composite.

a. $n = 6$ **b.** $n = 8$ **c.** $n = 13$ **d.** $n = 15$
   37, prime   49, comp.   79, prime   91, comp.

Exercises

Students' lists of primes will have the triplet 3, 5, 7. Challenge them to find another triplet between 2 and 100. **There is none.**

42. **[2] Answers may vary. Sample:**

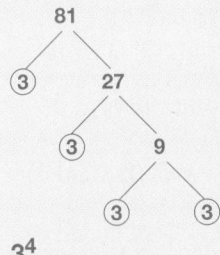

3^4

[1] The factor tree is complete, but the prime factorization is not written out, OR there is a small computational error, but all the work is present.

Lesson Preview

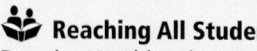

✓ **Check Skills You'll Need** 🔲 PowerPoint

Finding the Prime Factorization
Lesson 3-2: Example 3. Extra
Practice p. 644.

Lesson Resources

📁 **Teaching Resources**
Practice, Reteaching, Enrichment
Checkpoint Quiz 1

👥 **Reaching All Students**
Practice Workbook 3-3
Spanish Practice Workbook 3-3
Reading and Math Literacy 3B
Spanish Reading and Math
Literacy 3B
Spanish Checkpoint Quiz 1
Guided Problem Solving 3-3
Hands-On Activities 10

🕐 **Presentation Assistant Plus!**
Transparencies
• Check Skills You'll Need 3-3
• Problem of the Day 3-3
• Additional Examples 3-3
• Student Edition Answers 3-3
• Lesson Quiz 3-1
PH Presentation Pro CD-ROM 3-3

(ASSESSMENT *SYSTEM*)

Checkpoint Quiz 1
Computer Test Generator CD

💻 **Technology**
Resource Pro® CD-ROM
Computer Test Generator CD
PH Presentation Pro CD-ROM

💻 **www.PHSchool.com**
Student Site
• Teacher Web Code: aak-5500
• Algebra Readiness Puzzles 48
• Self-grading Lesson Quiz

PH SuccessNet Teacher Center
• Lesson Planner
• Resources

Plus 📘**iTEXT**

3-3

Greatest Common Factor

What You'll Learn

▼ **OBJECTIVE 1** To find the greatest common factor of two or more numbers

. . . And Why

To equally distribute stamps, as in Example 1

✓ **Check Skills You'll Need** ❓ For help, go to Lesson 3-2.

Find the prime factorization of each number.

1. 45 $3^2 \times 5$
2. 21 3×7
3. 99 $3^2 \times 11$
4. 93 3×31
5. 39 3×13
6. 128 2^7

7. **Error Analysis** Explain why the expression $2 \times 3 \times 13 \times 21 \times 31$ is not a correct prime factorization. **21 is not prime.**

New Vocabulary • common factor • greatest common factor (GCF)

OBJECTIVE

1 📘**iTEXT** Interactive lesson includes instant self-check, tutorials, and activities.

Finding the Greatest Common Factor

Real-World 🌐 Connection

Careers Collectors buy and sell rare items including stamps, coins, antiques, and sports memorabilia.

Suppose a stamp club president equally distributes two different sets of stamps among the club members. One set contains 18 stamps. The other set contains 30 stamps. There are no stamps left undistributed. What is the greatest possible number of club members?

The number of possible club members depends on the common factors of 18 and 30. A factor that two or more numbers share is a **common factor.**

The **greatest common factor (GCF)** of two or more numbers is the greatest factor shared by all the numbers. You can find the GCF of two numbers by listing their factors.

① **EXAMPLE** **Using Lists of Factors**

Find the greatest common factor of 18 and 30.

List the factors of 18 and the factors of 30. Then circle the common factors.

Factors of 18: ①, ②, ③, ⑥, 9, 18
Factors of 30: ①, ②, ③, 5, ⑥, 10, 15, 30

← The common factors are 1, 2, 3, and 6.

The greatest common factor (GCF) is 6.

✓ **Check Understanding** ① List the factors to find the GCF of each set of numbers.

1a–c. See back of book for lists.

a. 6, 21 **3**
b. 18, 49 **1**
c. 14, 28 **14**

d. **Number Sense** Based on Example 1, no more than six people can share equally 18 stamps from one set and 30 stamps from another set. How many stamps from each set will each person receive? **three from the set of 18 stamps and five from the set of 30 stamps**

128 Chapter 3 Number Theory and Fractions

📘 **Ongoing Assessment and Intervention**

Before the Lesson	**During the Lesson**	**After the Lesson**
Diagnose prerequisite skills using:	Monitor progress using:	Assess knowledge using:
• Check Skills You'll Need	• Check Understanding	• Lesson Quiz
	• Additional Examples	• Computer Test Generator CD
	• Test Prep	• Chapter Checkpoint 1 (p. 131)

You can also use a division ladder or factor trees to find the greatest common factor of two or more numbers.

2a. $2\overline{)24\quad 54}$
$\;\;\;3\overline{)12\quad 27}$
$\;\;\;\;\;\;\;4\quad\;\; 9$

GCF = 6

b. $3\overline{)18\quad 27\quad 36}$
$\;\;3\overline{)6\quad\;\; 9\quad\; 12}$
$\;\;\;\;\;\;2\quad\;\; 3\quad\;\; 4$

GCF = 9

(2) EXAMPLE   Using a Division Ladder

Use a division ladder to find the GCF of 42 and 56.

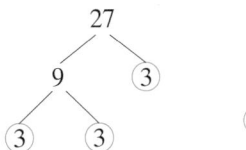

$2\overline{)42\quad 56}$ ← **Divide by 2, a common factor of 42 and 56.**
$7\overline{)21\quad 28}$ ← **Divide by 7, a common factor of 21 and 28.**
$\quad\;\; 3\quad\;\; 4$ ← **3 and 4 have no common factors.**

Multiply the common factors: 2 × 7 = 14.

○ The GCF of 42 and 56 is 14.

✔ **Check Understanding** ② Use a division ladder to find the GCF of each set of numbers.
   a. 24, 54   **b.** 18, 27, 36
   2a–b. See above left.

(3) EXAMPLE   Using Factor Trees

Use factor trees to find the GCF of 27 and 36.

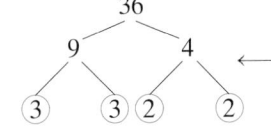

← **Make a factor tree for each number.**

$27 = \boxed{3} \times \boxed{3} \times 3$
$36 = \boxed{3} \times \boxed{3} \times 2 \times 2$

← **Write the prime factorization for each number.**

← **Identify common factors.**

$3 \times 3 = 9$ ← **Multiply the common factors.**

○ The GCF of 27 and 36 is 9.

3a–b. See back of book for factor trees.

✔ **Check Understanding** ③ Use factor trees to find the GCF of each set of numbers.
   a. 12, 32 **4**   **b.** 18, 42 **6**

EXERCISES

🔖 **For more practice, see _Extra Practice_.**

1–6. See back of book for lists.

List the factors to find the GCF of each set of numbers.

Example 1
(page 128)

1. 14, 35 **7**   **2.** 24, 45 **3**   **3.** 26, 34 **2**

4. 30, 35 **5**   **5.** 48, 88 **8**   **6.** 36, 63 **9**

👥 Reaching All Students

| **Below Level** Have students find the GCF of pairs of numbers that are already in factored form. For example: $2 \times 2 \times 3$ **GCF** $\quad 2 \times 3 \times 3 \times 5$ **GCF** $2 \times 3 \times 7 = 6 \quad 3 \times 3 \times 5 \times 5 = 45$ | **Advanced Learners** A number is a _perfect number_ if the sum of all its factors (including 1) is equal to twice the number. Find all the perfect numbers in this list: 4, 6, 8, 14, 18, 34, 28, 32 **6, 28** | **Inclusion** See note on page 130. **Tactile Learners** See note on page 129. |

Math Background

If two numbers are each divisible by a third number, the third number is a _common factor_ of the other two. In this lesson, students learn three methods for identifying the _greatest common factor_, or the _GCF_.

Teaching Notes

① EXAMPLE Tactile Learners

Students can model the problem using two colors of tiles or cubes. One color can represent the set of 18 stamps, and another color can represent the set of 30 stamps.

Error Prevention!

Students might name the greatest common _prime_ factor instead of the GCF.

PowerPoint

🖳 Additional Examples

① List the factors to find the GCF of 48 and 64. **16**
   48: ①, ②, 3, ④, 6, ⑧, 12, ⑯, 24, 48
   64: ①, ②, ④, ⑧, ⑯, 32, 64

② Use a division ladder to find the GCF of 84 and 90. **6**

   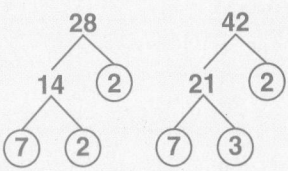

③ Use factor trees to find the GCF of 28 and 42. **14**

Closure

Describe three ways to find the GCF. **1. List all the factors of each number. Find the greatest factor common to all the numbers. 2. Use a division ladder and multiply the common factors. 3. Use factor trees to find the prime factorization of each number. Multiply the prime factors common to all the numbers.**

129

3. Practice

Assignment Guide

1 **Objective 1**
Ⓐ Ⓑ Core 1–33
Ⓒ Extension 34

Test Prep 35–38
Mixed Review 39–43

Inclusion
Exercises 7–12 Make sure students always divide by a prime number.

7. $\begin{array}{r} 2\overline{\smash{)}10\quad 18} \\ 5\quad 9 \end{array}$

GCF = 2

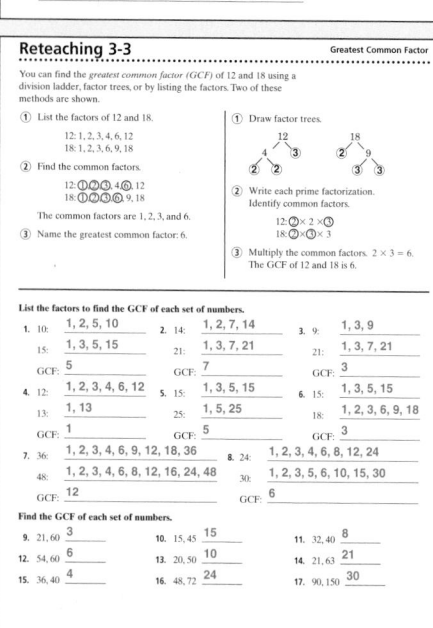
130

Example 2
(page 129)

Use a division ladder to find the GCF of each set of numbers.
7–11. See margin for division ladders. 12. See back of book.

7. 10, 18   2   8. 24, 60   12   9. 11, 23   1

10. 27, 30   3   11. 12, 16, 28   4   12. 33, 55, 132   11

Example 3
(page 129)

Use factor trees to find the GCF of each set of numbers.
Exercise 13 has been started for you.
13–19. See back of book for factor trees.

13. 22, 110 $22 = 2 \times 11;$ $110 = 2 \times 5 \times 11;$ GCF = ▉ 22

14. 20, 60   20   15. 54, 84   6   16. 72, 120   24

17. 64, 125   1   18. 117, 130   13   19. 45, 150   15

Ⓑ Apply Your Skills   **Find the GCF of each set of numbers.**

20. 300, 450   150   21. 280, 420   140   22. 200, 300, 400   100

23. 50, 250, 425   25   24. 31, 32, 33   1   25. 16, 60, 90   2

26. **Summer Camp** At a camp, 14 counselors and 77 campers will be split into groups for activities. Each group will have the same number of counselors and the same number of campers. At most, how many groups can there be? How many counselors will be in each group? How many campers? **7 groups; 2 counselors; 11 campers**

27. **Baseball Cards** Three friends pool their money to buy baseball cards. GPS Brand A has 8 cards in each pack, Brand B has 12 cards, and Brand C has 15 cards. If they want to split the cards equally, which two brands should they buy? Explain. **Brand B with 12 cards and Brand C with 15 cards because 12 and 15 are divisible by 3.**

28. **Writing in Math** Suppose several people are going to share equally 24 stamps from one set and 36 stamps from another set. Explain why 9 people cannot share the stamps equally. **Nine is not a common factor of 24 and 36.**

Real-World 🌐 Connection
Over six million children attend camp in the United States each summer.
SOURCE: National Camp Association

Mental Math   **Find the GCF of each set of numbers.**

29. 8, 12, 20   4   30. 3, 5, 7   1   31. 30, 50, 70   10

32. **Error Analysis** Find and correct the error(s) in the following statement.
Since $36 = 6^2$ and $18 = 3 \cdot 6$, the GCF of 36 and 18 is 6.
The GCF of 36 and 18 is 18.

33. **Reasoning** Which number less than 50 has the most factors? List the factors of that number. **48; 1, 2, 3, 4, 6, 8, 12, 16, 24, 48**

Ⓒ Challenge

34. **Stretch Your Thinking** Below are three different two-digit numbers. Each is less than 50 and ends in 6. Find the GCF of the numbers.
2
▉6; ▉6; ▉6

8. $\begin{array}{r} 2\overline{\smash{)}24\quad 60} \\ 2\overline{\smash{)}12\quad 30} \\ 3\overline{\smash{)}6\quad 15} \\ 2\quad 5 \end{array}$
GCF = 12

9. GCF = 1

10. $\begin{array}{r} 3\overline{\smash{)}27\quad 30} \\ 9\quad 10 \end{array}$
GCF = 3

11. $\begin{array}{r} 2\overline{\smash{)}12\quad 16\quad 28} \\ 2\overline{\smash{)}6\quad 8\quad 14} \\ 3\quad 4\quad 7 \end{array}$
GCF = 4

GPS Use the Guided Problem Solving worksheet with Exercise 27.

Test Prep

Multiple Choice

35. What is the greatest common factor of 56 and 84?   **D**
  A. 4   **B.** 12   **C.** 14   **D.** 28

Take It to the NET
Online lesson quiz at
www.PHSchool.com
Web Code: aaa-0303

36. What are the common factors of 36 and 54?   **H**
  F. 1, 2, 3, 6, 9   **G.** 1, 2, 3, 4, 6, 9
  H. 1, 2, 3, 6, 9, 18   **I.** 1, 2, 4, 6, 9, 18

37. What is the greatest common factor of 60 and 132?   **B**
  A. 2×3 **B.** $2^2 \times 3$ **C.** 2×3^2 **D.** $2^2 \times 3^2$

Short Response

38. For a field day, 84 girls and 78 boys will be split into teams. Each team will have the same number of girls and the same number of boys.
  a. At most, how many teams are possible?
  b. How many girls and how many boys will be on each team?
  38a–b. See margin.

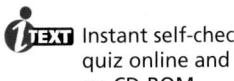
Mixed Review

Lesson 1-10

39. You buy 3 packs of notebook paper at $1.25 each and a binder for $1.50.
  a. Write an expression for the total cost of the items you want.
  b. Find the total cost. $3 \times \$1.25 + \$1.50$
      $5.25

Lesson 1-2

Write each decimal in words.

40. 0.6   **41.** 0.9   **42.** 0.10   **43.** 0.80
  six tenths   nine tenths   ten hundredths   eighty
                                                     hundredths

Checkpoint Quiz 1   Lessons 3-1 through 3-3

Instant self-check quiz online and on CD-ROM

Test each number for divisibility by 2, 3, 5, 9, or 10.

1. 375 3, 5   **2.** 1,402 2   **3.** 240 2, 3, 5, 10

Find the prime factorization of each number.

4. 48   **5.** 80   **6.** 1,000
  $2^4 \times 3$ $2^4 \times 5$ $2^3 \times 5^3$

Find the GCF of each set of numbers.

7. 45, 80 5   **8.** 24, 72 24   **9.** 9, 18, 51 3

10. Find all the common factors of 18 and 48.
  1, 2, 3, 6

3-3 Greatest Common Factor   **131**

---

38. [2] a. $84 = 2^2 \times 3 \times 7$
    $78 = 2 \times 3 \times 13$
    The GCF of 84 and 78 is 6. Six teams are possible.

  b. **14 girls and 13 boys on each team.**

[1] Prime factorization is correct, but GCF is incorrect, OR number of girls and/or boys per team is incorrect.

Alternative Assessment

Provide pairs of students with pairs of composite numbers such as those in Exercises 1–19. Each partner draws a factor tree to find the prime factorization for one of the composite numbers. Partners then work together to find the GCF of each set of numbers.

---

4. Assess

PowerPoint Lesson Quiz 3-3
Find the GCF of each set of numbers.

1. 60, 80 20

2. 24, 57 3

3. 36, 48 12

4. 115, 70, 200 5

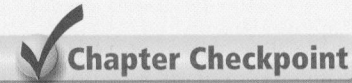
Chapter Checkpoint

To check understanding of Lessons 3-1 to 3-3:

Checkpoint Quiz 1 (p. 131)

  Teaching Resources
Checkpoint Quiz 1 (also in *Prentice Hall Assessment System*)

  Reaching All Students
Reading and Math Literacy 3B

Spanish versions available

Test Prep

Resources
For additional practice with a variety of test item formats:
• Test-Prep, p. 165
• Test-Taking Strategies, p. 161
• Test-Taking Strategies With Transparencies

Enrichment 3-3   Greatest Common Factor
Critical Thinking

Use each set of clues to find the number being described.

1. *Clues:* a. The greatest common factor (GCF) of two numbers is 6.
   b. The sum of the two numbers is 30.
   c. The difference between the two numbers is 6.
   12 and 18

2. *Clues:* a. The greatest common factor of two numbers is 8.
   b. If you divide the sum of the two numbers by the GCF, the answer is 10.
   c. The difference between the two numbers is 32.
   24 and 56

3. *Clues:* a. The greatest common factor of three numbers is 8.
   b. The sum of the numbers is 48.
   8, 16, and 24

4. *Clues:* a. The greatest common factor of two numbers is 3.
   b. The sum of the numbers is divisible by the GCF.
   c. The difference between the numbers is 15.
   21 and 36

The following puzzles have more than one answer. Find as many solutions as you can.

5. *Clues:* a. The greatest common factor of two numbers is 9.
   b. The sum of the numbers is 63.
   9 and 54, 18 and 45, 27 and 36

6. *Clues:* a. The greatest common factor of three different numbers is 5.
   b. The sum of the numbers is 45.
   5, 15, and 25; 5, 10, and 30

7. Write your own puzzle like the ones on the page. Check to see how many solutions your puzzle has.
   Check students' answers.

131

Modeling Fractions

In this investigation for use with Lesson 3-4, students model fractions in a variety of ways: as part of a set or whole, on a number line, and with a ruler.

Optional Materials

• inch ruler
• graph paper
• Classroom Aid 2, 12–14

Teaching Notes

English Learners
Use plain language to review the parts of a fraction. The *numerator* is the "top" number and shows the number of parts. The *denominator* is the "bottom" number and shows the total number of parts. Each model gives both numbers.

① EXAMPLE Teaching Tip

After you have worked through the Example, ask the following questions to check student understanding:
• *What fraction of flowers is not red?* $\frac{7}{16}$
• *What fraction of the pie is gone?* $\frac{3}{8}$

Error Prevention!

Exercise 1 Students might write a fraction relating the shaded parts to the unshaded parts, such as $\frac{4}{2}$ or $\frac{2}{4}$. Suggest that they write the words *shaded* and *total* next to the numerator and denominator as shown below.

$$\text{shaded} \rightarrow 4$$
$$\text{total} \rightarrow 6$$

Exercises 5–7 Have students work in pairs or small groups. This helps students who might have difficulty drawing the fraction models.

132

Investigation — Modeling Fractions

A fraction describes a part of a set of items, or a part of a whole item. The whole item must be split into equal parts.

$\frac{3}{4}$ ← The numerator shows how many parts are being considered.
← The denominator shows the total number of parts.

① EXAMPLE   Writing Fractions

Write a fraction for each situation.

a. What fraction of the flowers are red?

There are 9 red flowers and 16 flowers altogether. So, $\frac{9}{16}$ of the flowers are red.

b. What fraction of the pie is left?

The pie had 8 equal pieces. Five are left. So $\frac{5}{8}$ of the pie is left.

c. On the number line, what fraction describes point *A*?

The segment from 0 to 1 is divided into 5 equal parts. So, $\frac{3}{5}$ describes point *A*.

EXERCISES

Name the fraction represented by each model.

1.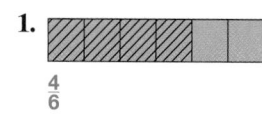
$\frac{4}{6}$

2.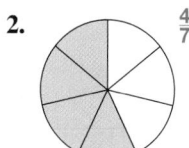
$\frac{4}{7}$

3.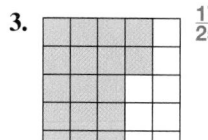
$\frac{17}{25}$

4.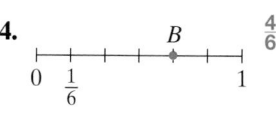
$\frac{4}{6}$

Draw a fraction model for each situation. **5–7. See margin.**

5. $\frac{3}{4}$ as part of a set

6. $\frac{4}{7}$ as part of a whole

7. $\frac{5}{8}$ on a number line

8. At the grocery store, you purchase 5 apples and 7 oranges. What fraction of the fruit is apples? $\frac{5}{12}$

9. Number Sense What fraction is represented when all parts of a fraction model are shaded? When no parts are shaded? $\frac{n}{n}$ (where *n* is the total number of parts); $\frac{0}{n}$

Investigation

5.

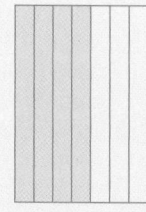

6.

7.

The marks on an inch ruler are based on fractions.

2 EXAMPLE Fractions on a Ruler  Real World

Biology Find the length shown for each insect.

a.

inches

The ruler is marked every $\frac{1}{8}$ inch.
The insect extends over seven
$\frac{1}{8}$-inch spaces.

So, the length of the insect is $\frac{7}{8}$ inch.

b.

inches

The ruler is marked every
$\frac{1}{16}$ inch. The insect extends over
ten $\frac{1}{16}$-inch spaces.

So, the length of the insect is $\frac{10}{16}$, or $\frac{5}{8}$ inch.

EXERCISES

Find the length of each segment.

10. 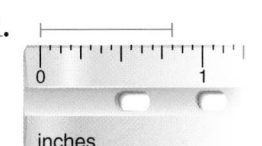 $\frac{6}{8}$ in. or $\frac{3}{4}$ in. **11.** 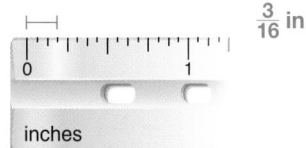 $\frac{13}{16}$ in. **12.** $\frac{3}{16}$ in.

inches

inches

inches

Use a ruler to measure the length of each segment or object. Measure to the nearest sixteenth of an inch.

13. ——— $\frac{8}{16}$ in. or $\frac{1}{2}$ in. **14.** ——— $\frac{12}{16}$ or $\frac{3}{4}$ in. **15.** ——— $\frac{15}{16}$ in. **16.** ——— $\frac{7}{16}$ in.

17.  $\frac{7}{16}$ in. **18.**  $\frac{14}{16}$ in. or $\frac{7}{8}$ in. **19.**  $\frac{10}{16}$ in. or $\frac{5}{8}$ in. **20.** $\frac{11}{16}$ in.

2 EXAMPLE Auditory Learners

Some students might find it easier to measure by counting the marks on the ruler aloud. In part a, for instance, they might softly say to themselves, "one eighth, two eighths, three eighths, four eighths, five eighths, six eighths, seven eighths."

Inclusion
Ask: *How can you determine what the smallest mark is on an inch ruler?* Sample: Count the number of small segments between 0 and 1.

Teaching Tip
Ask: *Why is the "zero mark" not placed at the edge of the ruler?* Guide students to observe that the edges of rulers can be easily "rounded." Such damage would make the ruler difficult to use.

Exercises
Exercises 13–20 Have students work in pairs or small groups. Students take turns making the measurements and must agree on each answer.

Inclusion
As a summary, review the four distinct models that students used to name fractions in the Investigation. (1) a part of a set of objects such as flowers, (2) a part of a region such as a rectangle or pie, (3) a point on a line, and (4) a length on a ruler.

3-4

Equivalent Fractions

1. Plan

Lesson Preview

✓ **Check Skills You'll Need**

Finding the GCF
Lesson 3-3: Examples 1–3. Extra Practice p. 644.

Lesson Resources

📁 **Teaching Resources**
Practice, Reteaching, Enrichment

👥 **Reaching All Students**
Practice Workbook 3-4
Spanish Practice Workbook 3-4
Guided Problem Solving 3-4
Hands-On Activities 11

⏰ **Presentation Assistant Plus!**
Transparencies
• Check Skills You'll Need 3-4
• Problem of the Day 3-4
• Additional Examples 3-4
• Student Edition Answers 3-4
• Lesson Quiz 3-4
• Classroom Aid 11, 12, 13, 14, 15, 16, 17, 18, 19
PH Presentation Pro CD-ROM 3-4

Computer Test Generator CD

💻 **Technology**
Resource Pro® CD-ROM
Computer Test Generator CD
PH Presentation Pro CD-ROM

💻 **www.PHSchool.com**
Student Site
• Teacher Web Code: aak-5500
• Algebra Readiness Puzzles 51
• Self-grading Lesson Quiz

PH SuccessNet Teacher Center
• Lesson Planner
• Resources

Plus

What You'll Learn

OBJECTIVE 1 To find equivalent fractions

OBJECTIVE 2 To write fractions in simplest form

. . . And Why

To simplify statistics, as in Exercise 17

✓ **Check Skills You'll Need** ❓ For help, go to Lesson 3-3.

Find the GCF of each set of numbers.

1. 8, 12 **4**
2. 20, 25 **5**
3. 12, 30 **6**
4. 5, 18 **1**
5. 36, 100 **4**
6. 7, 21, 28 **7**

New Vocabulary   • equivalent fractions   • simplest form

OBJECTIVE 1

💻 Interactive lesson includes instant self-check, tutorials, and activities.

Finding Equivalent Fractions

The two fraction models at the right have the same amount shaded. **Equivalent fractions** are fractions that name the same amount.

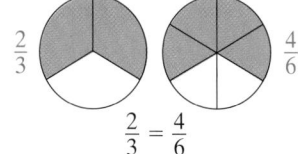

You form equivalent fractions by multiplying (or dividing) the numerator and denominator of a fraction by the same nonzero number.

① **EXAMPLE**   **Equivalent Fractions**

Write three fractions equivalent to $\frac{6}{8}$.

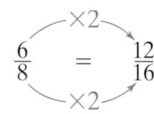
$\frac{6}{8} = \frac{12}{16}$ ← Multiply the numerator and denominator by 2.

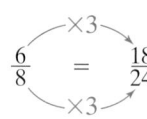
$\frac{6}{8} = \frac{18}{24}$ ← Multiply the numerator and denominator by 3.

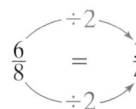
$\frac{6}{8} = \frac{3}{4}$ ← Divide the numerator and denominator by 2.

So, $\frac{3}{4} = \frac{6}{8} = \frac{12}{16} = \frac{18}{24}$.

✓ **Check Understanding** ① Write three fractions equivalent to each fraction.

1a–c. **Answers may vary. Samples are given.**

a. $\frac{4}{10}$ $\frac{2}{5}, \frac{8}{20}, \frac{12}{30}$

b. $\frac{5}{8}$ $\frac{10}{16}, \frac{15}{24}, \frac{25}{40}$

c. $\frac{2}{6}$ $\frac{1}{3}, \frac{4}{12}, \frac{6}{18}$

134   Chapter 3   Number Theory and Fractions

Ongoing Assessment and Intervention

Before the Lesson
Diagnose prerequisite skills using:
• Check Skills You'll Need

During the Lesson
Monitor progress using:
• Check Understanding
• Additional Examples
• Test Prep

After the Lesson
Assess knowledge using:
• Lesson Quiz
• Computer Test Generator CD

Writing Fractions in Simplest Form

A fraction is in **simplest form** when the only common factor of the numerator and denominator is 1. For example, $\frac{2}{3}$ is in simplest form, since 2 and 3 have only 1 as a common factor.

One way to write a fraction in simplest form is to divide both the numerator and denominator by their greatest common factor.

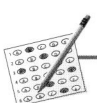

Test-Prep Tip

Some standardized tests may ask you to write a fraction in lowest terms, which is the same as simplest form.

2 EXAMPLE **Fractions in Simplest Form**

Write $\frac{20}{28}$ in simplest form.

20: 1, 2, ④, 5, 10, 20 ← List the factors for the numerator and denominator.
28: 1, 2, ④, 7, 14, 28 ← Find the greatest common factor.

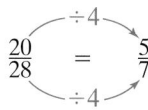

$\frac{20}{28} = \frac{5}{7}$ ← Divide the numerator and denominator by the GCF.

The fraction $\frac{20}{28}$ written in simplest form is $\frac{5}{7}$.

✓ **Check Understanding** ② Write each fraction in simplest form.

a. $\frac{24}{32}$ $\frac{3}{4}$ **b.** $\frac{14}{49}$ $\frac{2}{7}$ **c.** $\frac{20}{100}$ $\frac{1}{5}$

3 EXAMPLE **Real-World 🌐 Problem Solving**

Pet Foods A pet store stocks 36 different types of cat food, 42 types of dog food, 18 types of bird food, and 24 other pet foods. In simplest form, what fraction of the types of foods are cat foods?

Add to find the total number of foods: 36 + 42 + 18 + 24 = 120.

Write the fraction.

$\frac{36}{120}$ ← number of types of cat foods
       ← total number of types of foods

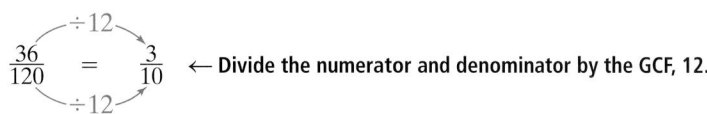

$\frac{36}{120} = \frac{3}{10}$ ← Divide the numerator and denominator by the GCF, 12.

So, $\frac{3}{10}$ of the types of foods are cat foods.

✓ **Check Understanding** ③ **a.** In simplest form, what fraction of the types of foods are dog foods? $\frac{7}{20}$

b. **Reasoning** Which two types of foods together make up $\frac{1}{2}$ of the foods? Explain your reasoning.
dog food and bird food; 42 + 18 = 60, and $\frac{60}{120} = \frac{1}{2}$

3-4 Equivalent Fractions   **135**

🧑‍🤝‍🧑 Reaching All Students

| **Below Level** Have students identify groups of equivalent fractions among the fractions represented by a set of fraction bars. For example:
$\frac{1}{2} = \frac{2}{4} = \frac{3}{6} = \frac{4}{8} = \frac{5}{10} = \frac{6}{12}$; $\frac{2}{3} = \frac{4}{6} = \frac{8}{12}$ | **Advanced Learners** Find all the fractions equivalent to $\frac{8,085}{14,553}$ in which both numerator and denominator are whole numbers less than 50. $\frac{5}{9}, \frac{10}{18}, \frac{15}{27}, \frac{20}{36}, \frac{25}{45}$ | **English Learners**
See note on page 135.
Alternative Method
See note on page 135. |

---

2. Teach

Professional Development

Math Background

Fractions that name the same amount are called *equivalent fractions*. You can find an equivalent fraction by either multiplying or dividing both numerator and denominator by the same number.

Teaching Notes

① EXAMPLE **English Learners**

Relate the word *equivalent* to the word *equal*. *Equivalent fractions* are fractions that name *equal* amounts.

② EXAMPLE **Error Prevention**

Some students might multiply or divide the numerator and denominator of a fraction by different numbers. Encourage them to write the number by which they are multiplying or dividing.

③ EXAMPLE **Alternative Method**

Some students find that successive divisions by common factors is easier than using the GCF. For instance, $\frac{36 \div 6}{120 \div 6} = \frac{6}{20}$ and $\frac{6 \div 2}{20 \div 2} = \frac{3}{10}$. Make sure students recognize that the simplification process is complete when the only common factor of the numerator and denominator is 1.

PowerPoint
📖 Additional Examples

① Write three fractions equivalent to $\frac{6}{9}$. Samples: $\frac{12}{18}$, $\frac{18}{27}$, $\frac{2}{3}$

② Write $\frac{16}{40}$ in simplest form. $\frac{2}{5}$

③ A store stocks 12 types of blue pens, 6 types of black pens, and 2 types of red pens. In simplest form, what fraction of the pens are blue? $\frac{3}{5}$

Closure

• *What are equivalent fractions?* fractions that name the same amount

• *When is a fraction in simplest form?* when the only common factor of the numerator and denominator is 1

135

3. Practice

Assignment Guide

1 Objective 1
Ⓐ Ⓑ Core 1–8, 31–32, 34–38

2 Objective 2
Ⓐ Ⓑ Core 9–30, 33
Ⓒ Extension 39–40

Test Prep 41–45
Mixed Review 46–53

EXERCISES

Ⓐ **Practice by Example**

1–8. Answers may vary. Samples are given.

Write two fractions equivalent to each fraction.

Example 1
(page 134)

1. $\frac{2}{4}$ $\frac{1}{2}, \frac{4}{8}$
2. $\frac{6}{7}$ $\frac{12}{14}, \frac{24}{28}$
3. $\frac{12}{18}$ $\frac{2}{3}, \frac{4}{6}$
4. $\frac{3}{16}$ $\frac{6}{32}, \frac{9}{48}$

5. $\frac{3}{10}$ $\frac{6}{20}, \frac{9}{30}$
6. $\frac{3}{9}$ $\frac{1}{3}, \frac{6}{18}$
7. $\frac{1}{20}$ $\frac{2}{40}, \frac{3}{60}$
8. $\frac{15}{20}$ $\frac{3}{4}, \frac{30}{40}$

Example 2
(page 135)

Write each fraction in simplest form.

9. $\frac{4}{6}$ $\frac{2}{3}$
10. $\frac{10}{35}$ $\frac{2}{7}$
11. $\frac{10}{20}$ $\frac{1}{2}$
12. $\frac{40}{50}$ $\frac{4}{5}$

13. $\frac{15}{45}$ $\frac{1}{3}$
14. $\frac{6}{8}$ $\frac{3}{4}$
15. $\frac{12}{18}$ $\frac{2}{3}$
16. $\frac{9}{21}$ $\frac{3}{7}$

Example 3
(page 135)

17. **Sports** Over the last three seasons, a school football team has won 15 out of 25 games. In simplest form, what fraction of their games have they won? $\frac{3}{5}$

18. **Greeting Cards** A store stocks 50 birthday cards, 10 anniversary cards, and 45 get-well cards. In simplest form, what fraction of the cards are get-well cards? $\frac{3}{7}$

Ⓑ **Apply Your Skills**

State whether each fraction is in simplest form. If it is not, write it in simplest form.

19. $\frac{3}{6}$ no; $\frac{1}{2}$
20. $\frac{1}{7}$ yes
21. $\frac{15}{18}$ no; $\frac{5}{6}$
22. $\frac{4}{5}$ yes

23. $\frac{24}{56}$ no; $\frac{3}{7}$
24. $\frac{21}{77}$ no; $\frac{3}{11}$
25. $\frac{25}{150}$ no; $\frac{1}{6}$
26. $\frac{3}{50}$ yes

27. $\frac{15}{135}$ no; $\frac{1}{9}$
28. $\frac{17}{51}$ no; $\frac{1}{3}$
29. $\frac{10}{65}$ no; $\frac{2}{13}$
30. $\frac{120}{150}$ no; $\frac{4}{5}$

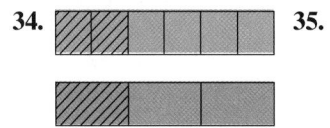

31. **Traffic Planning** Two traffic engineers are writing about the average driving time between two towns. One engineer writes the time as 45, but the other writes it as $\frac{3}{4}$. What could explain the difference? See margin.

32. **Data File, p. 117** Indicate which size wrenches are equivalent to $\frac{6}{16}$ inch, $\frac{12}{16}$ inch, and $\frac{30}{32}$ inch. $\frac{3}{8}, \frac{3}{4},$ and $\frac{15}{16}$

33. **Writing in Math** How can you use the GCF of the numerator and the denominator to write a fraction in simplest form? **Divide the numerator and the denominator by their GCF.**

Real-World 🌐 Connection

Careers Traffic engineers study things that influence traffic conditions, such as traffic volume and signals.

Name the fractions modeled and determine if they are equivalent.

34.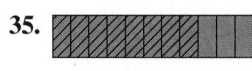
$\frac{2}{6}, \frac{1}{3};$ yes

35.
$\frac{8}{12}, \frac{3}{5};$ no

36.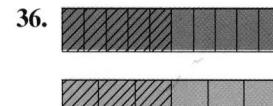
$\frac{5}{10}, \frac{3}{6};$ yes

GPS Use the Guided Problem Solving worksheet with Exercise 31.

31. The first engineer is recording time in minutes. The second engineer is recording fractions of an hour.

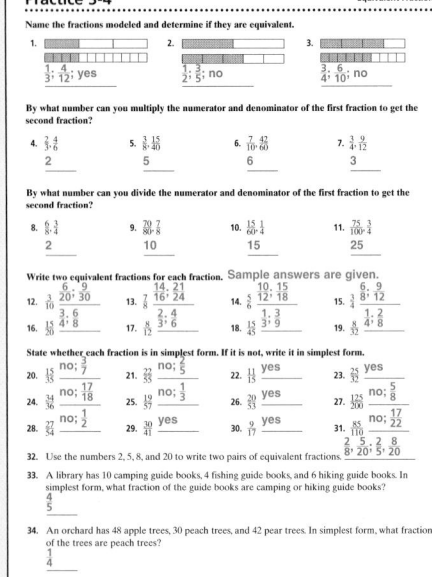

Practice 3-4 — Equivalent Fractions

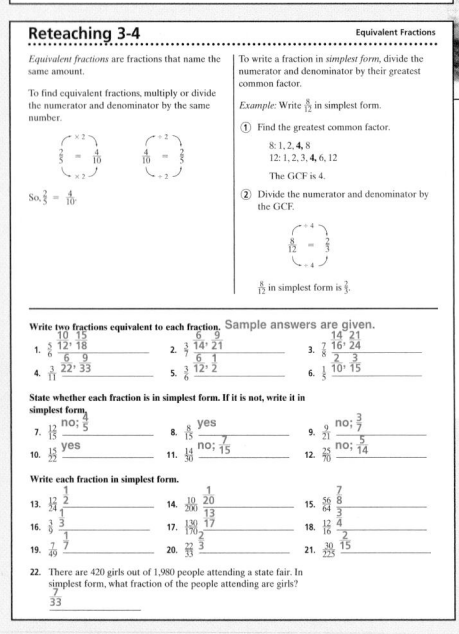

Reteaching 3-4 — Equivalent Fractions

136

37. Games On a chessboard, 32 of the squares are white. At the start of a game, each player places half of her 16 pieces on white squares. What fraction of the white squares have pieces on them? $\frac{1}{2}$

38. Open-Ended Choose from the numbers 2, 3, 4, 6, 12, 18, and 24. Write three pairs of equivalent fractions. **Answers may vary.** Sample: $\frac{2}{3}, \frac{4}{6}, \frac{12}{18}$

C Challenge

39b. $\frac{2}{3}$; when you divide the numerator and the denominator by the common factor *a*, the result is in simplest terms.

39. a. (Algebra) Evaluate $\frac{2a}{3a}$ for $a = 1, 2, 5,$ and 10. Write each result as a fraction. $\frac{2}{3}, \frac{4}{6}, \frac{10}{15}, \frac{20}{30}$

   b. When *a* is a nonzero whole number, what do you think is the simplest form for $\frac{2a}{3a}$? Explain. **See left.**

40. Stretch Your Thinking A fraction greater than $\frac{1}{8}$ and less than $\frac{1}{4}$ is in simplest form. Its denominator is four more than its numerator. What is the fraction? $\frac{1}{5}$

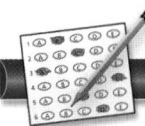

Test Prep

Gridded Response

41. How do you write $\frac{80}{100}$ as a fraction in simplest form? $\frac{4}{5}$

42. The length of a segment is $\frac{3}{8}$ inch. How do you write the length as a fraction with 16 as its denominator? $\frac{6}{16}$

43. In simplest form, what fraction of an hour is 40 minutes? $\frac{2}{3}$

44. Samantha made 45 out of 75 free throw attempts. In simplest form, what fraction of her attempts did she make? $\frac{3}{5}$

Take It to the NET
Online lesson quiz at
www.PHSchool.com
Web Code: aaa-0304

45. A newsstand stocks 21 different newspapers and 35 different magazines. In simplest form, what fraction represents the portion that is newspapers? $\frac{3}{8}$

Mixed Review

Lesson 3-3 **Find the GCF of each set of numbers.**

46. 48, 56 **8**   **47.** 15, 21 **3**   **48.** 42, 72 **6**   **49.** 300, 450 **150**

Lesson 2-7 (Algebra) **Solve each equation. Check your solution.**

50. $4x = 36$ **9**   **51.** $6x = 5.4$ **0.9**   **52.** $20x = 1$ **0.05**   **53.** $0.5x = 10$ **20**

137

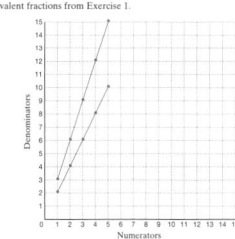

Simplifying Fractions

Students use a fraction calculator to simplify fractions. They extend their knowledge, learned in Lesson 3-5, of finding equivalent fractions and expressing fractions in simplest form.

Optional Materials

• fraction calculator
• Classroom Aid 11

Teaching Notes

EXAMPLE

Guide students to work through the steps, as presented, for simplifying $\frac{9}{27}$.

Error Prevention!

Students may have difficulty following the steps used to simplify a fraction with a fraction calculator. One way to remediate this is to draw a flow chart on the board that describes the steps. Students can follow the flow chart to complete the exercises.

Teaching Tip

For extra practice, have students work through the steps to simplify another fraction that requires more than one step, such as $\frac{12}{30}$. Ask a volunteer to share the series of keystrokes he or she used to display that fraction in simplest form.

Inclusion

You may wish to have students work in pairs to complete the exercises.

You can use a fraction calculator to simplify a fraction. The calculator divides the numerator and denominator by a common factor and rewrites the fraction. Repeat the process until the fraction is in simplest form.

EXAMPLE

Use a fraction calculator to simplify $\frac{9}{27}$.

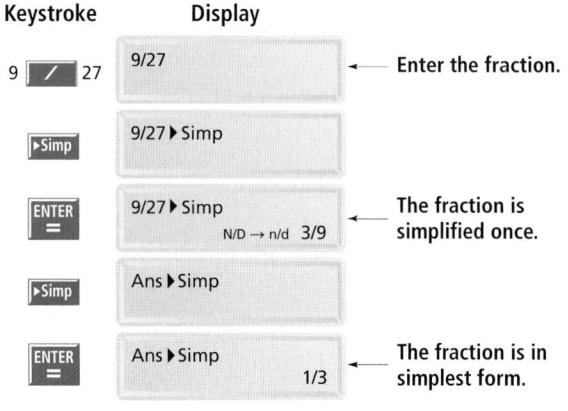

In simplest form, $\frac{9}{27} = \frac{1}{3}$.

EXERCISES

Use a fraction calculator to simplify each fraction.

1. $\frac{18}{51}$ $\frac{6}{17}$
2. $\frac{21}{49}$ $\frac{3}{7}$
3. $\frac{102}{387}$ $\frac{34}{129}$
4. $\frac{35}{56}$ $\frac{5}{8}$

5. $\frac{20}{65}$ $\frac{4}{13}$
6. $\frac{17}{68}$ $\frac{1}{4}$
7. $\frac{12}{15}$ $\frac{4}{5}$
8. $\frac{28}{32}$ $\frac{7}{8}$

9. $\frac{12}{30}$ $\frac{2}{5}$
10. $\frac{45}{75}$ $\frac{3}{5}$
11. $\frac{24}{32}$ $\frac{3}{4}$
12. $\frac{12}{96}$ $\frac{1}{8}$

13. $\frac{35}{45}$ $\frac{7}{9}$
14. $\frac{14}{63}$ $\frac{2}{9}$
15. $\frac{40}{48}$ $\frac{5}{6}$
16. $\frac{105}{180}$ $\frac{7}{12}$

17. $\frac{92}{132}$ $\frac{23}{33}$
18. $\frac{39}{117}$ $\frac{1}{3}$
19. $\frac{126}{324}$ $\frac{7}{18}$
20. $\frac{200}{385}$ $\frac{40}{77}$

21. **Writing in Math** How do you know from the calculator procedures shown in the example that the calculator does not use the greatest common factor (GCF) when simplifying?

The calculator first simplifies $\frac{9}{27}$ as $\frac{3}{9}$ and then as $\frac{1}{3}$. If the GCF had been used, the calculator would not have had the $\frac{3}{9}$ step.

3-5 Mixed Numbers and Improper Fractions

What You'll Learn

 OBJECTIVE 1
To write numbers as improper fractions

 OBJECTIVE 2
To write fractions as mixed numbers

. . . And Why

To convert measurements, as in Example 2

For help, go to Lesson 3-4.

✓ **Check Skills You'll Need**

Write each fraction in simplest form.

1. $\frac{9}{27}$ $\frac{1}{3}$

2. $\frac{18}{27}$ $\frac{2}{3}$

3. $\frac{20}{64}$ $\frac{5}{16}$

4. $\frac{3}{51}$ $\frac{1}{17}$

5. $\frac{36}{40}$ $\frac{9}{10}$

6. Explain how to write 35 minutes as a fraction of an hour.

See margin.

New Vocabulary • proper fraction • improper fraction • mixed number

 Interactive lesson includes instant self-check, tutorials, and activities.

OBJECTIVE 1
Writing Mixed Numbers as Improper Fractions

> **Investigation:** Comparing Numerators and Denominators
>
> 1. Which fractions below are less than 1? Equal to 1? Greater than 1?
>
> 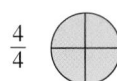 $\frac{4}{4}$ equal
> $\frac{5}{2}$ greater
> 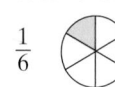 $\frac{1}{6}$ less
>
> 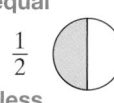 $\frac{1}{2}$ less
>  $\frac{11}{8}$ greater
> $\frac{3}{3}$ equal
>
> 2. Explain how comparing the numerator to the denominator shows whether a fraction is less than, equal to, or greater than 1.
>
> **2–3. See back of book.**
>
> 3. Use a ruler to draw a line segment for each length.
>
>   a. $1\frac{3}{8}$ inches   b. $2\frac{3}{4}$ inches   c. $3\frac{5}{8}$ inches
>
>   d. How many eighths are there in each measurement? Explain.

Examples

A **proper fraction** has a numerator that is less than its denominator.

$\frac{1}{2}$ $\frac{3}{8}$ $\frac{4}{5}$

An **improper fraction** has a numerator that is greater than or equal to its denominator.

$\frac{5}{2}$ $\frac{11}{8}$ $\frac{5}{5}$

A **mixed number** shows the sum of a whole number and a proper fraction: $2\frac{1}{2} = 2 + \frac{1}{2}$.

$2\frac{1}{2}$ $1\frac{3}{8}$ $1\frac{1}{5}$

Ongoing Assessment and Intervention

Before the Lesson
Diagnose prerequisite skills using:
• Check Skills You'll Need

During the Lesson
Monitor progress using:
• Check Understanding
• Additional Examples
• Test Prep

After the Lesson
Assess knowledge using:
• Lesson Quiz
• Computer Test Generator CD

Lesson Preview

 PowerPoint

✓ **Check Skills You'll Need**

Writing Fractions in Simplest Form
Lesson 3-4: Example 2. Extra Practice p. 644.

Lesson Resources

Optional Materials
• inch ruler

 **Teaching Resources**
Practice, Reteaching, Enrichment

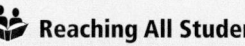 **Reaching All Students**
Practice Workbook 3-5
Spanish Practice Workbook 3-5
Guided Problem Solving 3-5

Presentation Assistant Plus!
Transparencies
• Check Skills You'll Need 3-5
• Problem of the Day 3-5
• Additional Examples 3-5
• Student Edition Answers 3-5
• Lesson Quiz 3-5
• Classroom Aid 12, 13, 14, 15, 16, 17, 18, 19
PH Presentation Pro CD-ROM 3-5

PRENTICE HALL ASSESSMENT SYSTEM
Computer Test Generator CD

 Technology
Resource Pro® CD-ROM
Computer Test Generator CD
PH Presentation Pro CD-ROM

www.PHSchool.com
Student Site
• Teacher Web Code: aak-5500
• Self-grading Lesson Quiz

PH SuccessNet Teacher Center
• Lesson Planner
• Resources

Plus

6. There are 60 minutes in an hour, so compare 35 to 60 by using the fraction $\frac{35}{60}$. In simplest form, $\frac{35}{60}$ is $\frac{7}{12}$.

139

Math Background

A *mixed number* is a "mixture" of two types of numbers: a whole number and a fraction. It represents one or more identical whole quantities, plus some fractional part of the whole. It is possible to rewrite any mixed number as a single fraction, which is called an *improper fraction*.

Teaching Notes

Investigation (Optional)
Make sure students understand that each circle represents 1. So if the model for a fraction involves more than one complete circle, the fraction must be greater than 1.

1 EXAMPLE Error Prevention

Students might multiply the numerator by the whole number, then add the denominator.

2 EXAMPLE Tactile Learners

Students can act out this problem using water in quart and gallon measuring jars or pitchers.

PowerPoint

Additional Examples

1. Write $4\frac{3}{5}$ as an improper fraction. $\frac{23}{5}$

2. A chef needs $2\frac{3}{4}$ quarts of water to make soup. How many cups will the chef need? (*Hint:* 1 cup $= \frac{1}{4}$ quart) **11 cups**

3. Write $\frac{42}{9}$ as a mixed number in simplest form. $4\frac{2}{3}$

Closure

- *How do you write a mixed number as an improper fraction?* **Sample: Multiply the denominator by the whole number. Then add this product to the numerator.**

- *How do you write an improper fraction as a whole or mixed number?* **Divide the numerator by the denominator. The remainder over the denominator is the fractional part of the mixed number, if not equal to zero.**

140

$6\frac{2}{3} = \frac{20}{3}$

1 EXAMPLE   Writing Mixed Numbers as Improper Fractions

Write $6\frac{2}{3}$ as an improper fraction.

Multiply the whole number by the denominator. (6 × 3 thirds is 18 thirds.) $\rightarrow$ $6\frac{2}{3} = \frac{(6 \times 3) + 2}{3}$ ← Add the numerator. (There are 2 more thirds.)

$= \frac{20}{3}$ ← Write as an improper fraction.

✓ **Check Understanding** ① Write $3\frac{4}{7}$ as an improper fraction. $\frac{25}{7}$

2 EXAMPLE   Real-World Problem Solving

Engines A mechanic needs $3\frac{1}{4}$ gallons of oil to fill a diesel engine. How many quarts will the mechanic need? (*Hint:* 1 quart $= \frac{1}{4}$ gallon)

Change $3\frac{1}{4}$ to an improper fraction.

$3\frac{1}{4} = \frac{3 \times 4 + 1}{4} = \frac{13}{4}$

Since there are 13 fourths in $3\frac{1}{4}$, the mechanic will need 13 quarts of oil.

✓ **Check Understanding** ② **Reasoning** What does the denominator in the improper fraction $\frac{7}{1}$ represent? **whole units**

OBJECTIVE

2 Writing Improper Fractions as Mixed Numbers

Use division to write an improper fraction as a mixed number.

3 EXAMPLE   Writing Improper Fractions as Mixed Numbers

Each orange slice is $\frac{1}{6}$ of an orange. How many oranges are represented by 9 slices?

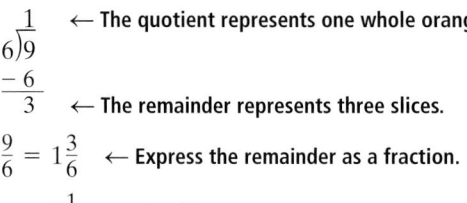

Write $\frac{9}{6}$ as a mixed number. Begin by dividing 9 by 6.

$$6\overline{)9}$$

← The quotient represents one whole orange.

-6

3 ← The remainder represents three slices.

$\frac{9}{6} = 1\frac{3}{6}$ ← Express the remainder as a fraction.

$= 1\frac{1}{2}$ ← Simplify.

Nine slices represent $1\frac{1}{2}$ oranges.

✓ **Check Understanding** ③ Write each improper fraction as a mixed number in simplest form.

a. $\frac{40}{9}$ $4\frac{4}{9}$ b. $\frac{32}{6}$ $5\frac{1}{3}$ c. $\frac{23}{4}$ $5\frac{3}{4}$ d. $\frac{30}{18}$ $1\frac{2}{3}$

Reaching All Students

Below Level Review divisions involving whole-number remainders using several exercises like these.	Advanced Learners Fill in the boxes with the numbers 4, 8, 12, 24, and 36 to make a true statement. Use each number exactly once.	Tactile Learners See note on page 140. Error Prevention See note on page 140.
$9 \div 5$ **1 R4** $11 \div 5$ **2 R1** $30 \div 4$ **7 R2** $29 \div 12$ **2 R5**	$\frac{\square}{\square} = \square\frac{\square}{\square}$ $\frac{36}{8} = 4\frac{12}{24}$	

? For more practice, see *Extra Practice.*

A Practice by Example

Write each mixed number as an improper fraction. Exercise 1 has been started for you.

Examples 1, 2
(page 140)

1. $3\frac{5}{6} = \frac{(3 \times 6) + 5}{6} = \blacksquare \quad \frac{23}{6}$

2. $1\frac{2}{9} \quad \frac{11}{9}$

3. $4\frac{3}{5} \quad \frac{23}{5}$

4. $1\frac{4}{15} \quad \frac{19}{15}$

5. $7\frac{1}{7} \quad \frac{50}{7}$

6. $21\frac{1}{3} \quad \frac{64}{3}$

7. $5\frac{1}{2} \quad \frac{11}{2}$

8. $1\frac{3}{11} \quad \frac{14}{11}$

9. $3\frac{3}{8} \quad \frac{27}{8}$

10. $2\frac{1}{16} \quad \frac{33}{16}$

11. $3\frac{1}{4} \quad \frac{13}{4}$

 12. **Engines** Your family car needs $1\frac{1}{4}$ gallons of oil. How many $\frac{1}{4}$'s are in $1\frac{1}{4}$? 5

Example 3
(page 140)

Write each improper fraction as a mixed number in simplest form.

13. $\frac{17}{5} \quad 3\frac{2}{5}$

14. $\frac{10}{4} \quad 2\frac{1}{2}$

15. $\frac{27}{12} \quad 2\frac{1}{4}$

16. $\frac{9}{4} \quad 2\frac{1}{4}$

17. $\frac{21}{14} \quad 1\frac{1}{2}$

18. $\frac{18}{11} \quad 1\frac{7}{11}$

19. $\frac{21}{10} \quad 2\frac{1}{10}$

20. $\frac{16}{12} \quad 1\frac{1}{3}$

B Apply Your Skills

Write each mixed number as an improper fraction. Write each improper fraction as a mixed number in simplest form.

21. $4\frac{5}{7} \quad \frac{33}{7}$

22. $\frac{68}{8} \quad 8\frac{1}{2}$

23. $\frac{106}{5} \quad 21\frac{1}{5}$

24. $11\frac{13}{15} \quad \frac{178}{15}$

25. $\frac{232}{12} \quad 19\frac{1}{3}$

26. $15\frac{1}{10} \quad \frac{151}{10}$

27. $1\frac{11}{12} \quad \frac{23}{12}$

28. $\frac{80}{9} \quad 8\frac{8}{9}$

Find the length of each segment. Write mixed numbers in simplest form.

29.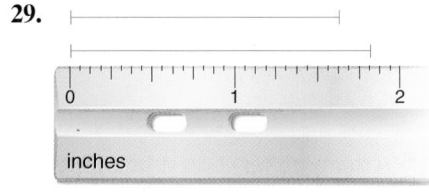

30.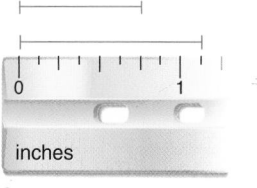

$1\frac{5}{8}$ in.; $1\frac{13}{16}$ in.

$\frac{3}{4}$ in.; $1\frac{1}{8}$ in.

Write each number as an improper fraction and as a mixed number.

31. 33 halves $\frac{33}{2}$; $16\frac{1}{2}$

32. 7 fifths $\frac{7}{5}$; $1\frac{2}{5}$

33. 106 fourths $\frac{106}{4}$, $26\frac{1}{2}$

34. 2 and 3 fifths $\frac{13}{5}$; $2\frac{3}{5}$

35. 8 and 7 ninths $\frac{79}{9}$; $8\frac{7}{9}$

36. 6 and 3 sevenths $\frac{45}{7}$; $6\frac{3}{7}$

 37. **Food** A caterer plans to serve two slices of melon to each of 50 guests. GPS She estimates getting 12 slices from each melon. Write the number of melons she will use as a mixed number. How many whole melons does she need? $8\frac{1}{3}$ melons; 9 melons

GPS Use the Guided Problem Solving worksheet with Exercise 37.

Assignment Guide

1 Objective 1
A **B** Core 1–12, 21, 24, 26–27

2 Objective 2
A **B** Core 13–20, 22–23, 25, 28–37
C Extension 38–39

Test Prep 40–43
Mixed Review 44–49

Error Prevention!

Exercises 13–20 Watch for students who reverse the numerator and denominator when reading improper fractions.

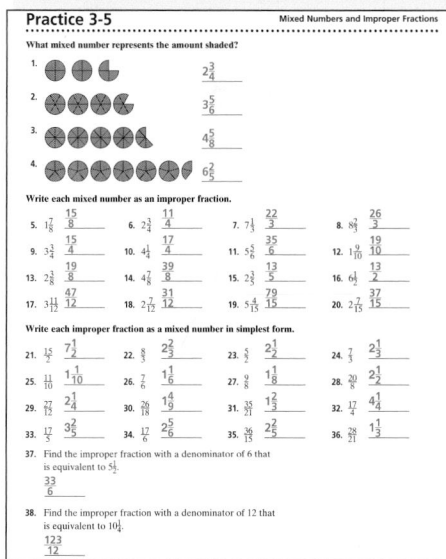

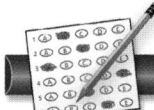

Write each as an improper fraction.

1. $3\frac{5}{8}$ $\frac{29}{8}$ **2.** $6\frac{4}{7}$ $\frac{46}{7}$

Write each as a mixed number in simplest form.

3. $\frac{38}{5}$ $7\frac{3}{5}$ **4.** $\frac{100}{9}$ $11\frac{1}{9}$

Alternative Assessment

Have students use customary rulers with each inch marked in sixteenths. Make sure students can read the ruler. Give mixed numbers such as $3\frac{1}{4}$, $2\frac{5}{8}$, and $4\frac{5}{16}$. Students count the tick marks on the rulers to help them write improper fractions for the mixed numbers. $\frac{13}{4}$, $\frac{21}{8}$, $\frac{69}{16}$ Then give improper fractions such as $\frac{45}{8}$, $\frac{9}{2}$, and $\frac{25}{4}$ and have students name each as a mixed number. $5\frac{5}{8}$, $4\frac{1}{2}$, $6\frac{1}{4}$

Test Prep

Resources

For additional practice with a variety of test item formats:
• Test-Prep, p. 165
• Test-Taking Strategies, p. 161
• Test-Taking Strategies With Transparencies

C Challenge

38. Open-Ended Find a number that is between $\frac{6}{4}$ and $\frac{7}{4}$. Write your answer as an improper fraction and as a mixed number. **Answers may vary. Sample:** $\frac{13}{8}$, $1\frac{5}{8}$

39. Stretch Your Thinking Replace each ■ with either the number 5 or an addition sign to get the sum shown.

■ ■ ■ ■ ■ ■ ■ ■ ■ ■ ■ = 1,165
555 + 555 + 55

Test Prep

Reading Comprehension   Read the passage and answer the questions below.

Gifts From the Sea

Pearls are the only gems that come from the sea. They are also the only gems made by living things—mollusks.

The largest pearl was found in the Philippines in 1934. It was $9\frac{1}{2}$ inches long. It had a diameter of $5\frac{1}{2}$ inches. The pearl weighed 14 pounds 1 ounce.

40. Which improper fraction represents the diameter of the pearl? **C**
   A. $5\frac{1}{2}$ inches   **B.** $\frac{7}{2}$ inches   **C.** $\frac{11}{2}$ inches   **D.** $\frac{19}{2}$ inches

41. Which number represents the weight of the pearl in pounds? (*Hint:* There are 16 ounces in a pound.) **H**
   F. $1\frac{1}{4}$ **G.** $1\frac{14}{16}$ **H.** $14\frac{1}{16}$ **I.** $14\frac{1}{4}$

Short Response   **42. a.** A number pattern begins $1\frac{1}{2}$, $2\frac{1}{4}$, 3, $3\frac{3}{4}$, $4\frac{1}{2}$, ... Write the next three numbers in the pattern. **42a–b. See margin.**
   b. Explain your reasoning.

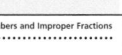

Take It to the NET
Online lesson quiz at
www.PHSchool.com
Web Code: aaa-0305

43. A chef cuts his spice cakes into 16 servings each. **43a–b. See margin.**
   a. How many cakes should he prepare in order to serve 150 people?
   b. What part of a cake will be left over?

Mixed Review

Lesson 2-5   **Tell whether each equation is true or false.**

44. $48 \div 6 = 8$ **45.** $0.7 + 0.8 = 15$ **46.** $1.8 = 5.4 \div 3$
   true   false   true

Lesson 2-2   **Algebra**   **Evaluate each expression for $x = 7$.**

47. $3x + 5$ 26   **48.** $42 \div x$ 6   **49.** $(x + 3) - 4$ 6

142   Chapter 3   Number Theory and Fractions

42. [2]a. $5\frac{1}{4}$, 6, $6\frac{3}{4}$
   b. Each number in the pattern is the sum of the number before it and $\frac{3}{4}$.

[1] correct numbers in the pattern with no explanation OR error in the numbers with correct explanation.

43. [2]a. 10
   b. $\frac{5}{8}$

[1] only one part is correct.

Least Common Multiple

What You'll Learn

 OBJECTIVE 1 To find the least common multiple of numbers

. . . And Why

To find when three trains will arrive at a station, as in Example 2

 Check Skills You'll Need

 For help, go to Lesson 3-2.

Find the prime factorization of each number.

1. 80 $2^4 \times 5$
2. 32 2^5
3. 95 5×19
4. 500 $2^2 \times 5^3$
5. 208 $2^4 \times 13$
6. 625 5^4

New Vocabulary
- multiple
- common multiple
- least common multiple (LCM)

Lesson Preview

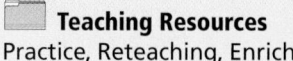

 **Check Skills You'll Need**

Finding Prime Factorization
Lesson 3-2: Example 3. Extra Practice p. 644.

Lesson Resources

📁 **Teaching Resources**
Practice, Reteaching, Enrichment

 Reaching All Students
Practice Workbook 3-6
Spanish Practice Workbook 3-6
Guided Problem Solving 3-6

 Presentation Assistant Plus!
Transparencies
- Check Skills You'll Need 3-6
- Problem of the Day 3-6
- Additional Examples 3-6
- Student Edition Answers 3-6
- Lesson Quiz 3-6
PH Presentation Pro CD-ROM 3-6

ASSESSMENT SYSTEM
Computer Test Generator CD

 **Technology**
Resource Pro® CD-ROM
Computer Test Generator CD
PH Presentation Pro CD-ROM

💻 **www.PHSchool.com**
Student Site
- Teacher Web Code: aak-5500
- Self-grading Lesson Quiz

PH SuccessNet Teacher Center
- Lesson Planner
- Resources

Plus 📘**TEXT**

OBJECTIVE
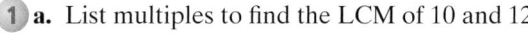
1 Finding the Least Common Multiple

*i***TEXT** Interactive lesson includes instant self-check, tutorials, and activities.

Peg gets a haircut every four weeks. Pam gets a haircut every six weeks at the same time and place as Peg. If Peg meets Pam while getting a haircut, when would they meet again?

You can list *multiples* of 4 and 6 to answer this question. A **multiple** of a number is the product of that number and a nonzero whole number.

$6 \times 1 = 6$
$6 \times 2 = 12$
$6 \times 3 = 18$
$6 \times 4 = 24$
$6 \times \blacksquare = $ multiple of 6

A number that is a multiple of each of two or more numbers is a **common multiple.** The **least common multiple (LCM)** of two or more numbers is the least multiple that is common to all the numbers.

Real-World 🌐 Connection

Americans spend $45 billion on haircuts and hair care each year.

1 EXAMPLE Finding the LCM Using Lists of Multiples

Find the least common multiple of 4 and 6.

multiples of 4: 4, 8, ⑫, 16, 20, ㉔
multiples of 6: 6, ⑫, 18, ㉔

← List multiples of each number. 12 and 24 are common multiples.

● The least common multiple is 12.

✓ **Check Understanding** ① **a.** List multiples to find the LCM of 10 and 12. **60**
b. **Number Sense** Name the first five common multiples of 4 and 6.
12, 24, 36, 48, 60

🔍 Ongoing Assessment and Intervention

Before the Lesson
Diagnose prerequisite skills using:
- Check Skills You'll Need

During the Lesson
Monitor progress using:
- Check Understanding
- Additional Examples
- Test Prep

After the Lesson
Assess knowledge using:
- Lesson Quiz
- Computer Test Generator CD

Math Background

A *multiple* of a number is a product of that number and a nonzero whole number. You can make a list of multiples to find the *least common multiple*, or *LCM*, of a set of numbers. You can also use prime factorizations to find the LCM.

Teaching Notes

Auditory Learners

Students might confuse LCM with GCF because the two acronyms sound similar. Suggest that they say "least common multiple" softly whenever they encounter *LCM*, and say "greatest common factor" whenever they encounter *GCF*.

2 EXAMPLE Inclusion

Some students might circle every occurrence of the common prime factors. Remind them to circle each prime factor in just one number, wherever it appears the greatest number of times.

Careers

Transportation planners make sure that all types of traffic—bus, subway, railway, taxicab, commercial trucking, private automobile, and pedestrian—flow as smoothly as possible.

PowerPoint Additional Examples

1 List multiples to find the LCM of 6 and 9. **18**
6: 6, 12, ⑱, 24, 30, ㊱
9: 9, ⑱, 27, ㊱

2 Use prime factorizations to find the LCM of each: 6, 9, 15. **90**
6 = ② × 3   9 = ③ × ③   15 = 3 × ⑤

Closure

• *What is the LCM of two or more numbers?* the least multiple that is common to all the numbers
• *How do you find the LCM by using prime factorization?* Write the prime factorization for each number. Circle each different factor where it appears the most times. Multiply these factors.

144

REGULAR SERVICE
EVERY
YELLOW LINE   8 min
GREEN LINE   10 min
PURPLE LINE 20 min

2 EXAMPLE LCM From Prime Factorizations    Real World

Scheduling Suppose the three trains in the table have just arrived together. In how many minutes will they arrive together again?

Write the prime factorizations for 8, 10, and 20. Then circle each different factor where it appears the greatest number of times.

$8 = (2 \times 2 \times 2)$ ← 2 appears three times.
$10 = 2 \times (5)$ ← 5 appears once.
$20 = 2 \times 2 \times 5$ ← Don't circle 5 again.
$2 \times 2 \times 2 \times 5 = 40$ ← Multiply the circled factors.

The LCM of 8, 10, and 20 is 40. So, it will be 40 minutes until the trains again arrive at the same time.

✓ **Check Understanding** 2 Use prime factorizations to find the LCM of: 25, 35, and 50.   **350**

More Than One Way

Find the LCM of 20, 30, and 45.

Michael's Method

I can use the prime factorizations of 20, 30, and 45 to find the LCM.

$20 = (2 \times 2) \times (5)$ ← 2 appears twice. 5 appears once.
$30 = 2 \times 3 \times 5$ ← Don't circle 2 or 5 again.
$45 = (3 \times 3) \times 5$ ← 3 appears twice.
$2 \times 2 \times 3 \times 3 \times 5 = 180$ ← Multiply the circled factors.

The LCM of 20, 30, and 45 is 180.

Amanda's Method

The greatest number is 45. I will list the multiples of 45 until I find one that is also a multiple of 20 and 30.

90 is a multiple of 30, but not of 20.
45, 90, 135, 180 ← 180! That's a multiple of both 20 and 30.

So, the LCM of 20, 30, and 45 is 180.

Choose a Method

Find the LCM of 6, 9, and 10. Explain which method you chose and why.
90; explanations may vary.

👥 Reaching All Students

| Below Level Have students find the LCM of pairs of numbers that are already in factored form. For example: $2 \times 2 \times 7$ LCM $2 \times 3 \times 3 \times 5$ LCM $2 \times 3 \times 7 = 84$ $2 \times 2 \times 3 \times 5 = 180$ | Advanced Learners The pennies in a jar can be shared equally by 2, 3, 4, 5, 6, 7, 8, 9, or 10 friends, with no pennies left over. What is the least number of pennies in the jar? 2,520 pennies | Inclusion See note on page 144. Auditory Learners See note on page 144. |

 **EXERCISES**

? For more practice, see *Extra Practice*.

For more practice, see *Extra Practice*.

A Practice by Example

List multiples to find the LCM of each pair of numbers.

Example 1
(page 143)

1. 4, 9 36   **2.** 5, 6 30   **3.** 12, 15 60   **4.** 10, 16 80

5. 14, 21 42   **6.** 20, 30 60   **7.** 25, 75 75   **8.** 8, 10 40

Example 2
(page 144)

Use prime factorizations to find the LCM of each set of numbers. Exercise 9 has been started for you.

9. 16, 24;   16 = 2 × 2 × 2 × 2;   24 = 2 × 2 × 2 × 3;   LCM = ■ 48

10. 9, 21 63   **11.** 18, 24 72   **12.** 75, 100 300

13. 8, 14 56   **14.** 22, 55 110   **15.** 18, 108 108

B Apply Your Skills

16. Travel Two ships sail between New York and London. One makes the round trip in 12 days. The other takes 16 days. They both leave London today. In how many days will both ships leave London together again? **in 48 days**

17. Business During a promotion, a music store gives a free CD to every fifteenth customer and a free DVD to every fortieth customer. Which customer will be the first to get both a free CD and a free DVD? **120th customer**

Find the LCM of each set of numbers.

18. 7, 10 70   **19.** 7, 12 84   **20.** 7, 14 14

21. 35, 45 315   **22.** 22, 25 550   **23.** 60, 100 300

24. 4, 7, 20 140   **25.** 6, 8, 16 48   **26.** 30, 50, 200 600

27. $2^2 \times 7, 2 \times 7^2$
196

28. $2^3 \times 7, 2^2 \times 3, 2 \times 3^2 \times 5$
2,520

29b. If Monday is day 1, then the first time both items are picked up on a Sunday will be on day 91.

29. Recycling City recycling trucks pick up plastic from a collection bin every 3 days and glass every 5 days.
  a. Suppose both items are picked up today. In how many days will both items again be picked up on the same day? **15 days**
  b. Suppose both items are picked up on a Monday. In how many days will they be picked up together on a Sunday? **See left.**

30. Answers may vary. Sample: The LCM is the product of the two numbers. For example, 5 and 6 have no common factors. Since no number less than 30 is divisible by both 5 and 6, the LCM is 30, and 5 × 6 = 30.

30. Writing in Math What is the LCM for two numbers that have no common factors greater than 1? Give examples and explain your reasoning.

31. Number Sense A number *N* has both 8 and 10 as factors.
  a. Name three other factors of the number *N*, other than 1. **2, 4, 5**
  b. What is the smallest the number *N* could be? **40**

3-6 Least Common Multiple **145**

 Use the Guided Problem Solving worksheet with Exercise 17.

---

3. Practice

Assignment Guide

1 Objective 1
  A B Core 1–33
  C Extension 34–40

Test Prep 41–44
Mixed Review 45–52

Error Prevention!

Exercises 18–26 Encourage students to check the LCM by dividing it by each of the original numbers.

Practice 3-6 — Least Common Multiple

List multiples to find the LCM of each set of numbers.

1. 5, 10 — 10   2. 2, 3 — 6   3. 6, 8 — 24   4. 4, 6 — 12
5. 8, 10 — 40   6. 5, 6 — 30   7. 12, 15 — 60   8. 8, 12 — 24
9. 9, 15 — 45   10. 6, 15 — 30   11. 6, 9 — 18   12. 6, 18 — 18
13. 3, 5 — 15   14. 4, 5 — 20   15. 9, 21 — 63   16. 7, 28 — 28
17. 4, 6, 8 — 24   18. 6, 8, 12 — 24   19. 4, 9, 12 — 36   20. 6, 9, 12 — 36
21. 6, 12, 15 — 60   22. 8, 12, 15 — 120   23. 2, 4, 5 — 20   24. 5, 10, 15 — 30

Use prime factorization to find the LCM of each set of numbers.

25. 18, 21 — 126   26. 15, 21 — 105   27. 18, 24 — 72   28. 21, 24 — 168
29. 15, 30 — 30   30. 24, 30 — 120   31. 24, 72 — 72   32. 18, 72 — 72
33. 8, 42 — 168   34. 16, 42 — 336   35. 8, 56 — 56   36. 6, 81 — 162
37. 8, 30 — 120   38. 16, 30 — 240   39. 18, 30 — 90   40. 45, 60 — 180
41. 12, 24, 16 — 48   42. 8, 16, 20 — 80   43. 12, 16, 20 — 240   44. 15, 20, 25 — 300

45. At a store, hot dogs come in packages of eight and hot dog buns come in packages of twelve. What is the least number of packages of each type that you can buy and have no hot dogs or buns left over?
3 packages of hot dogs, 2 packages of buns

Reteaching 3-6 — Least Common Multiple

Find the *least common multiple (LCM)* of 8 and 12.

① Begin listing multiples of each number.
  8: 8, 16, 24, 32, 40
  12: 12, 24

② Continue the lists until you find the first multiple that is common to both lists. That is the LCM.

The least common multiple of 8 and 12 is 24.

List multiples to find the LCM of each pair of numbers.

1. 4: 4, 8, 12, 16, 20   2. 6: 6, 12, 18, 24, 30, 36, 42
   5: 5, 10, 15, 20   7: 7, 14, 21, 28, 35, 42
   LCM: 20   LCM: 42
3. 9: 9, 18, 27, 36, 45   4. 10: 10, 20, 30, 40, 50
   15: 15, 30, 45   25: 25, 50
   LCM: 45   LCM: 50
5. 8: 8, 16, 24   6. 8: 8, 16, 24
   24: 24   12: 12, 24
   LCM: 24   LCM: 24
7. 4: 4, 8, 12, 16, 20, 24, 28   8. 15: 15, 30, 45, 60, 75
   7: 7, 14, 21, 28   25: 25, 50, 75
   LCM: 28   LCM: 75
9. 15: 15, 30, 45, 60   10. 4: 4, 8, 12, 16, 20, 24, 28, 32, 36
   20: 20, 40, 60   9: 9, 18, 27, 36
   LCM: 60   LCM: 36

Use prime factorization to find the LCM of each set of numbers.

11. 9, 21 — 63   12. 6, 8 — 24
13. 18, 24 — 72   14. 40, 50 — 200
15. 42, 49 — 294   16. 6, 12 — 12

145

Lesson Quiz 3-6

Find the LCM of each set of numbers.

1. 3, 7 **21**

2. 12, 18 **36**

3. 5, 6 **30**

4. 4, 9, 12 **36**

Alternative Assessment

Each student in a pair writes a whole number. Partners exchange numbers and write at least 10 multiples of the number. Working together, partners find the LCM of each set of numbers. Students repeat the activity as time permits.

Test Prep

Resources

For additional practice with a variety of test item formats:
• Test-Prep, p. 165
• Test-Taking Strategies, p. 161
• Test-Taking Strategies With Transparencies

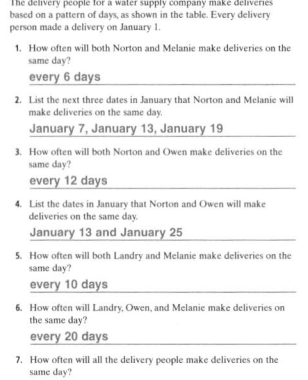

Enrichment 3-6 — Least Common Multiple
Visual Thinking

The delivery people for a water supply company make deliveries based on a pattern of days, as shown in the table. Every delivery person made a delivery on January 1.

Landry	Every 5 days
Melanie	Every 2 days
Norton	Every 6 days
Owen	Every 4 days

1. How often will both Norton and Melanie make deliveries on the same day?
every 6 days

2. List the next three dates in January that Norton and Melanie will make deliveries on the same day.
January 7, January 13, January 19

3. How often will both Norton and Owen make deliveries on the same day?
every 12 days

4. List the dates in January that Norton and Owen will make deliveries on the same day.
January 13 and January 25

5. How often will both Landry and Melanie make deliveries on the same day?
every 10 days

6. How often will Landry, Owen, and Melanie make deliveries on the same day?
every 20 days

7. How often will all the delivery people make deliveries on the same day?
every 60 days

8. All four employees make a delivery on January 1 of a year that is not a leap year. What is the next date when all four employees will make deliveries on the same day?
March 2

32. Fitness Suppose you lift weights every third day and swim every fourth day. If you do both activities today, in how many days will you again do both activities on the same day? **in 12 days**

33. (**Algebra**) The LCM of 3 and 6 is 6. The LCM of 5 and 10 is 10. The LCM of x and $2x$ is ■. **2x**

C Challenge

Find the LCM of each set of numbers.

34. 3, 8, 12, 15 **120**

35. 4, 7, 12, 21 **84**

36. 25, 50, 125, 200 **1,000**

37. 2, 3, 5, 7, 11 **2,310**

38. $2^2, 2^4, 2^5$ **32**

39. 100, 200, 300, 400 **1,200**

40. Stretch Your Thinking A gross is a dozen dozens. How many items are in a gross? Write "a dozen dozens" using an exponent. **144 items, 12^2**

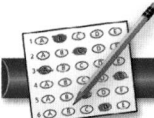

Test Prep

Multiple Choice

41. What is the least common multiple of 24 and 28? **C**
A. 4   **B.** 84   **C.** 168   **D.** 336

42. The least common multiple of 20 and another number is 80. What is the other number? **G**
F. 10   **G.** 16   **H.** 40   **I.** 160

Take It to the NET
Online lesson quiz at
www.PHSchool.com
Web Code: aaa-0306

43. What is the least common multiple of 20 and 30? **B**
A. $2 \times 3 \times 5$ **B.** $2^2 \times 3 \times 5$ **C.** $2^2 \times 3^2 \times 5$ **D.** $2^2 \times 3 \times 5^2$

Short Response

44. Folders are sold in packs of 6. Stickers are sold in packs of 10. What is the least number of folders and stickers you can buy so that so you have a sticker for each folder? Explain your reasoning. **See margin.**

Mixed Review

Lesson 1-3 **Order each set of decimals on a number line.**

45. 0.51, 0.3, 0.49, 0.37, 0.6
0.3, 0.37, 0.49, 0.51, 0.6

46. 9.2, 9.28, 9.13, 9.25, 9.26
9.13, 9.2, 9.25, 9.26, 9.28

Lesson 2-8 **Write each expression using an exponent. Name the base and the exponent.**

47. $5 \times 5 \times 5$ **5^3; 5, 3**

48. $4 \times 4 \times 4 \times 4$ **4^4; 4, 4**

49. $7 \times 7 \times 7$ **7^3; 7, 3**

50. $2 \times 2 \times 2 \times 2 \times 2$ **2^5; 2, 5**

51. 12×12 **12^2; 12, 2**

52. 1.5×1.5 **1.5^2; 1.5, 2**

44. [2] 5 packs of folders, 3 packs of stickers. The least number of folder/sticker pairs will be the LCM of 6 and 10, which is 30. Divide 30 by 6 to find the number of packs of folders and divide 30 by 10 to find the number of packs of stickers.

[1] correct answer, no explanation

Learning Vocabulary

For Use With Lesson 3-6

You can learn new vocabulary by building your own index-card word list.

- Write the term. Then, write the definition.
- Include any math symbols related to the term.
- Give an example that shows how the term is used.
- Give a nonexample showing how the term might *not* apply.

EXAMPLE

Make an index card for the vocabulary term *greatest common factor* (*GCF*).

Greatest Common Factor (GCF)	← **Write the term.**
Definition: The GCF of two or more numbers is the greatest factor shared by all the numbers.	← **Write the definition.**
Example: The GCF of 12 and 20 is 4.	← **Give an example using numbers.**
Nonexample: 2 is a common factor of 12 and 20, but is not the GCF.	← **Give a nonexample.**

Sometimes you can use the everyday meaning of the word as a connection to the mathematical meaning.

A *factor in a decision* forms part of the decision.

A *greatest common factor* is the largest "part" some numbers have in common.

A *composite picture* is a picture made up of many parts.

A *composite number* is a number with more than two factors.

EXERCISES

**Make an index card, like the one shown above, for each vocabulary term.
Include any helpful everyday meanings.** 1–6. **Check students' work.**

1. least common multiple

2. equivalent fractions

3. exponent

4. prime number

5. divisible

6. improper fraction

Learning Vocabulary

Students who grasp the precision of math vocabulary will improve their ability to fully comprehend and share mathematical ideas. This feature guides students to create an index-card dictionary to help them learn new math vocabulary.

Teaching Notes

Go over all the parts of the sample card and the samples of everyday meanings of the words. Discuss the advantages of including symbols and non-examples of the defined terms on the cards.

Inclusion
Encourage students to refer to the English/Spanish Illustrated Glossary (p. 669) and the Table of Symbols (p. 666) to help build their vocabulary cards.

Activating Prior Knowledge
Elicit from students the value of applying knowledge and understandings they already have to learn new concepts. Discuss that they can more successfully acquire new vocabulary by relating the new terms to terms they already know and use.

English Learners
Modify the features of the index cards to meet the language needs of your students. Additionally, you may wish to allow students to write their definitions in their native language. Call attention to the English/Spanish Illustrated Glossary that begins on page 669 of the textbook.

Exercises
Have students work individually to complete the exercises. Invite them to compare their dictionary cards with those of classmates.

Encourage students to keep a personal ongoing index-card math dictionary, adding new entries throughout the year.

Lesson Preview

 Check Skills You'll Need PowerPoint

Writing Equivalent Fractions
Lesson 3-4: Example 1. Extra
Practice p. 644.

Lesson Resources

 Teaching Resources
Practice, Reteaching, Enrichment
Checkpoint Quiz 2

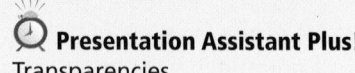 **Reaching All Students**
Practice Workbook 3-7
Spanish Practice Workbook 3-7
Reading and Math Literacy 3C
Spanish Reading and Math
   Literacy 3C
Spanish Checkpoint Quiz 2
Guided Problem Solving 3-7

 Presentation Assistant Plus!
Transparencies
• Check Skills You'll Need 3-7
• Problem of the Day 3-7
• Additional Examples 3-7
• Student Edition Answers 3-7
• Lesson Quiz 3-7
PH Presentation Pro CD-ROM 3-7

PRENTICE HALL ASSESSMENT SYSTEM

Checkpoint Quiz 2
Computer Test Generator CD

 Technology
Resource Pro® CD-ROM
Computer Test Generator CD
PH Presentation Pro CD-ROM

 **www.PHSchool.com**
Student Site
• Teacher Web Code: aak-5500
• Self-grading Lesson Quiz

PH SuccessNet Teacher Center
• Lesson Planner
• Resources

Plus *i* TEXT

What You'll Learn

OBJECTIVE 1 To compare fractions

OBJECTIVE 2 To order fractions

. . . And Why

To solve carpentry problems, as in Example 2

New Vocabulary • least common denominator (LCD)

  Check Skills You'll Need   For help, go to Lesson 3-4.

1–9. Answers may vary. Samples are given.
Write two fractions equivalent to each given fraction.

1. $\frac{3}{7}$ $\frac{6}{14}, \frac{15}{35}$ 2. $\frac{7}{21}$ $\frac{1}{3}, \frac{21}{63}$ 3. $\frac{8}{40}$ $\frac{1}{5}, \frac{2}{10}$

4. $\frac{2}{3}$ $\frac{4}{6}, \frac{20}{30}$ 5. $\frac{10}{12}$ $\frac{5}{6}, \frac{20}{24}$ 6. $\frac{25}{150}$ $\frac{1}{6}, \frac{5}{30}$

7. $\frac{6}{8}$ $\frac{3}{4}, \frac{12}{16}$ 8. $\frac{40}{100}$ $\frac{4}{10}, \frac{120}{300}$ 9. $\frac{8}{5}$ $\frac{16}{10}, \frac{24}{15}$

OBJECTIVE 1 **Comparing Fractions**

 Interactive lesson includes instant self-check, tutorials, and activities.

Investigation: Comparing Fractions

1a. $\frac{1}{3} < \frac{2}{3}$

b. $\frac{5}{8} > \frac{3}{8}$

c. $\frac{5}{6} < \frac{6}{6}$

d. $\frac{3}{5} < \frac{3}{4}$

e. $\frac{1}{6} > \frac{1}{8}$

f. $\frac{7}{8} > \frac{7}{10}$

2. The fraction with the greater numerator is greater.

3. The fraction with the lesser denominator is greater.

1–3. See left.

1. Look at the fraction models below. In each pair, tell whether the top model is less than, equal to, or greater than the bottom model.

a. 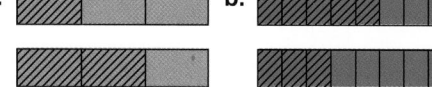 b. c.

d. e. f.

2. Describe a rule to compare fractions with the same denominator.

3. Describe a rule to compare fractions with the same numerator.

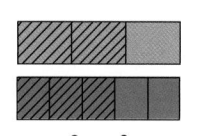

$\frac{2}{3} > \frac{3}{5}$

Which is greater: $\frac{2}{3}$ of an hour or $\frac{3}{5}$ of an hour? Models like those at the left can help you decide. To compare fractions without using models, you can find equivalent fractions that have the same denominator.

Sometimes it is easiest to use the least common denominator. The **least common denominator (LCD)** of two or more fractions is the least common multiple (LCM) of their denominators.

Ongoing Assessment and Intervention

Before the Lesson	During the Lesson	After the Lesson
Diagnose prerequisite skills using:	Monitor progress using:	Assess knowledge using:
• Check Skills You'll Need	• Check Understanding • Additional Examples • Test Prep	• Lesson Quiz • Computer Test Generator CD • Chapter Checkpoint 2 (p. 152)

① EXAMPLE Comparing Fractions With Unlike Denominators

Compare $\frac{5}{6}$ and $\frac{3}{4}$. Use $<$, $=$, or $>$.

Method 1 Multiply denominators to find a common denominator.
Use 6×4, or 24, as a common denominator.

$$\frac{5}{6} \overset{\times 4}{\underset{\times 4}{=}} \frac{20}{24} \qquad \frac{3}{4} \overset{\times 6}{\underset{\times 6}{=}} \frac{18}{24} \quad \leftarrow \text{Find equivalent fractions and compare.}$$

$\frac{20}{24} > \frac{18}{24}$. So, $\frac{5}{6} > \frac{3}{4}$.

Method 2 Use the least common denominator.
The least common multiple of 6 and 4 is 12. Use 12 as the LCD.

$$\frac{5}{6} = \frac{10}{12} \qquad \frac{3}{4} = \frac{9}{12} \quad \leftarrow \text{Find equivalent fractions and compare.}$$

$\frac{10}{12} > \frac{9}{12}$. So, $\frac{5}{6} > \frac{3}{4}$.

✔ **Check Understanding** ① Compare each pair of fractions. Use $<$, $=$, or $>$.

    a. $\frac{6}{8} \overset{<}{\blacksquare} \frac{7}{9}$
    b. $\frac{6}{10} \overset{=}{\blacksquare} \frac{9}{15}$
    c. $\frac{2}{3} \overset{>}{\blacksquare} \frac{5}{8}$

    d. Number Sense Use the common denominator 60 to compare $\frac{2}{3}$ and $\frac{3}{5}$. How many minutes are in $\frac{2}{3}$ of an hour? In $\frac{3}{5}$ of an hour? Which is greater? 40 min, 36 min; $\frac{2}{3}$

Real-World  **Connection**

Careers Carpenters cut, fit, and assemble wood used in the construction of structures.

② EXAMPLE Comparing Mixed Numbers 🌎 Real World

Carpentry "Measure twice, cut once" is the carpenters' motto. A carpenter needs a piece of lumber that is at least $6\frac{27}{32}$ inches wide. Is a $6\frac{3}{4}$-inch piece wide enough?

Since the whole numbers are the same, compare $\frac{27}{32}$ and $\frac{3}{4}$.

$$\frac{27}{32} = \frac{27}{32} \qquad \frac{3}{4} = \frac{24}{32} \quad \leftarrow \text{Write equivalent fractions. Use the LCD 32.}$$

$\frac{27}{32} > \frac{24}{32}$. So, $6\frac{27}{32} > 6\frac{3}{4}$. $\leftarrow$ Compare fractions and mixed numbers.

The $6\frac{3}{4}$-inch piece is not wide enough.

✔ **Check Understanding** ② Compare each pair of mixed numbers using $<$, $=$, or $>$.

    a. $4\frac{2}{5} \overset{<}{\blacksquare} 4\frac{3}{7}$
    b. $1\frac{2}{3} \overset{>}{\blacksquare} 1\frac{6}{11}$
    c. $2\frac{12}{21} \overset{=}{\blacksquare} 2\frac{4}{7}$

    d. Number Sense In Example 2, would a $6\frac{7}{8}$-inch piece of lumber be wide enough? Explain. Yes; $\frac{7}{8} = \frac{28}{32}$ and $\frac{28}{32} > \frac{27}{32}$. So $6\frac{7}{8} > 6\frac{27}{32}$.

👥 Reaching All Students

Below Level Review the meanings of the symbols $<$ (is less than), $>$ (is greater than), and $=$ (is equal to). Have students practice using the symbols by asking them to make some simple whole-number comparisons.	**Advanced Learners** Show how to compare $\frac{a}{b}$ and $\frac{c}{d}$ using ad and bc. Assume a, b, c, and d are nonzero whole numbers. $ad = bc \rightarrow \frac{a}{b} = \frac{c}{d}$; $ad < bc \rightarrow \frac{a}{b} < \frac{c}{d}$; $ad > bc \rightarrow \frac{a}{b} > \frac{c}{d}$	**Inclusion** See note on page 150. **Visual Learners** See note on page 149.

---

2. Teach

Professional Development

Math Background

Fractions represent amounts, and there are many real-world situations in which it is necessary to compare amounts. When fractions have like denominators, you compare them by comparing numerators. For instance, $\frac{3}{5} > \frac{2}{5}$ because $3 > 2$.

When fractions have unlike denominators, comparing them involves rewriting the fractions with a common denominator. For instance, $\frac{1}{3} > \frac{1}{4}$ because $\frac{4}{12} > \frac{3}{12}$. Their *least common denominator*, or LCD, is the least common multiple (LCM) of their denominators. So, 12 is the LCM of 3 and 4, and 12 is the LCD of $\frac{1}{3}$ and $\frac{1}{4}$.

Teaching Notes

Investigation (Optional)
Students may recognize that the fraction model with the larger part of the whole is greater. However, they might have difficulty expressing it in a rule. For Question 2, have students complete the statement: "If two models are divided into the same number of parts, then. . . ."
Sample: ". . . the model with the greater number of shaded parts is greater."

② EXAMPLE Visual Learners

Have students verify that the lumber is too narrow by locating $6\frac{27}{32}$ inches and $6\frac{3}{4}$ inches on a ruler. If students' rulers are marked only in sixteenths of an inch, lead them to see that a length of $6\frac{27}{32}$ inches is halfway between $6\frac{13}{16}$ inches and $6\frac{14}{16}$ inches.

PowerPoint
📖 **Additional Examples**

① Compare $\frac{5}{8}$ and $\frac{7}{10}$. Use $<$, $=$, or $>$. $\frac{5}{8} < \frac{7}{10}$

② If you need a piece of lumber that is $4\frac{3}{16}$ feet long, is a $4\frac{1}{4}$-foot piece long enough? yes

14

OBJECTIVE
2 Ordering Fractions

To order fractions with like denominators, you can compare numerators.

To order fractions with unlike denominators, first write the fractions with common denominators.

③ EXAMPLE   Ordering Fractions

Order from least to greatest: $\frac{3}{8}, \frac{2}{5}$, and $\frac{1}{4}$.

Any multiple of 8 is also a multiple of 4. So, you can multiply 8×5 to find a common multiple. A common multiple of 8, 5, and 4 is 40.

$$\frac{3}{8} = \frac{15}{40} \qquad \frac{2}{5} = \frac{16}{40} \qquad \frac{1}{4} = \frac{10}{40} \quad \leftarrow \text{Write equivalent fractions.}$$

$$10 < 15 < 16 \qquad\qquad\qquad \leftarrow \text{Arrange the numerators in order.}$$

$\frac{10}{40} < \frac{15}{40} < \frac{16}{40}$. So, $\frac{1}{4} < \frac{3}{8} < \frac{2}{5}$.

✓ **Check Understanding** ③ Order $2\frac{5}{6}, 2\frac{4}{5}$, and $2\frac{2}{3}$ from least to greatest. $2\frac{2}{3}, 2\frac{4}{5}, 2\frac{5}{6}$

EXERCISES

? For more practice, see *Extra Practice*.

Ⓐ Practice by Example   **Compare each pair of numbers. Use <, =, or >.**

Example 1
(page 149)

1. $\frac{3}{5} \; \boxed{<} \; \frac{5}{8}$ 2. $\frac{3}{4} \; \boxed{>} \; \frac{3}{5}$ 3. $\frac{1}{2} \; \boxed{>} \; \frac{7}{16}$

4. $\frac{3}{5} \; \boxed{=} \; \frac{12}{20}$ 5. $\frac{5}{7} \; \boxed{<} \; \frac{5}{6}$ 6. $\frac{3}{11} \; \boxed{>} \; \frac{1}{4}$

7. $\frac{2}{9} \; \boxed{<} \; \frac{4}{15}$ 8. $\frac{15}{16} \; \boxed{>} \; \frac{7}{8}$ 9. $\frac{9}{24} \; \boxed{=} \; \frac{3}{8}$

Example 2
(page 149)

10. $3\frac{1}{8} \; \boxed{<} \; 3\frac{1}{4}$ 11. $7\frac{2}{3} \; \boxed{=} \; 7\frac{4}{6}$ 12. $8\frac{7}{10} \; \boxed{>} \; 8\frac{3}{5}$

13. $2\frac{17}{18} \; \boxed{>} \; 2\frac{13}{16}$ 14. $5\frac{4}{6} \; \boxed{<} \; 5\frac{5}{7}$ 15. $3\frac{1}{4} \; \boxed{>} \; 3\frac{1}{5}$

16. Tim ran $1\frac{3}{4}$ miles. Naomi ran $1\frac{7}{10}$ miles. Who ran farther? **Tim**

Example 3
(page 150)

Order each set of numbers from least to greatest.

17. $\frac{2}{3}, \frac{5}{6}, \frac{3}{4}$ $\frac{2}{3}, \frac{3}{4}, \frac{5}{6}$ 18. $\frac{5}{8}, \frac{3}{4}, \frac{1}{2}$ $\frac{1}{2}, \frac{5}{8}, \frac{3}{4}$ 19. $\frac{1}{8}, \frac{7}{40}, \frac{3}{10}$ $\frac{1}{8}, \frac{7}{40}, \frac{3}{10}$

20. $3\frac{2}{3}, 3\frac{2}{5}, 3\frac{7}{15}$ 21. $2\frac{8}{9}, 2\frac{5}{6}, 2\frac{11}{12}$ 22. $6\frac{7}{12}, 6\frac{2}{3}, 6\frac{1}{5}$
    $3\frac{2}{5}, 3\frac{7}{15}, 3\frac{2}{3}$ $2\frac{5}{6}, 2\frac{8}{9}, 2\frac{11}{12}$ $6\frac{1}{5}, 6\frac{7}{12}, 6\frac{2}{3}$

150   Chapter 3   Number Theory and Fractions

B **Apply Your Skills**

23. Shopping Two sports drinks have the same price. The cherry-flavored drink is $12\frac{9}{20}$ ounces. The blueberry-flavored drink is $12\frac{7}{16}$ ounces. Assuming you like both flavors, which drink is the better buy?
GPS
the cherry-flavored drink

24. Construction Plywood comes in a variety of thicknesses for different uses. Put these thicknesses in order from least to greatest.

$\frac{3}{4}$ inch, $\frac{3}{8}$ inch, $\frac{1}{2}$ inch, $\frac{1}{4}$ inch, $\frac{5}{8}$ inch $\frac{1}{4}, \frac{3}{8}, \frac{1}{2}, \frac{5}{8}, \frac{3}{4}$

25. Music Musical notes are based on fractions of a whole note.
  a. Order the fractions shown from greatest to least. $\frac{1}{2}, \frac{1}{4}, \frac{1}{8}, \frac{1}{16}$
  b. Redraw the note symbols so they are in order. **See margin.**
  c. Patterns Do the symbols change in a pattern? Explain. **See margin.**

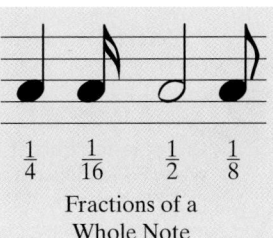

| $\frac{1}{4}$ | $\frac{1}{16}$ | $\frac{1}{2}$ | $\frac{1}{8}$ |

Fractions of a Whole Note

Number Sense Without using a common denominator, compare each pair of fractions using <, =, or >. Explain your reasoning.

26. $\frac{3}{7}$ **>** $\frac{3}{8}$ **27.** $\frac{11}{16}$ **<** $\frac{11}{12}$ **28.** $\frac{1}{8}$ **>** $\frac{1}{18}$

26–28. See margin for explanations.

Mental Math Compare each pair of numbers. Use <, =, or >.

29. $\frac{1}{15}$ **>** $\frac{1}{20}$ **30.** $\frac{3}{4}$ **<** $\frac{3}{2}$ **31.** $\frac{2}{45}$ **>** $\frac{1}{30}$

Determine if each statement is true or false.

32. $\frac{13}{14} > \frac{25}{28}$ **true**   **33.** $\frac{21}{45} > \frac{4}{9}$ **true**   **34.** $\frac{2}{11} < \frac{15}{100}$ **false** **35.** $\frac{9}{3} < \frac{13}{4}$ **true**

36. Data File, p. 117 If a $\frac{7}{16}$-inch wrench is too big for a bolt, and a $\frac{5}{16}$-inch wrench is too small, what size wrench should you try on the bolt? $\frac{3}{8}$

37. Writing in Math Write a rule to compare fractions that have the same numerator and different denominators. **See margin.**

C **Challenge**

Order each set of numbers from least to greatest.

38. $\frac{3}{2}, \frac{9}{7}, \frac{8}{5}, \frac{13}{10}$ **39.** $\frac{11}{10}, \frac{21}{20}, \frac{12}{10}, \frac{23}{10}$ **40.** $\frac{55}{45}, \frac{60}{50}, \frac{50}{40}, \frac{65}{55}$

38. $\frac{9}{7}, \frac{13}{10}, \frac{3}{2}, \frac{8}{5}$

39. $\frac{21}{20}, \frac{11}{10}, \frac{12}{10}, \frac{23}{10}$

40. $\frac{65}{55}, \frac{60}{50}, \frac{55}{45}, \frac{50}{40}$

41. Algebra Find a whole number x so that $\frac{2}{3} < \frac{x}{8} < 1$.

41. Answers may vary. Sample: 7

42. Stretch Your Thinking Copy the diagram. Fill in the squares with the digits 1–9. The sum of the numbers in each indicated row, column, and diagonal must be 15. **See margin.**

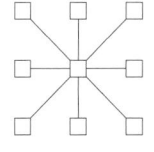

37. In fractions with the same numerators, the fraction with the greater denominator is the lesser fraction.

42.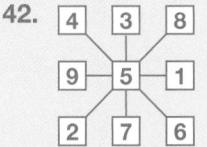

GPS Use the Guided Problem Solving worksheet with Exercise 23.

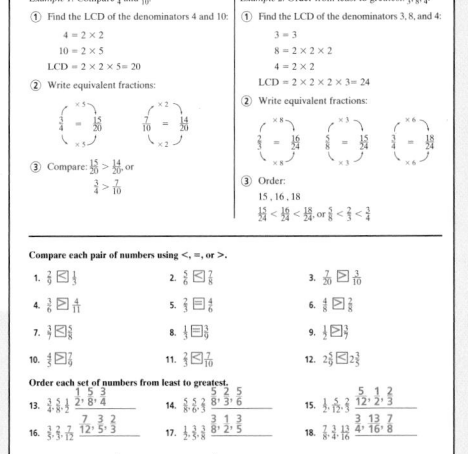

Lesson Quiz 3-7

Compare. Use $<$, $=$, or $>$.

1. $\frac{2}{3}$ ■ $\frac{9}{12}$ $<$ 2. $4\frac{3}{8}$ ■ $4\frac{3}{7}$ $<$

Order from least to greatest.

3. $\frac{3}{5}, \frac{4}{20}, \frac{5}{15}$ $\frac{4}{20}, \frac{5}{15}, \frac{3}{5}$

4. $1\frac{5}{8}, 1\frac{13}{24}, 1\frac{5}{16}$ $1\frac{5}{16}, 1\frac{13}{24}, 1\frac{5}{8}$

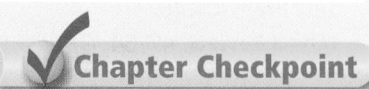

✔ Chapter Checkpoint

To check understanding of Lessons 3-4 to 3-7:

Checkpoint Quiz 2 (p. 152)

📁 **Teaching Resources**
Checkpoint Quiz 2 (also in *Prentice Hall Assessment System*)

👥 **Reaching All Students**
Reading and Math Literacy 3C

Spanish versions available

Test Prep

Resources
For additional practice with a variety of test item formats:
• Test-Prep, p. 165
• Test-Taking Strategies, p. 161
• Test-Taking Strategies With Transparencies

Enrichment 3-7   Comparing and Ordering Fractions
Decision Making

An important thing to learn about fractions is that the size of the fraction is related to the size of the whole. For instance, ½ of a large pizza is much larger than ½ of a small pizza even though each is a half. A half of a dime is much less than a half of a dollar!

1. Would you rather have ½ of two pounds of pennies or ⅓ of one pound of silver dollars? Explain your reasoning.
Sample answer: ⅓ of one pound of silver dollars. Even though there are fewer pounds, the value is greater.

2. Would you rather have ⅓ of one million dollars or ⅓ of two million dollars? Explain your reasoning.
Sample answer: ⅓ of two million dollars; ⅓ of two million dollars is about $666,667; ½ of one million is only $500,000.

3. Which would be less, ⅞ of a collection of 250,000 baseball cards, or ½ of another collection of 500,000 baseball cards? How did you find the answer?
Sample answer: ⅞ of 250,000; ½ of 500,000 is 250,000, which is more than any fraction of 250,000.

4. Which would be more, ½ of 3 dozen chocolate chip cookies or ⅙ of 12 dozen chocolate chip cookies? How do you know?
Sample answer: ⅙ of 12 dozen; ⅙ of 12 is 2, which is greater than ½ of 3, or 1½.

5. Write a similar problem that has you compare the value of fractions. Trade problems with a classmate and solve.
Check students' work.

152

Test Prep

Multiple Choice

43. Which set of fractions is NOT in order from least to greatest? **A**

A. $\frac{3}{8}, \frac{3}{9}, \frac{5}{12}$ B. $\frac{1}{2}, \frac{7}{12}, \frac{5}{6}$ C. $\frac{2}{3}, \frac{3}{4}, \frac{4}{5}$ D. $\frac{2}{9}, \frac{3}{10}, \frac{4}{11}$

44. What is the order of $\frac{7}{20}, \frac{15}{40}, \frac{10}{30}$ from least to greatest? **G**

F. $\frac{7}{20}, \frac{10}{30}, \frac{15}{40}$ G. $\frac{10}{30}, \frac{7}{20}, \frac{15}{40}$ H. $\frac{15}{40}, \frac{10}{30}, \frac{7}{20}$ I. $\frac{15}{40}, \frac{10}{30}, \frac{7}{20}$

Short Response

Take It to the NET
Online lesson quiz at
www.PHSchool.com
Web Code: aaa-0307

45. a. What mixed number is halfway between $1\frac{1}{8}$ and $1\frac{3}{8}$?
    b. Show your answer on a number line.
    45a–b. See margin.

46. Use the lengths shown for each side of the triangle at the right. Put the lengths in order from least to greatest. Explain your reasoning.
See back of book.

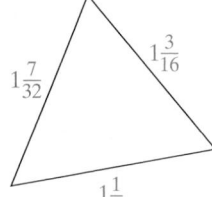

Mixed Review

Lesson 3-5   **Write each mixed number as an improper fraction.**

47. $5\frac{2}{3}$ $\frac{17}{3}$ 48. $1\frac{8}{9}$ $\frac{17}{9}$ 49. $1\frac{15}{21}$ $\frac{36}{21}$, or $\frac{12}{7}$ 50. $13\frac{1}{4}$ $\frac{53}{4}$

Lesson 3-4   **Write each fraction in simplest form.**

51. $\frac{18}{42}$ $\frac{3}{7}$ 52. $\frac{16}{36}$ $\frac{4}{9}$ 53. $\frac{36}{132}$ $\frac{3}{11}$ 54. $\frac{36}{153}$ $\frac{4}{17}$

✔ Checkpoint Quiz 2   Lessons 3-4 through 3-7

 iTEXT Instant self-check quiz online and on CD-ROM

Write each fraction in simplest form.

1. $\frac{8}{12}$ $\frac{2}{3}$ 2. $\frac{21}{28}$ $\frac{3}{4}$ 3. $\frac{16}{64}$ $\frac{1}{4}$

4. $\frac{16}{5}$

4. Write $3\frac{1}{5}$ as an improper fraction.   5. Write $\frac{13}{8}$ as a mixed number. $1\frac{5}{8}$

6. Find the least common multiple of 4, 5, and 12. **60**

7. Order these fractions from least to greatest: $\frac{3}{16}, \frac{1}{8}, \frac{1}{3}$. $\frac{1}{8}, \frac{3}{16}, \frac{1}{3}$

Compare. Use $<$, $=$, or $>$.

8. $\frac{5}{8}$ ■ $\frac{5}{6}$ $<$ 9. $3\frac{2}{3}$ ■ $3\frac{7}{12}$ $>$ 10. $\frac{13}{16}$ ■ $\frac{4}{5}$ $>$

Alternative Assessment

Provide pairs of students with fraction models. Give them two fractions with unlike denominators such as $\frac{3}{7}$ and $\frac{4}{10}$, or $\frac{2}{5}$ and $\frac{3}{8}$. One partner models one fraction; the other partner models the other fraction. Then partners compare the models to determine which is greater. Students write the comparison using mathematical notation.

45. [2]
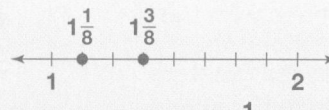

Halfway between $1\frac{1}{8}$ and $1\frac{3}{8}$ is $1\frac{2}{8}$, or $1\frac{1}{4}$.

[1] Correct number line is shown OR correct statement of answer is given.

3-8 Fractions and Decimals

What You'll Learn

OBJECTIVE 1 To write decimals as fractions

OBJECTIVE 2 To write fractions as decimals

. . . And Why

To convert measurements, as in Example 2

✔ **Check Skills You'll Need**　　　❓ For help, go to Lesson 1-9.

Find each quotient. Identify each as a terminating or a repeating decimal.

1. $3 \div 2$ 1.5; term.
2. $2 \div 3$ $0.\overline{6}$; repeat.
3. $8 \div 5$ 1.6; term.
4. $3 \div 8$ 0.375; term.
5. $3 \div 10$ 0.3; term.
6. $24 \div 100$ 0.24; term.
7. $36 \div 150$ 0.24; term.
8. $25 \div 125$ 0.2; term.
9. $16 \div 5$ 3.2; term.

Lesson Preview

✔ **Check Skills You'll Need**　PowerPoint

Finding a Decimal Quotient
Lesson 1–9: Example 2. Extra Practice p. 642.

Lesson Resources

📁 **Teaching Resources**
Practice, Reteaching, Enrichment

👥 **Reaching All Students**
Practice Workbook 3-8
Spanish Practice Workbook 3-8
Guided Problem Solving 3-8
Technology Activities 8

⏱ **Presentation Assistant Plus!**
Transparencies
• Check Skills You'll Need 3-8
• Problem of the Day 3-8
• Additional Examples 3-8
• Student Edition Answers 3-8
• Lesson Quiz 3-8
• Classroom Aid 9, 11
PH Presentation Pro CD-ROM 3-8

PRENTICE HALL ASSESSMENT SYSTEM

Computer Test Generator CD

💻 **Technology**
Resource Pro® CD-ROM
Computer Test Generator CD
PH Presentation Pro CD-ROM

💻 **www.PHSchool.com**
Student Site
• Teacher Web Code: aak-5500
• Self-grading Lesson Quiz

PH SuccessNet Teacher Center
• Lesson Planner
• Resources

Plus 🄸TEXT

OBJECTIVE 1

Writing Decimals as Fractions

🄸TEXT Interactive lesson includes instant self-check, tutorials, and activities.

To write a decimal as a fraction, write the fraction as you would say the decimal. Then simplify.

Reading Math

Reading 0.225 as "two hundred twenty-five thousandths" can help you write 0.225 as a fraction.

1 EXAMPLE　**Writing Decimals as Fractions**

a. Write 0.225 as a fraction in simplest form.

$$0.225 = \frac{225}{1,000}$$ ← Use the place value of the 5 to write a fraction.

$$\frac{225}{1,000} \overset{\div 25}{\underset{\div 25}{=}} \frac{9}{40}$$ ← Simplify. The GCF of 225 and 1,000 is 25.

So, $0.225 = \frac{9}{40}$.

b. Write 2.06 as a mixed number in simplest form.

$$2\frac{6}{100} \overset{\div 2}{\underset{\div 2}{=}} 2\frac{3}{50}$$ ← Write "two and six hundredths" as a mixed number. Then simplify.

So, $2.06 = 2\frac{3}{50}$.

✔ **Check Understanding** ① Write each decimal as a fraction or mixed number in simplest form.
a. 0.6 $\frac{3}{5}$
b. 0.35 $\frac{7}{20}$
c. 5.08 $5\frac{2}{25}$
d. 7.405 $7\frac{81}{200}$
e. **Reasoning** How does saying or writing the decimal in words help you to write the decimal as a fraction? Using the digits to the right of the decimal point, the number you say first tells you the numerator, and the number that is read with "-th" at the end tells you the denominator.

Ongoing Assessment and Intervention

Before the Lesson
Diagnose prerequisite skills using:
• Check Skills You'll Need

During the Lesson
Monitor progress using:
• Check Understanding
• Additional Examples
• Test Prep

After the Lesson
Assess knowledge using:
• Lesson Quiz
• Computer Test Generator CD

2. Teach

Math Background

The fraction $\frac{a}{b}$, where a and b are whole numbers and b is not zero, represents $a \div b$. This quotient is the decimal equivalent of $\frac{a}{b}$. For denominators whose only prime factors are 2 or 5—denominators such as 2, 4, 5, 8, 10, 16, 20, 25, 32, 40, 50, and so on—the decimal is a *terminating decimal*. Otherwise, the decimal is a *repeating decimal* with a block of digits that repeats forever.

Teaching Notes

① EXAMPLE Alternative Method

For part a, some students might prefer to find the simplest form by performing two successive divisions by 5.

$$\frac{225}{1,000} = \frac{225 \div 5}{1,000 \div 5} = \frac{45}{200}$$
$$\frac{45}{200} = \frac{45 \div 5}{200 \div 5} = \frac{9}{40}$$

② EXAMPLE Teaching Tip

Students might wonder if they can write 0.6 as a fraction and compare it to $\frac{5}{8}$. This is a valid method, but it involves comparing fractions with unlike denominators. Therefore, it may be more difficult.

📊 PowerPoint

Additional Examples

① Write 0.028 as a fraction in simplest form. $\frac{7}{250}$

② You need at least $\frac{3}{4}$ pound of dried apricots for a recipe. You find a bag that contains 0.8 pound. Is this enough? **yes**

③ Write $\frac{5}{6}$ as a decimal. $0.8\overline{3}$

Closure

- *How do you write a terminating decimal as a fraction?* **Sample: Write the fraction as you would say the decimal. Then simplify the fraction, if possible.**
- *How do you write a fraction as a decimal?* **Sample: Divide the numerator by the denominator.**

154

A fraction indicates division. To write a fraction as a decimal, divide the numerator by the denominator.

② EXAMPLE Writing a Fraction as a Decimal  Real World

Construction A construction worker wants to drill a hole with a diameter that is no more than 0.6 inch. Can she use a $\frac{5}{8}$-inch drill bit?

To write $\frac{5}{8}$ as a decimal, divide 5 by 8.

$$\begin{array}{r} 0.625 \\ 8\overline{)5.000} \\ \underline{4\,8} \\ 20 \\ \underline{16} \\ 40 \\ \underline{40} \\ 0 \end{array}$$

$\leftarrow \frac{5}{8} = \mathbf{0.625}$

Since 0.625 > 0.6, the $\frac{5}{8}$-inch drill bit is too big.

✓ **Check Understanding** ② **a.** Write $\frac{9}{20}$ as a decimal. **0.45**

b. Reasoning Explain how to write $2\frac{3}{4}$ as a decimal.
$2\frac{3}{4}$ **is really** $2 + \frac{3}{4}$. **Divide 3 by 4 to get 0.75.**
$2 + 0.75 = 2.75$.

③ EXAMPLE Repeating Decimals

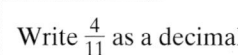
Need Help?
For help with repeating decimals, go to Lesson 1-9.

Write $\frac{4}{11}$ as a decimal.

Method 1 Divide.

$$\begin{array}{r} 0.3636 \\ 11\overline{)4.0000} \\ \underline{3\,3} \\ 70 \\ \underline{66} \\ 40 \\ \underline{33} \\ 70 \\ \underline{66} \\ 4 \end{array}$$

$\leftarrow$ **The digits 3 and 6 repeat.**

$\frac{4}{11} = 0.\overline{36}$

Method 2 Use a calculator.

4 ➗ 11 🟰 0.363636364

The calculator rounds the last digit in the display to 4. Look for the repeated digits: 3636. . .

$$\frac{4}{11} = 0.\overline{36}$$

✓ **Check Understanding** ③ Write each fraction as a decimal. Use a bar to show repeating digits.

a. $\frac{2}{3}$ $0.\overline{6}$　　　**b.** $\frac{1}{6}$ $0.1\overline{6}$　　　**c.** $\frac{5}{9}$ $0.\overline{5}$　　　**d.** $\frac{4}{3}$ $1.\overline{3}$

e. Number Sense Examine the fractions $\frac{2}{3}, \frac{3}{3}, \frac{4}{3}, \frac{5}{3}$, and $\frac{6}{3}$. Explain when a denominator of 3 will result in a repeating decimal.
when the numerator is not divisible by 3

👥 Reaching All Students

Below Level Have students write the names of several sets of decimals like the following.	Advanced Learners If n is a whole number from 1 to 98, what is the decimal form of $\frac{n}{99}$? If $n < 10$, $\frac{n}{99} = 0.\overline{0n}$. If n is 10 or greater, $\frac{n}{99} = 0.\overline{n}$.	Alternative Method See note on page 154. Error Prevention See note on page 155.
0.27 **27 hundredths** 2.7 **2 and 7 tenths** 0.027 **27 thousandths**		

 For more practice, see *Extra Practice*.

3. Practice

Assignment Guide

1 **Objective 1**
   Ⓐ Ⓑ Core 1–12, 27–28
   Ⓒ Extension 43

2 **Objective 2**
   Ⓐ Ⓑ Core 13–26, 29–37
   Ⓒ Extension 38–42, 44

Test Prep 45–48
Mixed Review 49–54

Ⓐ Practice by Example

Example 1
(page 153)

Write each decimal as a fraction or mixed number in simplest form.

1. 0.3 $\frac{3}{10}$ **2.** 0.8 $\frac{4}{5}$ **3.** 0.75 $\frac{3}{4}$ **4.** 0.04 $\frac{1}{25}$

5. 0.15 $\frac{3}{20}$ **6.** 0.17 $\frac{17}{100}$ **7.** 0.008 $\frac{1}{125}$ **8.** 5.5 $5\frac{1}{2}$

9. 4.25 $4\frac{1}{4}$ **10.** 3.149 $3\frac{149}{1,000}$ **11.** 5.075 $5\frac{3}{40}$ **12.** 8.32 $8\frac{8}{25}$

Examples 2, 3
(page 154)

Write each fraction or mixed number as a decimal.

13. $\frac{2}{5}$ 0.4   **14.** $\frac{3}{4}$ 0.75   **15.** $\frac{3}{8}$ 0.375   **16.** $\frac{9}{10}$ 0.9

17. $\frac{5}{6}$ $0.8\overline{3}$ **18.** $\frac{7}{15}$ $0.4\overline{6}$ **19.** $\frac{11}{8}$ 1.375   **20.** $\frac{10}{9}$ $1.\overline{1}$

21. $4\frac{7}{10}$ 4.7   **22.** $1\frac{1}{10}$ 1.1   **23.** $2\frac{7}{12}$ $2.58\overline{3}$ **24.** $5\frac{3}{20}$ 5.15

Ⓑ Apply Your Skills

25. Shopping You order $1\frac{1}{4}$ pounds of cheese at a deli. What decimal number should the digital scale show? 1.25

26. Sports During the 2001 baseball season, Vladimir Guerrero had 184 hits in 599 official at bats. Use a calculator to change the fraction $\frac{184}{599}$ to a decimal. Round your answer to the nearest thousandth. 0.307

27. Writing in Math Explain the steps you would use to write 0.125 as a fraction in simplest form. See below left.

28. Data File, p. 117 Which wrenches measure 0.375 inch, 0.4375 inch, and 0.8125 inch? $\frac{3}{8}, \frac{7}{16}, \frac{13}{16}$

State whether each fraction is less than, equal to, or greater than 0.75.

29. $\frac{7}{8}$ greater than **30.** $\frac{4}{5}$ greater than **31.** $\frac{21}{28}$ equal to **32.** $\frac{11}{15}$ less than

27. Write 0.125 as $\frac{125}{1,000}$. Divide numerator and denominator by 125 to express the fraction in simplest form as $\frac{1}{8}$.

Write each measurement as a mixed number and as a decimal.

33. four and three-fourths pounds $4\frac{3}{4}$ lb, 4.75 lb

34. five and seven-eighths inches $5\frac{7}{8}$ in., 5.875 in.

Order each set of numbers from least to greatest.

35. $\frac{7}{8}$, 0.8, 0.87   **36.** 1.65, $1\frac{2}{3}$, $1\frac{3}{5}$, 1.7
   0.8, 0.87, $\frac{7}{8}$ $1\frac{3}{5}$, 1.65, $1\frac{2}{3}$, 1.7

37. Stocks Until 2001, stock prices were reported as mixed numbers. Find the dollar amounts represented by $6\frac{5}{8}$ and $8\frac{1}{2}$. $6.625, $8.50

3-8 Fractions and Decimals **155**

GPS Use the Guided Problem Solving worksheet with Exercise 25.

Error Prevention!

Exercises 4–11 Students might ignore zeros after the decimal point, and write the wrong denominator.

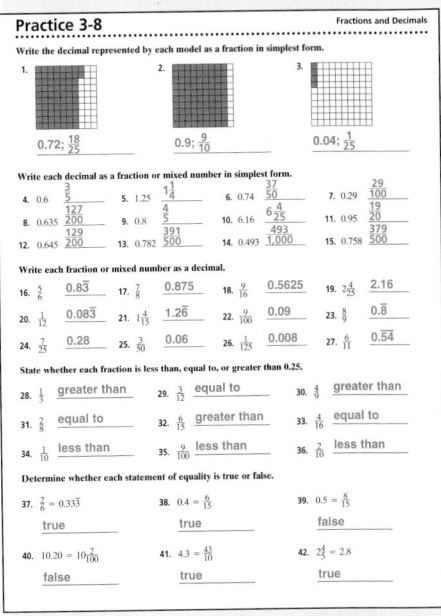

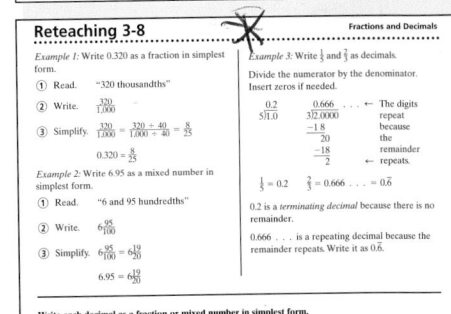

 **PowerPoint** **Lesson Quiz 3-8**

Write each as a fraction in simplest form.

1. 0.7 $\frac{7}{10}$

2. 0.008 $\frac{1}{125}$

Write each as a decimal. Use a bar to indicate repeating digits.

3. $\frac{9}{16}$ 0.5625

4. $1\frac{4}{15}$ $1.2\overline{6}$

Alternative Assessment

Each student in a pair writes a decimal and a fraction. Partners exchange papers and write each other's decimal as a fraction in simplest form and each other's fraction as a decimal.

Test Prep

Resources

For additional practice with a variety of test item formats:
• Test-Prep, p. 165
• Test-Taking Strategies, p. 161
• Test-Taking Strategies With Transparencies

C Challenge **Match each number with its location on the number line.**

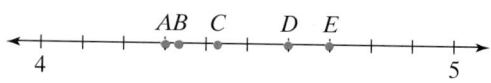

38. $4\frac{3}{5}$ D **39.** 4.3 A **40.** 4.43 C **41.** $4\frac{1}{3}$ B **42.** 4.7 E

43. Write the decimal $0.0\overline{3}$ as a fraction. (*Hint*: How is the decimal different than $\frac{1}{3} = 0.\overline{3}$?) $\frac{1}{30}$

44. Stretch Your Thinking Copy and fill in both blanks with the same digit to make the equation true. $\frac{\blacksquare 6}{125} = 0.\blacksquare 08$

$\frac{26}{125} = 0.208$

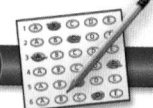

Test Prep

Multiple Choice

45. A carton of juice contains 1 liter, or about 33.8 fluid ounces. What is 33.8 as a mixed number in simplest form? A

A. $33\frac{4}{5}$ **B.** $33\frac{8}{10}$ **C.** $33\frac{9}{10}$ **D.** $34\frac{4}{5}$

46. Which decimal is equivalent to $\frac{8}{15}$? G
F. 0.53 **G.** $0.5\overline{3}$ **H.** 0.54 **I.** 0.6

Take It to the NET
Online lesson quiz at
www.PHSchool.com
Web Code: aaa-0308

47. On a digital scale, some sliced ham weighs 1.38 pounds. Which amount is nearest this weight? C

A. $1\frac{1}{4}$ pounds **B.** $1\frac{1}{3}$ pounds **C.** $1\frac{3}{8}$ pounds **D.** $1\frac{1}{2}$ pounds

Short Response

48. Three paint brushes have widths of $\frac{1}{2}$ inch, $\frac{3}{8}$ inch, and $\frac{3}{4}$ inch.
a. Which brush is the least wide?
b. Justify your answer.
48a–b. See margin.

Mixed Review

Lesson 2-9 **Use the Distributive Property to simplify each expression.**

49. 3×42 126 **50.** 9×68 612 **51.** 7×2.9 20.3 **52.** 4×9.1 36.4

Lesson 1-6 **Choose a strategy to solve each problem.**

53. Delino lives 0.5 mile from the bus stop. How many miles does he walk going to and from the bus stop five days a week for 36 weeks? 180 miles

54. Gardening Your uncle is planting a row of tomato plants along his back fence. The fence is 30 feet long. If he places the plants 30 inches apart, how many plants does he have room for? 13 plants

---

Enrichment 3-8 Fractions and Decimals
Patterns in Numbers

When some fractions are converted to decimals, they create a pattern.

1. Write each fraction as a decimal.
$\frac{1}{9}$ $0.\overline{1}$ $\frac{1}{11}$ $0.\overline{09}$
$\frac{2}{9}$ $0.\overline{2}$ $\frac{2}{11}$ $0.\overline{18}$
$\frac{3}{9}$ $0.\overline{3}$ $\frac{3}{11}$ $0.\overline{27}$
$\frac{4}{9}$ $0.\overline{4}$ $\frac{4}{11}$ $0.\overline{36}$
$\frac{5}{9}$ $0.\overline{5}$ $\frac{5}{11}$ $0.\overline{45}$
$\frac{6}{9}$ $0.\overline{6}$ $\frac{6}{11}$ $0.\overline{54}$
$\frac{7}{9}$ $0.\overline{7}$ $\frac{7}{11}$ $0.\overline{63}$

2. Look at the decimals you wrote for the fractions with a denominator of 9. What pattern do you see?
Sample answer: The decimal is a repeating decimal. The repeating part of the decimal is the same as the numerator of the fraction.

3. Look at the decimals you wrote for the fractions with a denominator of 11. What pattern do you see?
Sample answer: The decimal is a repeating decimal. The repeating part of the decimal is the product of 9 and the numerator of the fraction.

4. Use the patterns to write the decimal for each fraction.
a. $\frac{8}{9}$ $0.\overline{8}$ b. $\frac{8}{11}$ $0.\overline{72}$
c. $\frac{9}{11}$ $0.\overline{81}$ d. $\frac{10}{11}$ $0.\overline{90}$

Match each number with its location on the number line.

A B C DE F
├──┼──┼──┼──┼──┼──┼──┤
1   2

5. $1.\overline{72}$ D 6. $1\frac{1}{9}$ A 7. $1\frac{10}{11}$ F
8. $1.\overline{3}$ C 9. $1\frac{5}{9}$ E 10. $1\frac{3}{11}$ B

---

48. [2] a. $\frac{3}{8}$ in.
b. Write equivalent fractions using LCD 8: $\frac{4}{8}, \frac{3}{8}, \frac{6}{8}$. The least fraction is $\frac{3}{8}$ because with the

same denominators, the lesser the numerator, the lesser the fraction size.

[1] correct answer with no explanation

3-9 Try, Check, and Revise

What You'll Learn

OBJECTIVE 1 To solve problems by trying, checking, and revising

...And Why

To solve a problem involving different prices, as in Example 1

✓ Check Skills You'll Need

❓ For help, go to Lesson 2-1.

Write the next three terms in each pattern.

1. 2, 4, 6, 8, ...   10, 12, 14
2. 2, 4, 8, 16, ...   32, 64, 128
3. 2, 6, 18, ...   54, 162, 486
4. 100, 95, 90, ...   85, 80, 75
5. 1, 6, 11, 16, ...   21, 26, 31
6. 1, 3, 5, 7, ...   9, 11, 13

Lesson Preview

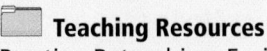

✓ **Check Skills You'll Need**

Finding Number Patterns
Lesson 2-1: Example 1. Extra Practice p. 643.

Lesson Resources

📁 **Teaching Resources**
Practice, Reteaching, Enrichment

👥 **Reaching All Students**
Practice Workbook 3-9
Spanish Practice Workbook 3-9
Guided Problem Solving 3-9

🕐 **Presentation Assistant Plus!**
Transparencies
• Check Skills You'll Need 3-9
• Problem of the Day 3-9
• Additional Examples 3-9
• Student Edition Answers 3-9
• Lesson Quiz 3-9
• Classroom Aid 10
PH Presentation Pro CD-ROM 3-9

PRENTICE HALL ASSESSMENT SYSTEM

Computer Test Generator CD

💻 **Technology**
Resource Pro® CD-ROM
Computer Test Generator CD
PH Presentation Pro CD-ROM

💻 **www.PHSchool.com**
Student Site
• Teacher Web Code: aak-5500
• Algebra Readiness Puzzles 111
• Self-grading Lesson Quiz

PH SuccessNet Teacher Center
• Lesson Planner
• Resources

Plus 📘TEXT

OBJECTIVE

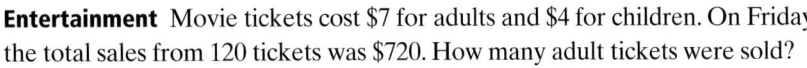

1 Solving Problems by Trying, Checking, and Revising

📘TEXT Interactive lesson includes instant self-check, tutorials, and activities.

When to Use This Strategy You can use the *Try, Check, and Revise* strategy when the solution to a problem involves several related numbers.

To use this strategy, first *try* to make a reasonable estimate of the solution. Then *check* against the given information. If your estimate is incorrect, *revise* it to make it more reasonable. Keep trying, checking, and revising until you find the correct answer.

1 EXAMPLE Real-World 🌐 Problem Solving

Entertainment Movie tickets cost $7 for adults and $4 for children. On Friday the total sales from 120 tickets was $720. How many adult tickets were sold?

Read and Understand Adult tickets cost $7. Child tickets cost $4. The theater collected $720 by selling 120 tickets. You need to find how many adult tickets were sold.

Plan and Solve To help determine how many adult tickets were sold, try, check, and revise a reasonable combination of numbers.

Try: Since 120 tickets were sold, try 40 adult tickets and 80 child tickets.

You can organize your data in a table.

Adult Tickets	Child Tickets	Total Sales
40 × $7 = $280	80 × $4 = $320	$280 + $320 = $600

Check: With 40 adult tickets, the total sales of $600 is too low.

Ongoing Assessment and Intervention

Before the Lesson
Diagnose prerequisite skills using:
• Check Skills You'll Need

During the Lesson
Monitor progress using:
• Check Understanding
• Additional Examples
• Test Prep

After the Lesson
Assess knowledge using:
• Lesson Quiz
• Computer Test Generator CD

Math Background

The *try, check, and revise* strategy is sometimes called *guess and check*. Students make a reasonable estimate of the solution, check if the estimate satisfies the conditions of the problem, and revise the number if necessary. Students arrive at the correct solution by making increasingly more reasonable tries and revisions.

Teaching Notes

① EXAMPLE Technology Tip

Students can use spreadsheet software to make their tables. In cell A1 of the first row, enter the number of adult tickets. In cell B1, enter =120−A1, the number of child tickets. In cell C1, enter =7*A1+4*B1, the total sales. Repeat these steps in succeeding rows to try other numbers.

Error Prevention!

Students might focus on one condition of a problem and forget another. For instance, in Check Understanding 1, they might say there were 60 adult tickets (and 30 child tickets) because $60 \times \$7 + 30 \times \$4 = \$540$. While $540 is the correct total sales, the total number of tickets would be $60 + 30 = 90$, which is incorrect.

PowerPoint
Additional Examples

① There are exactly 50 coins in a bank. Their total value is $9.50. The coins are either quarters or dimes. How many dimes are there? **20 dimes**

Closure

Explain the *try, check, and revise* strategy. Try to make a reasonable attempt to solve the problem. Check the result against the given information. If it is incorrect, revise it to make it more reasonable. Keep trying, checking, and revising until you find the correct answer.

158

Since $600 is too low, increase the number of tickets that are more expensive.

Revise: Increase the number of adult tickets. Keep a total of 120 tickets.

Adult Tickets	Child Tickets	Total Sales
$50 \times \$7 = \$350$	$70 \times \$4 = \$280$	$630
$90 \times \$7 = \$630$	$30 \times \$4 = \$120$	$750

You can see that 50 adult tickets is too low, and 90 adult tickets is too high. But the total sales of $750 with 90 adult tickets is close to $720. Revise once more. Try 80 adult tickets.

Adult Tickets	Child Tickets	Total Sales
$80 \times \$7 = \$560$	$40 \times \$4 = \$160$	$720

Look Back and Check With 80 adult tickets and 40 child tickets, the number of tickets sold is equal to 120 and the total sales are $720.

✓ Check Understanding ① If the theater collected $540 by selling 120 tickets at the same prices as those in Example 1, how many adult tickets were sold? **20 adult tickets**

EXERCISES

? For more practice, see *Extra Practice*.

Ⓐ Practice by Example **Solve each problem using the strategy Try, Check, and Revise.**

Example 1
(page 157)

1. **Business** A vendor sells salads and juices. A salad costs $3.00 and juice costs $2.50. The vendor collected $216 by selling 80 items. How many juices were sold? **48 juices**

Need Help?
• Reread the problem.
• Identify the key facts and details.
• Tell the problem in your own words.
• Try a different strategy.
• Check your work.

2. **Pet Care** A rectangular turtle cage is made with 40 feet of wire fence. The length is 6 feet more than the width. What are the length and width of the turtle cage? **length = 13 ft, width = 7 ft**

3. The Kinjo family has two children. The sum of their ages is 27. They were born 5 years apart. How old are the two children? **11 years old and 16 years old.**

4. **Sports** The junior high school soccer team played a total of 24 games. They won 6 more games than they lost. They tied in 4 games. How many games did they win? **13 games**

5.

5. Split the face of the clock at the right into two halves so that the sum of the clock's numbers in each of the halves is equal. **See left.**

158 Chapter 3 Number Theory and Fractions

👥 Reaching All Students

Below Level Have students solve several simple problems like these.

Find two numbers whose:
sum is 20 and product is 36 **2, 18**
sum is 40 and difference is 8 **16, 24**

Advanced Learners There are 20 animals in a barnyard. Some are cows and some are chickens. The number of legs is 8 more than twice the number of heads. How many chickens are there? **16 chickens**

Diversity See note on page 159.
Error Prevention See note on page 158.

B Apply Your Skills

Choose a strategy to solve each problem.

Strategies

Draw a Diagram
Make a Graph
Make an Organized List
Make a Table and
    Look for a Pattern
Simulate a Problem
Solve a Simpler Problem
Try, Check, and Revise
Use Logical Reasoning
Work Backward
Write an Equation

6. Music Wayne gives piano and voice lessons. Piano lessons are 30 minutes long and voice lessons are 45 minutes long. Wayne spent a total of $4\frac{1}{2}$ hours giving 8 different lessons. How many piano lessons did Wayne give?
6 piano lessons

7. Trains leave Farmville for Lexinburg GPS every 40 minutes. The first train leaves at 5:00 A.M. What is the departure time closest to 12:35 P.M.?
12:20 P.M.

8. Money Suppose you save quarters and dimes in a jar. Last night you counted $6.75. The number of dimes is one more than the number of quarters. How many quarters are there? **19 quarters**

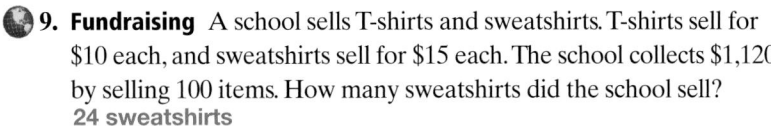

9. Fundraising A school sells T-shirts and sweatshirts. T-shirts sell for $10 each, and sweatshirts sell for $15 each. The school collects $1,120 by selling 100 items. How many sweatshirts did the school sell?
24 sweatshirts

10. Writing in Math Rearrange the boxes so that the weight of each pile is equal. Explain the steps you took in trying, checking, and revising.

1 lb	4 lb	7 lb
2 lb	5 lb	8 lb
3 lb	6 lb	9 lb

1 lb, 5 lb, 9 lb;
2 lb, 6 lb, 7 lb;
3 lb, 4 lb, 8 lb;
**check students'
work.**

C Challenge

11. Place the digits 2, 3, 4, 6, and 8 in a copy of the figure below so the product is the same in both directions. Find the product.
**Answers may vary.
Sample:**

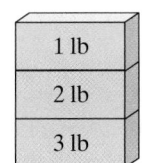 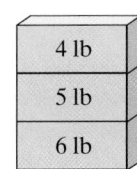
; 96

12. Stretch Your Thinking The puzzle below is a cryptarithm. Each letter represents a different digit. Find a value for each letter. (*Hint:* What is the only possible value for M?)

```
  FUN
+  I S
-----
 MATH
```

**Answers may vary.
Sample: 984
      + 72

      1,056**

GPS **Use the Guided Problem Solving worksheet with Exercise 7.**

Assignment Guide

1 Objective 1
    A **B** Core 1–10
    C Extension 11–13

Test Prep **14–17**
Mixed Review **18–32**

Diversity
Exercise 6 Ask volunteers who play the piano or sing to describe how they practice and what lessons they have received.

Practice 3-9   Problem Solving: Try, Check, and Revise

Solve each problem by trying, checking, and revising.

1. A deli sells ham sandwiches for $2 and roast beef sandwiches for $3. A group organizing a family reunion placed orders for 85 sandwiches. The bill came to $218 before tax. How many ham sandwiches were ordered?
   37 ham sandwiches

2. Tickets for a community dinner cost $4 for adults and $3 for children. A total of 390 tickets was sold, earning $1,380. How many of each type of ticket were sold?
   210 adult, 180 children

3. Place the digits 3, 4, 7, 9, and 12 in the circles at the right so that the product of these numbers is the same left to right and up and down. What is the product?
   252

Choose a strategy to solve each problem.

4. Two numbers have a sum of 42 and a product of 432. What are the two numbers?
   18 and 24

5. Two numbers have a sum of 70 and a product of 1,189. What are the two numbers?
   29 and 41

6. Louise, Bill, and Fran each had a different piece of fruit packed in their lunches. An apple, an orange, and a banana were packed. Louise won't eat apples. Bill is allergic to oranges. Fran eats only bananas. What piece of fruit did each person have?
   Louise: orange; Bill: apple;
   Fran: banana

7. Paco joins a baseball card club. He brings 2 cards to the first meeting, 3 cards to the second meeting, 5 cards to the third meeting, and 8 cards to the fourth meeting. If he continues this pattern, how many cards will he bring to the fifth meeting?
   12 cards

8. The floor plan of the first floor of a museum is shown at the right. If you enter at A, is it possible to go through each doorway only one time, see each room, and exit at B? If this can be done, show how. You may enter each room more than once.
   Sample answer shown.

Reteaching 3-9   Problem Solving: Try, Check, and Revise

Lincoln Middle School needs new smoke alarms. The school has $415 to spend. Alarms with escape lights cost $18, and alarms with a false-alarm silencer cost $11. The school wants 4 times as many escape-light alarms as silencer alarms. How many of each kind can the school purchase?

Read and Understand What facts are needed to solve the problem? *You need the costs of the alarms, $18 and $11; the amount to be spent, $415; and the fact that 4 times as many escape-light alarms as silencer alarms will be bought.*

Plan and Solve You can try, check, and revise to solve this problem.
Try: Buy 12 escape-light alarms and 3 silencer alarms.
Check: 12 × $18 = $216
          3 × $11 = $ 33
     Add: $249

$249 is a lot less than the $415 that the school has to spend. Revise with different combinations until you solve the problem.

Buy 20 escape-light alarms and 5 silencer alarms.
Check: 20 × $18 = $360
          5 × $11 = $ 55
     Add: $415

Look Back and Check Check to see whether your answer agrees with the information in the problem. *Is the total amount spent $415, or slightly less? Are there 4 times as many escape-light alarms as silencer alarms?*

Solve each problem by trying, checking, and revising.

1. Tina needs batteries. AA batteries cost $3 per pack. D batteries cost $4 per pack. If she has $26 to spend and buys 3 times as many packs of AA batteries as D batteries, how many packs of each does she buy?
   6 packs of AA, 2 packs of D

2. Ian needs CDs for his CD burner. One package of 3 CDs sells for $5. Another pack of 2 costs $4. If Ian has $19 and buys 11 CDs, how many packs of each kind does he buy?
   three $5 packs and one $4 pack

3. Hyugen has $50 to spend on CDs. New ones cost $9 and used ones cost $7. He wants to buy more new CDs than used. How many of each can he buy?
   4 new CDs and 2 used CDs

4. Frank has $41 to spend on computer disks. A pack of 10 ES brand disks costs $13, and a pack of 11 CW brand disks costs $14. How many packs of each can he buy if he spends all his money?
   1 ES brand and 2 CW brand

 **Lesson Quiz 3-9**

Solve using try, check, and revise.

1. The difference between two whole numbers is 66. One of the numbers is $\frac{1}{4}$ of the other. What are the two numbers? **88 and 22**

Alternative Assessment

Each student in a pair writes a problem similar to Exercises 1–5. Suggest that students work backward from a solution to the given information. Partners exchange problems and then solve. Partners then discuss how they found their solutions.

Test Prep

Resources

For additional practice with a variety of test item formats:
• Test-Prep, p. 165
• Test-Taking Strategies, p. 161
• Test-Taking Strategies With Transparencies

Enrichment 3-9   Problem Solving: Try, Check, and Revise
Decision Making

You want to make a meat loaf. You need to go to the grocery store to purchase each ingredient. You only have $15. If you do not have enough money for any item, your neighbor says that you can borrow the item from her.

Grocery Store Prices	
Ground beef	$1.29/lb
Catsup	$1.79/bottle
Eggs	$1.69/dozen
Tomato juice	$3.99/bottle
Bran cereal	$3.79/box
Onion flakes	$1.10/container
Worcestershire sauce	$4.19/bottle
Rice	$1.89/box

Check students' answers.

1. Determine which items you plan to buy from the grocery store.
   Since this is a meat loaf, ground beef must be purchased.

2. Which items do you not have enough money for?

3. You only want to borrow as few of the inexpensive items as possible. How does this affect your decisions from Questions 1 and 2?

4. What items do you plan to borrow from your neighbor?

---

13. 25, 25;
    25, 19, 6;
    25, 19, 3, 3;
    19, 19, 12;
    19, 19, 9, 3;
    19, 19, 6, 6;
    19, 19, 6, 3, 3;
    19, 19, 3, 3, 3, 3

 13. **Carnivals** A game at a carnival involves throwing two or more bean bags through target holes for different numbers of points. The object of the game is to score exactly 50 points. What are the different ways you can score exactly 50 points?

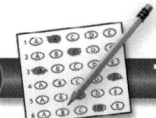 **Test Prep**

Multiple Choice

14. What is 0.24 as a fraction in simplest form? **B**
   A. $\frac{1}{4}$ B. $\frac{6}{25}$ C. $\frac{12}{50}$ D. $\frac{24}{100}$

Take It to the NET
Online lesson quiz at
www.PHSchool.com
Web Code: aaa-0309

15. Which number is both a factor and a multiple of 26? **H**
   F. 1   G. 13   H. 26   I. 52

16. Which of the following numbers is a prime number? **C**
   A. 9   B. 16   C. 23   D. 57

17. Which of the following numbers is NOT a prime number? **G**
   F. 53   G. 63   H. 73   I. 83

Mixed Review

Lesson 3-7

Compare each pair of numbers. Use <, =, or >.

18. $\frac{3}{4}$ ■ $\frac{7}{8}$ **<**   19. $\frac{1}{5}$ ■ $\frac{4}{20}$ **=**   20. $\frac{4}{7}$ ■ $\frac{3}{6}$ **>**

21. $2\frac{3}{5}$ ■ $\frac{13}{5}$ **=**   22. $\frac{10}{8}$ ■ $\frac{5}{2}$ **<**   23. $6\frac{1}{3}$ ■ $6\frac{3}{8}$ **<**

Lesson 2-6

Algebra Solve each equation.

24. $x + 35 = 90$ **55**   25. $x + 0.6 = 0.92$ **0.32**   26. $5 = x + 3.1$ **1.9**

27. $x + 8 = 18.5$ **10.5**   28. $1.2 = x + 0.05$ **1.15**   29. $x + 2.4 = 2.7$ **0.3**

Lesson 2-3

Algebra Write an expression for each word phrase.

30. 6 times r
    $6r$

31. 3 less than p
    $p - 3$

32. 15 more than y
    $y + 15$

Writing Extended Responses

Writing Extended Responses

This feature gives an example for students to see how to receive full credit on extended-response questions.

An extended-response question in this book is worth a total of 4 points. To get full credit, you must show your work and explain your reasoning.

Resources

 PRENTICE HALL **ASSESSMENT SYSTEM**

Test-Taking Strategies With Transparencies
• Transparency 4
• Practice master, p. 3

● EXAMPLE

Mary plans to fence 80 square feet of her backyard for her dog. She wants the length and width to be whole numbers (in feet). What dimensions can she use? Tell how you know that you have found all possible pairs.

Here are four responses with the points each received.

---

4 points

1 ft by 80 ft, 2 ft by 40 ft, 4 ft by 20 ft, 5 ft by 16 ft, and 8 ft by 10 ft

These are all the pairs because there are no other whole numbers that divide 80 without a remainder.

---

3 points

8 and 10, 4 and 20, 5 and 14, 2 and 40, 1 and 80

There are no other whole numbers that divide 80 with no remainder, so this must be the answer.

The 4-point response shows all of the correct whole-number factors of 80 and the student's explanation of why the answer is complete.

The 3-point response has one error and the student's explanation of why the answer is complete.

---

2 points

8 ft by 10 ft, 1 ft by 80 ft, 2 ft by 40 ft, 5 ft by 16 ft, and 4 ft by 20 ft

---

1 point

2 and 40, 1 and 80, 8 and 10

The 2-point response gives all pairs of factors but does not have an explanation.

The 1-point response is missing some pairs and does not have an explanation.

Teaching Notes

Emphasize to students the importance of providing complete answers to extended-response questions, of showing all work, and of writing a clear and full explanation of their reasoning. Encourage students always to check their work.

● EXAMPLE Error Prevention

Some students may omit 1 and 80 as dimensions of one of the fenced-in rectangles. Remind them that every number has 1 and itself as factors.

EXERCISES

Use the example above to answer each question.

1. Read the 3-point response. What error did the student make? **5 and 14 are not a pair of factors of 80.**

2. Read the 1-point response. Which dimensions are missing? **4 and 20, 5 and 16**

Test-Taking Strategies With Transparencies

Chapter 3: Writing Extended Responses
Exercises

David has one quarter, three dimes, and five nickels. How many different ways can he combine the coins to make 45¢?

Scoring Rubric

• **4 points:** Student correctly answers question in a complete sentence, provides an explanation, and shows all possible combinations.

• **3 points:** Student answers question in a complete sentence, provides an explanation, and shows possible combinations, but makes minor calculation errors.

• **2 point:** Student provides an incorrect explanation and does not completely answer the question.

• **1 point:** Student incorrectly answers the question and does not provide an explanation.

• **0 points:** No response or answer is completely incorrect.

Three responses to the question are shown below.

4 point response	3 point response	1 point response
1 quarter, 2 dimes	1 quarter, 2 dimes	1 quarter, 2 dimes
1 quarter, 1 dime, 2 nickels	1 quarter, 1 dime, 2 nickels	
1 quarter, 4 nickels	1 quarter, 3 nickels	1 quarter, 1 dime, 2 nickels
3 dimes, 3 nickels	3 dimes, 3 nickels	
2 dimes, 5 nickels	2 dimes, 5 nickels	1 quarter, 4 nickels
There are no other possible ways for the coins to add up to 45¢ so this must be the complete answer.	These are the only combinations that add up to 45¢.	2 dimes, 5 nickels

1. Tell why the 4-point response received the points it did.
   It shows all work and answers to both parts of the problem. The
   response includes an explanation of why this is the complete answer.

2. Read the 3-point response. What error did the student make?
   1 quarter + 3 nickels equals 40¢, not 45¢.

3. Write a 2-point response that has an incorrect explanation.
   Sample answer: 1 quarter and 2 dimes, 1 quarter and 4 nickels,
   3 dimes and 3 nickels; all these add up to 45¢.

Resources

Student Edition
Extra Practice, Ch. 3, p. 644
English/Spanish Glossary, p. 669
Table of Symbols, p. 666

 Reaching All Students
Reading and Math Literacy 3D
Spanish Reading and Math
Literacy 3D

PRENTICE HALL
ASSESSMENT SYSTEM

Test Preparation
• Chapter 3 practice in test
  formats

 www.PHSchool.com
Student Site
• Self-grading vocabulary test

PH SuccessNet Teacher Center
• Resources

Plus  iTEXT

Chapter 3 Chapter Review

Vocabulary

common factor (p. 128)   factor (p. 123)   multiple (p. 143)
common multiple (p. 143)   greatest common factor (p. 128)   odd number (p. 120)
composite number (p. 124)   improper fraction (p. 139)   prime factorization (p. 124)
divisible (p. 119)   least common denominator (p. 148)   prime number (p. 124)
equivalent fractions (p. 134) least common multiple (p. 143)   proper fraction (p. 139)
even number (p. 120)   mixed number (p. 139)   simplest form (p. 135)

 Reading Math:
Understanding
Vocabulary

Choose the vocabulary term from the column on the right that best completes each sentence.

1. Fractions that represent the same amount are __?__. **B**

2. The number $5\frac{1}{8}$ is a(n) __?__. **D**

Take It to the NET
Online vocabulary quiz
at www.PHSchool.com
Web Code: aaj-0351

3. The __?__ of 42 is $2 \times 3 \times 7$. **A**

4. Every __?__ is divisible by 2. **C**

5. The numbers 2, 3, 5, 7, and 11 are __?__. **E**

A. prime
   factorization

B. equivalent
   fractions

C. even number

D. mixed number

E. prime numbers

Skills and Concepts

3-1 and 3-2 Objectives

▼ To identify numbers
  divisible by 2, 3, 5, 9,
  or 10

▼ To find factors of a
  number

▼ To find the prime
  factorization of a
  number

A **prime number** has exactly two factors, 1 and the number itself.
A **composite number** has more than two whole-number factors. Writing a composite number as a product of prime numbers is the **prime factorization** of the number.

Test each number for divisibility by 2, 3, 5, 9, or 10.

6. 207 3 and 9   7. 585 3, 5, and 9   8. 756 2, 3, and 9   9. 3,330
                                                                    2, 3, 5, 9,
                                                                    and 10

Find the prime factorization of each number.

10. 28   11. 51   12. 100   13. 250
    $2^2 \times 7$ 3×17 $2^2 \times 5^2$ 2×5^3

3-3 Objective

▼ To find the greatest
  common factor of
  two or more numbers

The **greatest common factor (GCF)** of two or more numbers is the greatest factor shared by all the numbers.

Find the GCF of each set of numbers.

14. 18, 28 2   15. 12, 62 2   16. 25, 35 5   17. 16, 40 8

Spanish Reading and Math Literacy

Reading and Math Literacy

3D: Vocabulary   For use with the Chapter Review

Study Skill: Combine clue words and pictures to prompt your memory.

Use the word list below to find hidden words in the puzzle. Once you have found a word, draw a circle around it and cross the word off in the word list. Words can be displayed forwards, backwards, up, down, or diagonally but they are always in a straight line.

divisible   common factor   fraction   factor tree
multiple   prime factor   improper fraction   least common multiple
mixed number   composite number equivalent fractions expression
range   conjecture   exponent   equation
solution   variable   power   identity
associative   commutative   distributive   decimal

```
Q E C I E L P I T L U M N O M M O C T S A E L T B
W A V S A Z W B Z P T D A N O I S S E R P X E D S
I T G I N P M E P F R A C T I O N O B H L D D P R
L R P N T H B E L L M G O M W F S Z O X Y I Y Y U
X N G I U A J I M P R O P E R F R A C T I O N J H
L I V T S K T Y O J I K U Z V W B N M K I Y E N V
E A K Q O H J U E V I T A I C O S S A C A B U T A
V M M B N W E D M H O Z L P R I M E F A C T O R E
I M R I K A B L H M K K H U E F M E J W A Y W O F
T M X B C Q P L B W O B M Y M L O N U E L R N W Y
U Q F H O E K L U I G C L S O L U T I O N A D L Y
B Z P I V F D M Z Q S E B L B F R J Y V I N Y X X
I U Q L X R A E L B A I R A V F P O W E R G S T E
R J P E I D J R X G O X V F A C T O R T R E E E U
T R O T C A F N O M M O C I X Z Q W X O S A X X K
S Q Y N Z U G J U O N O T Z D B O N M W R X B P Y
I N O I T A U Q E B T Q J J L U T V O S L E O M
D H Z O C Z V G C R S D H Z W V Y Y Z F K A H N U
J X A F B A D I C B U S K U K S Y C H V K Z Z E O
O F J K R E B M U N E T I S O P M O C K E T K N Z
V M E Q U I V A L E N T F R A C T I O N S G X T X
R E B M U N D E X I M H H W D G J Z Q S D V T I H
M J R I J O V A T H Z T M K A Y D D V G L L W H Y
I U I D E N T I T Y L G A C B M Y R O S S J H D D
N P S L E H Z J Z D N C O N J E C T U R E T H O E
```

3-4 and 3-5 Objectives

- To find equivalent fractions
- To write fractions in simplest form
- To write mixed numbers as improper fractions
- To write improper fractions as mixed numbers

Equivalent fractions are fractions that name the same amount. A fraction is in **simplest form** when the only common factor of the numerator and the denominator is 1. A **mixed number** shows the sum of a whole number and a fraction. An **improper fraction** has a numerator that is greater than or equal to its denominator.

State whether each fraction is in simplest form. If not, write it in simplest form. Then, write two other equivalent fractions for each fraction.

18. $\frac{5}{20}$ no; $\frac{1}{4}$; $\frac{2}{8}$, $\frac{3}{12}$ **19.** $\frac{4}{6}$ no; $\frac{2}{3}$; $\frac{8}{12}$, $\frac{20}{30}$ **20.** $\frac{1}{3}$ yes; $\frac{2}{6}$, $\frac{6}{18}$ **21.** $\frac{2}{9}$ yes; $\frac{4}{18}$, $\frac{6}{27}$

Write each number as an improper fraction or a mixed number.

22. $4\frac{2}{3}$ $\frac{14}{3}$ **23.** $8\frac{1}{5}$ $\frac{41}{5}$ **24.** $\frac{13}{3}$ $4\frac{1}{3}$ **25.** $\frac{58}{6}$ $9\frac{2}{3}$

3-6 Objective

- To find the least common multiple

A number that is a multiple of each of two or more numbers is a **common multiple.** The **least common multiple** is abbreviated **LCM.**

Find the LCM of each set of numbers.

26. 2, 10 10 **27.** 6, 9 18 **28.** 12, 22 132 **29.** 10, 20, 35 140

3-7 and 3-8 Objectives

- To compare fractions
- To order fractions
- To write decimals as fractions
- To write fractions as decimals

To compare fractions with unlike denominators, find equivalent fractions that have a common denominator. To write a fraction as a decimal, divide the numerator by the denominator. Write a fraction for a decimal just as you would say the decimal.

Order the numbers from least to greatest.

30. $\frac{1}{2}, \frac{1}{4}, \frac{1}{6}$ $\frac{1}{6}, \frac{1}{4}, \frac{1}{2}$ **31.** $2\frac{4}{15}, 2\frac{1}{3}, 2\frac{2}{5}$ $2\frac{4}{15}, 2\frac{1}{3}, 2\frac{2}{5}$ **32.** $\frac{17}{40}, \frac{7}{20}, \frac{5}{16}$ $\frac{5}{16}, \frac{7}{20}, \frac{17}{40}$

Write each number as a fraction or mixed number in simplest form or as a decimal.

33. $\frac{3}{16}$ 0.1875 **34.** $6\frac{5}{24}$ $6.208\overline{3}$ **35.** 0.06 $\frac{3}{50}$ **36.** 4.52 $4\frac{13}{25}$

3-9 Objective

- To solve problems by trying, checking, and revising

You can try, check, and revise to solve some problems.

37. Catering The caterer at a banquet prepared twice as many chicken dinners as turkey dinners. A total of 114 dinners were prepared. How many chicken dinners were prepared? 76 chicken dinners

38. Film Rich bought 7 rolls of film, some with 36 exposures and some with 24 exposures. He can take 192 pictures in all. How many of each type of film did he buy? two 36-exposure rolls, five 24-exposure rolls

Quarter 1 Test – Form B

Quarter 1 Test – Form A

Quarter 1 Test **Form A**

Chapters 1–3

1. Write the decimal that the model represents. Then write a decimal for the portion of the model that is not shaded.

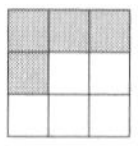

2. Write 11.017 in words.
3. Write the number in standard form. 200,000 + 6,000 + 90 + 6 + 0.04
4. Use <, >, or = to complete the statement. 0.35 _?_ 0.4
5. Round 19.082 to the nearest tenth.
6. Use compatible numbers to estimate. 47.9 ÷ 5.99
7. Allen had $312.18 in his checking account. He wrote a check for $37.12. Find his new balance.
8. Use the data in the chart below. Suppose you have to limit your sugar intake to 2 oz per day.

Food	Sugar Content
Orange Juice (4 oz)	0.417 oz
Plain Granola Bar	0.333 oz
Raisins (7 oz)	0.75 oz
Yogurt (8 oz)	1 oz

a. How many ounces of sugar did you consume if you drank 8 oz of orange juice and ate two Granola Bars?

b. Did you go over your daily limit?

9. Place the decimal point in the product. Write zeros as necessary.

$$\begin{array}{r} 1.03 \\ \times\ 0.04 \\ \hline 412 \end{array}$$

10. At $1.75 per pound, what will 2.25 pounds of grapes cost?
11. Divide. 644.8 ÷ 0.8
12. Use mental math to find the product. 123.62 × 1,000
13. Evaluate. 8 × (45 ÷ 4.5) + 20
14. Write the next two terms in the pattern. 1, 3.5, 6, 8.5, . . .
15. Evaluate the expression. $6p - 11$ for $p = 5$
16. In the expression $m - 5$, replace m with $4m + 10$. Write the resulting solution.
17. Write an algebraic expression for the word phrase "p decreased by 9."
18. Tell whether the given number is a solution to the equation. $7x - 5 = 16$; 3
19. Explain what you would do to each side of the equation to solve it. $x - 17 = 30$
20. Tom weighs 42 pounds more than his sister. If Tom weighs 90 pounds, how much does his sister weigh?

Alternative Assessment Form C

Alternative Assessment **Form C**

Chapter 3

THE PERFECT BIRDHOUSE

Did you know that birds will not move into just any birdhouse? A bird wants a house that fits; most prefer houses that are just big enough for them to squeeze into.

The drawing below shows an entrance hole that is just the right size for a downy woodpecker. The table beside it lists the right size hole for some other kinds of birds.

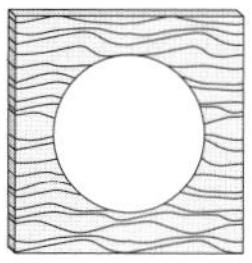

Bird	Minimum Diameter of Entrance Hole
Chickadee	$1\frac{1}{8}$ in.
House wren	$1\frac{1}{8}$ in.
Downy woodpecker	$1\frac{1}{4}$ in.
Hairy woodpecker	$1\frac{1}{2}$ in.
Red-headed woodpecker	2 in.
Great crested flycatcher	2 in.
Bluebird	$1\frac{1}{2}$ in.
Tree swallow	$1\frac{1}{2}$ in.
Purple martin	$2\frac{1}{2}$ in.
Screech owl	$3\frac{1}{4}$ in.

Show all of your work on a separate sheet of paper.

1. Why do you suppose birds are so particular about the size of their entrance hole?
2. Make a circle that shows the size of the entrance hole you would need to make in a birdhouse for a chickadee. You can use a ruler and a compass to help you.
3. Three woodpeckers are pictured on the next page. One is a red-headed woodpecker, one is a downy woodpecker, and one is a hairy woodpecker. Next to each picture is the bird's length. Use the information in the table above to help you identify each woodpecker. Write the name of each under its correct drawing. Explain your thinking.

Resources

Teaching Resources
Ch. 3 Test, Forms A & B
Ch. 3 Alternative Assessment, Form C

Reaching All Students
Spanish Ch. 3 Test, Forms A & B
Spanish Ch. 3 Alternative Assessment, Form C

PRENTICE HALL ASSESSMENT SYSTEM

Assessment Resources
• Ch. 3 Test, Forms A & B
• Ch. 3 Alternative Assessment, Form C

Computer Test Generator CD
• Ch. 3 Instant Chapter Test™
• Make your own Ch. 3 test

www.PHSchool.com
Student Site
• Self-grading Ch. 3 test

PH SuccessNet Teacher Center
• Resources

Plus *i*TEXT

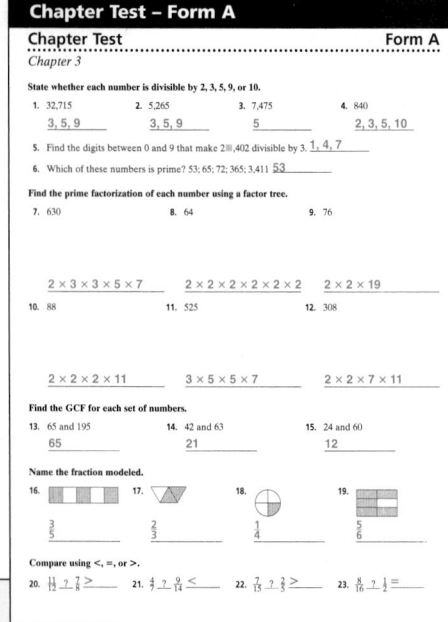

164

Take It to the NET
Online chapter test at
www.PHSchool.com
Web Code: aaa-0352

Test each number for divisibility by 2, 3, 5, 9, or 10.

1. 70
2, 5, and 10

2. 405
3, 5, and 9

3. 628
2

4. 837
3 and 9

Tell whether each number is prime or composite.

5. 19 prime

6. 39 comp.

7. 51 comp.

8. 67 prime

Find the prime factorization of each number.

9. 72
$2^3 \times 3^2$

10. 80
$2^4 \times 5$

11. 120
$2^3 \times 3 \times 5$

Find the GCF of each set of numbers.

12. 24, 36 12

13. 20, 25, 30 5

14. 7, 19 1

15. For a writing workshop, 15 coaches and 35 students will be split into groups, each with the same number of coaches and the same number of students. At most, how many groups can there be? **5 groups**

16. Find the length of each segment.
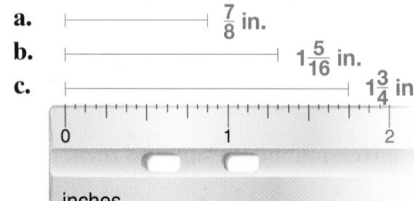
a. $\frac{7}{8}$ in.
b. $1\frac{5}{16}$ in.
c. $1\frac{3}{4}$ in.

inches

17. Lawns Today, two neighbors water their lawns. One neighbor waters her lawn every four days. The other neighbor waters his lawn every three days. In how many days will they next water their lawns on the same day? **12 days**
18a–d. Answers may vary. Samples are given.

18. Write two fractions equivalent to each.
a. $\frac{6}{18}$ $\frac{1}{3}, \frac{2}{6}$
b. $\frac{9}{24}$ $\frac{3}{8}, \frac{12}{32}$
c. $\frac{18}{20}$ $\frac{9}{10}, \frac{27}{30}$
d. $\frac{60}{100}$ $\frac{3}{5}, \frac{6}{10}$

19. Write $\frac{34}{51}$ in simplest form. $\frac{2}{3}$

20. Writing in Math Explain how to use prime factorizations to find the LCM of two numbers. Include an example. **See margin.**

Write as a mixed number and as an improper fraction.

21. one and two thirds $1\frac{2}{3}, \frac{5}{3}$

22. five and four fifths $5\frac{4}{5}, \frac{29}{5}$

23. eight and one sixth $8\frac{1}{6}, \frac{49}{6}$

24. three and one half $3\frac{1}{2}, \frac{7}{2}$

Find the LCM for each set of numbers.

25. 4, 8 8

26. 6, 11 66

27. 10, 12, 15 60

Compare each set of numbers using <, =, or >.

28. $1\frac{2}{5}$ > $1\frac{1}{5}$

29. $\frac{15}{4}$ > $\frac{17}{5}$

30. $\frac{7}{14}$ = $\frac{1}{2}$

31. $2\frac{3}{5}$ < $2\frac{7}{11}$

32. Order from least to greatest: $1\frac{5}{6}, 1\frac{7}{9}, \frac{35}{36}, 1\frac{3}{4}$.
$\frac{35}{36}, 1\frac{3}{4}, 1\frac{7}{9}, 1\frac{5}{6}$

33. Fitness Lee jogged $\frac{1}{2}$ mile, Orlando jogged $\frac{2}{3}$ mile, and Holden jogged $\frac{3}{8}$ mile. Who jogged the longest distance? **Orlando**

Write each decimal as a fraction or mixed number in simplest form. Write each fraction as a decimal.

34. 0.04 $\frac{1}{25}$

35. $\frac{17}{40}$ 0.425

36. 3.875 $3\frac{7}{8}$

37. $\frac{8}{9}$ $0.\overline{8}$

38. 2.14 $2\frac{7}{50}$

39. $\frac{6}{11}$ $0.\overline{54}$

40. Field Trips Students at Gale Middle School are going to a museum. The entrance fee is $1.75 per student and $3.25 per adult. The bus fee is $189 per bus. Each bus holds 44 people. Find the cost for 182 students and 14 adults. **$1,309**

---

20. Answers may vary. Sample: Write the prime factorization of each number greater than 1. Write an expression that involves the product of powers of the prime factors in one or both numbers. For each prime factor in this product, use the greatest exponent found in the individual prime factorizations. Then find the product. Example: Find the LCM of 6 and 10. $6 = 2 \times 3$, $10 = 2 \times 5$, LCM of 6 and $10 = 2 \times 3 \times 5 = 30$

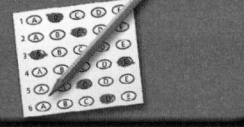

Test Prep

 **Test Prep**

Students must be able to extract information from reading passages, answer multiple-choice questions, and construct responses in order to be successful in current state and national assessments.

Reading Comprehension Read each passage and answer the questions that follow.

16	3	2	a
5	b	11	c
d	6	7	e
f	15	14	1

Sum Art Artists have often used mathematics in their work. The artist M. C. Escher used math ideas in many of his drawings. In the early sixteenth century, Albrecht Dürer included a 4 × 4 number square in one of his engravings, *Melancholia*. A number square has numbers arranged so that each row, column, and main diagonal has the same sum. Part of Dürer's number square is shown at the left.

1. What must be the sum of each row, column, and diagonal in Dürer's number square? **C**
- **A.** 21
- **B.** 23
- **C.** 34
- **D.** 38

2. What numbers do *a* and *f* represent? **I**
- **F.** 13 and 6
- **G.** 14 and 4
- **H.** 14 and 3
- **I.** 13 and 4

3. What is the sum of $b + c$? **D**
- **A.** 15
- **B.** 16
- **C.** 17
- **D.** 18

4. Two squares next to each other contain the year that Dürer made the engraving. In what year did Dürer engrave *Melancholia*? **I**
- **F.** 715
- **G.** 911
- **H.** 1112
- **I.** 1514

Something to Prove One of the most famous unsolved math problems is Goldbach's Conjecture. In 1742, Christian Goldbach made the conjecture that every even number greater than 2 can be written as the sum of two prime numbers. For example, $6 = 3 + 3$ and $10 = 3 + 7$. Today, mathematicians are still trying to prove Goldbach's Conjecture.

5. To which of the following numbers does Goldbach's Conjecture apply? **D**
- **A.** 1
- **B.** 2
- **C.** 3
- **D.** 4

6. Which of the following illustrates Goldbach's Conjecture for 100? **I**
- **F.** $100 = 35 + 65$
- **G.** $100 = 37 + 63$
- **H.** $100 = 39 + 61$
- **I.** $100 = 41 + 59$

7. Which of the following does NOT illustrate Goldbach's Conjecture for 30? **B**
- **A.** $30 = 7 + 23$
- **B.** $30 = 21 + 9$
- **C.** $30 = 11 + 19$
- **D.** $30 = 17 + 13$

8. Which of the following odd numbers would NOT be used to illustrate Goldbach's Conjecture? **H**
- **F.** 5
- **G.** 7
- **H.** 9
- **I.** 11

Resources

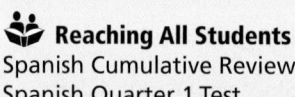 **Teaching Resources**
Cumulative Review
Quarter 1 Test, Forms A & B

 **Reaching All Students**
Spanish Cumulative Review
Spanish Quarter 1 Test

PRENTICE HALL **ASSESSMENT SYSTEM**

Test Preparation
• Ch. 3 standardized test prep

Assessment Resources
• Cumulative Review
• Quarter 1 Test, Forms A & B

Computer Test Generator CD
• Standardized test prep

 **www.PHSchool.com**
• Standardized test prep
• Resources

Plus **iTEXT**

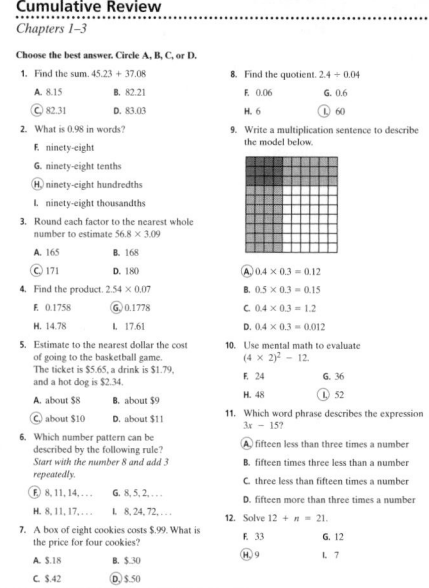

Cumulative Review

Chapters 1–3

Choose the best answer. Circle A, B, C, or D.

1. Find the sum. $45.23 + 37.08$
   - A. 8.15
   - B. 82.21
   - **C.** 82.31
   - D. 83.03

2. What is 0.98 in words?
   - F. ninety-eight
   - G. ninety-eight tenths
   - **H.** ninety-eight hundredths
   - I. ninety-eight thousandths

3. Round each factor to the nearest whole number to estimate 56.8×3.09
   - A. 165
   - B. 168
   - **C.** 171
   - D. 180

4. Find the product. 2.54×0.07
   - F. 0.1758
   - **G.** 0.1778
   - H. 14.78
   - I. 17.61

5. Estimate to the nearest dollar the cost of going to the basketball game. The ticket is $5.65, a drink is $1.79, and a hot dog is $2.34.
   - A. about $8
   - B. about $9
   - **C.** about $10
   - D. about $11

6. Which number pattern can be described by the following rule?
   Start with the number 8 and add 3 repeatedly.
   - **F.** 8, 11, 14, …
   - G. 8, 5, 2, …
   - H. 8, 11, 17, …
   - I. 8, 24, 72, …

7. A box of eight cookies costs $.99. What is the price for four cookies?
   - A. $.18
   - B. $.30
   - C. $.42
   - **D.** $.50

8. Find the quotient. $2.4 \div 0.04$
   - F. 0.06
   - G. 0.6
   - H. 6
   - **I.** 60

9. Write a multiplication sentence to describe the model below.
   - **A.** $0.4 \times 0.3 = 0.12$
   - B. $0.5 \times 0.3 = 0.15$
   - C. $0.4 \times 0.3 = 1.2$
   - D. $0.4 \times 0.3 = 0.012$

10. Use mental math to evaluate $(4 \times 2)^2 - 12$.
   - F. 24
   - G. 36
   - H. 48
   - **I.** 52

11. Which word phrase describes the expression $3x - 15$?
   - **A.** fifteen less than three times a number
   - B. fifteen times three less than a number
   - C. three less than fifteen times a number
   - D. fifteen more than three times a number

12. Solve $12 + n = 21$.
   - F. 33
   - G. 12
   - **H.** 9
   - I. 7

165

Lifting With Levers

🕮 **Real-World Snapshots**

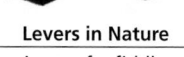

Lifting With Levers

Applying Fractions The simplest machines have only a few moving parts and can be powered by hand. For example, you can use a lever like the one in the diagram below to help lift a heavy load. If you know the distances *a* and *b* in the diagram, and the weight of a load, you can find the force needed to lift the load.

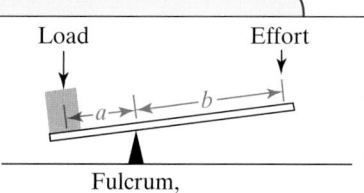

Levers in Nature
The pincer of a fiddler crab is a Class 3 lever.

How to Measure Force
$$\text{force} = \frac{a}{b} \times \text{weight of load}$$

Put It All Together

Data File Use the information on these two pages and on page 117 to answer these questions.

1. **a.** Suppose $a = 3$ and $b = 6$. Find the fraction of the load the force will be.
   b. How much force would it take to lift 100 pounds?

Load   Effort

Fulcrum, or pivot point

a = distance from fulcrum to load
b = distance from fulcrum to effort

Lever	Muscle Multiplier	Great Lifter	Load Lifter	Extra Muscle	Effort Less	Lever Greatness
a	6	4	5	10	8	5
b	10	6	8	15	14	9

2. The table shows the values of *a* and *b* in feet for six different levers.
   a. Use the force formula to write the fraction of the load required to work each lever. Write each fraction in simplest form.
   b. List the levers in order from least to most force required. Which levers need the same force?
   c. Convert each of the fractions to a decimal. Round to the nearest hundredth. Use the decimals to check the order of your list.

3. **Open-Ended** Make up your own set of levers.
   a. Choose *a* and *b* for six levers (make *a* less than *b*).
   b. Make a table to record the data about your levers. Name each lever.
   c. Exchange tables with a classmate. Write the fraction of the load required by each lever (in simplest form). Arrange the levers in order from least to most force required.

4. **Reasoning** For the levers on this page, $a < b$. What would happen if $a > b$? Can you think of a use for such a lever?

5. **Writing in Math** What class of lever is a wrench? Explain.

Levers in Playgrounds
A seesaw is a Class 1 lever. The fulcrum is between the load (one child) and the effort (the other child). The load and effort positions change as the seesaw rocks.

1a. $\frac{1}{2}$

b. 50 pounds

2a. $\frac{3}{5}, \frac{2}{3}, \frac{5}{8}, \frac{2}{3}, \frac{4}{7}, \frac{5}{9}$

b. Lever Greatness, Effort Less, Muscle Multiplier, Load Lifter, Extra

Muscle, Great Lifter; Extra Muscle and Great Lifter need the same force.

c. 0.56, 0.57, 0.6, 0.63, 0.67, 0.67

3a-c. Check students' work.

4. Answers may vary. Sample: if $a > b$, then the required force is greater than the weight of the load. You could use such a lever to move objects under a microscope.

Reaching All Students
Additional Instructional Options in Chapter 4

Reading and Math Literacy

📖 Reading Math

Understanding Word Problems, p.195

Reading-Comprehension Questions, p. 209

Understanding Vocabulary, p. 210

✏️ Writing in Math

Daily Writing Practice, pp. 173, 177, 183, 188, 193, 198, 200, 204, 207, 212

Above Level

🄲 Challenge exercises

pp. 174, 178, 183, 188, 194, 199, 204, 208

Hands-On and Technology

🔍 Investigations

Estimating Fractions, p. 171

Modeling Like Denominators, p. 175

Modeling Unlike Denominators, p. 179

Using Mixed Numbers, p. 185

Exploring Differences, p. 196

Exploring Elapsed Time, p. 201

💻 Technology

Computing With a Fraction Calculator, p. 200

Activities and Projects

📖 Real-World Snapshots

Applying Mixed Numbers pp. 214–215

📁 Chapter Project

Seeing is Believing, p. 637

Test Prep

📝 Daily Test Prep

pp. 174, 178, 184, 189, 194, 199, 205, 208

📝 Test-Taking Strategies

Reading-Comprehension Questions, p. 209

📝 Test Prep

Cumulative Review (Chapters 1–4), p. 213

Chapter Assessment

✅ Checkpoint Quiz

pp. 184, 205

⬤ Chapter Review

pp. 210–211

⬤ Chapter Test

p. 212

Pacing Options

This chart suggests pacing only for the core lessons and their parts. It is provided as a possible guide. It will help you determine how much time you have in your schedule to cover the additional features and assessment, as described at the left.

Day	Traditional 45-minute class periods	Block 90-minute class periods
1	4-1 ▽	4-1 ▽
		4-2 ▽
2	4-2 ▽	4-2 ▽
		4-3 ▽
3	4-2 ▽	4-3 ▽
		4-4 ▽
4	4-3 ▽	4-4 ▽
		4-5 ▽
5	4-3 ▽	4-5 ▽
		4-6 ▽
6	4-4 ▽	4-6 ▽
		4-7 ▽
7	4-4 ▽	4-7 ▽
		4-8 ▽
8	4-5 ▽	
9	4-5 ▽	
10	4-6 ▽	
11	4-6 ▽	
12	4-7 ▽	
13	4-7 ▽	
14	4-8 ▽	

NCTM STANDARDS 2000

1 Number and Operations
2 Algebra
3 Geometry
4 Measurement
5 Data Analysis and Probability
6 Problem Solving
7 Reasoning and Proof
8 Communication
9 Connections
10 Representation

Math Background

Skills Trace

BEFORE Chapter 4
Grade 5 presented fraction addition and subtraction.

DURING Chapter 4
Course 1 reviews and extends adding and subtracting fractions to like and unlike denominators as well as mixed numbers.

AFTER Chapter 4
Throughout this course students add and subtract fractions to solve problems.

4-1 Estimating Sums and Differences

Math Understandings
- You can find approximate answers by using estimation.
- You can estimate the value of fractions between 0 and 1 by comparing the size of the numerator and denominator.
- You estimate the sum or difference of two mixed numbers by rounding the mixed numbers to the nearest whole number.

A **benchmark** is a number that is close to a fraction and easy to use when you estimate. The chart below describes when to round to the benchmarks 0, $\frac{1}{2}$, and 1.

Description	Examples	Benchmark
Numerator is close to 0. Denominator is not close to 0.	$\frac{1}{8}, \frac{3}{16}, \frac{2}{25}, \frac{9}{100}$	0
Numerator is about half of denominator.	$\frac{3}{8}, \frac{9}{16}, \frac{11}{25}, \frac{52}{100}$	$\frac{1}{2}$
Numerator and denominator are close to each other.	$\frac{7}{8}, \frac{14}{16}, \frac{23}{25}, \frac{95}{100}$	1

4-2 Fractions With Like Denominators

Math Understandings
- In order to add or subtract fractions, both fractions must be written with the same denominator.

To add fractions with like denominators, add the numerators and keep the same denominator. Then write the sum in simplest form, which may involve writing an improper fraction as a mixed number. To subtract fractions with like denominators, subtract the numerators and keep the same denominator. Write the difference in simplest form.

Example: Find $\frac{5}{6} - \frac{1}{6}$.

$$\frac{5}{6} - \frac{1}{6} = \frac{4}{6} = \frac{2}{3}$$

4-3 Fractions With Unlike Denominators

Math Understandings
- To find the sum or difference of two fractions with different denominators, you must first rewrite each fraction using a common denominator.
- Any common denominator may be used, but using the Least Common Denominator (LCD) may save steps and make it easier to simplify the final answer.
- The product of the denominators will always give a common denominator, but it may not be the lowest common denominator.

To find the sum or difference of two fractions with different denominators, rewrite each fraction using a common denominator, add or subtract numerators, and simplify.

Example: Find $\frac{1}{2} - \frac{1}{3}$.

$$\frac{1}{2} - \frac{1}{3} = \frac{1 \times 3}{2 \times 3} - \frac{1 \times 2}{3 \times 2} = \frac{3}{6} - \frac{2}{6} = \frac{1}{6}$$

4-4 Adding Mixed Numbers

Math Understandings
- To find the sum of two mixed numbers with unlike denominators, you first rewrite each fraction part as an equivalent fraction using a common denominator.

You can find the sum of mixed numbers by adding the whole number and fraction parts separately, and then combining the two parts to find the total. If the sum of the fraction parts is an improper fraction, rename it as a mixed number and simplify.

Example: Find $3\frac{5}{6} + 2\frac{1}{4}$.

$$3\frac{5}{6} \rightarrow 3\frac{10}{12} \leftarrow \text{Rename } \frac{5}{6} \text{ as } \frac{10}{12}.$$
$$+5\frac{1}{4} \rightarrow 5\frac{3}{12} \leftarrow \text{Rename } \frac{1}{4} \text{ as } \frac{3}{12}.$$
$$8\frac{13}{12} = 8 + 1\frac{1}{12} = 9\frac{1}{12}$$

 **4-5**

Subtracting Mixed Numbers

Math Understandings

- To find the difference of two mixed numbers with unlike denominators, you first rewrite each fraction part as an equivalent fraction using a common denominator.
- In order to subtract from a mixed number, it may be necessary to rename the mixed number.

You can find the difference of mixed numbers by subtracting the whole number and fraction parts separately, and then combining the two parts. Sometimes you need to rename whole numbers or fractions in order to subtract from them.

Example: Find $11\frac{1}{6} - 5\frac{2}{3}$.

$$11\frac{1}{6} \rightarrow 10\frac{7}{6} \leftarrow \text{Rename } 11\frac{1}{6} \text{ as } 10\frac{7}{6}.$$
$$-5\frac{2}{3} \rightarrow 5\frac{4}{6} \leftarrow \text{Rename } \frac{2}{3} \text{ as } \frac{4}{6}.$$
$$5\frac{3}{6} = 5\frac{1}{2}$$

 4-6

Equations With Fractions

Math Understandings

- You solve an equation with fractions in the same way you solve an equation with whole numbers: you get the variable alone on one side of the equal sign using properties of equality and inverse operations.

You can solve equations with fractions and mixed numbers by applying the addition and subtraction properties of equality and inverse operations. Then write the answer in simplest form.

 4-7

Measuring Elapsed Time

Math Understandings

- The standard unit of time is the second.

You can use equivalent units to change from one unit of time to another.

Units of Time	
second (s)	
minute (min)	1 min = 60 s
hour (h)	1 h = 60 min = 3,600 s
day	1 day = 24 h = 1,440 min
week (wk)	1 wk = 7 days = 188 h
year (yr)	1 yr ≈ 52 wk ≈ 365 days

 4-8

Draw a Diagram

You can use the problem-solving strategy draw a diagram when the situation in a word problem is hard to picture mentally.

Additional Professional Development Opportunities

 Professional Development

Chapter 4 Math Background notes: pp. 172, 176, 181, 186, 191, 197, 202, 206

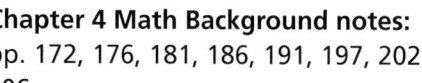 Additional resources available from SkyLight Professional Development:

On-site courses, workshops, summer institutes. Online courses and chat rooms. Videocassettes and books. Visit www.skylightedu.com.

Ongoing Assessment and Intervention

The *Prentice Hall Mathematics* program provides many options for assessment in the Student Edition, Teacher's Edition, and teaching resources. From these options you may choose instructional materials that are appropriate for your students and that support your district's curriculum requirements.

Daily Assessment

 Instant Check System™ in Chapter 4

Allows students to check their own learning before, during, and after each lesson.

Diagnosing Readiness before the chapter (p. 170)

Check Skills You'll Need exercises in each lesson (pp. 171, 175, 180, 185, 190, 196, 201, 206)

Check Understanding questions with each Example (pp. 172, 175, 176, 180, 181, 182, 185, 186, 187, 190, 191, 196, 197, 202, 203, 207)

Checkpoint Quiz (pp. 184, 205)

Formal Assessment

Assessment in the Student Text and in Additional Resources

Assess student progress throughout the Course 1 textbook and with blackline masters and CD-ROM.

Student Edition
- Chapter 4 Review, with Vocabulary, Skills, and Concepts Review, pp. 210–211
- Chapter 4 Test, p. 212

Assessment Resources
- Checkpoint Quizzes 1 & 2
- Chapter Test, forms A & B
- Chapter Alternative Assessment

Spanish versions available.

 Computer Test Generator CD-ROM
- Instant Chapter Tests™—pre-made tests with items that vary every time you print.
- Online Testing allows you to give tests online and receive progress reports.
- Prepare students by making tests based on standardized test objectives.

Algebra Readiness Tests
- Includes Basic Skills Tests and Concept-Readiness Tests.
- Assess understanding of skills and concepts needed for success in algebra.

Intervention

 Skills Intervention Kit

Online Intervention
Integrated within the iText, this online intervention system includes diagnostic tests and prescribed remediation, plus reports to track student mastery.

A *complete* system for the student who is struggling with course-level work

Eight intervention units cover core skills and allow you to:
- **Diagnose** students' gaps in basic skills
- **Prescribe** an individualized course of study
- **Monitor** student progress

Includes print workbooks, tutorial CD-ROM, teacher editions, progress folders, and more. *Available in Spanish.*

How to Use with Chapter 4

4-1	Operations with Fractions, Skill 1
4-2	Operations with Fractions, Skills 2, 5
4-3	Operations with Fractions, Skills 3, 5
4-4	Operations with Fractions, Skill 4
4-5	Operations with Fractions, Skills 6–7
4-7	Measurement, Skill 6

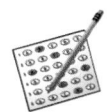

Standardized Test Preparation

The *Prentice Hall Mathematics* program integrates preparation for high-stakes standardized tests in every lesson of the Student Edition and continues this support in the Prentice Hall Assessment System.

Test Prep

In Student Text, Chapter 4

Teaches students strategies and gives them practice with all the test item formats they will encounter on high-stakes tests.

Test Prep exercises in each lesson (pp. 174, 178, 184, 189, 194, 199, 205, 208)

Test-Taking Strategies (p. 209: Reading-Comprehension Questions)

Test Prep (p. 213: Cumulative Review Chapters 1–4)

A three-step approach to preparing students for high stakes, national, and state exams.

① Diagnose & Prescribe

Content Diagnostic Tests
- Diagnose strengths and weaknesses with ongoing benchmark tests.
- Prescribe individualized reteaching opportunities.

② Review & Reteach

Skills and Concepts Review
- Provides reteaching worksheets with instruction and practice for each skill.
- Includes course prerequisite skills.

③ Practice & Assess

Standardized Test Preparation
- Features practice for national standardized exams.
- Includes practice tests for NAEP, SAT10, ITBS, and Terra Nova.

Test-Taking Strategies with Transparencies
- Support the Test-Taking Strategies pages in the Student Edition.
- Provide a transparency and a worksheet for each strategy.

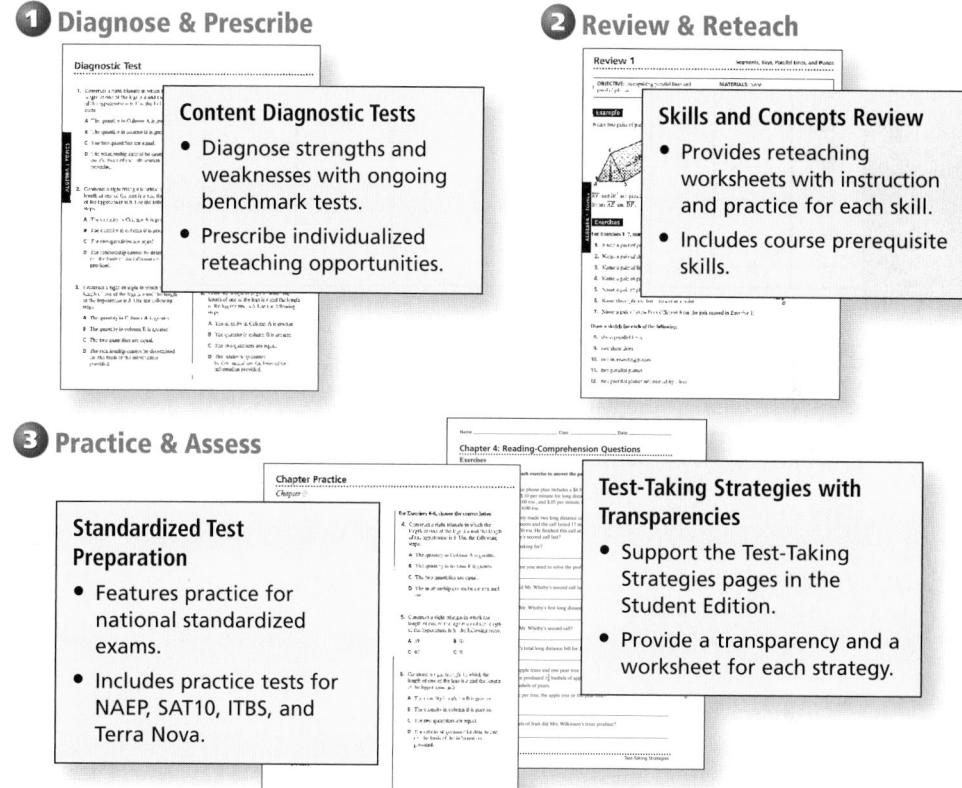

Correlation to Standardized Tests

Lesson		NAEP	Terra Nova				Local Test
			CAT6	CTBS	ITBS	SAT10	
4-1	Estimating Sums and Differences	N2a	■	■		■	
4-2	Fractions With Like Denominators	N3a	■	■	■	■	
4-3	Fractions With Unlike Denominators	N3a	■	■		■	
4-4	Adding Mixed Numbers	N3a	■	■			
4-5	Subtracting Mixed Numbers	N3a	■	■			
4-6	Equations With Fractions	A4c		■			
4-7	Measuring Elapsed Time			■		■	
4-8	Problem Solving: Draw a Diagram						

NAEP National Assessment of Educational Progress
CAT6/Terra Nova California Achievement Test, 6th Ed.

CTBS/Terra Nova Comprehensive Test of Basic Skills
ITBS Iowa Test of Basic Skills, Form M.

SAT10 Stanford Achievement Test, 10th Ed.

Program Resources

	Resources in Grab & Go™ Files				Resources for Reaching All Students				Spanish Resources			Presentation Assistant Plus! Transparencies					Prentice Hall Presentation Pro CD-ROM
	Practice	Reteach	Enrich	Checkpt Quiz	Reading & Math Literacy	Technology Activities	Hands-On Activities	Guided Problem Solving	Practice	Reading & Math Literacy	Checkpt Quiz	Skills Check	Problem of the Day	Additional Examples	Answers to Exercises	Lesson Quiz	
4-1	■	■	■		■			■	■			■	■	■	■	■	■
4-2	■	■	■				■	■	■			■	■	■	■	■	■
4-3	■	■	■	■	■	■	■	■	■	■	■	■	■	■	■	■	■
4-4	■	■	■				■	■	■			■	■	■	■	■	■
4-5	■	■	■				■	■	■			■	■	■	■	■	■
4-6	■	■	■				■	■	■			■	■	■	■	■	■
4-7	■	■	■	■	■			■	■	■	■	■	■	■	■	■	■
4-8	■	■	■					■	■								
For the Chapter	Chapter Projects, Chapter Tests, Alternative Assessment, Cumulative Review, Cumulative Assessment				On web site only: Home Activities, Interdisciplinary Activities, Algebra Readiness Puzzles				Spanish Chapter Tests, Alternative Assessment, Cumulative Review, Cumulative Assessment			Classroom Aid Transparencies					

Also available for use with the chapter:

 PRENTICE HALL **ASSESSMENT SYSTEM** *See page 168F.*

- Practice Workbook
- Solution Key
- MathNotes folder

- For teacher support and access to student Web materials, use the Web Code aak-5500.
- For additional online and technology resources, *see below.*

 **Technology**

 **Online and on CD-ROM**

Complete Interactive Student Text online and on CD-ROM—with instant feedback assessment, tutorial help, dynamic activities, instructional and real-world videos, audio, and additional practice.

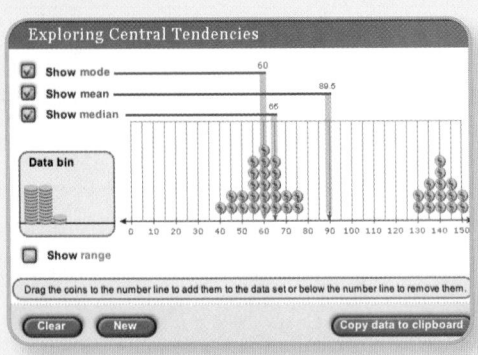

 www.PHSchool.com For Students

Use Web codes for easy access to online activities, chapter projects, self-grading lesson quizzes, chapter tests, vocabulary quizzes, updated data sources, graphing calculator procedures, and more.

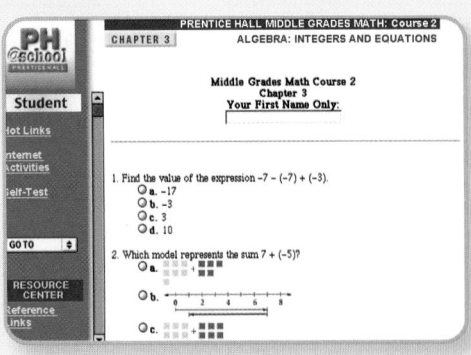

PH SuccessNet **For Teachers**

Online lesson planning with built-in state correlations, all the teaching resources, complete reference library, your own calendar and Teacher Web page, professional development, and more.

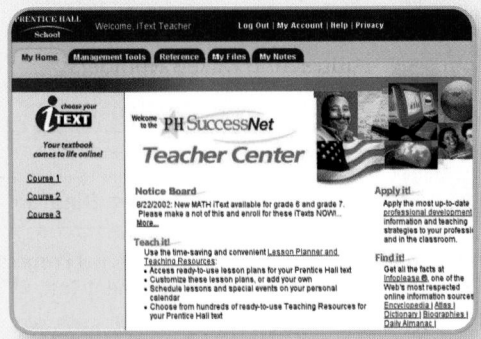

Presentation Assistant Plus!

The *Prentice Hall Presentation Assistant Plus!* provides you with the material you need to teach a lesson from beginning to end. Two easy-to-use formats—Transparencies and PowerPoint®—allow you to present a lesson the way you are most comfortable.

 Transparencies

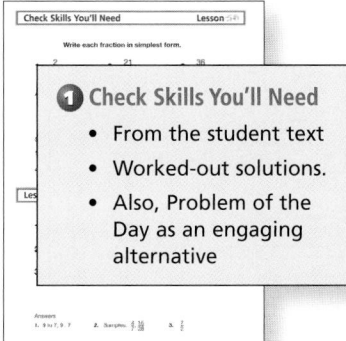

1 Check Skills You'll Need
- From the student text
- Worked-out solutions.
- Also, Problem of the Day as an engaging alternative

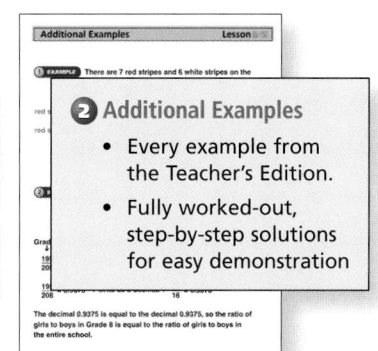

2 Additional Examples
- Every example from the Teacher's Edition.
- Fully worked-out, step-by-step solutions for easy demonstration

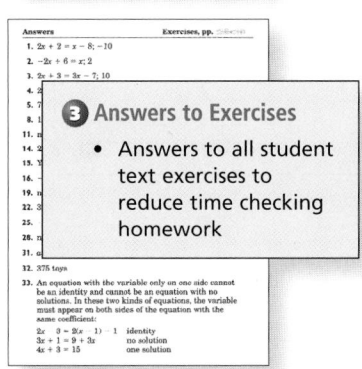

3 Answers to Exercises
- Answers to all student text exercises to reduce time checking homework

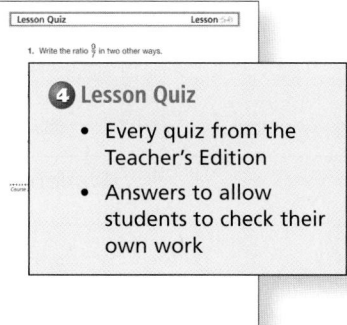

4 Lesson Quiz
- Every quiz from the Teacher's Edition
- Answers to allow students to check their own work

 **PowerPoint** Throughout the Teacher's Edition, this symbol indicates material that is available in the Presentation Assistant Plus!

PowerPoint **Prentice Hall Presentation Pro CD-ROM**

- Includes all Transparencies.
- Conveniently organized by lesson so you can easily **1** Introduce, **2** Teach, **3** Check Homework, and **4** Assess each lesson.
- Animated examples allow step-by-step instruction at your own pace.
- Easy to edit so you can create custom presentations.

Teaching Chapter 4 Using Presentation Assistant Plus!

	1 Introduce	**2 Teach**	**3 Check Homework**	**4 Assess**
	Check Skills You'll Need	Additional Examples	Student Edition Answers	Lesson Quiz
4-1	p. 30	p. 47	✔	p. 30
4-2	p. 31	p. 48	✔	p. 31
4-3	p. 32	pp. 49–50	✔	p. 32
4-4	p. 33	pp. 51–52	✔	p. 33
4-5	p. 34	pp. 53–54	✔	p. 34
4-6	p. 35	pp. 55–56	✔	p. 35
4-7	p. 36	pp. 57–58	✔	p. 36
4-8	p. 37	pp. 59–60	✔	p. 37

 Prentice Hall Presentation Pro

CD-ROM with dynamic PowerPoint® presentations for every lesson. Helps you introduce and develop concepts, check homework, and assess progress. Part of Presentation Assistant Plus! *(See above.)*

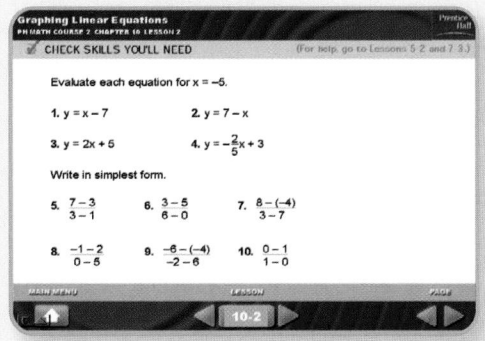

 Computer Test Generator

CD-ROM to create practice sheets and tests for course objectives and standardized tests. Includes Instant Chapter Tests™, online testing, and student reports. Part of the PH Assessment System. *(See page 168F.)*

 Resource Pro® with Planning Express®

CD-ROM with a lesson planning tool that allows you to import state and local objectives. Includes electronic versions of all the teaching resources.

Chapter Resources

Reading and Math Support

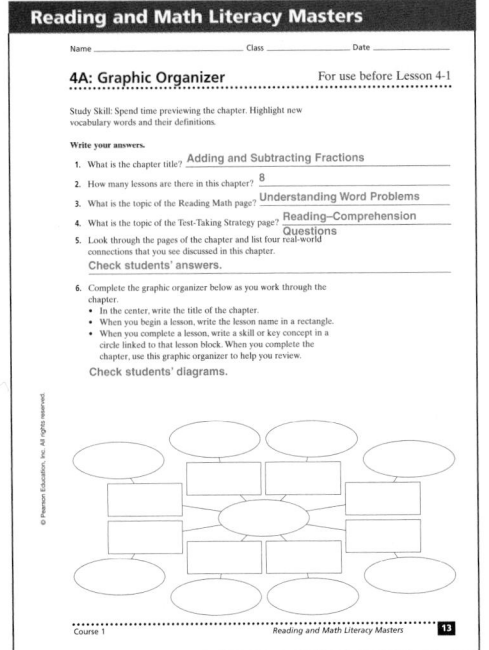

Available in Spanish

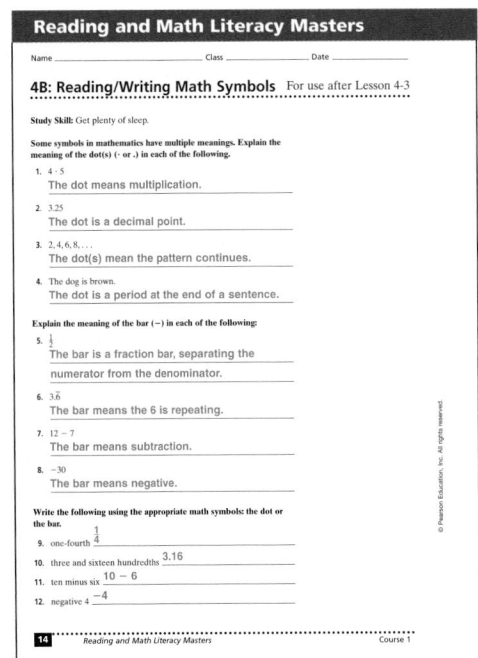

Available in Spanish

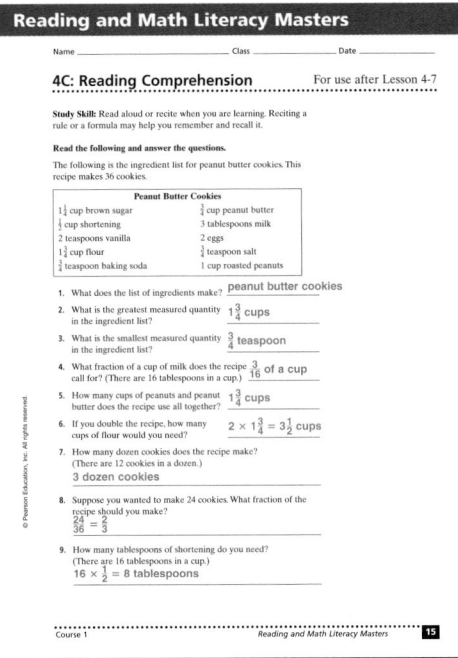

Available in Spanish

Problem Solving

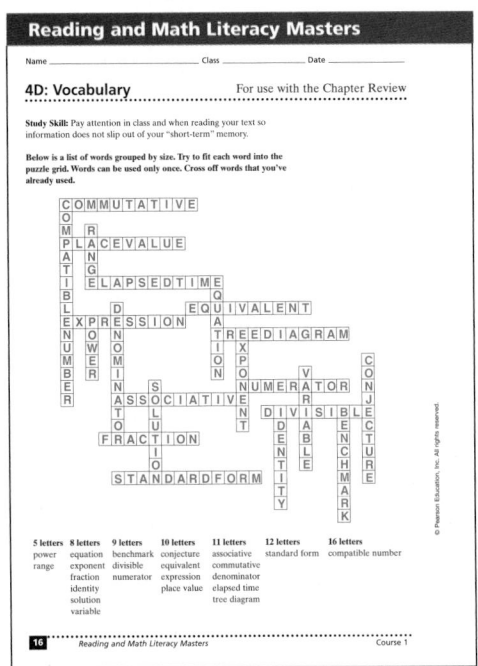

Available in Spanish

Name _____ Class _____ Date _____

4-3 • Guided Problem Solving

GPS Student Page 183, Exercise 25:

Weather A weather reporter records the rainfall as $\frac{2}{10}$ inch between 9:00 and 10:00 and $\frac{7}{8}$ inch between 10:00 and 11:00.

  a. **Estimation** Estimate the total rainfall between 9:00 and 11:00.

  b. What is the total rainfall between 9:00 and 11:00?

Read and Understand

1. What is the difference between part *a* and part *b*?
   In part *a*, you estimate the total rainfall; in part *b*, you find the actual sum.

Plan and Solve

2. Estimate $\frac{2}{10}$ and $\frac{7}{8}$ separately. 0; 1 inch

3. Use the answers to Step 3 to estimate the total rainfall between 9:00 and 11:00. 0 + 1 = 1 inch

4. What do you need to find the sum of the two measurements?
   common denominator

5. What is the least common denominator for $\frac{2}{10}$ and $\frac{7}{8}$? 40

6. Rewrite each fraction using the answer to Step 6. $\frac{8}{40}, \frac{35}{40}$

7. What is the total rainfall between 9:00 and 11:00?
   $\frac{47}{40}$ or $1\frac{7}{40}$ inches of rainfall

Look Back and Check

8. Does your answer match your estimate? Explain.
   Yes, because $1\frac{7}{40}$ is close to 1.

Solve Another Problem

9. A recipe for party mix calls for $\frac{3}{4}$ cup of cereal, $\frac{1}{4}$ cup of walnuts, $\frac{5}{8}$ cup of crackers, and $\frac{1}{2}$ cup of raisins. Estimate the number of cups in the mix. Determine the actual number of cups in the mix.
   Sample answer: $1 + 0 + 1 + \frac{1}{2} = 2\frac{1}{2}$; $2\frac{1}{8}$ cups

---

Name _____ Class _____ Date _____

4-4 • Guided Problem Solving

GPS Student Page 188, Exercise 18a:

Tides At low tide, the water is $4\frac{11}{12}$ feet deep. At high tide, the water depth increases by $2\frac{3}{4}$ feet. How deep is the water at high tide?

Read and Understand

1. Circle the information you will need to solve.

2. What operation do you need to answer the question?
   addition

Plan and Solve

3. What is the least common denominator for $4\frac{11}{12}$ feet and $2\frac{3}{4}$ feet?
   12

4. Rewrite both fractions using the least common denominator.
   $4\frac{11}{12}$ feet and $2\frac{9}{12}$ feet

5. Write an expression you can use to answer the question.
   $4\frac{11}{12}$ feet $+ 2\frac{9}{12}$ feet

6. How deep is the water at high tide?
   $6\frac{20}{12} = 7\frac{8}{12} = 7\frac{2}{3}$ feet

Look Back and Check

7. How can you check your answer?
   Sample answer: Subtract $4\frac{11}{12}$ feet from $7\frac{2}{3}$ feet
   and see if the answer is $2\frac{3}{4}$ feet.

Solve Another Problem

8. Suppose Don will need to leave his fishing spot when the river reaches 30 feet. The river is predicted to rise $5\frac{1}{12}$ feet from its present level of $21\frac{7}{10}$ feet. Will he need to leave?
   No, it is not quite 30 feet.

Name _____ Class _____ Date _____

4-5 • Guided Problem Solving

GPS Student Page 193, Exercise 28:

On Monday, the snowfall in the mountains was $15\frac{3}{4}$ inches. On Tuesday, the snowfall was $18\frac{1}{2}$ inches. What was the difference in snowfall?

Read and Understand

1. Circle the information you will need to solve.

2. What are you being asked to do?
   Find the difference in the snowfall amounts.

Plan and Solve

3. How many inches fell on Monday?
   $15\frac{3}{4}$ inches

4. How many inches fell on Tuesday?
   $18\frac{1}{2}$ inches

5. What common denominator do you need to use?
   4

6. Rewrite each fraction using the least common denominator.
   $15\frac{3}{4}, 18\frac{2}{4}$

7. What was the difference in snowfall?
   $2\frac{3}{4}$ inches

Look Back and Check

8. How can you check your answer? Sample answer:
   Add $15\frac{3}{4}$ and $2\frac{3}{4}$; the answer should be $18\frac{2}{4}$.

Solve Another Problem

9. The perimeter of the lid to a rectangular box is $\frac{14}{6}$ yards. If the longer sides are $\frac{5}{6}$ yard, how long are the shorter sides? Explain.
   $\frac{14}{6} - 2(\frac{5}{6}) = \frac{14}{6} - \frac{10}{6} = \frac{4}{6} \div 2 = \frac{1}{3}$ yard

---

Name _____ Class _____ Date _____

4-6 • Guided Problem Solving

GPS Student Page 198, Exercise 22:

Landscaping The Service Club bought a 10-yard roll of edging to put around two trees in front of the school. They use $5\frac{2}{3}$ yards of edging for one tree and $3\frac{3}{4}$ yards for the other tree. How much edging is left?

Read and Understand

1. Circle the information you will need to solve.

2. How do you plan to solve this problem?
   Add the two lengths of edging and subtract from 10 yards.

Plan and Solve

3. How much of the edging has been used?
   $5\frac{2}{3}$ yards, $3\frac{3}{4}$ yards

4. Add these amounts together using a common denominator.
   $9\frac{5}{12}$ yards

5. How much edging did the club purchase?
   10 yards

6. How much edging is left over?
   $\frac{7}{12}$ yard

Look Back and Check

7. Explain how you can check your answer.
   Add all of the numbers; the answer is 10 yards.

Solve Another Problem

8. Linda bought a 15-yard roll of fabric to make a dress. She used $8\frac{1}{3}$ yards for the blouse and $5\frac{1}{4}$ yards for the pants. How much fabric is left?
   $1\frac{5}{12}$ yards

Name _____ Class _____ Date _____

4-7 • Guided Problem Solving

GPS Student Page 204, Exercise 22:

Clowns A clown wants to perform a 45-minute show at each of three birthday parties on the same Saturday. The first party must begin at 10:00 A.M. and he needs to leave the third party by 2:15 P.M. He wants to allow one hour between each party. Make a schedule for the clown.

Read and Understand

1. Circle the information you will need to solve.

2. What are you being asked to do?
   Create a schedule.

3. What problem-solving method can you use to help create the schedule?
   Create a table or work backward.

Plan and Solve

4. If the clown starts the first show at 10:00 A.M. when will he finish?
   10:45 A.M.

5. If he allows an hour between each show, when will the next show begin?
   11:45 A.M.

6. When will he finish the second show? 12:30 P.M.

7. If he allows an hour between each show, when will the next show begin?
   1:30 P.M.

8. When will he finish the third show? 2:15 P.M.

Look Back and Check

9. Did the clown finish when he was supposed to? yes

Solve Another Problem

10. If the clown's schedule changed and he doesn't have to leave until 6:00 P.M., how many more shows with breaks can the clown have?
    3:15–4:00, 5:00–5:45; 2 more shows

Name _____ Class _____ Date _____

4-8 • Guided Problem Solving

GPS Student Page 207, Exercise 5:

Lighting Lights are placed every $1\frac{3}{4}$ feet along both sides of a 14-foot driveway. How many lights are needed?

Read and Understand

1. Circle the information you will need to solve.

2. Which strategy can you use to answer this question?
   Draw a diagram.

Plan and Solve

3. Draw a number line to represent one side of the driveway. What will you use for intervals? $\frac{1}{4}$ ft

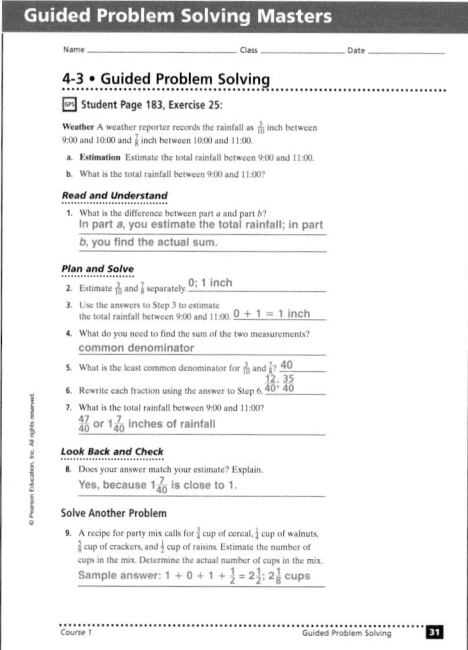

0 1 2 3 4 5 6 7 8 9 10 11 12 13 14

4. Start at zero. Plot a point for each light along the driveway. How many lights will there be? 9 lights

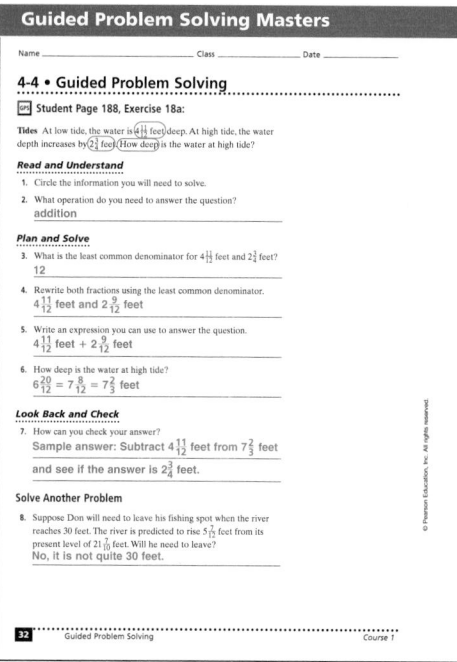

0 1 2 3 4 5 6 7 8 9 10 11 12 13 14

5. Use your answer from Step 4 to write an expression for the total number of lights. total = 9 × 2

6. How many lights do you need total? 18 lights

Look Back and Check

7. Can you think of another way to solve this problem?
   Sample answer: Use the equation $14 \div 1\frac{3}{4} + 1$
   to find the number of lights one one side of
   the driveway.

Solve Another Problem

8. You are planting bushes every $2\frac{1}{4}$ feet along the side of a house that is $29\frac{1}{4}$ feet long. How many bushes do you need?
   $29\frac{1}{4} \div 2\frac{1}{4} + 1 = 14$; 14 bushes

168J

Activities and Projects

Hands-On Activities

Activity 13: Fraction Bar Explorations

Materials needed: fraction bars, snap cubes (red and blue)

Work with a partner.

1. Snap 6 red cubes together. Then add 3 blue cubes to one end.

   a. Write a fraction that names the blue part of the bar.

   b. Write the fraction in simplest form.

   c. Build 3 more fraction bars with snap cubes. Write fractions to represent them. Simplify the fractions, if possible.

2. One partner builds a fraction bar from 5 red and 3 blue cubes; the other partner builds one from 4 red and 4 blue cubes.

   a. Add the 2 fractions.

   b. Add the 2 fractions using the cubes.

   c. Build 3 fraction bars and use them to add or subtract the fractions. Simplify your answers, if possible.

3. Make a fraction bar. Then make 3 more fraction bars that are equivalent to the amount shaded on the first fraction bar. Write a fraction for each bar picked. Circle the fraction that is in simplest form.

4. Put the fraction bars in order from smallest amount to greatest amount shaded. Write the fractions in order using simplest form.

5. Group the fraction bars according to common denominators. Write a fraction for each bar. Tell which fraction has the least common denominator.

6. Use fraction bars to find each sum or difference. Show your answer in simplest form.

   a. $\frac{7}{12} - \frac{5}{12}$

   b. $\frac{3}{4} + \frac{1}{12}$

   c. $\frac{5}{8} + \frac{7}{9}$

   d. $\frac{4}{5} - \frac{1}{2}$

   e. $\frac{5}{6} + \frac{1}{2}$

   f. $\frac{9}{10} - \frac{1}{2}$

Hands-On Activities

Activity 14: Adding and Subtracting Mixed Numbers

Materials needed: yardsticks

Work with a partner.

1. Copy the table below on a separate sheet of paper.

A in inches	A in feet	B in inches	B in feet	A+B in feet	C in inches	C in feet	(A+B)−C in feet

Measurement A:

2. a. Measure the height of your classroom chair. Round your measurement to the nearest inch and record the result in your table.

   b. Rewrite measurement A as a mixed number in feet. Be sure to write your answer in simplest terms. For example, if measurement A is 14 inches, this would be $1\frac{2}{12} = 1\frac{1}{6}$ ft. Record the answer in your table.

Measurement B:

3. a. Measure the height of your classroom desk or table. Round your measurement to the nearest inch and record the result in your table.

   b. In simplest terms, rewrite measurement B as a mixed number in feet. Record the answer in your table.

   c. Find the sum of measurements A and B and record the answer in simplest terms in your table.

Measurement C:

4. a. Measure the height of the classroom. Round your measurement to the nearest inch and record the result in your table.

   b. In simplest terms, rewrite measurement C as a mixed number in feet. Record the answer in your table.

   c. Is the sum of measurements A and B less than, greater than, or equal to measurement C? By how much? Record the difference in your table.

5. If you stacked your chair on top of the table or desk, would the total height be less than, greater than, or equal to the height of the classroom? How do you know?

6. If a mobile was hanging $2\frac{3}{4}$ ft above your desk, and you stacked your chair on top of your desk to vacuum the carpeting, might the chair hit the mobile? Explain.

Technology Activities

Finding the LCD   Activity 9

Use your scientific calculator to do this activity.

Example 1: Find $\frac{1}{4} + \frac{1}{6}$.

① First, find the LCD of $\frac{1}{4}$ and $\frac{1}{6}$. The LCD for the two fractions is the same as the Lowest Common Multiple of 4 and 6, the two denominators.

② Press [2nd] [MATH]. Press the right arrow key to move across the menu items until you see the underline under **lcm**. Press [ENTER].

③ Enter 4 [2nd] [,] 6 [ENTER]. The calculator gives you a 12. The LCD of $\frac{1}{4}$ and $\frac{1}{6}$ is 12.

④ Now write both fractions with a denominator of 12 and find the sum.

$$\left(\frac{1}{4} + \frac{1}{6}\right) = \left(\frac{1}{4} \times \frac{3}{3}\right) + \left(\frac{1}{6} \times \frac{2}{2}\right)$$
$$= \frac{3}{12} + \frac{2}{12}$$
$$= \frac{5}{12}$$

Example 2: Find $\frac{11}{14} - \frac{5}{8}$.

Another method is to let the calculator add the fractions directly.

① Press [2nd] [FracMode]. Press the right arrow key until you see **Auto** underlined. Press [ENTER]. Note: Once you've done this step, the calculator will automatically simplify fractions until someone changes it.

② Enter 11 [/] 14 [−] 5 [/] 8 [ENTER]. The calculator gives you 9 / 56. The difference is $\frac{9}{56}$.

(*Note:* If you see **N/D → n/d** displayed at the bottom of the display after adding or subtracting fractions, then the calculator is not in auto simplification mode. Press [2nd] [FracMode], select **Auto** and press [ENTER] again. Then try the addition or subtraction again.)

Exercises

Find each sum or difference.

1. $\frac{5}{13} - \frac{2}{39}$

2. $\frac{20}{21} - \frac{2}{7}$

3. $\frac{5}{8} + \frac{1}{16}$

4. $\frac{29}{32} - \frac{3}{8}$

5. $\frac{7}{12} + \frac{5}{24}$

6. $\frac{45}{53} - \frac{7}{15}$

7. $\frac{69}{96} + \frac{7}{16}$

8. $\frac{30}{33} - \frac{5}{11}$

9. $\frac{15}{108} + \frac{5}{12}$

Sample pages; see p. G for complete list.

Chapter Project

Chapter 4 Project: Seeing is Believing

Design a Demonstration

Beginning the Chapter Project

Have you ever conducted a science experiment? Scientists perform experiments to prove if an idea is correct or incorrect. You can prove if something is correct or not in math class, too.

You will learn ways to add fractions and mixed numbers with unlike denominators, but can you prove these techniques *really* work? Your goal is to prove that they do by giving several demonstrations.

Activities

Activity 1: Researching Check students' work.

Look around for items that are typically divided into equal parts, or fractions. Some suggestions are rulers, pizzas, and cakes. How are these items usually divided — into halves, thirds, eighths? Make a list of items you could use to demonstrate the proofs you develop. Gather as many of these items as you can.

Activity 2: Demonstrating

Using some of the items you have gathered, create a demonstration showing the addition of fractions that have the same denominator. You could use a ruler to add eighths of an inch, a measuring cup to add thirds of a cup of water, or a clock to add sixths of an hour. Make sure you prove that the two fractions add up to the expected sum.

Activity 3: Modeling

Now create a demonstration to calculate the sum of fractions with unlike denominators. See whether or not the sum agrees with the measured results. Again, use items you have gathered, visual models, or other methods. Expand your demonstration to illustrate the addition of mixed numbers.

Chapter Project

Chapter 4 Project: Seeing is Believing (continued)

Finishing the Project

Imagine you are a scientist who has just discovered something very important. Demonstrate the results of your work and proofs to your classmates. Imagine that there are other scientists in your field and you are presenting your proofs to them to show them your discovery.

Reflect and Revise

Show your proofs to some of your classmates. Discuss whether or not these same techniques would work to show subtraction of fractions and mixed numbers. Work together to devise a method for proving that fraction multiplication techniques work. Are your proofs logical and correct? Are your calculations accurate? Revise your demonstration or proofs as necessary.

Extending the Project

Study the scientific method. Use the Internet to learn about a recent scientific discovery. Create a display to show the process the scientist went through to prove the discovery.

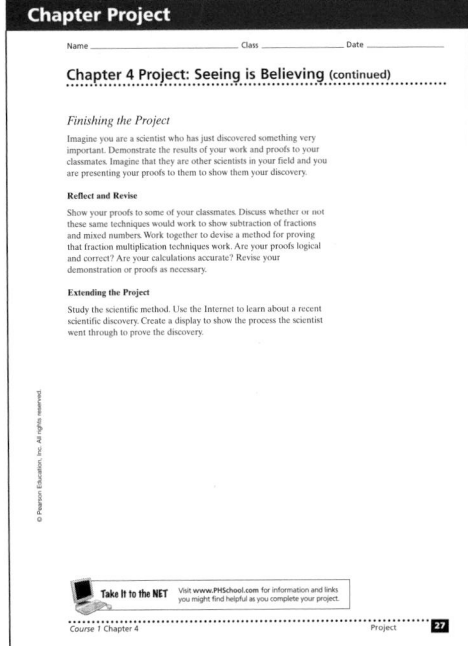

Take It to the NET Visit www.PHSchool.com for information and links you might find helpful as you complete your project.

Chapter Project

Chapter Project Manager

Chapter 4: Seeing is Believing

Getting Started

Read about the project. As you work on it, you will need several sheets of paper. If available, a spreadsheet program can be used. Keep all your work for the project in a folder, along with this Project Manager.

Checklist

☐ Activity 1: researching
☐ Activity 2: demonstrating
☐ Activity 3: modeling
☐ Recommendations

Suggestions

☐ Pizzas, cakes, rulers, and football fields are all good examples.
☐ Help students determine the denominator based on the sections of the divided object.
☐ Make a video or poster of the proofs from the items gathered.
☐ Review the scientific method before you begin the project.

Scoring Rubric

3 You provide a step-by-step proof showing that addition of fractions with unlike denominations really works. This proof includes a description of at least two experiments you conducted using items you collected. The sums you found by experiment are compared to the results of actual calculations in a table. Your presentation is clear and complete.

2 You provide a proof that includes evidence of only one experiment. The results of the experiment are compared to actual calculations. Your work is neat and easy to follow.

1 You provide the results of one experiment and accompanying calculations, but your work is disorganized or unclear.

0 You failed to conduct any experiments or to prepare a written description of your work.

Your Evaluation of the Project Evaluate your work based on the Scoring Rubric.

Teacher's Evaluation of the Project

Transparencies

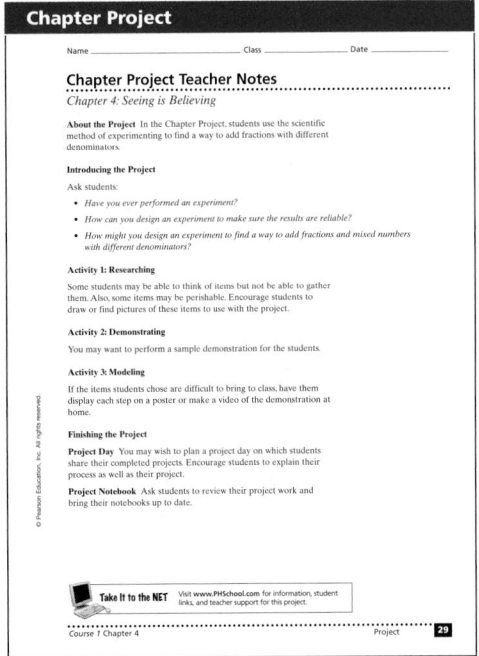

Chapter Project

Name _____ Class _____ Date _____

Chapter Project Teacher Notes
Chapter 4: Seeing is Believing

About the Project In the Chapter Project, students use the scientific method of experimenting to find a way to add fractions with different denominators.

Introducing the Project

Ask students:
- *Have you ever performed an experiment?*
- *How can you design an experiment to make sure the results are reliable?*
- *How might you design an experiment to find a way to add fractions and mixed numbers with different denominators?*

Activity 1: Researching

Some students may be able to think of items but not be able to gather them. Also, some items may be perishable. Encourage students to draw or find pictures of these items to use with the project.

Activity 2: Demonstrating

You may want to perform a sample demonstration for the students.

Activity 3: Modeling

If the items students chose are difficult to bring to class, have them display each step on a poster or make a video of the demonstration at home.

Finishing the Project

Project Day You may wish to plan a project day on which students share their completed projects. Encourage students to explain their process as well as their project.

Project Notebook Ask students to review their project work and bring their notebooks up to date.

Take It to the NET Visit www.PHSchool.com for information, student links, and teacher support for this project.

Course 1 Chapter 4 — Project — 29

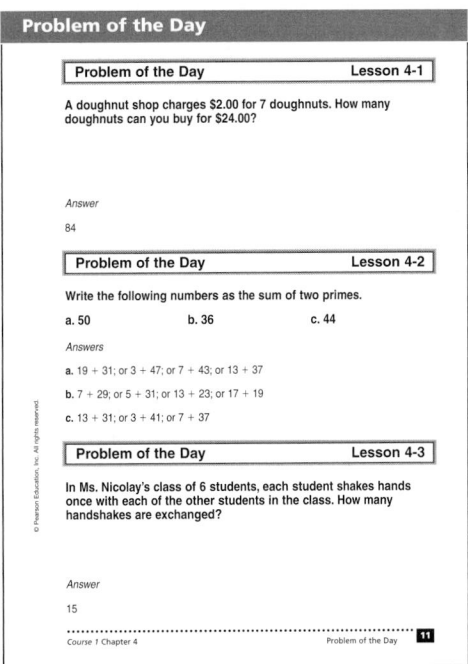

Problem of the Day

Problem of the Day — Lesson 4-1

A doughnut shop charges $2.00 for 7 doughnuts. How many doughnuts can you buy for $24.00?

Answer

84

Problem of the Day — Lesson 4-2

Write the following numbers as the sum of two primes.

a. 50   b. 36   c. 44

Answers

a. 19 + 31; or 3 + 47; or 7 + 43; or 13 + 37

b. 7 + 29; or 5 + 31; or 13 + 23; or 17 + 19

c. 13 + 31; or 3 + 41; or 7 + 37

Problem of the Day — Lesson 4-3

In Ms. Nicolay's class of 6 students, each student shakes hands once with each of the other students in the class. How many handshakes are exchanged?

Answer

15

Course 1 Chapter 4 — Problem of the Day — 11

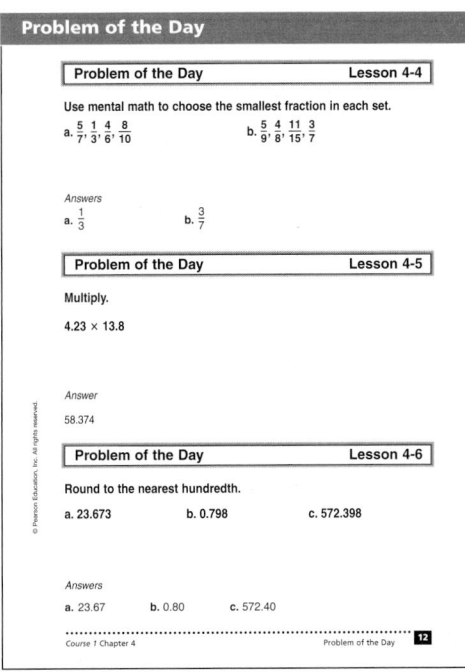

Problem of the Day

Problem of the Day — Lesson 4-4

Use mental math to choose the smallest fraction in each set.

a. $\frac{5}{7}, \frac{1}{3}, \frac{4}{6}, \frac{8}{10}$ b. $\frac{5}{9}, \frac{4}{8}, \frac{11}{15}, \frac{3}{7}$

Answers

a. $\frac{1}{3}$ b. $\frac{3}{7}$

Problem of the Day — Lesson 4-5

Multiply.

4.23×13.8

Answer

58.374

Problem of the Day — Lesson 4-6

Round to the nearest hundredth.

a. 23.673   b. 0.798   c. 572.398

Answers

a. 23.67   b. 0.80   c. 572.40

Course 1 Chapter 4 — Problem of the Day — 12

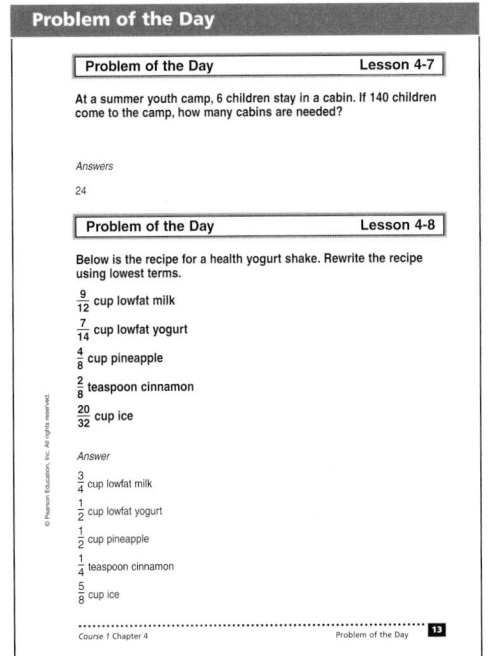

Problem of the Day

Problem of the Day — Lesson 4-7

At a summer youth camp, 6 children stay in a cabin. If 140 children come to the camp, how many cabins are needed?

Answers

24

Problem of the Day — Lesson 4-8

Below is the recipe for a health yogurt shake. Rewrite the recipe using lowest terms.

$\frac{9}{12}$ cup lowfat milk

$\frac{7}{14}$ cup lowfat yogurt

$\frac{4}{8}$ cup pineapple

$\frac{2}{8}$ teaspoon cinnamon

$\frac{20}{32}$ cup ice

Answer

$\frac{3}{4}$ cup lowfat milk

$\frac{1}{2}$ cup lowfat yogurt

$\frac{1}{2}$ cup pineapple

$\frac{1}{4}$ teaspoon cinnamon

$\frac{5}{8}$ cup ice

Course 1 Chapter 4 — Problem of the Day — 13

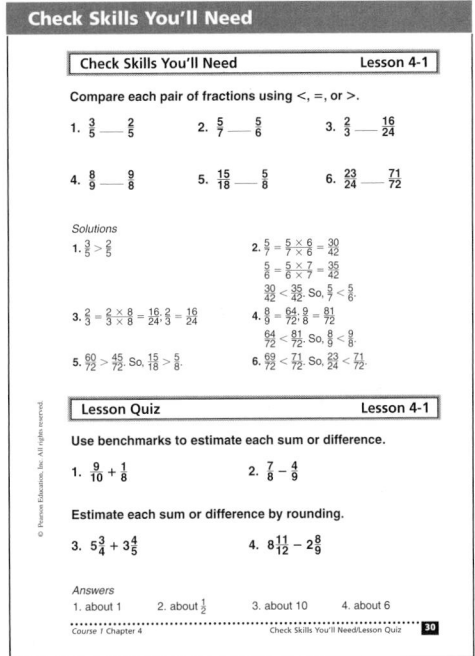

Check Skills You'll Need

Check Skills You'll Need — Lesson 4-1

Compare each pair of fractions using <, =, or >.

1. $\frac{3}{5}$ ___ $\frac{2}{5}$ 2. $\frac{5}{7}$ ___ $\frac{5}{6}$ 3. $\frac{2}{3}$ ___ $\frac{16}{24}$

4. $\frac{8}{9}$ ___ $\frac{9}{8}$ 5. $\frac{15}{18}$ ___ $\frac{5}{6}$ 6. $\frac{23}{24}$ ___ $\frac{71}{72}$

Solutions

1. $\frac{3}{5} > \frac{2}{5}$

2. $\frac{5}{7} = \frac{5 \times 6}{7 \times 6} = \frac{30}{42}$
$\frac{5}{6} = \frac{5 \times 7}{6 \times 7} = \frac{35}{42}$
$\frac{30}{42} < \frac{35}{42}$. So, $\frac{5}{7} < \frac{5}{6}$.

3. $\frac{2}{3} = \frac{2 \times 8}{3 \times 8} = \frac{16}{24}$. $\frac{2}{3} = \frac{16}{24}$

4. $\frac{8}{9} = \frac{64 \times 9}{72}, \frac{9}{8} = \frac{81}{72}$
$\frac{64}{72} < \frac{81}{72}$. So, $\frac{8}{9} < \frac{9}{8}$.

5. $\frac{60}{72} > \frac{45}{72}$. So, $\frac{15}{18} > \frac{5}{6}$.

6. $\frac{69}{72} < \frac{71}{72}$. So, $\frac{23}{24} < \frac{71}{72}$.

Lesson Quiz — Lesson 4-1

Use benchmarks to estimate each sum or difference.

1. $\frac{9}{10} + \frac{1}{8}$ 2. $\frac{7}{8} - \frac{4}{9}$

Estimate each sum or difference by rounding.

3. $5\frac{3}{4} + 3\frac{4}{5}$ 4. $8\frac{11}{12} - 2\frac{8}{9}$

Answers

1. about 1   2. about $\frac{1}{2}$ 3. about 10   4. about 6

Course 1 Chapter 4 — Check Skills You'll Need/Lesson Quiz — 30

Sample page; see p. H for complete list.

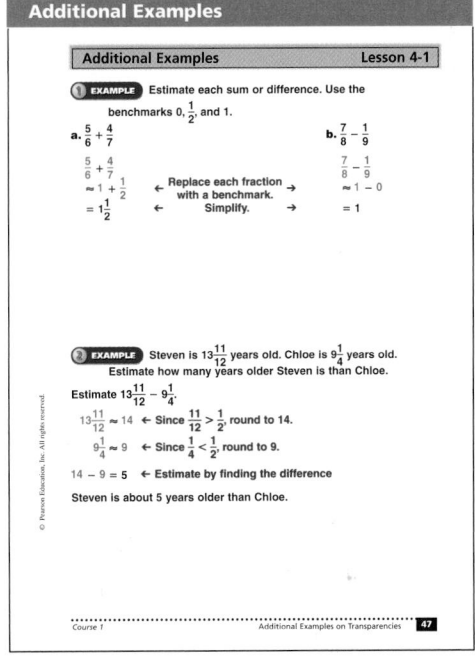

Additional Examples

Additional Examples — Lesson 4-1

1 EXAMPLE Estimate each sum or difference. Use the benchmarks 0, $\frac{1}{2}$, and 1.

a. $\frac{5}{6} + \frac{4}{7}$ b. $\frac{7}{8} - \frac{1}{9}$

$\frac{5}{6} + \frac{4}{7}$ ← Replace each fraction → $\frac{7}{8} - \frac{1}{9}$
$\approx 1 + \frac{1}{2}$ with a benchmark. $\approx 1 - 0$
$= 1\frac{1}{2}$ ← Simplify. → $= 1$

2 EXAMPLE Steven is $13\frac{11}{12}$ years old. Chloe is $9\frac{1}{4}$ years old. Estimate how many years older Steven is than Chloe.

Estimate $13\frac{11}{12} - 9\frac{1}{4}$.

$13\frac{11}{12} \approx 14$ ← Since $\frac{11}{12} > \frac{1}{2}$, round to 14.

$9\frac{1}{4} \approx 9$ ← Since $\frac{1}{4} < \frac{1}{2}$, round to 9.

$14 - 9 = 5$ ← Estimate by finding the difference

Steven is about 5 years older than Chloe.

Course 1 — Additional Examples on Transparencies — 47

Sample page; see p. H for complete list.

Sample page.

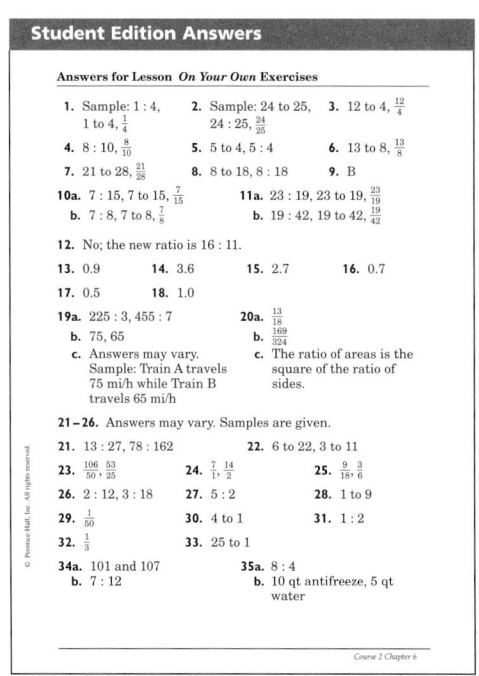

Sample page; see p. H for complete list.

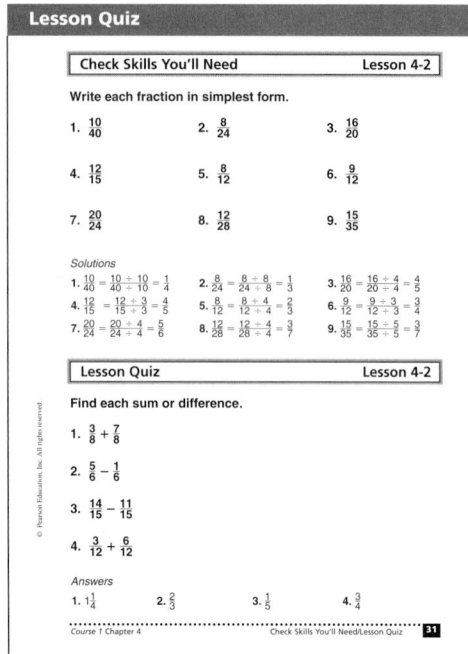

Sample page; see p. H for complete list.

Assessment

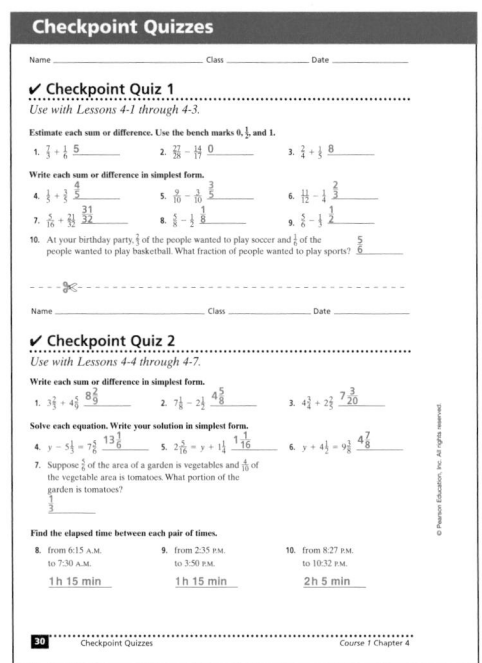

Available in Spanish

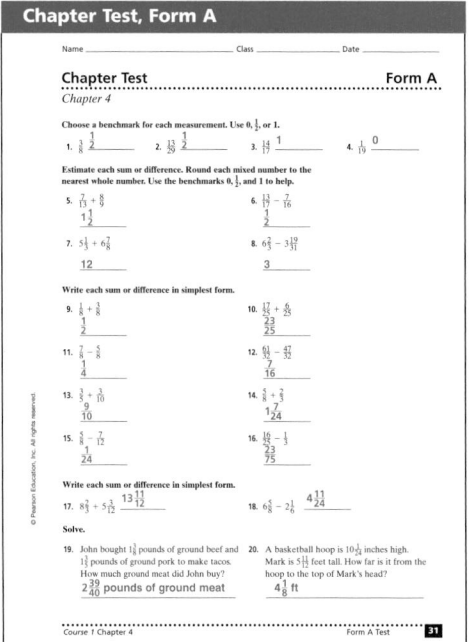

Available in Spanish

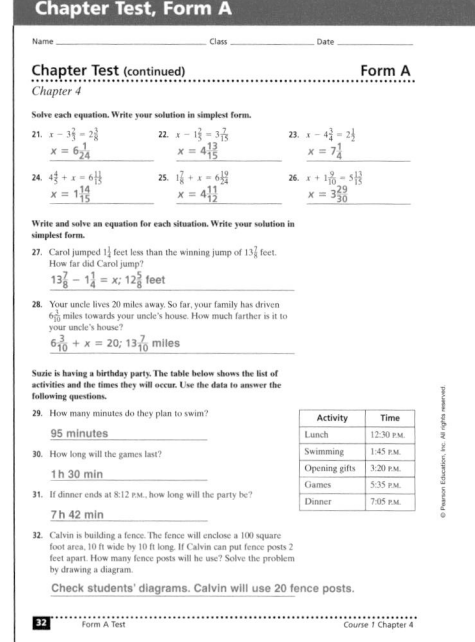

Available in Spanish

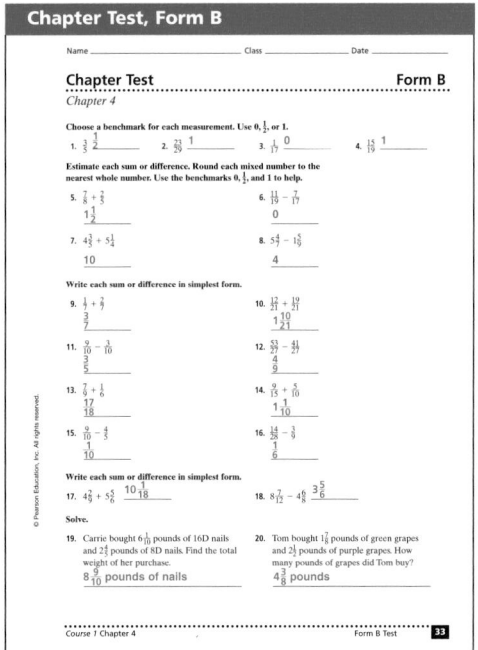

Chapter Test, Form B

Name _____ Class _____ Date _____

Chapter Test

Form B

Chapter 4

Choose a benchmark for each measurement. Use $0, \frac{1}{2}$, or 1.

1. $\frac{3}{5}$ $\frac{1}{2}$
2. $\frac{23}{50}$ $\frac{1}{2}$
3. $\frac{23}{17}$ 1
4. $\frac{1\frac{4}{9}}{}$ 1

Estimate each sum or difference. Round each mixed number to the nearest whole number. Use the benchmarks $0, \frac{1}{2}$, and 1 to help.

5. $\frac{2}{9} + \frac{3}{5}$ $1\frac{1}{2}$
6. $\frac{1}{17} + \frac{2}{17}$ 0
7. $4\frac{3}{8} + 5\frac{1}{4}$ 10
8. $5\frac{3}{4} - 1\frac{4}{5}$ 4

Write each sum or difference in simplest form.

9. $\frac{1}{7} + \frac{4}{7}$ $\frac{5}{7}$
10. $\frac{17}{21} + \frac{19}{21}$ $1\frac{10}{21}$
11. $\frac{9}{10} - \frac{3}{10}$ $\frac{4}{9}$
12. $\frac{53}{29} - \frac{21}{41}$ $\frac{4}{9}$
13. $\frac{5}{9} + \frac{1}{4}$ $\frac{17}{18}$
14. $\frac{9}{15} + \frac{5}{10}$ $1\frac{1}{10}$
15. $\frac{9}{10} - \frac{4}{5}$ $\frac{1}{10}$
16. $\frac{4\frac{5}{3}}{} - \frac{3}{6}$ $\frac{1}{6}$

Write each sum or difference in simplest form.

17. $4\frac{3}{8} + 5\frac{5}{6}$ $10\frac{5}{18}$
18. $8\frac{7}{12} - 4\frac{5}{8}$ $3\frac{5}{6}$

Solve.

19. Carrie bought $6\frac{3}{10}$ pounds of 16D nails and $2\frac{4}{5}$ pounds of 8D nails. Find the total weight of her purchase. $8\frac{9}{10}$ pounds of nails

20. Tom bought $1\frac{5}{6}$ pounds of green grapes and $2\frac{1}{3}$ pounds of purple grapes. How many pounds of grapes did Tom buy? $4\frac{3}{8}$ pounds

Available in Spanish

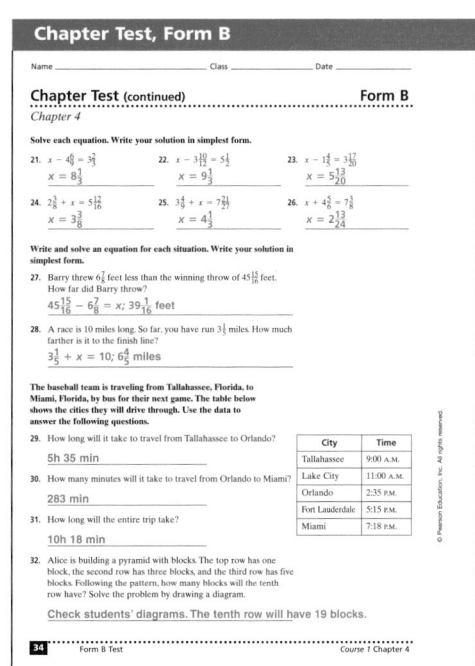

Chapter Test, Form B

Name _____ Class _____ Date _____

Chapter Test (continued)

Form B

Chapter 4

Solve each equation. Write your solution in simplest form.

21. $x - 4\frac{2}{9} = 3\frac{4}{9}$
$x = 8\frac{1}{3}$

22. $x - 3\frac{10}{12} = 5\frac{1}{2}$
$x = 9\frac{1}{3}$

23. $x - 1\frac{3}{4} = 3\frac{17}{20}$
$x = 5\frac{13}{20}$

24. $2\frac{3}{8} + x = 5\frac{12}{16}$
$x = 3\frac{3}{8}$

25. $3\frac{1}{4} + x = 7\frac{3}{4}$
$x = 4\frac{1}{2}$

26. $x + 4\frac{5}{8} = 7\frac{3}{4}$
$x = 2\frac{13}{24}$

Write and solve an equation for each situation. Write your solution in simplest form.

27. Barry threw $6\frac{7}{8}$ feet less than the winning throw of $45\frac{15}{16}$ feet. How far did Barry throw?
$45\frac{15}{16} - 6\frac{7}{8} = x; \ 39\frac{1}{16}$ feet

28. A race is 10 miles long. So far, you have run $3\frac{1}{5}$ miles. How much farther is it to the finish line?
$3\frac{1}{5} + x = 10; \ 6\frac{4}{5}$ miles

The baseball team is traveling from Tallahassee, Florida, to Miami, Florida, by bus for their next game. The table below shows the cities they will drive through. Use the data to answer the following questions.

City	Time
Tallahassee	9:00 A.M.
Lake City	11:00 A.M.
Orlando	2:35 P.M.
Fort Lauderdale	5:15 P.M.
Miami	7:18 P.M.

29. How long will it take to travel from Tallahassee to Orlando?
5h 35 min

30. How many minutes will it take to travel from Orlando to Miami?
283 min

31. How long will the entire trip take?
10h 18 min

32. Alice is building a pyramid with blocks. The top row has one block, the second row has three blocks, and the third row has five blocks. Following the pattern, how many blocks will the tenth row have? Solve the problem by drawing a diagram.
Check students' diagrams. The tenth row will have 19 blocks.

Available in Spanish

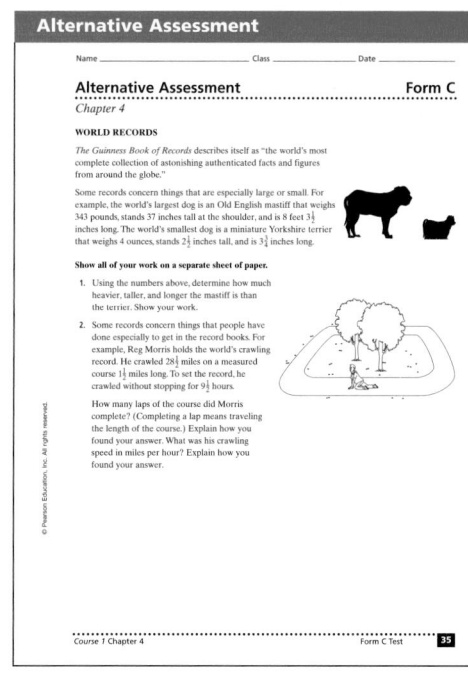

Alternative Assessment

Name _____ Class _____ Date _____

Alternative Assessment

Form C

Chapter 4

WORLD RECORDS

The Guinness Book of Records describes itself as "the world's most complete collection of astonishing authenticated facts and figures from around the globe."

Some records concern things that are especially large or small. For example, the world's largest dog is an Old English mastiff that weighs 343 pounds, stands 37 inches tall at the shoulder, and is 8 feet $3\frac{1}{2}$ inches long. The world's smallest dog is a miniature Yorkshire terrier that weighs 4 ounces, stands $2\frac{1}{2}$ inches tall, and is $3\frac{1}{4}$ inches long.

Show all of your work on a separate sheet of paper.

1. Using the numbers above, determine how much heavier, taller, and longer the mastiff is than the terrier. Show your work.

2. Some records concern things that people have done especially to get in the record books. For example, Reg Morris holds the world's crawling record. He crawled $28\frac{1}{2}$ miles on a measured course $1\frac{1}{2}$ miles long. To set the record, he crawled without stopping for $9\frac{1}{2}$ hours. How many laps of the course did Morris complete? (Completing a lap means traveling the length of the course.) Explain how you found your answer. What was his crawling speed in miles per hour? Explain how you found your answer.

Available in Spanish

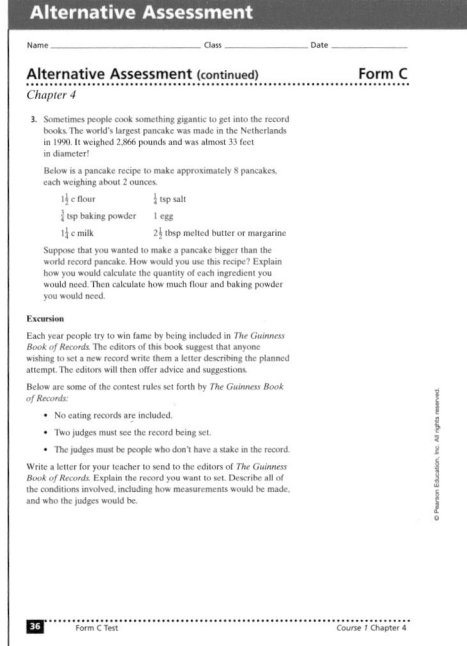

Alternative Assessment

Name _____ Class _____ Date _____

Alternative Assessment (continued)

Form C

Chapter 4

3. Sometimes people cook something gigantic to get into the record books. The world's largest pancake was made in the Netherlands in 1990. It weighed 2,866 pounds and was almost 33 feet in diameter!

Below is a pancake recipe to make approximately 8 pancakes, each weighing about 2 ounces.

$1\frac{1}{2}$ c flour $\frac{1}{4}$ tsp salt

$\frac{3}{4}$ tsp baking powder   1 egg

$1\frac{1}{4}$ c milk $2\frac{1}{2}$ tbsp melted butter or margarine

Suppose that you wanted to make a pancake bigger than the world record pancake. Explain how you would use this recipe. Explain how you would calculate the quantity of each ingredient you would need. Then calculate how much flour and baking powder you would need.

Excursion

Each year people try to win fame by being included in *The Guinness Book of Records*. The editors of this book suggest that anyone wishing to set a new record write them a letter describing the planned attempt. The editors will then offer advice and suggestions.

Below are some of the contest rules set forth by *The Guinness Book of Records*:

- No eating records are included.
- Two judges must see the record being set.
- The judges must be people who don't have a stake in the record.

Write a letter for your teacher to send to the editors of *The Guinness Book of Records*. Explain the record you want to set. Describe all of the conditions involved, including how measurements would be made, and who the judges would be.

Available in Spanish

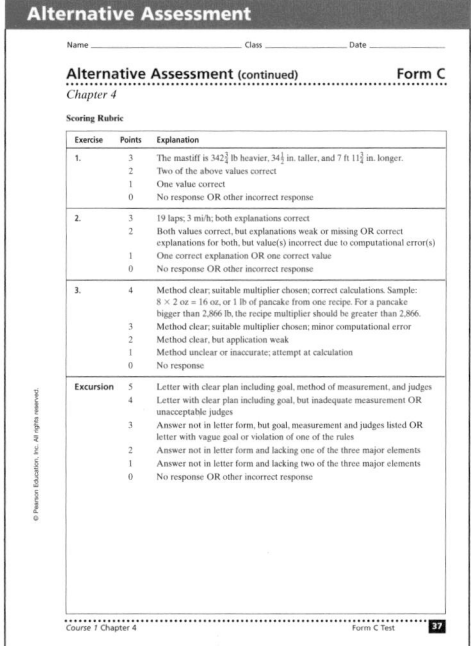

Alternative Assessment

Name _____ Class _____ Date _____

Alternative Assessment (continued)

Form C

Chapter 4

Scoring Rubric

Exercise	Points	Explanation
1.	3	The mastiff is $342\frac{3}{4}$ lb heavier, $34\frac{1}{2}$ in. taller, and 7 ft $11\frac{1}{4}$ in. longer.
	2	Two of the above values correct
	1	One value correct
	0	No response OR other incorrect response
2.	3	19 laps; 3 mi/h; both explanations correct
	2	Both values correct, but explanations weak or missing OR correct explanations for both, but value(s) incorrect due to computational error(s)
	1	One correct explanation OR one correct value
	0	No response OR other incorrect response
3.	4	Method clear; suitable multiplier chosen; correct calculations. Sample: 8×2 oz $= 16$ oz, or 1 lb of pancake from one recipe. For a pancake bigger than 2,866 lb, the recipe multiplier should be greater than 2,866.
	3	Method clear; suitable multiplier chosen; minor computational error
	2	Method clear, but application weak
	1	Method unclear or inaccurate; attempt at calculation
	0	No response
Excursion	5	Letter with clear plan including goal, method of measurement, and judges
	4	Letter with clear plan including goal, but inadequate measurement OR unacceptable judges
	3	Answer not in letter form, but goal, measurement and judges listed OR letter with vague goal or violation of one of the rules
	2	Answer not in letter form and lacking one of the three major elements
	1	Answer not in letter form and lacking two of the three major elements
	0	No response OR other incorrect response

Available in Spanish

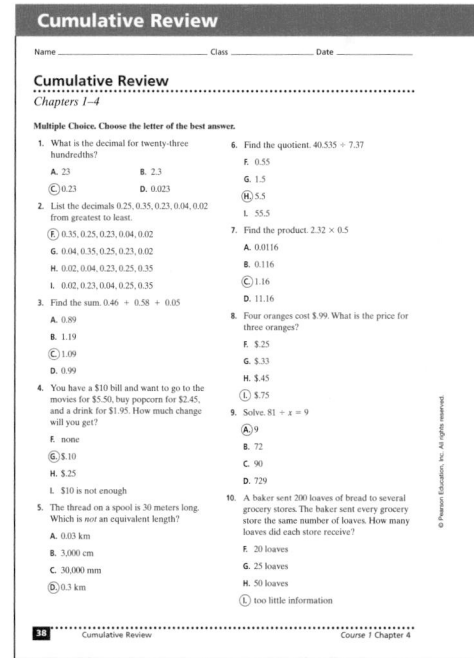

Cumulative Review

Name _____ Class _____ Date _____

Cumulative Review

Chapters 1–4

Multiple Choice. Choose the letter of the best answer.

1. What is the decimal for twenty-three hundredths?
A. 23   B. 2.3
(C.) 0.23   D. 0.023

2. List the decimals 0.25, 0.35, 0.23, 0.04, 0.02 from greatest to least.
(F.) 0.35, 0.25, 0.23, 0.04, 0.02
G. 0.04, 0.35, 0.25, 0.23, 0.02
H. 0.02, 0.04, 0.23, 0.25, 0.35
I. 0.02, 0.23, 0.04, 0.25, 0.35

3. Find the sum. $0.46 + 0.58 + 0.05$
A. 0.89
B. 1.19
(C.) 1.09
D. 0.99

4. You have a $10 bill and want to go to the movies for $5.50, buy popcorn for $2.45, and a drink for $1.95. How much change will you get?
F. none
(G.) $.10
H. $.25
I. $10 is not enough

5. The thread on a spool is 30 meters long. Which is *not* an equivalent length?
A. 0.03 km
B. 3,000 cm
C. 30,000 mm
(D.) 0.3 km

6. Find the quotient. $40.535 \div 7.37$
F. 0.55
G. 1.5
(H.) 5.5
I. 55.5

7. Find the product. 2.32×0.5
A. 0.0116
B. 0.116
(C.) 1.16
D. 11.16

8. Four oranges cost $.99. What is the price for three oranges?
F. $.25
G. $.33
H. $.45
(I.) $.75

9. Solve. $81 + x = 9$
(A.) 9
B. 72
C. 90
D. 729

10. A baker sent 200 loaves of bread to several grocery stores. The baker sent every grocery store the same number of loaves. How many loaves did each store receive?
F. 20 loaves
G. 25 loaves
H. 50 loaves
(I.) too little information

Available in Spanish

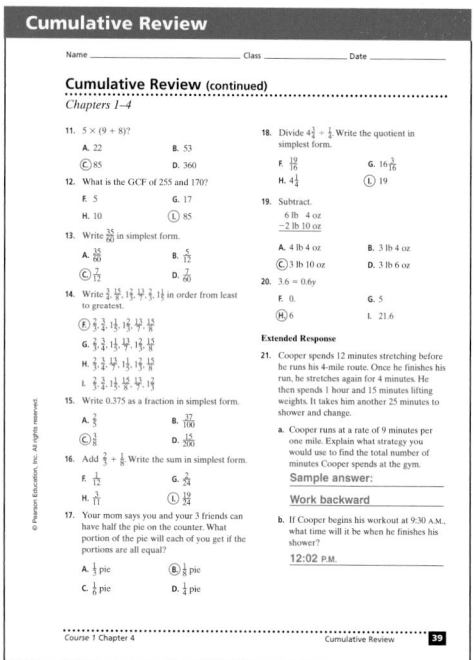

Cumulative Review (continued)
Chapters 1–4

11. $5 \times (9 + 8)$?
   A. 22   B. 53
   C. 85   D. 360

12. What is the GCF of 255 and 170?
   F. 5   G. 17
   H. 10   I. 85

13. Write $\frac{24}{60}$ in simplest form.
   A. $\frac{35}{60}$ B. $\frac{5}{12}$
   C. $\frac{2}{15}$ D. $\frac{7}{60}$

14. Write $\frac{3}{4}, \frac{13}{16}, 1\frac{1}{8}, \frac{17}{2}, \frac{9}{8}, 1\frac{1}{4}$ in order from least to greatest.

15. Write 0.375 as a fraction in simplest form.

16. Add $\frac{5}{6} + \frac{1}{8}$. Write the sum in simplest form.

17. Your mom says you and your 3 friends can have half the pie on the counter. What portion of the pie will each of you get if the portions are all equal?

18. Divide $4\frac{3}{4} \div \frac{1}{4}$. Write the quotient in simplest form.

19. Subtract.
   6 lb 4 oz
   − 2 lb 10 oz

20. $3.6 = 0.6y$

Extended Response

21. Cooper spends 12 minutes stretching before he runs his 4-mile route. Once he finishes his run, he stretches again for 4 minutes. He then spends 1 hour and 15 minutes lifting weights. It takes him another 25 minutes to shower and change.
   a. Cooper runs at a rate of 9 minutes per one mile. Explain what strategy you would use to find the total number of minutes Cooper spends at the gym.
   Sample answer:
   Work backward
   b. If Cooper begins his workout at 9:30 A.M., what time will it be when he finishes his shower?
   12:02 P.M.

Course 1 Chapter 4 — Cumulative Review — 39

Available in Spanish

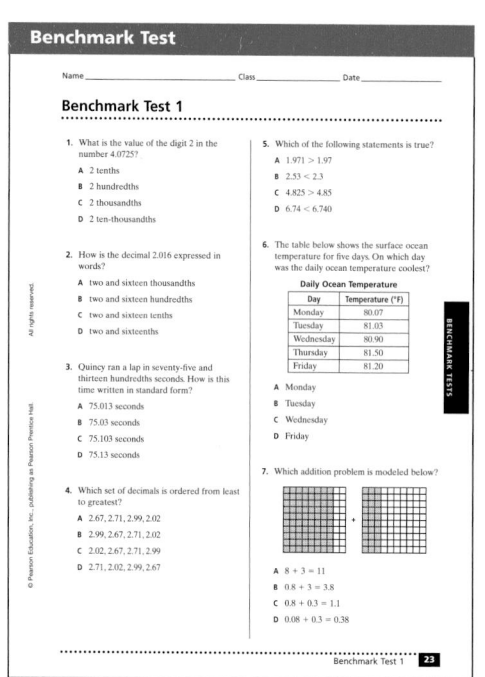

Benchmark Test 1

1. What is the value of the digit 2 in the number 4.0725?
   A 2 tenths
   B 2 hundredths
   C 2 thousandths
   D 2 ten-thousandths

2. How is the decimal 2.016 expressed in words?
   A two and sixteen thousandths
   B two and sixteen hundredths
   C two and sixteen tenths
   D two and sixteen

3. Quincy ran a lap in seventy-five and thirteen hundredths seconds. How is this time written in standard form?
   A 75.013 seconds
   B 75.03 seconds
   C 75.103 seconds
   D 75.13 seconds

4. Which set of decimals is ordered from least to greatest?
   A 2.67, 2.71, 2.99, 2.02
   B 2.99, 2.67, 2.71, 2.02
   C 2.02, 2.67, 2.71, 2.99
   D 2.71, 2.02, 2.99, 2.67

5. Which of the following statements is true?
   A 1.971 > 1.97
   B 2.53 < 2.3
   C 4.825 > 4.85
   D 6.74 < 6.740

6. The table below shows the surface ocean temperature for five days. On which day was the daily ocean temperature coolest?

   Daily Ocean Temperature

Day	Temperature (°F)
Monday	80.07
Tuesday	81.03
Wednesday	80.90
Thursday	81.50
Friday	81.20

   A Monday
   B Tuesday
   C Wednesday
   D Friday

7. Which addition problem is modeled below?

   A 8 + 3 = 11
   B 0.8 + 3 = 3.8
   C 0.8 + 0.3 = 1.1
   D 0.08 + 0.3 = 0.38

Benchmark Test 1 — 23

Test-Taking Strategies: Reading-Comprehension Questions

Reading comprehension questions are based on a passage that gives information and facts.

To solve a problem use these steps:
- Read the directions and the passage.
- Read the questions carefully.
- Look for information that helps answer the questions.

EXAMPLE
Read the passage and answer the questions below.

> Each year, more than 775,000 children and teenagers are treated in the emergency room for sports injuries. In a recent study, doctors found that 10 years ago, up to 70 percent of sports injuries in kids were acute injuries, such as a sprained ankle or a fracture. Over the past five years, however, overuse accounted for about half of all sports injuries among youngsters. Doctors are seeing a lot more elbow injuries from too much pitching and a lot more heel pain from tendinitis due to too much soccer.

This year about 25 athletes in your school will be injured. About how many of them will have injuries due to overuse?

What are you being asked?
How many of the 25 athletes will have injuries due to overuse?

What information helps you to solve the problem?
Over the past five years overuse accounted for about half of all sports injuries among youngsters.

Solve the problem: 50% of 25 students is about 13 students.

Transparency 5

On PH Website

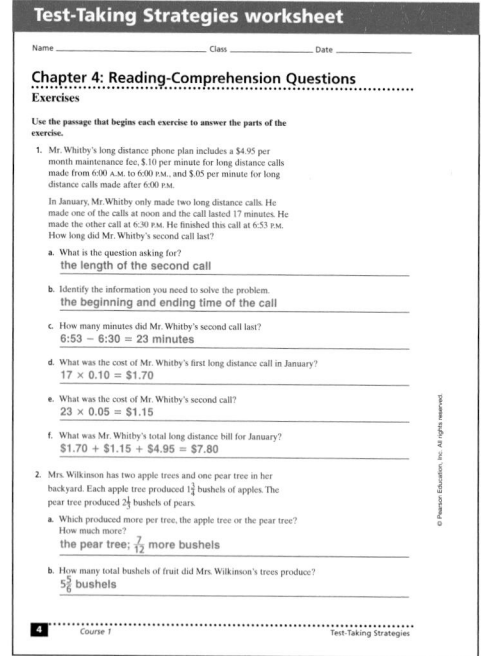

Chapter 4: Reading-Comprehension Questions
Exercises

Use the passage that begins each exercise to answer the parts of the exercise.

1. Mr. Whitby's long distance phone plan includes a $4.95 per month maintenance fee, $.10 per minute for long distance calls made from 6:00 A.M. to 6:00 P.M., and $.05 per minute for long distance calls made after 6:00 P.M.

   In January, Mr. Whitby only made two long distance calls. He made one of the calls at noon and the call lasted 17 minutes. He made the other call at 6:30 P.M. He finished this call at 6:53 P.M. How long did Mr. Whitby's second call last?

   a. What is the question asking for?
   the length of the second call
   b. Identify the information you need to solve the problem.
   the beginning and ending time of the call
   c. How many minutes did Mr. Whitby's second call last?
   6:53 − 6:30 = 23 minutes
   d. What was the cost of Mr. Whitby's first long distance call in January?
   17 × 0.10 = $1.70
   e. What was the cost of Mr. Whitby's second call?
   23 × 0.05 = $1.15
   f. What was Mr. Whitby's total long distance bill for January?
   $1.70 + $1.15 + $4.95 = $7.80

2. Mrs. Wilkinson has two apple trees and one pear tree in her backyard. Each apple tree produced $1\frac{3}{4}$ bushels of apples. The pear tree produced $2\frac{1}{3}$ bushels of pears.
   a. Which produced more per tree, the apple tree or the pear tree? How much more?
   the pear tree; $\frac{7}{12}$ more bushels
   b. How many total bushels of fruit did Mrs. Wilkinson's trees produce?
   $5\frac{5}{6}$ bushels

4 — Course 1 — Test-Taking Strategies

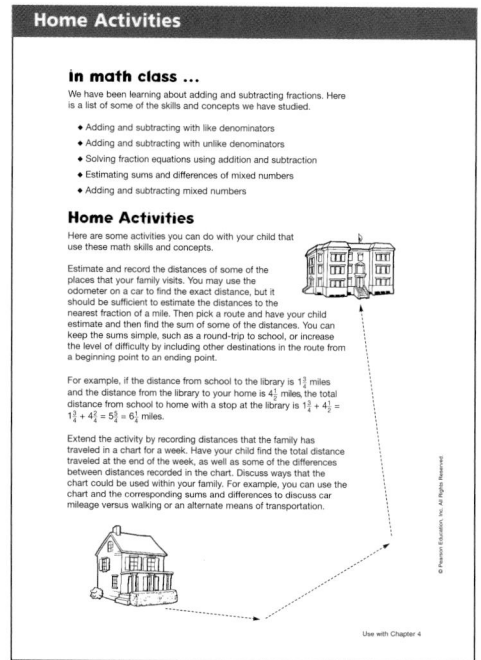

in math class ...
We have been learning about adding and subtracting fractions. Here is a list of some of the skills and concepts we have studied.

- Adding and subtracting with like denominators
- Adding and subtracting with unlike denominators
- Solving fraction equations using addition and subtraction
- Estimating sums and differences of mixed numbers
- Adding and subtracting mixed numbers

Home Activities
Here are some activities you can do with your child that use these math skills and concepts.

Estimate and record the distances of some of the places that your family visits. You may use the odometer on a car to find the exact distance, but it should be sufficient to estimate the distances to the nearest fraction of a mile. Then pick a route and have your child estimate and then find the sum of some of the distances. You can keep the sums simple, such as a round-trip to school, or increase the level of difficulty by including other destinations in the route from a beginning point to an ending point.

For example, if the distance from school to the library is $1\frac{3}{4}$ miles and the distance from the library to your home is $4\frac{1}{2}$ miles, the total distance from school to home with a stop at the library is $1\frac{3}{4} + 4\frac{1}{2} = 5\frac{5}{4} = 6\frac{1}{4}$ miles.

Extend the activity by recording distances that the family has traveled in a chart over a week. Have your child find the total distance traveled at the end of the week, as well as some of the differences between distances recorded in the chart. Discuss ways that the chart could be used within your family. For example, you can use the chart and the corresponding sums and differences to discuss car mileage versus walking or an alternate means of transportation.

Use with Chapter 4

Available in Spanish;
Web Code: aak-5500

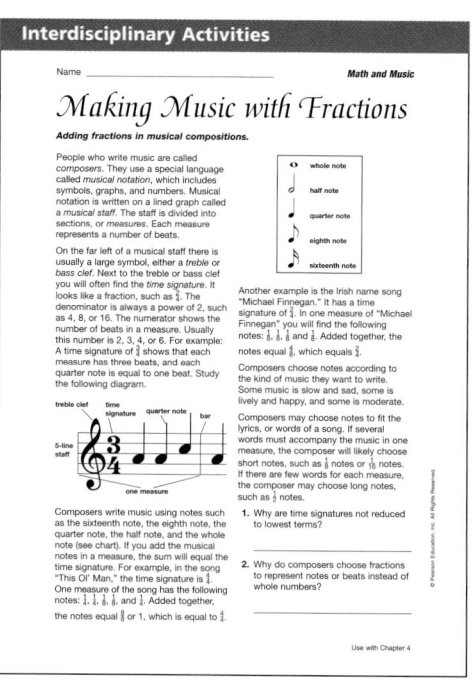

Math and Music

Making Music with Fractions
Adding fractions in musical compositions.

People who write music are called *composers*. They use a special language called *musical notation*, which includes symbols, graphs, and numbers. Musical notation is written on a lined graph called a *musical staff*. The staff is divided into sections, or *measures*. Each measure represents a number of beats.

On the far left of a musical staff there is usually a large symbol, either a *treble* or *bass clef*. Next to the treble or bass clef you will often find the *time signature*. It looks like a fraction, such as $\frac{3}{4}$. The denominator is always a power of 2, such as 4, 8, or 16. The numerator shows the number of beats in a measure. Usually this number is 2, 3, 4, or 6. For example: A time signature of $\frac{3}{4}$ shows that each measure has three beats, and each quarter note is equal to one beat. Study the following diagram.

Composers write music using notes such as the sixteenth note, the eighth note, the quarter note, the half note, and the whole note (see chart). If you add the musical notes in a measure, the sum will equal the time signature. For example, in the song "This Ol' Man," the time signature is $\frac{1}{4}$. One measure of the song has the following notes: $\frac{1}{8}, \frac{1}{8}, \frac{1}{8}, \frac{1}{8}$, and $\frac{1}{4}$. Added together, the notes equal $\frac{6}{8}$ or 1, which is equal to $\frac{4}{4}$.

●	whole note
♩	half note
♩	quarter note
♪	eighth note
♬	sixteenth note

Another example is the Irish name song "Michael Finnegan." It has a time signature of $\frac{1}{4}$. In one measure of "Michael Finnegan" you will find the following notes: $\frac{1}{8}, \frac{1}{8}, \frac{1}{4},$ and $\frac{1}{8}$. Added together, the notes equal $\frac{4}{8}$, which equals $\frac{1}{4}$.

Composers choose notes according to the kind of music they want to write. Some music is slow and sad, some is lively and happy, and some is moderate.

Composers may choose notes to fit the lyrics, or words of a song. If several words must accompany the music in one measure, the composer will likely choose short notes, such as $\frac{1}{8}$ notes or $\frac{1}{16}$ notes. If there are few words for each measure, the composer may choose long notes, such as $\frac{1}{2}$ notes.

1. Why are time signatures not reduced to lowest terms?

2. Why do composers choose fractions to represent notes or beats instead of whole numbers?

Use with Chapter 4

Web Code: aak-5500

Interdisciplinary Activities

Math and Music

3. Study the musical notes in the following parts of songs. Then answer the questions that follow.

- The "Wassail Song" is from England, where "wassailers" go house to house, singing carols.

Here   we come   a - was - sail - ing   A- mong the leaves   so   green——

- The song, "We Shall Overcome," was sung by Civil Rights marchers in the 1960s. They made up verses to express their beliefs and hopes.

We shall   o - ver - come,——   We shall   o - ver - come.——

- The song, "Rain Dance," is from the great rain dance of the Zuni Indians of New Mexico.

Rain   now   is   here with us,   We   will   be   pros - per - ous!

- Almost everyone knows "Happy Birthday to You." Here's another birthday song called "Birthday Song."

Oh,   Birth-day Pal,   we sing-a-ling-a-ling   With   all   our   hearts to   you,   We

a. Write the time signature for each song above. Next to the time signature, write the value of the notes from the first full measure. Add them together. What does each sum match?

b. Look at the second full measure in the "Birthday Song." Show how it is equal to the third full measure.

4. A composer has chosen the following time signatures. Show two combinations of notes that equal each time signature:

a. $\frac{4}{4}$

b. $\frac{6}{8}$

c. $\frac{2}{4}$

5. On a separate sheet of paper, make a list of things you do, or see others do, in which fractions are used. Tell about the fractions that are used.

Use with Chapter 4

Web Code: aak-5500

Algebra Readiness Puzzles

Fraction Fun   Puzzle 4

Adding and Subtracting Fractions

Use the following digits to make the sentences true. Each digit may be used in the boxes no more than two times.

```
0      3      8

    4    9    1    5

2      6      7
```

$\frac{6}{9} - \frac{2}{3} = \square$

$\frac{\square}{\square} + \frac{6}{5} = 2$

$\frac{8}{9} + \frac{\square}{3} = 1\frac{5}{\square}$

$\frac{9}{\square} - \frac{\square}{4} = 1\frac{1}{28}$

$\frac{\square}{2} + \frac{\square}{\square} = \frac{7}{8}$

$\frac{5}{\square} - \frac{\square}{\square} = \frac{1}{30}$

$\frac{\square}{9} + \frac{6}{\square} = 3$

Web Code: aak-5500
Sample pages.

Algebra Readiness Puzzles

Solutions in Need of Equations   Puzzle 68

Ring the equation or equations that give the solution.

1. $y = 5$

$y - 6 = 11$ $y + 15 = 20$ $6 \times y = 60$

2. $n = 12$

$4n = 48$ $n - 12 = 1$ $12 + n = 1$

3. $t = 10$

$5 + t = 10$ $t - 10 = 10$ $t \times 6 = 60$

4. $p = \frac{5}{12}$

$p + \frac{7}{12} = 1$ $p - \frac{3}{12} = \frac{8}{12}$ $p - \frac{4}{12} = \frac{1}{12}$

5. $r = \frac{1}{8}$

$r + \frac{1}{8} = \frac{1}{4}$ $r - \frac{3}{8} = \frac{1}{4}$ $\frac{5}{8} + r = \frac{7}{8}$

Ring the equation or equations in which s is greater than r.

6. $r = 4$ $s - 2 = 3$ $10 - s = 6$ $3s = 9$

7. $r = 10$ $s - 2 = 6$ $4 \times s = 36$ $s + 10 = 22$

8. $r = \frac{7}{10}$ $s + \frac{4}{10} = 1$ $s - \frac{3}{10} = \frac{1}{2}$ $2 - s = 1\frac{1}{10}$

Web Code: aak-5500

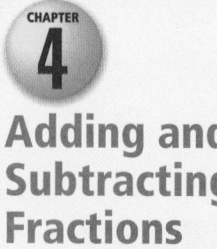

CHAPTER 4

Adding and Subtracting Fractions

Chapter 4 Overview

In this chapter students estimate and find sums and differences of fractions and mixed numbers with the same denominators and with different denominators. They also solve one-step equations involving fractions.

 **Reading Math**
- Understanding Word Problems, p. 195
- **Vocabulary:** A complete list, plus exercises, in the Chapter Review, p. 210
- **Illustrated Glossary:** Examples for each vocabulary term, plus definitions in English and Spanish, on p. 669

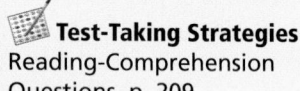 **Test-Taking Strategies**
Reading-Comprehension Questions, p. 209

Real-World Problem Solving
- **Strategies:** Draw a Diagram, pp. 206–208
- **Real-World Snapshots:** Fast Fractions, pp. 214–215
- **Chapter Project:** Seeing is Believing, p. 637

 **www.PHSchool.com**
Internet support includes:
- Self-grading Vocabulary and Chapter 4 Tests
- Activity Masters
- Chapter Project support
- Chapter Planner
- Ch. 4 Resources

Plus **iTEXT**

CHAPTER 4

Lessons

4-1 Estimating Sums and Differences

4-2 Fractions With Like Denominators

4-3 Fractions With Unlike Denominators

4-4 Adding Mixed Numbers

4-5 Subtracting Mixed Numbers

4-6 Equations With Fractions

4-7 Measuring: Elapsed Time

4-8 Problem Solving: Draw a Diagram

Key Vocabulary
- benchmark (p. 171)
- elapsed time (p. 202)

Adding and Subtracting Fractions

Real-World Snapshots

You can determine running speeds for many types of races, including a soapbox derby. Finding speeds for animals is more of a challenge. However, scientists have been able to determine approximate animal speeds, as shown in the chart below.

Data File Top Speeds in Miles per Minute

Animal	Top Speed
Black mamba snake	$\frac{1}{3}$
Cheetah	$\frac{7}{6}$
Chicken	$\frac{3}{20}$
Giant tortoise	$\frac{1}{300}$

Animal	Top Speed
Peregrine falcon	$\frac{10}{3}$
Rabbit	$\frac{3}{5}$
Spider	$\frac{1}{25}$
Whippet	$\frac{71}{120}$

SOURCE: *Natural History Magazine*

You will use the data above in this chapter:

- p. 177 Lesson 4-2
- p. 183 Lesson 4-3
- p. 193 Lesson 4-5

Real-World Snapshots On pages 214 and 215, you will solve problems involving speeds.

Teaching Notes

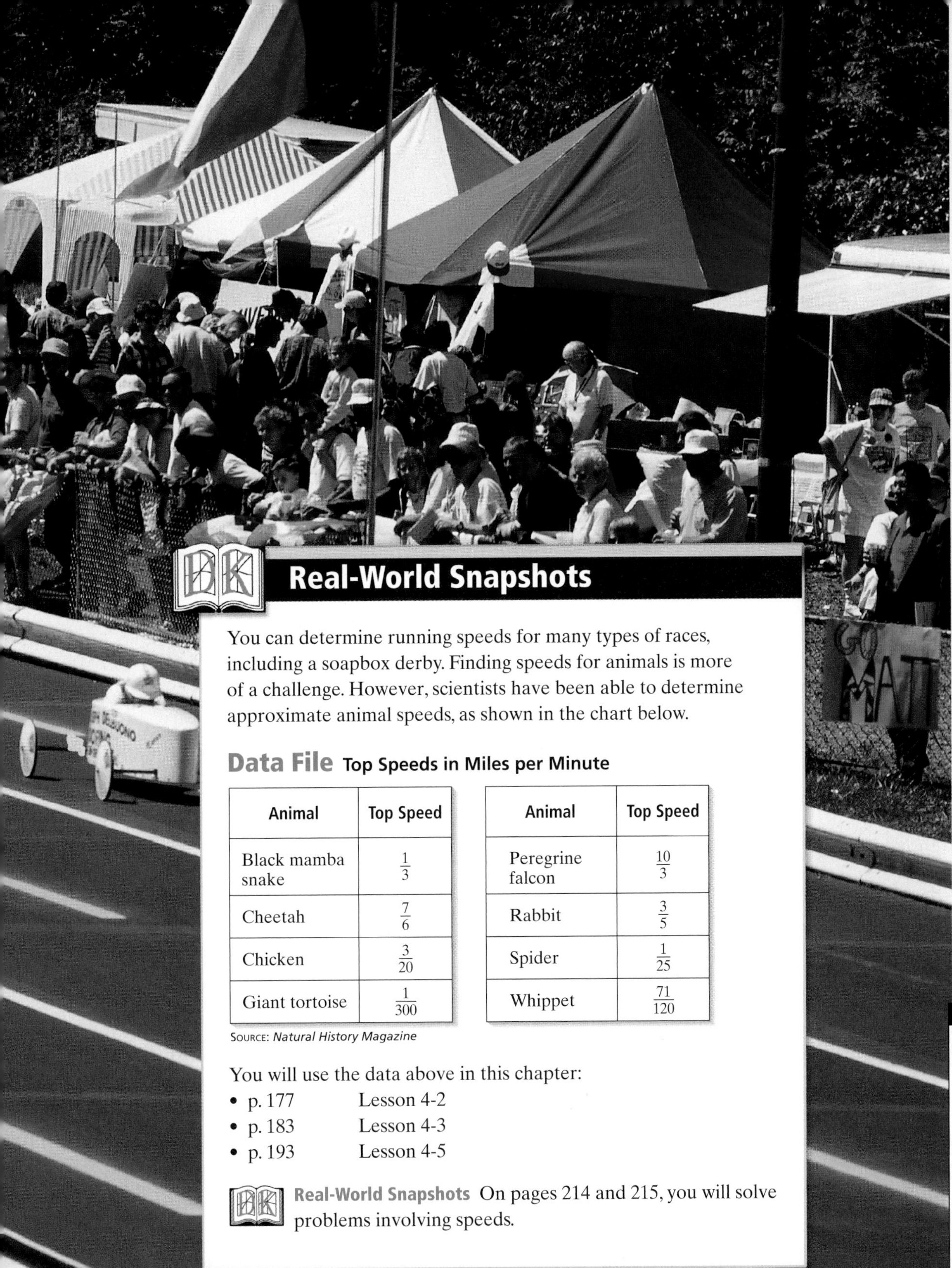

Activating Prior Knowledge

In this chapter students build on and extend their knowledge of fraction concepts to add and subtract fractions and mixed numbers. They also draw upon their understanding of time measurement to find elapsed time. Ask questions such as:

- *Write the mixed number $4\frac{4}{6}$ as an improper fraction in simplest form.* $\frac{14}{3}$
- *What is the GCF of 24 and 18?* 6
- *What is the LCM of 24 and 18?* 72
- *Write in order from least to greatest: $\frac{1}{2}$, 0.8, $\frac{3}{8}$.* $\frac{3}{8}$, $\frac{1}{2}$, 0.8

Real-World Snapshots

The data here will be used throughout the chapter. Have a volunteer read the opening sentence and the title of the chart, which contains information that compares speeds of different animals. Focus students on the data in the chart and ask:

- *Which is the slowest animal?* giant tortoise
- *Which animals can attain speeds that are greater than a mile a minute? Explain how you can tell.* Cheetah, peregrine falcon; top speed fraction is greater than 1.

Reading and Math Literacy

4A: Graphic Organizer For use before Lesson 4-1

Study Skill: Spend time previewing the chapter. Highlight new vocabulary words and their definitions.

Write your answers.

1. What is the chapter title? Adding and Subtracting Fractions
2. How many lessons are there in this chapter? 8
3. What is the topic of the Reading Math page? Understanding Word Problems
4. What is the topic of the Test-Taking Strategy page? Reading Comprehension Questions
5. Look through the pages of the chapter and list four real-world connections that you see discussed in this chapter. Answers will vary.
6. Complete the graphic organizer below as you work through the chapter.
   - In the center, write the title of the chapter.
   - When you begin a lesson, write the lesson name in a rectangle.
   - When you complete a lesson, write a skill or key concept in a circle linked to that lesson block. When you complete the chapter, use this graphic organizer to help you review.

Available in Spanish

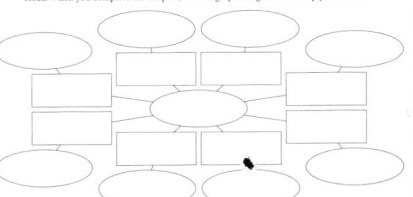

Diagnosing Readiness

Prescribing Intervention
For intervention, direct students to:

Estimating With Decimals
Lesson 1-4: Example 1. Extra Practice, p. 642.

Finding Equivalent Fractions
Lesson 3-4: Example 2. Extra Practice, p. 644.

Writing Mixed Numbers and Improper Fractions
Lesson 3-5 Example 3. Extra Practice, p. 644.

Finding the Least Common Multiple
Lesson 3-6: Examples 1–2. Extra Practice, p. 644.

Chapter 4 Preview

Where You've Been

- In Chapter 1, you learned to add, subtract, and estimate using decimals.

- In Chapter 2, you learned to solve equations.

- In Chapter 3, you learned to write and compare fractions and mixed numbers.

Where You're Going

- In Chapter 4, you will add and subtract fractions and mixed numbers.

- You will also solve equations with fractions.

- Applying what you learn, you will find elapsed time.

Pilots calculate elapsed time to determine if a flight is on schedule.

iTEXT Instant self-check online and on CD-ROM

 **Diagnosing Readiness** ? **For help, go to the lesson in green.**

Estimating With Decimals (Lesson 1-4)

Round each decimal to the nearest hundredth.

1. 2.58796 2.59   **2.** 1.98637 1.99   **3.** 6.219054 6.22

Finding Equivalent Fractions (Lesson 3-4)

Write each fraction in simplest form.

4. $\frac{5}{10}$ $\frac{1}{2}$ **5.** $\frac{6}{15}$ $\frac{2}{5}$ **6.** $\frac{12}{16}$ $\frac{3}{4}$

Writing Mixed Numbers and Improper Fractions (Lesson 3-5)

Write each improper fraction as a mixed number.

7. $\frac{87}{9}$ $9\frac{2}{3}$ **8.** $\frac{21}{4}$ $5\frac{1}{4}$ **9.** $\frac{15}{2}$ $7\frac{1}{2}$

Write each mixed number as an improper fraction.

10. $8\frac{2}{3}$ $\frac{26}{3}$ **11.** $5\frac{3}{4}$ $\frac{23}{4}$ **12.** $16\frac{7}{9}$ $\frac{151}{9}$

Finding the Least Common Multiple (Lesson 3-6)

Find the LCM of each pair of numbers.

13. 8, 18 72   **14.** 5, 16 80   **15.** 14, 30 210

Estimating Sums and Differences

What You'll Learn

OBJECTIVE 1 To estimate sums and differences

...And Why

To estimate the difference of two measurements, as in Example 2

 Check Skills You'll Need

? For help, go to Lesson 3-7.

Compare each pair of fractions using <, =, or >.

1. $\dfrac{3}{5} \boxed{>} \dfrac{2}{5}$

2. $\dfrac{5}{7} \boxed{<} \dfrac{5}{6}$

3. $\dfrac{2}{3} \boxed{=} \dfrac{16}{24}$

4. $\dfrac{8}{9} \boxed{<} \dfrac{9}{8}$

5. $\dfrac{15}{18} \boxed{>} \dfrac{5}{8}$

6. $\dfrac{23}{24} \boxed{<} \dfrac{71}{72}$

New Vocabulary • benchmark

OBJECTIVE 1

Estimating Sums and Differences

iTEXT Interactive lesson includes instant self-check, tutorials, and activities.

Investigation: Estimating Fractions

Estimate the shaded part of each figure using $0, \frac{1}{4}, \frac{1}{2}, \frac{3}{4}$, and 1.

1. 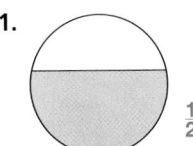 $\frac{1}{2}$

2. 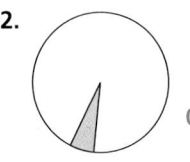 0

3.  $\frac{3}{4}$

4. 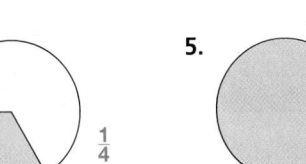 $\frac{1}{4}$

5. 1

6. 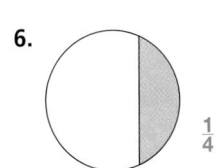 $\frac{1}{4}$

Reading Math

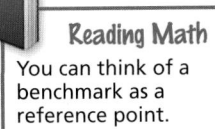 You can think of a benchmark as a reference point.

A **benchmark** is a whole number or fraction that is easy to use when you estimate. The benchmarks $0, \frac{1}{2}$, and 1 are particularly useful when estimating sums and differences of fractions. The following table will help you determine which benchmarks to use when estimating.

Description	Examples	Benchmark
Numerator is close to 0. Denominator is not close to 0.	$\dfrac{1}{8}, \dfrac{3}{16}, \dfrac{2}{25}, \dfrac{9}{100}$	0
Numerator is about one half of denominator.	$\dfrac{3}{8}, \dfrac{9}{16}, \dfrac{11}{25}, \dfrac{52}{100}$	$\dfrac{1}{2}$
Numerator and denominator are close to each other.	$\dfrac{7}{8}, \dfrac{14}{16}, \dfrac{23}{25}, \dfrac{95}{100}$	1

Lesson Preview

PowerPoint

 **Check Skills You'll Need**

Comparing Fractions
Lesson 3-7: Example 1. Extra Practice p. 644.

Lesson Resources

Teaching Resources
Practice, Reteaching, Enrichment

Reaching All Students
Practice Workbook 4-1
Spanish Practice Workbook 4-1
Guided Problem Solving 4-1

Presentation Assistant Plus!
Transparencies
• Check Skills You'll Need 4-1
• Problem of the Day 4-1
• Additional Examples 4-1
• Student Edition Answers 4-1
• Lesson Quiz 4-1
• Classroom Aid 7
PH Presentation Pro CD-ROM 4-1

 PRENTICE HALL ASSESSMENT SYSTEM

Computer Test Generator CD

 Technology
Resource Pro® CD-ROM
Computer Test Generator CD
PH Presentation Pro CD-ROM

 **www.PHSchool.com**
Student Site
• Teacher Web Code: aak-5500
• Self-grading Lesson Quiz

PH SuccessNet Teacher Center
• Lesson Planner
• Resources

Plus **iTEXT**

Ongoing Assessment and Intervention

Before the Lesson
Diagnose prerequisite skills using:
• Check Skills You'll Need

During the Lesson
Monitor progress using:
• Check Understanding
• Additional Examples
• Test Prep

After the Lesson
Assess knowledge using:
• Lesson Quiz
• Computer Test Generator CD

Math Background

A *benchmark* is a number that is easy to use when you estimate. You can use the benchmark values of 0, $\frac{1}{2}$, and 1 to estimate sums and differences of fractions. For instance, the fraction $\frac{4}{7}$ would have a benchmark estimate of $\frac{1}{2}$ and $\frac{7}{8}$ would have a benchmark of 1. You can estimate the sum $\frac{4}{7} + \frac{7}{8}$ as about $\frac{1}{2} + 1$, or $1\frac{1}{2}$. For mixed numbers, simply round to the nearest whole number when making estimates.

Teaching Notes

Investigation (Optional)
Some students may have difficulty relating a fraction to a shaded region. Have them read $\frac{1}{4}$ as "one quarter," $\frac{1}{2}$ as "one half," and $\frac{3}{4}$ as "three quarters." Then discuss what each word phrase represents.

1 EXAMPLE Alternative Method
For students who have difficulty identifying fractions close to $\frac{1}{2}$, suggest that they change the numerator or denominator to find a fraction that is exactly $\frac{1}{2}$. For example, $\frac{7}{12}$ is close to $\frac{6}{12}$ and to $\frac{7}{14}$.

English Learners
Make sure students understand that a *sum* is the result of adding.

PowerPoint
Additional Examples

1. Estimate each sum or difference. Use the benchmarks 0, $\frac{1}{2}$, and 1.
   a. $\frac{5}{6} + \frac{4}{7}$ $1\frac{1}{2}$ b. $\frac{7}{8} - \frac{1}{9}$ 1

2. Steven is $13\frac{11}{12}$ years old. Chloe is $9\frac{1}{4}$ years old. Estimate how many years older Steven is than Chloe. about 5 years

Closure

- *When is 0 a good benchmark value for a fraction?* Sample: when the numerator is much smaller than the denominator
- *When is $\frac{1}{2}$ a good benchmark value for a fraction?* Sample: when the denominator is about twice as large as the numerator

172

Determine the benchmark for each fraction. Then estimate the sum or difference using the benchmarks 0, $\frac{1}{2}$, and 1.

1 EXAMPLE   Estimating Sums and Differences

Estimate.

a. $\dfrac{7}{12} + \dfrac{4}{5}$

b. $\dfrac{9}{10} - \dfrac{1}{7}$

$$\dfrac{7}{12} + \dfrac{4}{5} \qquad \dfrac{9}{10} - \dfrac{1}{7}$$

$\approx \dfrac{1}{2} + 1$ ← Replace each fraction with a benchmark. → $\approx 1 - 0$

$= 1\dfrac{1}{2}$ ← Simplify. → $= 1$

✔ **Check Understanding** 1 Estimate each sum or difference.   a. $\dfrac{5}{6} + \dfrac{3}{7}$ b. $\dfrac{12}{13} - \dfrac{2}{25}$ 1

$1\dfrac{1}{2}$

You can round mixed numbers to the nearest whole number. The diagram below shows how to round $7\frac{9}{16}$ inches and $6\frac{1}{8}$ inches.

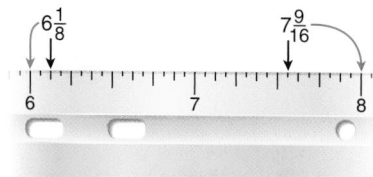

You can round before estimating the sum or difference of two mixed numbers. If a mixed number has a fraction of $\frac{1}{2}$, round up.

2 EXAMPLE   Estimating With Mixed Numbers    Real World

Measurement Dave's hand span is $7\frac{9}{16}$ inches. Galina's hand span is $6\frac{1}{8}$ inches. Estimate the difference between their hand spans.

Estimate $7\frac{9}{16} - 6\frac{1}{8}$.

$7\dfrac{9}{16} \approx 8$ ← Since $\frac{9}{16} > \frac{1}{2}$, round to 8.

$6\dfrac{1}{8} \approx 6$ ← Since $\frac{1}{8} < \frac{1}{2}$, round to 6.

$8 - 6 = 2$ ← Estimate by finding the difference.

Dave's hand span is about 2 inches greater than Galina's hand span.

✔ **Check Understanding** 2 **Travel** It takes $3\frac{3}{4}$ hours to drive to the beach. It takes $8\frac{1}{2}$ hours to drive to the mountains. Estimate the difference in driving times.   5 hours

172   Chapter 4   Adding and Subtracting Fractions

👥 Reaching All Students

| **Below Level** Give students fractions with benchmark values of $\frac{1}{2}$ such as $\frac{2}{5}$, $\frac{6}{10}$, $\frac{5}{8}$, and $\frac{5}{12}$. Have them shade fraction bars for each fraction. | **Advanced Learners** Write a mixed number that rounds up to 4. Then write five other mixed numbers that are between that number and 4. Sample: $3\frac{7}{8}$; $3\frac{9}{10}$; $3\frac{29}{32}$; $3\frac{15}{16}$; $3\frac{39}{40}$; $3\frac{319}{320}$ | **English Learners** See note on page 172. **Alternative Method** See note on page 172. |

A Practice by Example

Example 1
(page 172)

Estimate each sum or difference. Use the benchmarks $0, \frac{1}{2}$, or 1.

1. $\frac{5}{13} + \frac{4}{25}$ $\frac{1}{2}$

2. $\frac{17}{19} - \frac{2}{13}$ 1

3. $\frac{70}{85} + \frac{32}{51}$ $1\frac{1}{2}$

4. $\frac{11}{20} - \frac{2}{15}$ $\frac{1}{2}$

5. $\frac{9}{16} - \frac{18}{37}$ 0

6. $\frac{5}{16} + \frac{7}{15}$ 1

Example 2
(page 172)

Estimate each sum or difference.

7. $4\frac{2}{9} + 6\frac{13}{27}$ 10

8. $9\frac{7}{15} - 3\frac{1}{2}$ 5

9. $22\frac{1}{9} - 16\frac{9}{11}$ 5

10. $22\frac{8}{14} - 17\frac{3}{7}$ 6

11. $76\frac{6}{23} - 45\frac{1}{5}$ 31

12. $84\frac{3}{36} + 41\frac{7}{8}$ 126

13. **Life Science** In an experiment, a kudzu plant is $1\frac{1}{12}$ feet tall. Over time, the plant grows to $4\frac{7}{12}$ feet. About how much did the plant grow?
about 4 ft

B Apply Your Skills

Choose a benchmark for each measurement. Use $0, \frac{1}{2}$, or 1.

14. $\frac{1}{8}$ inch 0

15. $\frac{4}{8}$ inch $\frac{1}{2}$

16. $\frac{15}{16}$ inch 1

17. $\frac{3}{8}$ inch $\frac{1}{2}$

18. $\frac{11}{16}$ inch $\frac{1}{2}$

19. $\frac{3}{16}$ inch 0   inches

20a. Jocelyn: 0 in.;
Carlos: 1 in.;
Amanda: 2 in.

20. **a. Measurement** Use the table. About how much did each person grow during the summer? See left.
   b. Who grew the most? Amanda

21. **Error Analysis** Your friend says that when you estimate the sum of two fractions, the estimate is never a whole number. Do you agree? Explain.   No; for instance, $\frac{7}{8} + \frac{9}{10}$ ≈ 1 + 1 = 2.

Heights (inches)

Person	June	Sept.
Jocelyn	$61\frac{7}{8}$	$62\frac{1}{4}$
Carlos	$60\frac{3}{4}$	$61\frac{5}{8}$
Amanda	$59\frac{1}{8}$	$60\frac{5}{8}$

22. Answers may vary.
Sample: Whole numbers are easier to add and subtract; yes.

22. **Writing in Math** Why does it make sense to round a mixed number to the nearest whole number before adding or subtracting? Could you round to the nearest $\frac{1}{2}$ instead? See above left.

U.S. Coins

Coin	Diameter (inches)
Dime	$\frac{11}{16}$
Penny	$\frac{3}{4}$
Nickel	$\frac{13}{16}$
Quarter	$\frac{15}{16}$

23. **Coins** Use the table at the left to estimate the total width of the coins in the picture below.   about $3\frac{1}{2}$ in.

4-1 Estimating Sums and Differences **173**

GPS Use the Guided Problem Solving worksheet with Exercise 23.

3. Practice

Assignment Guide

Objective 1
Ⓐ Ⓑ Core 1–23
Ⓒ Extension 24–27

Test Prep 28–32
Mixed Review 33–43

Error Prevention!

Exercises 1–12 Have students write the original problem and then the benchmark (or rounded whole number) below each fraction (or mixed number). This helps students check their work.

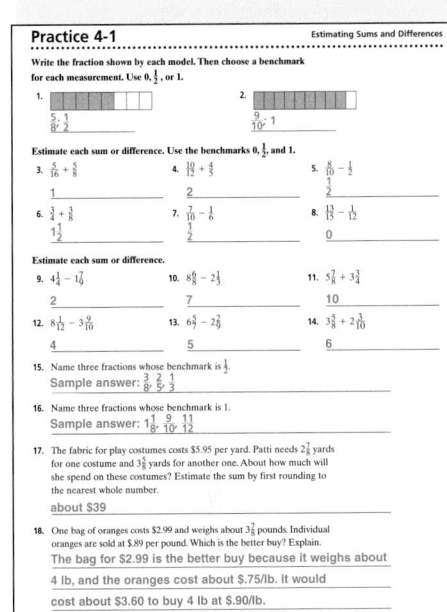

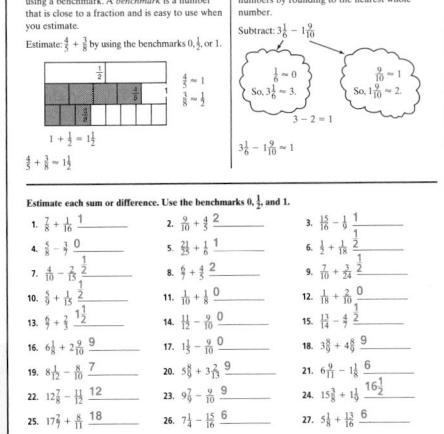

Use benchmarks to estimate each sum or difference.

1. $\frac{9}{10} + \frac{1}{8}$ about 1

2. $\frac{7}{8} - \frac{4}{9}$ about $\frac{1}{2}$

Estimate each sum or difference by rounding.

3. $5\frac{3}{4} + 3\frac{4}{5}$ about 10

4. $8\frac{11}{12} - 2\frac{8}{9}$ about 6

Alternative Assessment

Provide pairs of students with number lines. Partners work together using the number lines to determine whether the given fractions in Exercises 1–6 are closer to 0, $\frac{1}{2}$, or 1.

Test Prep

Resources

For additional practice with a variety of test item formats:
• Test-Prep, p. 213
• Test-Taking Strategies, p. 209
• Test-Taking Strategies With Transparencies

C Challenge

27. Answers may vary. Sample:

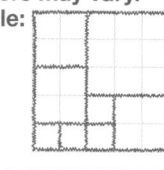

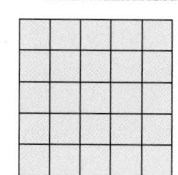

Estimation Use $<$ or $>$ to compare.

24. $14\frac{9}{10} - \left(8\frac{1}{7} + 1\frac{8}{9}\right) \overset{<}{\blacksquare} 14\frac{9}{10} - 8\frac{1}{7} + 1\frac{8}{9}$

25. $\left(13\frac{5}{8} - 10\frac{2}{5}\right) - 2\frac{1}{3} \overset{<}{\blacksquare} 13\frac{5}{8} - \left(10\frac{2}{5} - 2\frac{1}{3}\right)$

26. Less than; each addend is greater than $\frac{1}{2}$, so the actual sum will be greater than the estimate $1\frac{1}{2}$.

26. Number Sense You estimate $\frac{5}{8} + \frac{9}{16} + \frac{17}{32}$ using the benchmarks $0, \frac{1}{2}$, and 1. Is the estimate less than or greater than the actual sum? Explain. See above right.

27. Stretch Your Thinking Divide the grid at the left into eight squares. The squares do not need to be the same size. There can be no overlaps and no space can be left over. See above left.

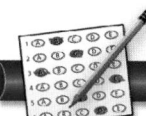

Test Prep

Multiple Choice

28. Which number is closest to 5? **C**

A. $4\frac{3}{4}$　　B. $4\frac{2}{6}$　　C. $4\frac{7}{8}$　　D. $4\frac{1}{3}$

29. Which number is closest to $\frac{1}{2}$? **G**

F. $\frac{3}{4}$　　G. $\frac{3}{8}$　　H. $\frac{3}{9}$　　I. $\frac{3}{10}$

30. Which is the best estimate of $1\frac{8}{9} - \frac{17}{20}$? **C**

A. 0　　B. $\frac{1}{2}$　　C. 1　　D. $1\frac{1}{2}$

31. Which is the best estimate of $\frac{5}{11} + \frac{12}{13}$? **I**

F. 0　　G. $\frac{1}{2}$　　H. 1　　I. $1\frac{1}{2}$

Take It to the NET
Online lesson quiz at
www.PHSchool.com
Web Code: aaa-0401

Short Response

32. Fabric costs $7.00 per yard. Suppose you need $1\frac{5}{8}$ yards of solid-colored fabric and $\frac{3}{4}$ yard of print fabric for a quilt. **(a)** What is the best estimate of the total amount of fabric you need? **(b)** About how much will the fabric cost? Justify your answer. See margin.

Mixed Review

Lesson 3-8　**Write each fraction as a decimal.**

33. $\frac{47}{1,000}$　　**34.** $\frac{4}{5}$ 0.8　　**35.** $\frac{3}{500}$　　**36.** $\frac{17}{20}$ 0.85　　**37.** $\frac{1}{8}$
0.047　　　　　　　　　　　　　　0.006　　　　　　　　　　　　0.125

Lesson 2-3　**Algebra** **Write an algebraic expression for each word phrase.**

38. 10 more than g
$g + 10$

39. 20 times h　 20h

40. 5 less than m
$m - 5$

41. 12 added to s
$s + 12$

42. r decreased by 6
$r - 6$

43. 14 divided by t　$\frac{14}{t}$

174　　Chapter 4　Adding and Subtracting Fractions

32. [2] $2\frac{1}{2}$ yd; $1\frac{5}{8} + \frac{3}{4} \approx 1\frac{1}{2} + 1 = 2\frac{1}{2}$. About $17.50;
$7.00 \times 2\frac{1}{2} = $7.00 \times 2.5 = $17.50

[1] correct answers, but no work shown

4-2 Fractions With Like Denominators

What You'll Learn

 OBJECTIVE 1 To add fractions

 OBJECTIVE 2 To subtract fractions

...And Why

To solve problems involving measurement, as in Exercise 28

 Check Skills You'll Need

? For help, go to Lesson 3-4.

Write each fraction in simplest form.

1. $\frac{10}{40}$ $\frac{1}{4}$

2. $\frac{8}{24}$ $\frac{1}{3}$

3. $\frac{16}{20}$ $\frac{4}{5}$

4. $\frac{12}{15}$ $\frac{4}{5}$

5. $\frac{8}{12}$ $\frac{2}{3}$

6. $\frac{9}{12}$ $\frac{3}{4}$

7. $\frac{20}{24}$ $\frac{5}{6}$

8. $\frac{12}{28}$ $\frac{3}{7}$

9. $\frac{15}{35}$ $\frac{3}{7}$

Lesson Preview

 PowerPoint

✓ Check Skills You'll Need 🖥

Simplifying Fractions
Lesson 3-4: Example 2. Extra Practice p. 644.

Lesson Resources

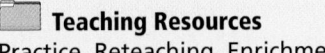

📁 **Teaching Resources**
Practice, Reteaching, Enrichment

👥 **Reaching All Students**
Practice Workbook 4-2
Spanish Practice Workbook 4-2
Guided Problem Solving 4-2
Hands-On Activities 12–13

⏱ **Presentation Assistant Plus!**
Transparencies
• Check Skills You'll Need 4-2
• Problem of the Day 4-2
• Additional Examples 4-2
• Student Edition Answers 4-2
• Lesson Quiz 4-2
PH Presentation Pro CD-ROM 4-2

PRENTICE HALL **ASSESSMENT SYSTEM**

Computer Test Generator CD

💻 **Technology**
Resource Pro® CD-ROM
Computer Test Generator CD
PH Presentation Pro CD-ROM

💻 **www.PHSchool.com**
Student Site
• Teacher Web Code: aak-5500
• Algebra Readiness Puzzles 52
• Self-grading Lesson Quiz

PH SuccessNet Teacher Center
• Lesson Planner
• Resources

Plus

 **OBJECTIVE 1** Adding Fractions

iTEXT Interactive lesson includes instant self-check, tutorials, and activities.

Investigation: Modeling Like Denominators

A pizza has 8 equal slices. You eat 2 and a friend eats 3.

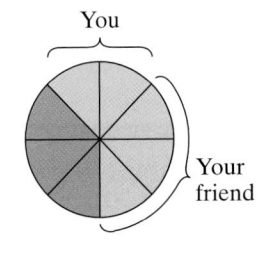
You

Your friend

1. **a.** Write a fraction for the amount of pizza you eat. Do not simplify your answer. Then write a fraction for the amount of the pizza your friend eats. $\frac{2}{8}$; $\frac{3}{8}$

   b. Write a fraction for the total eaten. $\frac{5}{8}$

   c. When you add fractions, do you add the denominators? Explain.
   No; you add the numerators together.

To add fractions with like denominators, add the numerators and keep the same denominator.

1 EXAMPLE   Adding With Like Denominators

Find $\frac{4}{15} + \frac{7}{15}$.

$\frac{4}{15} + \frac{7}{15} = \frac{4+7}{15}$ ← The fractions have like denominators. Add the numerators. The denominator stays the same.

$= \frac{11}{15}$ ← Simplify the numerator.

 **Check Understanding** **1** Add.   **a.** $\frac{1}{6} + \frac{4}{6}$ $\frac{5}{6}$ **b.** $\frac{2}{5} + \frac{1}{5}$ $\frac{3}{5}$

⚡ Ongoing Assessment and Intervention

Before the Lesson
Diagnose prerequisite skills using:
• Check Skills You'll Need

During the Lesson
Monitor progress using:
• Check Understanding
• Additional Examples
• Test Prep

After the Lesson
Assess knowledge using:
• Lesson Quiz
• Computer Test Generator CD

Math Background

To add and subtract fractions with like denominators, simply add or subtract the numerators and keep the denominator the same. Then write the answer in simplest form.

Teaching Notes

Investigation (Optional)
To help with Question 2, ask:
• *What is the same in each of your fractions?* same denominator, 8
• *What does the denominator represent?* the total number of equal slices

Teaching Tip
Write the fractions $\frac{1}{2}$ and $\frac{47}{94}$ on the board. Have students try to quickly picture them in their minds. Then point out that the quantities are equal. Guide students to recognize that it is usually much easier to understand a fraction when it is written in its simplest form. Likewise, the mixed number $4\frac{2}{5}$ is easier to picture than the improper fraction $\frac{22}{5}$. So improper fractions should be changed into mixed numbers for final answers.

Error Prevention!

Some students have difficulty writing fractions neatly on their papers. Provide them with graph paper and emphasize that the numerators and denominators are aligned.

Additional Examples

1 Find $\frac{2}{9} + \frac{4}{9}$. $\frac{2}{3}$
2 Find $\frac{3}{4} + \frac{3}{4}$. $1\frac{1}{2}$
3 Find $\frac{7}{8} - \frac{1}{8}$. $\frac{3}{4}$

Closure

• *How do you add fractions with like denominators?* Add the numerators and keep the denominator, then simplify.
• *How do you subtract fractions with like denominators?* Subtract the numerators and keep the denominator, then simplify.

If the sum of fractions results in an improper fraction, rename the improper fraction as a mixed number.

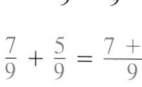 **2 EXAMPLE** **Sums Greater Than 1**

Find $\frac{7}{9} + \frac{5}{9}$.

$\frac{7}{9} + \frac{5}{9} = \frac{7 + 5}{9}$ ← Add the numerators. The denominator remains the same.

$= \frac{12}{9}$ ← Simplify the numerator.

$= 1\frac{3}{9}$ ← Write as a mixed number.

$= 1\frac{1}{3}$ ← Divide the numerator and denominator by the GCF, 3.

✔ **Check Understanding** 2 Find each sum. **a.** $\frac{5}{16} + \frac{13}{16}$ $1\frac{1}{8}$ **b.** $\frac{11}{20} + \frac{17}{20}$ $1\frac{2}{5}$

c. Number Sense Explain how you can recognize when your answer needs to be written in simplest form. Answers may vary. Sample: If the numerator and denominator have a common factor, the fraction is not in simplest form.

OBJECTIVE

2 **Subtracting Fractions**

To subtract fractions with like denominators, subtract the numerators and keep the same denominator. Write the answer in simplest form.

 **3 EXAMPLE** **Subtracting With Like Denominators** Real World

Circus There are 10 sections in a circular seating area for a circus. Three sections are empty. Just before the show begins, a large group completely fills one section. How much of the seating area is empty?

Three sections out of ten means $\frac{3}{10}$. One section out of 10 means $\frac{1}{10}$. The number of sections empty is $\frac{3}{10} - \frac{1}{10}$.

$\frac{3}{10} - \frac{1}{10} = \frac{3 - 1}{10}$ ← Subtract the numerators. The denominator remains the same.

$= \frac{2}{10}$ ← Simplify the numerator.

$= \frac{1}{5}$ ← Write the fraction in simplest form.

In the circus, $\frac{1}{5}$ of the sections are empty.

✔ **Check Understanding** 3 Find each difference. **a.** $\frac{3}{5} - \frac{2}{5}$ $\frac{1}{5}$ **b.** $\frac{3}{4} - \frac{1}{4}$ $\frac{1}{2}$

c. Suppose you are building a tree house. A board is $\frac{11}{12}$ yard long. You need $\frac{7}{12}$ yard of the board for a brace. How much is left after you cut off the piece you need? $\frac{1}{3}$ yard

 ## Reaching All Students

Below Level	Advanced Learners	Auditory Learners
Have students write a new fraction that has the same denominator but a different numerator. Samples: $\frac{1}{4}$ $\frac{3}{4}$ $\frac{5}{8}$ $\frac{3}{8}$ $\frac{7}{12}$ $\frac{5}{12}$ $\frac{2}{9}$ $\frac{4}{9}$ $\frac{2}{3}$ $\frac{1}{3}$ $\frac{6}{10}$ $\frac{9}{10}$	Write five sums, each with a different denominator, that equal $\frac{2}{3}$ when simplified. Sample: $\frac{7}{12} + \frac{1}{12}$; $\frac{2}{9} + \frac{1}{9} + \frac{2}{9} + \frac{1}{9}$; $\frac{1}{3} + \frac{1}{3}$; $\frac{3}{6} + \frac{1}{6}$; $\frac{5}{18} + \frac{5}{18} + \frac{2}{18}$	See note on page 177. **Error Prevention** See note on page 176.

A Practice by Example

Examples 1, 2
(pages 175, 176)

Find each sum.

1. $\frac{1}{4} + \frac{1}{4}$ $\frac{1}{2}$

2. $\frac{2}{5} + \frac{3}{5}$ 1

3. $\frac{2}{9} + \frac{4}{9}$ $\frac{2}{3}$

4. $\frac{1}{6} + \frac{3}{6}$ $\frac{2}{3}$

5. $\frac{2}{3} + \frac{2}{3}$ $1\frac{1}{3}$

6. $\frac{9}{10} + \frac{7}{10}$ $1\frac{3}{5}$

7. $\frac{7}{12} + \frac{6}{12}$ $1\frac{1}{12}$

8. $\frac{4}{5} + \frac{3}{5}$ $1\frac{2}{5}$

Find each difference.

Example 3
(page 176)

9. $\frac{17}{18} - \frac{5}{18}$ $\frac{2}{3}$

10. $\frac{15}{20} - \frac{3}{20}$ $\frac{3}{5}$

11. $\frac{4}{5} - \frac{3}{5}$ $\frac{1}{5}$

12. $\frac{6}{7} - \frac{3}{7}$ $\frac{3}{7}$

13. $\frac{5}{9} - \frac{2}{9}$ $\frac{1}{3}$

14. $\frac{9}{16} - \frac{3}{16}$ $\frac{3}{8}$

15. $\frac{8}{12} - \frac{5}{12}$ $\frac{1}{4}$

16. $\frac{17}{24} - \frac{7}{24}$ $\frac{5}{12}$

17. **Spiders** A typical garden spider is $\frac{7}{8}$ inch long. A typical black widow spider is $\frac{3}{8}$ inch long. How much longer is the garden spider? $\frac{1}{2}$ in.

18. **Office Supplies** White correction fluid is sold in a $\frac{7}{10}$-ounce bottle. Blue correction fluid is sold in a $\frac{6}{10}$-ounce bottle. You buy one bottle of each color. How much more white correction fluid than blue do you get? $\frac{1}{10}$ oz

B Apply Your Skills

Write an addition or subtraction sentence for each model.

19.

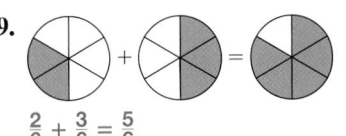

$\frac{2}{6} + \frac{3}{6} = \frac{5}{6}$

20.

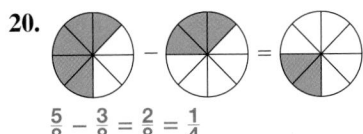

$\frac{5}{8} - \frac{3}{8} = \frac{2}{8} = \frac{1}{4}$

21. **Biology** Plasma makes up $\frac{11}{20}$ of your blood. Blood cells make up the other $\frac{9}{20}$. How much more of your blood is plasma than blood cells? $\frac{1}{10}$

GPS

22. **Data File, p. 169** How much faster is the running speed of a rabbit than the running speed of a squirrel? $\frac{2}{5}$ mi per min

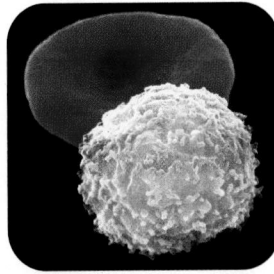

Real-World Connection

Most cells in your blood are red blood cells (top), white blood cells (bottom), or platelets (not shown).

27. Answers may vary. Sample: Add the numerators, and keep the denominator. Change the improper fraction $\frac{12}{9}$ to the mixed number $1\frac{3}{9}$. Reduce to $1\frac{1}{3}$.

Find each sum.

23. $\frac{1}{20} + \frac{3}{20} + \frac{5}{20}$ $\frac{9}{20}$

24. $\frac{27}{100} + \frac{41}{100} + \frac{3}{100}$ $\frac{71}{100}$

25. $\frac{4}{15} + \frac{1}{15} + \frac{7}{15}$ $\frac{4}{5}$

26. **Error Analysis** One of your classmates says $\frac{3}{5} + \frac{1}{5} = \frac{4}{10}$. Explain the error and find the correct sum. **Sample: The denominators were added in error; the correct sum is $\frac{4}{5}$.**

27. **Writing in Math** Explain how to find the sum of $\frac{5}{9}$ and $\frac{7}{9}$.

28. **Rainfall** Suppose it rains $\frac{3}{8}$ inch on Friday and $\frac{7}{8}$ inch on Saturday.
   a. What is the total rainfall during the two days? $1\frac{1}{4}$ in.
   b. What is the difference in rainfall for the two days? $\frac{1}{2}$ in.

4-2 Fractions With Like Denominators **177**

GPS Use the Guided Problem Solving worksheet with Exercise 21.

Assignment Guide

1 **Objective 1**
   A **B** Core 1–8, 19, 23–28a
   C Extension 29, 32–33

2 **Objective 2**
   A **B** Core 9–18, 20–22, 28b
   C Extension 30–31

Test Prep 34–37
Mixed Review 38–44

Auditory Learners
Exercises 1–16 Read these exercises aloud and have students solve them using mental math.

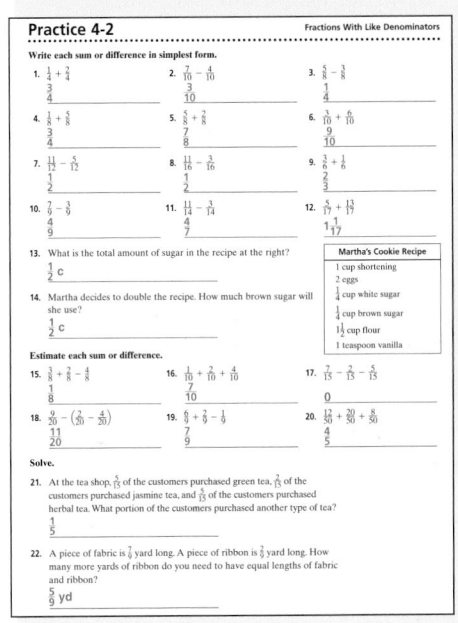

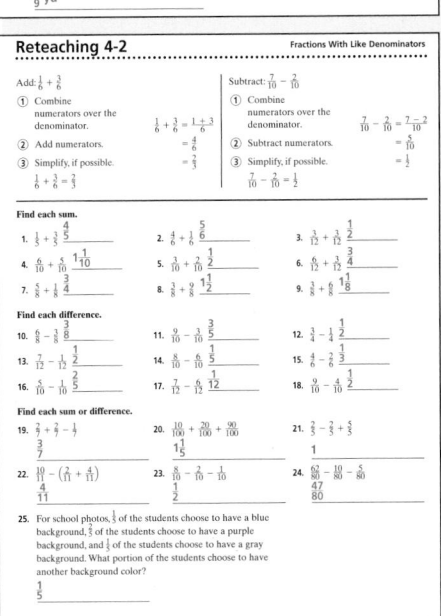

4. Assess

Lesson Quiz 4-2

Find each sum or difference.

1. $\frac{3}{8} + \frac{7}{8}$ $1\frac{1}{4}$

2. $\frac{5}{6} - \frac{1}{6}$ $\frac{2}{3}$

3. $\frac{14}{15} - \frac{11}{15}$ $\frac{1}{5}$

4. $\frac{3}{12} + \frac{6}{12}$ $\frac{3}{4}$

Alternative Assessment

Provide pairs of student with fraction bars. Partners work together, using the fraction bars, to model addition and subtraction exercises from Exercises 1–16. Have students record their work.

Test Prep

Resources

For additional practice with a variety of test item formats:
• Test-Prep, p. 213
• Test-Taking Strategies, p. 209
• Test-Taking Strategies With Transparencies

Enrichment 4-2 — Fractions With Like Denominators

Decision Making

You want to make a meat loaf. The only measuring cups in the house measure $\frac{1}{3}$ cup and $\frac{1}{4}$ cup. There are only $\frac{1}{2}$, $\frac{1}{4}$, and $\frac{1}{8}$ teaspoon measuring spoons. Since you don't want to continually wash and dry the measuring cups, you want to use certain ones for dry ingredients and the rest for wet ingredients.

Meat Loaf

$\frac{1}{2}$ lb ground beef W
$\frac{1}{4}$ c catsup W
2 eggs W
$\frac{1}{4}$ c tomato juice W
$\frac{3}{4}$ c bran cereal D
$1\frac{1}{4}$ tsp onion flakes D
$\frac{1}{8}$ tsp Worcestershire sauce W
$\frac{1}{4}$ tsp salt D
$\frac{1}{8}$ tsp pepper D

Topping
2 tsp mustard W
$\frac{1}{4}$ c catsup W
2 tsp brown sugar D

Mix ingredients in column 1. Place in 9 × 5 pan. Combine topping ingredients. Spread over meat loaf. Bake at 400° F for 45 minutes.

1. Identify the dry and wet ingredients in the recipe by placing a *D* beside the dry ingredients and a *W* beside the wet ingredients.

2. Which measuring cups and spoons will you use only for dry ingredients? Which for wet ingredients?
Dry: $\frac{1}{3}$ c, $\frac{1}{8}$ tsp, $\frac{1}{4}$ tsp;
Wet: $\frac{1}{4}$ c, $\frac{1}{2}$ tsp

3. Show how you will measure each quantity using the measuring cups you decided to use in Exercise 2.
$\frac{1}{4}$ c juice; ($\frac{1}{8}+\frac{1}{8}+\frac{1}{8}+\frac{1}{8}+\frac{1}{8}+\frac{1}{8}$) c cereal; ($\frac{1}{4}+\frac{1}{4}$ + $\frac{1}{4}+\frac{1}{4}+\frac{1}{4}+\frac{1}{4}$) tsp onion; $\frac{1}{4}$ tsp Worcestershire sauce; ($\frac{1}{4}+\frac{1}{4}$) tsp salt; $\frac{1}{8}$ tsp pepper; ($\frac{1}{2}+\frac{1}{2}+$ $\frac{1}{2}$) tsp mustard; ($\frac{1}{4}+\frac{1}{4}$) c catsup; ($\frac{1}{4}+\frac{1}{4}+\frac{1}{4}$ + $\frac{1}{4}+\frac{1}{4}+\frac{1}{4}$) tsp brown sugar

4. Rewrite the recipe so that it makes two meat loaves.
1 lb beef; 1 c catsup; 4 eggs; $\frac{1}{2}$ c juice; $1\frac{1}{2}$ c cereal; 3 tsp onion; 1 tsp Worcest. sauce; 1 tsp salt; $\frac{1}{4}$ tsp pepper; 4 tsp mustard; $\frac{1}{2}$ c catsup; 4 tsp brown sugar

178

© Challenge

PEANUT SAUCE
2 cups chopped onion
1 tablespoon peanut oil
$\frac{1}{4}$ tablespoon cayenne
$\frac{1}{4}$ teaspoon ground ginger
1 ripe banana
1 cup tomato juice
$\frac{1}{2}$ cup apple or apricot juice
$\frac{1}{2}$ cup peanut butter
$\frac{1}{2}$ teaspoon salt

Algebra Replace each ■ with a number to make the equation true.

29. $\frac{3}{5} + \frac{■}{5} = \frac{4}{5}$ 1

30. $\frac{■}{10} - \frac{1}{10} = 0$ 1

31. $\frac{7}{12} - \frac{■}{12} = \frac{1}{6}$ 5

32. **Recipes** Use the recipe card shown at the left for peanut sauce.
   a. To make the sauce spicier, you decide to double the amount of cayenne. How much cayenne should you use? $\frac{1}{2}$ tbsp
   b. You decide to use equal amounts of apple and apricot juices. In simplest form, how much of each type of juice should you use? $\frac{1}{4}$ c

33. **Stretch Your Thinking** In a jar, 26 out of 27 marbles are the same weight. One marble weighs less. You have a balance scale to find the odd marble. What is the least number of weighings you need to find the marble?
   1 weighing; if 13 marbles placed on one pan balance 13 marbles placed on the other pan, the leftover marble is the light one.

Test Prep

Multiple Choice

34. What is the sum of $\frac{9}{16}$ and $\frac{3}{16}$? **A**
   A. $\frac{3}{4}$ B. $\frac{2}{3}$ C. $\frac{11}{16}$ D. $\frac{9}{16}$

35. What is the difference of $\frac{35}{60}$ and $\frac{11}{60}$? **G**
   F. $\frac{4}{15}$ G. $\frac{2}{5}$ H. $\frac{3}{4}$ I. $\frac{5}{6}$

Take It to the NET
Online lesson quiz at
www.PHSchool.com
Web Code: aaa-0402

36. Two students explore a cove along an old road. One student explores $\frac{1}{8}$ mile of the cove. The other explores $\frac{3}{8}$ mile of the cove at the opposite end. Together, how much of the cove do they explore? **C**
   A. $\frac{1}{8}$ mile   B. $\frac{3}{8}$ mile   C. $\frac{1}{2}$ mile   D. $\frac{3}{4}$ mile

Short Response

37. In an archery tournament, a team hits the target 9 times out of 12 in the first round. **(a)** What fraction of the team's arrows did NOT hit the target? **(b)** Explain how you found your answer. See margin.

Mixed Review

Lesson 3-4 Write two fractions equivalent to each fraction. 38–41. Answers may vary. Samples are given.

38. $\frac{3}{8}$ $\frac{6}{16}, \frac{15}{40}$ 39. $\frac{1}{6}$ $\frac{2}{12}, \frac{5}{30}$ 40. $\frac{2}{5}$ $\frac{4}{10}, \frac{10}{25}$ 41. $\frac{7}{10}$ $\frac{14}{20}, \frac{35}{50}$

Lesson 2-8 Simplify each expression.

42. $3^2 + 5.1$ 14.1   43. $500 \div 10^2$ 5   44. $6^2 \times 10^3$ 36,000

178 Chapter 4 Adding and Subtracting Fractions

---

37. [2] a. $\frac{3}{12}$ or $\frac{1}{4}$
   b. Answers may vary. Sample: The arrows hit the target 9 times out of 12, and missed the target the other 3 times out of 12. Simplify $\frac{3}{12}$ to $\frac{1}{4}$.
   [1] correct answer without work shown, OR work shown with minor computational error

Modeling Unlike Denominators

For Use With Lesson 4-3

In Lesson 4-2, you added and subtracted fractions that had like denominators. To add or subtract fractions such as $\frac{5}{8}$ and $\frac{1}{4}$, first you must write the fractions with like denominators.

EXAMPLE

Use models to find each sum or difference.

a. $\frac{5}{8} + \frac{1}{4}$

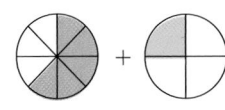

$\frac{5}{8}$ $\frac{1}{4}$

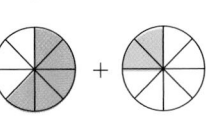

← Change the model for $\frac{1}{4}$ so that it has the same number of sections as the model for $\frac{5}{8}$.

$\frac{5}{8}$ $\frac{2}{8}$

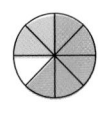

← Add $\frac{2}{8}$ to the model for $\frac{5}{8}$.

$\frac{7}{8}$

b. $\frac{5}{6} - \frac{2}{3}$

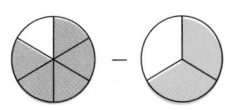

$\frac{5}{6}$ $\frac{2}{3}$

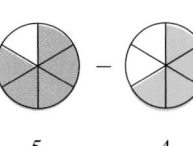

← Change the model for $\frac{2}{3}$ so that it has the same number of sections as the model for $\frac{5}{6}$.

$\frac{5}{6}$ $\frac{4}{6}$

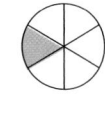

← Take away $\frac{4}{6}$ from the model for $\frac{5}{6}$.

$\frac{1}{6}$

EXERCISES

Use models to find each sum or difference. 1–7. See margin for models. 8–9. See back of book.

1. 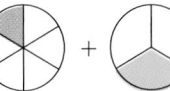 $\frac{3}{6}$ or $\frac{1}{2}$

2. 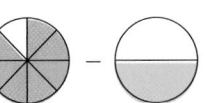 $\frac{3}{8}$

3. 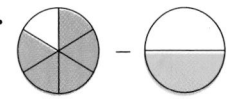 $\frac{2}{6}$ or $\frac{1}{3}$

Draw models to find each sum or difference.

4. $\frac{1}{8} + \frac{3}{4}$ $\frac{7}{8}$

5. $\frac{2}{3} - \frac{1}{6}$ $\frac{3}{6}$ or $\frac{1}{2}$

6. $\frac{1}{2} + \frac{3}{8}$ $\frac{7}{8}$

7. $\frac{5}{6} - \frac{1}{3}$ $\frac{3}{6}$ or $\frac{1}{2}$

8. $\frac{1}{2} + \frac{1}{3}$ $\frac{5}{6}$

9. $\frac{5}{8} - \frac{1}{2}$ $\frac{1}{8}$

Investigation

1. $\frac{1}{6} + \frac{1}{3}$;

2. $\frac{7}{8} - \frac{1}{2}$;

3. $\frac{5}{6} - \frac{1}{2}$;

4. ⊕ + ◯ = ⊕

5. ◷ − ⊕ = ⊕

6. ◖ + ⊕ = ⊕

7. ⊗ − ◖ = ⊗

Investigation

Modeling Unlike Denominators

In Lesson 4-2, students learned to add and subtract fractions with like denominators. In this Investigation for use with Lesson 4-3, students rename fraction models so that they have the same number of sections.

Optional Materials

- graph paper
- color pencils or markers
- fraction strips
- Classroom Aid 2, 12–15

Teaching Notes

Alternative Method
For a more hands-on approach, students can use fraction strips to model adding fractions with unlike denominators. You can begin by demonstrating how to use the strips to model fractions that are easy to rename, such as $\frac{1}{2} = \frac{2}{4}$, before modeling those presented in the Exercises.

Inclusion
Make sure all students understand the meaning of LCD (Least Common Denominator), and that they know how to find it.

Exercises
Have students work in small groups to work through and complete the exercises. Ask groups to share and explain their answers with the class.

1. Plan

Lesson Preview

Check Skills You'll Need `PowerPoint`

Finding the LCM
Lesson 3-6: Examples 1–2. Extra Practice p. 644.

Lesson Resources

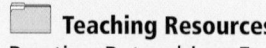

Teaching Resources
Practice, Reteaching, Enrichment
Checkpoint Quiz 1

Reaching All Students
Practice Workbook 4-3
Spanish Practice Workbook 4-3
Reading and Math Literacy 4B
Spanish Reading and Math Literacy 4B
Spanish Checkpoint Quiz 1
Guided Problem Solving 4-3
Technology Activities 9
Hands-On Activities 12, 13

Presentation Assistant Plus!
Transparencies
• Check Skills You'll Need 4-3
• Problem of the Day 4-3
• Additional Examples 4-3
• Student Edition Answers 4-3
• Lesson Quiz 4-1
PH Presentation Pro CD-ROM 4-3

ASSESSMENT SYSTEM

Checkpoint Quiz 1
Computer Test Generator CD

Technology
Resource Pro® CD-ROM
Computer Test Generator CD
PH Presentation Pro CD-ROM

www.PHSchool.com
Student Site
• Teacher Web Code: aak-5500
• Algebra Readiness Puzzles 4, 53
• Self-grading Lesson Quiz

PH SuccessNet Teacher Center
• Lesson Planner
• Resources

Plus

180

What You'll Learn

OBJECTIVE 1 To add fractions

OBJECTIVE 2 To subtract fractions

. . . And Why

To find survey results, as in Example 2

OBJECTIVE 1
Adding Fractions

✓ Check Skills You'll Need

? For help, go to Lesson 3-6.

Find the LCM.

1. 6, 9 18   **2.** 12, 18 36   **3.** 5, 24 120

4. 40, 48 240   **5.** 30, 75 150   **6.** 4, 6, 15 60

7. Explain your method for finding the LCM of 8 and 12.
24. Explanations may vary. Sample: List multiples of 8: 8, 16, 24. List multiples of 12: 12, 24. The LCM is 24.

 Interactive lesson includes instant self-check, tutorials, and activities.

When the denominators of fractions are different, you can use fraction models, or you can write equivalent fractions with the same denominator to add the fractions.

1 EXAMPLE   **Adding Fractions With Unlike Denominators**

Find $\frac{1}{4} + \frac{1}{3}$.

Method 1 Model $\frac{1}{4} + \frac{1}{3}$.

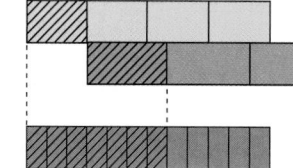

← Use the fraction model for $\frac{1}{4}$.
← Use the fraction model for $\frac{1}{3}$.

$$\frac{1}{4} + \frac{1}{3} = \frac{7}{12}$$

Method 2 Use a common denominator.

$$\frac{1}{4} \rightarrow \frac{1 \times 3}{4 \times 3} \rightarrow \frac{3}{12}$$

← The LCD is 12. Write the fractions with the same denominator.

$$+\frac{1}{3} \rightarrow \frac{1 \times 4}{3 \times 4} \rightarrow +\frac{4}{12}$$

$$\frac{7}{12}$$ ← Subtract the numerators.

Real-World 🌐 Connection
The LCM of 4 and 3 is 12. You can model this with a dozen eggs.

✓ Check Understanding ① Find $\frac{3}{5} + \frac{1}{10}$. Use a model or a common denominator. $\frac{7}{10}$

180   Chapter 4   Adding and Subtracting Fractions

Ongoing Assessment and Intervention

Before the Lesson	During the Lesson	After the Lesson
Diagnose prerequisite skills using:	Monitor progress using:	Assess knowledge using:
• Check Skills You'll Need	• Check Understanding	• Lesson Quiz
	• Additional Examples	• Computer Test Generator CD
	• Test Prep	• Chapter Checkpoint 1 (p. 184)

2 **EXAMPLE** Real-World Problem Solving

Art Class Students in art class completed a survey about their favorite activity. Ceramics is the favorite of $\frac{2}{5}$ of the students. Drawing is the favorite of $\frac{3}{8}$ of the students. What fraction of the students chose either ceramics or drawing as their favorite art class activity?

Add $\frac{2}{5}$ and $\frac{3}{8}$ to find the fraction of students who chose ceramics or drawing.

$$\begin{array}{ccccc} \frac{2}{5} & & \frac{2 \times 8}{5 \times 8} & & \frac{16}{40} \\ & \rightarrow & & \rightarrow & \\ +\frac{3}{8} & & \frac{3 \times 5}{8 \times 5} & & +\frac{15}{40} \\ \hline & & & & \frac{31}{40} \end{array}$$

← The LCD is 40. Write the fractions with the same denominator.

← Add the numerators.

The favorite art activity of $\frac{31}{40}$ of the students is either ceramics or drawing.

Real-World  Connection

The oven, or kiln, used for ceramics can reach a temperature of over 2,000°F.

✔ **Check Understanding** **2** You exercise $\frac{3}{4}$ hour on Monday and $\frac{2}{3}$ hour on Tuesday. How long did you exercise on Monday and Tuesday? $1\frac{5}{12}$ h

OBJECTIVE

2 **Subtracting Fractions**

You can subtract fractions that have unlike denominators.

3 **EXAMPLE** **Subtracting Fractions**

Find $\frac{1}{2} - \frac{1}{3}$.

Method 1 Model $\frac{1}{2} - \frac{1}{3}$.

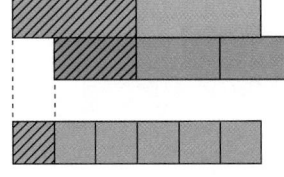

← Use the fraction model for $\frac{1}{2}$.

← Use the fraction model for $\frac{1}{3}$.

$$\frac{1}{2} - \frac{1}{3} = \frac{1}{6}$$

Method 2 Use a common denominator.

$$\begin{array}{ccccc} \frac{1}{2} & & \frac{1 \times 3}{2 \times 3} & & \frac{3}{6} \\ & \rightarrow & & \rightarrow & \\ -\frac{1}{3} & & \frac{1 \times 2}{3 \times 2} & & -\frac{2}{6} \\ \hline & & & & \frac{1}{6} \end{array}$$

← The LCD is 6. Write the fractions with the same denominator.

← Subtract the numerators.

✔ **Check Understanding** **3** Find $\frac{3}{4} - \frac{5}{8}$. Use a model or common denominators. $\frac{1}{8}$

👥 **Reaching All Students**

| **Below Level** Give students equivalent fractions like these. Have them explain how to find the missing numerator.

$\frac{3}{4} = \frac{\blacksquare}{12}$ Multiply 3 by 3; 9.

$\frac{2}{3} = \frac{\blacksquare}{12}$ Multiply 2 by 4; 8. | **Advanced Learners** Add a set of parentheses to each equation so that both will equal $\frac{1}{2}$.

$\frac{3}{4} - \left(\frac{1}{6} + \frac{1}{12}\right) = \frac{1}{2}$

$\left(\frac{17}{18} - \frac{2}{3}\right) + \frac{2}{9} = \frac{1}{2}$ | **Visual Learners** See note on page 181.

Error Prevention See note on page 181. |

---

2. Teach

Professional Development

Math Background

In order to add or subtract fractions, the fractions must have the same denominator, known as a *common denominator*. The least common denominator (LCD) is the smallest denominator that is common to both fractions. So, choosing the LCD may save the step of simplifying the sum or difference. When adding or subtracting fractions with unlike denominators, find a common denominator, write equivalent fractions with that denominator, add or subtract the numerators, and simplify as needed.

Teaching Notes

Teaching Tip

Here are two tips to make finding a common denominator easier.

The greater number of the denominators is often the LCD. For $\frac{1}{2}$ and $\frac{3}{4}$, the LCD is 4.

If the denominators are one number apart, such as 3 and 4, and each of the fractions is in its simplest form, the LCD will be the product of the denominators. For $\frac{1}{4}$ and $\frac{2}{3}$, the LCD is 12.

1 EXAMPLE Visual Learners

Use colored chalk to emphasize the multiplication step to help students see that the exact same operation is being done to both the numerator and the denominator.

3 EXAMPLE Error Prevention

Have students check the answer to a subtraction problem by adding.

PowerPoint
🖥 **Additional Examples**

1 Find $\frac{1}{3} + \frac{1}{2}$. $\frac{5}{6}$

2 In Ms. DeMarco's class, $\frac{3}{5}$ of the students chose cheese as their favorite pizza topping. Pepperoni was chosen by $\frac{1}{3}$ of the students. What fraction of the students chose either cheese or pepperoni as their favorite pizza topping? $\frac{14}{15}$

3 Find $\frac{5}{8} - \frac{1}{6}$. $\frac{11}{24}$

181

④ EXAMPLE Real-World Problem Solving

Parks A property owner donates $\frac{1}{4}$ acre to increase the size of a park next to his house to $\frac{5}{6}$ acre. Find the area of the park before the donation.

Subtract $\frac{1}{4}$ from $\frac{5}{6}$ to find the original size of the park.

Estimate Use benchmarks to estimate: $\frac{5}{6} - \frac{1}{4} \approx 1 - \frac{1}{2}$, or $\frac{1}{2}$.

$$
\begin{array}{c}
\frac{5}{6} \\
-\frac{1}{4}
\end{array}
\rightarrow
\begin{array}{c}
\frac{5 \times 2}{6 \times 2} \\
\frac{1 \times 3}{4 \times 3}
\end{array}
\rightarrow
\begin{array}{c}
\frac{10}{12} \\
-\frac{3}{12}
\end{array}
$$

← The LCD is 12. Write the fractions with the same denominator.

$$\frac{7}{12}$$ ← Subtract the numerators.

The park was originally $\frac{7}{12}$ acre.

Check for Reasonableness The answer $\frac{7}{12}$ is close to the estimate $\frac{1}{2}$.

✔ **Check Understanding** ④ Suppose you have $\frac{3}{5}$ yard of felt. You use $\frac{1}{2}$ yard of the felt for a display. How much felt do you have left? $\frac{1}{10}$ yard

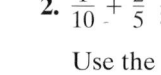

EXERCISES

❓ For more practice, see *Extra Practice*.

Ⓐ **Practice by Example**

Example 1 (page 180)

Find each sum. Exercises 1 and 2 have been started for you.

1. $\frac{2}{5} + \frac{1}{2}$ $\frac{9}{10}$

Use a model.

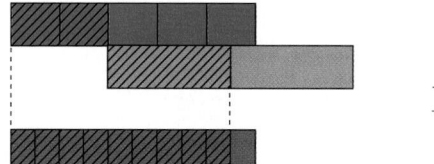

2. $\frac{1}{10} + \frac{2}{5}$ $\frac{1}{2}$

Use the LCD.

$$
\begin{array}{c}
\frac{1}{10} \\
+\frac{2}{5}
\end{array}
\rightarrow
\begin{array}{c}
\frac{1}{10} \\
\frac{2 \times 2}{5 \times 2}
\end{array}
\rightarrow
\begin{array}{c}
\frac{1}{10} \\
+\frac{4}{10}
\end{array}
$$

3. $\frac{1}{3} + \frac{1}{6}$ $\frac{1}{2}$

4. $\frac{1}{6} + \frac{1}{2}$ $\frac{2}{3}$

5. $\frac{8}{9} + \frac{5}{6}$ $1\frac{13}{18}$

6. $\frac{5}{6} + \frac{1}{4}$ $1\frac{1}{12}$

Example 2 (page 181)

7. Corky's house is $\frac{7}{10}$ mile farther from school than Diane's house is. Diane lives $\frac{7}{8}$ mile from school. How far from school does Corky live? $1\frac{23}{40}$ mi

8. Suppose you have two goldfish. One goldfish weighs $\frac{1}{6}$ ounce and the other weighs $\frac{1}{3}$ ounce. How much do the goldfish weigh together? $\frac{1}{2}$ oz

Example 3 (page 181)

Find each difference. Exercises 9 and 10 have been started for you.

9. $\frac{2}{3} - \frac{5}{12}$ $\frac{1}{4}$

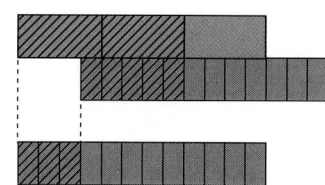

10. $\frac{7}{12} - \frac{1}{4}$ $\frac{1}{3}$

$$\begin{array}{ccccc} \frac{7}{12} & & \frac{7}{12} & & \frac{7}{12} \\ -\frac{1}{4} & \rightarrow & \frac{1\times 3}{4\times 3} & \rightarrow & -\frac{3}{12} \\ \hline & & & & \blacksquare \end{array}$$

11. $\frac{13}{16} - \frac{1}{4}$ $\frac{9}{16}$ 12. $\frac{17}{20} - \frac{2}{5}$ $\frac{9}{20}$ 13. $\frac{9}{10} - \frac{3}{5}$ $\frac{3}{10}$ 14. $\frac{3}{4} - \frac{1}{12}$ $\frac{2}{3}$

Example 4 (page 182) 15. **Cooking** A cook blends $\frac{1}{3}$ cup crushed raspberries into $\frac{3}{4}$ cup sugar for a sauce. How much more sugar than raspberries does the cook use? $\frac{5}{12}$ c

 16. **Leftovers** Suppose you have $\frac{3}{4}$ pound cooked salmon. You eat $\frac{1}{8}$ pound for dinner. How much salmon do you have for leftovers?
$\frac{5}{8}$ lb

B **Apply Your Skills**

Find each sum or difference.

17. $\frac{1}{3} + \frac{2}{5}$ $\frac{11}{15}$ 18. $\frac{13}{16} - \frac{1}{4}$ $\frac{9}{16}$ 19. $\frac{4}{5} - \frac{1}{2}$ $\frac{3}{10}$ 20. $\frac{3}{4} + \frac{1}{3}$ $1\frac{1}{12}$

21. $\frac{3}{5} + \frac{3}{20}$ $\frac{3}{4}$ 22. $\frac{7}{10} - \frac{1}{4}$ $\frac{9}{20}$ 23. $\frac{5}{6} - \frac{1}{2}$ $\frac{1}{3}$ 24. $\frac{3}{10} + \frac{1}{4}$ $\frac{11}{20}$

Real-World Connection

Central Florida is known as the "lightning capital" of the United States.

25. **Weather** A weather reporter records the rainfall as $\frac{3}{10}$ inch between
[GPS] 9:00 and 10:00 and $\frac{7}{8}$ inch between 10:00 and 11:00.
  a. Estimation Estimate the total rainfall between 9:00 and 11:00. $1\frac{1}{2}$ in.
  b. What is the total rainfall between 9:00 and 11:00? $1\frac{7}{40}$ in.

26. **Writing in Math** To add $\frac{5}{6}$ and $\frac{7}{12}$, you can use the LCD, 12, or another common denominator, such as 72. Find the sum each way. Which do you prefer, and why? $1\frac{5}{12}$; See margin for sample.

27. **Data File, p. 169** How much faster in miles per minute is the speed of a rabbit than the speed of a chicken? $\frac{9}{20}$ mi per min

Mental Math **Simplify by using mental math.**

28. $\frac{2}{3} + \frac{1}{6} - \frac{1}{6}$ $\frac{2}{3}$ 29. $\frac{9}{10} - \frac{7}{8} + \frac{1}{10}$ $\frac{1}{8}$ 30. $\frac{4}{5} - \left(\frac{1}{10} + \frac{1}{10}\right)$ $\frac{3}{5}$

C **Challenge**

34. Answers may vary. Sample:

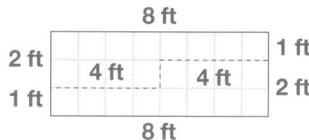

Use any method to add and subtract.

31. $\frac{5}{8} + \frac{9}{12} + \frac{1}{2}$ $1\frac{7}{8}$ 32. $\frac{11}{30} - \frac{1}{5} - \frac{1}{6}$ 0 33. $\frac{2}{5} + \frac{1}{2} - \frac{1}{10}$ $\frac{4}{5}$

34. **Stretch Your Thinking** How can you cut an 8-foot by 3-foot board into two pieces so that both pieces together cover a 12-foot by 2-foot hole?

4-3 Fractions With Unlike Denominators **183**

26. Sample: The LCD; the numerators and denominators will be smaller, and the answers will be easier to simplify.

 Use the Guided Problem Solving worksheet with Exercise 25.

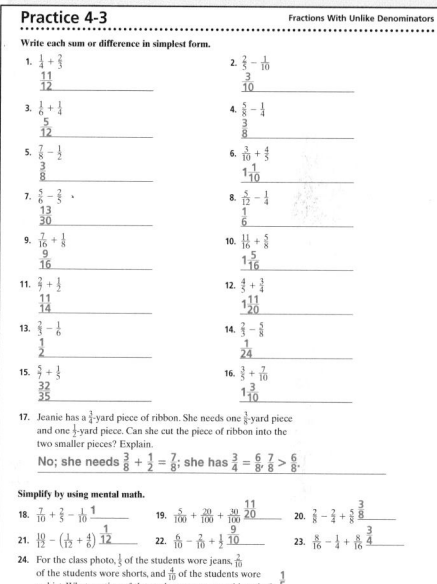

4. Assess

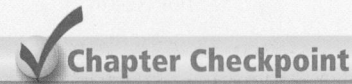

Find each sum or difference.

1. $\frac{8}{9} - \frac{4}{18}$ $\frac{2}{3}$

2. $\frac{5}{8} + \frac{1}{12}$ $\frac{17}{24}$

3. $\frac{3}{5} - \frac{2}{7}$ $\frac{11}{35}$

4. $\frac{13}{24} + \frac{3}{8}$ $\frac{11}{12}$

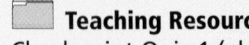 **Chapter Checkpoint**

To check understanding of
Lessons 4-1 to 4-3:

Checkpoint Quiz 1 (p. 184)

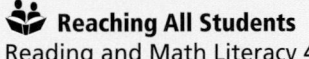 **Teaching Resources**
Checkpoint Quiz 1 (also in
Prentice Hall Assessment System)

Reaching All Students
Reading and Math Literacy 4B

Spanish versions available

Alternative Assessment

Each student in a pair writes
several exercises involving addition
and subtraction of fractions with
unlike denominators. Students
exchange papers and find each
sum or difference in simplest form.

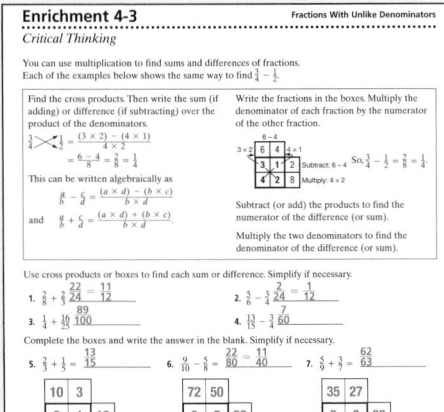

184

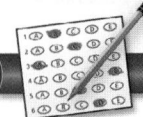 **Test Prep**

Gridded Response   Find each sum or difference.

35. $\frac{9}{16} + \frac{4}{32}$ $\frac{11}{16}$ 36. $\frac{2}{5} + \frac{3}{10}$ $\frac{7}{10}$ 37. $\frac{16}{24} - \frac{1}{2}$ $\frac{1}{6}$

38. $\frac{3}{4} - \frac{3}{8}$ $\frac{3}{8}$ 39. $\frac{9}{12} + \frac{4}{16}$ 1 40. $\frac{8}{12} - \frac{4}{9}$ $\frac{2}{9}$

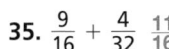
41. A package of sliced ham weighs $\frac{1}{2}$ pound. Another package of
ham weighs $\frac{1}{8}$ pound. What is the total weight in pounds of
both packages? $\frac{5}{8}$ lb

Mixed Review

Lesson 3-3   **List the factors to find the GCF of each set of numbers.**

42. 16, 64 16   43. 33, 121 11   44. 40, 72 8   45. 60, 210 30

Lesson 2-6   **Solve each equation. Then check the solution.**

46. $x + 2 = 5$ 3   47. $x - 12 = 4$ 16   48. $x - 0.5 = 1.6$ 2.1

Lesson 1-8   **Use mental math to find each product.**

49. 10×4.9 49   50. $100(3.14)$ 314   51. $1{,}000 \cdot 0.72$ 720

 Checkpoint Quiz 1   **Lessons 4-1 through 4-3**

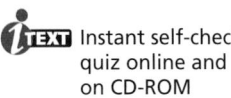 Instant self-check
quiz online and
on CD-ROM

Estimate each sum or difference. Use the benchmarks $0, \frac{1}{2}$, and 1.

1. $\frac{8}{9} + \frac{5}{16}$ $1\frac{1}{2}$ 2. $\frac{12}{13} - \frac{1}{9}$ 1

Find each sum or difference.

3. $\frac{3}{10} + \frac{9}{10}$ $1\frac{1}{5}$ 4. $\frac{5}{6} - \frac{1}{3}$ $\frac{1}{2}$ 5. $\frac{7}{12} + \frac{2}{3}$ $1\frac{1}{4}$

6. $\frac{9}{10} - \frac{1}{3}$ $\frac{17}{30}$ 7. $\frac{1}{7} + \frac{5}{14}$ $\frac{1}{2}$ 8. $\frac{17}{20} - \frac{3}{20}$ $\frac{7}{10}$

9. $\frac{11}{18}$ of the class   9. In a class, $\frac{1}{6}$ of the students have blue eyes and $\frac{7}{9}$ of the students have brown
eyes. Find how much more of the class has brown eyes than blue eyes.

10. **Cereal** Suppose you are still hungry after eating $\frac{2}{3}$ cup wheat flakes, so
you eat $\frac{1}{2}$ cup corn flakes. How much cereal do you eat that morning?
$1\frac{1}{6}$ c

184   **Chapter 4**   Adding and Subtracting Fractions

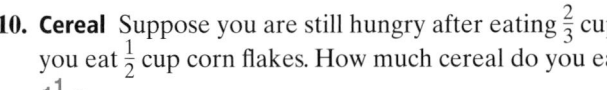

Test Prep

Resources
A sheet of blank grids is available in the *Test-Taking
Strategies With Transparencies* booklet. Give copies
of this sheet to students so they can practice filling
in the grids.

For additional practice with a variety of test item
formats:
• Test-Prep, p. 213
• Test-Taking Strategies, p. 209
• Test-Taking Strategies With Transparencies

4-4 Adding Mixed Numbers

What You'll Learn

OBJECTIVE 1 To add mixed numbers

OBJECTIVE 2 To add mixed numbers with renaming

. . . And Why

To find total distances, as in Example 2

 **Check Skills You'll Need**

 For help, go to Lesson 3-5.

Write each improper fraction as a mixed number in simplest form.

1. $\frac{9}{2}$ $4\frac{1}{2}$

2. $\frac{10}{3}$ $3\frac{1}{3}$

3. $\frac{8}{6}$ $1\frac{1}{3}$

4. $\frac{15}{6}$ $2\frac{1}{2}$

5. $\frac{7}{4}$ $1\frac{3}{4}$

6. $\frac{25}{10}$ $2\frac{1}{2}$

7. Explain how to simplify $\frac{36}{15}$. $2\frac{2}{5}$. Explanations may vary. Sample: Divide 36 by 15. The quotient 2 is the integer of the mixed number. The remainder 6 is the numerator, and 15 is the denominator: $2\frac{6}{15}$. Reduce to $2\frac{2}{5}$.

iTEXT Interactive lesson includes instant self-check, tutorials, and activities.

OBJECTIVE 1 Adding Mixed Numbers

Investigation: Using Mixed Numbers

Cut string into lengths of $1\frac{3}{8}$ inches, $2\frac{1}{4}$ inches, $1\frac{7}{8}$ inches, $3\frac{1}{8}$ inches, and $5\frac{3}{4}$ inches. Place two of the pieces end to end.

1. **a. Estimation** Estimate the total length of the two pieces.
   b. Find the actual length by adding. Check your sum by measuring the total length of the two pieces.   **1–2. Check student's work.**

2. Repeat for several different pairs of pieces.

You can find the sum of mixed numbers by adding the whole number and fraction parts separately. Then combine the two parts to find the total.

1 EXAMPLE   **Adding Mixed Numbers Mentally**

Mental Math Find $10\frac{1}{5} + 6\frac{2}{5}$.

$10 + 6 = 16$ ← Add the whole numbers.

$\frac{1}{5} + \frac{2}{5} = \frac{3}{5}$ ← Add the fractions.

$16 + \frac{3}{5} = 16\frac{3}{5}$ ← Combine the two parts.

1. Answers may vary. Sample: It doesn't matter because addition is commutative.

 **Check Understanding** **1 Reasoning** In Example 1, does it matter whether you add the whole numbers or the fractions first to get the correct answer? Explain. See above left.

Lesson Preview

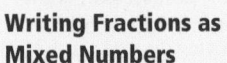
PowerPoint

✓ **Check Skills You'll Need**

Writing Fractions as Mixed Numbers
Lesson 3-5: Example 3. Extra Practice p. 644.

Lesson Resources

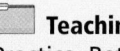 **Teaching Resources**
Practice, Reteaching, Enrichment

 Reaching All Students
Practice Workbook 4-4
Spanish practice Workbook 4-4
Guided Problem Solving 4-4
Hands-On Activities 14

Presentation Assistant Plus!
Transparencies
• Check Skills You'll Need 4-4
• Problem of the Day 4-4
• Additional Examples 4-4
• Student Edition Answers 4-4
• Lesson Quiz 4-4
PH Presentation Pro CD-ROM 4-4

 **PRENTICE HALL ASSESSMENT SYSTEM**

Computer Test Generator CD

 Technology
Resource Pro® CD-ROM
Computer Test Generator CD
PH Presentation Pro CD-ROM

 www.PHSchool.com
Student Site
• Teacher Web Code: aak-5500
• Self-grading Lesson Quiz

PH SuccessNet Teacher Center
• Lesson Planner
• Resources

Plus **iTEXT**

 Ongoing Assessment and Intervention

Before the Lesson
Diagnose prerequisite skills using:
• Check Skills You'll Need

During the Lesson
Monitor progress using:
• Check Understanding
• Additional Examples
• Test Prep

After the Lesson
Assess knowledge using:
• Lesson Quiz
• Computer Test Generator CD

Math Background

Professional Development

Adding mixed numbers involves finding a common denominator for the fraction parts, adding the fractions, and then adding the whole numbers separately. If the fraction portion of the sum is an improper fraction, you need to change it to a mixed number and add it to the whole number portion of the sum.

Teaching Notes

Error Prevention!

Watch for students who confuse LCD (Least Common Denominator), LCM (Least Common Multiple), and GCF (Greatest Common Factor).

Inclusion

You may need to review how to find the LCD of two fractions.

1 EXAMPLE Visual Learners

Write or circle the denominators, using the same color to emphasize that they need to be the same.

PowerPoint

Additional Examples

1. Use mental math to find $3\frac{1}{9} + 5\frac{3}{9}$. $8\frac{4}{9}$

2. Tyler juggled for $1\frac{1}{3}$ hr during the school week. He juggled for $2\frac{1}{4}$ hr over the weekend. How many hours did he juggle in all that week? $3\frac{7}{12}$ hr

3. Find $5\frac{4}{5} + 3\frac{9}{10}$. $9\frac{7}{10}$

4. A mother cat weighs $14\frac{5}{8}$ lb. Her kitten weighs $1\frac{1}{2}$ lb. How much do they weigh together? $16\frac{1}{8}$ lb

Closure

- *How do you add mixed numbers?* Add the fraction parts, finding a common denominator, if needed. Then add the whole numbers.
- *What do you need to do if the sum of mixed numbers includes an improper fraction?* Change the improper fraction to a mixed number and add the whole numbers.

186

Real-World Connection

The top speed of a giant tortoise is about $\frac{1}{5}$ mile per hour.

2 EXAMPLE Real-World Problem Solving

Animals A giant tortoise traveled $8\frac{1}{3}$ yards and stopped. Then it traveled $6\frac{1}{2}$ yards. Find the total distance the giant tortoise traveled.

Find $8\frac{1}{3} + 6\frac{1}{2}$.

Estimate $8\frac{1}{3} + 6\frac{1}{2} \approx 8 + 7 = 15$

$$
\begin{array}{c}
8\frac{1}{3} \\
+ 6\frac{1}{2}
\end{array}
\rightarrow
\begin{array}{c}
8\frac{2}{6} \\
+ 6\frac{3}{6}
\end{array}
\qquad \leftarrow \text{The LCD is 6. Write the fractions with the same denominator.}
$$

$$14\frac{5}{6} \qquad \leftarrow \text{Add the whole numbers. Then add the fractions.}$$

The giant tortoise traveled a total of $14\frac{5}{6}$ yards.

Check for Reasonableness The answer $14\frac{5}{6}$ is close to the estimate of 15.

✓ **Check Understanding** 2 **a.** Some students spent $2\frac{1}{3}$ hours on Friday and $3\frac{1}{4}$ hours on Saturday working on a science project. How long did the students work? $5\frac{7}{12}$ h

b. Estimation Use estimation to check the reasonableness of your sum. $2\frac{1}{3} + 3\frac{1}{4} \approx 2 + 3$, or 5

OBJECTIVE

2 Adding Mixed Numbers With Renaming

The sum of the fraction parts may be an improper fraction. If so, rename it as a mixed number. Then write the answer in simplest form.

Reading Math

You can read the mixed number $18\frac{8}{6}$ as "18 and $\frac{8}{6}$."

3 EXAMPLE Adding Mixed Numbers

Find $15\frac{5}{6} + 3\frac{1}{2}$.

$$
\begin{array}{c}
15\frac{5}{6} \\
+ 3\frac{1}{2}
\end{array}
\rightarrow
\begin{array}{c}
15\frac{5}{6} \\
+ 3\frac{3}{6}
\end{array}
\qquad \leftarrow \text{The LCD is 6. Write } \frac{1}{2} \text{ as } \frac{3}{6}.
$$

$$18\frac{8}{6} \qquad \leftarrow \text{Add the whole numbers. Then add the fractions.}$$

$$= 18 + 1\frac{2}{6} \qquad \leftarrow \text{Rename } \frac{8}{6} \text{ as } 1\frac{2}{6}.$$

$$= 19\frac{2}{6} \qquad \leftarrow \text{Add the whole numbers.}$$

$$= 19\frac{1}{3} \qquad \leftarrow \text{Simplify.}$$

✓ **Check Understanding** 3 Find each sum. **a.** $3\frac{5}{6} + 5\frac{11}{12}$ **b.** $12\frac{3}{8} + 6\frac{3}{4}$ **c.** $7\frac{3}{5} + 13\frac{2}{3}$

$9\frac{3}{4}$ $19\frac{1}{8}$ $21\frac{4}{15}$

Reaching All Students

Below Level Give students mixed number sums to rewrite with the LCD.	Advanced Learners Match up A, B, C, and D to the digits 1, 2, 3, and 4 to solve this mystery problem.	Inclusion See note on page 186.
Change to tenths: Change to eighths: $1\frac{1}{2}$ $1\frac{5}{10}$ $5\frac{3}{8}$ $5\frac{3}{8}$ $+ 4\frac{2}{5}$ $+ 4\frac{4}{10}$ $+ 2\frac{1}{4}$ $+ 2\frac{2}{8}$	$A\frac{B}{A} + C\frac{C}{D} = 4\frac{11}{12}$ A = 3, B = 2, $3\frac{2}{3} + 1\frac{1}{4} = 4\frac{11}{12}$ C = 1, D = 4	Visual Learners See note on page 186.

Hours at Practice

Total	
$2\frac{1}{2}$	$1\frac{3}{4}$
Monday	Tuesday

④ EXAMPLE Real-World Problem Solving

Sports Practice A sports team practiced for $2\frac{1}{2}$ hours on Monday and for $1\frac{3}{4}$ hours on Tuesday. How long did the team practice?

Find $2\frac{1}{2} + 1\frac{3}{4}$.

$$
\begin{array}{ll}
2\frac{1}{2} & 2\frac{2}{4} \\
+1\frac{3}{4} \rightarrow & +1\frac{3}{4} \\
\hline
& 3\frac{5}{4}
\end{array}
$$

← The LCD is 4. Write $\frac{1}{2}$ as $\frac{2}{4}$.

← Add the whole numbers. Then add the fractions.

$= 3 + 1\frac{1}{4}$ ← Rename $\frac{5}{4}$ as $1\frac{1}{4}$.

$= 4\frac{1}{4}$ ← Add the whole numbers.

The team practiced for $4\frac{1}{4}$ hours.

✓ **Check Understanding** ④ **Number Sense** One recipe uses $1\frac{3}{4}$ cups of milk. Another recipe uses $1\frac{1}{2}$ cups of milk. You have 3 cups of milk at home. Do you have enough milk to make both recipes? Explain. **No; you need $3\frac{1}{4}$ c of milk, but you have only 3 c.**

EXERCISES

? For more practice, see *Extra Practice*.

Ⓐ Practice by Example

Example 1 (page 185)

Mental Math Find each sum.

1. $1 + 2\frac{1}{6}$ $3\frac{1}{6}$ **2.** $2\frac{2}{3} + 4$ $6\frac{2}{3}$ **3.** $3\frac{5}{7} + 1\frac{1}{7}$ $4\frac{6}{7}$ **4.** $8\frac{1}{5} + 3\frac{2}{5}$ $11\frac{3}{5}$

Example 2 (page 186)

🌐 **5. Apples** You have $1\frac{3}{4}$ pounds of red apples and $2\frac{1}{2}$ pounds of golden apples. How many pounds of apples do you have? $4\frac{1}{4}$ lb

Examples 3, 4 (pages 186, 187)

Find each sum. Exercise 6 has been started for you.

6. $11\frac{1}{3} + 6\frac{7}{9}$ $11\frac{1}{3}$

$18\frac{1}{9}$ $+6\frac{7}{9} \rightarrow +6\frac{7}{9}$

7. $8\frac{5}{6} + 2\frac{1}{3}$ $11\frac{1}{6}$ **8.** $5\frac{2}{3} + 4\frac{1}{2}$ $10\frac{1}{6}$

9. $2\frac{3}{4} + 1\frac{5}{8}$ $4\frac{3}{8}$ **10.** $4\frac{5}{8} + 1\frac{3}{4}$ $6\frac{3}{8}$ **11.** $3\frac{1}{3} + 2\frac{5}{6}$ $6\frac{1}{6}$ **12.** $1\frac{1}{2} + 3\frac{5}{6}$ $5\frac{1}{3}$

🌐 **13. Soccer** Suppose you play $12\frac{3}{8}$ minutes during the first half of a soccer game and $8\frac{3}{4}$ minutes during the second half. How many total minutes do you play? $21\frac{1}{8}$ min

4-4 Adding Mixed Numbers **187**

GPS Use the Guided Problem Solving worksheet with Exercise 18.

187

B **Apply Your Skills**

Mental Math **Compare using <, =, or >.**

14. $5\frac{8}{9} + 7\frac{5}{6}$ $\overset{>}{\blacksquare}$ 13

15. $17\frac{3}{5} + 12\frac{7}{10}$ $\overset{>}{\blacksquare}$ $29\frac{1}{2}$

16. $7\frac{1}{6} + 3\frac{6}{18}$ $\overset{<}{\blacksquare}$ 11

17. $4\frac{5}{13} + 5\frac{4}{9}$ $\overset{<}{\blacksquare}$ $10\frac{12}{13}$

Real-World 🌐 **Connection**

Careers Oceanographers study water, plants, and animals in the ocean.

19. Answers may vary. Sample: Add like fractions: $\frac{1}{3} + \frac{2}{3} + \frac{4}{5} + \frac{1}{5} = 1 + 1 = 2$; Add 2 to the sum of the whole numbers: $5 + 3 + 3 + 6 + 2 = 19$.

20. Sometimes; answers may vary. Sample: mixed number: $4\frac{1}{3} + 2\frac{1}{6} = 6\frac{1}{2}$; whole number: $8\frac{3}{8} + 7\frac{5}{8} = 16$

18. **a. Tides** At low tide, the water is $4\frac{11}{12}$ feet deep. At high tide, the water depth increases by $2\frac{3}{4}$ feet. How deep is the water at high tide? $7\frac{2}{3}$ ft
    b. The next day, the depth is $5\frac{1}{2}$ feet at low tide. The depth increases the same amount as the day before. What is the water depth at high tide? $8\frac{1}{4}$ ft

19.  **Writing in Math** Explain how you can use mental math to find the sum $5\frac{1}{3} + 3\frac{4}{5} + 3\frac{2}{3} + 6\frac{1}{5}$. See below left.

20. **Number Sense** Is the sum of two mixed numbers *always*, *sometimes*, or *never* a mixed number? Give examples to support your answer. See below left.

21. **Publishing** In a newspaper, an article is $1\frac{1}{4}$ inches long. Another article is $2\frac{7}{8}$ inches long. How much space is needed for both articles? $4\frac{1}{8}$ in.

Find each sum.

22. $4\frac{7}{8} + 5\frac{3}{16} + 3\frac{1}{8}$ $13\frac{3}{16}$

23. $6\frac{7}{24} + 2\frac{7}{12} + 2\frac{2}{24}$ $10\frac{23}{24}$

24. $11\frac{2}{3} + 4\frac{7}{9} + 1\frac{5}{9}$ 18

25. **Fabric** Suppose you need the amounts of fabric shown in the table to make a flag. How much total fabric do you need? 13 yd

26. **a. Dogs** You walk your dog $1\frac{1}{8}$ miles to your friend's house, $1\frac{3}{4}$ miles to the park, and 1 mile back to your house. How far do you walk your dog? $3\frac{7}{8}$ mi
    b. Suppose a friend claims to walk a dog twice as far as you do. How far does your friend walk? $7\frac{3}{4}$ mi

Fabric Colors

Color	Length (yards)
Red	$3\frac{1}{4}$
White	$5\frac{1}{2}$
Blue	$4\frac{1}{4}$

C **Challenge**

Find each sum.

27. $5\frac{1}{2} + 2\frac{3}{4} + 5\frac{3}{8}$ $13\frac{5}{8}$

28. $7\frac{1}{3} + 7\frac{1}{6} + 7\frac{1}{9}$ $21\frac{11}{18}$

29. $4\frac{2}{3} + 3\frac{5}{9} + 6$ $14\frac{2}{9}$

30. Answers may vary. Sample:

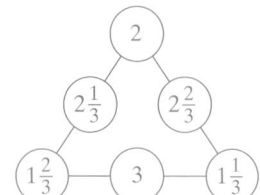

30. **Stretch Your Thinking** Copy the diagram. Write the numbers $1\frac{1}{3}$, $1\frac{2}{3}$, 2, $2\frac{1}{3}$, $2\frac{2}{3}$, and 3 in the circles so that the sum of the numbers along each side of the triangle is 6. See left.

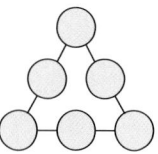

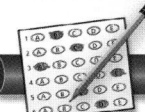

Multiple Choice

31. What is the sum of $2\frac{2}{3}$ and $1\frac{7}{8}$? C

 A. $3\frac{9}{11}$ B. $4\frac{9}{11}$ C. $4\frac{13}{24}$ D. $4\frac{14}{24}$

32. What is the sum of $9\frac{1}{10}$ and $1\frac{2}{5}$? I

 F. $10\frac{3}{15}$ G. $10\frac{2}{50}$ H. $10\frac{1}{10}$ I. $10\frac{1}{2}$

Take It to the NET
Online lesson quiz at
www.PHSchool.com
Web Code: aaa-0404

33. Which two numbers have a sum of $15\frac{3}{8}$? B

 A. $8\frac{1}{4}$ and $7\frac{3}{16}$ B. $8\frac{1}{8}$ and $7\frac{1}{4}$ C. $8\frac{1}{2}$ and $7\frac{1}{8}$ D. $8\frac{1}{3}$ and $7\frac{2}{5}$

Short Response

34. Ruth's house is near a park that has a $2\frac{3}{10}$-mile rollerblading path. Ruth rollerblades $1\frac{1}{4}$ miles from her house to the park. She goes once around the path and then rollerblades home.
 a. What is the total distance she rollerblades? a-b. See margin.
 b. Explain how you found your answer.

Mixed Review

Lesson 3-9 🌐 **35. Vacation** Pedro's family drives 600 miles in two days. The second day they drive 120 miles less than the first day. How many miles did they drive the first day? 360 mi

Lesson 2-8   **Simplify each expression.**

 36. $2^3 \times 3^2 + 5$ 77   **37.** $5^3 \times 2^2 \div 10^2$ 5   **38.** $6^2 \times 10^3$ 36,000

Practice Game

That's Some Sum!

How to Play
- Draw a square game board and divide it into 16 smaller squares. Write fractions in half of the squares and mixed numbers in the other half.
- Player 1 circles any two numbers and then finds their sum. The sum is added to the player's score.
- Player 2 circles two different numbers, finds the sum, and adds it to his or her score. Players take turns until all numbers have been chosen.
- Any answer may be challenged. If the answer is correct, the challenger loses a turn. If the challenger corrects the answer, that sum is added to the challenger's score. The other player's turn is over without any change to his or her score.
- The player with the greater total score wins.

4-4 Adding Mixed Numbers **189**

 **Lesson Quiz 4-4**

Write each sum.

1. $4\frac{1}{5} + 6\frac{3}{10}$ $10\frac{1}{2}$

2. $1\frac{1}{2} + 5\frac{3}{4}$ $7\frac{1}{4}$

3. $7\frac{7}{8} + 4\frac{5}{6}$ $12\frac{17}{24}$

5. $9\frac{1}{12} + 8\frac{7}{12}$ $17\frac{2}{3}$

Alternative Assessment

Each student in a pair writes several problems involving addition of mixed numbers. Students exchange papers and write the sums in simplest form. You may wish to allow students to use fraction bars to help them add the fractional parts of the mixed numbers. Have partners record how they found the sums.

Test Prep

Resources
For additional practice with a variety of test item formats:
- Test-Prep, p. 213
- Test-Taking Strategies, p. 209
- Test-Taking Strategies With Transparencies

Exercises 31–32 Encourage students to estimate before they find the sum to eliminate answer choices.

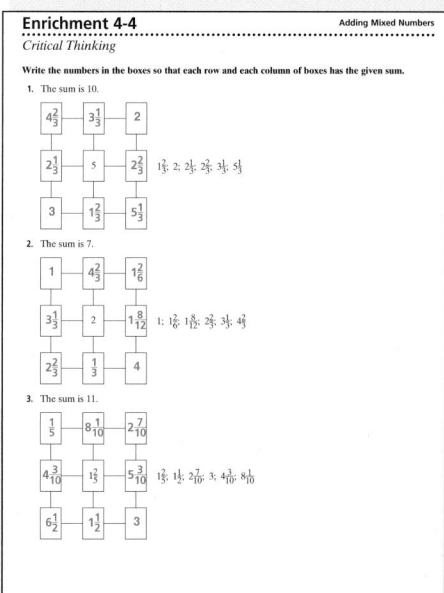

---

34. [2] a. $4\frac{4}{5}$ mi

 b. by an appropriate method such as finding the sum of the distance from her house to the park, distance around the lake, and distance back home; $1\frac{1}{4} + 2\frac{3}{10} + 1\frac{1}{4} = 4\frac{4}{5}$; OR $4\frac{4}{5}$ with a correct method shown

 [1] correct total without work shown OR correct explanation with a computational error

1. Plan

Lesson Preview

 Check Skills You'll Need PowerPoint

Writing Fractions as Mixed Numbers
Lesson 3-5: Example 3. Extra Practice p. 644.

Lesson Resources

 Teaching Resources
Practice, Reteaching, Enrichment

 Reaching All Students
Practice Workbook 4-5
Spanish Practice Workbook 4-5
Guided Problem Solving 4-5
Hands-On Activities 14

 Presentation Assistant Plus!
Transparencies
• Check Skills You'll Need 4-5
• Problem of the Day 4-5
• Additional Examples 4-5
• Student Edition Answers 4-5
• Lesson Quiz 4-5
PH Presentation Pro CD-ROM 4-5

 ASSESSMENT *SYSTEM*

Computer Test Generator CD

 Technology
Resource Pro® CD-ROM
Computer Test Generator CD
PH Presentation Pro CD-ROM

 www.PHSchool.com
Student Site
• Teacher Web Code: aak-5500
• Self-grading Lesson Quiz

PH SuccessNet Teacher Center
• Lesson Planner
• Resources

Plus **iTEXT**

190

What You'll Learn

 OBJECTIVE 1 To subtract mixed numbers

 OBJECTIVE 2 To subtract mixed numbers with renaming

... And Why

To subtract two weights, as in Example 1

 **Check Skills You'll Need**   🔍 For help, go to Lesson 3-5.

Write each improper fraction as a mixed number in simplest form.

1. $\frac{3}{2}$ $1\frac{1}{2}$ **2.** $\frac{8}{3}$ $2\frac{2}{3}$ **3.** $\frac{23}{5}$ $4\frac{3}{5}$

4. $\frac{20}{8}$ $2\frac{1}{2}$ **5.** $\frac{15}{6}$ $2\frac{1}{2}$ **6.** $\frac{24}{10}$ $2\frac{2}{5}$

7. Explain the steps you used to write $\frac{24}{10}$ as a mixed number in simplest form. **Divide 24 by 10. The quotient 2 is the integer of the mixed number. The remainder 4 is the numerator, and 10 is the denominator: $2\frac{4}{10}$. Reduce to $2\frac{2}{5}$.**

iTEXT Interactive lesson includes instant self-check, tutorials, and activities.

OBJECTIVE
 1 Subtracting Mixed Numbers

To subtract mixed numbers, first you may need to write the fractions with a common denominator. Then subtract the whole numbers and the fraction parts separately.

1 EXAMPLE Real-World 🌐 Problem Solving

Lions At birth, one lion cub weighs $3\frac{3}{4}$ pounds. Another cub in the same litter weighs $2\frac{5}{8}$ pounds. How much more does the heavier cub weigh?

To calculate the difference in weights, find $3\frac{3}{4} - 2\frac{5}{8}$.

$$3\frac{3}{4} \qquad 3\frac{6}{8} \quad \leftarrow \text{The LCD is 8. Write } \frac{3}{4} \text{ as } \frac{6}{8}.$$

$$\rightarrow$$

$$-2\frac{5}{8} \qquad -2\frac{5}{8}$$

$$\overline{\qquad 1\frac{1}{8}} \quad \leftarrow \begin{array}{l}\text{Subtract the whole numbers.}\\ \text{Then subtract the fractions.}\end{array}$$

The heavier cub weighs $1\frac{1}{8}$ pounds more than the other cub.

Check for Reasonableness Round each mixed number: $3\frac{3}{4} \approx 4$; $2\frac{5}{8} \approx 3$. Then subtract: $4 - 3 = 1$. The answer $1\frac{1}{8}$ is close to the estimate. So, the answer is reasonable.

Real-World 🌐 Connection
Male cubs grow to an adult weight of 600 pounds.

 Check Understanding ① **a.** A supporting wedge for a window is $2\frac{3}{16}$ inches wide and $2\frac{7}{8}$ inches long. How much longer is the wedge than it is wide? $\frac{11}{16}$ **in.**

b. Reasoning In Example 1, could you use 32 as the common denominator? Explain your answer. **Yes; answers may vary. Sample: 32 is a common multiple of 8 and 4, so it is also a common denominator.**

190 Chapter 4 Adding and Subtracting Fractions

Ongoing Assessment and Intervention

Before the Lesson	During the Lesson	After the Lesson
Diagnose prerequisite skills using:	**Monitor progress using:**	**Assess knowledge using:**
• Check Skills You'll Need	• Check Understanding • Additional Examples • Test Prep	• Lesson Quiz • Computer Test Generator CD

Sometimes you need to rename whole numbers or fractions in order to subtract from them. Here is how to rename $3\frac{1}{4}$.

Need Help?
For help writing mixed numbers as improper fractions, go to Lesson 3-5.

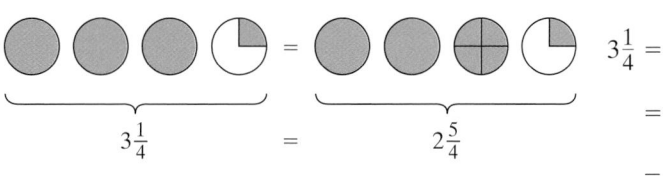

$3\frac{1}{4}$ = $2\frac{5}{4}$

$3\frac{1}{4} = 2 + 1\frac{1}{4}$

$= 2 + \frac{5}{4}$

$= 2\frac{5}{4}$

---

2 EXAMPLE **Renaming Whole Numbers**

Find $7 - 2\frac{5}{8}$.

Write 7 as a mixed number. Use 8 for the denominator since you must subtract $\frac{5}{8}$.

$$\begin{array}{c} 7 \\ -2\frac{5}{8} \end{array} \rightarrow \begin{array}{c} 6\frac{8}{8} \quad \leftarrow \text{Rename 7 as } 6 + 1 = 6 + \frac{8}{8}, \text{ or } 6\frac{8}{8}. \\ -2\frac{5}{8} \\ \hline 4\frac{3}{8} \quad \begin{array}{l} \leftarrow \text{Subtract the whole numbers.} \\ \text{Then subtract the fractions.} \end{array} \end{array}$$

✔ **Check Understanding** **2** Find each difference.   **a.** $5 - 3\frac{2}{3}$ $1\frac{1}{3}$ **b.** $10 - 4\frac{1}{4}$ $5\frac{3}{4}$

---

3 EXAMPLE **Renaming Mixed Numbers**

Distance (miles)

Moth $11\frac{1}{6}$	
$5\frac{2}{3}$ Bee	▨ Difference

Biology In one hour, a bee can fly $5\frac{2}{3}$ miles and a moth can fly $11\frac{1}{6}$ miles. How much farther can the moth fly in one hour?

To answer the question, find $11\frac{1}{6} - 5\frac{2}{3}$. Since $\frac{1}{6} < \frac{2}{3}$, rename $11\frac{1}{6}$.

Estimate $11\frac{1}{6} - 5\frac{2}{3} \approx 11 - 6 = 5$

$$\begin{array}{c} 11\frac{1}{6} \\ -5\frac{2}{3} \end{array} \rightarrow \begin{array}{c} 10\frac{7}{6} \quad \leftarrow \text{Rename } 11\frac{1}{6} \text{ as } 10 + 1\frac{1}{6} = 10\frac{7}{6}. \\ -5\frac{4}{6} \quad \leftarrow \text{The LCD is 6. Write } \frac{2}{3} \text{ as } \frac{4}{6}. \\ \hline = 5\frac{3}{6} \quad \leftarrow \text{Subtract.} \\ = 5\frac{1}{2} \quad \leftarrow \text{Simplify.} \end{array}$$

Check for Reasonableness The answer $5\frac{1}{2}$ is close to the estimate of 5.

The moth can fly $5\frac{1}{2}$ miles farther than the bee.

3. Answers may vary. Sample: If the benchmark of the first fraction is less than the benchmark of the second fraction, then rename before subtracting.

✔ **Check Understanding** **3 Number Sense** How can you use benchmarks to tell whether you will have to rename before subtracting? **See above left.**

Reaching All Students

Below Level Have students rename mixed numbers as improper fractions. $1\frac{2}{3} = \frac{3}{3} + \frac{2}{3} = \frac{5}{3}$ $1\frac{4}{9} = \frac{9}{9} + \frac{4}{9} = \frac{13}{9}$ $1\frac{5}{6} = \frac{6}{6} + \frac{5}{6} = \frac{11}{6}$	**Advanced Learners** Match up E, F, G, and H to the digits 1, 2, 5, and 8 to solve this mystery problem. $H\frac{G}{E} - F\frac{F}{G} = 6\frac{9}{10}$ E = 5, F = 1, $8\frac{2}{5} - 1\frac{1}{2} = 6\frac{9}{10}$ G = 2, H = 8	**Inclusion** See note on page 191. **Visual Learners** See note on page 192.

---

2. Teach

Professional Development

Math Background

Subtracting mixed numbers is similar to adding mixed numbers in that whole numbers and fraction parts are dealt with separately and the results are combined. The new step in subtracting mixed numbers involves renaming. If the fraction being subtracted is greater than the one from which it is being subtracted, the fraction from which you are subtracting must be renamed. This requires also renaming the whole number part of the mixed number. For instance, in subtracting $4\frac{1}{5} - 2\frac{2}{5}$, you rename $4\frac{1}{5}$ as $3\frac{6}{5}$. First you subtract the fractions. Then you subtract the whole numbers.

$$3\frac{6}{5} - 2\frac{2}{5} = 1\frac{4}{5}$$

Teaching Notes

Inclusion
You may need to review how to find the LCD (Least Common Denominator) of two fractions.

1 EXAMPLE Error Prevention

Guide students to begin with the fractions' column when they subtract mixed numbers. In Example 1 no renaming is required; but in problems that do require renaming, subtracting the whole numbers first can cause errors.

2 EXAMPLE Teaching Tip

Call attention to Check Understanding 2b. Review that 10 is the same as $10\frac{0}{4}$. Ask: *How do you rename 10?* $9\frac{4}{4}$

PowerPoint

Additional Examples

1 A black bear is about $5\frac{1}{4}$ ft long. An Alaskan brown bear is about $7\frac{1}{2}$ ft long. How much longer is an Alaskan brown bear than a black bear? $2\frac{1}{4}$ ft

2 Find $9 - 1\frac{2}{3}$. $7\frac{1}{3}$

3 A two-week-old panda bear weighed $\frac{3}{4}$ pound. At age one-month, the cub weighed $2\frac{3}{10}$ pounds. How many pounds did it gain? $1\frac{11}{20}$ lb

191

Visual Learners
For the More Than One Way
feature, have students make a
drawing to help them visualize
the problem situation. Then work
through both solution methods
using colors to illustrate each step.
For instance, have volunteers write
the subtraction on the board or
an overhead transparency and use
a color to circle the denominators.
Then have students use another
color to circle the numerators that
will be subtracted, and a third
color for the number that has
been renamed.

Closure

- *When do you have to rename
  when you are subtracting mixed
  numbers?* when the fraction
  being subtracted is greater
  than the one from which it is
  being subtracted
- Explain how you would rename
  $9\frac{1}{8}$. Sample: Think of $9\frac{1}{8}$ as
  $8 + 1 + \frac{1}{8}$. Change the 1 to
  eighths, or $\frac{8}{8}$. Combine
  $8 + \frac{8}{8} + \frac{1}{8}$ to get $8\frac{9}{8}$.

More Than One Way

Suppose you caught two fish. The first one is $4\frac{1}{8}$ inches long. The second one is $2\frac{1}{4}$ inches long. How much longer is the first fish?

Leon's Method

I need to subtract the lengths. Since $\frac{1}{8} < \frac{1}{4}$, I will rename $4\frac{1}{8}$.

$$4\frac{1}{8} \quad \rightarrow \quad 3\frac{9}{8} \quad \leftarrow \text{Rename } 4\frac{1}{8} \text{ as } 3 + 1\frac{1}{8} = 3\frac{9}{8}.$$
$$-\,2\frac{1}{4} \qquad -\,2\frac{2}{8} \quad \leftarrow \text{The LCD is 8. Write } \frac{1}{4} \text{ as } \frac{2}{8}.$$
$$\qquad\qquad\quad 1\frac{7}{8} \quad \leftarrow \text{Find the difference.}$$

The first fish is $1\frac{7}{8}$ inches longer than the second one.

Lauren's Method

I need to subtract the lengths. I will change both mixed numbers to improper fractions with the same denominator.

$$4\frac{1}{8} - 2\frac{1}{4} = \frac{33}{8} - \frac{9}{4} \quad \leftarrow \text{Write as improper fractions.}$$
$$= \frac{33}{8} - \frac{18}{8} \quad \leftarrow \begin{array}{l}\text{Rename as equivalent fractions}\\\text{with a like denominator.}\end{array}$$
$$= \frac{15}{8}, \text{ or } 1\frac{7}{8} \quad \leftarrow \begin{array}{l}\text{Subtract. Write the difference}\\\text{in simplest form.}\end{array}$$

The first fish is $1\frac{7}{8}$ inches longer than the second one.

Choose a Method

Find $10\frac{1}{3} - 7\frac{8}{9}$. Describe your method and explain your choice.

$2\frac{4}{9}$; Sample: I renamed $10\frac{1}{3}$ as $9\frac{12}{9}$ and subtracted $7\frac{8}{9}$; the difference is $2\frac{4}{9}$.

EXERCISES

? For more practice, see *Extra Practice*.

Ⓐ Practice by Example

Example 1
(page 190)

1. $2\frac{3}{8}$

Find each difference. Exercise 1 has been started for you.

1. $\begin{array}{r} 12\frac{3}{4} \\ -\,10\frac{3}{8} \end{array} \rightarrow \begin{array}{r} 12\frac{6}{8} \\ -\,10\frac{3}{8} \end{array}$
2. $7\frac{3}{4} - 6\frac{2}{5}$ $1\frac{7}{20}$
3. $2\frac{5}{8} - 1\frac{1}{4}$ $1\frac{3}{8}$
4. $9\frac{4}{5} - 4\frac{4}{15}$ $5\frac{8}{15}$

5. $21\frac{3}{8} - 11\frac{1}{4}$ $10\frac{1}{8}$
6. $15\frac{11}{12} - 11\frac{1}{2}$ $4\frac{5}{12}$
7. $12\frac{1}{4} - 4\frac{1}{8}$ $8\frac{1}{8}$
8. $3\frac{2}{3} - 1\frac{1}{6}$ $2\frac{1}{2}$

9. You spend $2\frac{2}{3}$ hours reading and $1\frac{1}{2}$ hours watching a movie. How much more time did you spend reading than watching a movie? $1\frac{1}{6}$ h

Example 2
(page 191)

Find each difference. Exercise 10 has been started for you.

10. $\quad 4 \qquad 3\frac{4}{4} \quad 1\frac{1}{4}$

$\quad \underline{-2\frac{3}{4}} \;\to\; \underline{-2\frac{3}{4}}$

11. $\quad 23 \quad 3\frac{3}{8}$
$\qquad \underline{-19\frac{5}{8}}$

12. $\quad 32 \quad 15\frac{1}{2}$
$\qquad \underline{-16\frac{1}{2}}$

Example 3
(page 191)

13. $10\frac{1}{10} - 3\frac{2}{5}$ 14. $3\frac{3}{8} - 1\frac{3}{4}$ $1\frac{5}{8}$ 15. $4\frac{5}{12} - 1\frac{3}{4}$ $2\frac{2}{3}$ 16. $6\frac{1}{5} - 2\frac{2}{3}$

$6\frac{7}{10}$ $3\frac{8}{15}$

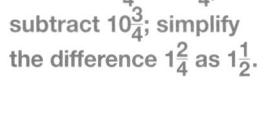 17. **Science** You and your partner are growing bean plants for a science project. After one week, one plant is $7\frac{7}{8}$ inches tall and another plant is $5\frac{15}{16}$ inches tall. Find the difference in the heights of the two plants. $1\frac{15}{16}$ in.

B Apply Your Skills

Find each difference.

$\qquad\qquad\qquad\qquad\qquad\qquad\qquad\qquad\qquad\qquad\qquad\qquad\qquad 2\frac{1}{2}$

18. $9\frac{2}{3} - 5\frac{2}{3}$ 4   19. $1 - \frac{1}{6}$ $\frac{5}{6}$ 20. $3 - 1\frac{2}{3}$ $1\frac{1}{3}$ 21. $12\frac{3}{4} - 10\frac{1}{4}$

22. $5\frac{7}{9} - 2\frac{1}{9}$ $3\frac{2}{3}$ 23. $8 - 3\frac{5}{11}$ $4\frac{6}{11}$ 24. $5\frac{1}{5} - 4\frac{4}{5}$ $\frac{2}{5}$ 25. $9\frac{1}{8} - 6\frac{3}{4}$ $2\frac{3}{8}$

26. **Data File, p. 169** Find the difference in the top speed of a peregrine falcon and the top speed of a cheetah. $2\frac{1}{6}$ mi per min

27. **Answers may vary. Sample: Mentally rename $12\frac{1}{4}$ as $11\frac{5}{4}$; subtract $10\frac{3}{4}$; simplify the difference $1\frac{2}{4}$ as $1\frac{1}{2}$.**

27. **Writing in Math** Explain how you can use mental math to find $12\frac{1}{4} - 10\frac{3}{4}$. **See left.**

28. On Monday, the snowfall in the mountains was $15\frac{3}{4}$ inches. On Tuesday, the snowfall was $18\frac{1}{2}$ inches. What was the difference in snowfall? $2\frac{3}{4}$ in.

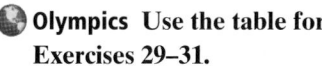 **Olympics** Use the table for Exercises 29–31.

29. How much farther did Heike Drechsler jump in 1992 than in 2000?   6 in.

30. Which two jumps were closest in length? Explain. **See below right.**

31. Find the difference between the longest and the shortest winning jumps shown.
    1 ft $5\frac{1}{2}$ in.

30. 1992 and 1996; the 1992 jump is $\frac{3}{4}$ in. longer than the 1996 jump.

Women's Olympic Long Jump Winners

Year	Winner, Country	Distance
1984	Anisoara Stanciu, Romania	22 ft 10 in.
1988	Jackie Joyner-Kersee, U.S.A.	24 ft $3\frac{1}{2}$ in.
1992	Heike Drechsler, Germany	23 ft $5\frac{1}{4}$ in.
1996	Chioma Ajunwa, Nigeria	23 ft $4\frac{1}{2}$ in.
2000	Heike Drechsler, Germany	22 ft $11\frac{1}{4}$ in.

 32. **Gardening** Carlos plants a spruce tree in a garden of a new school. The height of the tree when he plants it is $3\frac{1}{2}$ feet. He measures the tree two years later. It is $4\frac{3}{8}$ feet tall. How much has the tree grown? $\frac{7}{8}$ ft

4-5 Subtracting Mixed Numbers   **193**

GPS Use the Guided Problem Solving worksheet with Exercise 28.

Assignment Guide

1 Objective 1
Ⓐ Ⓑ Core 1–9, 18, 21–22, 27–31

2 Objective 2
Ⓐ Ⓑ Core 10–17, 19–20, 23–26, 32
Ⓒ Ⓑ Extension 33–35, 36

Test Prep 37–39
Mixed Review 40–49

Auditory Learners
Exercises 13–16 Have students verbalize to a partner the steps they used to rename mixed numbers.

Practice 4-5   Subtracting Mixed Numbers

Write each difference in simplest form.

1. $10\frac{11}{16} - 3\frac{7}{8}$ $6\frac{13}{16}$ 2. $8\frac{1}{3} - 2\frac{5}{8}$ $5\frac{23}{24}$ 3. $9 - 3\frac{2}{5}$ $5\frac{3}{5}$

4. $5\frac{1}{16} - 2\frac{3}{8}$ $2\frac{13}{16}$ 5. $8\frac{1}{6} - 3\frac{2}{5}$ $4\frac{23}{30}$ 6. $7\frac{1}{4} - 3$ $4\frac{1}{4}$

7. $2\frac{3}{8} - 1\frac{1}{4}$ $1\frac{1}{8}$ 8. $4\frac{1}{8} - 2\frac{1}{16}$ $2\frac{1}{16}$ 9. $9\frac{3}{8} - 3\frac{5}{6}$ $5\frac{5}{6}$

10. $2\frac{1}{10} - 1\frac{2}{5}$ $\frac{7}{10}$ 11. $15\frac{1}{2} - 8\frac{1}{3}$ $7\frac{7}{12}$ 12. $6\frac{7}{16} - 2\frac{2}{3}$ $3\frac{9}{16}$

13. $27\frac{1}{4} - 13\frac{11}{12}$ $13\frac{1}{3}$ 14. $5\frac{2}{3} - 1\frac{1}{4}$ $4\frac{3}{20}$ 15. $10\frac{5}{8} - 7\frac{3}{4}$ $6\frac{1}{12}$

16. $5\frac{3}{4} - 2\frac{1}{2}$ $3\frac{1}{4}$ 17. $16\frac{5}{12} - 10\frac{1}{3}$ $6\frac{1}{12}$ 18. $23\frac{7}{8} - 9\frac{1}{16}$ $14\frac{13}{16}$

19. $35\frac{1}{2} - 32\frac{1}{5}$ $3\frac{3}{10}$ 20. $25\frac{1}{3} - 17\frac{3}{4}$ $7\frac{7}{12}$ 21. $33\frac{1}{2} - 27\frac{1}{10}$ $6\frac{2}{5}$

22. $24\frac{1}{8} - 18\frac{5}{6}$ $5\frac{13}{24}$ 23. $12\frac{1}{8} - 8\frac{1}{16}$ $4\frac{3}{16}$ 24. $9\frac{1}{4} - 5\frac{1}{2}$ $3\frac{3}{4}$

Solve.

25. Robbie needs to buy fencing for his square vegetable garden that measures $16\frac{1}{4}$ feet on a side. One side borders the back of the garage. The fencing costs $4 per feet. Estimate how much the fencing will cost. about $204

26. Paula has 2 yards of elastic. One project needs a piece $\frac{3}{4}$ yard. Does she have enough for another project that needs $1\frac{1}{3}$ yards? Explain. No. Sample answer: she will have only $1\frac{1}{4}$ yd left after the first project and $1\frac{1}{4} < 1\frac{1}{3}$.

27. Use a ruler or measuring tape to find the perimeter of your desk. Measure to the nearest half inch. Check students' work.
   width: ___ length: ___ perimeter: ___
   Now find the perimeter of your teacher's desk.
   width: ___ length: ___ perimeter: ___
   Subtract to find the difference in the perimeters. ___

Reteaching 4-5   Subtracting Mixed Numbers

Some mixed numbers can be subtracted mentally.

Example 1: Find $5\frac{2}{3} - 2\frac{1}{6}$.

① Subtract the whole numbers.
   $5 - 2 = 3$

② Then, subtract the fractions.
   $\frac{2}{3} - \frac{1}{6} = \frac{4}{6} - \frac{1}{6} = \frac{3}{6} = \frac{1}{2}$

③ Combine the two parts.
   $3 + \frac{1}{2} = 3\frac{1}{2}$

$5\frac{2}{3} - 2\frac{1}{6} = 3\frac{1}{2}$

Sometimes you must *rename* the first fraction before subtracting.

Example 2: Find $6\frac{1}{2} - 2\frac{3}{4}$.

① Write with a common denominator.
   $6\frac{1}{2} - 2\frac{3}{4} = 6\frac{2}{4} - 2\frac{3}{4}$

② Rename $6\frac{2}{4}$. $= 5\frac{6}{4} - 2\frac{3}{4}$

③ Subtract the whole numbers. Then, subtract the fractions. Simplify, if necessary. $= 3\frac{3}{4}$

$6\frac{1}{2} - 2\frac{3}{4} = 3\frac{3}{4}$

Find each difference.

1. $7\frac{7}{10} - 2\frac{1}{10}$ $5\frac{3}{5}$ 2. $3\frac{3}{4} - 1\frac{1}{2}$ $2\frac{1}{4}$ 3. $6\frac{5}{6} - 2\frac{1}{6}$ $4\frac{2}{3}$

4. $9\frac{7}{8} - 7\frac{3}{4}$ $2\frac{1}{8}$ 5. $8\frac{1}{4} - 3\frac{1}{6}$ $5\frac{1}{12}$ 6. $14\frac{1}{4} - 8\frac{1}{6}$ $6\frac{1}{12}$

7. $12\frac{1}{2} - 9\frac{2}{3}$ $2\frac{5}{6}$ 8. $6\frac{5}{8} - 2\frac{1}{4}$ $4\frac{3}{8}$ 9. $7\frac{2}{7} - 4\frac{11}{14}$ $2\frac{11}{14}$

10. $10\frac{3}{4} - 7\frac{5}{6}$ $2\frac{11}{12}$ 11. $5\frac{7}{16} - 1\frac{1}{2}$ $3\frac{15}{16}$ 12. $8\frac{2}{5} - 3\frac{4}{15}$ $4\frac{11}{15}$

13. $6\frac{1}{16} - 3\frac{3}{16}$ $2\frac{7}{8}$ 14. $9\frac{2}{15} - 5\frac{4}{5}$ $3\frac{1}{3}$ 15. $12\frac{2}{3} - 6\frac{1}{6}$ $6\frac{1}{2}$

16. $7\frac{3}{4} - 2\frac{1}{5}$ $5\frac{11}{20}$ 17. $15\frac{5}{12} - 8\frac{1}{3}$ $7\frac{1}{12}$ 18. $4\frac{7}{10} - 2\frac{3}{5}$ $2\frac{1}{10}$

193

Lesson Quiz 4-5

Find each difference.

1. $7\frac{7}{8} - 4\frac{1}{4}$ $3\frac{5}{8}$

2. $8\frac{2}{5} - 6\frac{8}{10}$ $1\frac{3}{5}$

3. $9\frac{1}{3} - 5\frac{11}{12}$ $3\frac{5}{12}$

4. $14\frac{1}{3} - 6\frac{5}{8}$ $7\frac{17}{24}$

Alternative Assessment

Have students work in pairs. Refer them to Exercises 13–16. For each exercise, partners must verify with one another that they have found a common denominator and have renamed the mixed number accurately before subtracting. Partners should then compare their answers before moving to the next exercise.

Test Prep

For additional practice with a variety of test item formats:
• Test-Prep, p. 213
• Test-Taking Strategies, p. 209
• Test-Taking Strategies With Transparencies

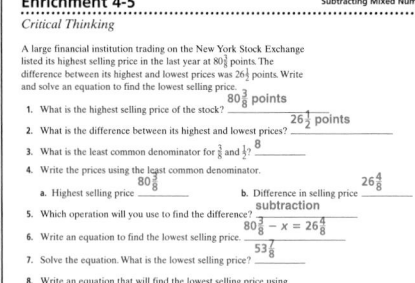

Enrichment 4-5 — Subtracting Mixed Numbers
Critical Thinking

194

 **Challenge**

Algebra Solve each equation.

33. $x = 9\frac{4}{7} - \frac{13}{14}$ $8\frac{9}{14}$ 34. $x = 6\frac{3}{16} - 2\frac{2}{3}$ $3\frac{25}{48}$ 35. $x + 3\frac{1}{2} = 4\frac{3}{4}$ $1\frac{1}{4}$

36. **Stretch Your Thinking** Fill in each ☐ with one of the digits 4, 5, 6, 7, 8, or 9 to find the least possible whole number difference. Use each digit only once.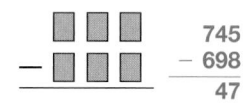

Test Prep

Reading Comprehension   Read the passage and answer the questions below.

Time of Day

Latitude	Jun. 21	Dec. 21
20°N	$13\frac{1}{5}$ h	$10\frac{4}{5}$ h
40°N	$14\frac{1}{2}$ h	$9\frac{1}{6}$ h
60°N	$18\frac{1}{2}$ h	$5\frac{1}{2}$ h

The tilt of Earth's axis affects the length of daylight in a given region throughout the year. Latitude, the measure of the distance from the equator toward the poles, also affects the length of daylight. In the Northern Hemisphere, June 21 is sometimes referred to as the "longest day of the year." December 21 is the "shortest day of the year." The table shows the number of daylight hours for some latitudes in the Northern Hemisphere.

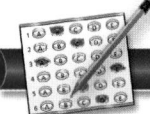

Take It to the NET
Online lesson quiz at
www.PHSchool.com
Web Code: aaa-0405

37. On December 21, what is the difference between the number of daylight hours at 20° latitude and 60° latitude? $5\frac{3}{10}$ h

38. For 20° latitude, what is the difference in daylight hours between the shortest and longest days of the year? $2\frac{2}{5}$ h

39. For 60° latitude, what is the difference in daylight hours between the shortest and longest days of the year? 13 h

 **Mixed Review**

Lesson 4-2   **Find each sum or difference.**

40. $\frac{10}{15} + \frac{7}{15}$ $1\frac{2}{15}$ 41. $\frac{9}{10} + \frac{6}{10}$ $1\frac{1}{2}$ 42. $\frac{21}{24} - \frac{5}{24}$ $\frac{2}{3}$

43. $\frac{23}{25} - \frac{3}{25}$ $\frac{4}{5}$ 44. $\frac{11}{18} + \frac{5}{18}$ $\frac{8}{9}$ 45. $\frac{9}{28} - \frac{3}{28}$ $\frac{3}{14}$

Lesson 3-4   **Write each fraction in simplest form.**

46. $\frac{15}{25}$ $\frac{3}{5}$ 47. $\frac{16}{56}$ $\frac{2}{7}$ 48. $\frac{36}{54}$ $\frac{2}{3}$ 49. $\frac{8}{4}$ 2

Reading Math

Understanding Word Problems

For Use With Lesson 4-5

Some problems contain **too much information.** You need to decide which information is necessary for solving the problem. You can use the problem-solving plan you learned in Lesson 1-6. Start by asking yourself, "What do I know?" and "What do I need to find out?"

 **EXAMPLE**  Real World

Track Team Each member of the track team runs 15 miles each week. On Monday, Celine runs $2\frac{7}{8}$ miles. She runs $3\frac{1}{4}$ miles on Tuesday and $2\frac{1}{2}$ miles on Wednesday. She runs 11 miles per hour. How many more miles does she need to run?

Read and Understand Read for understanding. Summarize the problem.

What do I know?
- Each team member runs 15 miles each week.
- Celine has already run $2\frac{7}{8}$, $3\frac{1}{4}$, and $2\frac{1}{2}$ miles.
- Celine runs 11 miles per hour.

What do I need to find out?
- How many miles must Celine run on Thursday and Friday?

What information is not needed?
- How fast Celine runs is not needed to solve the problem.

EXERCISES

For each word problem, answer the questions "What do I know?" and "What do I need to find out?" Identify any information not needed to solve the problem. 1–2. See margin.

1. **Dressmaking** A dressmaker sends 250 dresses to several stores. The same number of dresses is sent to each store. The dressmaker charges $59 for each dress. How much money does the dressmaker receive?

2. Carey worked $3\frac{3}{4}$ hours on Monday. Ricky worked $4\frac{1}{2}$ hours on Monday and 2 hours on Tuesday. Who worked more hours on Monday? How many more?

Reading Math

Understanding Word Problems

Students need to be able to read with comprehension to understand and solve problems. This page presents two basic questions: "What do I know?" and "What do I need to find out?" to help students identify the key information in word problems. A third related question is "What information is not needed?"

Teaching Notes

Discuss with students the need to read and solve word problems. Because real-world problems usually come in either written or verbal form, students must be able to extract relevant information, ignore extra information, and figure out what the problem asks.

Have a volunteer read the opening paragraph. Ask: *What are the steps in the Problem-Solving Plan you learned in Chapter 1?* **Read and understand; plan and solve; look back and check.**

EXAMPLE Teaching Tip

Have a volunteer read through the example. Have students summarize the problem using their own plain language. You may want to write a list as shown on the student page to summarize the three types of information. Remind students that these questions are part of the first step of the problem-solving plan.

Exercises

Have students work independently on the Exercises. Then have them form groups in which members share and evaluate their answers. Students should make adjustments in their work based upon their group discussions. Group members can work together to solve the problems.

1. I know 250 dresses were sent, the same number was sent to each store, and the dressmaker charges $59 for each dress. I need to find how much money the dressmaker receives.

The fact that the same number of dresses was sent to each store is not needed.

2. I know Carey worked $3\frac{3}{4}$ h on Monday. Ricky worked $4\frac{1}{2}$ h on Monday and 2 h on Tuesday. I need to find out whose work time on Monday is greater and the difference between the two work times. The time Ricky worked on Tuesday is not needed.

Lesson Preview

 **Check Skills You'll Need**

Solving Equations by Adding or Subtracting
Lesson 2-6: Examples 1, 3. Extra Practice p. 643.

Lesson Resources

📁 **Teaching Resources**
Practice, Reteaching, Enrichment

👥 **Reaching All Students**
Practice Workbook 4-6
Spanish Practice Workbook 4-6
Guided Problem Solving 4-6

⏲ **Presentation Assistant Plus!**
Transparencies
• Check Skills You'll Need 4-6
• Problem of the Day 4-6
• Additional Examples 4-6
• Student Edition Answers 4-6
• Lesson Quiz 4-6
PH Presentation Pro CD-ROM 4-6

PRENTICE HALL
ASSESSMENT SYSTEM

Computer Test Generator CD

💻 **Technology**
Resource Pro® CD-ROM
Computer Test Generator CD
PH Presentation Pro CD-ROM

💻 **www.PHSchool.com**
Student Site
• Teacher Web Code: aak-5500
• Algebra Readiness Puzzles 68
• Self-grading Lesson Quiz

PH SuccessNet Teacher Center
• Lesson Planner
• Resources

Plus

4-6 Equations With Fractions

What You'll Learn

OBJECTIVE 1 To use mental math to solve equations

OBJECTIVE 2 To solve equations with fractions

...And Why

To find the missing amount, as in Example 3

✓ **Check Skills You'll Need**

Solve each equation.

❓ For help, go to Lesson 2-6.

1. $17 + x = 43$ **26**
2. $x - 123 = 145$ **268**
3. $4.2 + x = 8$ **3.8**
4. $10.7 = x - 8.2$ **18.9**
5. $2.5 = 2.5 + x$ **0**
6. $x - 5 = 9.2$ **14.2**

OBJECTIVE 1

 Interactive lesson includes instant self-check, tutorials, and activities.

Using Mental Math to Solve Equations

Investigation: Exploring Differences

1–2. Check students' work.

1. Write your age in years and months. Use $\frac{1}{12}$ to represent each month. For example, write 11 years 4 months as $11\frac{4}{12}$ years.

2. **a.** In how many years will you be $14\frac{11}{12}$ years old?
   b. **Reasoning** Explain how you found your answer.

You can sometimes use mental math to solve equations that involve fractions or mixed numbers.

1 EXAMPLE Using Mental Math in Equations

Solve $x + 3\frac{1}{8} = 15\frac{7}{8}$ using mental math.

$15\frac{7}{8}$	
$3\frac{1}{8}$	x

$12 + 3 = 15$ ← Use mental math to find the missing whole number and missing fraction.

$\frac{6}{8} + \frac{1}{8} = \frac{7}{8}$

$x = 12\frac{6}{8}$ ← Combine the two parts.

$= 12\frac{3}{4}$ ← Simplify.

✓ **Check Understanding** 1 Solve each equation using mental math.

a. $5\frac{5}{6} - x = 2\frac{1}{6}$ $3\frac{2}{3}$ **b.** $14\frac{1}{4} + x = 25\frac{1}{2}$ $11\frac{1}{4}$ **c.** $x - 1\frac{3}{8} = 1\frac{3}{8}$ $2\frac{3}{4}$

196 Chapter 4 Adding and Subtracting Fractions

Ongoing Assessment and Intervention

Before the Lesson
Diagnose prerequisite skills using:
• Check Skills You'll Need

During the Lesson
Monitor progress using:
• Check Understanding
• Additional Examples
• Test Prep

After the Lesson
Assess knowledge using:
• Lesson Quiz
• Computer Test Generator CD

2 Solving Equations With Fractions

You can use inverse operations to get the variable alone on one side of the equation. Write the answer in simplest form.

2 EXAMPLE Solving Equations With Fractions

Solve $x - \frac{1}{3} = \frac{5}{6}$.

$$x - \frac{1}{3} = \frac{5}{6}$$
$$\underline{+\frac{1}{3} \quad +\frac{1}{3}} \quad \leftarrow \text{Add } \frac{1}{3} \text{ to each side.}$$
$$x = \frac{5}{6} + \frac{1}{3} \quad \leftarrow \text{Write the sum.}$$
$$= \frac{5}{6} + \frac{2}{6} \quad \leftarrow \text{The LCD is 6. Write } \frac{1}{3} \text{ as } \frac{2}{6}.$$
$$= \frac{7}{6}, \text{ or } 1\frac{1}{6} \quad \leftarrow \text{Simplify.}$$

 **Check Understanding** 2 Solve each equation. **a.** $n + \frac{1}{3} = \frac{11}{12}$ $\frac{7}{12}$ **b.** $\frac{2}{5} + a = \frac{13}{20}$ $\frac{1}{4}$

3 EXAMPLE Real-World Problem Solving

Rainfall During the first week of January, a rain gauge collected $\frac{1}{2}$ inch of rain. By the end of the month, the rain gauge showed that the total January rainfall was $2\frac{3}{5}$ inches. How much rain fell after the first week of January?

Words	rainfall in first week of January	+	rainfall after first week of January	=	total rainfall in January

Let r = the rainfall in inches after the first week of January.

Equation	$\frac{1}{2}$	+	r	=	$2\frac{3}{5}$

$$\frac{1}{2} + r = 2\frac{3}{5}$$
$$\underline{-\frac{1}{2} \qquad -\frac{1}{2}} \quad \leftarrow \text{Subtract } \frac{1}{2} \text{ from each side.}$$
$$r = 2\frac{3}{5} - \frac{1}{2} \quad \leftarrow \text{Write the difference.}$$
$$= 2\frac{6}{10} - \frac{5}{10} \quad \leftarrow \text{The LCD is 10. Write each fraction with a denominator of 10.}$$
$$= 2\frac{1}{10} \quad \leftarrow \text{Subtract.}$$

The January rainfall after the first week was $2\frac{1}{10}$ inches.

Check Understanding 3 You drive a nail that is $2\frac{3}{8}$ inches long through a wooden block. The nail extends beyond the board by $\frac{5}{8}$ inches. How thick is the wooden block? $1\frac{3}{4}$ in.

Math Background

You can solve equations with fractions in a manner similar to that of solving equations with whole numbers. To solve equations involving fractions and mixed numbers, you need to use the Addition Property of Equality or the Subtraction Property of Equality. These properties allow you to add the same number to, or subtract the same number from, both sides of an equation without changing the value of the equation.

Teaching Notes

Investigation (Optional)
Have students round their ages to the nearest whole number of months. Then have them divide by 12, and write the result as a mixed number in simplest form.

1 EXAMPLE Inclusion
Have students share with the class the methods they used to solve the Check Understanding exercises.

Visual Learners
Discuss the visual model in Example 1. Then have students draw and label similar models for Check Understanding 1a–c.

PowerPoint
Additional Examples

1. Solve $12\frac{7}{9} = x + 3\frac{4}{9}$ using mental math. $x = 9\frac{1}{3}$
2. Solve $x - \frac{1}{8} = \frac{3}{4}$. $x = \frac{7}{8}$
3. An empty container weighs $\frac{1}{12}$ lb. The same container full of chopped fruit weighs $\frac{7}{8}$ lb. How much does the fruit weigh? $\frac{19}{24}$ lb

Closure

How is solving equations with fractions similar to solving equations with whole numbers?
Sample: Both use the properties of equality to get the variable alone on one side of an equation.

👥 Reaching All Students

Below Level Write equations with like denominators for students to solve. $x - \frac{1}{9} = \frac{4}{9}$ $x = \frac{5}{9}$ $x + \frac{4}{8} = \frac{7}{8}$ $x = \frac{3}{8}$	**Advanced Learners** Write two one-step equations that have the solution $x = 5\frac{1}{9}$. Sample: $x - 1\frac{1}{3} = 3\frac{7}{9}, x + 5\frac{1}{6} = 10\frac{5}{18}$	**Inclusion** See note on page 197. **Visual Learners** See note on page 197.

3. Practice

For more practice, see *Extra Practice*.

EXERCISES

Assignment Guide

1 Objective 1
  Ⓐ Ⓑ Core 1–6, 25

2 Objective 2
  Ⓐ Ⓑ Core 7–24, 26
  Ⓒ Extension 27, 28

Test Prep 29–32
Mixed Review 33–39

Error Prevention!

Exercises 9–12 Watch for students who apply the inverse operation to only one side of the equation.

Ⓐ **Practice by Example**

Example 1
(page 196)

Mental Math Solve each equation using mental math.

1. $x + 4\frac{2}{5} = 7\frac{4}{5}$ $3\frac{2}{5}$ **2.** $a + 6\frac{1}{3} = 20\frac{2}{3}$ $14\frac{1}{3}$ **3.** $c - \frac{3}{10} = 6\frac{9}{10}$ $7\frac{1}{5}$

4. $7\frac{4}{5} = 2\frac{3}{5} + n$ $5\frac{1}{5}$ **5.** $4\frac{3}{8} = k - 7\frac{1}{8}$ $11\frac{1}{2}$ **6.** $12\frac{5}{6} = s + 2\frac{5}{6}$ 10

Example 2
(page 197)

Solve each equation.

7. $x = \frac{2}{7} + \frac{5}{6}$ $1\frac{5}{42}$ **8.** $\frac{2}{5} - \frac{1}{9} = x$ $\frac{13}{45}$ **9.** $x - \frac{5}{6} = \frac{7}{8}$ $1\frac{17}{24}$

10. $\frac{5}{24} + g = \frac{1}{3}$ $\frac{1}{8}$ **11.** $\frac{4}{9} = y - \frac{2}{5}$ $\frac{38}{45}$ **12.** $t - \frac{7}{9} = \frac{1}{3}$ $1\frac{1}{9}$

Example 3
(page 197)

Write and solve an equation for each situation.

13. Sample: Let b = amount of book read; $b = \frac{1}{3} + \frac{1}{4}$; $\frac{7}{12}$ of the book.

🌐 **13. Reading** You read $\frac{1}{3}$ of a book one week and $\frac{1}{4}$ of the book the following week. How much of the book have you read?

14. Your frog won second place in a jumping contest. The jump was $\frac{2}{3}$ foot less than the winning jump of $11\frac{1}{2}$ feet. How far did your frog jump?
Sample: Let f = length of your frog's jump; then $f = 11\frac{1}{2} - \frac{2}{3}$; $f = 10\frac{5}{6}$ ft.

Ⓑ **Apply Your Skills**

Solve each equation.

15. $\frac{11}{12} = n + \frac{2}{3}$ $\frac{1}{4}$ **16.** $y - 2\frac{8}{9} = \frac{5}{6}$ $3\frac{13}{18}$ **17.** $3\frac{1}{5} = x - \frac{12}{25}$ $3\frac{17}{25}$

18. $\frac{5}{8} = a + \frac{1}{3}$ $\frac{7}{24}$ **19.** $k - 4\frac{5}{6} = 2\frac{1}{4}$ $7\frac{1}{12}$ **20.** $9\frac{7}{8} = b - \frac{3}{4}$ $10\frac{5}{8}$

Write and solve an equation for each situation.

🌐 **21. Bridges** The Brooklyn Bridge in New York is approximately $\frac{3}{10}$ mile long. The Golden Gate Bridge in California is approximately $\frac{1}{2}$ mile longer than the Brooklyn Bridge. How long is the Golden Gate Bridge?
$g = \frac{3}{10} + \frac{1}{2}$; $g = \frac{4}{5}$ mi

🌐 **22. Landscaping** The Service Club bought a 10-yard roll of edging to put [GPS] around two trees in front of the school. They use $5\frac{2}{3}$ yards of edging for one tree and $3\frac{3}{4}$ yards for the other tree. How much edging is left?
$t = 10 - 5\frac{2}{3} - 3\frac{3}{4}$; $t = \frac{7}{12}$ yd

23. Your teacher asks your class to name a primary color. If $\frac{2}{5}$ of the class chooses blue and $\frac{1}{3}$ of the class chooses yellow, what fraction of the class chooses red? $r = 1 - \frac{2}{5} - \frac{1}{3}$; $r = \frac{4}{15}$

24. Patterns Solve each equation.

a. $\frac{1}{3} + x = \frac{1}{2}$ $\frac{1}{6}$ **b.** $\frac{1}{4} + x = \frac{1}{3}$ $\frac{1}{12}$ **c.** $\frac{1}{5} + x = \frac{1}{4}$ $\frac{1}{20}$

d. Writing in Math Predict the solution of $\frac{1}{9} + x = \frac{1}{8}$. Explain your reasoning. $\frac{1}{72}$; answers may vary. Sample: Subtract $\frac{1}{9}$ from $\frac{1}{8}$ by giving the fractions a common denominator of 72.

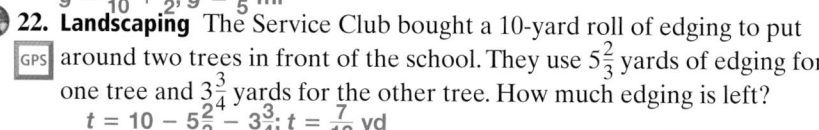

Real-World 🌐 Connection

The total length of the steel wires used in the cables of the Golden Gate Bridge would circle Earth three times.

---

198 Chapter 4 Adding and Subtracting Fractions

[GPS] Use the Guided Problem Solving worksheet with Exercise 22.

(Left sidebar — Practice 4-6 and Reteaching 4-6 worksheets)

Practice 4-6   Equations With Fractions

Solve each equation using mental math. Write your solution in simplest form.

1. $\frac{5}{17} + x = \frac{8}{17}$ $\frac{3}{17}$
2. $\frac{2}{7} + x = \frac{5}{7}$ $\frac{3}{7}$
3. $x - \frac{1}{2} = \frac{1}{10}$ $\frac{3}{5}$
4. $\frac{7}{16} - x = \frac{13}{16}$ $\frac{1}{16}$
5. $\frac{4}{5} - x = \frac{6}{25}$ $\frac{2}{5}$
6. $x - \frac{1}{5} = \frac{3}{10}$ $\frac{1}{2}$
7. $x + \frac{7}{22} = \frac{13}{22}$ $\frac{3}{11}$
8. $\frac{7}{9} - x = \frac{1}{36}$ $\frac{3}{4}$
9. $x - \frac{1}{6} = \frac{1}{6}$ $\frac{1}{3}$
10. $x + \frac{1}{4} = \frac{7}{16}$ $\frac{3}{16}$
11. $\frac{5}{9} + x = \frac{17}{18}$ $\frac{1}{9}$
12. $\frac{7}{8} - x = \frac{5}{24}$ $\frac{1}{3}$

Write and solve an equation for each situation.

13. Lori and Fraz ate $\frac{7}{12}$ of a vegetable pizza. If Lori ate $\frac{1}{3}$ of the pizza, how much of it did Fraz eat?
Sample answer: $\frac{1}{3} + x = \frac{7}{12}$; $\frac{1}{4}$

14. Irene's gas tank was $\frac{9}{10}$ full when she left her house, and it was $\frac{7}{15}$ full when she arrived for her vacation. What fraction of a tank of gas did she use driving there?
Sample answer: $\frac{9}{10} - x = \frac{7}{15}$; $\frac{13}{30}$

15. Last year, Wyatt weighed $74\frac{1}{8}$ pounds at football camp. When he weighed in this year, he was $4\frac{5}{12}$ pounds heavier. How much does Wyatt currently weigh?
$78\frac{13}{24}$ lb

16. Nora bought 3 bottles of juice for a picnic. After the picnic she had $\frac{3}{8}$ bottle left. How much juice did Nora and her friends drink?
Sample answer: $3 - x = \frac{3}{8}$; $2\frac{5}{8}$ bottles

Reteaching 4-6   Equations With Fractions

You can use mental math to solve addition and subtraction equations that involve fractions or mixed numbers. To solve equations involving fractions with unlike denominators, you need to change the fractions to equivalent fractions with like denominators.

Solve $x - \frac{3}{8} = \frac{5}{16}$.

$x - \frac{3}{8} = \frac{5}{16}$
$+ \frac{3}{8} \quad + \frac{3}{8}$ Add $\frac{3}{8}$ to each side.
$x = \frac{5}{16} + \frac{3}{8}$ Write the sum.
$= \frac{5}{16} + \frac{6}{16}$ The LCD is 16. Write $\frac{3}{8}$ as $\frac{6}{16}$.
$= \frac{11}{16}$ Simplify.

Solve each equation.

1. $x + \frac{1}{5} = \frac{4}{5}$ $\frac{3}{5}$
What number plus $\frac{1}{5}$ equals $\frac{4}{5}$? $\frac{3}{5}$ So, $x = \frac{3}{5}$.
Show that the equation is true. $\frac{3}{5} + \frac{1}{5} = \frac{4}{5}$; $\frac{4}{5} = \frac{4}{5}$

2. $x - \frac{1}{3} = \frac{2}{9}$ $\frac{5}{9}$
What is the least common multiple of 3 and 9?   9
Rewrite the equation using like denominators. $x - \frac{3}{9} = \frac{2}{9}$
What number minus $\frac{3}{9}$ equals $\frac{2}{9}$? $\frac{5}{9}$ So, $x = \frac{5}{9}$.
Show that the equation is true. $\frac{5}{9} - \frac{3}{9} = \frac{2}{9}$; $\frac{2}{9} = \frac{2}{9}$

Solve each equation.

3. $\frac{1}{4} + x = \frac{3}{4}$ $x = \frac{2}{4} = \frac{1}{2}$
4. $y - \frac{5}{8} = \frac{1}{8}$ $y = \frac{6}{8} = \frac{3}{4}$
5. $\frac{7}{10} - c = \frac{2}{5}$ $c = \frac{3}{10}$
6. $\frac{5}{12} + r = \frac{3}{4}$ $r = \frac{23}{12} = 1\frac{11}{12}$
7. $\frac{1}{12} + b = \frac{1}{4}$ $b = \frac{2}{12} = \frac{1}{6}$
8. $s - \frac{1}{6} = \frac{1}{6}$ $s = \frac{4}{6} = \frac{2}{3}$
9. $d + \frac{1}{3} = \frac{7}{12}$ $d = \frac{3}{12} = \frac{1}{4}$
10. $\frac{5}{6} - f = \frac{7}{12}$ $f = \frac{3}{12} = \frac{1}{4}$
11. $x + \frac{3}{8} = \frac{3}{4}$ $x = \frac{3}{8}$
12. $t - \frac{1}{10} = \frac{5}{8}$ $t = \frac{37}{40}$

198

25a. Answers may vary. Sample: No; rounding each number to its benchmark gives $2 + 1\frac{1}{2} + 2 + 1$, or $6\frac{1}{2}$, which is more than 6 min.

25. a. Mental Math Without computing, do you think the relay team at the right beat their best time of 6 minutes for this 1600-meter relay? Explain.

b. Find the team's total time. $5\frac{7}{8}$ min.

Relay Times (minutes)	
Kim	$1\frac{1}{2}$
Alison	$1\frac{3}{8}$
Laura	$1\frac{3}{4}$
Jamie	$1\frac{1}{4}$

26. You have a rope that is $18\frac{1}{2}$ feet long to use for a tug-of-war. The team captains agree to shorten the rope by cutting off $3\frac{3}{4}$ feet. Now how long is the rope? $14\frac{3}{4}$ ft

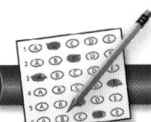 **Challenge**

27. Number Sense Which variable, m or n, has the greater value? n has the greater value.

$$m - \frac{3}{4} = \frac{37}{50} \qquad\qquad n - \frac{4}{5} = \frac{37}{50}$$

28. Stretch Your Thinking If one girl eats $\frac{1}{2}$ apple in $\frac{1}{2}$ minute, how many apples do two girls eat in two minutes? 4 apples

Test Prep

Multiple Choice

29. What is the solution of $\frac{4}{5} + x = 4\frac{3}{10}$? A

A. $3\frac{1}{2}$ **B.** $3\frac{7}{10}$ **C.** $4\frac{1}{2}$ **D.** $5\frac{1}{10}$

30. A roll of wrapping paper is 84 inches long. You cut lengths of $23\frac{1}{2}$ inches and $15\frac{1}{4}$ inches to wrap two gifts. How much paper is left? G

F. $38\frac{3}{4}$ inches **G.** $45\frac{1}{4}$ inches **H.** $46\frac{1}{4}$ inches **I.** $75\frac{3}{4}$ inches

31. A baby weighed $6\frac{3}{16}$ pounds at birth and gained $2\frac{1}{8}$ pounds. What is the weight of the baby? C

A. $4\frac{1}{16}$ pounds **B.** $8\frac{1}{4}$ pounds **C.** $8\frac{5}{16}$ pounds **D.** $9\frac{5}{16}$ pounds

Extended Response

Take It to the NET
Online lesson quiz at **www.PHSchool.com**
Web Code: aaa-0406

32. You buy the following vegetables: $2\frac{1}{2}$ pounds of onions, $1\frac{7}{8}$ pounds of corn, and 1 pound of carrots. You buy the following fruit: $1\frac{3}{8}$ pounds of apples, $2\frac{5}{8}$ pounds of grapes, and $1\frac{1}{4}$ pounds of bananas. Do you buy more vegetables or more fruit? How much more? Justify your answer. See margin.

Mixed Review

Lesson 4-3

Find each sum or difference.

33. $\frac{5}{6} - \frac{7}{12}$ $\frac{1}{4}$ **34.** $\frac{2}{5} + \frac{3}{10}$ $\frac{7}{10}$ **35.** $\frac{1}{4} + \frac{2}{3}$ $\frac{11}{12}$ **36.** $\frac{4}{5} - \frac{1}{2}$ $\frac{3}{10}$

Lesson 3-7

Order each set of numbers from least to greatest.

37. $\frac{1}{2}, \frac{2}{3}, \frac{4}{7}, \frac{3}{10}$ $\frac{3}{10}, \frac{1}{2}, \frac{4}{7}, \frac{2}{3}$ **38.** $\frac{3}{4}, \frac{4}{3}, \frac{1}{9}, \frac{11}{12}$ $\frac{1}{9}, \frac{3}{4}, \frac{11}{12}, \frac{4}{3}$ **39.** $\frac{2}{11}, \frac{0}{5}, \frac{5}{9}, \frac{8}{7}$ $\frac{0}{5}, \frac{2}{11}, \frac{5}{9}, \frac{8}{7}$

Solve each equation.

1. $x + \frac{1}{3} = \frac{14}{15}$ $x = \frac{3}{5}$

2. $x + 10\frac{5}{8} = 16\frac{1}{4}$ $x = 5\frac{5}{8}$

3. $17\frac{3}{4} + x = 18\frac{1}{12}$ $x = \frac{1}{3}$

4. $x - \frac{9}{10} = 3\frac{7}{10}$ $x = 4\frac{3}{5}$

Alternative Assessment

Have students work in pairs. One partner completes Exercises 7, 9, and 11 while the other completes Exercises 8, 10, and 12. Students explain to their partners how they found the solution to each equation.

Test Prep

Resources
For additional practice with a variety of test item formats:
• Test-Prep, p. 213
• Test-Taking Strategies, p. 209
• Test-Taking Strategies With Transparencies

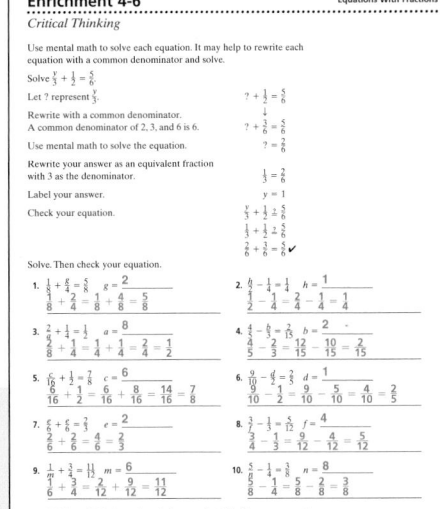

32. [4] $2\frac{1}{2} + 1\frac{7}{8} + 1 = 5\frac{3}{8}$ lb vegetables; $1\frac{3}{8} + 2\frac{5}{8} + 1\frac{1}{4} = 5\frac{1}{4}$ lb fruit; you buy more vegetables; $5\frac{3}{8} - 5\frac{1}{4} = \frac{1}{8}$. You buy $\frac{1}{8}$ lb more vegetables.

[3] 1 computational error with work shown

[2] 2 computational errors with work shown

[1] correct answer with no work shown

Computing With a Fraction Calculator

For Use With Lesson 4-6

In this activity, students use a fraction calculator to add and subtract fractions and mixed numbers with different denominators and learn how to express the answers in simplest form.

Optional Materials

- fraction calculator
- Classroom Aid 11

Teaching Notes

Allow students time to familiarize themselves with the special keys, particularly the ▶Simp key, on their fraction calculators.

① EXAMPLE Teaching Tip

After students have worked through this subtraction, ask: *How can you use the calculator to find the sum of $\frac{5}{6}$ and $\frac{3}{8}$?* Sample: Use the ➕ key instead of the ➖ key.

② EXAMPLE Teaching Tip

After students have completed the second example, ask: *How can you use your calculator to check that $5\frac{1}{4}$ is the correct answer?* Sample: Subtract either addend from $5\frac{1}{4}$ to obtain the other addend.

Exercises
Auditory Learners

Have students work in pairs and take turns completing the Exercises. One student reads an exercise and records the answer; the partner presses the keys on the calculator. Partners must agree on the keystrokes and the answers.

Error Prevention!

Watch for students who do not recognize when an answer is not displayed in simplest form.

You can use a fraction calculator to add and subtract fractions. Use the ⑦ key, which indicates division, for the fraction bar.

① EXAMPLE

Find $\frac{5}{6} - \frac{3}{8}$.

Enter 5 ⑦ 6 ➖ 3 ⑦ 8 ⬛ *11/24*.

$\frac{5}{6} - \frac{3}{8} = \frac{11}{24}$

You can also use a fraction calculator to add or subtract mixed numbers. Use the UNIT key to enter the whole number. If you do not use the unit key, the calculator will interpret $1\frac{3}{4}$ as $\frac{13}{4}$.

② EXAMPLE

Find $1\frac{3}{4} + 3\frac{1}{2}$.

Enter 1 UNIT 3 ⑦ 4 ➕ 3 UNIT 1 ⑦ 2 ⬛ *21/4*.

To rename this number, press 2nd a^b/c ⬛ *5u1/4*.

In simplest form, $1\frac{3}{4} + 3\frac{1}{2} = 5\frac{1}{4}$.

EXERCISES

Use a fraction calculator to find each sum or difference.

1. $\frac{3}{4} - \frac{2}{5}$ $\frac{7}{20}$
2. $\frac{5}{8} + \frac{1}{4}$ $\frac{7}{8}$
3. $\frac{9}{10} - \frac{1}{5}$ $\frac{7}{10}$
4. $\frac{8}{9} + \frac{1}{12}$ $\frac{35}{36}$

5. $\frac{11}{12} - \frac{3}{8}$ $\frac{13}{24}$
6. $\frac{4}{5} + \frac{1}{20}$ $\frac{17}{20}$
7. $\frac{3}{10} - \frac{2}{9}$ $\frac{7}{90}$
8. $\frac{22}{25} + \frac{9}{100}$ $\frac{97}{100}$

9. $\frac{5}{9} - \frac{2}{5}$ $\frac{7}{45}$
10. $\frac{2}{3} + \frac{4}{5}$ $1\frac{7}{15}$
11. $9\frac{3}{4} + 3\frac{3}{4}$ $13\frac{1}{2}$
12. $5\frac{3}{8} + 8\frac{1}{8}$ $13\frac{1}{2}$

13. $11\frac{8}{9} - 7\frac{1}{2}$ $4\frac{7}{18}$
14. $6\frac{9}{10} + 2\frac{1}{12}$ $8\frac{59}{60}$
15. $18\frac{5}{12} - 9\frac{1}{2}$ $8\frac{11}{12}$
16. $1\frac{1}{10} + 8\frac{1}{12}$ $9\frac{11}{60}$

17. $13\frac{5}{12} - 5\frac{1}{3}$ $8\frac{1}{12}$
18. $4\frac{1}{4} + 2\frac{1}{3}$ $6\frac{7}{12}$
19. $14\frac{3}{10} - 3\frac{1}{2}$ $10\frac{4}{5}$
20. $7\frac{8}{9} - 3\frac{1}{6}$ $4\frac{13}{18}$

21. **Writing in Math** How can you use a fraction calculator to simplify an improper fraction? Answers may vary. Sample: Enter the improper fraction. Press the 2nd key followed by the A^b/_c key. Then press the enter key.

4-7 Measuring Elapsed Time

What You'll Learn

OBJECTIVE 1 To add and subtract measures of time

OBJECTIVE 2 To read and use schedules

. . . And Why

To read bus schedules, as in Example 4

 Check Skills You'll Need   ❓ For help, go to Lesson 3-4.

Write an equivalent fraction with a denominator of 60.

1. $\frac{4}{15}$ $\frac{16}{60}$ 2. $\frac{3}{12}$ $\frac{15}{60}$ 3. $\frac{1}{5}$ $\frac{12}{60}$

4. $\frac{2}{6}$ $\frac{20}{60}$ 5. $\frac{2}{3}$ $\frac{40}{60}$ 6. $\frac{7}{12}$ $\frac{35}{60}$

New Vocabulary   • elapsed time

Lesson Preview

✔ **Check Skills You'll Need**

Finding Equivalent Fractions
Lesson 3-4: Example 1. Extra Practice p. 644.

Lesson Resources

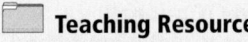 **Teaching Resources**
Practice, Reteaching, Enrichment
Checkpoint Quiz 2

 **Reaching All Students**
Practice Workbook 4-7
Spanish Practice Workbook 4-7
Reading and Math Literacy 4C
Spanish Reading and Math
  Literacy 4C
Spanish Checkpoint Quiz 2
Guided Problem Solving 4-7

🕐 **Presentation Assistant Plus!**
Transparencies
• Check Skills You'll Need 4-7
• Problem of the Day 4-7
• Additional Examples 4-7
• Student Edition Answers 4-7
• Lesson Quiz 4-7
PH Presentation Pro CD-ROM 4-7

PRENTICE HALL ASSESSMENT SYSTEM

Checkpoint Quiz 2
Computer Test Generator CD

 Technology
Resource Pro® CD-ROM
Computer Test Generator CD
PH Presentation Pro CD-ROM

 www.PHSchool.com
Student Site
• Teacher Web Code: aak-5500
• Self-grading Lesson Quiz

PH SuccessNet Teacher Center
• Lesson Planner
• Resources

 *Plus* **iTEXT**

OBJECTIVE 1   **iTEXT** Interactive lesson includes instant self-check, tutorials, and activities.

Adding and Subtracting Measures of Time

Investigation: Exploring Elapsed Time

6:30
1. a. What time does Clock 1 show?
   b. What time does Clock 2 show?
   7:10
2. **Reasoning** What is the least amount of time that has passed between the times shown on Clock 1 and Clock 2?   **40 min**

Clock 1   Clock 2

3. Draw a third clock showing the time 40 minutes after Clock 2.   **See left.**

 **Reading Math**
You can think of 6:30 A.M. as "6 hours and 30 minutes after midnight."

3.

The standard unit of time is the second (s). You use equivalent units to change from one unit of time to another.

Units of Time	
second (s)	
minute (min)	1 min = 60 s
hour (h)	1 h = 60 min
day	1 day = 24 h
week (wk)	1 wk = 7 days
year (yr)	1 yr ≈ 52 wk

Ongoing Assessment and Intervention

Before the Lesson
Diagnose prerequisite skills using:
• Check Skills You'll Need

During the Lesson
Monitor progress using:
• Check Understanding
• Additional Examples
• Test Prep

After the Lesson
Assess knowledge using:
• Lesson Quiz
• Computer Test Generator CD
• Chapter Checkpoint 2 (p. 205)

Professional Development

Math Background

Elapsed time is the time between two events. To calculate elapsed time, subtract one unit of time from another. Often you need to change from one unit of time to another unit before subtracting. For example, in order to change from years to months, multiply the number of years by 12.

Teaching Notes

Investigation (Optional)

Elicit the fact that the hour hand on a clock moves slowly from one hour to the next in 60 minutes. Furthermore, the minute hand makes one complete rotation in one hour. Ask:

- *How many hours does it take the hour hand to make one complete rotation on a clock?* **12 hours**
- *How many rotations does the minute hand make in 12 hours?* **12 rotations**

② EXAMPLE Inclusion

Demonstrate elapsed time on a clock face that has movable hands. Have volunteers take turns moving the hands on the clock to show the passing of time from 1:45 P.M. to 3:27 P.M.

③ EXAMPLE Teaching Tip

You might want students to break the problem into two separate parts relative to 12:00 noon as shown below.

8:15 → 12:00 A.M. = 3 h 45 min
12:00 → 3:25 P.M. = <u>3 h 25 min</u>
    Add the parts → 7 h 10 min

Diversity

Have students familiar with the 24-hour clock (military time) share their knowledge with the class.

④ EXAMPLE Error Prevention

Make sure students understand that "..." means buses leave every 30 minutes between 7:50 A.M. and 11:20 P.M.

---

① EXAMPLE Writing Equivalent Times

How many seconds are equivalent to 1 minute 20 seconds?

1 minute 20 seconds = 60 s + 20 s   ← **One minute is equivalent to 60 seconds.**
                    = 80 s   ← **Simplify.**

So, 1 minute 20 seconds is equivalent to 80 seconds.

✓ **Check Understanding** ① How many days are equivalent to 4 weeks 3 days? **31 days**

The time between two events is called **elapsed time.** To find elapsed time, you can subtract hours and minutes.

> **Test-Prep Tip**
> A drawing of a clock face can help you compute elapsed time.

② EXAMPLE Calculating Elapsed Time

Find the elapsed time between 1:45 P.M. and 5:27 P.M.

To find the elapsed time, subtract 1:45 from 5:27.

5:27 → 5 h 27 min →   4 h 87 min   ← **Rename 5 h 27 min as 4 h 87 min.**
1:45 → 1 h 45 min → <u>− 1 h 45 min</u>
                       3 h 42 min   ← **Subtract.**

The elapsed time is 3 hours 42 minutes.

✓ **Check Understanding** ② Find the elapsed time between 7:25 A.M. and 8:12 A.M. **47 min**

To find elapsed time between a morning and an afternoon or between an evening and the next morning, add 12 hours to the later time.

③ EXAMPLE Real-World 🌐 Problem Solving

School How long is a school day that goes from 8:15 A.M. to 3:25 P.M.?

Since 3:25 P.M. is later than 8:15 A.M., you need to add 12 hours to 3:25.

3:25 →   3 h 25 min
          <u>+ 12 h</u>   ← **Add 12 to the later time.**
           15 h 25 min

15:25 →   15 h 25 min
8:15 →   <u>− 8 h 15 min</u>   ← **Subtract the earlier time.**
            7 h 10 min   ← **Subtract.**

The school day that goes from 8:15 A.M. to 3:25 P.M. is 7 h 10 min long.

✓ **Check Understanding** ③ **a.** Find the elapsed time between 10:00 A.M. and 7:15 P.M. **9 h 15 min**
b. Reasoning Explain why you add 12 in Example 3. **Answers may vary. Sample: Adding 12 hours makes both times the hours elapsed since midnight, so they can be subtracted.**

202 Chapter 4 Adding and Subtracting Fractions

👥 Reaching All Students

Below Level	Advanced Learners	Inclusion
Below Level Have students write what the time will be 30 minutes later. 10:00 A.M. **10:30 A.M.** 2:07 P.M. **2:37 P.M.** 5:45 A.M. **6:15 A.M.**	Advanced Learners Which is longer—1,000,000 minutes or 1,000 days? Explain. **1,000 days; there are 1,440 minutes in one day (24 h × 60 min per h), and 1,440,000 minutes in 1,000 days.**	Inclusion See note on page 202. Diversity See note on page 202.

You think about elapsed time when reading and using schedules.

4 **EXAMPLE** **Reading and Using a Schedule**  Real World

Bus Schedules Use the bus schedule at the left. Suppose you arrive at the Willson Street bus stop 5 minutes after the 11:50 A.M. bus leaves.

Yellow Bus Line	
Buses Run Every 30 Minutes Monday–Friday	
Leave Willson St.	Arrive Kagy Blvd.
7:20 A.M.	7:45 A.M.
7:50 A.M.	8:15 A.M.
...	...
11:20 P.M.	11:45 P.M.

a. How long will you wait for the next bus?

The bus runs every 30 minutes. You will wait 30 − 5 min, or 25 minutes.

b. How long is the bus ride?

Using the first run, the elapsed time is 7:45 A.M − 7:20 A.M., or 25 min.

c. When will you arrive at Kagy Boulevard?

11:50 + 30 min = 11:80 min   ← Find when the next bus leaves.
= 11 h 80 min   ← Since 80 min is more than 1 h, rename.
= 12 h 20 min

The next bus will leave at 12:20 P.M. The trip takes 25 minutes. So, you will arrive at 12:20 + 25 min or 12:45 P.M.

✔ **Check Understanding** **4** It is a 5-minute walk from the bus stop on Kagy Boulevard to a gym. Which bus should you take from Willson Street to get to the gym by 6:00 P.M.? 5:20 P.M.

EXERCISES

? For more practice, see *Extra Practice.*

A Practice by Example

For each time, write an equivalent time using only the smaller unit.

Example 1 (page 202)

1. 1 h 30 min 90 min   **2.** 2 min 59 s 179 s   **3.** 8 h 2 min 482 min

4. 5 min 36 s 336 s   **5.** 3 wk 5 days 26 d   **6.** 2 days 17 h 65 h

Example 2 (page 202)

Find the elapsed time between each pair of times.

7. from 2:25 P.M. to 3:35 P.M. 1 h 10 min   **8.** from 8:25 A.M. to 10:52 A.M. 2 h 27 min

9. from 5:25 P.M. to 11:11 P.M. 5 h 46 min   **10.** from 9:28 A.M. to 11:07 A.M. 1 h 39 min

Example 3 (page 202)

11. from 11:25 A.M. to 2:45 P.M. 3 h 20 min   **12.** from 8:30 P.M. to 7:39 A.M. 11 h 9 min

13. How long is a car parked on the street if it arrives at 10:25 P.M. and leaves at 8:12 A.M.? 9 h 47 min

1 How many minutes are equivalent to 1 hr 45 min? 105 min

2 Find the elapsed time between 7:25 A.M. and 9:05 A.M. 1 h 40 min

3 Find the elapsed time between 10:15 A.M. and 2:25 P.M. 4 h 10 min

4 You arrive at the Glenmont bus stop at 8:00 A.M. and buy a ticket for the next bus.

a. How long will you wait for the next bus? 10 min.

b. What time will you arrive at the Reedville bus stop? 8:45 A.M.

Buses Run Every 15 min Monday–Friday	
LEAVE	**ARRIVE**
Glenmont	Reedville
7:40 A.M.	8:15 A.M.
7:55 A.M.	8:30 A.M.
...	...
9:55 A.M.	10:30 A.M.

Closure

What is elapsed time? the time between two events

3. Practice

Assignment Guide

1 Objective 1
  Ⓐ Ⓑ Core 1–13
  Ⓒ Extension 23–24

2 Objective 2
  Ⓐ Ⓑ Core 14–22
  Ⓒ Extension 25

Test Prep 26–29
Mixed Review 30–35

Error Prevention!

Exercises 11–12 Watch for students who neglect to add 12 hours to the later time.

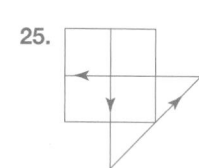

Practice 4-7   Measuring Elapsed Time

Clark is trying to plan his Saturday. He estimates each activity will take the following times.

Make a schedule for Clark's day if he wakes up at 7:00 A.M. Assume all his activities are done in the given order.

	Activity	Amount of Time	Time of Day
1.	Get up, eat breakfast	30 min	7:00 A.M. – 7:30 A.M.
2.	Mow lawn	1 h	7:30 A.M. – 8:30 A.M.
3.	Rake yard	2 h	8:30 A.M. – 10:30 A.M.
4.	Wash, wax car	45 min	10:30 A.M. – 11:15 A.M.
5.	Walk dog	15 min	11:15 A.M. – 11:30 A.M.
6.	Clean room	45 min	11:30 A.M. – 12:15 P.M.
7.	Eat lunch	30 min	12:15 P.M. – 12:45 P.M.
8.	Shop for school clothes	1 h 30 min	12:45 P.M. – 2:15 P.M.
9.	Read book	45 min	2:15 P.M. – 3:00 P.M.
10.	Do homework	1 h 15 min	3:00 P.M. – 4:15 P.M.
11.	Baby-sit brother	2 h	4:15 P.M. – 6:15 P.M.
12.	Eat supper	45 min	6:15 P.M. – 7:00 P.M.
13.	Get ready for party	30 min	7:00 P.M. – 7:30 P.M.
14.	Ride to party	20 min	7:30 P.M. – 7:50 P.M.
15.	Party	2 h	7:50 P.M. – 9:50 P.M.
16.	Ride home	20 min	9:50 P.M. – 10:10 P.M.

Find the elapsed time between each pair of times.

17. from 2:12 P.M. to 10:18 P.M.	18. from 9:35 A.M. to 8:48 P.M
8 h 6 min	11 h 13 min

19. from 6:45 P.M. to 11:24 A.M.	20. from 2:55 A.M. to 8:13 A.M.
16 h 39 min	5 h 18 min

21. from 7:00 P.M. to 8:56 P.M.	22. from 8:22 P.M. to 11:47 A.M.
1 h 56 min	15 h 25 min

23. The movie begins at 7:45 P.M. and lets out at 10:20 P.M. How long is the movie?
2 h 35 min

24. A plane left at 10:45 A.M. and landed at 4:37 P.M. How long was the flight?
5 h 52 min

Reteaching 4-7   Measuring Elapsed Time

Find the elapsed time between 6:15 A.M. and 11:10 A.M.

1. Set up as subtraction.	2. Rename 11:10 as 10:70.	3. Subtract.
11:10 −6:15	11:10 → 10:70 −6:15 → −6:15	10:70 −6:15 4:55

The elapsed time is 4 hours 55 minutes.

You can find elapsed time from a schedule.

Leave	Arrive
Boston 7:09 A.M.	New York 11:02 A.M.

For travel time, find the elapsed time between 7:09 A.M. and 11:02 A.M.

11:02 − 7:09 = 3 hours 53 minutes

For each time, write an equivalent time using only the smaller unit.

Example: 4 hours 55 minutes = 4 × 60 + 55 = 295 minutes

1. 3 hours 25 minutes	2. 2 hours 17 minutes	3. 2 hours 48 minutes
205 min	137 min	168 min

4. 5 hours 18 minutes	5. 6 hours 13 minutes	6. 5 hours 39 minutes
318 min	373 min	339 min

Find the elapsed time between each pair of times.

7. 6:45 P.M. and 9:20 P.M.	8. 9:36 A.M. and 11:50 A.M.
2 h 35 min	2 h 14 min

9. 5:45 A.M. and 11:30 A.M.	10. 3:11 P.M. and 10:40 P.M.
5 h 45 min	7 h 29 min

11. 8:15 A.M. and 10:09 P.M.	12. 1:00 A.M. and 7:28 P.M.
13 h 54 min	18 h 28 min

Use the schedule to answer the following questions.

13. How much time do you have to get to the game?	Leave for game 6:15 P.M. Game begins 7:35 P.M. Game ends 10:20 P.M.
1 h 20 min	

14. How long is the game?
2 h 45 min

204

Example 4
(page 203)

21. Answers may vary.
Sample: If it is 1:00 A.M. on a Tuesday in the Eastern time zone, it is 10:00 P.M. on Monday in the Pacific time zone.

22. 10:45 A.M. leave 1st party
11:45 A.M. arrive at 2nd party
12:30 P.M. leave 2nd party
1:30 P.M. arrive at 3rd party
2:15 P.M. leave 3rd party

Real-World 🌐 **Connection**

Careers Clowns often make balloon animals at children's parties.

Use the train schedule for Exercises 14–16.

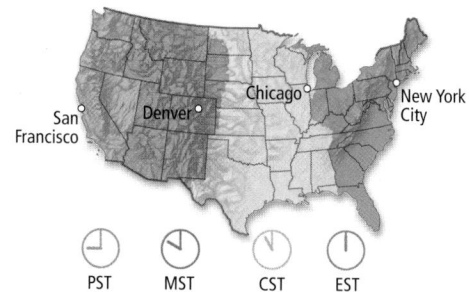

Train Schedule		
Station	**Train A**	**Train B**
Fairview	8:15 A.M.	8:42 A.M.
Huntville	8:26 A.M.	8:55 A.M.
Rush City	8:34 A.M.	9:04 A.M.
Grayland	8:45 A.M.	9:19 A.M.

14. Which train takes less time to travel from Fairview to Grayland?
Train A

15. How long do you wait for the train if you get to Rush City at 8:35 A.M.?
29 min

16. How long does it take to get to Grayland from Huntville on Train B?
24 min

Ⓑ Apply Your Skills 🌐 **Time Zones** The map below shows the time zones in the continental United States. Find the time for each city if it is 12:00 noon in Denver.

17. Chicago 1:00 P.M.
18. New York City 2:00 P.M.
19. San Francisco 11:00 A.M.

20. **Algebra** What time is it in New York if the time in San Francisco is x?
$x + 3$

21. **Writing in Math** Explain how it can be Monday in one part of the United States and Tuesday in another part of the United States.
See above left.

🌐 22. **Clowns** A clown wants to perform a 45-minute show at each of three
GPS   birthday parties on the same Saturday. The first party must begin at 10:00 A.M. and he needs to leave the third party by 2:15 P.M. He wants to allow one hour between each party. Make a schedule for the clown.
See above left.

23. **Estimation** Estimate each elapsed time.
a. from 1:38 A.M. to 4:50 A.M.   **b.** from 11:49 A.M. to 7:12 P.M.
    3 h   7 h 20 min

Ⓒ Challenge

24. Find the elapsed time from Saturday at 7:15 A.M. to Sunday at 3:05 P.M.
31 h 50 min

25. **Stretch Your Thinking** Draw a square. Then, without lifting your pencil, draw three line segments that divide it into four identical squares.
See above left.

GPS   Use the Guided Problem Solving worksheet with Exercise 22.

29. [2] a. 12:15 P.M.

b. Mix, bake, cool, frost cake; answers may vary. Sample: Yes;

decorate room while the cake bakes and cools.

c. Answers may vary. Sample: Start at 12:50 P.M. Mix cake (40 min), decorate room while cake

bakes and cools (80 min), frost cake (20 min), shower and dress (25 min).

[1] incorrect starting time OR incorrect explanation

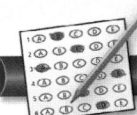

Multiple Choice

26. How many minutes are in 3 h 25 min? **D**

    A. 28 min   **B.** 75 min   **C.** 105 min   **D.** 205 min

27. What is the elapsed time between 4:25 A.M. and 7:24 A.M.? **G**

    F. 2 h 1 min   **G.** 2 h 59 min   **H.** 3 h 1 min   **I.** 3 h 59 min

28. Jack has 2 hours of homework. He will take one 30-minute break. To finish by 9:30 P.M., what is the latest time he can begin? **C**

    A. 6:00 P.M.   **B.** 6:30 P.M.   **C.** 7:00 P.M.   **D.** 7:30 P.M.

Short Response

29. You make a list of things to do before a party that starts today at 4:00 p.m.   **a–c.** See margin.

    a. If you follow the list in order, at what time should you begin?

    b. Which activities must you do in order? Can any be done at the same time? Revise the list.

    c. Use the revised list of part (b) to make a new schedule. Allow yourself an extra 25 minutes before the party.

> Decorate room (1 h)
> Mix cake (40 min)
> Bake cake (35 min)
> Cool cake (45 min)
> Frost cake (20 min)
> Shower and dress (25 min)

Take It to the NET
Online lesson quiz at
www.PHSchool.com
Web Code: aaa-0407

Lesson 2-6

Solve each equation.

30. $a + 14 = 31$ **17**   **31.** $t - 8 = 28$ **36**   **32.** $b - 2.4 = 5.1$ **7.5**

33. $9.1 - c = 5.3$ **3.8**   **34.** $15 = w + 9$ **6**   **35.** $23 = d - 16$ **39**

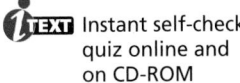

Checkpoint Quiz 2   **Lessons 4-4 through 4-7**

Instant Instant self-check quiz online and on CD-ROM

Find each sum or difference.

1. $2\frac{1}{2} + 3\frac{1}{8}$ $5\frac{5}{8}$ **2.** $9\frac{1}{2} - 4\frac{3}{4}$ $4\frac{3}{4}$ **3.** $6\frac{1}{3} + 8\frac{1}{2}$ $14\frac{5}{6}$ **4.** $7\frac{5}{9} - 1\frac{2}{3}$ $5\frac{8}{9}$

Solve each equation.

5. $a + \frac{2}{6} = \frac{5}{6}$ $\frac{1}{2}$ **6.** $p - \frac{5}{9} = \frac{2}{3}$ $1\frac{2}{9}$ **7.** $\frac{1}{5} + b = \frac{1}{2}$ $\frac{3}{10}$ **8.** $h + \frac{2}{3} = \frac{12}{15}$ $\frac{2}{15}$

9. Find the elapsed time between 8:42 A.M. and 3:29 P.M. **6 h 47 min**

10. Find the elapsed time between 6:35 P.M. and 4:18 A.M. **9 h 43 min**

---

4. Assess

PowerPoint **Lesson Quiz 4-7**

Find the elapsed time.

1. from 8:32 A.M. to 11:30 A.M.
    2 h 58 min

2. from 9:17 A.M. to 7:35 P.M.
    10 h 18 min

Trains Run Every 12 min	
LEAVE K St.	**ARRIVE Q St.**
6:30 A.M.	**6:50** A.M.
6:42 A.M.	**7:02** A.M.
. . .	. . .

3. How long is the train ride from K St. to Q St.? **20 min**

4. At 8:00 A.M. you arrive at K St. How long until the next train to Q St.? **6 min**

Chapter Checkpoint

To check understanding of Lessons 4-4 to 4-7:

Checkpoint Quiz 2 (p. 205)

Teaching Resources
Checkpoint Quiz 2 (also in *Prentice Hall Assessment System*)

Reaching All Students
Reading and Math Literacy 4C

Spanish versions available

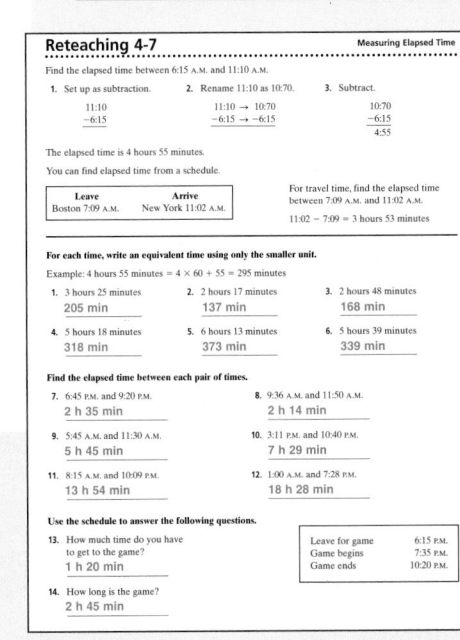

Test Prep

Resources
For additional practice with a variety of test item formats:
- Test-Prep, p. 213
- Test-Taking Strategies, p. 209
- Test-Taking Strategies With Transparencies

Alternative Assessment

Each student in a pair writes a time using A.M. or P.M. Partners designate one time as the starting time and the other as the ending time. They work together to find the elapsed time. Have pairs record their work.

1. Plan

Lesson Preview

✓ **Check Skills You'll Need**

Estimating Sums and Differences
Lesson 4-1: Examples 1–2. Extra
Practice p. 645.

Lesson Resources

Teaching Support includes:
Practice, Reteaching, Enrichment
Assessment, Reading & Literacy,
Activities, Transparencies,
Technology, CD-ROMs, Spanish,
and More

*See pp. 168G–168H for a complete
list of resources for this lesson.*

 **www.PHSchool.com**
• Teacher Web Code: aak-5500

Plus

2. Teach

Math Background

Drawing a diagram often helps to
clarify relationships among the
given numbers and provides a
concrete place for students to
start.

Additional Example

① A school is hosting a soccer
tournament. The field is
110 yards long and 80 yards
wide. It will be divided into
mini-soccer fields that are
25 yards long and 20 yards
wide. How many mini-fields
will fit on the large field?
Hint: Not all the space will be
used. **17 mini-fields**

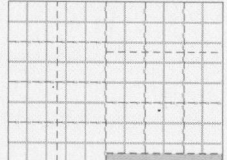

206

4-8 Draw a Diagram

What You'll Learn

OBJECTIVE 1 To solve problems
by drawing a
diagram

...And Why

To solve sports-related
problems, as in Example 1

✓ **Check Skills You'll Need**   ❓ For help, go to Lesson 4-1.

Estimate each sum or difference. 1–6. Answers may vary. Samples are given.

1. $3\frac{1}{12} + 2\frac{3}{4}$ 6
2. $15\frac{1}{5} - 5\frac{3}{10}$ 10
3. $1\frac{1}{3} + 9\frac{7}{12}$ 11
4. $5\frac{1}{8} - 2\frac{4}{5}$ 2
5. $7\frac{1}{6} + 12\frac{1}{5}$ 19
6. $18\frac{7}{8} - 17\frac{5}{15}$ 2

OBJECTIVE 1

 Interactive lesson includes instant self-check, tutorials, and activities.

Solving Problems by Drawing a Diagram

When to Use This Strategy Sometimes it is hard to picture a word problem.
By drawing a diagram, you can make a problem easier to solve.

① EXAMPLE Real-World 🌐 Problem Solving

Sports A volleyball tournament will be held on a soccer field that is
110 yards long and 80 yards wide. The game area for each volleyball court
allows space for the court and a safety zone around it. Each game area is
25 yards long by 15 yards wide. How many game areas will fit on the field?

Read and Understand The field is 110 yards by 80 yards. Each game area
is 25 yards by 15 yards. You are asked to find how many will fit on the field.

Plan and Solve To help decide, first *draw a diagram* of the field. Then
show how many game areas that are 25 yards by 15 yards fit on the field.

Mark off 7 game areas along the
length of the field and 3 game areas
along the width of the field. Since
$3 \times 7 = 21$, you can fit 21 in the field.

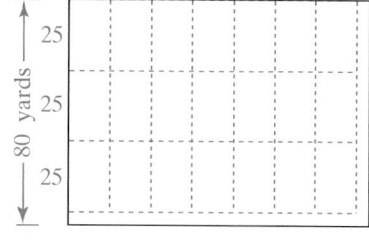

Look Back and Check Check the
answer by dividing the area of the field
by the area of a game area. Use the
formula area = length × width.

$$\frac{\text{area of the field}}{\text{area of a game area}} \rightarrow \frac{110 \text{ yards} \times 80 \text{ yards}}{25 \text{ yards} \times 15 \text{ yards}} \rightarrow \frac{8{,}800 \text{ square yards}}{375 \text{ square yards}} \approx 23$$

Twenty-one courts is a reasonable answer.

Real-World 🌐 Connection
Outdoors, volleyball is
played on grass or sand
courts.

Ongoing Assessment and Intervention

Before the Lesson	During the Lesson	After the Lesson
Diagnose prerequisite skills using:	**Monitor progress using:**	**Assess knowledge using:**
• Check Skills You'll Need	• Check Understanding	• Lesson Quiz
	• Additional Examples	• Computer Test Generator CD
	• Test Prep	

✓ **Check Understanding** ① A gymnastics floor exercise mat is 14 yards by 14 yards. How many floor exercise mats fit on a soccer field with no holes or overlaps? **35 mats**

Closure

How can drawing a diagram help you solve a problem? **Sample: It can help you visualize the given information and understand what you need to find.**

EXERCISES

❓ For more practice, see *Extra Practice.*

Ⓐ **Practice by Example**

Example 1
(page 206)

Solve each problem by drawing a diagram. 1–4. **Check students' diagrams.**

 1. **Merchandise Displays** A store owner stacks boxes in a pyramid shape like the one at the right. If the pattern continues, how many boxes are in a 10-high stack? **55**

Need Help?
• Reread the problem.
• Identify the key facts and details.
• Tell the problem in your own words.
• Try a different strategy.
• Check your work.

2. Each side of a square game board measures 16 inches.
   a. What is the perimeter of the game board? **64 in.**
   b. A 2-inch square is cut from each corner of the board. What is the perimeter of the new game board? **64 in.**

3. **Carpentry** A bookcase is made from wood that is $\frac{3}{4}$ inch thick. The bookcase has four shelves, including the top. The space between shelves is $12\frac{1}{2}$ inches. Find the total height of the bookcase. $40\frac{1}{2}$ in.

7. Answers may vary. Sample: The 4-cm rod covers 4 cm of the 6-cm rod, leaving 2 cm to add to the 9-cm rod.

4. **Gardening** A rectangular garden is 2 feet by $1\frac{1}{2}$ feet. A landscaper plants flowers $\frac{1}{2}$ foot apart along the edges and at the corners of the garden. How many plants does the landscaper need? **14 plants**

Ⓑ **Apply Your Skills**

Choose a strategy to solve each problem.

Strategies

Draw a Diagram
Make a Graph
Make an Organized List
Make a Table and
  Look for a Pattern
Simulate a Problem
Solve a Simpler Problem
Try, Check, and Revise
Use Logical Reasoning
Work Backward
Write an Equation

5. **Lighting** Lights are placed every $1\frac{3}{4}$ feet along both sides of a 14-foot driveway. How many lights are needed? **18 lights**
   GPS

6. **Tiles** An artist uses a tile design on a wall that is 6 feet by 10 feet. Tiles are placed at the border on all four sides. Each tile is a square that measures 0.5 foot on a side. How many tiles does the artist need for the entire border?

60 tiles

7. **Writing in Math** The lengths of three rods are 4 cm, 6 cm, and 9 cm. Explain how to arrange these rods to measure 11 cm. **See above left.**

The Alhambra in Spain has intricate tile designs.

4-8 Draw a Diagram   **207**

3. Practice

Assignment Guide

1 **Objective 1**
  Ⓐ Ⓑ Core 1–10
  Ⓒ Extension 11

Test Prep 12–15
Mixed Review 16–21

Error Prevention!

Exercises 1–4 Have students use graph paper for their drawings.

4. Assess

📽 **PowerPoint** **Lesson Quiz 4-8**

1. A rectangular swimming pool is 10 ft wide by 20 ft long. A landscaper wants to create a solid edge around the pool, including the corners, using concrete blocks that are 2 ft on each side. How many concrete blocks will be used? **34 blocks**

Alternative Assessment

Each student in a pair draws a diagram with only some dimensions labeled. Partners exchange their drawings, write a word problem for their partner's drawing, and solve the problem.

Test Prep

Resources
For additional practice with a variety of test item formats:
• Test-Prep, p. 213
• Test-Taking Strategies, p. 209
• Test-Taking Strategies With Transparencies

207

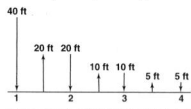

8. **Gymnastics** Suppose you take a total of 26 gymnastics lessons. A lesson lasts 45 minutes. A music lesson lasts a half hour. How much time, in hours, do you spend taking gymnastics lessons? 19.5 h

9. To celebrate its opening day, a store gives a free gift to every fifteenth customer. The store manager expects about 100 customers each hour. About how many gifts will the store give out in its 12-hour day? 80 gifts

10. **Patterns** Predict the next figure in the pattern and draw it.

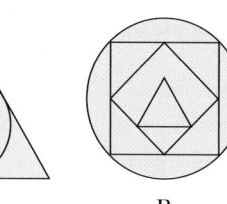  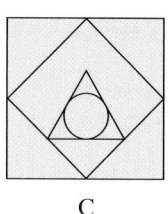 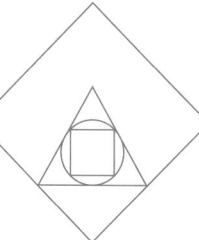

A   B   C

 Challenge

11. **Stretch Your Thinking** The sum of the digits in a 3-digit number is 6. Digits may be repeated. How many such 3-digit numbers are possible?
21 3-digit numbers

Test Prep

Multiple Choice

12. What is the difference between $9\frac{1}{2}$ and $2\frac{3}{4}$? B
A. $6\frac{1}{4}$ B. $6\frac{3}{4}$ C. $7\frac{1}{8}$ D. $7\frac{1}{4}$

13. What is the sum of $\frac{3}{5}$ and $\frac{3}{4}$? I
F. $1\frac{3}{10}$ G. $1\frac{9}{20}$ H. $1\frac{2}{3}$ I. $1\frac{7}{20}$

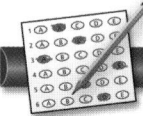
Take It to the NET
Online lesson quiz at
www.PHSchool.com
Web Code: aaa-0408

14. What is the difference between $\frac{11}{15}$ and $\frac{1}{3}$? A
A. $\frac{2}{5}$ B. $\frac{8}{15}$ C. $\frac{1}{2}$ D. $\frac{5}{6}$

Short Response

15. You have 24 feet of fencing for a rectangular dog pen. Each side must be a whole number of feet. List all possible dimensions for the dog pen. Which dimensions give your dog the most area? See margin.

Mixed Review

Lesson 4-6 **Algebra** Solve each equation.

16. $x - \frac{7}{10} = 4\frac{1}{2}$ $5\frac{1}{5}$ 17. $x + 2\frac{1}{3} = 5\frac{5}{6}$ $3\frac{1}{2}$ 18. $x - 3\frac{1}{4} = 2\frac{3}{5}$ $5\frac{17}{20}$

Lesson 4-4 Find each sum.

19. $4\frac{1}{16} + 9\frac{7}{8}$ $13\frac{15}{16}$ 20. $1\frac{1}{2} + 3\frac{1}{4}$ $4\frac{3}{4}$ 21. $2\frac{1}{5} + 5\frac{1}{2}$ $7\frac{7}{10}$

GPS Use the Guided Problem Solving worksheet with Exercise 5.

15. [2] The possible dimensions are 1 ft by 11 ft, 2 ft by 10 ft, 3 ft by 9 ft, 4 ft by 8 ft, and 5 ft by 7 ft, and 6 ft by 6 ft. 6 ft by 6 ft gives the dog the most area because 6 · 6 = 36, the greatest product of possible dimensions.

[1] one part correct

Reading-comprehension questions are based on a passage that gives facts. Read the directions and questions. Then read the passage. Look for information that helps answer the questions.

 **EXAMPLE**

Desert Area Deserts cover about $\frac{1}{5}$ of Earth's land surface. A *desert* is an area of land where less than 10 inches of precipitation (rain or snow) falls per year.

The Sahara Desert is the largest desert, covering about $3\frac{1}{2}$ million square miles. The Sahara Desert gets about 8 inches of rain each year.

Antarctica consists largely of desert. It is about 5 million square miles in area. Antarctica contains $\frac{7}{10}$ of the world's fresh water. The South Pole lies in the middle of the continent, and gets less than 1 inch of snow each year.

How much larger is Antarctica than the Sahara Desert?

What is the question asking? the difference in area between Antarctica and the Sahara Desert

Identify the information you need. Antarctica is about 5 million square miles in area. The Sahara Desert is about $3\frac{1}{2}$ million square miles.

Solve the problem

Difference in areas, in million square miles:
$$\begin{array}{c} 5 \\ -3\frac{1}{2} \end{array} \rightarrow \begin{array}{c} 4\frac{2}{2} \\ -3\frac{1}{2} \\ \hline 1\frac{1}{2} \end{array}$$

Antarctica is about $1\frac{1}{2}$ million square miles larger than the Sahara Desert.

EXERCISES

Use the passage above to answer Exercises 1 and 2.

1. How much more precipitation does the Sahara Desert get in a year than the South Pole? about 7 in.

2. Rain forests cover about $\frac{3}{50}$ of Earth's land surface. What fraction of Earth is covered by either desert or rain forest? $\frac{13}{50}$

Research shows that learning comprehension strategies helps students become purposeful, active readers who can gain control of their own reading comprehension.

Resources

PRENTICE HALL
ASSESSMENT SYSTEM

Test-Taking Strategies With Transparencies
• Transparency 4
• Practice master, p. 3

Teaching Notes

Teaching Tip
Encourage students to restate any difficult sentences in plain language. Remind them to look back through the passage to extract needed information.

Auditory Learners
Students may benefit from listing key words and information from the passage. Suggest they ask themselves:
• "What do I know?"
• "What do I need to find?"
• "What is not needed?"

Test-Taking Strategies With Transparencies

Chapter 4: Reading-Comprehension Questions
Exercises

Use the passage that begins each exercise to answer the parts of the exercise.

1. Mr. Whitby's long distance phone plan includes a $4.95 per month maintenance fee, $.10 per minute for long distance calls made from 6:00 A.M. to 6:00 P.M., and $.05 per minute for long distance calls made after 6:00 P.M.

   In January, Mr. Whitby only made two long distance calls. He made one of the calls at noon and the call lasted 17 minutes. He made the other call at 6:30 P.M. He finished this call at 6:53 P.M. How long did Mr. Whitby's second call last?

   a. What is the question asking for?
      the length of the second call

   b. Identify the information you need to solve the problem.
      the beginning and ending time of the call

   c. How many minutes did Mr. Whitby's second call last?
      6:53 − 6:30 = 23 minutes

   d. What was the cost of Mr. Whitby's first long distance call in January?
      17 × 0.10 = $1.70

   e. What was the cost of Mr. Whitby's second call?
      23 × 0.05 = $1.15

   f. What was Mr. Whitby's total long distance bill for January?
      $1.70 + $1.15 + $4.95 = $7.80

2. Mrs. Wilkinson has two apple trees and one pear tree in her backyard. Each apple tree produced $1\frac{3}{4}$ bushels of apples. The pear tree produced $2\frac{1}{3}$ bushels of pears.

   a. Which produced more per tree, the apple tree or the pear tree? How much more?
      the pear tree; $\frac{7}{12}$ more bushels

   b. How many total bushels of fruit did Mrs. Wilkinson's trees produce?
      $5\frac{5}{6}$ bushels

209

Resources

 **Reaching All Students**
Reading and Math Literacy 4D
Spanish Reading and Math
  Literacy 4D

 **ASSESSMENT SYSTEM**

Test Preparation
• Chapter 4 practice in test
  formats

 **www.PHSchool.com**
Student Site
• Self-grading vocabulary test
PH SuccessNet Teacher Center
• Resources

Plus

Chapter 4

Chapter Review

 **Take It to the NET**
Online vocabulary quiz
at **www.PHSchool.com**
Web Code: aaj-0451

Vocabulary

benchmark (p. 171)   elapsed time (p. 202)

 **Reading Math:**
Understanding
Vocabulary

Choose the vocabulary term that completes each sentence.

1. A(n) _?_ is a value that you use as an estimate for a fraction.
   benchmark
2. The time between two events is called _?_. elapsed time

Skills and Concepts

4-1 Objective
▼ To estimate sums and
  differences

A **benchmark** is a whole number or fraction that is easy to use when you estimate. You can use the benchmarks $0, \frac{1}{2}$, or 1 to estimate sums and differences of fractions.

To estimate sums and differences of mixed numbers, round to the nearest whole number.

3–10. Answers may vary. Samples are given.
Estimate each sum or difference. Use the benchmarks $0, \frac{1}{2}$, and 1.

3. $\frac{8}{9} + \frac{3}{7}$ $1\frac{1}{2}$ **4.** $\frac{5}{8} - \frac{3}{12}$ 0   **5.** $\frac{4}{5} + \frac{1}{6}$ 1   **6.** $\frac{23}{35} - \frac{4}{7}$ 0

Estimate each sum or difference.

7. $4\frac{1}{7} + 9\frac{7}{14}$ 14   **8.** $24\frac{11}{16} - 15\frac{1}{4}$ 10 **9.** $8\frac{5}{6} + 6\frac{3}{8}$ 15   **10.** $45\frac{33}{35} - 40\frac{2}{7}$ 6

11. You need $1\frac{1}{3}$ cups of lemon juice and $4\frac{3}{4}$ cups of water to make lemonade. Estimate the amount of lemonade you will make. about 6 c

---

4-2 and 4-3 Objectives
▼ To add fractions
  (like denominators)
▼ To subtract fractions
  (like denominators)
▼ To add fractions
  (unlike denominators)
▼ To subtract fractions
  (unlike denominators)

To add or subtract fractions, you may need to write each fraction using a common denominator. Then add or subtract the numerators.

Find each sum or difference.

12. $\frac{2}{5} + \frac{5}{5}$ $1\frac{2}{5}$ **13.** $\frac{7}{8} - \frac{3}{8}$ $\frac{1}{2}$ **14.** $\frac{3}{20} + \frac{9}{20}$ $\frac{3}{5}$ **15.** $\frac{25}{36} - \frac{5}{36}$ $\frac{5}{9}$

16. $\frac{1}{8} + \frac{3}{4}$ $\frac{7}{8}$ **17.** $\frac{4}{5} - \frac{3}{10}$ $\frac{1}{2}$ **18.** $\frac{17}{24} - \frac{7}{12}$ $\frac{1}{8}$ **19.** $\frac{11}{15} + \frac{1}{2}$ $1\frac{7}{30}$

20. You rode your bicycle $\frac{2}{3}$ mile to school and $\frac{1}{5}$ mile to a friend's house. How far did you ride your bicycle? $\frac{13}{15}$ mi

---

4-4 and 4-5 Objectives

▼ To add mixed numbers

▼ To add mixed numbers with renaming

▼ To subtract mixed numbers

▼ To subtract mixed numbers with renaming

You can add or subtract mixed numbers by first adding or subtracting the whole numbers and then adding or subtracting the fraction parts.

Find each sum or difference.

21. $3 + 4\frac{1}{8}$ $7\frac{1}{8}$

22. $9\frac{8}{9} + 7\frac{4}{9}$ $17\frac{1}{3}$

23. $35\frac{1}{5} - 28\frac{7}{10}$ $6\frac{1}{2}$

24. Your sister is 10 years old and $54\frac{1}{3}$ inches tall. Her doctor says she will grow about $2\frac{1}{2}$ inches during the next year and about $2\frac{3}{4}$ inches the year after that. About how tall will your sister be when she is 12 years old? about $59\frac{7}{12}$ in.

4-6 Objectives

▼ To use mental math to solve equations with fractions

▼ To solve equations with fractions

You can use mental math or the properties of inverse operations to solve equations involving fractions or mixed numbers.

Solve each equation.

25. $\frac{5}{7} = p + \frac{2}{7}$ $\frac{3}{7}$

26. $q + \frac{5}{8} = \frac{3}{4}$ $\frac{1}{8}$

27. $\frac{2}{3} = t - \frac{4}{9}$ $1\frac{1}{9}$

28. $4\frac{2}{3} = x + 1\frac{1}{3}$ $3\frac{1}{3}$

29. $k - 2\frac{1}{6} = 8\frac{8}{9}$ $11\frac{1}{18}$

30. $13\frac{3}{5} + h = 20$ $6\frac{2}{5}$

4-7 Objectives

▼ To add and subtract measures of time

▼ To read and use schedules

The time between two events is called **elapsed time.** You may need to rewrite hours and minutes before you can add or subtract time.

Find the elapsed time between each pair of times.

31. from 8:15 A.M. to 11:56 A.M. 3 h 41 min

32. from 9:33 P.M. to 6:21 A.M. 8 h 48 min

33. You start doing things on your to-do list at 6:00 P.M. If you take a 25-minute break while doing homework, at what time will you complete your list? 8:10 P.M.

Eat dinner	40 min
Homework	55 min
Walk dog	10 min

4-8 Objective

▼ To solve problems by drawing a diagram

You can draw diagrams to make problems easier to understand and solve.

Solve each problem by drawing a diagram.

34. Hobbies Baseball cards are $2\frac{1}{2}$ inches by $3\frac{1}{2}$ inches. How many baseball cards fit on a bulletin board that is 45 inches long and 36 inches wide? 180 cards

35. You want a plant at each corner and every 2 feet along the border of a square patio. The patio is 12 feet long. How many plants do you need? 24 plants

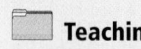 **Teaching Resources**
Ch. 4 Test, Forms A & B
Ch. 4 Alternative Assessment,
Form C

Reaching All Students
Spanish Ch. 4 Test, Forms A & B
Spanish Ch. 4 Alternative
Assessment, Form C

PRENTICE HALL
ASSESSMENT SYSTEM

Assessment Resources
• Ch. 4 Test, Forms A & B
• Ch. 4 Alternative Assessment,
Form C
Computer Test Generator CD
• Ch. 4 Instant Chapter Test™
• Make your own Ch. 4 test

 www.PHSchool.com
Student Site
• Self-grading Ch. 4 test

PH SuccessNet Teacher Center
• Resources

Plus

---

21. Answers may vary.

Sample: Rewrite $7\frac{4}{5}$ as

$7\frac{8}{10}$ and then add to $3\frac{1}{10}$

to get $10\frac{9}{10}$.

Chapter Test – Form B

Chapter Test – Form A

Chapter Test   Form A
Chapter 4

Choose a benchmark for each measurement. Use 0, ½, or 1.
1. ³⁄₈ ½   2. 12⅝ ½   3. 14⁄₁₇ 1   4. 1⁄₁₉ 0

Estimate each sum or difference. Round each mixed number to the
nearest whole number. Use the benchmarks 0, ½, and 1 to help.
5. 7⁄₁₃ + 8   6. 13⁄₁₄ − 7⁄₁₆
  1½   ½
7. 5⅓ + 6⅞   8. 6⅔ − 3¹⁰⁄₃₁
  12   3

Write each sum or difference in simplest form.
9. ⅛ + ⅜   10. 12⁄₂₅ + 6⁄₂₅
 ½   22⁄₂₅
11. ⅞ − ⅝   12. 9⁄₁₆ − 4⁄₃₂
 ¼   7⁄₁₆
13. ³⁄₅ + 7⁄₁₀   14. 8⁄₈ + ⅞
 9⁄₁₀   1⁷⁄₂₄
15. ⁵⁄₆ − 7⁄₁₂   16. 4⁶⁄₅ − ⅓
 5⁄₂₄   2⁷⁄₂₅

Write each sum or difference in simplest form.
17. 8⅞ + 5⁷⁄₁₂ 13¹¹⁄₁₂   18. 6⅝ − 2⅛ 4¹¹⁄₂₄

Solve.
19. John bought 1⅓ pounds of ground beef and 1⅓ pounds of ground pork to make tacos. How much ground meat did John buy? 2³⁹⁄₄₀ pounds of ground meat
20. A basketball hoop is 10¹⁄₄ feet high. Mark is 5¹¹⁄₁₂ feet tall. How far is it from the hoop to the top of Mark's head? 4⅓ ft

---

Chapter Test

 **Take It to the NET**
Online chapter test at
www.PHSchool.com
Web Code: aaa-0452

Estimate each sum or difference. Use the benchmarks 0, $\frac{1}{2}$, or 1.

1. $\frac{18}{35} + \frac{14}{16}$ $1\frac{1}{2}$ 2. $\frac{7}{50} + \frac{9}{16}$ $\frac{1}{2}$ 3. $\frac{9}{10} + \frac{2}{26}$ 1

4. How much did Sophia's hair grow during the month of May? $\frac{3}{16}$ in.

Sophia's Hair Length

May 1	$8\frac{1}{8}$ in.
May 31	$8\frac{5}{16}$ in.

Estimate each sum or difference.

5. $6\frac{5}{6} + 2\frac{1}{9}$ 9 6. $11\frac{6}{7} - 3\frac{7}{9}$ 8 7. $10\frac{5}{12} - 5\frac{1}{8}$ 5

8. **Lumber** You need $\frac{3}{8}$ foot of lumber to fix a fence and $\frac{3}{4}$ foot of lumber to fix a shed. How much lumber do you need? $1\frac{1}{8}$ ft

Find each sum or difference.

9. $\frac{4}{5} + \frac{2}{5}$ $1\frac{1}{5}$ 10. $\frac{11}{13} - \frac{7}{13}$ $\frac{4}{13}$ 11. $\frac{4}{7} + \frac{6}{7}$ $1\frac{3}{7}$

12. $1\frac{13}{15} - \frac{2}{3}$ $1\frac{1}{5}$ 13. $\frac{9}{20} + \frac{4}{5}$ $1\frac{1}{4}$ 14. $\frac{3}{4} - \frac{3}{8}$ $\frac{3}{8}$

15. $3\frac{3}{4} - 2\frac{8}{10}$ $\frac{19}{20}$ 16. $8\frac{1}{5} + 4\frac{1}{6}$ $12\frac{11}{30}$ 17. $5\frac{4}{9} + 7\frac{3}{5}$ $13\frac{2}{45}$

Find each sum.

18. $\frac{1}{7} + \frac{2}{7} + \frac{5}{7}$ $1\frac{1}{7}$ 19. $\frac{4}{12} + \frac{2}{12} + \frac{5}{12}$ $\frac{11}{12}$

20. Dan ran $\frac{5}{6}$ mile. Sol ran $\frac{7}{8}$ mile. $\frac{1}{24}$ mi
   a. How much farther did Sol run than Dan?
   b. What combined distance did they run? $1\frac{17}{24}$ mi

21. **Writing in Math** Explain how you could mentally solve the equation $x - 7\frac{4}{5} = 3\frac{1}{10}$.
   See margin.

Solve each equation.

22. $\frac{6}{9} = \frac{1}{3} + g$ $\frac{1}{3}$ 23. $y - \frac{4}{5} = \frac{11}{20}$ $1\frac{7}{20}$

24. $4\frac{3}{4} + v = 17\frac{1}{8}$ $12\frac{3}{8}$ 25. $13\frac{2}{3} = k - 10\frac{7}{9}$ $24\frac{4}{9}$

Use the table for Exercises 26–28.

Spruce Tree	Length of Cone (inches)
White	$1\frac{5}{8}$
Norway	$5\frac{1}{2}$
Black	$\frac{7}{8}$
Red	$1\frac{1}{4}$

26. Find the difference in length between the shortest and longest cones. $4\frac{5}{8}$ in.

27. **Estimation** Which two cones differ in length by about $\frac{1}{2}$ inch?   **White and Black**

28. What is the difference in length between the Red and White Spruce tree cones? $\frac{3}{8}$ in.

How many minutes are in each amount of time?

29. 5 h 47 min   347 min   30. 23 h 8 min   1,388 min

31. Find the elapsed time between 6:33 A.M. and 7:20 P.M.   12 h 47 min

32. **Trees** The roots of a tree reach $18\frac{1}{2}$ feet into the ground. A bird's nest is $6\frac{3}{4}$ feet from the top of the tree. The distance from the top of the tree to the bottom of the roots is 60 feet. How far above the ground is the bird's nest? $34\frac{3}{4}$ ft

33. **Business** A tailor buys $8\frac{1}{2}$ yards of fabric for a suit. After making a suit she has $1\frac{7}{8}$ yards left. How much fabric did she use to make the suit? $6\frac{5}{8}$ yd

---

Test Prep — Cumulative Review

12. [2] Methods may vary.
   $36 = 2^2 \times 3^2;$
   $45 = 3^2 \times 5;$
   LCM $= 2^2 \times 3^2 \times 5 = 180$

[1] incorrect LCM OR incorrect method

14. [4] a. 1 h, 4 p; 2 h, 5 p;
   3 h, 6 p; 4 h, 7 p; ...

   b. 3 h, 6 p: $3 \times 1.30 + 6 \times 0.35 = 6$;
   3 hardbacks and 6 paperbacks

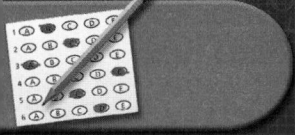

Test Prep

Multiple Choice

For Exercises 1–9, choose the correct letter.

1. On Venus the length of a day is 243.01 Earth days. On Mercury the length of a day is 58.65 Earth days. How much longer, in Earth days, is a Venus day than a Mercury day? **D**
   A. 301.66   B. 215.64
   C. 195.46   D. 184.36

2. Suppose you buy a shirt for x dollars with a twenty-dollar bill. The cashier gives you $5.35 back. Which equation can you use to find the cost of the shirt? **G**
   F. $5.35x = 20$ G. $x + 5.35 = 20$
   H. $x \div 20 = 5.35$ I. $5.35 - x = 20$

3. How much thicker is a quarter than a dime?
   C
    $1\frac{3}{4}$ mm

   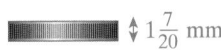 $1\frac{7}{20}$ mm

   A. $\frac{1}{20}$ mm   B. $\frac{1}{4}$ mm   C. $\frac{2}{5}$ mm   D. $\frac{1}{2}$ mm

4. Which equation is NOT an example of the Distributive Property? **I**
   F. $12(6.2) + 12(3.8) = 12(6.2 + 3.8)$
   G. $0.75(8.869) + 0.25(8.869) = 1(8.869)$
   H. $19.1(80) = 19.1(100) - 19.1(20)$
   I. $8.1 + 3.5 = 3.5 + 8.1$

5. Which set of numbers has a GCF of 3? **C**
   A. 15, 30, 45   B. 6, 30, 24
   C. 24, 36, 9   D. 36, 27, 18

6. Which number is divisible by 9? **G**
   F. 213,645   G. 31,392
   H. 285,137   I. 42,901

7. What is the best estimate for the sum of $12\frac{13}{16}$ and $23\frac{3}{8}$? **C**
   A. 30   B. 35   C. 36   D. 37

8. A store sells window glass that is $\frac{1}{8}$ inch, $\frac{3}{16}$ inch, $\frac{5}{16}$ inch, and $\frac{7}{32}$ inch thick. You need glass that is at least $\frac{1}{4}$ inch thick. **H** Which thickness, in inches, should you buy?
   F. $\frac{1}{8}$ G. $\frac{3}{16}$ H. $\frac{5}{16}$ I. $\frac{7}{32}$

9. What is the sum of $6\frac{3}{5}$ and $2\frac{4}{5}$? **C**
   A. $8\frac{1}{5}$ B. $8\frac{12}{25}$ C. $9\frac{2}{5}$ D. $9\frac{4}{5}$

Gridded Response

10. Kerry boards the school bus at 7:48 A.M. and arrives at school at 8:13 A.M. How many minutes does he spend on the bus? **25**

11. What is the solution of $x + \frac{3}{16} = \frac{3}{4}$? Write your answer in simplest form. $\frac{9}{16}$

Short Response

12. What is the least common multiple of 36 and 45? Choose a method of either listing multiples or using prime factorizations. Show the steps you use to find this LCM. See margin.

13. From his home, a jogger ran 1 mile west, $3\frac{1}{2}$ miles north, 1 mile east, and $1\frac{1}{4}$ miles south. How far from home is he? (a) Draw a diagram to help solve the problem. (b) Solve the problem. See margin.

Extended Response

14. At a book fair, a paperback sells for $.35 and a hardcover sells for $1.30. Your friend spends $6.00 on books. She buys three more paperbacks than hardcovers. See margin.
    a. Write a list of possibilities for the number of books. Begin with one hardcover.
    b. How many paperbacks does your friend buy?

13. [2] Strategies may vary. Draw a diagram.
    a.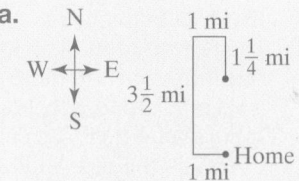
    N / W←→E / S ; 1 mi ; $1\frac{1}{4}$ mi ; $3\frac{1}{2}$ mi ; Home ; 1 mi

    b. $3\frac{1}{2} - 1\frac{1}{4} = 2\frac{1}{4}$
    $2\frac{1}{4}$ mi

    [1] incorrect distance OR incorrect method

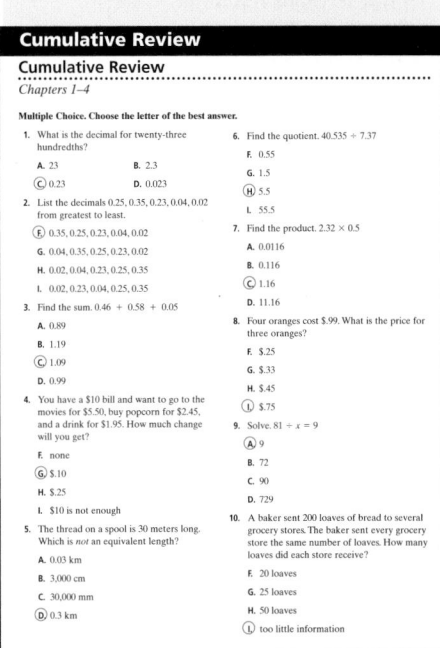

[3] appropriate methods, but with one computational error   [2] list of book combinations OR work shown for 3 h and 6 p   [1] correct book combination, without work shown

Item	1	2	3	4	5	6	7	8	9	10	11	12	13	14
Lesson	1-5	2-6	4-5	2-9	3-3	3-1	4-1	3-7	4-4	4-7	4-6	3-6	4-8	3-9

Fast Fractions

Students will use data from these two pages to answer the questions posed here in Put It All Together.

Activating Prior Knowledge

Have students share any experiences they have had watching any of the races described on these pages. Ask them to discuss what the events have in common and how they differ.

Teaching Notes

Have students read aloud the data about Marion Jones, the Iditarod, Catherine Raney, and the Tour de France. Ask students to explain how they could find the average speed that Raney skates. Sample: Divide the distance Raney skates by her time. Convert distance and time into miles and hours.

History Connection

The history of Alaska's Iditarod race from Anchorage to Nome is an interesting one. Invite some students to learn about the origins of the race and how it has developed into the modern race. Have students share their findings.

Physical Education Connection

Tell students that winning Olympic times in races have been getting faster over the years. Have students find and compare winning times for several races over a number of years. Challenge students to examine the data to determine which times—men's or women's—have been improving at a faster rate. Have students or small groups study different races. One way to display data is to make a double line graph to compare the changes in winning times over the years. Have groups share and compare findings.

Fast Fractions

Applying Mixed Numbers People love to race. Some races, like the Iditarod, the Tour de France, and the Paris–Dakar Rally, last days or even weeks. Other races can be over in a flash. The fastest runners can finish a 100-meter race in 10 or 11 seconds.

The Iditarod
The Iditarod is a dog sled race over at least 1,049 miles in Alaska. The fastest sled drivers, or mushers, finish in about 10 days.

Marion Jones
Marion Jones won three gold medals and two bronze medals at the 2000 Olympic Summer Games in Sydney, Australia.

Put It All Together

What You'll Need

- 3 number cubes

How to Play

- Work in a group. The goal of the game is to "run" each of four quarter-mile sections of a one-mile track.
- Roll three number cubes. Write a mixed number that includes a proper fraction. If all three numbers are the same, roll again.
- Take turns until each group member has times for each quarter-mile section of the track.
- If you roll the same three numbers more than once, you must make a different mixed number with them each time. If that is not possible, roll again.

1. Order your times from least to greatest.

2. **a. Estimation** Estimate the total time for each group member. Who do you think has the fastest time? Explain.
   b. Find your total time. Write your answer in simplest form.
   c. Compare your total to the totals for the others in your group. Who won the race?

3. **Number Sense** The record time for "running" this track is 4.95 minutes. Is it possible to beat this time? Explain.

4. **Data File** Pick one of the animals from page 169. How long would it take the animal to "run" the track? Who runs faster, you or the animal? Explain.

1. Check students' work.

2. Check students' work.

3. No; your fastest possible time is $1\frac{1}{6} + 1\frac{1}{5} + 1\frac{1}{4} + 1\frac{1}{3}$, which is $4\frac{19}{20}$, or 4.95 min.

4. Answers may vary. Sample: A black mamba snake can run the track in 3 min. The snake runs faster, because you would take at least 4.95 min.

Take It to the NET For more information about racing, go to **www.PHSchool.com**.

Web Code: aae-0453

Speed Skater

Catherine Raney of the 2002 U.S. Olympic team skated between 20 and 25 miles per hour during the women's 5,000-meter final.

Tour de France

The Tour de France bicycle race lasts about three weeks and covers about 2,000 miles.

Put It All Together

Have students work in groups to play the game and then answer the questions.

Inclusion

Help students understand the rules of the game. Review the meanings of a *mixed number* and an *improper fraction*. Also review how to compare and order fractions and mixed numbers.

Teaching Tip

Invite students to formulate and try out their own new versions of the game. Invite them to share their adjustments with other groups. Possibilities include:

- Have students compete for the greatest total.
- Have players wait until they have four sets of three digits before forming the mixed numbers. Have them form mixed numbers to make the *least* total. Ask students to explain how this change affects the strategy they use to win.

215

CHAPTER 5 Multiplying and Dividing Fractions

Chapter at a Glance

5-1 Multiplying Fractions
pp. 219–223

Objectives
1. Multiplying Two Fractions
2. Multiplying Fractions by Whole Numbers

NCTM Standards
1, 3, 4, 6, 7, 8, 9, 10

Local Standards

5-2 Multiplying Mixed Numbers
pp. 224–228

Objectives
1. Estimating Products of Mixed Numbers
2. Multiplying Mixed Numbers

NCTM Standards
1, 3, 4, 6, 7, 8, 9, 10

Local Standards

5-3 Dividing Fractions
pp. 230–234

Objectives
1. Dividing Whole Numbers by Fractions
2. Dividing Fractions by Fractions

New Vocabulary
reciprocal

NCTM Standards
1, 3, 4, 6, 7, 8, 9, 10

Local Standards

5-4 Dividing Mixed Numbers
pp. 236–240

Objectives
1. Estimating Quotients of Mixed Numbers
2. Dividing Mixed Numbers

NCTM Standards
1, 3, 4, 6, 7, 8, 9, 10

Local Standards

✓ Checkpoint Quiz 1

5-5 Algebra — Solving Fraction Equations by Multiplying
pp. 242–245

Objectives
1. Solving Fraction Equations

NCTM Standards
1, 2, 6, 7, 8, 9, 10

Local Standards

5-6 Problem Solving — Solving a Simpler Problem
pp. 246–249

Objectives
1. Solving a Simpler Problem

NCTM Standards
1, 3, 6, 7, 8, 9, 10

Local Standards

5-7 The Customary System
pp. 250–253

Objectives
1. Choosing Appropriate Units of Measurement

NCTM Standards
1, 4, 6, 7, 8, 9, 10

Local Standards

✓ Checkpoint Quiz 2

5-8 Changing Units in the Customary System
pp. 254–257

Objectives
1. Changing Units of Measurement
2. Computing with Units

NCTM Standards
1, 3, 4, 5, 6, 7, 8, 9, 10

Local Standards

Reaching All Students
Additional Instructional Options in Chapter 5

Reading and Math Literacy

📖 Reading Math

Reading Expressions, p. 258

Reading Math hints, pp. 221, 230

Reading Comprehension, p. 263

✎ Writing in Math

Writing to Explain, p. 235

Daily Writing Practice, pp. 222, 227, 233, 239, 244, 248, 252, 256, 262

Above Level

🅒 Challenge exercises

pp. 223, 227, 234, 239, 245, 249, 253, 257

Hands-On and Technology

🔍 Investigations

Modeling Multiplication of Fractions, p. 219

Fraction Division, p. 229

Solving Equations Mentally, p. 242

Customary Units, p. 252

💻 Technology

Using a Calculator for Fractions, p. 241

Activities and Projects

🄳🄺 Real-World Snapshots

Applying Fractions pp. 264–265

📁 Chapter Project

Crack It and Cook It!, p. 638

Test Prep

✅ Daily Test Prep

pp. 223, 228, 234, 240, 245, 249, 253, 257

✅ Test-Taking Strategies

Eliminating Answers, p. 259

✅ Test Prep

Reading Comprehension, p. 263

Chapter Assessment

✔️ Checkpoint Quiz

pp. 240, 253

⬤ Chapter Review

pp. 260–261

⬤ Chapter Test

p. 262

Pacing Options

This chart suggests pacing only for the core lessons and their parts. It is provided as a possible guide. It will help you determine how much time you have in your schedule to cover the additional features and assessment, as described at the left.

Day	Traditional 45-minute class periods	Block 90-minute class periods
1	5-1 ▽	5-1 ▽ ▽
2	5-1 ▽	5-2 ▽ ▽
3	5-2 ▽	5-3 ▽ ▽
4	5-2 ▽	5-4 ▽ ▽
5	5-3 ▽	5-5 ▽
6	5-3 ▽	5-6 ▽
		5-7 ▽
7	5-4 ▽	5-8 ▽ ▽
8	5-4 ▽	
9	5-5 ▽	
10	5-6 ▽	
11	5-7 ▽	
12	5-8 ▽	
13	5-8 ▽	

NCTM STANDARDS 2000

1 Number and Operations	6 Problem Solving
2 Algebra	7 Reasoning and Proof
3 Geometry	8 Communication
4 Measurement	9 Connections
5 Data Analysis and Probability	10 Representation

Math Background

Skills Trace

BEFORE Chapter 5

Grade 5 presented multiplication and division of fractions.

▼

DURING Chapter 5

Course 1 reviews and extends multiplying and dividing fractions to mixed numbers and the solving of equations with fractions.

▼

AFTER Chapter 5

Throughout this course students multiply and divide fractions to solve real-world problems.

5-1 Multiplying Fractions

Math Understandings

- Finding half of a number is the same as multiplying that number by $\frac{1}{2}$ and as dividing that number by 2.
- The product of two fractions, each less than one, is less than either factor.

You can find the product of two fractions by multiplying the numerators and multiplying the denominators.

Multiplying Fractions	
Arithmetic	**Algebra**
$\frac{3}{4} \times \frac{1}{2} = \frac{3 \times 1}{4 \times 2} = \frac{3}{8}$	$\frac{a}{b} \times \frac{c}{d} = \frac{ac}{bd}$ where b and $d \neq 0$.

Sometimes you can simplify before multiplying fractions by dividing out factors common to both numerator and denominator. To multiply a fraction by a whole number, write the whole number as a fraction with a denominator of 1. Then multiply the two fractions.

Example: Find $\frac{5}{6} \times 12$.

$$\frac{5}{6} \times 12 = \frac{5}{\underset{1}{6}} \times \frac{\overset{2}{12}}{1} = \frac{10}{1} = 10$$

5-2 Multiplying Mixed Numbers

Math Understandings

- Multiplying fractions and mixed numbers does not necessarily give a product less than both factors.

To find the product of mixed numbers, write each mixed number as an improper fraction before multiplying.

Example: Find $2\frac{2}{3} \times 3\frac{1}{4}$.

$$2\frac{2}{3} \times 3\frac{1}{4} = \frac{\overset{2}{8}}{3} \times \frac{13}{\underset{1}{4}} = \frac{2 \times 13}{3 \times 1} = \frac{26}{3}, \text{ or } 8\frac{2}{3}$$

5-3 5-4 Dividing Fractions Dividing Mixed Numbers

Math Understandings

- You can rewrite dividing by a number as multiplying by the reciprocal of that number.
- Two numbers are reciprocals if their product is 1.

The numbers $\frac{2}{3}$ and $\frac{3}{2}$ are **reciprocals.** Notice that the numerators and denominators are switched in fractions that are reciprocals. To divide by a fraction, multiply by the reciprocal of the fraction. You can remember this by thinking "invert and multiply."

Dividing Fractions	
Arithmetic	**Algebra**
$\frac{5}{8} \div \frac{1}{8} = \frac{5}{8} \times \frac{8}{1}$	$\frac{a}{b} \div \frac{c}{d} = \frac{a}{b} \times \frac{d}{c}$ where b, c, and $d \neq 0$.

To divide a fraction by a whole number, first write the whole number as an improper fraction with a denominator of 1. You can divide a mixed number by a whole number or another mixed number. Start by writing the numbers as improper fractions.

Example: Find $2\frac{1}{4} \div 3$.

$$2\frac{1}{4} \div 3 = \frac{9}{4} \div \frac{3}{1} = \frac{\overset{3}{9}}{4} \times \frac{1}{\underset{1}{3}} = \frac{3}{4}$$

5-5 Solving Fraction Equations by Multiplying

Math Understandings
- You can use the Multiplication Property of Equality to multiply each side of an equation by the same number to write an equivalent simpler equation.

Multiplication and division are inverse operations that undo each other.

5-6 Solve a Simpler Problem

You can use simpler numbers to help you develop a plan for solving a difficult problem.

5-7 The Customary System

Math Understandings
- Unlike the metric system, the customary system does not use a base unit and prefixes.

Common customary units of measure with abbreviations follow.

Length	Weight	Capacity
inch (in.)	ounce (oz)	fluid ounce (fl oz)
foot (ft)	pound (lb)	cup (c)
yard (yd)	ton (t)	pint (pt)
mile (mi)		quart (qt)
		gallon (gal)

Example: Choose an appropriate customary unit of measure for each situation.
- weight of a bicycle   pounds
- length of a shoe   inches
- capacity of a bathtub   gallons

5-8 Changing Units in the Customary System

Math Understandings
- To change between customary units, use multiplication or division of equivalent measures.

You can convert between different customary units by using equivalent measures.

Length	Weight	Capacity
12 in. = 1 ft	16 oz = 1 lb	8 fl oz = 1 cup
36 in. = 1 yd	2,000 lb = 1 t	2 cups = 1 pt
3 ft = 1 yd		4 cups = 1 qt
5,280 ft = 1 mi		2 pt = 1 qt
		4 qt = 1 gal

The following rules can help you convert from one unit to another.

Start with	Convert	Get
Many small units $\rightarrow$	Divide $\rightarrow$	A few large units
A few large units $\rightarrow$	Multiply $\rightarrow$	Many small units

Example: Find the number of gallons in 13 quarts.

$$13 \text{ qt} = (13 \div 4) \text{ gal} \rightarrow 3\frac{1}{4} \text{ gal}$$

Additional Professional Development Opportunities

Chapter 5 Math Background notes: pp. 220, 225, 237, 243, 247, 251, 255

Additional resources available from SkyLight Professional Development:

On-site courses, workshops, summer institutes. Online courses and chat rooms. Videocassettes and books. Visit www.skylightedu.com.

 # Ongoing Assessment and Intervention

The *Prentice Hall Mathematics* program provides many options for assessment in the Student Edition, Teacher's Edition, and teaching resources. From these options you may choose instructional materials that are appropriate for your students and that support your district's curriculum requirements.

Daily Assessment

 ### Instant Check System™ in Chapter 5

Allows students to check their own learning before, during, and after each lesson.

Diagnosing Readiness before the chapter (p. 218)

Check Skills You'll Need exercises in each lesson (pp. 219, 224, 230, 236, 242, 246, 250, 254)

Check Understanding questions with each Example (pp. 220, 221, 224, 225, 230, 231, 232, 236, 237, 242, 243, 247, 251, 254, 255)

Checkpoint Quiz (pp. 240, 253)

Formal Assessment

Assessment in the Student Text and in Additional Resources

Assess student progress throughout the Course 1 textbook and with blackline masters and CD-ROM.

Student Edition
- Chapter 5 Review, with Vocabulary, Skills, and Concepts Review, pp. 260–261
- Chapter 5 Test, p. 262

Assessment Resources
- Checkpoint Quizzes 1 & 2
- Chapter Test, forms A & B
- Chapter Alternative Assessment
Spanish versions available.

 ### Computer Test Generator CD-ROM
- Instant Chapter Tests™—pre-made tests with items that vary every time you print.
- Online Testing allows you to give tests online and receive progress reports.
- Prepare students by making tests based on standardized test objectives.

Algebra Readiness Tests
- Includes Basic Skills Tests and Concept-Readiness Tests.
- Assess understanding of skills and concepts needed for success in algebra.

Intervention

 ### Skills Intervention Kit

 **Online Intervention**
Integrated within the iText, this online intervention system includes diagnostic tests and prescribed remediation, plus reports to track student mastery.

A *complete* system for the student who is struggling with course-level work

Eight intervention units cover core skills and allow you to:
- **Diagnose** students' gaps in basic skills
- **Prescribe** an individualized course of study
- **Monitor** student progress

Includes print workbooks, tutorial CD-ROM, teacher editions, progress folders, and more. *Available in Spanish.*

How to Use with Chapter 5

5-1   Operations with Fractions, Skills 10–11
5-2   Operations with Fractions, Skills 9, 12
5-3   Operations with Fractions, Skills 15–16
5-4   Operations with Fractions, Skills 14, 18
5-8   Measurement, Skill 3

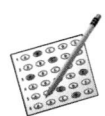

Standardized Test Preparation

The *Prentice Hall Mathematics* program integrates preparation for high-stakes standardized tests in every lesson of the Student Edition and continues this support in the Prentice Hall Assessment System.

Test Prep

In Student Text, Chapter 5

Teaches students strategies and gives them practice with all the test item formats they will encounter on high-stakes tests.

Test Prep exercises in each lesson (pp. 223, 228, 234, 240, 245, 249, 253, 257)

Test-Taking Strategies Eliminating Answers, p. 259

Test Prep Reading Comprehension, p. 263

A three-step approach to preparing students for high stakes, national, and state exams.

1 Diagnose & Prescribe

Content Diagnostic Tests
- Diagnose strengths and weaknesses with ongoing benchmark tests.
- Prescribe individualized reteaching opportunities.

2 Review & Reteach

Skills and Concepts Review
- Provides reteaching worksheets with instruction and practice for each skill.
- Includes course prerequisite skills.

3 Practice & Assess

Standardized Test Preparation
- Features practice for national standardized exams.
- Includes practice tests for NAEP, SAT10, ITBS, and Terra Nova.

Test-Taking Strategies with Transparencies
- Support the Test-Taking Strategies pages in the Student Edition.
- Provide a transparency and a worksheet for each strategy.

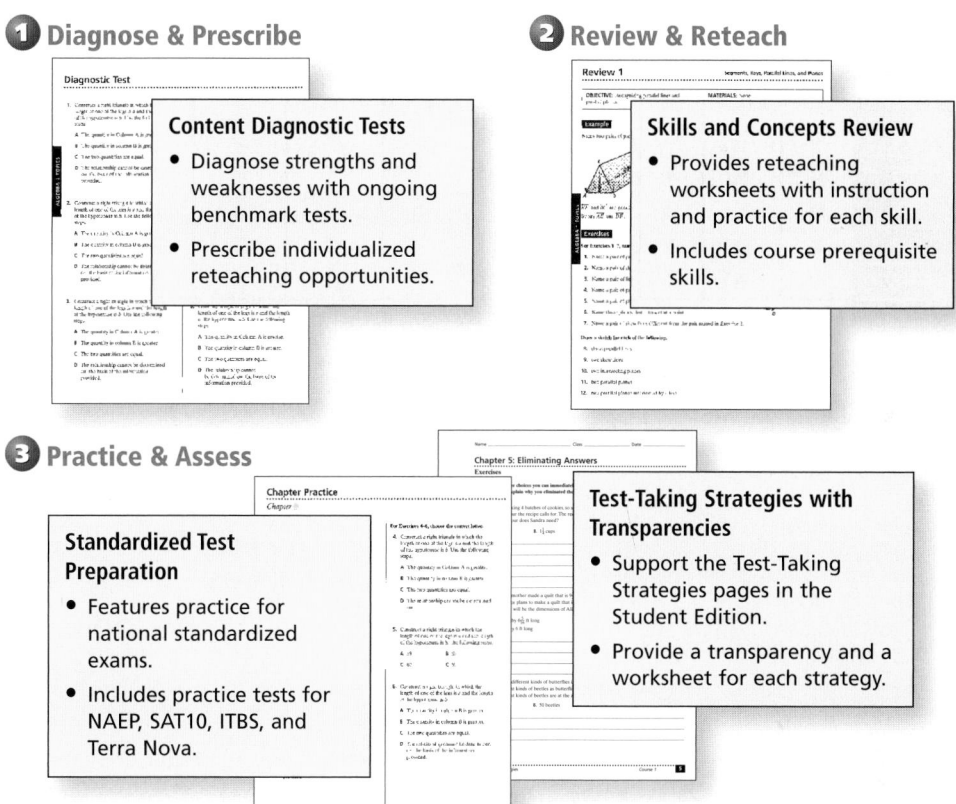

Correlation to Standardized Tests

Lesson		NAEP	Terra Nova		ITBS	SAT10	Local Test
			CAT6	CTBS			
5-1	Multiplying Fractions	N3a	■	■	■	■	
5-2	Multiplying Mixed Numbers	N3a	■	■		■	
5-3	Dividing Fractions	N3a		■	■		
5-4	Dividing Mixed Numbers	N3a		■			
5-5	Solving Fraction Equations by Multiplying	A4c					
5-6	Problem Solving: Solve a Simpler Problem						
5-7	The Customary System	M2a	■	■		■	
5-8	Changing Units in the Customary System	M2b	■				

NAEP National Assessment of Educational Progress
CAT6/Terra Nova California Achievement Test, 6th Ed.
CTBS/Terra Nova Comprehensive Test of Basic Skills
ITBS Iowa Test of Basic Skills, Form M.
SAT10 Stanford Achievement Test, 10th Ed.

Program Resources

	Resources in Grab & Go™ Files				Resources for Reaching All Students				Spanish Resources			Transparencies					Presentation Assistant Plus!
	Practice	Reteach	Enrich	Checkpt Quiz	Reading & Math Literacy	Technology Activities	Hands-On Activities	Guided Problem Solving	Practice	Reading & Math Literacy	Checkpt Quiz	Skills Check	Problem of the Day	Additional Examples	Answers to Exercises	Lesson Quiz	Prentice Hall Presentation Pro CD-ROM
5-1	■	■	■		■		■	■	■			■	■	■	■	■	■
5-2	■	■	■				■	■	■			■	■	■	■	■	■
5-3	■	■	■			■	■	■	■			■	■	■	■	■	■
5-4	■	■	■	■	■		■	■	■		■	■	■	■	■	■	■
5-5	■	■	■				■	■	■			■	■	■	■	■	■
5-6	■	■	■				■	■	■			■	■	■	■	■	■
5-7	■	■	■	■	■		■	■	■	■		■	■	■	■	■	■
5-8	■	■	■					■	■								
For the Chapter	Chapter Projects, Chapter Tests, Alternative Assessment, Cumulative Review, Cumulative Assessment				**On web site only:** Home Activities, Interdisciplinary Activities, Algebra Readiness Puzzles				Spanish Chapter Tests, Alternative Assessment, Cumulative Review, Cumulative Assessment			Classroom Aid Transparencies					

Also available for use with the chapter:

 *See page 216F.*

- Practice Workbook
- Solution Key
- MathNotes folder

- For teacher support and access to student Web materials, use the Web Code aak-5500.
- For additional online and technology resources, *see below.*

Technology

iTEXT Online and on CD-ROM

Complete Interactive Student Text online and on CD-ROM—with instant feedback assessment, tutorial help, dynamic activities, instructional and real-world videos, audio, and additional practice.

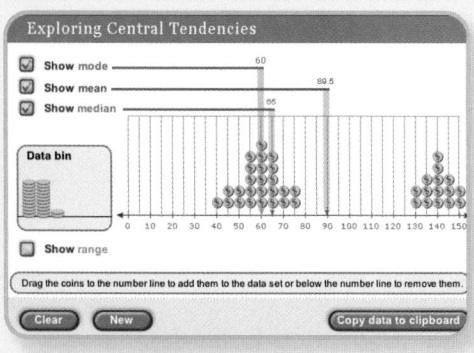

www.PHSchool.com For Students

Use Web codes for easy access to online activities, chapter projects, self-grading lesson quizzes, chapter tests, vocabulary quizzes, updated data sources, graphing calculator procedures, and more.

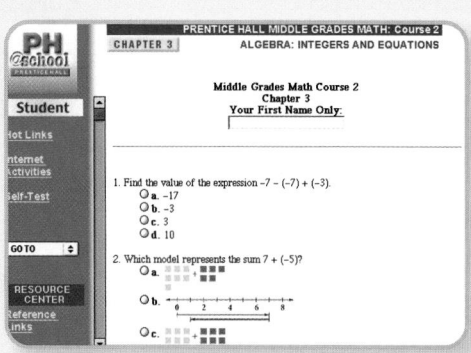

PH SuccessNet For Teachers

Online lesson planning with built-in state correlations, all the teaching resources, complete reference library, your own calendar and Teacher Web page, professional development, and more.

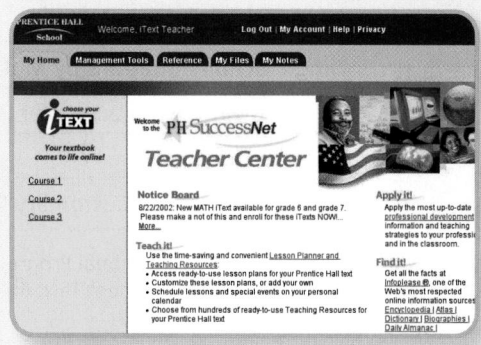

Presentation Assistant Plus!

The *Prentice Hall Presentation Assistant Plus!* provides you with the material you need to teach a lesson from beginning to end. Two easy-to-use formats—Transparencies and PowerPoint®—allow you to present a lesson the way you are most comfortable.

Transparencies

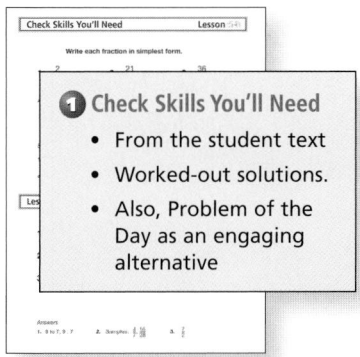

1 Check Skills You'll Need
- From the student text
- Worked-out solutions.
- Also, Problem of the Day as an engaging alternative

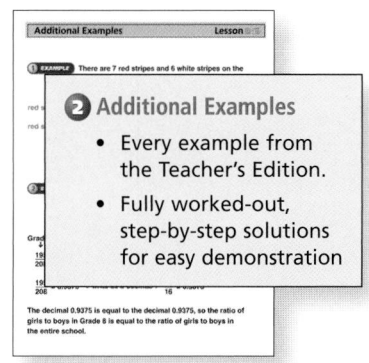

2 Additional Examples
- Every example from the Teacher's Edition.
- Fully worked-out, step-by-step solutions for easy demonstration

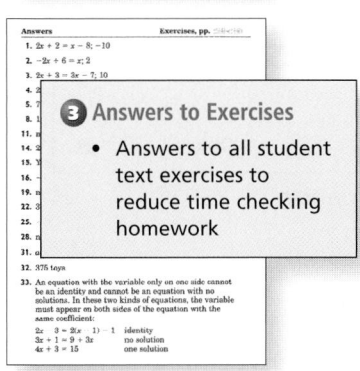

3 Answers to Exercises
- Answers to all student text exercises to reduce time checking homework

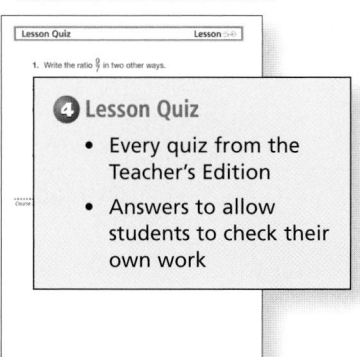

4 Lesson Quiz
- Every quiz from the Teacher's Edition
- Answers to allow students to check their own work

 Throughout the Teacher's Edition, this symbol indicates material that is available in the Presentation Assistant Plus!

PowerPoint Prentice Hall Presentation Pro CD-ROM

- Includes all Transparencies.
- Conveniently organized by lesson so you can easily **1** Introduce, **2** Teach, **3** Check Homework, and **4** Assess each lesson.
- Animated examples allow step-by-step instruction at your own pace.
- Easy to edit so you can create custom presentations.

Teaching Chapter 5 Using Presentation Assistant Plus!

	1 Introduce Check Skills You'll Need	**2 Teach** Additional Examples	**3 Check Homework** Student Edition Answers	**4 Assess** Lesson Quiz
5-1	p. 38	pp. 61–62	✔	p. 38
5-2	p. 39	pp. 63–64	✔	p. 39
5-3	p. 40	pp. 65–66	✔	p. 40
5-4	p. 41	pp. 67–68	✔	p. 41
5-5	p. 42	pp. 69–70	✔	p. 42
5-6	p. 43	pp. 71–72	✔	p. 44
5-7	p. 45	p. 73	✔	p. 45
5-8	p. 46	pp. 74–75	✔	p. 46

Prentice Hall Presentation Pro

CD-ROM with dynamic PowerPoint® presentations for every lesson. Helps you introduce and develop concepts, check homework, and assess progress. Part of Presentation Assistant Plus! *(See above.)*

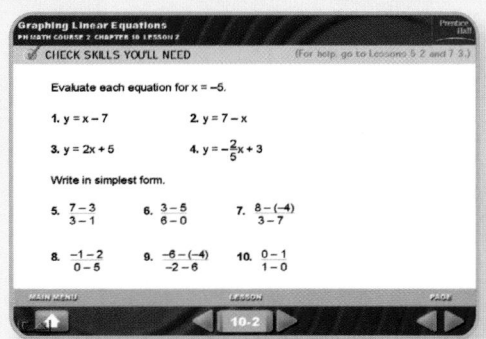

Computer Test Generator

CD-ROM to create practice sheets and tests for course objectives and standardized tests. Includes Instant Chapter Tests™, online testing, and student reports. Part of the PH Assessment System. *(See page 216F.)*

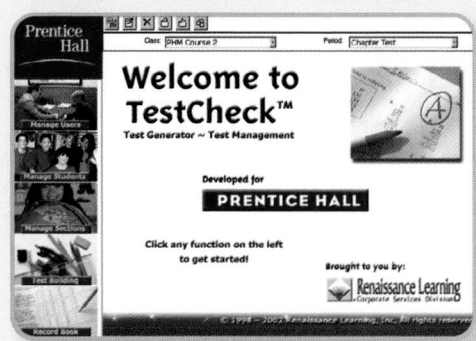

Resource Pro® with Planning Express®

CD-ROM with a lesson planning tool that allows you to import state and local objectives. Includes electronic versions of all the teaching resources.

Chapter Resources

Reading and Math Support

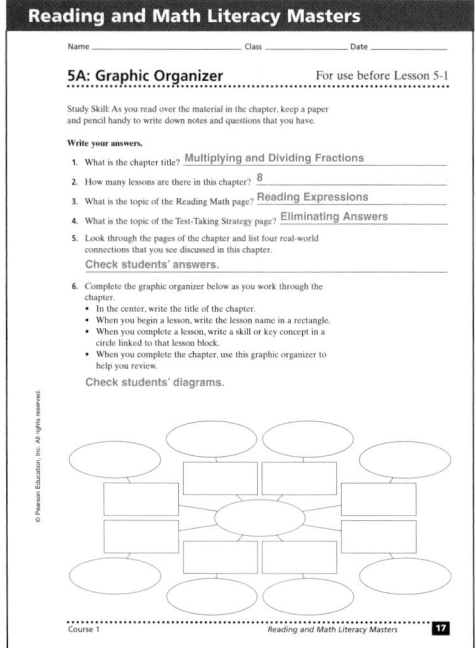

Available in Spanish

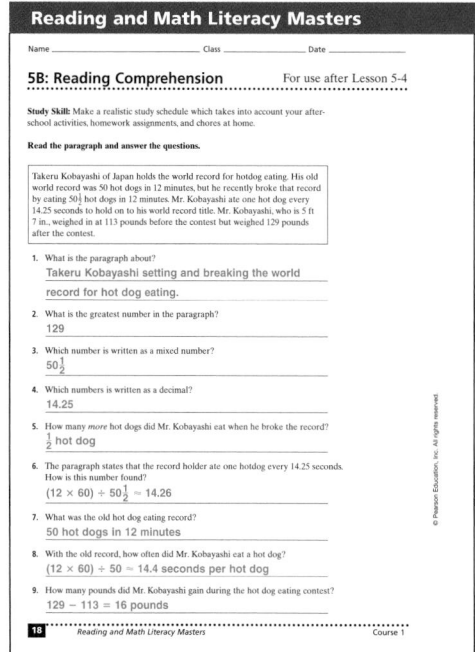

Available in Spanish

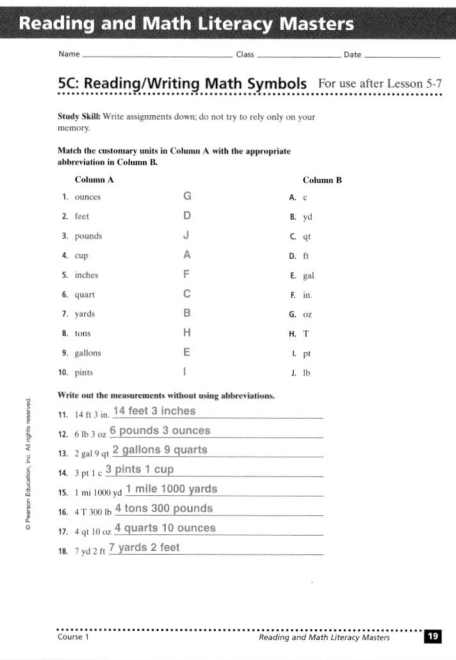

Available in Spanish

Problem Solving

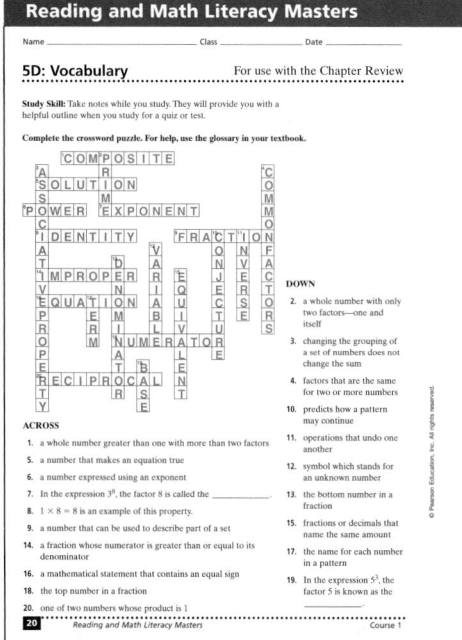

Available in Spanish

Guided Problem Solving Masters

Name _____ Class _____ Date _____

5-1 • Guided Problem Solving

GPS **Student Page 222, Exercise 36:**

Monuments The length of a side at the base of the Washington Monument is about $\frac{1}{10}$ of its height. The monument is about 555 feet tall. Find the length of a side at the base.

Read and Understand

1. What are you being asked to do?
   Find the length of a side at the base.

2. Which word group tells you what operation to perform?
   The words "$\frac{1}{10}$ of its height" tell you to multiply.

Plan and Solve

3. When multiplying a fraction by a whole number how do you rewrite the whole number?
   Write it as a fraction with a denominator of 1.

4. Write an expression to solve the problem. $\frac{1}{10} \times \frac{555}{1}$

5. Simplify the expression. $\frac{1}{(5 \cdot 2)} \times \frac{(5 \cdot 111)}{1} = \frac{1}{2} \times \frac{111}{1}$

6. Multiply the numerators, multiply the denominators, and simplify. $\frac{111}{2} = 55\frac{1}{2}$

7. What is the length of a side at the base of the monument? 55.5 feet

Look Back and Check

8. To estimate $\frac{1}{10}$ of 555, use compatible numbers. Find $\frac{1}{10}$ of 600. Is your answer reasonable?
   60; yes

Solve Another Problem

9. A concert hall has 12,360 seats. For the last concert, only $\frac{1}{3}$ of the hall was full. How many seats were unused?
   4,120 seats

Course 1   Guided Problem Solving   **37**

Guided Problem Solving Masters

Name _____ Class _____ Date _____

5-2 • Guided Problem Solving

GPS **Student Page 227, Exercise 18a:**

A mother is $1\frac{3}{8}$ times as tall as her daughter. The girl is $1\frac{1}{3}$ times as tall as her brother. The mother is how many times as tall as her son?

Read and Understand

1. What are you being asked to do?
   Find how many times taller the mother is than her son.

2. What do you do first when you multiply mixed numbers?
   Rewrite each number as an improper fraction.

Plan and Solve

3. Write an equation for the sentence "A mother is $1\frac{3}{8}$ times as tall as her daughter," where m represents the height of the mother and d represents the height of the daughter.
   $m = 1\frac{3}{8}d$

4. Write an equation for the sentence "The girl is $1\frac{1}{3}$ times as tall as her brother," where d represents the height of the girl and b represents the height of the brother.
   $d = 1\frac{1}{3}b$

5. Substitute the expression for d from Step 4 for d in the equation you wrote in Step 3. $m = (1\frac{3}{8})(1\frac{1}{3})b$

6. Simplify by multiplying the two mixed numbers. $m = (\frac{11}{8})(\frac{4}{3})b = 1\frac{5}{6}b$

7. The mother is how many time as tall as her son? $1\frac{5}{6}$

Look Back and Check

8. Divide $1\frac{5}{6}$ by either $1\frac{1}{3}$ or $1\frac{3}{8}$.
   $1\frac{5}{6} \div 1\frac{3}{8} = 1\frac{1}{3}; 1\frac{5}{6} \div 1\frac{1}{3} = 1\frac{3}{8}$

Solve Another Problem

9. Nora is building a birdhouse. The height of the birdhouse is $2\frac{1}{2}$ times the length of the birdhouse. If the length is $8\frac{2}{3}$ in. how tall is the birdhouse?
   $8\frac{2}{3} \times 2\frac{1}{2}$ or $21\frac{2}{3}$ in.

38   Guided Problem Solving   Course 1

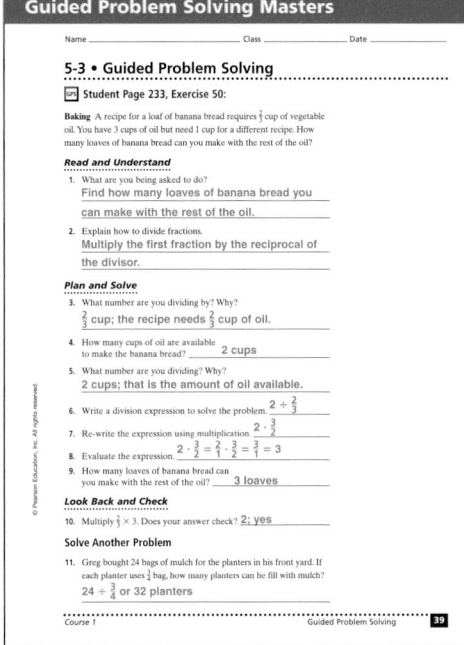

Guided Problem Solving Masters

Name _____ Class _____ Date _____

5-3 • Guided Problem Solving

GPS Student Page 233, Exercise 50:

Baking A recipe for a loaf of banana bread requires $\frac{2}{3}$ cup of vegetable oil. You have 3 cups of oil but need 1 cup for a different recipe. How many loaves of banana bread can you make with the rest of the oil?

Read and Understand

1. What are you being asked to do?
   Find how many loaves of banana bread you
   can make with the rest of the oil.

2. Explain how to divide fractions.
   Multiply the first fraction by the reciprocal of
   the divisor.

Plan and Solve

3. What number are you dividing by? Why?
   $\frac{2}{3}$ cup; the recipe needs $\frac{2}{3}$ cup of oil.

4. How many cups of oil are available
   to make the banana bread? 2 cups

5. What number are you dividing? Why?
   2 cups; that is the amount of oil available.

6. Write a division expression to solve the problem. $2 \div \frac{2}{3}$

7. Re-write the expression using multiplication. $2 \cdot \frac{3}{2}$

8. Evaluate the expression. $2 \cdot \frac{3}{2} = \frac{2}{1} \cdot \frac{3}{2} = 3$

9. How many loaves of banana bread can
   you make with the rest of the oil? 3 loaves

Look Back and Check

10. Multiply $\frac{2}{3} \times 3$. Does your answer check? 2; yes

Solve Another Problem

11. Greg bought 24 bags of mulch for the planters in his front yard. If
   each planter uses $\frac{3}{4}$ bag, how many planters can be fill with mulch?
   $24 \div \frac{3}{4}$ or 32 planters

Course 1   Guided Problem Solving   **39**

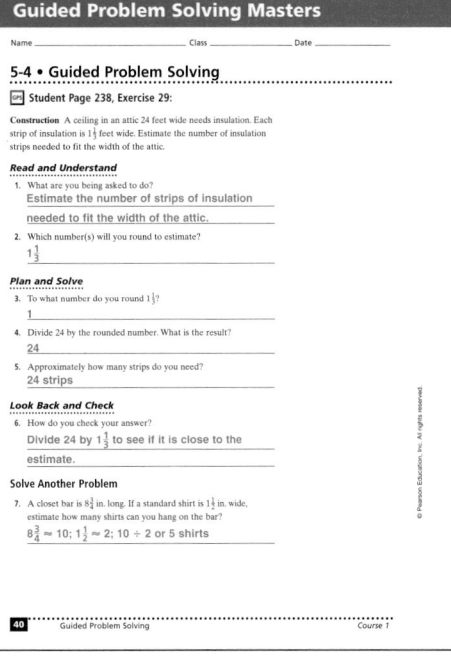

Guided Problem Solving Masters

Name _____ Class _____ Date _____

5-4 • Guided Problem Solving

GPS Student Page 238, Exercise 29:

Construction A ceiling in an attic 24 feet wide needs insulation. Each strip of insulation is $1\frac{1}{3}$ feet wide. Estimate the number of insulation strips needed to fit the width of the attic.

Read and Understand

1. What are you being asked to do?
   Estimate the number of strips of insulation
   needed to fit the width of the attic.

2. Which number(s) will you round to estimate?
   $1\frac{1}{3}$

Plan and Solve

3. To what number do you round $1\frac{1}{3}$?
   1

4. Divide 24 by the rounded number. What is the result?
   24

5. Approximately how many strips do you need?
   24 strips

Look Back and Check

6. How do you check your answer?
   Divide 24 by $1\frac{1}{3}$ to see if it is close to the
   estimate.

Solve Another Problem

7. A closet bar is $8\frac{3}{4}$ in. long. If a standard shirt is $1\frac{1}{2}$ in. wide,
   estimate how many shirts can you hang on the bar?
   $8\frac{3}{4} \approx 10$; $1\frac{1}{2} \approx 2$; $10 \div 2$ or 5 shirts

40   Guided Problem Solving   Course 1

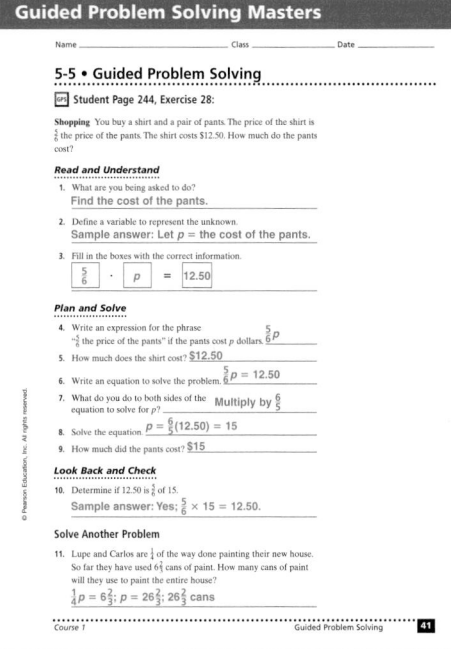

Guided Problem Solving Masters

Name _____ Class _____ Date _____

5-5 • Guided Problem Solving

GPS Student Page 244, Exercise 28:

Shopping You buy a shirt and a pair of pants. The price of the shirt is $\frac{5}{6}$ the price of the pants. The shirt costs $12.50. How much do the pants cost?

Read and Understand

1. What are you being asked to do?
   Find the cost of the pants.

2. Define a variable to represent the unknown.
   Sample answer: Let p = the cost of the pants.

3. Fill in the boxes with the correct information.
   $\boxed{\frac{5}{6}}$ · $\boxed{p}$ = $\boxed{12.50}$

Plan and Solve

4. Write an expression for the phrase
   "$\frac{5}{6}$ the price of the pants" if the pants cost p dollars. $\frac{5}{6}p$

5. How much does the shirt cost? $12.50

6. Write an equation to solve the problem. $\frac{5}{6}p = 12.50$

7. What do you do to both sides of the
   equation to solve for p? Multiply by $\frac{6}{5}$

8. Solve the equation $p = \frac{6}{5}(12.50) = 15$

9. How much did the pants cost? $15

Look Back and Check

10. Determine if 12.50 is $\frac{5}{6}$ of 15.
   Sample answer: Yes; $\frac{5}{6} \times 15 = 12.50$.

Solve Another Problem

11. Lupe and Carlos are $\frac{1}{4}$ of the way done painting their new house.
   So far they have used $6\frac{2}{3}$ cans of paint. How many cans of paint
   will they use to paint the entire house?
   $\frac{1}{4}p = 6\frac{2}{3}$; $p = 26\frac{2}{3}$; $26\frac{2}{3}$ cans

Course 1   Guided Problem Solving   **41**

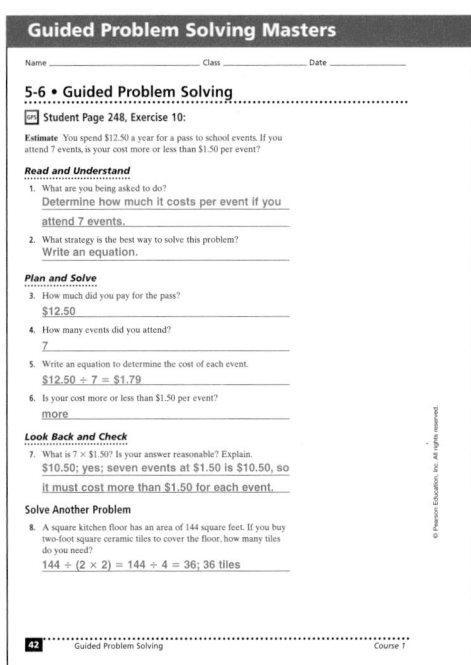

Guided Problem Solving Masters

Name _____ Class _____ Date _____

5-6 • Guided Problem Solving

GPS Student Page 248, Exercise 10:

Estimate You spend $12.50 a year for a pass to school events. If you attend 7 events, is your cost more or less than $1.50 per event?

Read and Understand

1. What are you being asked to do?
   Determine how much it costs per event if you
   attend 7 events.

2. What strategy is the best way to solve this problem?
   Write an equation.

Plan and Solve

3. How much did you pay for the pass?
   $12.50

4. How many events did you attend?
   7

5. Write an equation to determine the cost of each event.
   $12.50 \div 7 = $1.79

6. Is your cost more or less than $1.50 per event?
   more

Look Back and Check

7. What is $7 \times 1.50? Is your answer reasonable? Explain.
   $10.50; yes; seven events at $1.50 is $10.50, so
   it must cost more than $1.50 for each event.

Solve Another Problem

8. A square kitchen floor has an area of 144 square feet. If you buy
   two-foot square ceramic tiles to cover the floor, how many tiles
   do you need?
   $144 \div (2 \times 2) = 144 \div 4 = 36$; 36 tiles

42   Guided Problem Solving   Course 1

Guided Problem Solving Masters

Name _____ Class _____ Date _____

5-7 • Guided Problem Solving

GPS Student Page 252, Exercise 17:

Prehistoric Creatures In 2001, scientists discovered the fossil of a huge crocodile. This crocodile was more than 40 feet long and weighed over 10 tons. A Nile crocodile can weigh $\frac{3}{4}$ ton. How many times as heavy as the Nile crocodile was the prehistoric crocodile?

Read and Understand

1. Which weighs more, the Nile crocodile or the prehistoric
   crocodile? Explain.
   The prehistoric crocodile; 10 tons $> \frac{3}{4}$ ton.

2. What are you being asked to do?
   Find how many times heavier the prehistoric
   crocodile was than the Nile crocodile.

3. Define the variable for the unknown crocodile.
   Sample answer: Let n = number of times
   heavier the prehistoric crocodile is.

Plan and Solve

4. What is the least the prehistoric crocodile could weigh? 10 tons

5. How much does the Nile crocodile weigh? $\frac{3}{4}$ ton

6. Write an equation for the question, "$\frac{3}{4}$ ton
   times what number is 10 tons?" $\frac{3}{4}n = 10$

7. Solve the equation. $\frac{3}{4}n = 10$; $3n = 40$; $n = 13.\overline{3}$

8. How many times as heavy as the
   Nile crocodile was the prehistoric crocodile? $13.\overline{3}$ times

Look Back and Check

9. Is $\frac{3}{4}$ times your answer equal to 10? $\frac{3}{4} \times 13\frac{1}{3} = \frac{3}{4} \times \frac{40}{3} = 10$; yes

Solve Another Problem

10. Marie is 68 in. tall and her boyfriend Mario is 6 ft 2 in. tall. Who
   is taller? Explain.
   Mario is taller because Marie is 5 ft 8 in. tall.

Course 1   Guided Problem Solving   **43**

Guided Problem Solving Masters

Name _____ Class _____ Date _____

5-8 • Guided Problem Solving

GPS Student Page 256, Exercise 27:

Costume Design A costume designer is making a costume for a figure skater. To make the legs, she needs two strips of fabric that are each 34 inches long. How many yards of fabric does she need to make the legs?

Read and Understand

1. Circle the information you will need to solve.

2. What are you being asked to do?
   Find how many yards of fabric she needs to
   make the legs.

3. How many inches are in a yard?
   36 inches = 1 yard

Plan and Solve

4. How many strips of fabric does she need? 2 strips

5. How long does each strip need to be? 34 in.

6. How many inches of fabric do you need total? 68 in.

7. How do you convert this into yards? Divide by 36.

8. How many yards is it exactly?
   $\frac{68}{36} = 1\frac{17}{9} = 1.8$ yards

9. How many whole yards of fabric does she need? 2 yards

Look Back and Check

10. Approximately how many yards is each strip? Is your answer
   reasonable? Explain.
   1 yard; yes, if each leg is approximately 1 yard,
   then 2 yards of material are needed.

Solve Another Problem

11. Jessica is making fruit juice and it calls for 6 pints of water.
   Jessica only has a 2-quart pitcher. Will her fruit juice fit in the
   pitcher? Explain.
   Two quarts is only 4 pints, so her pitcher is
   not big enough for 6 pints.

44   Guided Problem Solving   Course 1

Activities and Projects

Hands-On Activities

Activity 16: Multiplying Fractions

Materials needed:	decimal grids

1. Model the problem $\frac{1}{2} \times \frac{1}{5}$ following these steps:

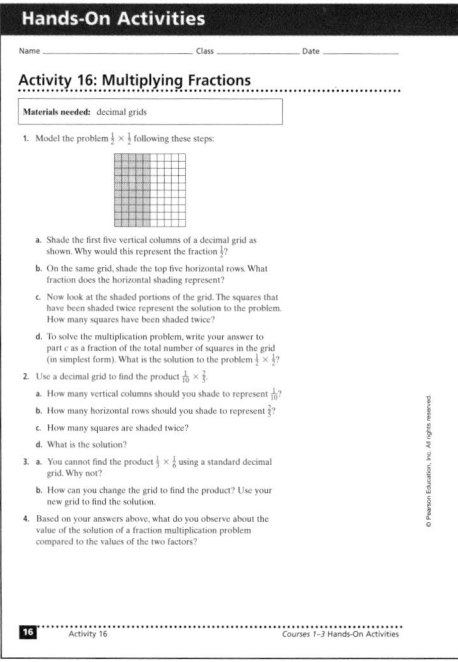

   a. Shade the first five vertical columns of a decimal grid as shown. Why would this represent the fraction $\frac{1}{2}$?

   b. On the same grid, shade the top five horizontal rows. What fraction does the horizontal shading represent?

   c. Now look at the shaded portions of the grid. The squares that have been shaded twice represent the solution to the problem. How many squares have been shaded twice?

   d. To solve the multiplication problem, write your answer to part c as a fraction of the total number of squares in the grid (in simplest form). What is the solution to the problem $\frac{1}{2} \times \frac{1}{5}$?

2. Use a decimal grid to find the product $\frac{3}{10} \times \frac{2}{5}$.

   a. How many vertical columns should you shade to represent $\frac{3}{10}$?

   b. How many horizontal rows should you shade to represent $\frac{2}{5}$?

   c. How many squares are shaded twice?

   d. What is the solution?

3. a. You cannot find the product $\frac{1}{2} \times \frac{1}{4}$ using a standard decimal grid. Why not?

   b. How can you change the grid to find the product? Use your new grid to find the solution.

4. Based on your answers above, what do you observe about the value of the solution of a fraction multiplication problem compared to the values of the two factors?

Hands-On Activities

Activity 19: Convert a Recipe

Materials needed:	flour, salt, powdered alum, water, food coloring, measuring cups, measuring spoons, plastic bag for storage, bowl, paper towels, rubber gloves

Work in small groups of 3–4 students.

Here is a recipe for modeling clay:

$2\frac{1}{2}$ cups flour

$1\frac{1}{4}$ cups salt

9 tablespoons powdered alum

$1\frac{1}{4}$ cup water

3 drops food coloring

The recipe makes 4 cups of clay. How would the recipe be modified to make 2 cups of clay?

1. Tell how you will change the recipe.

2. On a separate piece of paper, rewrite the recipe for making 2 cups of clay. Use the following calculations to find the amounts of the ingredients.

   a. $2\frac{1}{2} \div 2 =$

   b. $1\frac{1}{4} \div 2 =$

   c. $9 \div 2 =$

   d. $3 \div 2 =$

3. Follow these directions to make the clay.

   a. Mix the dry ingredients together (flour, salt, powdered alum).

   b. Add water and food coloring.

   c. Use rubber gloves to mix the ingredients with your hands.

   d. Store in a plastic bag in the refrigerator.

   e. Take out of refrigerator one hour before using.

4. Use the clay to form the following three-dimensional figures: cylinder, cone, sphere, pyramid, and prism.

Technology Activities

Calculating with Fractions   Activity 10

Use your scientific calculator to do this activity.

Example 1: Find $4 \div \frac{3}{5}$.

① You know that dividing by a fraction is the same as multiplying by the reciprocal of the fraction. So, you can rewrite $4 \div \frac{3}{5}$ as $4 \times \frac{5}{3}$.

② Press [2nd] [FracMode]. Press the right arrow key until you see **Auto** underlined. Press [ENTER]. *Note:* Once you've done this step, the calculator will automatically simplify fractions until someone changes it.

③ Enter 4 [×] 5 [/] 3 [2nd] [Ab/c ◄►a/c] [ENTER]. The calculator gives you 6u2/3, which is $6\frac{2}{3}$.

④ Check your answer by multiplying $6\frac{2}{3}$ by $\frac{3}{5}$ (because you originally divided by $\frac{3}{5}$). Enter 6 [UNIT] 2 [/] 3 [×] 3 [/] 5 [ENTER]. The calculator displays 4, so $6\frac{2}{3}$ is the correct quotient for $4 \div \frac{3}{5}$.

Example 2: Find $\frac{1}{7} \div \frac{2}{3}$.

Another method is to let the calculator divide the fractions directly.

Enter 1 [/] 7 [÷] 2 [/] 3 [ENTER]. The calculator gives you 3 / 14. The quotient is $\frac{3}{14}$.

(*Note:* If you ever see **N/D → n/d** displayed at the bottom of the display after multiplying or dividing fractions, then the calculator is not in auto simplification mode. Press [2nd] [FracMode], select **Auto** and press [ENTER] again. Then try the problem again.)

Exercises

Find each quotient.

1. $5 \div \frac{3}{8}$ 2. $11 \div \frac{5}{9}$ 3. $32 \div \frac{15}{16}$

4. $\frac{7}{15} \div \frac{1}{9}$ 5. $1\frac{1}{14} \div \frac{2}{17}$ 6. $\frac{24}{35} \div \frac{19}{22}$

7. $1\frac{4}{13} \div 7$ 8. $\frac{8}{15} \div 9$ 9. $\frac{57}{62} \div 12$

Sample pages; see p. G for complete list.

Chapter Project

Chapter 5 Project: Crack It and Cook It!

Create a Recipe

Beginning the Chapter Project

A hearty breakfast is a great way to start any day! You are probably familiar with pouring a bowl of cereal, making toast, or maybe even scrambling eggs. But, have you ever made an omelet? The basic omelet recipe can be pretty simple—some eggs, some water, and maybe some salt or pepper. However you can add other ingredients to this basic recipe to suit your tastes. For instance a cheese omelet is delicious; so is a bacon-and-tomato omelet. You might like mushrooms, onions, and peppers.

Put on your chef's hat! In this chapter project, you will write and name your own recipe for an omelet. Your final product will be a recipe that will feed everyone in your class.

Activities   Check students' answers.

Activity 1: Interviewing

Interview some people who know how to make omelets or start with a new recipe in a cookbook. Use that information to write your own recipe. Many of the ingredients will involve fractions. Include ingredients that you like, such as different types of cheese, meats, or vegetables. Give your recipe a unique name.

Activity 2: Researching

With an adult present, test your recipe by making omelets for your family. (You might want to ask an experienced chef to review your recipe if you do not have an opportunity to cook.) Revise your recipe if necessary. Adjust amounts so you have enough to feed your family.

Activity 3: Calculating

Now that you have a good omelet recipe for feeding your family, adjust it to serve the number of people that are in your class. Remember the number of eggs must be a whole number, even though many of the other ingredients use fractions. Did you multiply fractions or divide fractions to get the recipe large enough for the class? Explain.

Multiply; the class is larger than the family.

Chapter Project

Chapter 5 Project: Crack It and Cook It! (continued)

Finishing the Project

Present your recipe to the class. Tell your classmates how tasty your omelets are! Share your recipe with the class so that interested and hungry students can take your recipe home.

Be sure your work is neat and clear. Show all of your calculations. Write all explanations that you think are necessary.

Reflect and Revise

Think about the math that you used to complete this project. What did you learn in this chapter that helped you? What advice did you get from others to create a great recipe?

Ask a classmate to review your project with you. Are your calculations correct? Did you make the correct adjustments?

Extending the Project

Create a recipe for a different type of breakfast food, such as pancakes or waffles. Learn of all of the different toppings that can be used to create a unique breakfast experience.

Take It to the NET   Visit www.PHSchool.com for information and links you might find helpful as you complete your project.

Chapter Project

Chapter Project Manager

Chapter 5: Crack It and Cook It!

Getting Started

Read about the project. As you work on it, you will need several sheets of paper. If available, a spreadsheet program also can be used. Keep all your work for the project in a folder, along with this Project Manager.

Checklist	Suggestions
☐ Activity 1: interviewing	☐ Interview chefs in restaurants to learn how to make different types of omelets.
☐ Activity 2: researching	☐ Ask your family to fill out an evaluation form so you can see what they did or did not like about your omelets.
☐ Activity 3: calculating	☐ Write your fractions in simplest form.
☐ Recommendations	☐ Pass out samples of your omelets to prove how tasty they are.

Scoring Rubric

3   Your recipe produces good tasting omelets. You provided step-by-step explanations of how you calculated the amounts of ingredients required for your family and the class. You show proof that either you tested your recipe by making it for your family or you interviewed someone with cooking experience to make sure your recipe made sense.

2   You wrote an omelet recipe and explained how you calculated the amounts of ingredients required for your family and the class. But some of your calculations were inaccurate, or you did not prove that your recipe made sense.

1   You wrote an omelet recipe but did not calculate the amounts of ingredients required for either your family or the whole class.

0   You did not write an omelet recipe.

Your Evaluation of Project   Evaluate your work, based on the Scoring Rubric.

Teacher's Evaluation of Project

216K

Transparencies

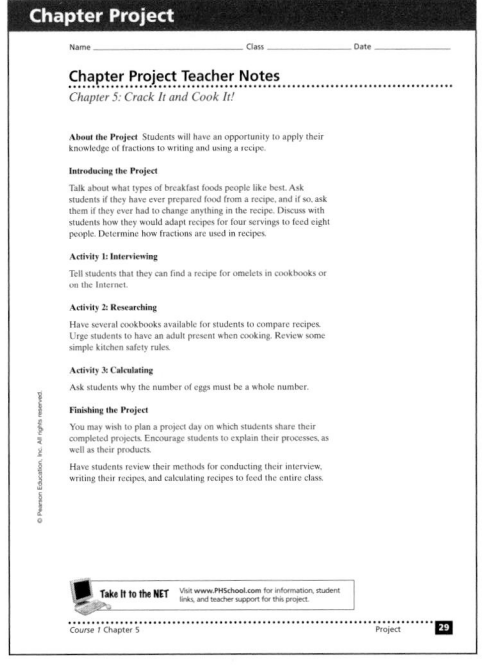

Chapter Project

Name _____ Class _____ Date _____

Chapter Project Teacher Notes
Chapter 5: Crack It and Cook It!

About the Project Students will have an opportunity to apply their knowledge of fractions to writing and using a recipe.

Introducing the Project

Talk about what types of breakfast foods people like best. Ask students if they have ever prepared food from a recipe, and if so, ask them if they ever had to change anything in the recipe. Discuss with students how they would adapt recipes for four servings to feed eight people. Determine how fractions are used in recipes.

Activity 1: Interviewing

Tell students that they can find a recipe for omelets in cookbooks or on the Internet.

Activity 2: Researching

Have several cookbooks available for students to compare recipes. Urge students to have an adult present when cooking. Review some simple kitchen safety rules.

Activity 3: Calculating

Ask students why the number of eggs must be a whole number.

Finishing the Project

You may wish to plan a project day on which students share their completed projects. Encourage students to explain their processes, as well as their products.

Have students review their methods for conducting their interview, writing their recipes, and calculating recipes to feed the entire class.

Take It to the NET Visit www.PHSchool.com for information, student links, and teacher support for this project.

Course 1 Chapter 5 · Project **29**

Problem of the Day

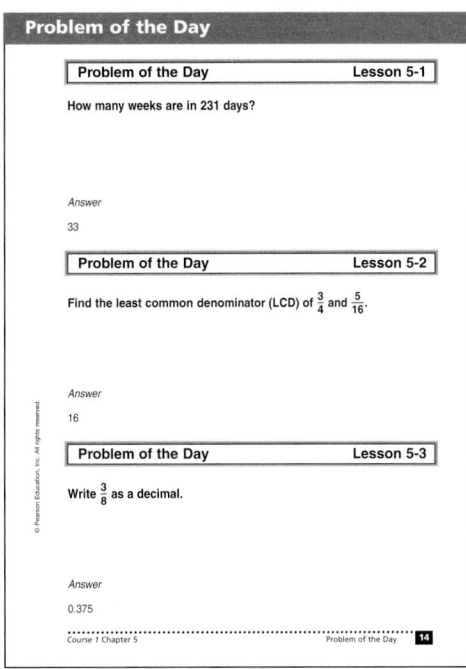

Problem of the Day	Lesson 5-1

How many weeks are in 231 days?

Answer

33

Problem of the Day	Lesson 5-2

Find the least common denominator (LCD) of $\frac{3}{4}$ and $\frac{5}{16}$.

Answer

16

Problem of the Day	Lesson 5-3

Write $\frac{3}{8}$ as a decimal.

Answer

0.375

Course 1 Chapter 5 · · · · · · · · · · · Problem of the Day **14**

Problem of the Day

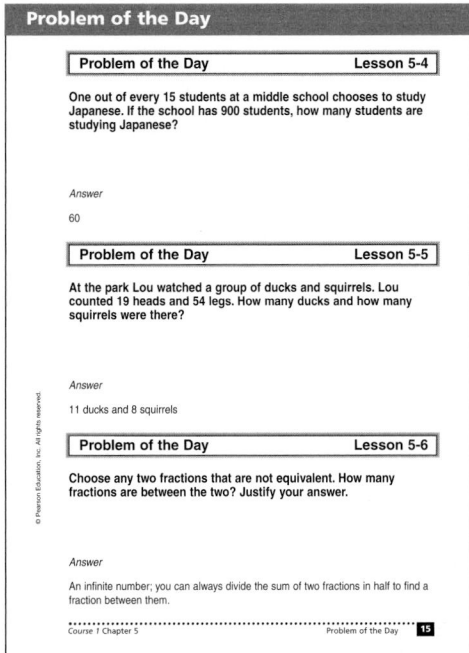

Problem of the Day	Lesson 5-4

One out of every 15 students at a middle school chooses to study Japanese. If the school has 900 students, how many students are studying Japanese?

Answer

60

Problem of the Day	Lesson 5-5

At the park Lou watched a group of ducks and squirrels. Lou counted 19 heads and 54 legs. How many ducks and how many squirrels were there?

Answer

11 ducks and 8 squirrels

Problem of the Day	Lesson 5-6

Choose any two fractions that are not equivalent. How many fractions are between the two? Justify your answer.

Answer

An infinite number; you can always divide the sum of two fractions in half to find a fraction between them.

Course 1 Chapter 5 · · · · · · · · · · · Problem of the Day **15**

Problem of the Day

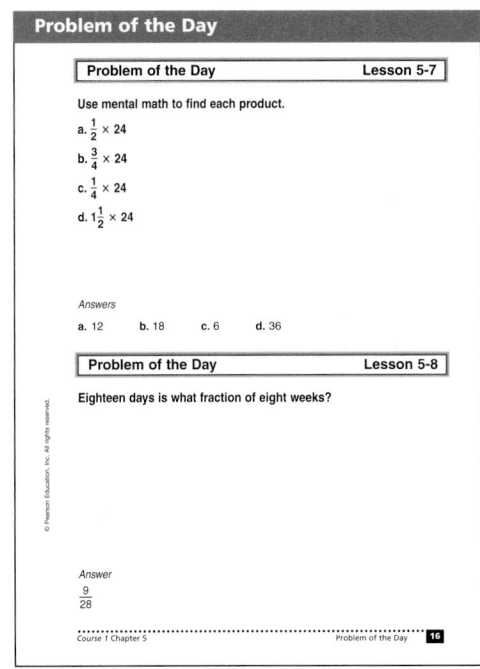

Problem of the Day	Lesson 5-7

Use mental math to find each product.

a. $\frac{1}{2} \times 24$

b. $\frac{3}{4} \times 24$

c. $\frac{1}{4} \times 24$

d. $1\frac{1}{2} \times 24$

Answers

a. 12   b. 18   c. 6   d. 36

Problem of the Day	Lesson 5-8

Eighteen days is what fraction of eight weeks?

Answer

$\frac{9}{28}$

Course 1 Chapter 5 · · · · · · · · · · · Problem of the Day **16**

Check Skills You'll Need

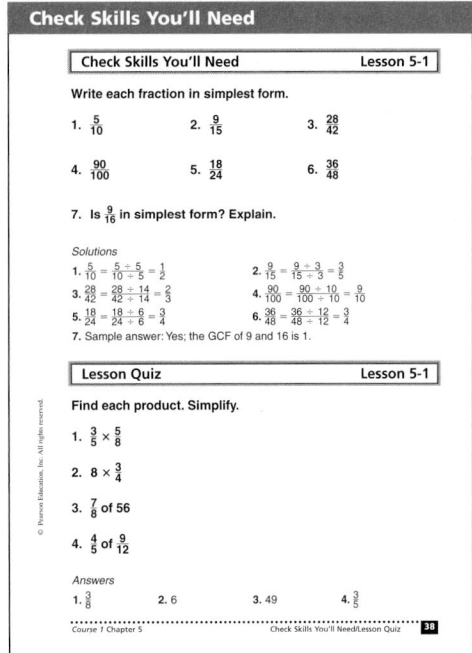

Check Skills You'll Need	Lesson 5-1

Write each fraction in simplest form.

1. $\frac{5}{10}$ 2. $\frac{9}{15}$ 3. $\frac{28}{42}$

4. $\frac{90}{100}$ 5. $\frac{18}{24}$ 6. $\frac{36}{48}$

7. Is $\frac{9}{16}$ in simplest form? Explain.

Solutions

1. $\frac{5}{10} = \frac{5 \div 5}{10 \div 5} = \frac{1}{2}$ 2. $\frac{9}{15} = \frac{9 \div 3}{15 \div 3} = \frac{3}{5}$

3. $\frac{28}{42} = \frac{28 \div 14}{42 \div 14} = \frac{2}{3}$ 4. $\frac{90}{100} = \frac{90 \div 10}{100 \div 10} = \frac{9}{10}$

5. $\frac{18}{24} = \frac{18 \div 6}{24 \div 6} = \frac{3}{4}$ 6. $\frac{36}{48} = \frac{36 \div 12}{48 \div 12} = \frac{3}{4}$

7. Sample answer: Yes; the GCF of 9 and 16 is 1.

Lesson Quiz	Lesson 5-1

Find each product. Simplify.

1. $\frac{3}{5} \times \frac{5}{8}$

2. $8 \times \frac{3}{4}$

3. $\frac{7}{8}$ of 56

4. $\frac{4}{5}$ of $\frac{9}{12}$

Answers

1. $\frac{3}{8}$ 2. 6   3. 49   4. $\frac{3}{5}$

Course 1 Chapter 5 · · · · · · · · · Check Skills You'll Need/Lesson Quiz **38**

Sample page; see p. H for complete list.

Additional Examples

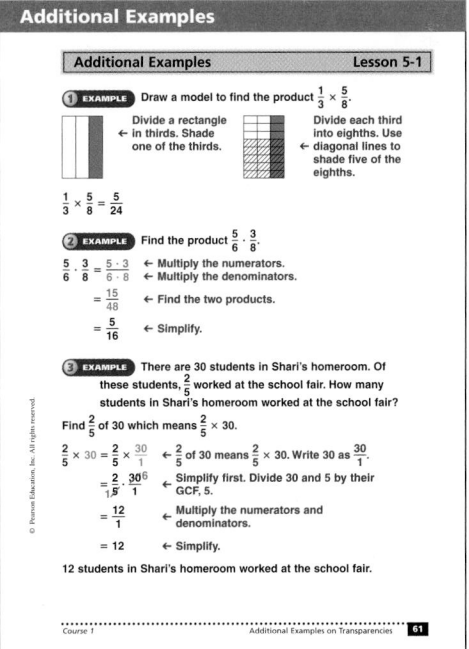

Additional Examples	Lesson 5-1

EXAMPLE Draw a model to find the product $\frac{1}{3} \times \frac{5}{8}$.

Divide a rectangle ← in thirds. Shade one of the thirds.

Divide each third into eighths. Use ← diagonal lines to shade five of the eighths.

$\frac{1}{3} \times \frac{5}{8} = \frac{5}{24}$

EXAMPLE Find the product $\frac{5}{6} \cdot \frac{3}{8}$.

$\frac{5}{6} \cdot \frac{3}{8} = \frac{5 \cdot 3}{6 \cdot 8}$ ← Multiply the numerators.
  ← Multiply the denominators.

$= \frac{15}{48}$ ← Find the two products.

$= \frac{5}{16}$ ← Simplify.

EXAMPLE There are 30 students in Shari's homeroom. Of these students, $\frac{2}{5}$ worked at the school fair. How many students in Shari's homeroom worked at the school fair?

Find $\frac{2}{5}$ of 30 which means $\frac{2}{5} \times 30$.

$\frac{2}{5} \times 30 = \frac{2}{5} \times \frac{30}{1}$ ← $\frac{2}{5}$ of 30 means $\frac{2}{5} \times 30$. Write 30 as $\frac{30}{1}$.

$= \frac{2}{1} \cdot \frac{30^6}{1}$ ← Simplify first. Divide 30 and 5 by their GCF, 5.

$= \frac{12}{1}$ ← Multiply the numerators and denominators.

$= 12$ ← Simplify.

12 students in Shari's homeroom worked at the school fair.

Course 1 · · · · · · · · · Additional Examples on Transparencies **61**

Sample page; see p. H for complete list.

Classroom Aid

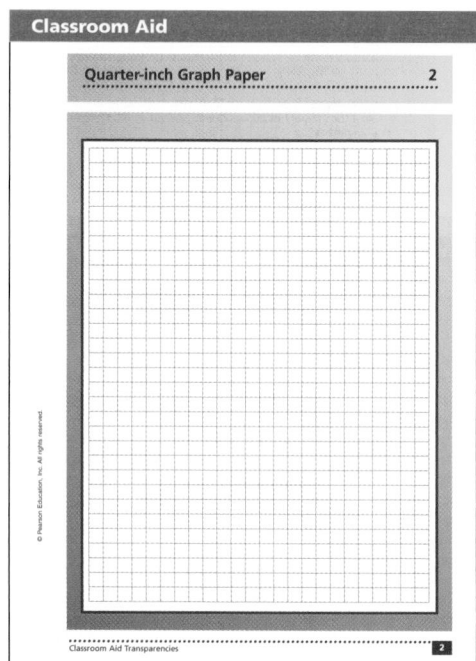

Sample page.

Student Edition Answers

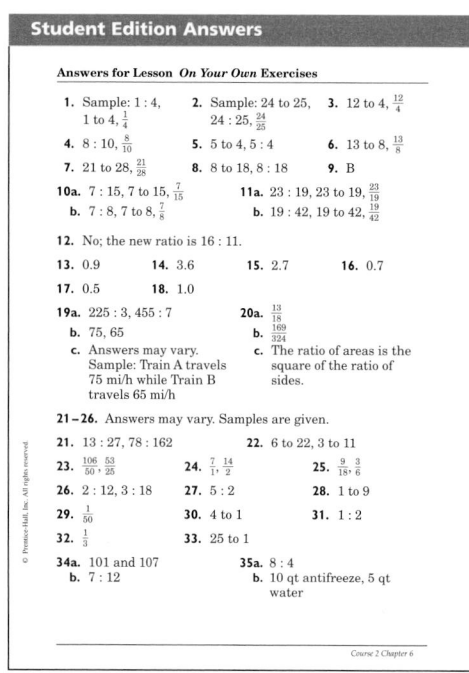

Sample page; see p. H for complete list.

Lesson Quiz

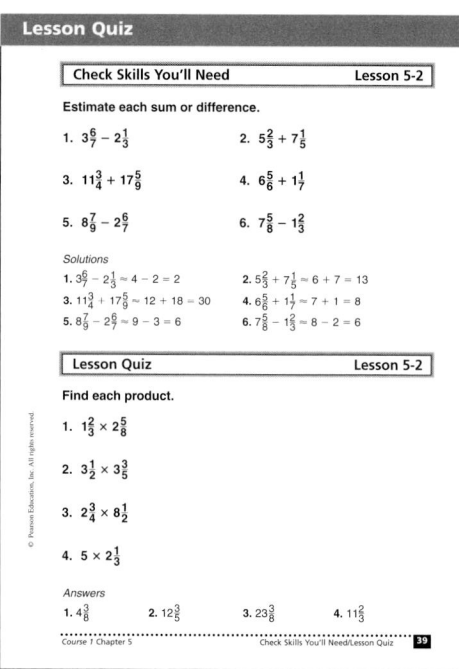

Sample page; see p. H for complete list.

Assessment

Checkpoint Quizzes

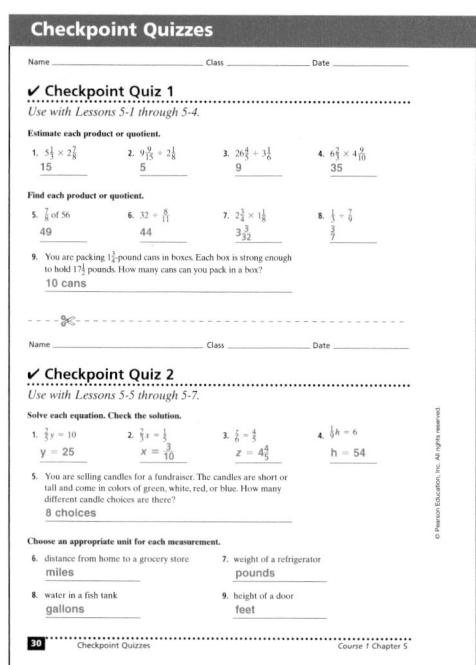

Available in Spanish

Chapter Test, Form A

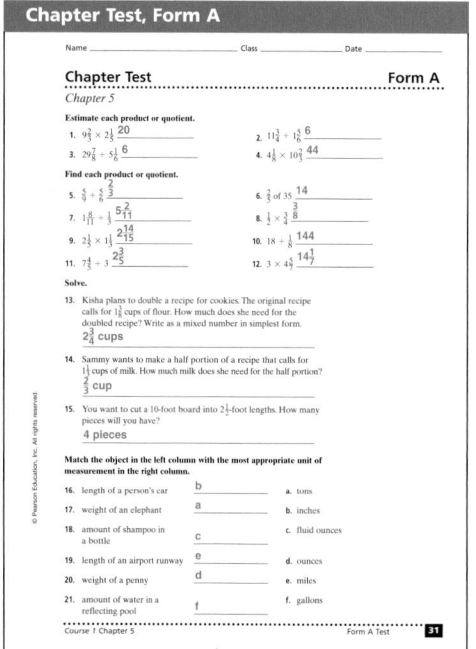

Available in Spanish

Chapter Test, Form A

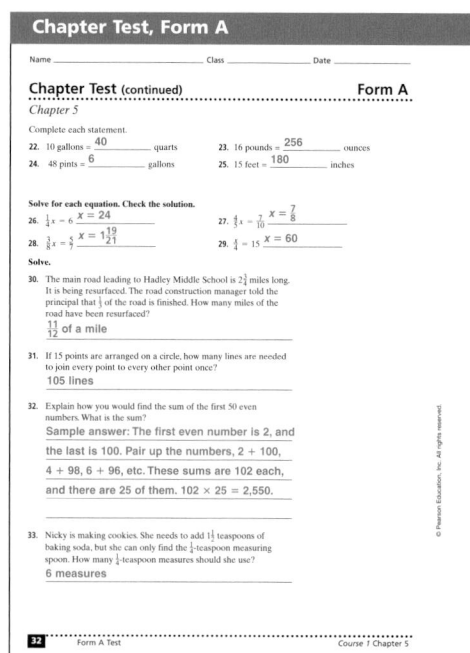

Available in Spanish

Name _____ Class _____ Date _____

Chapter Test   Form B
Chapter 5

Estimate each product or quotient.

1. $15\frac{1}{8} \times 5\frac{1}{4}$ 75
2. $42\frac{1}{3} \div 5\frac{6}{7}$ 7
3. $72\frac{7}{8} \div 8\frac{6}{9}$ 8
4. $12\frac{3}{8} \times 1\frac{9}{10}$ 24

Find each product or quotient.

5. $\frac{3}{8} \div \frac{1}{2}$ $\frac{7}{8}$
6. $\frac{3}{10}$ of 50   15
7. $2\frac{6}{11} \div \frac{1}{4}$ $10\frac{2}{11}$
8. $\frac{1}{3} \times 1\frac{1}{4}$ $\frac{1}{2}$
9. $2\frac{3}{4} \times 1\frac{1}{2}$ $4\frac{1}{8}$
10. $3\frac{1}{2} \div \frac{1}{8}$ 28
11. $9\frac{3}{8} \div 3$ $3\frac{1}{8}$
12. $5 \times 4\frac{4}{9}$ $22\frac{2}{9}$

Solve.

13. Joshua plans to double a recipe for muffins. The original recipe needs $2\frac{1}{4}$ cups of milk. How much does he need for the doubled recipe? Write as a mixed number in simplest form.
     $4\frac{1}{2}$ cups

14. Mark decides that a third of the recipe for hot chocolate will be just enough for himself. The recipe calls for $3\frac{1}{4}$ cups of milk. How much milk does he need for a third of the recipe?
     $1\frac{1}{12}$ cups

15. Ray has a 15-foot piece of lumber and he wants to cut it into $2\frac{1}{2}$-foot lengths. How many $2\frac{1}{2}$-foot pieces can he make from the original lumber?
     6 pieces

Match the object in the left column with the most appropriate unit of measurement in the right column.

16. length of a pencil   b   a. tons
17. weight of a centipede   d   b. inches
18. amount of hand cream in a bottle   c   c. fluid ounces
19. length of a classroom   e   d. ounces
20. weight of a full dump truck   a   e. feet
21. amount of water in a water tower   f   f. gallons

Available in Spanish

Name _____ Class _____ Date _____

Chapter Test (continued)   Form B
Chapter 5

Complete each statement.

22. 4 feet = 48 inches
23. 5 pounds = 80 ounces
24. 48 pints = 6 gallons
25. 5 gallons = 20 quarts

Solve each equation. Check the solution.

26. $\frac{1}{5}x = 8$ $x = 40$
27. $\frac{5}{6}x = \frac{10}{11}$ $x = 1\frac{1}{11}$
28. $1\frac{1}{2}x = 3\frac{1}{2}$ $x = 2$
29. $\frac{x}{6} = 5$ $x = 30$

Solve.

30. Alice's grandmother made a quilt that is $9\frac{1}{2}$ feet wide and $12\frac{5}{8}$ feet long. Alice plans to make a quilt that is half as wide and half as long. What will be the dimensions of Alice's quilt?
     $4\frac{3}{4}$ feet wide by $6\frac{5}{16}$ feet long

31. There are 7 players in a chess tournament. Each player must play each of the other players once. How many chess games will be played?
     21 games

32. Explain how you would find the sum of the first 20 odd numbers. What is the sum?
     Sample answer: The first odd number is 1 and the last in the list is 39. Pair up the numbers, 1 + 39, 3 + 37, 5 + 35, etc. These sums are 40, and there are 10 of them. 40 × 10 = 400.

33. Emma was making a cake. She needed to put in $2\frac{1}{4}$ teaspoons of brown sugar, but she could only find the $\frac{1}{4}$-teaspoon measure. How many $\frac{1}{4}$-teaspoon measures should she use?
     9 measures

Available in Spanish

Name _____ Class _____ Date _____

Alternative Assessment   Form C
Chapter 5

CHILI NIGHT

Your family moved recently. Before the move you used to help your parents out by making dinner every Wednesday night. One of your favorite dishes to prepare was chili, which you made by adding water and several fresh ingredients to Montana Martha's Chili Mix. Now, however, you live in a part of the country where Montana Martha's Chili Mix is not sold. But you have a plan to change that. Your first step was asking 240 people in your new town how often they eat chili. The circle graph shows the results of your survey.

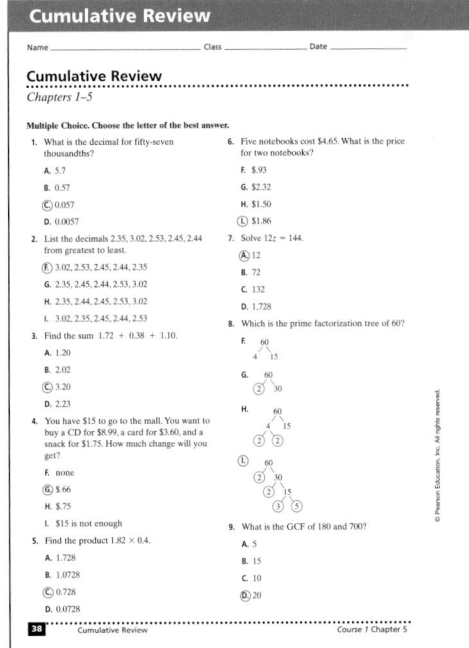

Show all of your work on a separate sheet of paper.

1. How many of the 240 people in your survey said they never eat chili?

2. Of the people who said they eat chili often, $\frac{3}{4}$ said they would be interested in trying Montana Martha's Chili Mix. What fraction of the survey group is this?

You think that grocery store managers will be more likely to carry Montana Martha's Chili Mix if you give them a sample of chili made from it. You have two packages left. You need to make a lot of chili to give away, but you want to save some of the mix to make a small batch for yourself.

3. You decide to use $1\frac{1}{3}$ packages of mix to make a large batch of chili for store managers to taste. The basic recipe calls for adding $\frac{2}{3}$ cup of water to each package. How much water will you need for $1\frac{1}{3}$ packages of mix?

Available in Spanish

Name _____ Class _____ Date _____

Alternative Assessment (continued)   Form C
Chapter 5

4. You make 7 quarts of chili to give away. How many $1\frac{3}{4}$-quart samples will you be able to make?

5. You will need to adjust the basic recipe again when you make a small batch of chili with the remaining half package. How many cups of chopped tomatoes will you need if the basic recipe calls for adding $1\frac{1}{2}$ cups of chopped tomatoes?

Excursion

Write a letter to a grocery store manager, and turn it in to your teacher. Explain why the grocery store should start selling Montana Martha's Chili Mix. Use the information in the circle graph and in Exercises 1 and 2 to support your argument. Include a table that shows your estimate of how many of your town's 5,967 residents eat chili often, occasionally, rarely, or never.

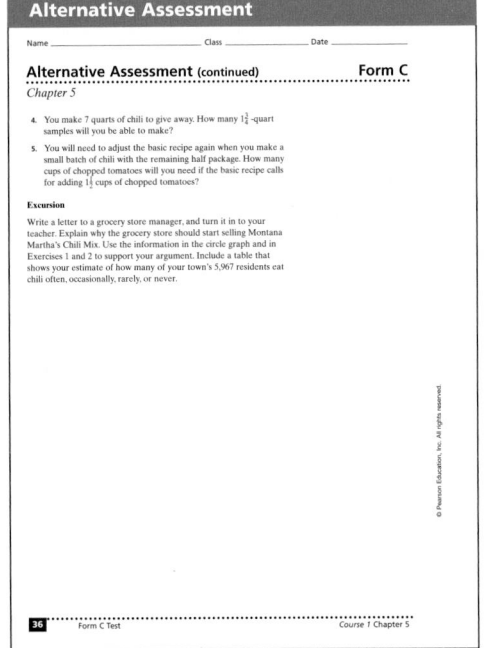

Available in Spanish

Name _____ Class _____ Date _____

Alternative Assessment (continued)   Form C
Chapter 5

Scoring Rubric

Exercise	Points	Explanation
1.	1	60 people
	0	No answer OR incorrect answer
2.	1	$\frac{1}{8}$
	0	No answer or incorrect answer
3.	1	1 cup
	0	No answer or incorrect answer
4.	1	4 containers
	0	No answer or incorrect answer
5.	1	$\frac{3}{4}$ cup
	0	No answer or incorrect answer
Excursion	4	The student demonstrates a clear understanding of multiplication and division with fractions. All calculations are accurate and complete. The student's letter is thorough, well organized, and easy to read.
	3	The student demonstrates a fundamental understanding of multiplication and division with fractions. The student does all necessary calculations but may make some minor errors. The student's letter is fairly well organized and easy to read but may contain minor computational errors.
	2	The student has some understanding of multiplication and division with fractions but requires assistance to apply this understanding to the given situation. One or more of the student's calculations contain major errors or omissions. The student requires some assistance to complete the letter.
	1	The student demonstrates little if any understanding of multiplication and division with fractions and cannot, even with assistance, apply this understanding to the given situation. The student attempts some calculations, but they are irrelevant or superfluous. The student requires a great deal of assistance to complete the letter.
	0	No response

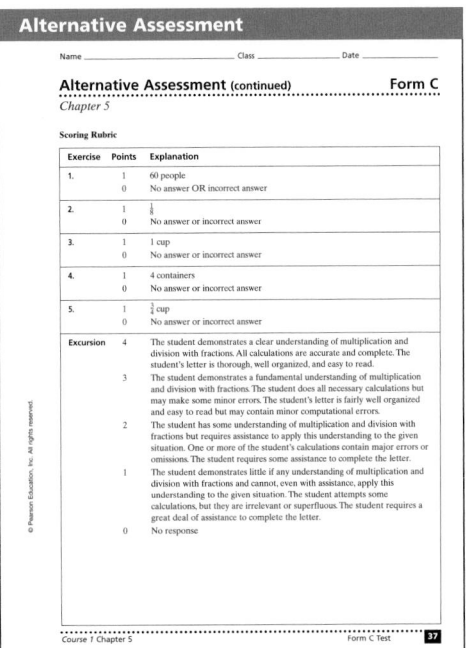

Available in Spanish

Name _____ Class _____ Date _____

Cumulative Review
Chapters 1–5

Multiple Choice. Choose the letter of the best answer.

1. What is the decimal for fifty-seven thousandths?
   A. 5.7
   B. 0.57
   C. 0.057
   D. 0.0057

2. List the decimals 2.35, 3.02, 2.53, 2.45, 2.44 from greatest to least.
   F. 3.02, 2.53, 2.45, 2.44, 2.35
   G. 2.35, 2.45, 2.44, 2.53, 3.02
   H. 2.35, 2.44, 2.45, 2.53, 3.02
   I. 3.02, 2.35, 2.45, 2.44, 2.53

3. Find the sum $1.72 + 0.38 + 1.10$.
   A. 1.20
   B. 2.02
   C. 3.20
   D. 2.23

4. You have \$15 to go to the mall. You want to buy a CD for \$8.99, a card for \$3.60, and a snack for \$1.75. How much change will you get?
   F. none
   G. \$.66
   H. \$.75
   I. \$15 is not enough

5. Find the product 1.82×0.4.
   A. 1.728
   B. 1.0728
   C. 0.728
   D. 0.0728

6. Five notebooks cost \$4.65. What is the price for two notebooks?
   F. \$.93
   G. \$2.32
   H. \$1.50
   I. \$1.86

7. Solve $12z = 144$.
   A. 12
   B. 72
   C. 132
   D. 1,728

8. Which is the prime factorization tree of 60?

9. What is the GCF of 180 and 700?
   A. 5
   B. 15
   C. 10
   D. 20

Available in Spanish

Name _____ Class _____ Date _____

Cumulative Review (continued)
Chapters 1–5

10. Write $\frac{45}{50}$ in simplest form.

   F. $\frac{45}{50}$ G. $\frac{5}{14}$

   H. $\frac{9}{14}$

11. Write $\frac{3}{4}, \frac{2}{3}, 1\frac{3}{5}, \frac{15}{4}, \frac{9}{2}, \frac{2}{5}$ in order from least to greatest.

   A. $\frac{2}{5}, \frac{2}{3}, 1\frac{3}{5}, \frac{15}{4}, \frac{9}{2}, \frac{3}{4}$

   B. $\frac{2}{5}, \frac{2}{3}, \frac{3}{4}, 1\frac{3}{5}, \frac{15}{4}, \frac{9}{2}$

   C. $\frac{15}{4}, \frac{9}{2}, \frac{3}{4}, \frac{2}{3}, 1\frac{3}{5}, \frac{2}{5}$

   D. $\frac{1}{2}, \frac{2}{3}, \frac{3}{4}, \frac{9}{2}, 1\frac{3}{5}, \frac{15}{4}$

12. Write 0.625 as a fraction in simplest form.

   F. $\frac{5}{8}$ G. $\frac{63}{100}$

   H. $\frac{5}{8}$

13. Your mom says you and two friends can have half of the whole pie on the counter. What portion of the pie will each of you get if the portions are all equal?

   A. $\frac{1}{3}$ pie

   B. $\frac{1}{6}$ pie

   C. $\frac{1}{2}$ pie

   D. $\frac{1}{4}$ pie

14. Divide $4\frac{3}{4} \div \frac{1}{4}$. Write in simplest form.

   F. $\frac{19}{16}$ G. $16\frac{1}{16}$

   H. $4\frac{1}{4}$ I. 19

15. Subtract.   6 lb 4 oz
               − 2 lb 10 oz

   A. 4 lb 4 oz

   B. 3 lb 4 oz

   C. 3 lb 10 oz

   D. 3 lb 6 oz

16. Solve. $\frac{1}{6}x = 4$

   F. $x = \frac{2}{3}$ G. $x = 10$

   H. $x = \frac{2}{3}$ I. $x = 24$

17. Solve. $\frac{5}{6}y = \frac{1}{5}$

   A. $y = \frac{5}{6}$ B. $y = \frac{6}{25}$

   C. $y = \frac{4}{5}$ D. $y = 6\frac{2}{3}$

18. There are 220 students in the marching band and $\frac{2}{5}$ of them play a brass instrument. What operation would you use to find the number of students who play a brass instrument?

   F. add

   G. subtract

   H. multiply

   I. divide

19. A piece of glass is 12.25 inches long. A glass cutter needs to shave 2.5 inches off of one end. How long will the glass be once the glass cutter is finished?

   A. 4.9 in.   B. 9.75 in.

   C. 10.2 in.   D. 14.75 in.

Gridded Response

20. Lena is sewing costumes for a children's ballet recital. She has 9 yards of fabric. She needs $1\frac{1}{2}$ yards for each costume. How many complete costumes can she make?

   6 complete costumes

21. If 16 points are arranged in a circle, how many lines are needed to join every point to every other point once?

   120 lines

Available in Spanish

Name _____ Class _____ Date _____

Benchmark Test 1

1. What is the value of the digit 2 in the number 4.0725?

   A. 2 tenths

   B. 2 hundredths

   C. 2 thousandths

   D. 2 ten-thousandths

2. How is the decimal 2.016 expressed in words?

   A. two and sixteen thousandths

   B. two and sixteen hundredths

   C. two and sixteen tenths

   D. two and sixteenths

3. Quincy ran a lap in seventy-five and thirteen hundredths seconds. How is this time written in standard form?

   A. 75.013 seconds

   B. 75.03 seconds

   C. 75.103 seconds

   D. 75.13 seconds

4. Which set of decimals is ordered from least to greatest?

   A. 2.67, 2.71, 2.99, 2.02

   B. 2.99, 2.67, 2.71, 2.02

   C. 2.02, 2.67, 2.71, 2.99

   D. 2.71, 2.02, 2.99, 2.67

5. Which of the following statements is true?

   A. 1.971 > 1.97

   B. 2.53 < 2.3

   C. 4.825 > 4.85

   D. 6.74 < 6.740

6. The table below shows the surface ocean temperature for five days. On which day was the daily ocean temperature coolest?

Daily Ocean Temperature

Day	Temperature (°F)
Monday	80.07
Tuesday	81.03
Wednesday	80.90
Thursday	81.50
Friday	81.20

   A. Monday

   B. Tuesday

   C. Wednesday

   D. Friday

7. Which addition problem is modeled below?

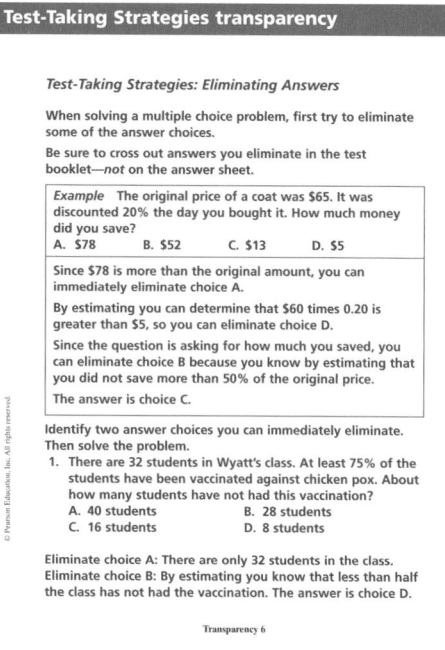

   A. 8 + 3 = 11

   B. 0.8 + 3 = 3.8

   C. 0.8 + 0.3 = 1.1

   D. 0.08 + 0.3 = 0.38

Test-Taking Strategies: Eliminating Answers

When solving a multiple choice problem, first try to eliminate some of the answer choices.

Be sure to cross out answers you eliminate in the test booklet—*not* on the answer sheet.

> *Example* The original price of a coat was $65. It was discounted 20% the day you bought it. How much money did you save?
>
> A. $78   B. $52   C. $13   D. $5
>
> Since $78 is more than the original amount, you can immediately eliminate choice A.
>
> By estimating you can determine that $60 times 0.20 is greater than $5, so you can eliminate choice D.
>
> Since the question is asking for how much you saved, you can eliminate choice B because you know by estimating that you did not save more than 50% of the original price.
>
> The answer is choice C.

Identify two answer choices you can immediately eliminate. Then solve the problem.

1. There are 32 students in Wyatt's class. At least 75% of the students have been vaccinated against chicken pox. About how many students have not had this vaccination?

   A. 40 students   B. 28 students

   C. 16 students   D. 8 students

Eliminate choice A: There are only 32 students in the class.
Eliminate choice B: By estimating you know that less than half the class has not had the vaccination. The answer is choice D.

On PH Website

Name _____ Class _____ Date _____

Chapter 5: Eliminating Answers
Exercises

Identify the answer choices you can immediately eliminate. Cross the choices out and explain why you eliminated them. Then solve the problem.

1. Sandra is making 4 batches of cookies, so she will need to use 4 times the amount of flour the recipe calls for. The recipe calls for $3\frac{1}{4}$ cups of flour. How much flour does Sandra need?

   A. 12 cups   B. $1\frac{1}{4}$ cups   C. 13 cups   D. 17 cups

   Since $1\frac{1}{4}$ is less than the original amount, you can immediately eliminate choice B. $4 \times 3 = 12$, so you can eliminate choice A since it would not take into account the extra $\frac{1}{4}$ cup. 17 is too large since 4 times 4 is only 16 and $3\frac{3}{4}$ is less than 4. So, you can rule out choice D. The answer is C.

2. Alice's grandmother made a quilt that is $9\frac{1}{8}$ feet wide and $12\frac{3}{8}$ feet long. Alice plans to make a quilt that is half as wide and half as long. What will be the dimensions of Alice's quilt?

   F. $4\frac{9}{16}$ ft wide by $6\frac{3}{16}$ ft long   G. $4\frac{9}{16}$ ft wide by $6\frac{9}{16}$ ft long

   H. $4\frac{9}{16}$ ft wide by 6 ft long   I. $18\frac{1}{4}$ ft wide by $24\frac{3}{4}$ ft long

   Since Alice's quilt will be half the size, you can eliminate choice I; the numbers are almost twice the original numbers. Since 4 is less than half of 9, you can eliminate choice H. The correct answer must be either choice F or G.

3. There are 95 different kinds of butterflies in a zoo. There are $\frac{4}{5}$ as many different kinds of beetles as butterflies at the zoo. How many different kinds of beetles are at the zoo?

   A. 76 beetles   B. 50 beetles   C. 120 beetles   D. 75 beetles

   Eliminate choice B; since $\frac{4}{5}$ is nearly equal to 1, 50 is too small. Eliminate choice C; $\frac{4}{5}$ is a fraction less than one, and the answer cannot be larger than the original number. The answer is A.

---

in math class ...

We have been learning about multiplying and dividing fractions. Here is a list of some of the skills and concepts we have studied.

♦ Multiplying by a whole number

♦ Multiplying by a fraction

♦ Dividing whole numbers by fractions

♦ Dividing fractions by fractions

♦ Solving fraction equations using multiplication and division

Home Activities

Here are some activities you can do with your child that use these math skills and concepts.

Find the recipes for some of your child's favorite foods. Have your child find how much of each ingredient would be needed if a recipe is doubled, tripled, or used to make enough servings for 50 people. Then have your child find the amount of each ingredient needed to make one half of the recipe(s) or one serving of a recipe.

Extend the activity by discussing how to measure ingredients with non-standard measures. A measuring cup may not have $\frac{1}{8}$-cup or $\frac{1}{3}$-cup marks. Have your child suggest ways to accurately measure these amounts. Also discuss measurement conversions when appropriate. For example, have your child explain how to easily measure 50 $\frac{1}{2}$-cups of milk. In addition, have your child suggest ways to measure very small fractional amounts that may arise, such as $\frac{1}{16}$ teaspoon of vanilla.

Your child can use multiple conversions to find easy ways to measure large amounts. For example, 2 cups = 1 pint, 2 pints = 1 quart, and 4 quarts = 1 gallon. So 4 cups = 1 quart and 16 cups = 1 gallon. Then there are 48 cups of milk in 3 gallons.

For small amounts, such as $\frac{1}{6}$-cup, your child could suggest ways to measure $\frac{1}{2}$ of a $\frac{1}{3}$-cup measuring cup.

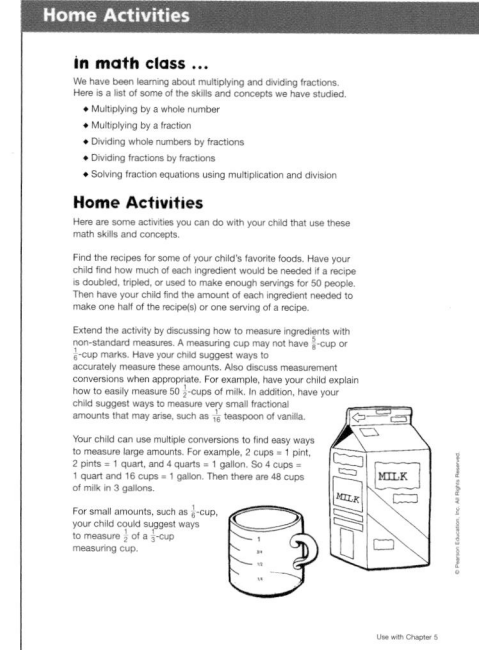

Available in Spanish;
Web Code: aak-5500

Name _____   *Math and Language Arts*

Newsy Fractions

Divide fractions to design and analyze newspaper page layouts.

The first successful American newspaper was printed in 1704 in Boston, Massachusetts. It was called the *Boston News-Letter*. It was very small—about the size of one sheet of notebook paper, with printing on both sides. The printing was divided into two columns. Today's newspapers are much larger, and they are divided into several pages.

The size of a newspaper and its staff is usually related to how many copies of the newspaper are sold. The average number of copies sold over a given period of time is called the newspaper's *circulation*. Some newspapers have a large circulation. *USA Today* has one of the largest circulations of any daily newspaper in the United States. More than 2 million copies are sold each day.

Large newspapers have several departments. The editorial department includes the people who prepare the stories for the newspapers. Reporters gather and write the news. Photographers take pictures to go with the news stories. Editors read the stories to make sure they are easy to follow and fit in the space allowed for them. Editors also choose the most important stories for the front page.

Another department of a large newspaper is the mechanical department. Its job is to print the newspaper. Most large newspapers have their own printing presses. Printing presses are machines that can print many copies of a

newspaper in a very short time. For instance, there are presses that print more than 70,000 newspapers per hour.

A third department of the newspaper is the business department. One of this department's biggest jobs is to sell advertising space. Many newspapers make more money from selling advertising space than from selling newspapers. Space is sold by the part of a page. A half-page ad, for example, would cost more than a quarter-page ad.

In every phase of newspaper production, newspaper personnel must consider how everything, including stories, photographs, sketches, cartoons, and advertisements, fits on the newspaper's pages. For this reason, a system of measurement is used by all newspapers. The basic units of this system are *points* and *picas*.

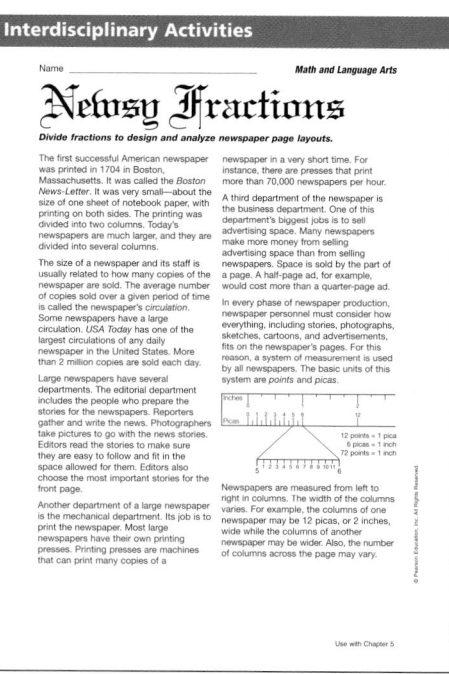

Newspapers are measured from left to right in columns. The width of the columns varies. For example, the width of one newspaper may be 12 picas, or 2 inches wide while the columns of another newspaper may be wider. Also, the number of columns across the page may vary.

Web Code: aak-5500

Web Code: aak-5500

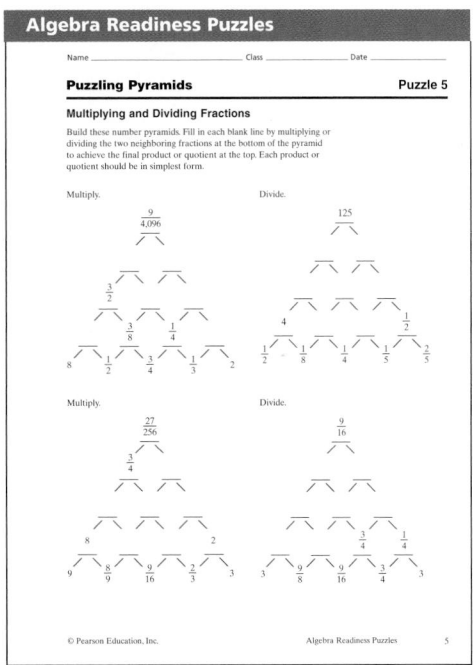

Web Code: aak-5500

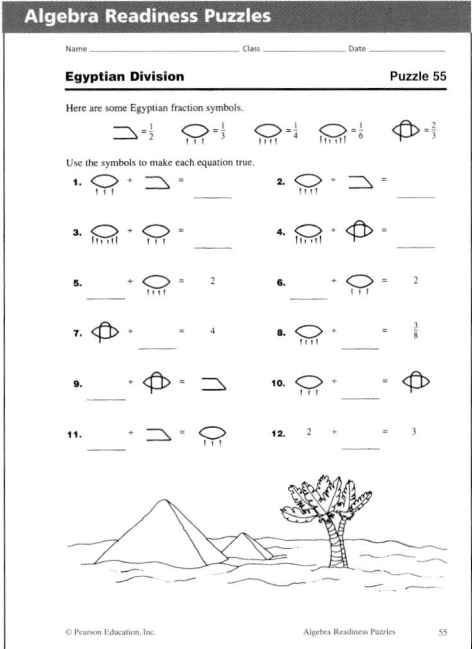

Web Code: aak-5500

CHAPTER 5

Multiplying and Dividing Fractions

Chapter 5 Overview

In this chapter students continue their study of fractions as they multiply and divide fractions and mixed numbers, and write and solve equations involving multiplication and division of fractions. In addition, students use their knowledge of fraction computation to change units within the customary system of measurement.

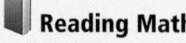 **Reading Math**
- Reading Expressions, p. 258
- **Vocabulary:** A complete list, plus exercises, in the Chapter Review, p. 260
- **Illustrated Glossary:** Examples for each vocabulary term, plus definitions in English and Spanish, on p. 669

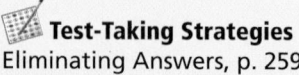 **Writing in Math**
Writing to Explain, p. 235

 **Test-Taking Strategies**
Eliminating Answers, p. 259

 **Real-World Problem Solving**
- **Strategies:** Solve a Simpler Problem, pp. 246–249
- **Real-World Snapshots:** Swimming to Win, pp. 264–265
- **Chapter Project:** Crack It and Cook It!, p. 638

💻 **www.PHSchool.com**
Internet support includes:
- Self-grading Vocabulary and Chapter 5 Tests
- Activity Masters
- Chapter Project support
- Chapter Planner
- Ch. 5 Resources

Plus **iTEXT**

Multiplying and Dividing Fractions

Key Vocabulary
- reciprocal (p. 230)

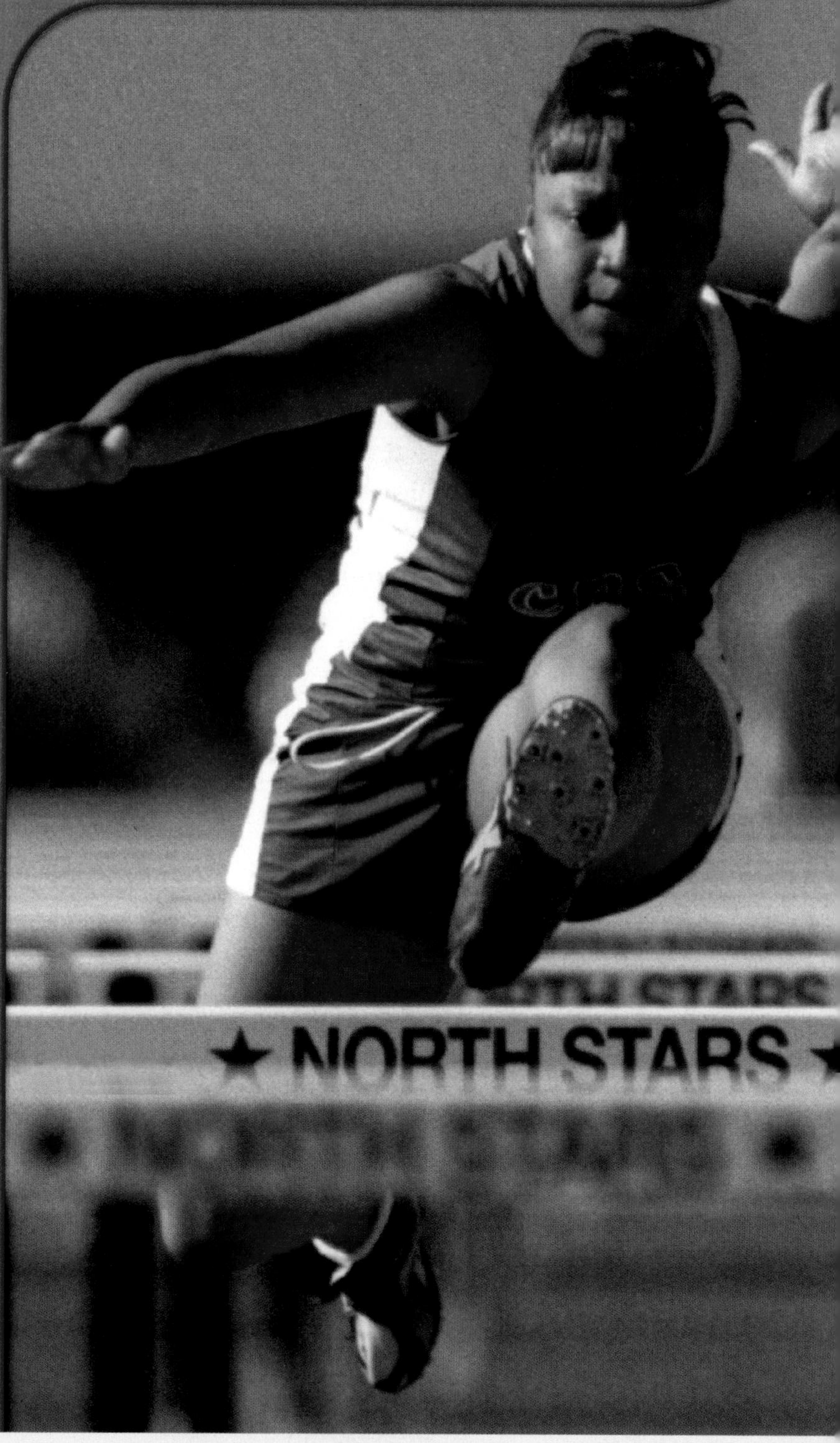

216

Real-World Snapshots

Track and field meets include events such as hurdles, relay races, high jump, long jump, and pole vault. Times are measured using decimals. Lengths and heights are measured using decimals or fractions.

Data File Junior Olympic Records for Long Jump

	Distance (feet)	
Age Group	Boys	Girls
10 and under	$15\frac{19}{24}$	$14\frac{29}{48}$
11–12	$18\frac{7}{16}$	$18\frac{5}{48}$
13–14	$21\frac{5}{8}$	$18\frac{23}{48}$
15–16	$24\frac{1}{8}$	$20\frac{3}{16}$
17–18	$24\frac{15}{16}$	$20\frac{7}{8}$

SOURCE: USA Track & Field

You will use the data above in this chapter:
- p. 227   Lesson 5-2
- p. 238   Lesson 5-4
- p. 256   Lesson 5-8

 Real-World Snapshots On pages 264 and 265, you will solve problems involving carpentry.

Teaching Notes

Activating Prior Knowledge
In this chapter students build on and extend their knowledge of fraction computation to multiply and divide fractions. They also draw upon their understanding of common multiples and factors, and of mental math strategies. Ask questions such as:
- *Write $\frac{20}{6}$ as a mixed number in simplest form.* $3\frac{1}{3}$
- *What is n in 3n = 42.* $n = 14$
- *What is the LCM of 4 and 18?* 36
- *What is the LCM of 12 and 30?* 60

 Real-World Snapshots
The data here will be used throughout the chapter. Have a volunteer read the opening passage and the title of the chart which contains information about long jump records for young athletes. Focus students on the data in the chart and ask:
- *Which category of competitors has the record that is closest to 24 ft?* boys 15–16 years old
- *What is the range of the records for boys?* $9\frac{7}{48}$ ft
- *What is the range of the records for girls?* $6\frac{13}{48}$ ft

Reading and Math Literacy

5A: Graphic Organizer   For use before Lesson 5-1

Study Skill: As you read over the material in the chapter, keep a paper and pencil handy to write down notes and questions that you have.

Write your answers.

1. What is the chapter title?
   Multiplying and Dividing Fractions

2. How many lessons are there in this chapter?
   8

3. What is the topic of the Reading Math page?
   Reading Expressions

4. What is the topic of the Test-Taking Strategy page?
   Eliminating Answers

5. Look through the pages of the chapter and list four real-world connections that you see discussed in this chapter.
   Answers will vary.

7. Complete the graphic organizer below as you work through the chapter.
   - In the center, write the title of the chapter.
   - When you begin a lesson, write the lesson name in a rectangle.
   - When you complete a lesson, write a skill or key concept in a circle linked to that lesson block.
   - When you complete the chapter, use this graphic organizer to help you review.

Available in Spanish

217

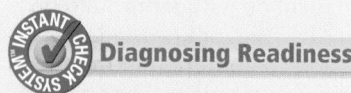

Students will find answers to these exercises in the back of their textbooks.

Prescribing Intervention
For intervention, direct students to:

Solving Equations by Multiplication and Division
Lesson 2-7: Examples 1, 3. Extra Practice, p. 643.

Finding the Greatest Common Factor
Lesson 3-3: Examples 1–3. Extra Practice, p. 644.

Writing Equivalent Fractions
Lesson 3-4: Example 2. Extra Practice, p. 644.

Chapter 5 Preview

Where You've Been

- In Chapter 3, you simplified and compared fractions. You also learned to express fractions as decimals.

- In Chapter 4, you added and subtracted fractions and mixed numbers.

Where You're Going

- In Chapter 5, you will multiply and divide fractions and mixed numbers.

- You will also change units in the customary system.

- Applying what you learn, you will change units as an architect does.

Architects often change units within the customary system.

Instant self-check online and on CD-ROM

Diagnosing Readiness

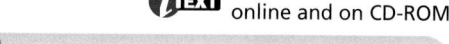

? For help, go to the lesson in green.

Solving Multiplication and Division Equations (Lesson 2-7)

Solve each equation.

1. $3a = 12$ **4**

2. $5x = 25$ **5**

3. $p \div 3 = 4$ **12**

4. $14 = x \div 8$ **112**

5. $0.1n = 10$ **100**

6. $750 = 150n$ **5**

7. $w \div 6 = 9$ **54**

8. $2 = g \div 0.3$ **0.6**

9. $48 = 16p$ **3**

Finding the Greatest Common Factor (Lesson 3-3)

Find the GCF of each set of numbers.

10. 12, 24 **12**

11. 28, 35 **7**

12. 27, 24 **3**

13. 80, 100 **20**

14. 36, 66 **6**

15. 21, 42 **21**

Writing Equivalent Fractions (Lesson 3-4)

Write each fraction in simplest form.

16. $\frac{15}{35}$ $\frac{3}{7}$

17. $\frac{24}{36}$ $\frac{2}{3}$

18. $\frac{16}{48}$ $\frac{1}{3}$

19. $\frac{24}{64}$ $\frac{3}{8}$

20. $\frac{18}{72}$ $\frac{1}{4}$

21. $\frac{21}{49}$ $\frac{3}{7}$

22. $\frac{32}{48}$ $\frac{2}{3}$

23. $\frac{49}{56}$ $\frac{7}{8}$

24. $\frac{36}{84}$ $\frac{3}{7}$

5-1 Multiplying Fractions

What You'll Learn

 OBJECTIVE 1 To multiply two fractions

 OBJECTIVE 2 To multiply fractions by whole numbers

...And Why

To find lengths, as in Example 4

 Check Skills You'll Need

$\text{\textbf{?}}$ For help, go to Lesson 3-4.

Write each fraction in simplest form.

1. $\frac{5}{10}$ $\frac{1}{2}$

2. $\frac{9}{15}$ $\frac{3}{5}$

3. $\frac{28}{42}$ $\frac{2}{3}$

4. $\frac{90}{100}$ $\frac{9}{10}$

5. $\frac{18}{24}$ $\frac{3}{4}$

6. $\frac{36}{48}$ $\frac{3}{4}$

7. Is $\frac{9}{16}$ in simplest form? Explain. **Answers may vary.**
Sample: Yes; the GCF of 9 and 16 is 1.

Lesson Preview

✔ **Check Skills You'll Need** [PowerPoint]

Writing Fractions in Simplest Form
Lesson 3-4: Example 2. Extra Practice p. 644.

Lesson Resources

📁 **Teaching Resources**
Practice, Reteaching, Enrichment

👥 **Reaching All Students**
Practice Workbook 5-1
Spanish Practice Workbook 5-1
Guided Problem Solving 5-1
Hands-On Activities 16

⏱ **Presentation Assistant Plus!**
Transparencies
• Check Skills You'll Need 5-1
• Problem of the Day 5-1
• Additional Examples 5-1
• Student Edition Answers 5-1
• Lesson Quiz 5-1
• Classroom Aid 2
PH Presentation Pro CD-ROM 5-1

PRENTICE HALL ASSESSMENT SYSTEM

Computer Test Generator CD

💻 **Technology**
Resource Pro® CD-ROM
Computer Test Generator CD
PH Presentation Pro CD-ROM

💻 **www.PHSchool.com**
Student Site
• Teacher Web Code: aak-5500
• Self-grading Lesson Quiz

PH SuccessNet Teacher Center
• Lesson Planner
• Resources

Plus 𝒊 **TEXT**

OBJECTIVE 1 Multiplying Two Fractions

𝒊 **TEXT** Interactive lesson includes instant self-check, tutorials, and activities.

$\frac{1}{4}$

Investigation: Modeling Multiplication of Fractions

Suppose you and your friend order a half-vegetable, half-cheese pizza. You like vegetable; your friend likes cheese.

1. Use a rectangular piece of paper to represent the pizza. Fold it in half as shown. Shade one of the two parts to represent your half. **Check students' work.**

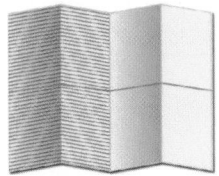

2. Refold the paper. Then fold it in half two more times. How many slices of pizza are there? **8**

3. Suppose you eat $\frac{3}{4}$ of your half. Draw an X on three of the four slices in your half. What fraction of the whole pizza have you eaten? $\frac{3}{8}$

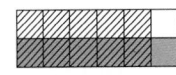

4. The third model represents $\frac{3}{4} \times \frac{1}{2}$. Use a model to find $\frac{1}{2} \times \frac{1}{2}$.

You can model the multiplication of fractions by shading parts of a rectangle. This type of model is an area model. The model at the right shows $\frac{5}{6} \times \frac{1}{2} = \frac{5}{12}$.

Ongoing Assessment and Intervention

Before the Lesson
Diagnose prerequisite skills using:
• Check Skills You'll Need

During the Lesson
Monitor progress using:
• Check Understanding
• Additional Examples
• Test Prep

After the Lesson
Assess knowledge using:
• Lesson Quiz
• Computer Test Generator CD

2. Teach

Professional Development

Math Background

The familiar rule for multiplying two fractions is $\frac{a}{b} \cdot \frac{c}{d} = \frac{ac}{bd}$, provided that neither b nor d is zero. This rule is, in fact, an algebraic *theorem*. That is, the rule can be justified by a logical argument that is supported by known algebraic properties. For students at this level, however, the rule can be justified in a much more concrete manner through the use of the area model that is presented in Example 1.

Teaching Notes

Investigation (Optional)
Students should observe that, in a situation like this, the word "of" signals a multiplication.

$$\frac{3}{4} \text{ of } \frac{1}{2}$$
$$\downarrow \quad \downarrow \quad \downarrow$$
$$\frac{3}{4} \quad \cdot \quad \frac{1}{2}$$

1 EXAMPLE Teaching Tip

Be sure students understand how to divide the rectangle into the correct number of parts. Ask:
• *Why was the width of the rectangle divided into two equal parts?* The denominator of one of the fractions is two.
• *Why was the length of the rectangle divided into five equal parts?* The denominator of the other fraction is five.

2 EXAMPLE Auditory Learners

Students might find it helpful to recite the fraction multiplication rule softly as they perform the steps. In Check Understanding 2a, for instance, they can say: "Multiply the numerators—three times one. Multiply the denominators—five times four."

Alternative Method

Emphasize, as shown below Example 2, that students can simplify fractions before multiplying. To help students understand that dividing the numerator and denominator by 2 is a justified simplification, show the following. $\frac{3}{8} \cdot \frac{2}{5} = \frac{3 \cdot 2}{8 \cdot 5} = \frac{3 \cdot \cancel{2}}{\cancel{2} \cdot 4 \cdot 5} = \frac{3}{4 \cdot 5}$, or $\frac{3}{20}$

220

---

1 EXAMPLE   Modeling Fraction Multiplication

Draw a model to find the product $\frac{3}{5} \times \frac{1}{2}$.

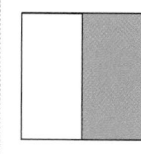 Divide a rectangle ← in half. Shade one of the halves.

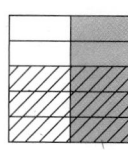 Divide each half into fifths. Use diagonal lines to shade three of the fifths.

$$\frac{3}{5} \times \frac{1}{2} = \frac{3}{10}$$

✔ **Check Understanding** ① Draw a model to find the product of $\frac{1}{3} \times \frac{2}{5}$. **See left.**

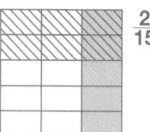 $\frac{2}{15}$

Example 1 shows that $\frac{3}{5} \times \frac{1}{2} = \frac{3}{10}$. You can get this product by multiplying the numerators and multiplying the denominators.

Key Concepts   **Multiplying Fractions**

Arithmetic	Algebra
$\frac{3}{4} \times \frac{1}{2} = \frac{3 \times 1}{4 \times 2} = \frac{3}{8}$	$\frac{a}{b} \cdot \frac{c}{d} = \frac{ac}{bd}$, where b and d are not zero.

---

2 EXAMPLE   Multiplying Two Fractions

? Need Help?
For help with simplifying fractions, go to Lesson 3-4.

Find the product $\frac{3}{8} \cdot \frac{2}{5}$.

$$\frac{3}{8} \cdot \frac{2}{5} = \frac{3 \cdot 2}{8 \cdot 5} \quad \leftarrow \text{Multiply the numerators.} \\ \leftarrow \text{Multiply the denominators.}$$

$$= \frac{6}{40} \quad \leftarrow \text{Find the two products.}$$

$$= \frac{3}{20} \quad \leftarrow \text{Simplify.}$$

✔ **Check Understanding** ② Find each product.   **a.** $\frac{3}{5} \cdot \frac{1}{4}$ $\frac{3}{20}$ **b.** $\frac{2}{9} \times \frac{5}{7}$ $\frac{10}{63}$

c. Reasoning How is adding $\frac{3}{8}$ and $\frac{5}{8}$ different from multiplying the two fractions? Explain.

When you add $\frac{3}{8}$ and $\frac{5}{8}$ you add numerators and keep the same denominator. When you multiply the fractions, you multiply numerators and multiply denominators.

Sometimes you can simplify before multiplying fractions.

$$\frac{3}{8} \cdot \frac{2}{5} = \frac{3}{\underset{4}{8}} \cdot \frac{\overset{1}{2}}{5} \quad \leftarrow \text{Divide 8 and 2 by their GCF, 2.}$$

$$= \frac{3 \cdot 1}{4 \cdot 5} \quad \leftarrow \text{Multiply the numerators and the denominators.}$$

$$= \frac{3}{20} \quad \leftarrow \text{Simplify.}$$

220   **Chapter 5**   Multiplying and Dividing Fractions

♥ Reaching All Students

Below Level Give students several blank forms like the one below to use for organizing their work.	**Advanced Learners** Find the product. Simplify before you multiply.	**Alternative Method** See note on page 220.
$\frac{\blacksquare}{\blacksquare} \cdot \frac{\blacksquare}{\blacksquare} = \frac{\blacksquare \cdot \blacksquare}{\blacksquare \cdot \blacksquare} = \frac{\blacksquare}{\blacksquare}$	$\frac{2}{3} \cdot \frac{9}{10} \cdot \frac{5}{14} \cdot \frac{7}{15}$ $\frac{1}{10}$	**Auditory Learners** See note on page 220.

To multiply a fraction by a whole number, write the whole number as an improper fraction with a denominator of 1. Then multiply the two fractions.

Reading Math
The word *of* usually indicates multiplication.

3 EXAMPLE Multiplying Fractions by Whole Numbers

Find $\frac{3}{4}$ of 20.

$\frac{3}{4} \times 20 = \frac{3}{4} \times \frac{20}{1}$ ← $\frac{3}{4}$ of 20 means $\frac{3}{4} \times 20$. Write 20 as $\frac{20}{1}$.

$= \frac{3}{{}_1 4} \times \frac{20^5}{1}$ ← Simplify first. Divide 20 and 4 by their GCF, 4.

$= \frac{15}{1}$ ← Multiply the numerators and the denominators.

$= 15$ ← Simplify.

✓ **Check Understanding** **3** Find each product.   **a.** $\frac{4}{5}$ of 7   **b.** $24 \cdot \frac{5}{9}$ $\frac{28}{5} = 5\frac{3}{5}$ $\frac{40}{3} = 13\frac{1}{3}$

4 EXAMPLE Real-World Problem Solving

Measurement Students in art class are using ribbon to decorate a bulletin board. A piece of green ribbon is $\frac{5}{6}$ yard long. A piece of yellow ribbon is nine times as long. How long is the piece of yellow ribbon?

Draw a diagram to help see how these lengths relate to each other.

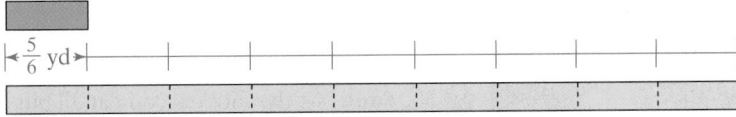

Find the length of the yellow ribbon by multiplying 9 and $\frac{5}{6}$.

$9 \cdot \frac{5}{6} = \frac{9}{1} \cdot \frac{5}{6}$ ← Write 9 as $\frac{9}{1}$.

$= \frac{{}^3 9}{1} \cdot \frac{5}{6_2}$ ← Divide 9 and 6 by their GCF, 3.

$= \frac{15}{2}$ ← Multiply the numerators and the denominators.

$= 7\frac{1}{2}$ ← Write as a mixed number.

The yellow ribbon is $7\frac{1}{2}$ yards long.

✓ **Check Understanding** **4** Juanita lives $\frac{3}{4}$ mile from school. Carlota lives 6 times as far away from school as Juanita. How far from school does Carlota live? $4\frac{1}{2}$ mi

Error Prevention!

When multiplying a fraction by a whole number, students might "distribute" the whole number over the numerator and denominator of the fraction. For instance, in Check Understanding 3a they might rewrite $\frac{4}{5} \times 7$ as $\frac{4 \times 7}{5 \times 7}$. Stress the importance of rewriting the whole number as a fraction before multiplying.

Additional Examples

1 Draw a model to find the product $\frac{1}{3} \times \frac{5}{8}$. $\frac{5}{24}$

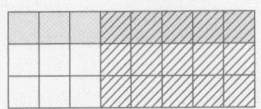

2 Find the product $\frac{5}{6} \cdot \frac{3}{8}$. $\frac{5}{16}$

3 There are 30 students in Shari's homeroom. Of these students, $\frac{2}{5}$ worked at the school fair. How many students in Shari's homeroom worked at the school fair? **12 students**

4 The width of a very old pipe is $\frac{3}{8}$ inch. A plumber must replace it with a new pipe that is 4 times as wide. What should be the width of the new pipe? $1\frac{1}{2}$ in.

Closure

• *How do you multiply fractions?* Multiply the numerators, multiply the denominators, and simplify.

• *How do you multiply a fraction by a whole number?* Write the whole number as a fraction with denominator 1. Then multiply numerators, multiply denominators, and simplify.

3. Practice

Assignment Guide

1 Objective 1
Ⓐ Ⓑ Core 1–13, 29–30, 32–35

2 Objective 2
Ⓐ Ⓑ Core 14–28, 31, 36
Ⓒ Extension 37–38

Test Prep 39–42
Mixed Review 43–58

Exercises 31–34 Remind students that these expressions represent products, even though there is no visible multiplication symbol.

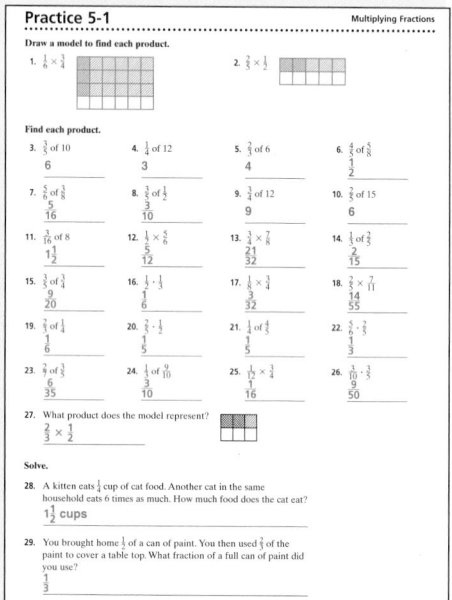

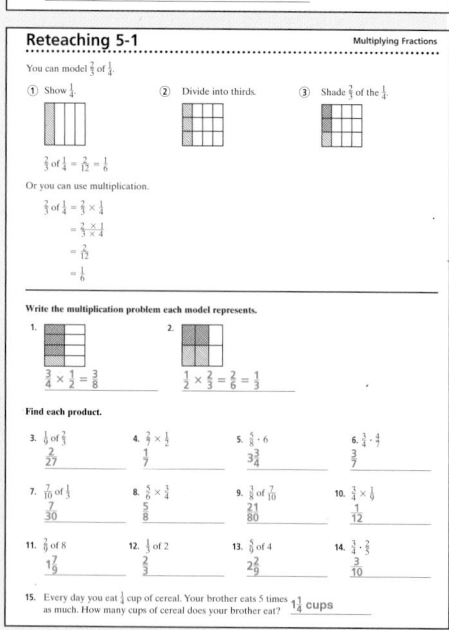

222

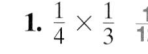
EXERCISES

For more practice, see *Extra Practice*.

Ⓐ **Practice by Example**

Draw a model to find each product. 1–4. See margin for models.

Example 1
(page 220)

1. $\frac{1}{4} \times \frac{1}{3}$ $\frac{1}{12}$
2. $\frac{1}{2} \times \frac{3}{4}$ $\frac{3}{8}$
3. $\frac{1}{5} \cdot \frac{5}{8}$ $\frac{5}{40} = \frac{1}{8}$
4. $\frac{2}{3} \cdot \frac{2}{5}$ $\frac{4}{15}$

Find each product. Exercises 5 and 14 have been started for you.

Example 2
(page 220)

5. $\frac{1}{2} \times \frac{3}{8} = \frac{1 \times 3}{2 \times 8}$ $\frac{3}{16}$
6. $\frac{5}{11} \times \frac{2}{7}$ $\frac{10}{77}$
7. $\frac{3}{4} \times \frac{11}{12}$ $\frac{11}{16}$

8. $\frac{2}{9} \times \frac{4}{8}$ $\frac{1}{9}$
9. $\frac{4}{9} \cdot \frac{3}{10}$ $\frac{2}{15}$
10. $\frac{3}{5} \cdot \frac{2}{3}$ $\frac{2}{5}$

11. $\frac{4}{11}$ of $\frac{5}{8}$ $\frac{5}{22}$
12. $\frac{9}{10}$ of $\frac{2}{5}$ $\frac{9}{25}$
13. $\frac{7}{15}$ of $\frac{3}{4}$ $\frac{7}{20}$

Examples 3, 4
(page 221)

14. $\frac{3}{8} \times 5 = \frac{3}{8} \times \frac{5}{1}$ $1\frac{7}{8}$
15. $\frac{11}{14}$ of 28 22
16. $\frac{5}{12} \cdot 30$ $12\frac{1}{2}$

17. $\frac{7}{9}$ of 21 $16\frac{1}{3}$
18. $\frac{1}{6} \cdot 6$ 1
19. $\frac{3}{10} \times 45$ $13\frac{1}{2}$

20. Fitness For gym class, you run $\frac{3}{4}$ of a mile. Your gym teacher runs that distance 3 times, since she teaches 3 classes. How far does she run? $2\frac{1}{4}$ mi

Ⓑ **Apply Your Skills**

Mental Math Find each product.

21. $\frac{1}{4} \cdot 44$ 11
22. $\frac{2}{7}$ of 63 18
23. $\frac{1}{12} \times 60$ 5
24. $\frac{4}{5}$ of 50 40

25. $\frac{1}{6}$ of 72 12
26. $\frac{3}{8}$ of 24 9
27. $\frac{5}{9}$ of 81 45
28. $\frac{7}{10}$ of 80 56

29. Writing in Math Explain how you can divide by common factors before you multiply to find $\frac{2}{3} \cdot \frac{4}{5} \cdot \frac{3}{4}$. See margin.

30. Food At the movies you eat all but $\frac{1}{3}$ of a box of popcorn. Your friend eats $\frac{2}{3}$ of what is left. What fraction of the popcorn does your friend eat? Who eats more? How much more? $\frac{2}{9}$ of the popcorn; you ate more; $\frac{4}{9}$ of the popcorn.

(**Algebra**) **Evaluate each expression for** $x = \frac{2}{3}$.

31. $15x$ 10
32. $\frac{3}{2}x$ 1
33. $\frac{9}{10}x$ $\frac{3}{5}$
34. $\frac{2}{3}x$ $\frac{4}{9}$

35. Landscaping Suppose $\frac{3}{5}$ of your yard will be grass and the rest will be plants. You plant flowers in $\frac{3}{4}$ of the plant area. What portion of the yard will have flowers? $\frac{3}{10}$

Real-World 🌐 Connection
The Washington Monument is the largest masonry structure in the world.

36. Monuments The length of a side at the base of the Washington [GPS] Monument is about $\frac{1}{10}$ of its height. The monument is about 555 feet tall. Find the length of a side at the base. about $55\frac{1}{2}$ ft

222 Chapter 5 Multiplying and Dividing Fractions

[GPS] Use the Guided Problem Solving worksheet with Exercise 36.

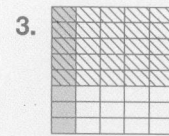
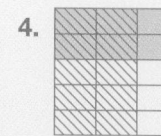

3. 4.

29. In the first and third fractions, divide denominator and

numerator by the common factor 3. In the second and third fractions, divide numerator and denominator by the common factor 4. You get

$\frac{2}{{}_1 3} \cdot \frac{4^1}{5} \cdot \frac{3^1}{4_1}$ or $\frac{2}{1} \cdot \frac{1}{5} \cdot \frac{1}{1}$.

1. 2.

37. Budgets Suppose the graph describes Paul's monthly spending. He makes $2,712 a month. How much does he spend each month on his rent and his car combined? **$1,017**

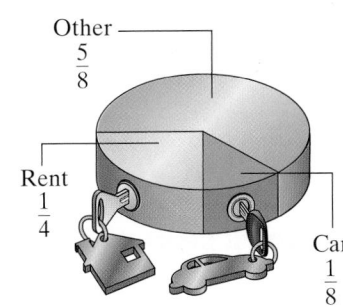

Other $\frac{5}{8}$

Rent $\frac{1}{4}$

Car $\frac{1}{8}$

38. Stretch Your Thinking In a three-digit number, the sum of its ones digit and tens digit is ten. Its tens digit is twice its hundreds digit, and its hundreds digit is twice its ones digit. What is the number? **482**

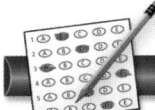

Test Prep

Multiple Choice

39. What is $\frac{3}{7}$ of 35? **D**

   A. $\frac{1}{15}$ **B.** $\frac{3}{5}$ **C.** 5   **D.** 15

40. What is the product of $\frac{5}{6}$ and $\frac{14}{15}$? **F**

   F. $\frac{7}{9}$ **G.** $\frac{7}{3}$ **H.** $1\frac{1}{2}$ **I.** $4\frac{1}{2}$

41. Which product is NOT equal to the others? **B**

   A. $\frac{4}{25} \cdot 20$ **B.** $\frac{4}{25} \cdot \frac{1}{20}$ **C.** $\frac{4}{5} \cdot \frac{4}{1}$ **D.** $\frac{20}{1} \cdot \frac{4}{25}$

Extended Response

Take It to the NET
Online lesson quiz at
www.PHSchool.com
Web Code: aaa-0501

42. You buy several items on sale. You buy a shirt for $\frac{4}{5}$ of its original cost of $21, jeans for $\frac{3}{4}$ of their original cost of $40, and shoes for $\frac{9}{10}$ of their original cost of $27. **42a–b. See margin.**

   a. How much money do you save on your shopping trip?

   b. What fraction of the total original cost do you pay?

Mixed Review

Lesson 4-3   **Find each sum or difference.**

43. $\frac{5}{6} + \frac{1}{3}$ $1\frac{1}{6}$ **44.** $\frac{4}{5} - \frac{1}{2}$ $\frac{3}{10}$ **45.** $\frac{7}{9} - \frac{3}{5}$ $\frac{8}{45}$ **46.** $\frac{3}{10} + \frac{5}{8}$ $\frac{37}{40}$

47. $\frac{7}{8} - \frac{5}{12}$ $\frac{11}{24}$ **48.** $\frac{3}{4} + \frac{1}{6}$ $\frac{11}{12}$ **49.** $\frac{2}{3} + \frac{1}{2}$ $1\frac{1}{6}$ **50.** $\frac{2}{3} - \frac{3}{7}$ $\frac{5}{21}$

Lesson 3-2   **Tell whether each number is prime or composite.**

51. 119   **52.** 10,101   **53.** 61   **54.** 135,792
    composite   composite   prime   composite

55. 231   **56.** 97   **57.** 441   **58.** 157
    composite   prime   composite   prime

---

4. Assess

PowerPoint Lesson Quiz 5-1

Find each product. Simplify.

1. $\frac{3}{5} \times \frac{5}{8}$ $\frac{3}{8}$ **2.** $8 \times \frac{3}{4}$ 6

3. $\frac{7}{8}$ of 56   49   **4.** $\frac{4}{5}$ of $\frac{9}{12}$ $\frac{3}{5}$

Alternative Assessment

Each student in a pair writes a fraction and a whole number. Partners work together to multiply each of their fractions and to multiply each fraction and whole number, resulting in five fraction multiplications.

Test Prep

Resources

For additional practice with a variety of test item formats:
• Test-Prep, p. 263
• Test-Taking Strategies, p. 259
• Test-Taking Strategies With Transparencies

[2] appropriate method with no computational errors for one part OR correct answers with no work shown

[1] appropriate method on one part with computational errors OR one correct answer

---

Enrichment 5-1   Multiplying Fractions

Critical Thinking

To make $1\frac{1}{2}$ cups of a fruit dessert, you use 1 cup of sour cream, $\frac{1}{2}$ cup of orange marmalade, $\frac{1}{4}$ cup of walnuts, 2 tablespoons of milk and one can of assorted fruit. Adjust this recipe to make 2 whole cups of the fruit dessert.

1. How many cups does the recipe make and how many cups do you need to make?
   The recipe makes $1\frac{1}{2}$ cups and 2 cups are needed.

2. Will you use more or less of each ingredient to make 2 cups of the dessert? How do you know?
   More, since 2 cups is greater than $1\frac{1}{2}$ cups.

3. Change $1\frac{1}{2}$ cups to a mixed number.
   $1\frac{1}{2} = \frac{3}{2}$

4. What fraction multiplied by the mixed number in Exercise 3 results in a product of 2.
   When $\frac{3}{2}$ is multiplied by $\frac{4}{3}$ the product is 2.

5. What factor will you multiply each ingredient by to make 2 whole cups of the fruit dessert?
   $\frac{4}{3}$ or $1\frac{1}{3}$

6. Complete the table to the find the quantities needed to make 2 cups of the fruit dessert.

Fruit Dessert Recipe		
Ingredient	$1\frac{1}{2}$ cups	2 cups
sour cream	1 cup	$1\frac{1}{3}$ cup
orange marmalade	$\frac{1}{2}$ cup	$\frac{2}{3}$ cup
walnuts	$\frac{1}{4}$ cup	$\frac{1}{3}$ cup
milk	2 tbsp	$2\frac{2}{3}$ tbsp
can of fruit	1 can	$1\frac{1}{3}$ can

7. Explain how you could use division to rewrite the recipe.
   Divide 2 cups by $1\frac{1}{2}$ cups. Then multiply the quotient by the amounts of the ingredients.

---

42. [4] a. The amount you save is the difference of the total original cost and what you pay. The total original cost is $21 + $40 + $27 = $88. The amount you pay is $\frac{4}{5} \cdot \$21 + \frac{3}{4} \cdot \$40 + \frac{9}{10} \cdot \$21 = \$16.80 + \$30.00 + \$24.30 = \$71.10$. So the amount you save is $88.00 − $71.10 = $16.90

b. $\frac{711}{880}$

The fraction of the total original cost you pay is $\frac{\$71.10}{\$88.00} = \frac{71.10 \times 10}{88.00 \times 10} = \frac{711}{880}$.

[3] appropriate methods with 1 or 2 computational errors

Multiplying Mixed Numbers

1. Plan

Lesson Preview

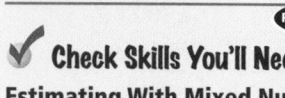

✓ **Check Skills You'll Need**

Estimating With Mixed Numbers
Lesson 4-1: Example 2. Extra
Practice p. 645.

Lesson Resources

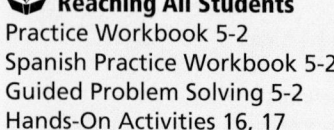

📁 **Teaching Resources**
Practice, Reteaching, Enrichment

👥 **Reaching All Students**
Practice Workbook 5-2
Spanish Practice Workbook 5-2
Guided Problem Solving 5-2
Hands-On Activities 16, 17

⏰ **Presentation Assistant Plus!**
Transparencies
• Check Skills You'll Need 5-2
• Problem of the Day 5-2
• Additional Examples 5-2
• Student Edition Answers 5-2
• Lesson Quiz 5-2
PH Presentation Pro CD-ROM 5-2

ASSESSMENT SYSTEM

Computer Test Generator CD

💻 **Technology**
Resource Pro® CD-ROM
Computer Test Generator CD
PH Presentation Pro CD-ROM

💻 **www.PHSchool.com**
Student Site
• Teacher Web Code: aak-5500
• Self-grading Lesson Quiz

PH SuccessNet Teacher Center
• Lesson Planner
• Resources

Plus 📘**TEXT**

Check Understanding

1d. The actual product is
greater than $80 \cdot \frac{1}{8}$,
since $82\frac{5}{7} > 80$.
So the actual product is
greater than 10. $83 \cdot 0$
would give an estimate
of 0, which is not
realistic.

What You'll Learn

 OBJECTIVE 1 To estimate
products of mixed
numbers

 OBJECTIVE 2 To multiply mixed
numbers

...And Why

To find how far a person
can ski, as in Example 3

✓ **Check Skills You'll Need**

❓ For help, go to Lesson 4-1.

Estimate each sum or difference.

1. $3\frac{6}{7} - 2\frac{1}{3}$ 2

2. $5\frac{2}{3} + 7\frac{1}{5}$ 13

3. $11\frac{3}{4} + 17\frac{5}{9}$ 30

4. $6\frac{5}{6} + 1\frac{1}{7}$ 8

5. $8\frac{7}{9} - 2\frac{6}{7}$ 6

6. $7\frac{5}{8} - 1\frac{2}{3}$ 6

OBJECTIVE 1

 **TEXT** Interactive lesson includes instant self-check, tutorials, and activities.

Estimating Products of Mixed Numbers

To estimate the product of mixed numbers, round the mixed numbers
to the nearest whole number and then multiply. If the fraction part of a
mixed number is $\frac{1}{2}$ or greater, round up.

1 **EXAMPLE** **Estimating Products**  **Real World**

Newspapers One of the smallest newspapers ever printed had a page size
of $1\frac{1}{4}$ inches wide by $2\frac{3}{4}$ inches long. Estimate the area of a page.

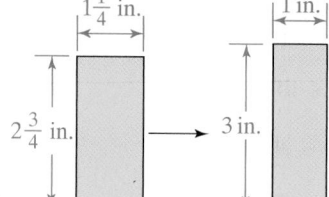

Real-World 🌐 **Connection**
The smallest newspaper in
circulation is the Brazilian
Vossa Senhoria. It measures
0.98 inch by 1.38 inches!

Step 1 Round the length and
width to the nearest whole numbers.

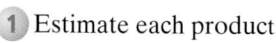

Original size   Rounded size
$1\frac{1}{4}$ in.   1 in.

$2\frac{3}{4}$ in.   →   3 in.

Step 2 Multiply to estimate
the area.

Area = length × width

$\approx 3 \times 1$

$= 3$

The area of a page is about
3 square inches.

✓ **Check Understanding** ① Estimate each product.

a. $5\frac{5}{6} \times 6\frac{4}{9}$ 36

b. $7\frac{11}{16} \cdot 7\frac{1}{5}$ 56

c. $12\frac{1}{2} \times 10\frac{2}{3}$ 143

d. **Reasoning** Suppose you want to estimate the product of $82\frac{5}{7}$ and $\frac{1}{8}$.
Explain why $80 \cdot \frac{1}{8}$ is a better estimate than $83 \cdot 0$. **See margin.**

Ongoing Assessment and Intervention

Before the Lesson
Diagnose prerequisite skills using:
• Check Skills You'll Need

During the Lesson
Monitor progress using:
• Check Understanding
• Additional Examples
• Test Prep

After the Lesson
Assess knowledge using:
• Lesson Quiz
• Computer Test Generator CD

To find the product of mixed numbers, write each mixed number as an improper fraction before multiplying.

2 EXAMPLE Multiplying Using Improper Fractions

Find the product $2\frac{2}{3} \times 3\frac{1}{4}$.

Test-Prep Tip
Estimate first and then check your computation to determine if your answer is reasonable.

Estimate $2\frac{2}{3} \times 3\frac{1}{4} \approx 3 \times 3$, or 9

$2\frac{2}{3} \times 3\frac{1}{4} = \frac{8}{3} \times \frac{13}{4}$ ← Write the mixed numbers as improper fractions.

$= \frac{\overset{2}{8}}{3} \times \frac{13}{\underset{1}{4}}$ ← Divide 8 and 4 by their GCF, 4.

$= \frac{26}{3}$, or $8\frac{2}{3}$ ← Multiply the numerators and the denominators. Then write as a mixed number.

Check for Reasonableness $8\frac{2}{3}$ is near the estimate of 9.

✓ **Check Understanding** 2 Find each product.

    a. $1\frac{1}{4} \times 2\frac{3}{4}$ $3\frac{7}{16}$ **b.** $7\frac{1}{3} \times 3\frac{3}{4}$ $27\frac{1}{2}$ **c.** $10\frac{4}{5} \cdot 1\frac{2}{3}$ 18

3 EXAMPLE Real-World 🌐 Problem Solving

Skiing A student can ski cross-country $3\frac{1}{2}$ miles in one hour. Her instructor can ski cross-country $1\frac{1}{3}$ times as far in the same amount of time. How far can the instructor ski in one hour?

The diagram at the left shows the distance that the instructor skis in one hour, which is $1\frac{1}{3}$ times as far as the student skis.

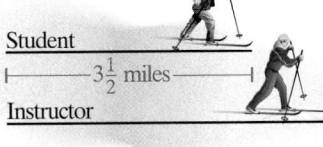

Student
$3\frac{1}{2}$ miles
Instructor

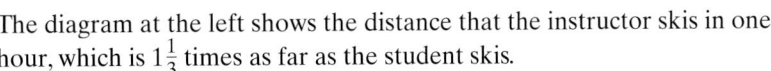

number of miles the instructor skis $= 1\frac{1}{3} \times$ number of miles the student skis

$= 1\frac{1}{3} \times 3\frac{1}{2}$

$= \frac{4}{3} \times \frac{7}{2}$ ← Write the mixed numbers as improper fractions.

$= \frac{\overset{2}{4}}{3} \times \frac{7}{\underset{1}{2}}$ ← Divide 4 and 2 by their GCF, 2.

$= \frac{14}{3}$, or $4\frac{2}{3}$ ← Multiply the numerators and the denominators. Then write as a mixed number.

The instructor can ski $4\frac{2}{3}$ miles in one hour.

✓ **Check Understanding** 3 How many miles can the student ski in $\frac{3}{4}$ hour? $2\frac{5}{8}$ mi

🌿 **Reaching All Students**

Below Level Have students perform multiplications using improper fractions, such as $\frac{5}{3} \times \frac{3}{2} = \frac{5}{2}$. Then have them rewrite the multiplications using mixed numbers. $1\frac{2}{3} \times 1\frac{1}{2} = 2\frac{1}{2}$	**Advanced Learners** Find two mixed numbers whose product is $2\frac{1}{10}$. Sample: $1\frac{1}{2}$ and $1\frac{2}{5}$ $\left(2\frac{1}{10} = \frac{21}{10} = \frac{3}{2} \cdot \frac{7}{5} = 1\frac{1}{2} \cdot 1\frac{2}{5}\right)$	**Inclusion** See note on page 225. **Diversity** See note on page 226.

---

2. Teach

Professional Development

Math Background

To many students, the task of performing a multiplication such as $2\frac{2}{3} \times 3\frac{1}{4}$ can be intimidating. In this lesson, however, they see how rewriting the mixed numbers as improper fractions transforms a multiplication like this to the familiar form $\frac{a}{b} \cdot \frac{c}{d}$. Then they need only apply the fraction multiplication rule that they learned in Lesson 5-1.

Teaching Notes

1 EXAMPLE Inclusion

You might want to review the process of rounding mixed numbers. Ask:
- *Why do you replace $1\frac{1}{4}$ inches with 1 inch?* Sample: $1\frac{1}{4}$ is closer to 1 than to 2.
- *Why do you replace $2\frac{3}{4}$ inches with 3 inches?* Sample: $2\frac{3}{4}$ is closer to 3 than to 2.

Error Prevention!

Some students might attempt to multiply mixed numbers by multiplying the whole numbers and multiplying the fractions. For instance, in Check Understanding 2a, they might calculate $1\frac{1}{4} \times 2\frac{3}{4}$ by multiplying $1 \times 2 = 2$ and $\frac{1}{4} \times \frac{3}{4} = \frac{3}{16}$, then giving the result as $2\frac{3}{16}$. Stress the importance of first rewriting the mixed numbers as improper fractions.

PowerPoint
🖥 Additional Examples

1 The pages of a book are $5\frac{1}{9}$ inches wide and $8\frac{3}{4}$ inches long. Estimate the area of a page in square inches. about 45 square inches

2 Find the product $3\frac{3}{8} \times 1\frac{5}{9}$. $5\frac{1}{4}$

3 A gear on a machine makes $2\frac{2}{3}$ turns in one minute. How many turns does this gear make in $4\frac{1}{2}$ minutes? 12 turns

Hummus is a popular Middle Eastern food. The recipe for hummus given on page 226 makes a thick sauce that is usually served as a dip with pita bread. Extend the *More Than One Way* discussion by asking students to bring in recipes for foods that are representative of other cultures and that might be suitable for a class picnic. Have them calculate the amount of each ingredient that would be needed if they were to make $2\frac{1}{2}$ times each recipe.

Closure

Explain how to multiply mixed numbers. **Write each mixed number as an improper fraction. Then multiply the numerators and multiply the denominators of the fractions. Simplify and rewrite improper fractions as mixed numbers.**

More Than One Way

How would you adjust the amount of tahini in the recipe at the right if you use $2\frac{2}{3}$ pounds of chick peas?

HUMMUS

1 lb chick peas
12 oz tahini
1 tbsp lemon juice
2 cloves garlic
Chop garlic and mix.
Add paprika, salt, cumin to taste.

Lauren's Method

Since I use $2\frac{2}{3}$ times as much chick peas, I will need $2\frac{2}{3}$ times as much tahini. I will multiply $2\frac{2}{3}$ by 12 ounces.

$2\frac{2}{3} \cdot 12 = \frac{8}{3} \cdot \frac{12}{1}$ ← **Write the numbers as improper fractions.**

$= \frac{8}{1\cancel{3}} \cdot \frac{\cancel{12}^4}{1}$ ← **Divide 3 and 12 by their GCF, 3.**

$= \frac{32}{1}$, or 32 ← **Multiply and simplify.**

I will need 32 ounces of tahini.

Derek's Method

I can think of $2\frac{2}{3}$ as the sum of two numbers, $2 + \frac{2}{3}$, and solve the problem using mental math.

I need two 12-ounce jars of tahini, and $\frac{2}{3}$ of another jar.

$2\frac{2}{3} \times 12 = 2 \times 12 + \frac{2}{3} \times 12$

$= 24 + 8$

$= 32$

I will need 32 ounces of tahini.

12 oz   12 oz $\frac{2}{3}$ full

Choose a Method

Find $10 \times 3\frac{2}{5}$. Describe your method and explain why you chose it.

I wrote both numbers as improper fractions and got $\frac{10}{1} \times \frac{17}{5} = \frac{170}{5} = 34$. I didn't see an easy way to multiply mentally.

Answers may vary. See left for sample.

EXERCISES

? For more practice, see *Extra Practice*.

A Practice by Example

Estimate each product. Exercises 1 and 2 have been started for you.

Example 1
(page 224)

1. $3\frac{1}{2} \cdot 1\frac{1}{4} \approx 4 \cdot 1$ 4   **2.** $14\frac{2}{3} \cdot 5\frac{1}{3} \approx 15 \cdot 5$ 75 **3.** $5\frac{1}{2} \cdot 10\frac{3}{10}$ 60

4. $7\frac{3}{4} \times 9\frac{1}{2}$ 80   **5.** $15\frac{9}{10} \cdot 3\frac{1}{5}$ 48   **6.** $2\frac{3}{4} \times 6\frac{1}{8}$ 18

More Than One Way

I wrote both numbers as improper fractions and got $\frac{10}{1} \times \frac{17}{5} = \frac{170}{5} = 34$. I didn't see an easy way to multiply mentally.

Examples 2, 3
(page 225)

Find each product. Exercise 7 has been started for you.

7. $7\frac{1}{2} \cdot 8\frac{2}{3} = \frac{15}{2} \cdot \frac{26}{3}$ 65 **8.** $5\frac{1}{3} \times 2\frac{1}{4}$ 12   **9.** $3\frac{1}{9} \cdot 3\frac{3}{8}$ $10\frac{1}{2}$

10. $2\frac{4}{5} \times 12\frac{1}{2}$ 35   **11.** $1\frac{1}{3} \cdot 10\frac{1}{2}$ 14   **12.** $3\frac{1}{5} \cdot 1\frac{7}{8}$ 6

13. $3\frac{5}{9} \times 4\frac{1}{2}$ 16   **14.** $1\frac{5}{8} \times 2\frac{2}{3}$ $4\frac{1}{3}$ **15.** $3\frac{3}{4} \times 5\frac{1}{3}$ 20

16. Estimate the area of a folder that measures $9\frac{3}{8}$ inches by $11\frac{3}{4}$ inches.
108 in.²

B Apply Your Skills

17. Sewing A quilt pattern uses a square with $7\frac{1}{2}$-inch sides. Patty wants to make each side $\frac{2}{3}$ of the pattern's length. Find the new dimensions.
5 in. by 5 in.

18. a. A mother is $1\frac{3}{8}$ times as tall as her daughter. The girl is $1\frac{1}{3}$ times as
GPS tall as her brother. The mother is how many times as tall as her son?
b. If the son is 3 feet tall, how tall is his mother?   18a. $1\frac{5}{6}$
$5\frac{1}{2}$ ft

(Algebra) **Evaluate each expression for $x = 5\frac{1}{3}$.**

19. $9x$ 48   **20.** $2\frac{5}{8} \cdot x$ 14   **21.** $3x + 2$ 18   **22.** $7\frac{1}{2}x + 5\frac{1}{4}x$
68

23. Carpentry A carpenter needs 6 pieces of wood that are $3\frac{1}{2}$ feet long. She has two 10-foot boards. Does she have enough wood? Explain.
See margin.

24. Data File, p. 217 The women's world outdoor long-jump record is about $1\frac{1}{5}$ the distance of the 15–16-year-old girls' record. Find the distance of this record to the nearest foot. **24 ft**

25. Construction A "2-by-4" board is $1\frac{1}{2}$ inches thick. How high is a stack of four boards? **6 in.**

Find each product.

26. $15\frac{1}{2} \times 3\frac{5}{8}$ $56\frac{3}{16}$ **27.** $12\frac{1}{10} \cdot 8\frac{2}{3}$ $104\frac{13}{15}$ **28.** $5\frac{3}{4} \cdot 8\frac{1}{12}$ $46\frac{23}{48}$

29. $2\frac{7}{8} \cdot 17\frac{1}{3}$ $49\frac{5}{6}$ **30.** $5\frac{5}{12} \times 4\frac{2}{5}$ $23\frac{5}{6}$ **31.** $5\frac{1}{5} \cdot 5\frac{5}{6}$ $30\frac{1}{3}$

32. Writing in Math Describe some items that have an area you can find by multiplying mixed numbers. **Check students' work.**

C Challenge

33. Design An artist is planning to make a painting that is $1\frac{3}{4}$ feet by $2\frac{5}{8}$ feet. The size of the painting may change depending on the available space. What size will the painting be if its length and width are increased to $1\frac{1}{3}$ of their original sizes? **$2\frac{1}{3}$ ft by $3\frac{1}{2}$ ft**

34. Stretch Your Thinking Every 15 minutes a cell divides into 2 cells. At 12:00 P.M., there are 256 cells. At what time were there 32 cells?
11:15 A.M.

Exercise 18

5-2 Multiplying Mixed Numbers   **227**

23. No; the carpenter needs $6 \times 3\frac{1}{2} = 21$ ft of wood for the slats; two 10-ft boards are only 20 ft.

Use the Guided Problem Solving worksheet with Exercise 18a.

Practice 5-2 Multiplying Mixed Numbers

Estimate each product.

1. $2\frac{5}{6} \times 1\frac{3}{4}$ **6**   2. $3\frac{3}{8} \times 7\frac{1}{4}$ **21**   3. $5\frac{3}{8} \times 2\frac{7}{8}$ **15**

4. $2\frac{3}{8} \times 4\frac{4}{5}$ **10**   5. $6\frac{7}{12} \times 5\frac{9}{10}$ **42**   6. $7\frac{1}{4} \times 10\frac{11}{12}$ **77**

7. $12\frac{1}{4} \times 3\frac{7}{8}$ **48**   8. $8\frac{4}{6} \times 2\frac{1}{4}$ **16**   9. $15\frac{2}{7} \times 5\frac{3}{4}$ **96**

Find each product.

10. $2\frac{5}{6} \times 1\frac{3}{4}$ $4\frac{23}{24}$ 11. $3\frac{3}{8} \times 7\frac{1}{4}$ $24\frac{15}{32}$ 12. $5\frac{3}{8} \times 2\frac{7}{8}$ $15\frac{29}{64}$

13. $2\frac{3}{8} \times 4\frac{4}{5}$ $11\frac{2}{5}$ 14. $6\frac{7}{12} \times 5\frac{9}{10}$ $38\frac{101}{120}$ 15. $7\frac{1}{4} \times 10\frac{11}{12}$ $80\frac{1}{18}$

16. $12\frac{1}{4} \times 3\frac{7}{8}$ $45\frac{15}{16}$ 17. $8\frac{4}{6} \times 2\frac{1}{4}$ $18\frac{3}{8}$ 18. $15\frac{2}{7} \times 5\frac{3}{4}$ $89\frac{11}{21}$

19. $\frac{1}{4} \times 5\frac{3}{5}$ $\frac{7}{20}$ 20. $2\frac{3}{8} \times \frac{4}{5}$ $1\frac{10}{10}$ 21. $1\frac{1}{2} \times 5\frac{1}{3}$ **8**

22. $3\frac{3}{8} \times 6$ $20\frac{1}{4}$ 23. $3\frac{1}{4} \times 1\frac{3}{5}$ $1\frac{1}{5}$ 24. $9\frac{3}{5} \times \frac{5}{8}$ $3\frac{5}{5}$

25. $1\frac{1}{4} \times 2\frac{3}{5}$ $3\frac{3}{5}$ 26. $1\frac{3}{5} \times \frac{4}{5}$ $\frac{7}{5}$ 27. $6\frac{1}{4} \times 1\frac{5}{12}$ $8\frac{3}{4}$

28. $\frac{7}{8} \times 3\frac{1}{4}$ $\frac{4}{5}$ 29. $5\frac{1}{3} \times 2\frac{1}{4}$ **12**   30. $\frac{3}{8} \times 4\frac{1}{5}$ $2\frac{7}{10}$

31. $\frac{5}{8} \times 7\frac{3}{4}$ $\frac{7}{4}$ 32. $5\frac{1}{3} \times 8$ $\frac{3}{5}$ 33. $2\frac{4}{5} \times \frac{4}{7}$ $1\frac{3}{5}$

34. $3\frac{1}{2} \times 3\frac{1}{10}$ **11**   35. $5\frac{1}{4} \times 2\frac{3}{7}$ $2\frac{2}{5}$ 36. $1\frac{5}{8} \times 3\frac{3}{4}$ $6\frac{1}{4}$

Solve.

37. Ken used a piece of lumber to build a bookshelf. If he made three shelves that are each $2\frac{1}{2}$ ft long, how long was the piece of lumber? $7\frac{1}{2}$ ft

38. Deanna's cake recipe needs to be doubled for a party. How much of each ingredient should Deanna use?

Cake Recipe

ingredient	amount	doubled amount
flour	$2\frac{1}{4}$ cups	$4\frac{1}{2}$ cups
sugar	$1\frac{3}{4}$ cups	$3\frac{1}{2}$ cups
butter	$1\frac{1}{2}$ cups	3 cups
milk	$\frac{3}{4}$ cup	$1\frac{1}{2}$ cups

Reteaching 5-2 Multiplying Mixed Numbers

Example 1: Multiply: $2\frac{1}{2} \times 2\frac{2}{3}$ *Example 2:* Multiply: $\frac{5}{6} \times 5\frac{1}{4}$

① Change to improper fractions. $\frac{15}{6} \times \frac{12}{5}$ $\frac{5}{6} \times \frac{21}{4}$

② Simplify. $\frac{3\frac{15}{6}}{1} \times \frac{\frac{12}{5}}{1}$ $\frac{\frac{5}{6}}{1} \times \frac{2\frac{21}{4}}{1}$

③ Multiply. $\frac{3 \times 12}{1 \times 1}$ $\frac{5 \times 7}{1 \times 2}$

④ Simplify. $5\frac{3}{5}$ $3\frac{1}{2}$

$2\frac{1}{2} \times 2\frac{2}{3} = 5\frac{3}{5}$ $\frac{5}{6} \times 5\frac{1}{4} = 3\frac{1}{2}$

Find each product.

1. $1\frac{1}{4} \times 2\frac{2}{3}$ $3\frac{1}{3}$ 2. $2\frac{2}{3} \times 4\frac{1}{4}$ $10\frac{4}{5}$ 3. $3\frac{1}{4} \times 2\frac{2}{3}$ $8\frac{2}{3}$ 4. $\frac{1}{5} \times 2\frac{7}{9}$ $\frac{5}{9}$ 5. $12\frac{1}{4} \times 2\frac{2}{3}$ **30**

6. $2\frac{1}{3} \times 2\frac{2}{5}$ $5\frac{3}{5}$ 7. $5\frac{1}{4} \times 1\frac{7}{8}$ **10**   8. $\frac{4}{5} \times 3\frac{1}{2}$ $1\frac{4}{5}$ 9. $2\frac{1}{2} \times 4\frac{2}{3}$ **10**   10. $1\frac{1}{3} \times 2\frac{9}{12}$ $4\frac{7}{9}$

11. $1\frac{5}{6} \times 2\frac{1}{4}$ $4\frac{1}{8}$ 12. $5\frac{1}{3} \times 2\frac{2}{3}$ **12**   13. $\frac{1}{4} \times 1\frac{2}{3}$ $\frac{2}{5}$ 14. $\frac{1}{2} \times 1\frac{1}{4}$ $\frac{1}{4}$ 15. $\frac{2}{3} \times 2\frac{1}{4}$ $\frac{1}{2}$

16. $3\frac{1}{4} \times 3\frac{3}{10}$ **11**   17. $1\frac{3}{4} \times 3\frac{1}{4}$ $5\frac{5}{6}$ 18. $1\frac{2}{3} \times 4\frac{1}{4}$ $6\frac{1}{15}$ 19. $\frac{1}{4} \times 1\frac{3}{5}$ $\frac{8}{35}$ 20. $\frac{3}{5} \times 3\frac{2}{5}$ $5\frac{1}{10}$

21. $3\frac{2}{5} \times 2\frac{1}{4}$ $8\frac{1}{2}$ 22. $1\frac{3}{4} \times 7\frac{1}{4}$ $12\frac{1}{2}$ 23. $1\frac{9}{10} \times 2\frac{2}{9}$ $3\frac{5}{7}$ 24. $\frac{7}{10} \times 1\frac{1}{4}$ $\frac{3}{14}$ 25. $2\frac{4}{9} \times 1\frac{2}{3}$ **4**

Solve.

26. Estimate the area of a window pane that has dimensions $6\frac{1}{8}$ by $11\frac{1}{4}$ inches.

66 square inches

27. A hamster is $2\frac{1}{2}$ inches long. A rabbit is $3\frac{1}{2}$ times as long as the hamster. How long is the rabbit?

$8\frac{3}{4}$ inches

Lesson Quiz 5-2

Find each product.

1. $1\frac{2}{3} \times 2\frac{5}{8}$ $4\frac{3}{8}$

2. $3\frac{1}{2} \times 3\frac{3}{5}$ $12\frac{3}{5}$

3. $2\frac{3}{4} \times 8\frac{1}{2}$ $23\frac{3}{8}$

4. $5 \times 2\frac{1}{3}$ $11\frac{2}{3}$

Alternative Assessment

Each student in a pair writes two mixed numbers. Partners work together to multiply each possible pair of their mixed numbers (6 possibilities).

Test Prep

Resources

For additional practice with a variety of test item formats:
• Test-Prep, p. 263
• Test-Taking Strategies, p. 259
• Test-Taking Strategies With Transparencies

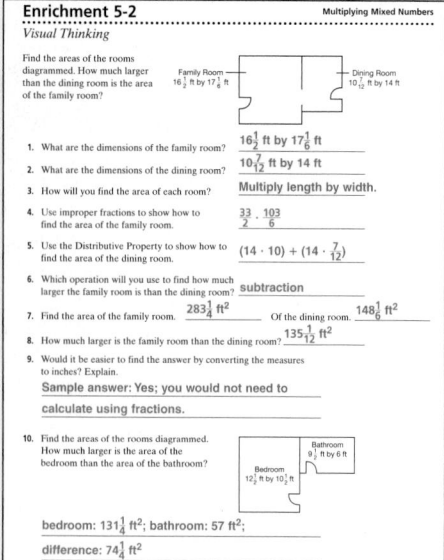

Enrichment 5-2   Multiplying Mixed Numbers
Visual Thinking

Find the areas of the rooms diagrammed. How much larger than the dining room is the area of the family room?

1. What are the dimensions of the family room? $16\frac{1}{2}$ ft by $17\frac{1}{6}$ ft
2. What are the dimensions of the dining room? $10\frac{7}{12}$ ft by 14 ft
3. How will you find the area of each room?   Multiply length by width.
4. Use improper fractions to show how to find the area of the family room. $\frac{33}{2} \cdot \frac{103}{6}$
5. Use the Distributive Property to show how to find the area of the dining room. $(14 \cdot 10) + (14 \cdot \frac{7}{12})$
6. Which operation will you use to find how much larger the family room is than the dining room?   subtraction
7. Find the area of the family room. $283\frac{3}{4}$ ft²   Of the dining room. $148\frac{1}{6}$ ft²
8. How much larger is the family room than the dining room? $135\frac{1}{12}$ ft²
9. Would it be easier to find the answer by converting the measures to inches? Explain.
Sample answer: Yes; you would not need to calculate using fractions.
10. Find the areas of the rooms diagrammed. How much larger is the area of the bedroom than the area of the bathroom?

bedroom: $131\frac{1}{4}$ ft²; bathroom: 57 ft²;
difference: $74\frac{1}{4}$ ft²

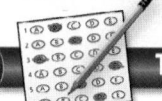
Test Prep

Multiple Choice

35. What is $3\frac{3}{4} \times 5\frac{1}{3}$?   C

    A. 12   **B.** $15\frac{1}{4}$ **C.** 20   **D.** 24

36. Which of the following is NOT equal to $8 \times 4\frac{1}{6}$?   I

    F. $8 \times \frac{25}{6}$ **G.** $\frac{8}{3} \times \frac{25}{2}$ **H.** $\frac{100}{3}$ **I.** $4 \times 8\frac{1}{6}$

Take It to the NET
Online lesson quiz at
www.PHSchool.com
Web Code: aaa-0502

37. Which number multiplied by $4\frac{1}{3}$ gives a product closest to 12?   C

    A. $1\frac{1}{5}$ **B.** $2\frac{1}{5}$ **C.** $3\frac{1}{5}$ **D.** $4\frac{1}{5}$

Short Response

38. Suppose Andrew earns $6.25 an hour. He works $4\frac{1}{2}$ hours per day, 5 days per week. **(a)** How much money does he earn per day? **(b)** How much money does he earn in 2 weeks?   See margin.

Mixed Review

Lesson 4-4   **Find each sum.**

39. $3\frac{2}{5} + 4\frac{1}{5}$ $7\frac{3}{5}$ **40.** $2\frac{1}{6} + 1\frac{5}{6}$ 4   **41.** $5\frac{3}{8} + 2\frac{1}{4}$ $7\frac{5}{8}$

42. $7\frac{5}{12} + 6\frac{3}{4}$ $14\frac{1}{6}$ **43.** $8\frac{1}{6} + 3\frac{1}{2}$ $11\frac{2}{3}$ **44.** $1\frac{2}{3} + 4\frac{2}{9}$ $5\frac{8}{9}$

Lesson 3-6   **Find the LCM of each set of numbers.**

45. 6, 15 30   **46.** 35, 40 280   **47.** 10, 20, 50 100   **48.** 15, 18, 24 360

Practice Game

Estimate That Product!

What You'll Need
• 20 cards or paper slips, each with a fraction or mixed number
• fraction calculator (optional)

How to Play
• One student acts as the game host. Two students are the players.
• The host shuffles the cards and then turns over two cards.
• Players have 10 seconds to write an estimate for the product.
• The host finds the product. The host also computes the difference between each player's estimate and the actual product.
• The player with the estimate closer to the actual product earns 1 point. If there is a tie, each player gets 1 point.
• The first player to earn 5 points wins.

228   **Chapter 5**   Multiplying and Dividing Fractions

38. **[2] a.** Since Andrew works $4\frac{1}{2}$ hours a day and makes $6.25 an hour, he earns $6.25 \times 4\frac{1}{2} = 28.125 for each day of work.

b. Andrew works 10 days in 2 weeks (5×2), so he earns $28.125 \times 10 = 281.25 in 2 weeks.

[1] one part correct OR correct answers with no work shown

Fraction Division

For Use With Lesson 5-3

Suppose you serve three large cheese quesadillas at a party. You divide the three quesadillas into eighths. How many pieces do you have?

You can use circle models to represent each quesadilla.

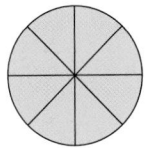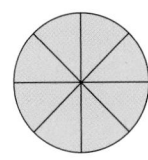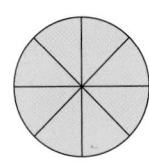

Each circle is divided into eighths. You see that there are 24 pieces.

So, $3 \div \frac{1}{8} = 24$.

Activity

1. **a.** Draw 3 circles. Divide each circle in half. How many halves are there? **6 halves**
   b. What is $3 \div \frac{1}{2}$? **6**

2. Divide 4, 5, and 6 circles into halves. Copy and complete the table.

Number of Circles	Fraction	Number of Pieces	Division Problem
3	$\frac{1}{2}$	■6	$3 \div \frac{1}{2} = $ ■6
4	$\frac{1}{2}$	■8	$4 \div \frac{1}{2} = $ ■8
5	$\frac{1}{2}$	■10	$5 \div \frac{1}{2} = $ ■10
6	$\frac{1}{2}$	■12	$6 \div \frac{1}{2} = $ ■12

3. **a. Patterns** How do the number of pieces relate to the number of circles in the table? **The number of pieces is double the number of circles.**
   b. What happens when you divide a number by $\frac{1}{2}$? **You get twice the number.**

4. **Number Sense** How are dividing by $\frac{1}{2}$ and multiplying by 2 related? Explain. **They produce the same result.**

EXERCISES

Find each quotient.

5. $4 \div \frac{1}{3}$ 12

6. $5 \div \frac{1}{3}$ 15

7. $4 \div \frac{1}{4}$ 16

8. $5 \div \frac{1}{4}$ 20

Investigation

Fraction Division

Students model division of a whole number by a fraction in preparation for learning an algorithm for dividing by fractions in Lesson 5-3 that follows.

Optional Materials

- compass
- straightedge

Teaching Notes

Discuss the 3 circle models that are each divided into eight equal-sized pieces. Make sure students understand how it represents $3 \div \frac{1}{8}$. Ask: *What can you say about the quotient when you divide a whole number by a fraction?* The quotient is greater than the whole number.

Inclusion

Students with impaired coordination might have difficulty drawing the circles for Step 1. Provide them with a sheet containing empty circles that they can use to make the models.

Tactile Learners

Some students may benefit from cutting out the semi-circles and then counting them to model the division.

English Learners

When a quantity is divided into two equal parts, people often say it has been "divided in half." This might lead students to believe that "dividing by 2" and "dividing by $\frac{1}{2}$" have the same meaning. Contrast $3 \div 2$, or $1\frac{1}{2}$, with $3 \div \frac{1}{2}$, or 6.

Exercises

Have students work independently on the exercises.

Lesson Preview

 Check Skills You'll Need

Multiplying Fractions
Lesson 5-1: Examples 2–3. Extra
Practice p. 646.

Lesson Resources

 Teaching Resources
Practice, Reteaching, Enrichment

 Reaching All Students
Practice Workbook 5-3
Spanish Practice Workbook 5-3
Guided Problem Solving 5-3
Technology Activites 10
Hands-On Activities 15, 18, 19

 Presentation Assistant Plus!
Transparencies
• Check Skills You'll Need 5-3
• Problem of the Day 5-3
• Additional Examples 5-3
• Student Edition Answers 5-3
• Lesson Quiz 5-3
PH Presentation Pro CD-ROM 5-3

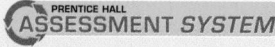 **ASSESSMENT SYSTEM**

Computer Test Generator CD

 Technology
Resource Pro® CD-ROM
Computer Test Generator CD
PH Presentation Pro CD-ROM

 www.PHSchool.com
Student Site
• Teacher Web Code: aak-5500
• Algebra Readiness Puzzles 5, 55
• Self-grading Lesson Quiz

PH SuccessNet Teacher Center
• Lesson Planner
• Resources

Plus

What You'll Learn

 OBJECTIVE 1 To divide whole numbers by fractions

 OBJECTIVE 2 To divide fractions by fractions

...And Why

To fill birdfeeders, as in Example 4

Check Skills You'll Need

 For help, go to Lesson 5-1.

Find each product.

1. $8 \times \frac{3}{4}$ 6

2. $\frac{2}{3} \times 6$ 4

3. $\frac{4}{5} \cdot \frac{1}{4}$ $\frac{1}{5}$

4. $8 \cdot \frac{1}{8}$ 1

5. $\frac{1}{3}$ of $\frac{3}{7}$ $\frac{1}{7}$

6. $\frac{10}{11} \cdot \frac{2}{5}$ $\frac{4}{11}$

New Vocabulary   • reciprocal

OBJECTIVE 1 Interactive lesson includes instant self-check, tutorials, and activities.

Dividing Whole Numbers by Fractions

Reading Math

Reciprocal comes from a Latin word meaning *alternating*.

The numbers $\frac{2}{3}$ and $\frac{3}{2}$ are reciprocals. Two numbers are **reciprocals** if their product is 1. Notice that the numerators and denominators are switched in fractions that are reciprocals.

1 EXAMPLE Writing a Reciprocal

Write the reciprocal of each number.

a. $\frac{7}{8}$

The reciprocal is $\frac{8}{7}$.

Check $\frac{7}{8} \times \frac{8}{7} = \frac{56}{56}$, or 1

b. 9

Write 9 as $\frac{9}{1}$. The reciprocal is $\frac{1}{9}$.

Check $\frac{9}{1} \times \frac{1}{9} = \frac{9}{9}$, or 1

✓ **Check Understanding** 1 Write the reciprocal of each number.

a. $\frac{3}{4}$ $\frac{4}{3}$ or $1\frac{1}{3}$

b. 7 $\frac{1}{7}$

c. $\frac{8}{7}$ $\frac{7}{8}$

To divide by a fraction, multiply by the reciprocal of the fraction. You can remember this by thinking "invert and multiply."

Key Concepts   **Dividing Fractions**

Arithmetic	Algebra
$\frac{3}{5} \div \frac{1}{3} = \frac{3}{5} \times \frac{3}{1}$	$\frac{a}{b} \div \frac{c}{d} = \frac{a}{b} \cdot \frac{d}{c}$, where b, c, and d are not 0.

230 Chapter 5 Multiplying and Dividing Fractions

 **Ongoing Assessment and Intervention**

Before the Lesson	During the Lesson	After the Lesson
Diagnose prerequisite skills using:	Monitor progress using:	Assess knowledge using:
• Check Skills You'll Need	• Check Understanding • Additional Examples • Test Prep	• Lesson Quiz • Computer Test Generator CD

2 EXAMPLE Using Reciprocals to Divide by a Fraction

Find $12 \div \frac{8}{9}$.

$12 \div \frac{8}{9} = 12 \times \frac{9}{8}$ ← Multiply 12 by $\frac{9}{8}$, the reciprocal of $\frac{8}{9}$.

$= \frac{12}{1} \times \frac{9}{8}$ ← Write 12 as $\frac{12}{1}$.

$= \frac{\overset{3}{12}}{1} \times \frac{9}{\underset{2}{8}}$ ← Divide 12 and 8 by their GCF, 4.

$= \frac{27}{2}$ ← Multiply.

$= 13\frac{1}{2}$ ← Write as a mixed number.

✓ **Check Understanding** 2 Find each quotient.

a. $8 \div \frac{3}{4}$ $10\frac{2}{3}$ **b.** $7 \div \frac{2}{9}$ $31\frac{1}{2}$ **c.** $12 \div \frac{8}{7}$ $10\frac{1}{2}$

OBJECTIVE

2 Dividing Fractions by Fractions

In the diagram at the right, a rectangle is divided into seven pieces. There are two groups of $\frac{3}{7}$ in $\frac{6}{7}$.

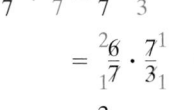

So, $\frac{6}{7} \div \frac{3}{7} = 2$.

$\frac{6}{7} \div \frac{3}{7} = \frac{6}{7} \cdot \frac{7}{3}$ ← Multiply $\frac{6}{7}$ by $\frac{7}{3}$, the reciprocal of $\frac{3}{7}$.

           Divide 6 and 3 by their GCF, 3.

$= \frac{\overset{2}{6}}{\underset{1}{7}} \cdot \frac{\overset{1}{7}}{\underset{1}{3}}$ ← Divide the numerator 7 and denominator 7 by their GCF, 7.

$= \frac{2}{1}$, or 2   ← Multiply and simplify.

3 EXAMPLE Dividing a Fraction by a Fraction

3d. $\frac{2}{3}$ is between $\frac{1}{2}$ and 1. There are 2 fourths in $\frac{1}{2}$, and 4 fourths in 1. So there must be between 2 and 4 fourths in $\frac{2}{3}$.

Find $\frac{5}{10} \div \frac{5}{6}$.

$\frac{5}{10} \div \frac{5}{6} = \frac{5}{10} \times \frac{6}{5}$ ← Multiply by $\frac{6}{5}$, the reciprocal of $\frac{5}{6}$.

$= \frac{\overset{1}{5}}{\underset{5}{10}} \times \frac{\overset{3}{6}}{\underset{1}{5}}$ ← Divide 5 and 5 by their GCF, 5. Divide 10 and 6 by their GCF, 2.

$= \frac{3}{5}$ ← Multiply.

✓ **Check Understanding** 3 Find each quotient.

a. $\frac{9}{16} \div \frac{3}{4}$ $\frac{3}{4}$ **b.** $\frac{5}{8} \div \frac{5}{6}$ $\frac{3}{4}$ **c.** $\frac{8}{15} \div \frac{2}{3}$ $\frac{4}{5}$

d. Number Sense Without dividing, how can you tell whether $\frac{2}{3} \div \frac{1}{4}$ is greater than or less than 2? *Answers may vary. See above left for sample.*

🫂 Reaching All Students

Below Level Give students several blank forms like the one below to use for organizing their work.

Advanced Learners Find the missing divisor.

$\frac{3}{8} \div \blacksquare = \frac{15}{16}$ $\frac{2}{5}$

$\frac{2}{5} \div \blacksquare = \frac{1}{15}$ 6

English Learners
See note on page 231.
Auditory Learners
See note on page 231.

---

2. Teach

Professional Development

Math Background

Algebraically, division is defined in terms of multiplication. That is, the quotient $m \div n$ is defined as $m \times \frac{1}{n}$, provided that the divisor n is not zero. The number $\frac{1}{n}$ is called the *reciprocal* of n. This definition of division is stated less formally as follows: *Dividing by a nonzero number is the same as multiplying by the reciprocal of that number.*

The reciprocal of a fraction $\frac{c}{d}$ is $\frac{d}{c}$. So, when a division involves fractions, the definition of division leads to the familiar rule for dividing fractions: $\frac{a}{b} \div \frac{c}{d} = \frac{a}{b} \times \frac{d}{c}$, provided that b, c, and d are not zero.

Teaching Notes

1 EXAMPLE English Learners

To help students remember the word *reciprocal*, discuss the related word *reciprocate*. Point out that, when you do a favor for a friend, the friend reciprocates by doing a favor for you. Tell students to think of a reciprocal as the result when the numerator and denominator of a fraction do a "favor" for each other: The numerator takes the place of the denominator, and the denominator takes the place of the numerator.

2 EXAMPLE Auditory Learners

Students might find it helpful to recite the "invert the second fraction and multiply" procedure softly as they work. In Check Understanding 2a, for instance, they might say: "Eight divided by three fourths" as they copy the exercise, then "Eight multiplied by four thirds" as they write the multiplication.

PowerPoint

Additional Examples

1 Write the reciprocal of each number.

a. $\frac{4}{9}$ $\frac{9}{4}$ **b.** 5 $\frac{1}{5}$

2 Find $4 \div \frac{6}{7}$. $4\frac{2}{3}$

3 Find $\frac{3}{8} \div \frac{7}{12}$. $\frac{9}{14}$

231

To divide a fraction by a whole number, first write the whole number as an improper fraction with a denominator of 1.

④ **EXAMPLE**   **Dividing a Fraction by a Whole Number**

Feeding Birds Suppose you plan to put the same amount of seed in three feeders. You have $\frac{7}{8}$ pound of seed. How much seed will each feeder get?

The $\frac{7}{8}$ pound of seed must be distributed evenly among three feeders, so divide $\frac{7}{8}$ by 3.

$$\frac{7}{8} \div 3 = \frac{7}{8} \div \frac{3}{1} \quad \leftarrow \text{Write 3 as } \frac{3}{1}.$$

$$= \frac{7}{8} \times \frac{1}{3} \quad \leftarrow \text{Multiply by } \frac{1}{3}, \text{ the reciprocal of } \frac{3}{1}.$$

$$= \frac{7}{24} \quad \leftarrow \text{Multiply.}$$

Each feeder will get $\frac{7}{24}$ pound of seed.

✔ **Check Understanding** ④ Find each quotient.   **a.** $\frac{3}{8} \div 12$ $\frac{1}{32}$ **b.** $\frac{11}{15} \div 110$ $\frac{1}{150}$

c. Your art teacher must cut $\frac{5}{6}$ yard of fabric into five equal pieces for his students. How much fabric does each student get?
Answers may vary. Sample: $\frac{1}{5}$ of the original piece, or $\frac{1}{6}$ yd.

EXERCISES

? For more practice, see *Extra Practice*.

Ⓐ **Practice by Example**   **Write the reciprocal of each number.**

Example 1
(page 230)
1. $\frac{2}{5}$ $\frac{5}{2}$, or $2\frac{1}{2}$ **2.** $\frac{1}{7}$ 7   **3.** 11 $\frac{1}{11}$ **4.** $\frac{5}{3}$ $\frac{3}{5}$ **5.** $\frac{4}{11}$ $\frac{11}{4}$, or $2\frac{3}{4}$

Example 2
(page 231)
Find each quotient. Exercise 6 has been started for you.

6. $5 \div \frac{3}{8} = 5 \times \frac{8}{3}$ $13\frac{1}{3}$ **7.** $4 \div \frac{3}{5}$ $6\frac{2}{3}$ **8.** $5 \div \frac{5}{16}$ 16

9. $7 \div \frac{3}{5}$ $11\frac{2}{3}$ **10.** $9 \div \frac{4}{9}$ $20\frac{1}{4}$ **11.** $6 \div \frac{2}{5}$ 15   **12.** $8 \div \frac{3}{7}$ $18\frac{2}{3}$

Example 3
(page 231)
13. $\frac{8}{9} \div \frac{1}{3}$ $2\frac{2}{3}$ **14.** $\frac{1}{4} \div \frac{1}{4}$ 1   **15.** $\frac{11}{2} \div \frac{3}{4}$ $7\frac{1}{3}$ **16.** $\frac{1}{5} \div \frac{1}{4}$ $\frac{4}{5}$

17. $\frac{4}{9} \div \frac{2}{3}$ $\frac{2}{3}$ **18.** $\frac{9}{2} \div \frac{1}{2}$ 9   **19.** $\frac{8}{9} \div \frac{4}{5}$ $1\frac{1}{9}$ **20.** $\frac{3}{4} \div \frac{1}{8}$ 6

Example 4
(page 232)
21. $\frac{3}{4} \div 3$ $\frac{1}{4}$ **22.** $\frac{1}{2} \div 5$ $\frac{1}{10}$ **23.** $\frac{11}{3} \div 4$ $\frac{11}{12}$ **24.** $\frac{5}{12} \div 15$ $\frac{1}{36}$

🌐 **25. Construction** Sam has $\frac{3}{4}$ ton of stones to divide evenly among four sidewalks. How much stone will be used in each sidewalk? $\frac{3}{16}$ t

44. 24;
four $\frac{1}{4}$ inches
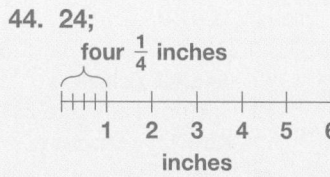
inches

46. Answers may vary. Sample: When you divide a number by 2, the quotient is less than the dividend. When you divide a number by $\frac{1}{2}$, the quotient is greater than the dividend. For instance: $3 \div 2 = 1\frac{1}{2}$

B **Apply Your Skills**

Find each quotient.

26. $\frac{4}{3} \div \frac{5}{3}$ $\frac{4}{5}$

27. $11 \div \frac{121}{10}$ $\frac{10}{11}$

28. $\frac{9}{8} \div 4$ $\frac{9}{32}$

29. $\frac{11}{9} \div 3$ $\frac{11}{27}$

30. $2 \div \frac{9}{7}$ $1\frac{5}{9}$

31. $\frac{5}{3} \div \frac{4}{3}$ $1\frac{1}{4}$

32. $\frac{15}{8} \div \frac{9}{5}$ $1\frac{1}{24}$

33. $8 \div \frac{15}{6}$ $3\frac{1}{5}$

🌎 **Geography** Use the table at the right.

34. About how many times more people live in Argentina than in Peru? **about $1\frac{1}{3}$ times more**

35. About how many times more people live in Brazil than in Colombia? **about $4\frac{1}{2}$ times more**

36. The population of Brasilia, the capital of Brazil, is about $\frac{1}{85}$ of the population of Brazil. What fraction of the total population of South America lives in Brasilia? **about $\frac{1}{170}$**

Country	Portion of South America's Population
Brazil	$\frac{1}{2}$
Colombia	$\frac{1}{9}$
Argentina	$\frac{1}{10}$
Peru	$\frac{1}{13}$

SOURCE: U.S. Census Bureau. Go to **www.PHSchool.com** for a data update. Web Code: aag-2041

43. Answers may vary. Sample: The reciprocal of $\frac{11}{9}$ was multiplied by $\frac{2}{3}$ instead of by the reciprocal of $\frac{2}{3}$. The correct answer is $1\frac{5}{6}$.

Writing in Math

For help with writing to explain, as in Exercise 43, see p. 235.

Algebra Evaluate each expression for $x = \frac{5}{6}$ and $n = 3$.

37. $30 \div x$ 36

38. $\frac{3}{5} \div x$ $\frac{18}{25}$

39. $x \div 2$ $\frac{5}{12}$

40. $\frac{n}{5} \div \frac{1}{3}$ $1\frac{4}{5}$

41. $\frac{51}{16} \div n$ $1\frac{1}{16}$

42. $\frac{1}{3} \div \frac{5}{n}$ $\frac{1}{5}$

43. **Error Analysis** Explain and correct the error in the work at the right. **See above left.**

$$\frac{11}{9} \div \frac{2}{3} = \frac{\overset{3}{9}}{11} \times \frac{2}{\underset{1}{3}}$$
$$= \frac{6}{11}$$

44. **Measurement** How many $\frac{1}{4}$ inches are in $\frac{1}{2}$ foot? Draw a diagram that shows the problem and your solution. **See margin.**

45. **Baking** You are baking an apple pie. The recipe calls for eight sliced apples. Suppose you cut the apples into eighths. How many pieces of apple would you have? **64 pieces**

46. **Writing in Math** How are dividing by 2 and dividing by $\frac{1}{2}$ different? Include a diagram. **See margin.**

Find the number that completes each equation.

47. $\frac{3}{2} \div \frac{1}{2} = \blacksquare$ 3

48. $\frac{3}{2} \div \blacksquare = 3$ $\frac{1}{2}$

49. $\frac{3}{2} \div \blacksquare = \frac{3}{4}$ 2

🌎 50. **Baking** A recipe for a loaf of banana bread requires $\frac{2}{3}$ cup of vegetable oil. You have 3 cups of oil but need 1 cup for a different recipe. How many loaves of banana bread can you make with the rest of the oil? **3 loaves**
GPS

GPS Use the Guided Problem Solving worksheet with Exercise 50.

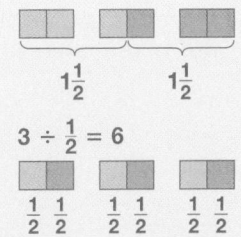

$1\frac{1}{2}$ $1\frac{1}{2}$

$3 \div \frac{1}{2} = 6$

$\frac{1}{2}$ $\frac{1}{2}$ $\frac{1}{2}$ $\frac{1}{2}$ $\frac{1}{2}$ $\frac{1}{2}$

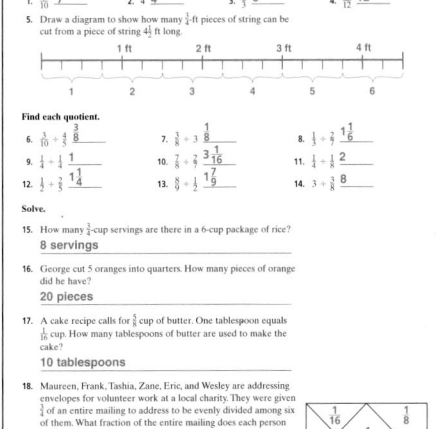

Practice 5-3   Dividing Fractions

Write the reciprocal of each number.

1. $\frac{7}{10}$ $\frac{10}{7}$ 2. 4 $\frac{1}{4}$ 3. $\frac{1}{3}$ 3 4. $\frac{1}{12}$ 12

5. Draw a diagram to show how many $\frac{3}{4}$-ft pieces of string can be cut from a piece of string $4\frac{1}{2}$ ft long.

Find each quotient.

6. $\frac{3}{10} \div \frac{3}{8}$ $\frac{3}{8}$
7. $\frac{3}{8} \div 3$ $\frac{1}{8}$
8. $\frac{1}{4} \div \frac{2}{7}$ $1\frac{1}{6}$
9. $\frac{1}{4} \div 4$ $\frac{1}{16}$
10. $\frac{7}{8} \div \frac{2}{7}$ $3\frac{1}{16}$
11. $\frac{4}{11} \div \frac{4}{6}$ 2
12. $\frac{5}{12} \div \frac{7}{4}$ $1\frac{1}{4}$
13. $\frac{9}{8} \div \frac{5}{2}$ $1\frac{7}{9}$
14. $3 \div \frac{3}{8}$ 8

Solve.

15. How many $\frac{3}{4}$-cup servings are there in a 6-cup package of rice? **8 servings**

16. George cut 5 oranges into quarters. How many pieces of orange did he have? **20 pieces**

17. A cake recipe calls for $\frac{5}{8}$ cup of butter. One tablespoon equals $\frac{1}{16}$ cup. How many tablespoons of butter are used to make the cake? **10 tablespoons**

18. Maureen, Frank, Tashia, Zane, Eric, and Wesley are addressing envelopes for volunteer work at a local charity. They were given $\frac{3}{4}$ of an entire mailing to address to be evenly divided among six of them. What fraction of the entire mailing does each person address? **$\frac{1}{8}$**

19. Study the tangram pieces at the right. If the entire square is 1, find the fractional value of each piece. You can copy the tangram and cut the pieces to compare them.

Reteaching 5-3   Dividing Fractions

Find $8 \div \frac{4}{5}$.
① The *reciprocal* of $\frac{4}{5}$ is $\frac{5}{4}$.

Find $\frac{4}{9} \div \frac{8}{15}$.
① The *reciprocal* of $\frac{8}{15}$ is $\frac{15}{8}$.

② Multiply 8 by the reciprocal.
$8 \div \frac{4}{5} = 8 \times \frac{5}{4} = \frac{2 \cdot 8}{1} \times \frac{5}{4_1} = \frac{2 \times 5}{1 \times 1} = 10$
$8 \div \frac{4}{5} = 10$

② Multiply $\frac{4}{9}$ by the reciprocal.
$\frac{4}{9} \div \frac{8}{15} = \frac{4}{9} \times \frac{15}{8} = \frac{1 \cdot 4}{3 \cdot 9} \times \frac{15^5}{8_2} = \frac{1 \times 5}{3 \times 2} = \frac{5}{6}$
$\frac{4}{9} \div \frac{8}{15} = \frac{5}{6}$

Write the reciprocal of each number.

1. $\frac{1}{4}$ 4
2. $\frac{3}{5}$ $\frac{5}{3}$
3. $\frac{1}{20}$ 20
4. $\frac{8}{8}$ $\frac{8}{8}$
5. 14 $\frac{1}{14}$
6. 18 $\frac{1}{18}$
7. $\frac{5}{9}$ $\frac{9}{5}$
8. $\frac{1}{3}$ $\frac{3}{1}$
9. $\frac{7}{9}$ $\frac{9}{7}$
10. $\frac{1}{12}$ $\frac{12}{11}$
11. $\frac{2}{7}$ $\frac{7}{2}$
12. $\frac{1}{15}$ $\frac{15}{3}$

Find each quotient.

13. $2 \div \frac{2}{3}$ 3
14. $7 \div \frac{7}{8}$ 8
15. $9 \div \frac{3}{4}$ 12
16. $6 \div \frac{2}{5}$ 15
17. $5 \div \frac{2}{3}$ $7\frac{1}{2}$
18. $14 \div \frac{5}{6}$ $16\frac{4}{5}$
19. $\frac{4}{5} \div \frac{4}{15}$ $\frac{1}{5}$
20. $\frac{7}{8} \div \frac{7}{9}$ $1\frac{1}{8}$
21. $\frac{4}{9} \div \frac{1}{6}$ $2\frac{2}{3}$
22. $\frac{7}{8} \div \frac{5}{2}$ $\frac{5}{16}$
23. $\frac{1}{2} \div 4$ $\frac{1}{8}$
24. $\frac{2}{3} \div \frac{5}{4}$ $\frac{8}{15}$
25. $\frac{9}{10} \div 3$ $\frac{3}{10}$
26. $\frac{3}{5} \div \frac{3}{5}$ $\frac{3}{25}$
27. $\frac{5}{8} \div 10$ $\frac{1}{16}$
28. $\frac{3}{4} \div \frac{7}{8}$ $\frac{6}{7}$
29. $\frac{5}{6} \div \frac{1}{3}$ $2\frac{1}{2}$
30. $\frac{11}{4} \div \frac{1}{4}$ $\frac{12}{19}$

Assignment Guide

1 Objective 1
A B Core 1–12, 27, 30, 33

2 Objective 2
A B Core 13–26, 28–29, 31–32, 34–50
C Extension 51–55

Test Prep 56–59
Mixed Review 60–67

4. Assess

PowerPoint **Lesson Quiz 5-3**

Find each quotient.

1. $\frac{4}{5} \div \frac{2}{3}$ $1\frac{1}{5}$ 2. $\frac{3}{8} \div \frac{5}{6}$ $\frac{9}{20}$
3. $7 \div \frac{3}{10}$ $23\frac{1}{3}$ 4. $\frac{7}{12} \div 4$ $\frac{7}{48}$

Alternative Assessment

Each student in a pair writes a fraction and a whole number. Partners work together to divide each of their whole numbers by a fraction (4 possibilities) and each of their fractions by the other fraction (2 possibilities).

Test Prep

Resources
For additional practice with a variety of test item formats:
- Test-Prep, p. 263
- Test-Taking Strategies, p. 259
- Test-Taking Strategies With Transparencies

Exercise 56 Have students discuss the steps they would take and the operation they would use to find the answer.

Enrichment 5-3 Dividing Fractions

Patterns in Numbers

You have found rules for number sequences. For example, you know that the rule for the sequence 3, 9, 27, 81 is *Multiply by 3.*

You can also find rules for sequences that contain fractions. Some rules also contain fractions. Write the next three terms in each sequence below. Then write the rule.

Sample answers: Exercises 1–10

1. 81, 27, 9, 3 1, $\frac{1}{3}$, $\frac{1}{9}$, … Rule: Divide by 3.
2. 250, 50, 10, 2 $\frac{2}{5}$, $\frac{2}{25}$, $\frac{2}{125}$, … Rule: Divide by 5.
3. 1, 8, 64, 512, 4,096, 32,768, 262,144, … Rule: Multiply by 8.
4. 1000, 100, 10, 1, $\frac{1}{10}$, $\frac{1}{100}$, $\frac{1}{1{,}000}$, … Rule: Divide by 10.
5. $\frac{1}{8}, \frac{1}{2}$, 2, 8, 32, 128, 512, … Rule: Multiply by 4.
6. $\frac{3}{2}$, 1, $\frac{2}{3}, \frac{4}{9}$, $\frac{8}{27}$, $\frac{16}{81}$, $\frac{32}{243}$, … Rule: Multiply by $\frac{2}{3}$.
7. How could you rewrite the rule *Divide by 2* using a fraction in the rule? Think: $4 \div 2 = 2, 4 \times x = 2$ Multiply by $\frac{1}{2}$.
8. Rewrite each rule for Exercises 1–6 above.
   a. 81, 27, 9, … Multiply by $\frac{1}{3}$.
   b. 250, 50, 10, … Multiply by $\frac{1}{5}$.
   c. 1, 8, 64, … Divide by $\frac{1}{8}$.
   d. 1000, 100, 10, … Multiply by $\frac{1}{10}$.
   e. $\frac{1}{8}, \frac{1}{2}$, 2, … Divide by $\frac{1}{4}$.
   f. $\frac{3}{2}$, 1, $\frac{2}{3}$, … Divide by $\frac{3}{2}$.
9. Draw the next figure in the pattern. Then write two rules for the pattern.

Multiply by $\frac{1}{2}$; divide by 2.

10. Draw the next figure in the pattern. Then write two rules for the pattern.

Multiply by 2; divide by $\frac{1}{2}$.

C Challenge **Simplify each expression.**

51. $\left(\frac{2}{7} \times \frac{2}{7}\right) \div \frac{2}{7}$ $\frac{2}{7}$ **52.** $\left(\frac{2}{7}\right)^2 \div \frac{2}{7}$ $\frac{2}{7}$ **53.** $\left(\frac{2}{7}\right)^2 \div 2^2$ $\frac{1}{49}$ **54.** $\left(\frac{2}{7}\right)^2 \div \left(\frac{1}{7}\right)^2$ 4

55. Stretch Your Thinking The numerator of a fraction is a two-digit prime number. The denominator is four more than the numerator. Three of the digits are the same prime number. What is the fraction? $\frac{73}{77}$

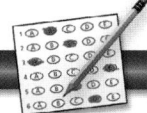

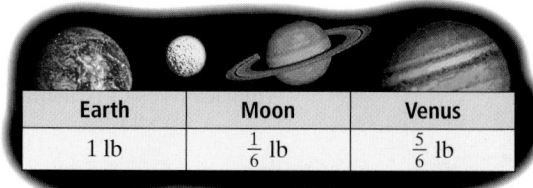

Test Prep

Multiple Choice

The table shows the different weights of the same object on Earth, on the moon, and on Venus.

Earth	Moon	Venus
1 lb	$\frac{1}{6}$ lb	$\frac{5}{6}$ lb

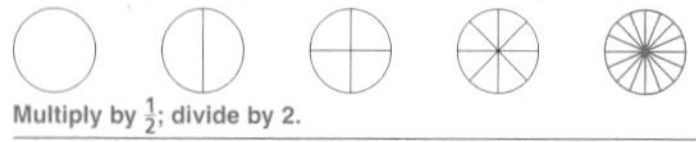

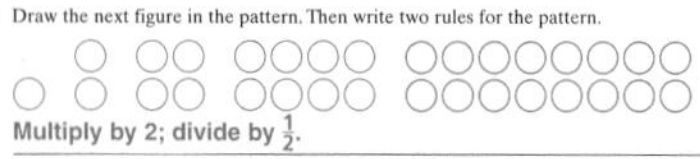

56. How many pounds would a 186-pound astronaut weigh on Venus? B
A. 31 **B.** 155 **C.** 186 **D.** 365

Take It to the NET
Online lesson quiz at
www.PHSchool.com
Web Code: aaa-0503

57. Suppose you weigh m pounds on the moon. Which expression represents your weight on Venus? H
F. $\frac{1}{5}m$ **G.** $1\frac{1}{5}m$ **H.** $5m$ **I.** $6m$

58. If Ezra weighs 150 pounds on Earth, what is his weight on the moon? B
A. 20 lb **B.** 25 lb **C.** 30 lb **D.** 35 lb

Short Response

59. Jaime bought a carton of juice containing 192 fluid ounces, or 24 cups of juice. **(a)** If a serving is $\frac{3}{4}$ cup, how many servings of juice are in the carton? **(b)** Explain in words how you found your answer. See margin.

Mixed Review

Lesson 5-2 **Find each product.**

60. $3\frac{3}{8} \times 2\frac{2}{9}$ $7\frac{1}{2}$ **61.** $8\frac{1}{3} \times 2\frac{2}{5}$ 20 **62.** $5\frac{1}{3} \cdot 8\frac{1}{4}$ 44 **63.** $4\frac{1}{2} \cdot 3\frac{1}{3}$ 15

Lesson 3-1 **Test each number for divisibility by 2, 3, 5, 9, or 10.**

64. 1,250 2, 5, 10 **65.** 372 2, 3 **66.** 55,600 2, 5, 10 **67.** 445 5

59. [2] 32 servings
To find how many servings of $\frac{3}{4}$ cup there are, divide the number of cups available, 24, by $\frac{3}{4}$.
$24 \div \frac{3}{4} = 24 \times \frac{4}{3} =$
$\frac{{}^{8}\cancel{24}}{1} \times \frac{4}{\cancel{3}_{1}} = \frac{32}{1} = 32.$
So there are 32 servings of $\frac{3}{4}$ cup each.
[1] correct expression, but wrong answer

In this book, there are many exercises that ask you to give an explanation. When you are asked to explain an error, consider the following:

- Find the error and explain what is wrong.
- Correct the error.
- Check your work, if possible.

On page 233, you will find the following exercise.

43. Error Analysis Explain and correct the error in the work at the right.

$$\frac{11}{9} \div \frac{2}{3} = \frac{\overset{3}{9}}{11} \times \frac{2}{\underset{1}{3}}$$
$$= \frac{6}{11}$$

Here is one student's response.

The answer must be wrong because $\frac{11}{9}$ is about 1, and there is one group of $\frac{2}{3}$ in 1.   ← **Explain what is wrong.**

The divisor is $\frac{2}{3}$. So $\frac{2}{3}$, not $\frac{11}{9}$, should be replaced with its reciprocal.   ← **Correct the error.**

$$\frac{11}{9} \div \frac{2}{3} = \frac{11}{\underset{3}{9}} \times \frac{\overset{1}{3}}{2} = \frac{11}{6}, \text{ or } 1\frac{5}{6}$$

Since $1\frac{5}{6}$ is more than 1, this answer makes sense.   ← **Check for reasonableness.**

EXERCISES

1–4. Answers may vary. See margin for samples.

1. A student has a bottle containing 4 cups of laundry detergent. The student thinks that, if each load of laundry requires $\frac{1}{3}$ cup, then there is enough detergent for $4 \times \frac{1}{3}$, or $\frac{4}{3}$ loads. Explain the error.

2. April rainfall is shown in the table. One person says the total rainfall is $2\left(\frac{3}{10}\right) + \frac{2}{5} + 1\frac{1}{10} = 3\frac{8}{10}$, or $3\frac{4}{5}$ inches. Explain the error.

April 7	$\frac{3}{10}$ inch
April 8	$\frac{3}{10}$ inch
April 12	$\frac{2}{5}$ inch
April 19	$1\frac{1}{10}$ inches

3. A student solves $10 \div \frac{5}{3}$ by finding $\frac{1}{10} \times \frac{3}{5}$. Her answer is $\frac{3}{50}$. Explain the error, and find the correct answer.

4. A model airplane sits on a base that is $19\frac{11}{16}$ inches by $10\frac{7}{8}$ inches. One estimate of the area of the base is 190 square inches. Why is 220 square inches a better estimate?

1. The answer is wrong because one cup of detergent will do 3 loads of laundry, already more than $\frac{4}{3}$. To find how many groups of $\frac{1}{3}$ are in 4, 4 should be divided by $\frac{1}{3}$, not multiplied by $\frac{1}{3}$. So, 4 $\div \frac{1}{3} = 4 \times 3 = 12$. Since 1 cup will do 3 loads, 4 cups will do 12 loads. The answer makes sense.

2, 3. See back of book.

4. 190 is 19 × 10, so there is almost 1 inch in each measure that is ignored. The two measures were rounded down to the nearest whole number. However, $19\frac{11}{16}$ is closer to 20, and $10\frac{7}{8}$ is closer to 11. A closer estimate would be 20 × 11 = 220 in.^{2}.

235

Writing in Math

Writing to Explain

When students do an exercise that asks them to analyze an error, they may respond that an operation is inappropriate or that a particular calculation is wrong. Guide students to understand that error analysis involves three key tasks beyond simply identifying the error: (1) explaining why a particular calculation or operation used is incorrect, (2) correcting the error or errors, and (3) checking to see that their answer makes sense.

Teaching Notes

Begin the lesson by asking students to suggest what they think is involved in an error analysis exercise. Ask a volunteer to record responses on the board or on an overhead transparency.

Next, tell students to read the division exercise with the error, directing them to think about what has gone wrong. Then work through the student's response, step-by-step. Ask:
- *Do you agree with the conclusion that the answer to the division is too small?* Yes. The answer must be greater than the dividend, $\frac{11}{9}$, because the divisor is a fraction.
- *Could you explain the error in another way?* Answers may vary; students may state that since multiplication and division are inverse operations, dividing by $\frac{2}{3}$ is equivalent to multiplying by its reciprocal, $\frac{3}{2}$.

Inclusion

Make sure students understand the type of exercise this lesson examines. Tell them that in their text, exercises of this kind are signaled by the words "Error Analysis," which appear in blue type just after the exercise number. Encourage students to flip through the book to find other examples of this type of exercise.

Lesson Preview

Check Skills You'll Need **PowerPoint**

Dividing Fractions
Lesson 5-3: Examples 3–4. Extra
Practice p. 646.

Lesson Resources

📁 **Teaching Resources**
Practice, Reteaching, Enrichment
Checkpoint Quiz 1

👥 **Reaching All Students**
Practice Workbook 5-4
Spanish Practice Workbook 5-4
Reading and Math Literacy 5B
Spanish Reading and Math
   Literacy 5B
Spanish Checkpoint Quiz 1
Guided Problem Solving 5-4
Hands-On Activities 19

⏱ **Presentation Assistant Plus!**
Transparencies
• Check Skills You'll Need 5-4
• Problem of the Day 5-4
• Additional Examples 5-4
• Student Edition Answers 5-4
• Lesson Quiz 5-4
• Classroom Aid 11
PH Presentation Pro CD-ROM 5-4

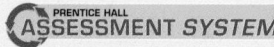
ASSESSMENT SYSTEM

Checkpoint Quiz 1
Computer Test Generator CD

💻 **Technology**
Resource Pro® CD-ROM
Computer Test Generator CD
PH Presentation Pro CD-ROM

💻 **www.PHSchool.com**
Student Site
• Teacher Web Code: aak-5500
• Self-grading Lesson Quiz

PH SuccessNet Teacher Center
• Lesson Planner
• Resources

Plus

5-4 Dividing Mixed Numbers

What You'll Learn

OBJECTIVE 1 To estimate quotients of mixed numbers

OBJECTIVE 2 To divide mixed numbers

. . . And Why

To solve carpentry problems, as in Example 1

✔ **Check Skills You'll Need**   ❓ For help, go to Lesson 5-3.

Find each quotient.

1. $8 \div \frac{2}{7}$ 28

2. $20 \div \frac{6}{7}$ $23\frac{1}{3}$

3. $\frac{7}{8} \div \frac{3}{1}$ $\frac{7}{24}$

4. $\frac{2}{3} \div 4$ $\frac{1}{6}$

5. $\frac{3}{8} \div \frac{2}{5}$ $\frac{15}{16}$

6. $\frac{15}{4} \div \frac{11}{8}$ $2\frac{8}{11}$

7. Explain what "invert and multiply" means. **When you divide by a fraction, find its reciprocal and multiply by it.**

OBJECTIVE 1

🖥 Interactive lesson includes instant self-check, tutorials, and activities.

Estimating Quotients of Mixed Numbers

To estimate the quotient of two mixed numbers, round each number to the nearest whole number. Then divide.

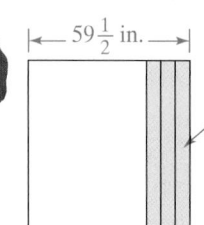

Real-World 🌐 Connection

Careers Carpenters use fractions when they measure, estimate, and cut.

1 EXAMPLE   **Estimating Quotients**   🌐 Real World

Carpentry Sharon wants to cover a $59\frac{1}{2}$-inch wide wall with narrow wood panels. Each panel is $4\frac{3}{8}$ inches wide. Estimate the number of panels she will need to cover the wall.

|← 59 ½ in. →|

← Draw a diagram to model the situation.

Panel $4\frac{3}{8}$ in.

$59\frac{1}{2} \div 4\frac{3}{8}$ ← Round each mixed number to the nearest whole number.
  ↓   ↓
$60 \div 4 = 15$ ← Divide.

Sharon needs about 15 panels.

✔ **Check Understanding** ① Estimate each quotient.

a. $7\frac{2}{5} \div 1\frac{3}{7}$ about 7   b. $14\frac{9}{16} \div 3\frac{8}{19}$ about 5   c. $100 \div 9\frac{2}{3}$ about 10

d. **Estimation** Suppose the panels are $6\frac{1}{4}$ inches wide in Example 1. Estimate the number of panels needed to cover the $59\frac{1}{2}$-inch wall. **Answers may vary. Sample: about 10**

Ongoing Assessment and Intervention

Before the Lesson	During the Lesson	After the Lesson
Diagnose prerequisite skills using:	**Monitor progress using:**	**Assess knowledge using:**
• Check Skills You'll Need	• Check Understanding	• Lesson Quiz
	• Additional Examples	• Computer Test Generator CD
	• Test Prep	• Chapter Checkpoint 1 (p. 240)

2. Teach

Math Background

There are two basic models for division. In the *partition model*, the number of groups is given and the size of each group must be found. In the *measurement model*, the size of each group is given and the number of groups must be found. In this lesson, students solve problems related to both models in the context of mixed-number division.

Need Help?

For help in writing mixed numbers as improper fractions, go to Lesson 3-5.

You can divide a mixed number by a whole number or another mixed number. Just as with multiplication, you start by writing the numbers as improper fractions.

2 EXAMPLE Real-World Problem Solving

Baking A baker has $2\frac{1}{4}$ cups of blueberries to make 3 batches of muffins. How many cups of blueberries should he put into each batch?

| blueberries | ÷ | batches |

← You need to divide the cups of blueberries by the number of batches.

$$2\frac{1}{4} \quad \div \quad 3 \quad = \frac{9}{4} \div \frac{3}{1}$$ ← Write the numbers as improper fractions.

$$= \frac{9}{4} \times \frac{1}{3}$$ ← Multiply by $\frac{1}{3}$, the reciprocal of 3.

$$= \frac{{}^3 9}{4} \times \frac{1}{3_1}$$ ← Divide 9 and 3 by their GCF, 3.

$$= \frac{3}{4}$$ ← Multiply.

Each batch of muffins gets $\frac{3}{4}$ cup of blueberries.

Check for Reasonableness When you estimate $2\frac{1}{4} \div 3$, the result is $2 \div 3$, or $\frac{2}{3}$ cup. So, $\frac{3}{4}$ cup is a reasonable answer.

✓ **Check Understanding** **2** Suppose the baker has $3\frac{3}{4}$ cups of blueberries. How many cups of blueberries should go in each batch to make 3 batches of muffins? $1\frac{1}{4}$ c

Teaching Notes

2 EXAMPLE Tactile Learners

Discuss with students the problem and solution as it is presented in the textbook. Then have students verify the solution by measuring $2\frac{1}{4}$ cups of rice or sand and dividing it into three portions of $\frac{3}{4}$ cup.

3 EXAMPLE Dividing Mixed Numbers

Find $10\frac{1}{2} \div 1\frac{3}{4}$.

$$10\frac{1}{2} \div 1\frac{3}{4} = \frac{21}{2} \div \frac{7}{4}$$ ← Write the mixed numbers as improper fractions.

$$= \frac{21}{2} \times \frac{4}{7}$$ ← Multiply by $\frac{4}{7}$, the reciprocal of $\frac{7}{4}$.

$$= \frac{{}^3 21}{{}_1 2} \times \frac{4^2}{7_1}$$ ← Divide 21 and 7 by their GCF, 7. Divide 2 and 4 by their GCF, 2.

$$= \frac{6}{1}, \text{ or } 6$$ ← Multiply and simplify.

✓ **Check Understanding** **3** Find each quotient.

a. $7 \div 1\frac{1}{6}$ 6

b. $6\frac{5}{6} \div 3\frac{1}{3}$ $2\frac{1}{20}$

c. $8\frac{3}{4} \div 2\frac{1}{2}$ $3\frac{1}{2}$

d. Number Sense How can you tell that $2\frac{1}{3} \div 3\frac{1}{2}$ will be less than 1? When you divide a number by a greater number, the quotient is less than 1.

Additional Examples

1 Paulo wants to put a row of decorative tiles along a wall. The wall is $72\frac{3}{8}$ inches wide. Each tile is $3\frac{3}{4}$ inches wide. Approximate how many tiles he will need. If each tile costs $7.00, will $100 cover the total cost? Paulo will need about 18 tiles; $100 will not cover the total cost.

2 Shaleen has enough oatmeal to make 5 batches of cookies. She wants to distribute $3\frac{1}{3}$ cups of raisins equally among each batch. What amount of raisins should she put into each batch? $\frac{2}{3}$ cup for each batch

3 Find $6\frac{1}{4} \div 1\frac{7}{8}$. $3\frac{1}{3}$

Closure

Explain how to divide mixed numbers. Write each mixed number as an improper fraction. Then find the reciprocal of the divisor and multiply.

👥 **Reaching All Students**

| **Below Level** Have students practice writing reciprocals of several mixed numbers such as the following. $1\frac{2}{3}$ $\frac{3}{5}$ $4\frac{1}{6}$ $\frac{6}{25}$ $2\frac{5}{7}$ $\frac{7}{19}$ | **Advanced Learners** Evaluate the expression. $3\frac{1}{5} \div 1\frac{1}{4} \div 5\frac{3}{5} \div 4\frac{4}{7}$ $\frac{1}{10}$ | **Tactile Learners** See note on page 237. **Error Prevention** See note on page 239. |

Assignment Guide

 **Objective 1**
Ⓐ Ⓑ Core 1–7, 29–33

Objective 2
Ⓐ Ⓑ Core 8–28, 34–52
Ⓒ Extension 53–56

Test Prep 57–60
Mixed Review 61–68

Ⓐ **Practice by Example**   **Estimate each quotient.**

Example 1
(page 236)

1. $50\frac{1}{4} \div 5\frac{3}{16}$ 10

2. $48\frac{8}{10} \div 7\frac{3}{7}$ 7

3. $99 \div 8\frac{2}{3}$ 11

4. $21\frac{1}{2} \div 1\frac{9}{16}$ 11

5. $100 \div \frac{9}{10}$ 100

6. $12 \div 2\frac{3}{10}$ 6

7. Stock Market The price of one technology stock rose $71\frac{5}{8}$ points in $7\frac{1}{2}$ hours. Estimate the number of points gained per hour during that time. **9 points**

Example 2
(page 237)

Find each quotient. Exercise 8 has been started for you.

8. $4\frac{1}{2} \div 3 = \frac{9}{2} \div \frac{3}{1}$ $1\frac{1}{2}$

9. $4\frac{3}{4} \div 5$ $\frac{19}{20}$

10. $5\frac{1}{10} \div 2$ $2\frac{11}{20}$

11. Anatomy An adult's height is about 8 times the length of his or her head. If a man is $6\frac{1}{2}$ feet tall, about how long is his head? $\frac{13}{16}$ ft

Example 3
(page 237)

Find each quotient. Exercise 12 has been started for you.

12. $3\frac{1}{3} \div 1\frac{1}{2} = \frac{10}{3} \div \frac{3}{2}$ $2\frac{2}{9}$

13. $7\frac{1}{3} \div 1\frac{5}{6}$ 4

14. $3\frac{1}{4} \div 1\frac{1}{2}$ $2\frac{1}{6}$

15. $2\frac{1}{2} \div 1\frac{1}{8}$ $2\frac{2}{9}$

16. $10\frac{1}{3} \div 3\frac{1}{3}$ $3\frac{1}{10}$

17. $2\frac{1}{10} \div 4\frac{2}{3}$ $\frac{9}{20}$

18. Astronomy Sunlight takes about $8\frac{1}{2}$ minutes to travel approximately 93 million miles from the sun to Earth. About how many miles does light travel in one minute? **about 11 million mi**

Ⓑ **Apply Your Skills**   **Find each quotient.**

19. $2\frac{1}{2} \div 7$ $\frac{5}{14}$

20. $4\frac{1}{6} \div \frac{15}{16}$ $4\frac{4}{9}$

21. $1 \div 4\frac{1}{2}$ $\frac{2}{9}$

22. $8\frac{2}{9} \div 4\frac{2}{3}$ $1\frac{16}{21}$

23. $5 \div 7\frac{2}{9}$ $\frac{9}{13}$

24. $6\frac{4}{5} \div 6\frac{9}{10}$ $\frac{68}{69}$

25. $1\frac{1}{9} \div 6\frac{2}{3}$ $\frac{1}{6}$

26. $3\frac{1}{6} \div 2$ $1\frac{7}{12}$

27. $7\frac{5}{7} \div 10\frac{2}{7}$ $\frac{3}{4}$

$1\frac{151}{887}$ times as long

28. Data File, p. 217 Look at the long jump records for the 13–14 age group. The boys' distance record is how many times as long as the girls' distance record? **See left.**

29. Construction A ceiling in an attic 24 feet wide needs insulation. Each GPS strip of insulation is $1\frac{1}{3}$ feet wide. Estimate the number of insulation strips needed to fit the width of the attic. **about 24 strips**

 Use the Guided Problem Solving worksheet with Exercise 29.

Practice 5-4   Dividing Mixed Numbers

Estimate each quotient.

1. $\frac{4}{5} \div \frac{7}{8}$ about 1

2. $2\frac{3}{8} \div \frac{5}{6}$ about 2

3. $12\frac{5}{6} \div 3\frac{1}{4}$ about 3

4. $\frac{1}{8} \div \frac{11}{12}$ about 0

5. $17\frac{1}{13} \div 2\frac{7}{9}$ about 6

6. $51\frac{1}{3} \div 4\frac{9}{10}$ about 10

7. $4 \div 1\frac{8}{11}$ about 2

8. $21\frac{2}{3} \div \frac{15}{17}$ about 22

9. $32\frac{5}{8} \div 2\frac{6}{11}$ about 11

Find each quotient.

10. $1\frac{4}{5} \div \frac{1}{3}$ $5\frac{2}{5}$

11. $1\frac{7}{9} \div \frac{2}{15}$ $13\frac{1}{3}$

12. $3\frac{4}{7} \div 3\frac{1}{2}$ $1\frac{1}{49}$

13. $3\frac{4}{5} \div 1\frac{5}{9}$ $2\frac{13}{60}$

14. $\frac{2}{3} \div 4\frac{3}{5}$ $\frac{2}{23}$

15. $4\frac{1}{6} \div \frac{4}{7}$ $9\frac{5}{8}$

16. $2\frac{4}{9} \div 4\frac{1}{4}$ $\frac{56}{95}$

17. $\frac{5}{6} \div 1\frac{3}{4}$ $\frac{10}{21}$

18. $1\frac{5}{9} \div 1\frac{3}{7}$ $1\frac{1}{35}$

19. $\frac{5}{7} \div 2\frac{1}{6}$ $\frac{2}{13}$

20. $1\frac{4}{9} \div \frac{6}{7}$ $1\frac{37}{54}$

21. $1\frac{5}{6} \div \frac{4}{5}$ $2\frac{7}{16}$

22. $\frac{1}{7} \div 3\frac{1}{4}$ $\frac{2}{13}$

23. $4\frac{4}{5} \div 1\frac{1}{6}$ $3\frac{33}{49}$

24. $\frac{4}{7} \div 3\frac{2}{5}$ $\frac{4}{17}$

25. $\frac{8}{9} \div 2\frac{4}{5}$ $\frac{56}{171}$

26. $\frac{1}{4} \div 1\frac{5}{9}$ $\frac{9}{56}$

27. $1\frac{3}{5} \div \frac{1}{5}$ $8\frac{3}{4}$

28. $4\frac{2}{3} \div 1\frac{1}{2}$ $2\frac{6}{7}$

29. $1\frac{1}{9} \div \frac{1}{5}$ $5\frac{5}{9}$

30. $1\frac{1}{5} \div 1\frac{1}{3}$ $\frac{9}{10}$

31. $1\frac{5}{8} \div \frac{4}{9}$ $2\frac{37}{40}$

32. $1\frac{3}{5} \div \frac{1}{3}$ $4\frac{4}{5}$

33. $\frac{1}{2} \div 3\frac{1}{3}$ $\frac{7}{52}$

Anna bought a strip of fabric 10 yd long. She needs a $1\frac{1}{3}$-yd piece to make a pillow.

34. How many pillows can Anna make?   **7 pillows**

35. Anna decides to make smaller pillows using $\frac{2}{3}$-yd pieces. How many small pillows can she make?   **15 pillows**

36. A bulletin board is 56 in. wide and 36 in. high. How many $3\frac{1}{2}$-in. columns can be created?   **16 columns**

Reteaching 5-4   Dividing Mixed Numbers

Example 1: Estimate $36\frac{1}{3} \div 5\frac{7}{8}$.

$36\frac{1}{3} \div 5\frac{7}{8}$ Round mixed numbers to nearest whole number.

$\downarrow$ $\downarrow$

$36 \div 6 = 6$ Find the quotient of the rounded values.

Example 2: Find $5\frac{1}{3} \div 2\frac{2}{5}$.

① Write each mixed number as an improper fraction.

$5\frac{1}{3} \div 2\frac{2}{5} = \frac{16}{3} \div \frac{12}{5}$

② The *reciprocal* of $\frac{12}{5}$ is $\frac{5}{12}$.

$\frac{12}{5} \times \frac{5}{12}$

③ Multiply $\frac{16}{3}$ by the reciprocal.

$\frac{16}{3} \div \frac{12}{5} = \frac{16}{3} \times \frac{5}{12} = \frac{\overset{4}{16}}{3} \times \frac{5}{\underset{3}{12}} = \frac{4 \times 5}{3 \times 3} = \frac{20}{9} = 2\frac{2}{9}$

$5\frac{1}{3} \div 2\frac{2}{5} = 2\frac{2}{9}$

Estimate each quotient.

1. $14\frac{4}{10} \div 5\frac{1}{3}$ 3

2. $19\frac{3}{4} \div 3\frac{7}{8}$ 5

3. $50\frac{1}{4} \div 2\frac{6}{9}$ 17

4. $5\frac{1}{3} \div 2\frac{2}{9}$ 2

5. $6\frac{1}{4} \div 2\frac{1}{3}$ 3

6. $9 \div 3\frac{1}{8}$ 3

7. $12 \div 6\frac{1}{9}$ 2

8. $5 \div 1\frac{1}{8}$ 5

9. $2\frac{7}{10} \div \frac{4}{5}$ 3

10. $6\frac{1}{4} \div 2\frac{3}{5}$ 3

11. $5\frac{3}{7} \div 1\frac{3}{4}$ 3

12. $5\frac{4}{6} \div 2\frac{1}{3}$ 2

Find each quotient.

13. $2\frac{1}{2} \div \frac{1}{4}$ 10

14. $100\frac{1}{2} \div 6\frac{1}{4}$ $16\frac{1}{50}$

15. $3\frac{5}{7} \div 1\frac{1}{2}$ $2\frac{4}{9}$

16. $6\frac{4}{9} \div 2\frac{3}{4}$ $2\frac{9}{20}$

17. $75\frac{1}{2} \div 5\frac{1}{2}$ $13\frac{8}{11}$

18. $1\frac{1}{8} \div 2\frac{3}{4}$ $\frac{7}{16}$

19. $10\frac{2}{3} \div 4\frac{1}{4}$ $2\frac{6}{13}$

20. $18\frac{5}{9} \div 1\frac{2}{3}$ $12\frac{4}{27}$

21. $1\frac{1}{10} \div 1\frac{5}{6}$ $\frac{3}{5}$

Estimation Estimate each quotient.

30. $121 \div 9\frac{7}{8}$ **12**   **31.** $210 \div 3\frac{1}{4}$ **70**   **32.** $12\frac{5}{8} \div 1\frac{1}{8}$ **13**   **33.** $9\frac{21}{32} \div 2\frac{1}{4}$ **5**

Real-World Connection

About 30 percent of U.S. households planted flower bulbs in 2001.

34. Gardening A gardener is building a border for a garden with a row of red bricks. The row is $136\frac{1}{2}$ inches long. Each brick is $10\frac{1}{2}$ inches long.
  a. How many bricks does the gardener need? **13 bricks**
  b. If each brick costs $.35, how much will the border cost? **$4.55**

35. Books A bookstore has a shelf that is $37\frac{1}{2}$ inches long. If each book is $1\frac{1}{4}$ inches thick, how many books can fit on the shelf? **30 books**

Algebra Evaluate each expression for $y = 3\frac{3}{10}$.

36. $11 \div y$ $3\frac{1}{3}$ **37.** $1\frac{1}{5} \div y$ $\frac{4}{11}$ **38.** $y \div \frac{11}{12}$ $3\frac{3}{5}$ **39.** $\frac{11}{12} \div y$ $\frac{5}{18}$

Simplify each expression.

40. $1\frac{2}{3} + \frac{3}{5}$ $2\frac{4}{15}$ **41.** $1\frac{2}{3} - \frac{3}{5}$ $1\frac{1}{15}$ **42.** $1\frac{2}{3} \times \frac{3}{5}$ 1   **43.** $1\frac{2}{3} \div \frac{3}{5}$ $2\frac{7}{9}$

44. Error Analysis At the right is Erica's solution to a division problem. Explain the error in her work and find the correct answer. **See margin.**

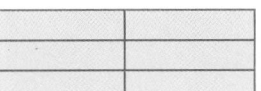

Find $7\frac{3}{8} \div 1\frac{1}{5}$.

$7\frac{3}{8} \div 1\frac{1}{5} = \frac{18}{8} \div \frac{6}{5}$

$\qquad = \frac{18}{8} \times \frac{5}{6}$

$\qquad = \frac{\overset{3}{\cancel{18}}}{8} \times \frac{5}{\underset{1}{\cancel{6}}}$

$\qquad \frac{15}{8}$, or $1\frac{7}{8}$

45a. 80; 800; 80,000

45b. As a gets larger, $8 \div \frac{1}{a}$ also gets larger.

45. a. Find the quotient $8 \div \frac{1}{a}$ for $a = 10, a = 100,$ and $a = 10,000$.
  b. Reasoning Describe the quotient $8 \div \frac{1}{a}$ as a gets larger.

46. Change $12 \div \frac{1}{5}$ to $12 \times \frac{5}{1}$. Since $\frac{5}{1} = 5$, find 12×5 to get 60.

46. Writing in Math Explain how you can use mental math to find $12 \div \frac{1}{5}$.

Find the number that correctly completes each equation.

47. $2\frac{3}{5} \div 2\frac{1}{2} = \blacksquare$ $1\frac{1}{25}$ **48.** $2\frac{3}{5} \div \blacksquare = 1$ $2\frac{3}{5}$ **49.** $\blacksquare \div \frac{1}{2} = 1\frac{3}{4}$ $\frac{7}{8}$

50. $2\frac{4}{9} \div \blacksquare = 2$ $1\frac{2}{9}$ **51.** $\blacksquare \div 2 = 3\frac{1}{8}$ $6\frac{1}{4}$ **52.** $4\frac{1}{2} \div 1\frac{1}{3} = \blacksquare$ $3\frac{3}{8}$

C Challenge

Algebra Evaluate each expression for $x = 1\frac{1}{3}$.

53. $(x + x) \div \frac{1}{2}$ $5\frac{1}{3}$ **54.** $(x + 1) \div 1\frac{1}{2}$ $1\frac{5}{9}$ **55.** $x^2 \div 4$ $\frac{4}{9}$

56. Stretch Your Thinking How many rectangles can you find in the figure at the right? **18 rectangles**

44. $7\frac{3}{8}$ is not equivalent to $\frac{18}{8}$. The correct work should be $\frac{59}{8} \div \frac{6}{5} = \frac{59}{8} \cdot \frac{5}{6} = \frac{295}{48} = 6\frac{7}{48}$

Error Prevention!

Exercises 19–27 Students might forget one or more of the multiple steps involved in the process of dividing mixed numbers. Suggest that they use a checklist like the following to help remember the steps.
1. Rewrite the mixed numbers as improper fractions.
2. Change the division to multiplication.
3. Write the reciprocal of the divisor.
4. Multiply the fractions.
5. Simplify the product.

Find each quotient.

1. $8 \div 2\frac{1}{2}$ $3\frac{1}{5}$

2. $6\frac{1}{3} \div 9$ $\frac{19}{27}$

3. $10\frac{3}{8} \div 4\frac{1}{6}$ $2\frac{49}{100}$

4. $3\frac{1}{4} \div 5\frac{1}{5}$ $\frac{5}{8}$

 Chapter Checkpoint

To check understanding of
Lessons 5-1 to 5-4:

Checkpoint Quiz 1 (p. 240)

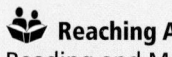 **Teaching Resources**
Checkpoint Quiz 1 (also in
Prentice Hall Assessment System)

Reaching All Students
Reading and Math Literacy 5B

Spanish versions available.

Test Prep

Resources
For additional practice with a
variety of test item formats:
• Test-Prep, p. 263
• Test-Taking Strategies, p. 259
• Test-Taking Strategies With
  Transparencies

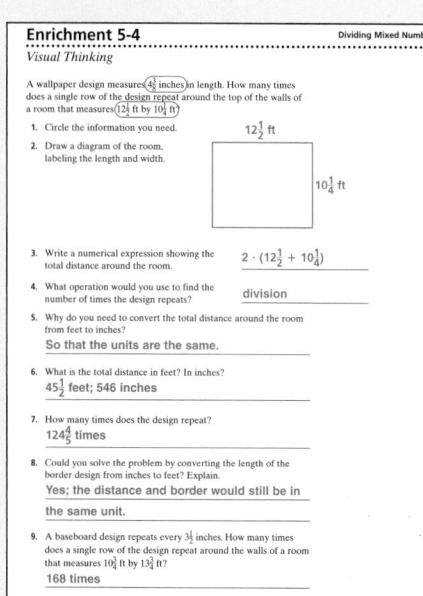
240

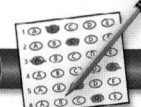

Test Prep

Reading Comprehension   Read the passage and answer the questions below.

What's in a Mile?

In England, farms used to be
measured in furlongs. The length of
a furlong depended on the distance
the horse could drag the plow
before needing to rest. The
standard length of one furlong is
660 feet. There are 8 furlongs in
1 mile, which is 5,280 feet.

 **Take It to the NET**
Online lesson quiz at
www.PHSchool.com
Web Code: aaa-0504

57. How many miles are in $5\frac{1}{3}$ furlongs? $\frac{2}{3}$ mi

58. How many furlongs are in $94\frac{2}{7}$ feet? $\frac{1}{7}$ furlong

59. How many miles are in $18\frac{2}{3}$ furlongs? $2\frac{1}{3}$ mi

Multiple Choice   60. You must cover a $72\frac{3}{8}$-inch wide wall with wood panels. If each panel
is $5\frac{5}{8}$ inches wide, about how many panels will you need? **B**

A. 10   B. 12   C. 15   D. 17

Mixed Review

Lesson 4-1   **Estimate each sum or difference.**

61. $5\frac{2}{3} + 2\frac{7}{8}$ 62. $12\frac{3}{7} - 9\frac{5}{6}$ 63. $13\frac{6}{17} + 7\frac{2}{11}$ 64. $4\frac{8}{9} - 4\frac{11}{23}$
    about 9   about 2   about 20   about $\frac{1}{2}$

Lesson 3-2   **Find the prime factorization of each number.**

65. 144   66. 98   67. 276   68. 5,000
    $2^4 \times 3^2$ 2×7^2 $2^2 \times 3 \times 23$ $2^3 \times 5^4$

 Checkpoint Quiz 1   **Lessons 5-1 through 5-4**

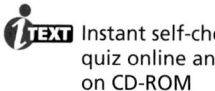 **Instant self-check
quiz online and
on CD-ROM**

Find each product or quotient.

1. $\frac{5}{12}$ of 36   15   2. $5\frac{1}{4} \times 4\frac{1}{2}$ $23\frac{5}{8}$ 3. $24 \div \frac{3}{8}$ 64   4. $1\frac{1}{9} \div 6\frac{2}{3}$ $\frac{1}{6}$

5. $\frac{2}{7} \cdot 5\frac{1}{3}$ $1\frac{11}{21}$ 6. $2\frac{2}{5} \div 4$ $\frac{3}{5}$ 7. $8\frac{1}{6} \times 2$ $16\frac{1}{3}$ 8. $7\frac{4}{9} \div 3\frac{1}{3}$ $2\frac{7}{30}$

9. How tall is a tree that is 9 times as tall as a $4\frac{1}{3}$-foot sapling?   **39 ft**

10. How many $\frac{1}{2}$-inch thick cookies can you slice from 1 foot of dough?
    24 cookies

Alternative Assessment

Provide pairs of students with exercises similar
to those in Exercises 12–17. For each exercise,
one partner renames each mixed number as an
improper fraction. The other makes any necessary
corrections, writes the reciprocal, and changes
the operation sign. Partners work together to find
the quotient. Have partners alternate roles for
each exercise.

Using a Calculator for Fractions

For Use With Lesson 5-4

Many calculators do not have fraction keys. You can still use a calculator without fraction keys to check your computations with fractions by changing the fractions to decimals. The example below is for a calculator that follows the order of operations.

Round repeating decimals to several decimal places. When you compute with rounded decimals, results may be slightly different.

EXAMPLE **Mixed Numbers to Decimals**

a. Check $2\frac{3}{8} \times 4\frac{7}{10} = 11\frac{13}{80}$.

Change the fraction part of each mixed number to a decimal by dividing the numerator by the denominator. Then add the whole number.

$$2\frac{3}{8} \qquad \times \qquad 4\frac{7}{10} \qquad \stackrel{?}{=} \qquad 11\frac{13}{80}$$

 2 ⊞ 3 ÷ 8 = 2.375   4 ⊞ 7 ÷ 10 = 4.7    11 ⊞ 13 ÷ 80 = 11.1625

2.375 ✕ 4.7 = 11.1625 ← Use a calculator to find 2.375 × 4.7.

Since $2.375 \times 4.7 = 11.1625$ and $11\frac{13}{80} = 11.1625$, the answer checks.

b. Check $2\frac{2}{7} \div 1\frac{1}{3} = 1\frac{5}{7}$.

Find the decimal equivalent of each fraction. Use three decimal places.

$$2\frac{2}{7} \qquad \div \qquad 1\frac{1}{3} \qquad \stackrel{?}{=} \qquad 1\frac{5}{7}$$

2 ⊞ 2 ÷ 7 = 2.285...   1 ⊞ 1 ÷ 3 = 1.333...   1 ⊞ 5 ÷ 7 = 1.714...

2.285 ÷ 1.333 = 1.715 ← Use a calculator to find 2.285 ÷ 1.333.

Since 1.715 is very close to 1.714, the answer $1\frac{5}{7}$ checks.

EXERCISES

Write a decimal number sentence to check each fraction sentence.
Round repeating decimals to three decimal places. 1–4. See margin.

1. $3\frac{1}{5} \times 1\frac{3}{4} = 5\frac{3}{5}$
2. $9\frac{3}{10} - 3\frac{2}{5} = 5\frac{9}{10}$
3. $6\frac{1}{2} \div 1\frac{3}{5} = 4\frac{1}{16}$
4. $2\frac{5}{7} + 7\frac{1}{2} = 10\frac{3}{14}$

1. $3.2 \times 1.75 \stackrel{?}{=} 5.6$ ✓

2. $9.3 - 3.4 \stackrel{?}{=} 5.9$ ✓

3. $6.5 \div 1.6 \stackrel{?}{=} 4.0625$ ✓

4. $2.714 + 7.5 \stackrel{?}{=} 10.214$ ✓

Using a Calculator for Fractions

Students can use a calculator to convert fractions to decimals in order to check computations with fractions and mixed numbers.

Optional Materials

- any calculator
- Classroom Aid 11

Teaching Notes

Circulate and watch as students work through the steps to rename each mixed number as a decimal and then multiply to confirm the product shown. Ask:

- *How else could you use your calculator to rename each factor as a decimal?* Sample: Find the improper fraction; divide numerator by denominator.
- *When you multiply mixed numbers, what is another way to check that your answer is reasonable?* Sample: Round each mixed number to the nearest whole number; multiply the whole numbers.

Inclusion
You may find it useful to review the relationship between fractions and decimals. In addition, you may wish to review the process of rounding decimals.

Exercises
When you assign the exercises, encourage students to round the mixed numbers to whole numbers as a way of checking for reasonableness.

Lesson Preview

 Check Skills You'll Need

Multiplying Two Fractions
Lesson 5-1: Example 2. Extra
Practice p. 646.

Lesson Resources

 Teaching Resources
Practice, Reteaching, Enrichment

Reaching All Students
Practice Workbook 5-5
Spanish Practice Workbook 5-5
Guided Problem Solving 5-5

Presentation Assistant Plus!
Transparencies
• Check Skills You'll Need 5-5
• Problem of the Day 5-5
• Additional Examples 5-5
• Student Edition Answers 5-5
• Lesson Quiz 5-5
PH Presentation Pro CD-ROM 5-5

 ASSESSMENT SYSTEM

Computer Test Generator CD

 Technology
Resource Pro® CD-ROM
Computer Test Generator CD
PH Presentation Pro CD-ROM

 www.PHSchool.com
Student Site
• Teacher Web Code: aak-5500
• Self-grading Lesson Quiz

PH SuccessNet Teacher Center
• Lesson Planner

Plus **iTEXT**

5-5 Solving Fraction Equations by Multiplying

What You'll Learn

OBJECTIVE 1 To solve fraction equations

. . . And Why

To solve measurement problems, as in Example 3

 Check Skills You'll Need For help, go to Lesson 5-1.

Find each product.

1. $\frac{1}{3} \times \frac{7}{10}$ $\frac{7}{30}$ **2.** $\frac{2}{3} \cdot \frac{9}{22}$ $\frac{3}{11}$ **3.** $\frac{3}{7} \times \frac{14}{15}$ $\frac{2}{5}$

OBJECTIVE 1   **iTEXT** Interactive lesson includes instant self-check, tutorials, and activities.

Solving Fraction Equations

Investigation: Solving Equations Mentally

1. Use mental math to find each numerator.

   a. $\frac{\blacksquare}{4} = 5$ 20   **b.** $\frac{\blacksquare}{3} = 12$ 36   **c.** $\frac{\blacksquare}{10} = 10$ 100   **d.** $\frac{\blacksquare}{10} = 100$ 1,000

2. How can you find the value of each numerator from the other two numbers in the equation? **Multiply the other two numbers.**

The Multiplication Property of Equality says that multiplying each side of an equation by the same number does not change the solution of an equation.

1 EXAMPLE   **Solving Equations by Multiplying**

Solve $\frac{x}{8} = 20$.

$$\frac{x}{8} = 20$$

$$8 \cdot \frac{x}{8} = 8 \cdot 20 \qquad \leftarrow \text{Multiply each side by 8.}$$

$$\frac{1}{8} \cdot \frac{x}{8_1} = 160 \qquad \leftarrow \text{Write 8 as } \frac{8}{1}. \text{ Simplify.}$$

$$\frac{x}{1} = 160 \qquad \leftarrow \text{Multiply the numerators and the denominators.}$$

$$x = 160 \qquad \leftarrow \text{Simplify.}$$

 Check Understanding ① Solve.   **a.** $\frac{x}{2} = 15$ 30   **b.** $\frac{n}{6} = 12$ 72

 ## Ongoing Assessment and Intervention

Before the Lesson	During the Lesson	After the Lesson
Diagnose prerequisite skills using:	Monitor progress using:	Assess knowledge using:
• Check Skills You'll Need	• Check Understanding	• Lesson Quiz
	• Additional Examples	• Computer Test Generator CD
	• Test Prep	

To solve $\frac{2}{3}x = 8$, multiply each side by $\frac{3}{2}$, since $\frac{3}{2} \cdot \frac{2}{3} = 1$.

2 EXAMPLE **Using Reciprocals to Solve Equations**

Solve $\frac{2}{3}x = 8$. Check the solution.

$$\frac{2}{3}x = 8$$

$$\frac{3}{2} \cdot \left(\frac{2}{3}x\right) = \frac{3}{2} \cdot (8) \quad \leftarrow \text{ Multiply each side by } \frac{3}{2}, \text{ the reciprocal of } \frac{2}{3}.$$

$$1 \cdot x = 12 \quad \leftarrow \textbf{Multiply.}$$

$$x = 12 \quad \leftarrow \textbf{Simplify.}$$

Check $\frac{2}{3}x = 8 \quad \leftarrow$ **Start with the original equation.**

$$\frac{2}{3}(12) \stackrel{?}{=} 8 \quad \leftarrow \textbf{Replace } x \textbf{ with 12.}$$

$$8 = 8 \checkmark \quad \leftarrow \textbf{The solution checks.}$$

✔ **Check Understanding** ② Solve each equation. Check the solution.

a. $\frac{9}{10}x = 18$ **20** **b.** $\frac{4}{5}x = 20$ **25** **c.** $\frac{7}{8}x = 42$ **48**

3 EXAMPLE **Writing and Solving Equations**  **Real World**

Spelling Bee Students are making banners to support friends in a national spelling bee. They have 6 yards of material. Each banner takes $\frac{5}{8}$ yard of material. How many banners can they make?

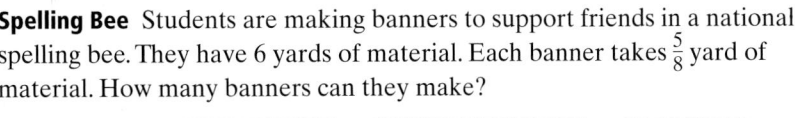

Words | yards per banner × number of banners = total yards

Let b = number of banners.

Equation | $\frac{5}{8}$ × b = 6

$$\frac{5}{8}b = 6 \quad \leftarrow \textbf{Write the equation.}$$

$$\frac{5}{8}b = \frac{6}{1} \quad \leftarrow \textbf{Write 6 as } \frac{6}{1}.$$

$$\frac{8}{5} \cdot \left(\frac{5}{8}b\right) = \frac{8}{5} \cdot \frac{6}{1} \quad \leftarrow \textbf{Multiply each side by } \frac{8}{5}, \textbf{ the reciprocal of } \frac{5}{8}.$$

$$1 \cdot b = \frac{48}{5} \quad \leftarrow \textbf{Multiply.}$$

$$b = 9\frac{3}{5} \quad \leftarrow \textbf{Write as a mixed number.}$$

The students can make 9 banners.

✔ **Check Understanding** ③ Beth needs boards that are $\frac{3}{4}$ foot long. She has a board that is 8 feet long. How many $\frac{3}{4}$-foot sections can she cut from it? **10 boards**

Real-World Connection

The first national spelling bee was held in 1925. Today more than 10 million students participate in local spelling bees.

👥 Reaching All Students

| **Below Level** Review the Multiplication Property of Equality by having students solve several equations like these.

$k \div 4 = 9$ $k = 36$
$z \div 6 = 10$ $z = 60$ | **Advanced Learners** Solve mentally.

$\frac{m}{12} = 4$ $\frac{12}{n} = 4$
$m = 48$ $n = 3$
$\frac{r}{3} = 6$ $\frac{3}{s} = 6$
$r = 18$ $s = 0.5 \text{ or } \frac{1}{2}$ | **Inclusion**
See note on page 243.
Error Prevention
See note on page 244. |

---

2. Teach

Professional Development

Math Background

In Lesson 2-7, students learned that an equation of the form $x \div a = b$ can be solved by applying the Multiplication Property of Equality. That is, they learned to solve by multiplying each side of the equation by a. Since a fraction bar represents division, the same method can be used to solve an equation that appears in the form $\frac{x}{a} = b$.

Teaching Notes

Investigation (Optional)
Have students read each equation silently. For instance, for $\frac{\blacksquare}{4} = 5$ they read "what number divided by 4 equals 5?" Students might also benefit from rewriting each equation without the fraction bar.

$$\frac{\blacksquare}{4} = 5 \rightarrow \blacksquare \div 4 = 5$$

2 EXAMPLE Inclusion

Use the reciprocal technique presented in Example 2 to solve Example 1 again. This may help students understand that $\frac{x}{8}$ and $\frac{1}{8}x$ are equivalent expressions.

$$\frac{x}{8} = 20$$

$$\frac{1x}{8} = 20$$

$$\frac{1}{8}x = 20$$

$$\frac{8}{1} \cdot \left(\frac{1}{8}x\right) = \frac{8}{1} \cdot (20)$$

$$1 \cdot x = 8 \cdot 20$$

$$x = 160$$

PowerPoint

📖 Additional Examples

① Solve $\frac{c}{3} = 14$. $c = 42$

② Solve $\frac{3}{4}m = 24$. Check the solution. $m = 32$

③ Mai Li worked $7\frac{1}{2}$ hours and earned \$150. What amount did she earn per hour? **\$20 per hour**

Closure

Explain how to solve a fraction equation by multiplying. **Sample:** For an equation like $\frac{a}{5} = 20$, multiply each side by the denominator of the fraction. For an equation like $\frac{4}{5}b = 20$, multiply each side by the reciprocal of the fraction.

3. Practice

Assignment Guide

1 Objective 1
- Ⓐ Ⓑ Core 1–32
- Ⓒ Extension 33–36

Test Prep 37–40
Mixed Review 41–46

Error Prevention!

Exercises 1–9 Students might simply divide the numbers they see. In Exercise 1, for instance, they might calculate $12 \div 3 = 4$ and give the solution $x = 4$. Stress the importance of checking the solution in the original equation.

Practice 5-5   Solving Fraction Equations by Multiplying

Solve each equation. Check the solution.

1. $\frac{1}{13}n = \frac{1}{3}$
$n = 2\frac{1}{6}$

2. $\frac{9}{7}f = \frac{1}{3}$
$f = \frac{7}{18}$

3. $\frac{7}{19}f = \frac{1}{2}$
$f = 1\frac{5}{14}$

4. $\frac{5}{18}n = 2$
$n = 7\frac{1}{5}$

5. $\frac{5}{8}n = 1$
$n = 1\frac{3}{5}$

6. $\frac{6}{7}u = \frac{3}{7}$
$u = 1\frac{1}{5}$

7. $\frac{3}{7}q = \frac{3}{8}$
$q = \frac{7}{8}$

8. $\frac{5}{14}c = \frac{1}{2}$
$c = 1\frac{2}{5}$

9. $\frac{3}{7}b = \frac{6}{7}$
$b = \frac{4}{7}$

10. $\frac{1}{4}n = 2$
$n = 8$

11. $\frac{8}{9}t = 3$
$t = 3\frac{3}{8}$

12. $\frac{5}{13}h = \frac{2}{5}$
$h = 1\frac{11}{25}$

13. $\frac{4}{9}v = \frac{1}{4}$
$v = \frac{9}{16}$

14. $\frac{8}{13}h = 2$
$h = 6\frac{1}{4}$

15. $\frac{10}{7}h = \frac{1}{2}$
$h = \frac{7}{20}$

16. $\frac{2}{3}w = 3$
$w = 4\frac{1}{2}$

17. $\frac{8}{9}d = \frac{1}{3}$
$d = \frac{17}{24}$

18. $\frac{3}{2}v = \frac{1}{2}$
$v = \frac{1}{3}$

19. $\frac{7}{9}z = 1$
$z = \frac{9}{7}$

20. $\frac{8}{9}z = \frac{1}{3}$
$z = \frac{3}{8}$

21. $\frac{10}{11}m = 4$
$m = 6\frac{4}{5}$

Solve.

22. The largest U.S. standard postage stamp ever issued has a width of about 1 inch, which is $\frac{3}{4}$ of the height of the stamp. Write and solve an equation to find the height of the stamp.
$\frac{3}{4}x = 1; 1\frac{1}{3}$ in.

23. Candace said, "I'm thinking of a fraction. If I divide it by $\frac{1}{2}$, I get $\frac{3}{11}$." What fraction was Candace thinking of?
$\frac{3}{22}$

Reteaching 5-5   Solving Fraction Equations by Multiplying

When solving multiplication equations, it may help to first find the numerator of the missing value and then the denominator. If the equation includes whole numbers or mixed numbers, you may need to rewrite these numbers as fractions.

Solve: $\frac{2}{3}x = \frac{4}{25}$

① Think: What number times $\frac{2}{3}$ equals $\frac{4}{25}$? $(2 \times 2 = 4)$

② Then use mental math to find the numerator. $\frac{2}{3} \times \frac{2}{?} = \frac{4}{25}$

③ Use mental math to find the denominator. $\frac{2}{3} \times \frac{2}{?} = \frac{4}{25}$ $(5 \times 5 = 25)$

④ Check to see that the equation is true. $\frac{2}{3} \times \frac{2}{5} = \frac{4}{25}$ ✓

So, $x = \frac{2}{5}$.

Solve each equation. Check the solution.

1. $\frac{2}{3}x = \frac{8}{15}$
$x = \frac{4}{5}$

2. $\frac{3}{4}x = \frac{9}{20}$
$x = \frac{3}{5}$

3. $\frac{1}{3}x = 4$
$x = 12$

4. $\frac{5}{6}x = \frac{18}{16}$
$\frac{6}{6} = 3$

5. $\frac{3}{2}x = \frac{6}{10}$
$x = \frac{2}{5}$

6. $\frac{9}{8}x = \frac{9}{25}$
$x = \frac{1}{5}$

7. $\frac{8}{9}x = \frac{16}{27}$
$x = \frac{2}{9}$

8. $\frac{5}{4}x = \frac{35}{48}$
$x = \frac{7}{12}$

9. $\frac{9}{7}x = \frac{27}{35}$
$x = \frac{3}{5}$

10. $\frac{10}{3}x = \frac{20}{27}$
$x = \frac{2}{9}$

11. A wrestler weighed $112\frac{1}{2}$ pounds before the state meet. After the meet, the wrestler weighed $\frac{49}{50}$ of his original weight. How much did the wrestler weigh after the meet?
$110\frac{1}{4}$ pounds

12. A number divided by 4 equals $10\frac{1}{8}$. What is the number?
$40\frac{1}{2}$

EXERCISES

Ⓐ Practice by Example

Solve each equation. Check the solution.

Example 1
(page 242)

1. $\frac{x}{3} = 12$ 36
2. $\frac{a}{7} = 8$ 56
3. $\frac{j}{12} = 27$ 324

4. $\frac{s}{5} = 35$ 175
5. $\frac{v}{4} = 11$ 44
6. $\frac{p}{9} = 9$ 81

7. $\frac{x}{15} = 3$ 45
8. $\frac{t}{2} = 75$ 150
9. $\frac{r}{12} = 1.5$ 18

Example 2
(page 243)

10. $\frac{1}{2}m = 6$ 12
11. $\frac{2}{3}r = 10$ 15
12. $\frac{3}{5}n = 9$ 15

13. $\frac{7}{8}p = 21$ 24
14. $\frac{4}{5}y = 8$ 10
15. $\frac{5}{9}z = 30$ 54

Example 3
(page 243)

$\frac{5}{6}c = 9$; 10 costumes

Write an equation for each problem. Then solve the equation.

16. **Costumes** Each ballerina's costume needs $\frac{5}{6}$ yard of ribbon trim. Joy has 9 yards of ribbon. How many costumes can she trim?   **See left.**

17. **Coin Collecting** Gerald's nickel collection weighs $7\frac{1}{2}$ times as much as his brother's nickel collection. If Gerald has 3 pounds of nickels, how many pounds of nickels does his brother have? $7\frac{1}{2} \times p = 3$; $\frac{2}{5}$ lb

Ⓑ Apply Your Skills

Solve each equation. Check the solution.

18. $11 = \frac{x}{5}$ 55
19. $\frac{9}{10}k = 18$ 20
20. $7 = \frac{n}{7}$ 49

21. $\frac{7}{8}b = \frac{1}{2}$ $\frac{4}{7}$
22. $\frac{3}{20}x = 5$ $33\frac{1}{3}$
23. $\frac{3}{4}y = \frac{3}{8}$ $\frac{1}{2}$

24. $2\frac{2}{5}p = 10$ $4\frac{1}{6}$
25. $\frac{1}{6}m = \frac{3}{20}$ $\frac{9}{10}$
26. $\frac{2}{7}n = \frac{1}{14}$ $\frac{1}{4}$

27. **Writing in Math** In the equation $\frac{3}{5}k = 11$, how can you tell k is greater than 11 without solving? k is greater than 11 because if it were 11 or less, multiplying it by $\frac{3}{5}$ would give a product less than 11.

Write an equation for each problem. Then solve the equation.

28. **Shopping** You buy a shirt and a pair of pants. The price of the shirt is $\frac{5}{6}$ the price of the pants. The shirt costs \$12.50. How much do the pants cost? $\frac{5}{6}p = 12.50$; \$15

29. **Running** Andrew and Keith are training for a marathon. On a given day, Andrew runs 12 miles, which is $\frac{8}{5}$ the distance Keith runs. How far does Keith run? $\frac{8}{5}k = 12$; $7\frac{1}{2}$ mi

30. **Architecture** The Sears Tower in Chicago is about 1,450 feet tall, which is $\frac{29}{25}$ as tall as the Empire State Building in New York City. How tall is the Empire State Building? $\frac{29}{25}h = 1$; 450; about 1,250 ft

GPS   Use the Guided Problem Solving worksheet with Exercise 28.

Travel Refer to the map.

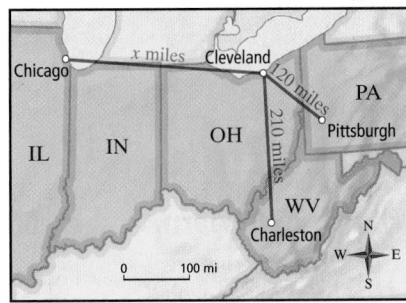

31. The distance from Cleveland to Pittsburgh is about $\frac{2}{5}$ the distance from Cleveland to Chicago. About how far is Cleveland from Chicago?
about 300 mi

32. Cleveland to Charleston is about how many times as far as Cleveland to Pittsburgh? about $1\frac{3}{4}$ times as far

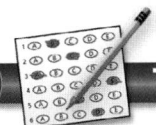

C **Challenge**

Solve each equation. Check the solution.

33. $\frac{1}{4}w = 2\frac{1}{2}$ 10

34. $2\frac{5}{8}y = 10\frac{1}{2}$ 4

35. $6\frac{4}{9}p = 9\frac{2}{3}$ $1\frac{1}{2}$

36. **Stretch Your Thinking** You have 48 yellow blocks and 40 green blocks. What is the greatest number of identical towers that you can build using all 88 blocks? 8 towers

Test Prep

Multiple Choice

37. What is the value of x in the equation $\frac{3}{4}x = 12$? C
A. 6   B. 9   C. 16   D. 48

38. If $15 = d - 7$, what is the value of $3d$? I
F. 8   G. 22   H. 45   I. 66

Take It to the NET
Online lesson quiz at
www.PHSchool.com
Web Code: aaa-0505

39. What is the value of t in the equation $\frac{3}{8}t = 6$? C
A. $\frac{1}{16}$ B. $2\frac{1}{4}$ C. 16   D. $48\frac{1}{3}$

Short Response

40. Pedro bikes $3\frac{1}{3}$ times as far as Pat, and Pat bikes $\frac{1}{5}$ as far as Jen.
a. If Pedro rides 8 miles a day, how far does Jen ride?
b. Explain in words how you found your answer. See margin.

Mixed Review

Lesson 4-5

Find each difference.

41. $15\frac{6}{9} - 13\frac{5}{12}$ $2\frac{1}{4}$

42. $23\frac{2}{3} - 4\frac{1}{2}$ $19\frac{1}{6}$

43. $26 - 4\frac{1}{9}$ $21\frac{8}{9}$

Lesson 3-8

Write each decimal as a fraction or mixed number in simplest form.

44. 0.375 $\frac{3}{8}$

45. 0.09 $\frac{9}{100}$

46. 2.125 $2\frac{1}{8}$

5-5 Solving Fraction Equations by Multiplying **245**

40. [2] a. Jen rides 12 miles.

b. Pedro bikes $\left(3\frac{1}{3} \times \frac{1}{5}\right)$ of Jen's distance. $3\frac{1}{3} \cdot \frac{1}{5} = \frac{2}{3}$. Pedro bikes $\frac{2}{3}$ of

Jen's distance. I solved the equation $8 = \frac{2}{3}j$ and got 12.

[1] incorrect explanation OR incorrect answer

4. Assess

PowerPoint Lesson Quiz 5-5

Solve each equation.

1. $\frac{n}{4} = 6$ 24

2. $\frac{2}{5}p = 30$ 75

3. $\frac{3}{8}h = \frac{1}{4}$ $\frac{2}{3}$

4. $\frac{1}{6}k = 4$ 24

Alternative Assessment

Provide pairs of students with equations similar to those in Exercises 1–15. Before working together to solve each equation, have partners first discuss and list the steps they will take.

Test Prep

Resources
For additional practice with a variety of test item formats:
• Test-Prep, p. 263
• Test-Taking Strategies, p. 259
• Test-Taking Strategies With Transparencies

Enrichment 5-5   Solving Fraction Equations by Multiplying

Critical Thinking

Many ancient peoples used various body distances as a means for measuring length. The Inka used measures such as the half arm-span (known as a *sikya*); the forearm, or cubit (known as a *cuchuch*); and the hand-span (called a *capa*). The Romans also used body distances to measure length, including the width of a finger (known as a *digitus*), the palm (called a *palmus*), and the length of two steps (called a *passus*).

Two of the more common measures of length were the *palm* and the *span* (or hand-span). A palm is defined as the width of four extended fingers; a span the width of a hand, from outspread thumb to the little finger. One inch equals $\frac{1}{3}$ of a palm and $\frac{1}{9}$ of a span.

1. How many palms equal 1 inch? $\frac{1}{3}$ palm

2. How many spans equal 1 inch? $\frac{1}{9}$ span

3. Which operation should you use to find how many
   a. palms are in 12 inches? division
   b. spans are in 18 inches? division

4. How are the equations used to find the number of palms in 12 inches and the number of spans in 18 inches similar?
   Sample answer: Both use the same operation and have fractional amounts.

5. Write an equation to find the number of palms in 12 inches. $p \div \frac{1}{3} = 12$

6. How many palms are in 12 inches? 4 palms

7. Write an equation to find the number of spans in 18 inches. $s \div \frac{1}{9} = 18$

8. How many spans are in 18 inches? 2 spans

9. How can you check your answer?
   Sample answer: Substitute the answer into the equation. Then solve.

10. Write and solve an equation to find the number of inches in 16 palms.
    Sample answer: $16 \div \frac{1}{3} = p$; $p = 48$; 48 in.

245

5-6

1. Plan

Lesson Preview

 Check Skills You'll Need

Dividing Mixed Numbers
Lesson 5-4: Example 3. Extra
Practice p. 646.

Lesson Resources

 Teaching Resources
Practice, Reteaching, Enrichment

Reaching All Students
Practice Workbook 5-6
Spanish Practice Workbook 5-6
Guided Problem Solving 5-6

Presentation Assistant Plus!
Transparencies
• Check Skills You'll Need 5-6
• Problem of the Day 5-6
• Additional Examples 5-6
• Student Edition Answers 5-6
• Lesson Quiz 5-6
PH Presentation Pro CD-ROM 5-6

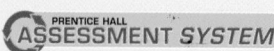 *ASSESSMENT SYSTEM*

Computer Test Generator CD

 Technology
Resource Pro® CD-ROM
Computer Test Generator CD
PH Presentation Pro CD-ROM

 www.PHSchool.com
Student Site
• Teacher Web Code: aak-5500
• Self-grading Lesson Quiz

PH SuccessNet Teacher Center
• Lesson Planner
• Resources

Plus 🅸TEXT

What You'll Learn

OBJECTIVE 1 To solve problems by solving a simpler problem

... And Why

To tile a floor, as in Example 1

 **Check Skills You'll Need**   ❓ For help, go to Lesson 5-4.

Find each quotient.

1. $5\frac{1}{2} \div 3\frac{2}{3}$ $1\frac{1}{2}$ **2.** $1\frac{1}{3} \div 3\frac{3}{5}$ $\frac{10}{27}$ **3.** $18 \div 1\frac{4}{5}$ 10

4. $1\frac{12}{13} \div 2\frac{10}{13}$ $\frac{25}{36}$ **5.** $56 \div 8\frac{3}{4}$ $6\frac{2}{5}$ **6.** $4\frac{1}{6} \div 4\frac{6}{11}$ $\frac{11}{12}$

OBJECTIVE

1 Solving a Simpler Problem

🅸TEXT Interactive lesson includes instant self-check, tutorials, and activities.

When to Use This Strategy Using simpler numbers can help you develop a plan for solving a difficult problem.

1 EXAMPLE   Real-World 🌐 Problem Solving

Tiling You are to tile a $17\frac{1}{2}$-foot by $13\frac{3}{4}$-foot rectangular floor with square tiles $1\frac{1}{4}$-foot on each side. How many tiles do you need?

Read and Understand The rectangular floor is $17\frac{1}{2}$ feet long and $13\frac{3}{4}$ feet wide. Each tile is a square with sides $1\frac{1}{4}$ feet long. You must find how many tiles are needed to cover the floor.

Plan and Solve To help you decide how many tiles are needed, **solve a simpler problem.** Replace $17\frac{1}{2}$ with 18, $13\frac{3}{4}$ with 14, and $1\frac{1}{4}$ with 1.

> **Simpler Problem** A rectangular floor is 18 feet by 14 feet. How many 1-foot by 1-foot tiles do you need to cover the floor?

Step 1 For one row of tiles to cover the length of the room, you need

$$18 \div 1 = 18 \text{ tiles.}$$

Step 2 For enough rows to cover the width of the room, you need

$$14 \div 1 = 14 \text{ rows.}$$

So, you need $14 \times 18 = 252$ tiles.

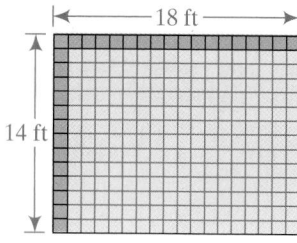

Ongoing Assessment and Intervention

Before the Lesson
Diagnose prerequisite skills using:
• Check Skills You'll Need

During the Lesson
Monitor progress using:
• Check Understanding
• Additional Examples
• Test Prep

After the Lesson
Assess knowledge using:
• Lesson Quiz
• Computer Test Generator CD

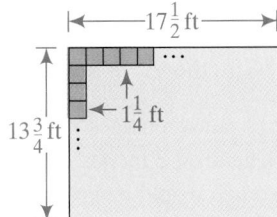

Solving the simpler problem helps you understand what operations and steps to use. Now solve the *original problem*, using the same steps.

Step 1 Divide to find the number of tiles in a row to cover the length of the room.

$$17\frac{1}{2} \div 1\frac{1}{4} = \frac{35}{2} \div \frac{5}{4}$$
$$= \frac{7\cancel{35}}{\cancel{2}_1} \cdot \frac{\cancel{4}^2}{\cancel{5}_1}$$
$$= 14 \text{ tiles}$$

Step 2 Divide to find the number of rows to cover the width of the room.

$$13\frac{3}{4} \div 1\frac{1}{4} = \frac{55}{4} \div \frac{5}{4}$$
$$= \frac{11\cancel{55}}{\cancel{4}_1} \cdot \frac{\cancel{4}^1}{\cancel{5}_1}$$
$$= 11 \text{ rows}$$

So, the floor will have 11 rows of tiles with 14 tiles per row. You need $11 \times 14 = 154$ tiles.

Look Back and Check The sides of each tile are slightly longer than 1 foot, so you will need fewer than $17\frac{1}{2}$ tiles along the length of the floor and fewer than $13\frac{3}{4}$ tiles along the width. It is reasonable that you need 14 tiles for the length and 11 rows for the width. The answer checks.

✓ **Check Understanding** **1** Each of 12 people from Company A gives a business card to each of 17 people from Company B. Each person from Company B gives a card to each person from Company A. How many cards are given? **408 cards**

EXERCISES

💡 For more practice, see *Extra Practice.*

Ⓐ Practice by Example

Example 1
(pages 246–247)

Solve each problem by first solving a simpler problem.

1. On a school day, Jose spends $5\frac{1}{4}$ hours in classes. Each class lasts $\frac{3}{4}$ hour. How many classes does he have? **7 classes**

2. A grandfather clock sounds a chime every 15 minutes. How many times in a 30-day month does the clock chime? **2,880 times**

Need Help?
• Reread the problem.
• Identify the key facts and details.
• Tell the problem in your own words.
• Try a different strategy.
• Check your work.

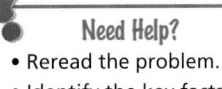

🌐 **3. Sewing** A tailor has a section of material that is $28\frac{1}{2}$ feet long. He wants to cut it into pieces that are each $1\frac{1}{2}$ feet long. How many cuts will he have to make? **18 cuts**

🌐 **4. Decorating** Nadine wants to cover a wall of her dining room with glass tiles. The wall is 8 feet by 8 feet, and the tiles are 16 inches by 16 inches. How many tiles will she need? **36 tiles**

🌐 **5. Baking** A baking pan of brownies measures 9 inches by 12 inches. How many $1\frac{1}{2}$-inch by $1\frac{1}{2}$-inch brownies can be cut from this batch? **48 brownies**

👫 Reaching All Students

Below Level Give students several mixed numbers and have them round to the nearest whole number. For example:

$17\frac{3}{4}$ 18 $12\frac{1}{5}$ 12 $22\frac{1}{2}$ 23

Advanced Learners Explain how to measure the thickness of a sheet of paper by solving a simpler problem.
Sample: Measure the thickness of 100 sheets, then divide by 100.

Visual Learners See note on page 247.
Error Prevention See note on page 248.

---

2. Teach

Professional Development

Math Background

Problems sometimes appear intimidating simply because they involve fractions, decimals, or greater whole numbers. In this lesson, students learn how to approach such problems by first considering numbers that are more manageable. With the "difficult" numbers temporarily set aside, students can focus their attention on making a plan for solving the problem. Once the plan has been determined, students can go back and apply it to the original problem. This strategy is referred to as *solving a simpler problem*.

Teaching Notes

1 EXAMPLE Visual Learners

In Check Understanding 1, students might draw a diagram like the one below to show the simpler situation of 3 people from Company A and 4 people from Company B. It clearly shows that there are $3 \times 4 = 12$ pairings between the people, requiring $2 \times 12 = 24$ business cards.

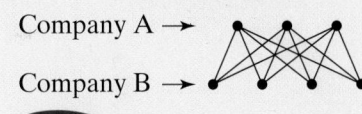
Company A →
Company B →

PowerPoint
🔲 **Additional Examples**

1 You and your friends are going to bake 48 loaves of bread for the bake sale. You need $1\frac{1}{4}$ cups of flour for each loaf. A bag of flour contains $18\frac{3}{4}$ cups. How many bags of flour do you need for all the loaves? $3\frac{1}{5}$ **bags**

Closure

• *When might it be a good idea to solve a simpler problem?* When it is difficult to get started and the problem involves numbers that appear "difficult."

• *How does solving a simpler problem help you solve the more complicated problem?* It might be easier to make a plan for solving the original problem.

Assignment Guide

1 Objective 1
Ⓐ Ⓑ **Core 1–12**
Ⓒ **Extension 13–15**

Test Prep 16–20
Mixed Review 21–30

Error Prevention!

Students might give the solution of the simpler problem as the solution of the original problem. Remind them to *Look Back and Check* to make sure that the answer satisfies the original problem.

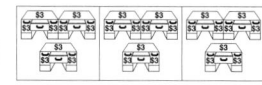

Practice 5-6   Problem Solving Strategy: Solve a Simpler Problem

Solve each problem by first solving a simpler problem.

1. At 8:00 P.M., there are 243 people in line for a ride at an amusement park. Every 12 minutes starting at 8 P.M., 42 people are able to enter the ride. A boy gets in line at 8:00 P.M. Will he get to ride before the ride shuts down at 9:00 P.M.? Explain.
No; if the last ride ends at 9 P.M.; Yes, if the last ride leaves at 9 P.M.

2. The astronauts who landed on the moon brought back about 842 pounds of moon rocks. Dividing the cost of these moon flights by the weight of the rocks, it is estimated that the rocks cost $3,000,000 per ounce. What was the approximate cost of these moon flights?
$40,416,000,000

3. While an adult is asleep, his or her heart can pump about 80 gal of blood per hour. About how many gallons of blood will the heart pump during a week of sleep if an adult sleeps 7 h each night?
3,920 gal

Choose a strategy to solve each problem.

4. The Language Club includes students who are enrolled in Latin, German, Spanish, or French. Each person, including John, is enrolled in only one foreign language. Christine does not speak French. Judy is enrolled in German or Latin. Pepe is enrolled in Latin or Spanish. Christine and the person taking Spanish often walk to school together. Christine and the person who is taking German are best friends. Who is enrolled in which course?
Christine: Latin; Judy: German; Pepe: Spanish; John: French

5. What is the sum of all odd numbers from 101 to 200?
7,500

6. A small hummingbird beats its wings 70 times per second. How many times will it beat its wings in 8 h?
about 2,016,000 times

7. It takes the sound of thunder five seconds to travel one mile. How far away is the thunder if it takes 45 s to reach you?
about 9 mi

8. A company with 628 employees is taking all the employees to see a baseball game. The company will hire buses. If each bus holds 34 passengers, will 15 buses be enough?
no

Reteaching 5-6   Problem Solving: Solve a Simpler Problem

A mystery game has 3 rooms. Each room has 3 desks. Each desk has 3 drawers, and each drawer has 3 dollars. If you are able to collect all the money, how many dollars would this be?

Read and Understand   What is the object of the game?
The object is to collect all the money.
What does the problem ask you to find?
Find how much money is hidden in all 3 rooms.

Plan and Solve   If you cannot solve the entire problem at once, how can you break it down into simpler problems?
Find the amount of money in one room.
Then multiply by 3.
For one room multiply:
3 (desks) × 3 (drawers) × 3 (dollars).
There is $27 in one room. 3 × $27 = $81. There is $81 in all three rooms.

Look Back and Check   How does solving a simpler problem help find the solution to the original problem?
The strategy allows you to work with easier numbers.

Solve each problem by first solving a simpler problem.

1. Another game has 7 rooms, each with 7 paintings. Behind each painting are 7 safes. Inside each safe are 7 security boxes, each with $70 in them. How much money is hidden in the house?
$168,070

2. If someone enters one of the 7 rooms while you are there collecting the money, you must give that person the contents of one safe. Suppose this happens to you in all 7 rooms. How much would you have at the end of the game?
$167,580

3. Six students are playing a game. Each student plays the game once with each of the other students. How many games are played?
15 games

4. Twelve students each have 2 bookbags. Each bookbag contains 4 books. Each book costs $10.95. How much do the books cost altogether?
$1,051.20

248

Ⓑ **Apply Your Skills**

Strategies

Draw a Diagram
Make a Graph
Make an Organized List
Make a Table and
  Look for a Pattern
Simulate a Problem
Solve a Simpler Problem
Try, Check, and Revise
Use Logical Reasoning
Work Backward
Write an Equation

Choose a strategy to solve each problem.

6. **Fundraising** The pep club sells shirts with the school logo. The shirts come with long sleeves or short sleeves. The color choices are orange, green, purple, and blue. How many different styles are there? **8 styles**

7. Between the ages of 5 and 10, Brian grew 27 inches. Between ages 10 and 15, he grew 9 inches. Between ages 15 and 20, he grew 3 inches.
   a. If Brian could continue to grow this way, how much would he grow between ages 20 and 25? **1 in.**
   b. At age 5, Brian was 30 inches tall. Based on your answer to part (a), what would his height be at age 25? **70 in.**

5 years   10 years   15 years   20 years

8. Find two consecutive odd numbers whose product is 399. (*Hint*: 11 and 13 are consecutive odd numbers.) **19 and 21**

9. **Biology** Two rats, Squeaky and Moe, are running through a 50-foot maze. Both run 10 feet in 10 seconds.
   - Squeaky's path has a food bin every 2 feet. She takes 3 seconds to eat at each bin.
   - Moe's path has a food bin every 5 feet. He takes 5 seconds to eat at each bin.
   a. Which rat will finish first? **Moe**
   b. **Writing in Math** Explain how you solved this problem. **See above left.**

9b. Answers may vary. Sample: I drew a diagram to help find the number of stops for each rat. Both ran the same distance for 50 seconds. Moe wins by 25 seconds.

10. **Estimation** You spend $12.50 a year for a pass to school events. If you attend 7 events, is your cost more or less than $1.50 per event? **more**
GPS

11. **Weaving** Jamal makes wall hangings and sells them for $4.95 per square foot. How much will he charge for a 4-foot by 4-foot hanging? **$79.20**

12. **Music** A chorus teacher can arrange singers in rows of 10, 12, or 15 with no one left over. What is the least possible number of singers in the chorus? **60 singers**

248   **Chapter 5**   Multiplying and Dividing Fractions

 GPS   Use the Guided Problem Solving worksheet with Exercise 10.

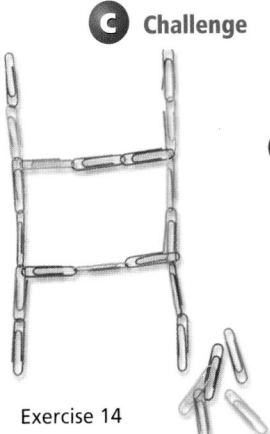

Exercise 14

C Challenge

13. Roz helps set the table every 5 days. David helps set the table every day. Chris helps set the table every 6 days. On May 9, all three set the table. In which month will they all set the table on the same day next? **June**

🌐 **14. Crafts** Meghan is making a paper clip ladder like the one at the left. The legs of the ladder must extend above the top rung and below the bottom rung. Each rung is three clips. To make a ladder with 15 rungs, how many paper clips will Meghan need? **109 clips**

15. Stretch Your Thinking In a two-digit prime number, the ones digit is four less than its tens digit. The number can be made by reversing the digits of another prime number. What is the number? **73**

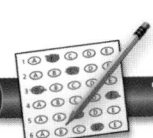

Test Prep

Multiple Choice

16. Which of the following is NOT a whole number? **C**

A. $24 \div 8$ B. $24 \div \frac{6}{7}$ C. $24 \div \frac{5}{6}$ D. $24 \div \frac{1}{3}$

17. Which of the following is greater than x for $x > 0$? **F**

F. $x \div \frac{16}{17}$ G. $x \div \frac{112}{97}$ H. $x \div \frac{7}{7}$ I. $x \div 11$

18. If $y = \frac{3}{4}$, which of the following is NOT a whole number? **B**

A. $y \div \frac{1}{8}$ B. $(y + 1) \div 7$ C. $12 \div y$ D. $9 \div \left(y - \frac{1}{2}\right)$

Take It to the NET
Online lesson quiz at
www.PHSchool.com
Web Code: aaa-0506

19. Which of the following is equivalent to $\frac{9}{8} \div \frac{3}{4}$? **I**

F. $\frac{27}{32}$ G. $\frac{8}{9} \cdot \frac{3}{4}$ H. $\frac{9 \div 4}{8 \div 3}$ I. $\frac{9 \div 3}{8 \div 4}$

Short Response

20. A bus arrives at the bus depot every half-hour from 6:00 A.M. until 7:00 P.M. every day. How many times in a week does a bus arrive at the depot? **See margin.**

Mixed Review

Lesson 4-6   (Algebra) **Solve each equation.**

21. $x - \frac{1}{2} = 2$ $2\frac{1}{2}$ **22.** $y + \frac{1}{5} = 7$ $6\frac{4}{5}$ **23.** $m - \frac{4}{7} = \frac{8}{21}$ $\frac{20}{21}$

24. $w - \frac{3}{4} = 3\frac{3}{4}$ $4\frac{1}{2}$ **25.** $b + 2\frac{1}{3} = 4\frac{1}{3}$ 2 **26.** $8\frac{1}{4} + g = 9\frac{1}{2}$ $1\frac{1}{4}$

Lesson 3-3   **Find the GCF of each set of numbers.**

27. $12, 30$ **6**   **28.** $75, 50$ **25**   **29.** $12, 16$ **4**   **30.** $28, 32$ **4**

5-6 Solve a Simpler Problem   **249**

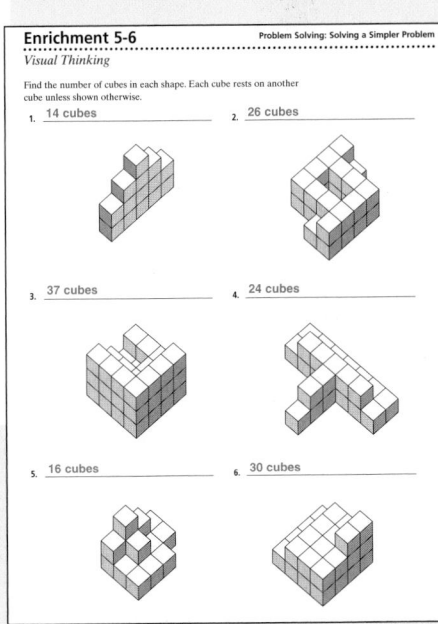
249

Lesson Preview

 **Check Skills You'll Need**

Comparing Fractions and Mixed Numbers
Lesson 3-7: Examples 1–2. Extra Practice p. 644.

Lesson Resources

 Teaching Resources
Practice, Reteaching, Enrichment
Checkpoint Quiz 2

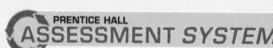 **Reaching All Students**
Practice Workbook 5-7
Spanish Practice Workbook 5-7
Reading and Math Literacy 5C
Spanish Reading and Math
  Literacy 5C
Spanish Checkpoint Quiz 2
Guided Problem Solving 5-7
Hands-On Activities 11

 Presentation Assistant Plus!
Transparencies
• Check Skills You'll Need 5-7
• Problem of the Day 5-7
• Additional Examples 5-7
• Student Edition Answers 5-7
• Lesson Quiz 5-7
PH Presentation Pro CD-ROM 5-7

PRENTICE HALL ASSESSMENT SYSTEM

Checkpoint Quiz 2
Computer Test Generator CD

 Technology
Resource Pro® CD-ROM
Computer Test Generator CD
PH Presentation Pro CD-ROM

 **www.PHSchool.com**
Student Site
• Teacher Web Code: aak-5500
• Self-grading Lesson Quiz

PH SuccessNet Teacher Center
• Lesson Planner
• Resources

Plus **iTEXT**

5-7 The Customary System

What You'll Learn

OBJECTIVE 1 To choose an appropriate unit of measurement

. . . And Why

To choose a unit for capacity, as in Example 3

 **Check Skills You'll Need**   For help, go to Lesson 3-7.

Compare each pair of numbers. Use <, =, or >.

1. $\frac{1}{2}$ $\boxed{>}$ $\frac{1}{3}$ 2. $\frac{5}{6}$ $\boxed{>}$ $\frac{5}{7}$ 3. 4 $\boxed{>}$ $3\frac{1}{4}$

4. 5 $\boxed{>}$ $\frac{1}{50}$ 5. $\frac{5}{8}$ $\boxed{<}$ $\frac{2}{3}$ 6. $9\frac{4}{8}$ $\boxed{=}$ $9\frac{2}{4}$

OBJECTIVE 1

iTEXT Interactive lesson includes instant self-check, tutorials, and activities.

Choosing Appropriate Units of Measurement

The customary system of measurement was established in 1824. Today, it is still used by the United States and some other countries. Unlike the metric system, the customary system does not use a base unit and prefixes. Each unit has a separate name.

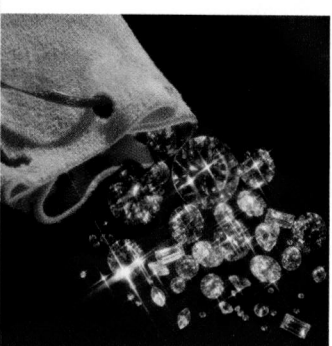

Real-World Connection
There are several kinds of ounces. Jewelers measure the weights of precious stones or metals in troy ounces.

Customary Units of Measure

	Name	Symbol	Approximate Comparison
Length	inch	in.	Length of soda bottle cap
	foot	ft	Length of an adult male's foot
	yard	yd	Length across a door
	mile	mi	Length of 14 football fields
Weight	ounce	oz	Weight of a slice of bread
	pound	lb	Weight of a loaf of bread
	ton	t	Weight of two grand pianos
Capacity	fluid ounce	fl oz	Amount in a mouthful of mouthwash
	cup	c	Amount of milk in a single-serving carton
	pint	pt	Amount in a container of cream
	quart	qt	Amount in a bottle of fruit punch
	gallon	gal	Amount in a large can of paint

You can describe 128 ounces of juice as 16 cups, 8 pints, 4 quarts, or 1 gallon. Usually the most appropriate name is the one with the smallest number.

Quantity	Measurement	Less Helpful Measurement
Weight of a person	160 pounds	2,560 ounces
Distance from home to school	About 1 mile	About 63,360 inches

Ongoing Assessment and Intervention

Before the Lesson
Diagnose prerequisite skills using:
• Check Skills You'll Need

During the Lesson
Monitor progress using:
• Check Understanding
• Additional Examples
• Test Prep

After the Lesson
Assess knowledge using:
• Lesson Quiz
• Computer Test Generator CD
• Chapter Checkpoint 2 (p. 253)

1 EXAMPLE   Choosing a Unit of Length    Real World

Flagpoles Choose an appropriate customary unit of measure to describe the height of a flagpole.

● The unit "mile" is too large and "inches" is too small. Use feet or yards.

✔ **Check Understanding**

1a. Inches; pencils are shorter than a foot.

b. Feet or yards; adult whales are longer than humans.

c. Inches are a short unit of measure. Inches are too small to measure a walking distance.

① Choose an appropriate unit for each length. Explain. **a–c. See left.**
   a. length of a pencil
   b. length of an adult whale
   c. Reasoning Explain why inches are *not* an appropriate unit of measure for the distance from your home to school.

2 EXAMPLE   Choosing a Unit of Weight    Real World

Ice What customary unit describes the weight of a bag of ice?

● The customary units that describe weight are ounces, pounds, and tons. The weight of a bag of ice is best described in pounds.

✔ **Check Understanding**

2a. Pounds; a refrigerator weighs less than a grand piano.

b. Ounces; an ice cube weighs about the same as a slice of bread.

② Choose an appropriate unit for each weight. Explain. **a–b. See left.**
   a. weight of a refrigerator
   b. weight of an ice cube

You use a unit of capacity to describe amounts of liquid. Some sample units of capacity are shown below.

1 fluid   1 cup   1 pint   1 quart   1 gallon
ounce

3 EXAMPLE   Choosing a Unit of Capacity    Real World

Beverages Choose an appropriate customary unit of measure to describe the amount of lemonade in a pitcher.

● The customary units that describe capacity are fluid ounces, cups, pints, quarts, and gallons. The capacity of a pitcher is best described in quarts.

3a–d. See back of book.

✔ **Check Understanding** ③ Choose an appropriate unit for each capacity. Explain.
   a. gasoline in a tanker truck
   b. serving of yogurt
   c. water in a bathtub
   d. bottle of cough syrup

👥 Reaching All Students

Below Level Give students measures like 2 feet and 2 pounds. Have them identify objects that are about those sizes. Samples: 2 feet—width of a student desk; 2 pounds—a textbook	**Advanced Learners** Have students research the customary units of dry capacity (pint, quart, peck, bucket, bushel) and use them to create problems.	**English Learners** See note on page 251. **Tactile Learners** See note on page 251.

---

2. Teach

 Professional Development

Math Background

The purpose of this lesson is not so much to teach the customary units of measurement as it is to heighten students' awareness of them. Specifically, given an object to be measured, students learn to recognize the type of measurement involved—length, liquid capacity, or weight—and to choose an appropriate unit of that type.

Teaching Notes

English Learners
The words *yard* and *pound* might be difficult because they have other meanings in the English language. Students also might have difficulty with the distinction between *fluid ounce* as a unit of capacity and *ounce* as a unit of weight.

Tactile Learners
Have students actually measure objects using customary units of length, weight, and capacity.

Investigation (Optional)
Have volunteers share their examples of units with the class.

PowerPoint
▦ Additional Examples

① Choose an appropriate customary unit of measure to describe the length of an automobile. **feet**

② Choose an appropriate customary unit of measure to describe the weight of a bag of popcorn. **ounces**

③ Choose an appropriate customary unit of measure to describe the capacity of a household bucket. **gallons**

Closure

How do you choose an appropriate unit of measurement?
Sample: Choose a unit that roughly matches what you are measuring—a small unit to measure smaller quantities, a large unit to measure larger quantities.

251

Assignment Guide

 **Objective 1**

Ⓐ Ⓑ **Core** 1–18

Ⓒ **Extension** 19–20

Test Prep 21–25
Mixed Review 26–30

Error Prevention!

Exercises 9–12 Students often confuse cups, pints, quarts, and gallons. Share this memory device.

lesser unit → greater unit

| cup | pint | quart | gallon |
| (3) | (4) | (5) | (6) |

fewer letters → more letters

Practice 5-7   The Customary System

Use the table to choose an appropriate unit of measurement for each item. Explain.

Customary Units of Measure

	Name	Approximate Comparison
Length	inch	Length of a soda bottle cap
	foot	Length of an adult male's foot
	mile	Length of 14 football fields
Weight	ounce	Weight of a slice of bread
	pound	Weight of a loaf of bread
	ton	Weight of two grand pianos
Capacity	cup	Amount of water in a drinking glass
	quart	Amount in a bottle of fruit punch
	gallon	Amount in a large can of paint

1. height of a stop sign
Feet; a stop sign is much taller than a bottle cap.

2. length of a leaf
Inches; a leaf is shorter than a male's foot.

3. width of a door
Feet; a door is much narrower than a football field.

4. depth of the ocean
Miles; the ocean is deeper than 14 football fields in most places.

5. weight of a small notebook
Ounces; a notebook is lighter than a loaf of bread.

6. weight of a couch
Pounds; a couch is lighter than two pianos.

7. weight of a garbage truck
Tons; a garbage truck is heavier than two pianos.

8. weight of a box of books
Pounds; a box of books is lighter than two pianos.

9. water in a swimming pool
Gallons; there is more water than in a can of paint.

10. water in a bathtub
Gallons; a bathtub holds more water than a paint can.

11. a soup in a can
Cups; a soup can is about the size of a drinking glass.

12. milk in a carton
Quarts; a milk carton is about the size of a juice bottle.

Compare using <, =, or >.

13. water you use to wash dishes [>] 1 cup

14. the depth of the Grand Canyon [<] 30 miles

15. the weight of a cereal bowl [≈] 6 ounces

Reteaching 5-7   The Customary System

Choose an appropriate customary unit of measure to describe the following:

length of a train engine	weight of a train engine
You need a unit to measure length. A train engine will be quite long, so choose feet or yards.	You need a unit to measure weight. Since a train engine will be quite heavy, choose tons.
amount of liquid in a large bucket	length of a CD case
You need a unit to measure capacity. A bucket is likely to contain quite a bit of water, so choose quarts or gallons.	You need a unit to measure length. A CD case is quite small, so choose inches.
weight of a bale of straw	amount of liquid in a bottle of eye drops
You need a unit to measure weight. A bale of straw is heavy, so choose pounds.	You need a unit to measure capacity. Since a bottle of eye drops will be very small, so choose fluid ounces.

Choose an appropriate unit for each measurement. Explain.

1. the length of a garden
Gardens can be quite long, so use feet or yards.

2. the length of a hummingbird
Hummingbirds are quite small, so use inches.

Choose an appropriate unit for each weight. Explain.

3. the weight of a letter
A letter is not heavy, so use ounces.

4. the weight of steel girders
Steel girders are heavy, so use tons.

Choose an appropriate unit for each capacity. Explain.

5. a pitcher of juice
A pitcher is usually less than a gallon, so use quarts.

6. the water in an aquarium
There is a lot of water in an aquarium, so use gallons.

Compare using <, ≈, or >.

7. weight of a tank [>] 100 pounds

8. length of a TV remote [≈] 5 inches

Investigation: Customary Units

Make a study card for each customary unit found on page 250.

On your card, record the name of the unit, its symbol, and 3 or 4 examples.
Check students' work.

pound (lb)
• bag of carrots
• regular size box of cereal
• 3 large apples

 EXERCISES

❓ For more practice, see *Extra Practice*.

Ⓐ **Practice by Example** 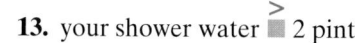 **Choose an appropriate unit for each length. Explain.** 1–12. **See back of book for explanations.**

Example 1
(page 251)

1. length of a back yard **feet**

2. distance to the moon **miles**

3. length of a car's license plate **inches**

4. width of a photograph **inches**

Example 2
(page 251)

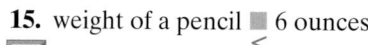 **Choose an appropriate unit for each weight. Explain.**

5. bag of oranges **pounds**

6. package of chewing gum **ounces**

7. bowling ball **pounds**

8. pickup truck **tons**

Example 3
(page 251)

🌎 **Choose an appropriate unit for each capacity. Explain.**

9. sample-size bottle of shampoo **fluid ounces**

10. bowl of soup **cup**

11. gasoline in a lawnmower **gallon**

12. tube of toothpaste **fluid ounces**

Ⓑ **Apply Your Skills** 🌎 **Compare using <, ≈, or >.**

13. your shower water **■** 2 pints **>**

14. a raindrop **■** 1 fluid ounce **<**

15. weight of a pencil **■** 6 ounces **<**

16. height of a tree **■** 0.5 mile **<**

GPS

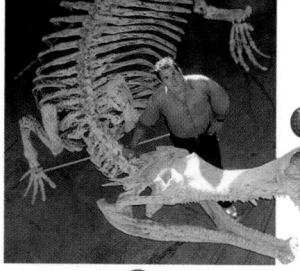

Real-World 🌎 Connection
This prehistoric crocodile was discovered in Africa.

🌎 **17. Prehistoric Creatures** In 2001, scientists discovered the fossil of a huge crocodile. This crocodile was more than 40 feet long and weighed over 10 tons. A Nile crocodile can weigh $\frac{3}{4}$ ton. How many times as heavy as the Nile crocodile was the prehistoric crocodile? **about $13\frac{1}{3}$ times as heavy**

18. **Writing in Math** What is the difference when you measure in fluid ounces or ounces? Explain. **Answers may vary. Sample: A fluid ounce is a measure of capacity for liquids. An ounce is a measure of weight.**

252 **Chapter 5** Multiplying and Dividing Fractions

GPS Use the Guided Problem Solving worksheet with Exercise 17.

19. The variable *x* represents the number of feet, since there are 12 inches in each foot. I need to multiply the number of feet by 12 to find the number of inches.

C Challenge

19.  Jill is 5 feet 1 inch tall. The expression $12x + y$ can be used to find her height in inches. Which variable represents the number of feet? Explain. **See margin.**

20. **Stretch Your Thinking** The product of two mixed numbers x and y is 10. If $x = \blacksquare\frac{2}{3}$ and $y = \blacksquare\frac{3}{4}$, find x and y. $x = 2\frac{2}{3}; y = 3\frac{3}{4}$

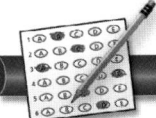

Test Prep

Gridded Response

For gridded responses, write mixed numbers as improper fractions or decimals. For the mixed number $3\frac{4}{5}$, you must grid 19/5 or 3.8. Simplify each expression. Show the answer you would use for a gridded response.

21. $\frac{21}{25} \times \frac{10}{27}$ $\frac{14}{45}$ 22. $1\frac{7}{9} \div 5\frac{1}{3}$ $\frac{1}{3}$ 23. $4\frac{2}{5} \cdot \frac{2}{11}$ $\frac{4}{5}$

Take It to the NET
Online lesson quiz at
www.PHSchool.com
Web Code: aaa-0507

24. Jai alai is a game played in Cuba, Spain, Mexico, and the United States. The ball, or *pelota*, weighs $4\frac{1}{2}$ ounces. How many ounces are in 16 *pelotas*? **72**

25. Sally plans to make bows from 200 yards of ribbon. If she needs $1\frac{1}{6}$ yards of ribbon for each bow, how many bows can she complete? **171**

Mixed Review

Lesson 5-5

Algebra Solve each equation. Check the solution.

26. $\frac{1}{2}x = 36$ **72**   27. $\frac{2}{5}z = \frac{8}{15}$ $1\frac{1}{3}$ 28. $4m = \frac{10}{3}$ $\frac{5}{6}$

Lesson 4-7

Find the elapsed time between each pair of times.

29. 9:30 A.M. and 11:29 A.M.
1 h 59 min

30. 8:15 A.M. and 2:30 P.M.
6 h 15 min

Checkpoint Quiz 2
Lessons 5-5 through 5-7

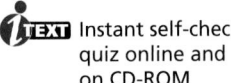
Instant self-check quiz online and on CD-ROM

1. Solve $\frac{2}{3}x = 7$. $10\frac{1}{2}$ 2. Solve $\frac{1}{3} = \frac{5}{6}h$. $\frac{2}{5}$

Choose an appropriate unit for each measurement.

3. distance from school to a park
mile

4. weight of your gym shoes
pound

5. A 25-mile course has markers at the start, the end, and every $\frac{1}{2}$ mile. How many markers are there? **51 markers**

5-7 The Customary System   **253**

Test Prep

Resources
A sheet of blank grids is available in the *Test-Taking Strategies With Transparencies* booklet. Give copies of this sheet to students so they can practice filling in grids.

For additional practice with a variety of test item formats:
• Test-Prep, p. 263
• Test-Taking Strategies, p. 259
• Test-Taking Strategies With Transparencies

4. Assess

 **Lesson Quiz 5-7**

Choose an appropriate customary unit for each item.

1. the length of a pen **in.**

2. the weight of a dog **lb**

3. the capacity of a mug **fl oz**

4. the length of a bed **ft**

✔ Chapter Checkpoint

To check understanding of Lessons 5-5 to 5-7:

Checkpoint Quiz 2 (p. 253)

📁 **Teaching Resources**
Checkpoint Quiz 2 (also in *Prentice Hall Assessment System*)

👥 **Reaching All Students**
Reading and Math Literacy 5C

Spanish versions available.

Alternative Assessment

Provide pairs of students with customary measuring tools. Partners list four measurable classroom objects and record estimated lengths. Then they measure and record the actual lengths.

Enrichment 5-7   The Customary System
Patterns in Measurement

The history of many of the different measuring systems relate back to the dimensions of the human body. For instance, the inch represents the width of a thumb. In some languages, the word for inch is also the word for thumb. As you can imagine, the foot was based on the length of a human foot, and the yard was the measure from the tip of the nose to the end of the middle finger of the outstretched hand. One other measure, the fathom (6 feet), is the measure of a person's arm span. (Stretch your arms out to the sides as far as possible.)

Exercises 1-12: Check students' answers.

1. Measure the width of your thumb. _____

2. How much more or less than one inch does the width of your thumb measure? _____

3. How accurate was the historical definition of an inch? _____

4. Measure the length of your foot. _____

5. How much more or less than 12 inches does your foot measure? _____

6. How accurate was the historical definition of a foot? _____

7. Have a partner measure the length of your arm span. _____

8. How much more or less than 6 feet does your arm span measure? _____

Some other historical measurements include the digit (the width of a finger, 0.75 inch), the nail (the length of the last two joints of the middle finger, 3 digits or 2.25 inches), the palm (the width of the palm, 3 inches), and the hand (4 inches).

9. Measure the widths of your finger. _____

10. How much more or less than 0.75 inch does the width of your finger measure? _____

11. How accurate was the historical definition of a digit? _____

12. Do you think the historical definitions of a nail, a palm, and a hand are accurate? Explain.

1. Plan

Lesson Preview

 Check Skills You'll Need PowerPoint

Multiplying Fractions
Lesson 5-1: Examples 2–3. Extra Practice p. 646.

Lesson Resources

 Teaching Resources
Practice, Reteaching, Enrichment

 Reaching All Students
Practice Workbook 5-8
Spanish Practice Workbook 5-8
Guided Problem Solving 5-8

 Presentation Assistant Plus!
Transparencies
• Check Skills You'll Need 5-8
• Problem of the Day 5-8
• Additional Examples 5-8
• Student Edition Answers 5-8
• Lesson Quiz 5-8
PH Presentation Pro CD-ROM 5-8

 **ASSESSMENT SYSTEM**

Computer Test Generator CD

 Technology
Resource Pro® CD-ROM
Computer Test Generator CD
PH Presentation Pro CD-ROM

 www.PHSchool.com
Student Site
• Teacher Web Code: aak-5500
• Self-grading Lesson Quiz

PH SuccessNet Teacher Center
• Lesson Planner
• Resources

Plus

Check Skills You'll Need

7.
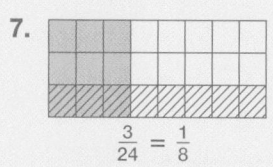
$$\frac{3}{24} = \frac{1}{8}$$

254

What You'll Learn

OBJECTIVE 1 To change units of measurement

OBJECTIVE 2 To compute with units

...And Why

To determine a person's growth, as in Example 3

✔ **Check Skills You'll Need**

❓ For help, go to Lesson 5-1.

Find each product.

1. $\frac{1}{2} \times 51$ $25\frac{1}{2}$
2. $\frac{3}{4} \cdot 14$ $10\frac{1}{2}$
3. $\frac{2}{3} \times 36$ 24
4. $\frac{5}{6} \times \frac{11}{13}$ $\frac{55}{78}$
5. $\frac{2}{3} \cdot \frac{9}{16}$ $\frac{3}{8}$
6. $\frac{2}{3} \times 1\frac{1}{9}$ $\frac{20}{27}$

7. Draw an area model to find the product $\frac{3}{8} \times \frac{1}{3}$. **See margin.**

OBJECTIVE 1

Changing Units of Measurement

 Interactive lesson includes instant self-check, tutorials, and activities.

To solve many problems, you must change units of measurement. To do this, you need to know how the units are related.

Conversions for Customary Units

Length	Weight	Capacity
12 in. = 1 ft	16 oz = 1 lb	8 fl oz = 1 cup
36 in. = 1 yd	2,000 lb = 1 t	2 cups = 1 pt
3 ft = 1 yd		4 cups = 1 qt
5,280 ft = 1 mi		2 pt = 1 qt
		4 qt = 1 gal

1 EXAMPLE Changing Units of Length  Real World

Costume Design Suppose you need $8\frac{1}{2}$ feet of fabric to make a costume. Fabric is sold in yards. How many yards of fabric should you buy?

Since 3 feet = 1 yard, you need to find how many groups of 3 feet there are in $8\frac{1}{2}$ feet. This is shown by the diagram at the left.

$8\frac{1}{2}$ ft = $\left(8\frac{1}{2} \div 3\right)$ yd ← **Divide $8\frac{1}{2}$ by 3.**

= $\left(\frac{17}{2} \times \frac{1}{3}\right)$ yd ← **Multiply by $\frac{1}{3}$, the reciprocal of 3.**

= $\frac{17}{6}$ yd, or $2\frac{5}{6}$ yd

You should buy $2\frac{5}{6}$ yards of fabric.

✔ **Check Understanding** ① Complete each statement. **a.** 45 in. = ■ ft $3\frac{3}{4}$ **b.** $56\frac{1}{3}$ in. = ■ ft $4\frac{25}{36}$

c. How many yards of fabric are in $7\frac{1}{2}$ feet of fabric? $2\frac{1}{2}$ yd

Diagram labels: 1 ft, 1 ft, 1 ft (= 1 yd); $8\frac{1}{2}$ ft; 1 yd; $\frac{1}{2}$ ft

---

 **Ongoing Assessment and Intervention**

Before the Lesson
Diagnose prerequisite skills using:
• Check Skills You'll Need

During the Lesson
Monitor progress using:
• Check Understanding
• Additional Examples
• Test Prep

After the Lesson
Assess knowledge using:
• Lesson Quiz
• Computer Test Generator CD

In Example 1, the goal was to go from a smaller unit (feet) to a larger unit (yards). To do this, you divided. Here are some rules to keep in mind.

Start With	Convert	Get
Many small units $\longrightarrow$	Divide $\longrightarrow$	A few large units
A few large units $\longrightarrow$	Multiply $\longrightarrow$	Many small units

2 EXAMPLE   **Changing Units of Weight and Capacity**

a. Find the number of pounds in 28 ounces.

$28 \text{ oz} = (28 \div 16) \text{ lb}$ $\leftarrow$ **Divide to go from a smaller unit to a larger unit.**

$= \left(\dfrac{\overset{7}{28}}{1} \times \dfrac{1}{\underset{4}{16}} \right) \text{ lb}$ $\leftarrow$ **Multiply by $\frac{1}{16}$, the reciprocal of 16.**

$= \dfrac{7}{4} \text{ lb, or } 1\dfrac{3}{4} \text{ lb}$ $\leftarrow$ **Multiply and simplify.**

b. Find the number of quarts in $2\frac{1}{2}$ gallons.

$2\frac{1}{2} \text{ gal} = \left(2\frac{1}{2} \times 4 \right) \text{ qt}$ $\leftarrow$ **Multiply to go from a larger unit to a smaller unit.**

$= \left(\dfrac{5}{\underset{1}{2}} \times \dfrac{\overset{2}{4}}{1} \right) \text{ qt}$ $\leftarrow$ **Write the numbers as improper fractions.**

$= \dfrac{10}{1} \text{ qt, or } 10 \text{ qt}$ $\leftarrow$ **Multiply and simplify.**

✔ **Check Understanding** ② Complete each statement.   **a.** $13 \text{ c} = \blacksquare \text{ pt } 6\frac{1}{2}$ **b.** $2\frac{1}{4} \text{ t} = \blacksquare \text{ lb } 4{,}500$

OBJECTIVE

 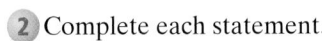

2 **Computing With Units**

Sometimes you need to rename units before you subtract or after you add.

3 EXAMPLE   **Computing With Units**    **Real World**

Growth At age 12, Robert Wadlow was 6 feet 11 inches tall. At age 19, he was 8 feet 7 inches tall. How much did he grow from age 12 to age 19?

Think: $8 \text{ ft } 7 \text{ in.} = 7 \text{ ft} + 1 \text{ ft} + 7 \text{ in.}$ $\leftarrow$ **Write 8 ft as 7 ft + 1 ft.**

$= 7 \text{ ft} + 12 \text{ in.} + 7 \text{ in.}$ $\leftarrow$ **Rename 1 ft as 12 in.**

$= 7 \text{ ft } 19 \text{ in.}$ $\leftarrow$ **Combine 12 in. and 7 in.**

Now subtract: $\begin{array}{r} 8 \text{ ft } 7 \text{ in.} \\ - 6 \text{ ft } 11 \text{ in.} \end{array} \rightarrow \begin{array}{r} 7 \text{ ft } 19 \text{ in.} \\ - 6 \text{ ft } 11 \text{ in.} \\ \hline 1 \text{ ft } 8 \text{ in.} \end{array}$

Robert grew 1 foot 8 inches between the ages of 12 and 19.

✔ **Check Understanding** ③ Your baby cousin was 6 pounds 8 ounces at birth. She gained 1 pound 9 ounces. How much does she weigh now? **8 lb 1 oz**

Reaching All Students

Below Level Review the symbols $<$ and $>$ by giving students true-or-false items about units of time. For example: True or false? 16 days $<$ 2 weeks **false**	**Advanced Learners** Have students list other relationships that can be derived from the conversion chart on page 254. **Samples: 1,760 yd = 1 mi; 16 fl oz = 1 pt; 8 pt = 1 gal**	**Alternative Method** See note on page 255. **Auditory Learners** See note on page 255.

Professional Development

Math Background

To add, subtract, or compare two measurements, the measurements must be expressed in the same units. To convert one of the measurements to a different unit, you can use the following rules.

To convert from a larger unit to a smaller unit, you multiply.

To convert from a smaller unit to a larger unit, you divide.

Teaching Notes

① EXAMPLE **Alternative Method**

Some students prefer to use the relationship equation, as shown.

$3 \text{ ft} = 1 \text{ yd}$

$1 \text{ ft} = \frac{1}{3} \text{ yd}$

$8\frac{1}{2} \text{ ft} = \left(8\frac{1}{2} \times \frac{1}{3} \right) \text{ yd}$

The solution then proceeds as indicated in the text.

② EXAMPLE **Auditory Learners**

Have students softly recite the appropriate conversion rule. In Check Understanding 2a, for instance, they might say: "cups to pints—smaller to larger—divide."

PowerPoint

Additional Examples

① Complete each statement.
  a. $111 \text{ in} = \blacksquare \text{ ft } 9\frac{1}{4}$
  b. $14 \text{ ft} = \blacksquare \text{ yd } 4\frac{2}{3}$

② Complete each statement.
  a. $19 \text{ cups} = \blacksquare \text{ qt } 4\frac{3}{4}$
  b. $4\frac{1}{2} \text{ lb} = \blacksquare \text{ oz } 72$

③ A craftsperson is shipping a ceramic vase that weighs 3 lb 12 oz. The weight of the packing crate is 2 lb 6 oz. What is the total weight of the vase and the packing crate? **6 lb 2 oz**

Closure

When do you need to convert units of measure? **Samples: when adding or subtracting measures; when comparing measures**

255

Assignment Guide

1 Objective 1
 Ⓐ Ⓑ Core 1–7, 12–17, 20–25

2 Objective 2
 Ⓐ Ⓑ Core 8–11, 18–19, 26–27
 Ⓒ Extension 28–32

Test Prep 33–34
Mixed Review 35–41

Error Prevention!

Exercises 1–7 Students might choose the incorrect operation.

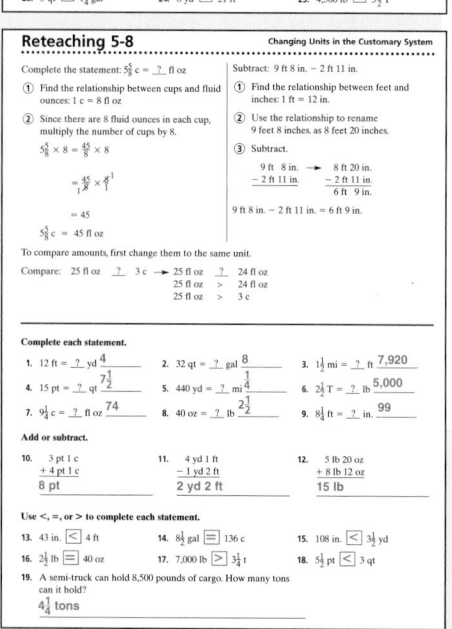

 EXERCISES

🔎 For more practice, see *Extra Practice*.

Ⓐ **Practice by Example**

Complete each statement.

Examples 1, 2
(pages 254, 255)

1. 6 lb = ■ oz 96

2. 3 mi = ■ ft 15,840

3. $5\frac{1}{2}$ ft = ■ in. 66

4. 5,500 lb = ■ t $2\frac{3}{4}$

5. $27\frac{1}{4}$ c = ■ pt $13\frac{5}{8}$

6. 40 in. = ■ ft $3\frac{1}{3}$

🌐 **7. Animals** In parts of Alaska, moose cause traffic jams. An adult moose weighs about 1,000 pounds. How many tons does an adult moose weigh? about $\frac{1}{2}$ t

Example 3
(page 255)

Add or subtract.

8. 6 gal 3 qt
    +4 gal 1 qt
    11 gal

9. 4 ft 10 in.
    +1 ft 9 in.
    6 ft 7 in.

10. 8 qt 1 pt
    − 6 qt 1 pt
    2 qt

11. Maria bought 2 pounds of ricotta cheese. She used 15 ounces to make manicotti. How much does she have left to make a ricotta cheese pie? 1 lb 1 oz

Ⓑ **Apply Your Skills**

Use <, =, or > to complete each statement.

12. 91 in. ■ 8 ft <

13. $3\frac{1}{2}$ lb ■ 56 oz =

14. $1\frac{1}{2}$ t ■ 4,000 lb <

15. 3 lb ■ 50 oz <

16. 18 fl oz ■ 2 c >

17. 4 ft ■ 66 in. <

the Channel Tunnel

🌐 **18. Tunnels** The 38,000-foot Mont Blanc Tunnel connects Italy and France through a mountain. The 31-mile Channel Tunnel connects France and England under the English Channel. Which tunnel is longer? **See left.**

19. Writing in Math Describe a situation in daily life in which you need to change from one unit of measure to another. **See margin.**

Complete each statement.

20. 42 in. = ■ ft $3\frac{1}{2}$

21. 30,000 lb = ■ t 15

22. 105,600 ft = ■ mi 20

23. $4\frac{1}{4}$ pt = ■ fl oz 68

24. 880 yd = ■ mi $\frac{1}{2}$

25. $3\frac{1}{2}$ yd = ■ in. 126

26. Data File, p. 217 How much farther in inches would the 15–16-year-old Junior Olympic record holder for boys need to jump to match the world record of $29\frac{3}{8}$ feet? **63 in.**

🌐 **27. Costume Design** A costume designer is making a costume for a figure GPS skater. To make the legs, she needs two strips of fabric that are each 34 inches long. How many yards of fabric does she need to make the legs? $1\frac{8}{9}$, or about 2 yd

Real-World 🌐 Connection

Careers Costume designers use measurements involving mixed numbers.

 GPS Use the Guided Problem Solving worksheet with Exercise 27.

19. Answers may vary.
Sample: When following a recipe you might need to convert pints to cups or cups to pints.

C Challenge

Add or subtract.

28.   6 yd 1 ft 7 in.
    +   1 ft 11 in.
    ─────────────────
      7 yd 6 in.

29.   8 gal   5 fl oz
    −   3 c 7 fl oz
    ─────────────────
      7 gal 3 qt 6 fl oz

30.   2 t
    −   15 lb 8 oz
    ─────────────────
      1 t 1,984 lb 8 oz

A: 5½ lb; B: 9 lb; C: 15 lb

31. **Stretch Your Thinking** Use the drawings to find the weight of each block.

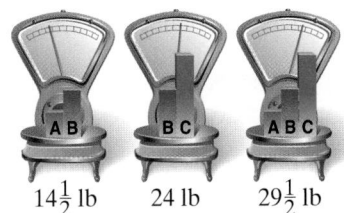

A B   B C   A B C

14½ lb   24 lb   29½ lb

32. (**Algebra**) The equation $3x = y$ can be used to convert feet to yards or yards to feet. Which variable represents the number of feet and which represents the number of yards? Explain. **See margin.**

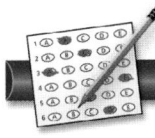

Test Prep

Reading Comprehension   Read the passage and answer the questions below.

Latest News From the American Heart Association

The American Heart Association recommends that an adult eat about 6 ounces of cooked poultry, fish, or lean red meat each day.

Meat, fish, and poultry are the major contributors of iron, zinc, and B vitamins in most American diets.

Take It to the NET
Online lesson quiz at
www.PHSchool.com
Web Code: aaa-0508

33. What is the weight of the recommended daily serving of red meat in pounds? $\frac{3}{8}$ lb

34. Five adults share $2\frac{1}{2}$-pounds of boneless chicken for dinner. Each adult eats about the same amount. Should they eat all of the chicken? Explain in words how you found your answer.
    No; recommended amount for 5 people is 5 × 6 = 30 oz; $2\frac{1}{2}$ lb = 40 oz.

Mixed Review

Lesson 4-5   **Write each difference in simplest form.**

35. $8\frac{4}{7} - 3\frac{5}{14}$ $5\frac{3}{14}$

36. $4\frac{3}{8} - 1\frac{5}{16}$ $3\frac{1}{16}$

37. $7\frac{2}{9} - 5\frac{5}{6}$ $1\frac{7}{18}$

Lesson 3-5   **Write each improper fraction as a mixed number in simplest form.**

38. $\frac{49}{5}$ $9\frac{4}{5}$

39. $\frac{17}{3}$ $5\frac{2}{3}$

40. $\frac{49}{6}$ $8\frac{1}{6}$

41. $\frac{51}{4}$ $12\frac{3}{4}$

5-8   Changing Units in the Customary System   **257**

32. x represents yards,
    y represents feet; Since 3 ft
    = 1 yd, you have to multiply
    the number of yards by 3 to
    get the number of feet. x is
    the variable multiplied by
    3 in the equation, so
    x represents yards.

Reading Expressions

In this feature, students learn that a fraction or mixed number can supply useful information that may be lost when it is simplified.

Teaching Notes

① EXAMPLE Teaching Tip

Many students may know their height in terms of feet and inches, such as 5 feet 4 inches. Some students may be interested to know that measurements in feet and inches are often abbreviated with single and double apostrophes. So, 5 feet 4 inches would be 5' 4".

② EXAMPLE Teaching Tip

For another example, ask: *If you were going to write your age as a mixed number, what denominator might be practical for the fraction part? Explain.* Twelfths; because there are 12 months in a year, the numerator would give the number of months. This allows someone to quickly know in how many months you will be a certain age.

Exercises

Exercises 1–5 Preview these exercises with students. Have them examine each fraction and ask: *What smaller unit is the denominator of the given unit?* In Exercise 1, for instance, 36 inches is equal to 1 yard.

You usually show fractions in simplest form. Sometimes, a fraction that has not been simplified gives you useful information.

① EXAMPLE

Suppose you add the lengths of three boards and get $2\frac{4}{12}$, or $2\frac{1}{3}$ feet. Which form, $2\frac{4}{12}$ or $2\frac{1}{3}$, helps you read the answer in feet and inches?

The form $2\frac{4}{12}$ allows you to read the measurement as *2 feet 4 inches* since there are 12 inches in a foot.

② EXAMPLE

You are shipping four books. Each weighs $1\frac{7}{16}$ pounds. How should you fill in the shipping information at the right?   Weight of contents: ☐ lb ☐ oz

$$4 \cdot 1\frac{7}{16} = \frac{4}{1} \cdot \frac{23}{16} \quad \leftarrow \text{Write 4 and } 1\frac{7}{16} \text{ as improper fractions.}$$

$$= \frac{92}{16} \quad \leftarrow \text{Multiply.}$$

$$= 5\frac{12}{16} \quad \leftarrow \text{Write as a mixed number.}$$

Weight of contents: ⑤ lb ⑫ oz

EXERCISES

For each fraction, tell why the fraction that has not been simplified is useful. You may wish to refer to the table on page 250. 1–5. See margin.

1. $2\frac{12}{36}$ yd

2. $5\frac{2}{4}$ gal

3. $7\frac{15}{60}$ min

4. $5\frac{7}{12}$ ft

5. $59\frac{32}{100}$ dollars

6. A dram is a measure of weight equal to $\frac{1}{8}$ ounce.
   a. What denominator would be useful if you wish to write $5\frac{1}{4}$ ounces as ounces and drams? 8
   b. Write $5\frac{1}{4}$ ounces as ounces and drams. 5 oz 2 drams

7. a. A group of students goes on a hike. They travel for $1\frac{1}{6}$ hours, take a break, and then continue for $2\frac{1}{10}$ hours. How much time, in hours, do they spend hiking? Write your fraction with a denominator of 60. $3\frac{16}{60}$ h
   b. Write the answer from part (a) so that it can be read as hours and minutes. 3 h 16 min

1. $2\frac{12}{36}$ yd tells you that you have 2 yd 12 in.

2. $5\frac{2}{4}$ gal tells you that you have 5 gal 2 qt.

3. $7\frac{15}{60}$ min tells you that you have 7 min 15 sec.

4. $5\frac{7}{12}$ ft tells you that you have 5 ft 7 in.

5. $59\frac{32}{100}$ dollars tells you that you have $59.32.

Eliminating Answers

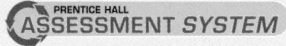

In a multiple-choice problem, you can often eliminate some of the answer choices.

1 EXAMPLE

Mary jogged $4\frac{1}{2}$ miles. Dan jogged $\frac{2}{3}$ as far as Mary. How far did Dan jog?

A. $\frac{2}{3}$ mile   **B.** 3 miles   **C.** 6 miles   **D.** $6\frac{3}{4}$ miles

- The phrase "$\frac{2}{3}$ as far as Mary" means Dan jogged a shorter distance than Mary. Eliminate choices C and D; they are greater than $4\frac{1}{2}$.
- Dan actually jogged $\frac{2}{3} \times 4\frac{1}{2}$ miles. An estimate that is less than the actual measure is $\frac{1}{2} \times 4$, or 2 miles. Choice A is too small.
- The correct answer is B.

2 EXAMPLE

A truck carries machines that each weigh $\frac{4}{5}$ ton. If the total load is $5\frac{3}{5}$ tons, how many machines are on the truck?

F. 2 machines   **G.** 4 machines   **H.** 7 machines   **I.** 11 machines

- To solve this problem, divide the total weight by the weight of one machine: $5\frac{3}{5} \div \frac{4}{5}$.
- Estimate the quotient: $6 \div 1 = 6$ machines. Eliminate choices F and I, since they are far from the estimate. Eliminate choice G because the answer must be greater than $5\frac{3}{5}$.
- The correct answer must be H.

EXERCISES

Identify two choices you can easily eliminate and explain why. 1–2. See margin.

1. June and Franklin are making posters for the school election. Together they can make a poster in $\frac{3}{4}$ of an hour. How many posters can June and Franklin make in 6 hours?

   A. 4 posters   **B.** 6 posters   **C.** 8 posters   **D.** 10 posters

2. Mike is planting a garden that is $5\frac{1}{3}$ feet by $6\frac{3}{4}$ feet. What is the area?

   F. $24\frac{1}{3}$ square feet   **G.** 30 square feet

   H. 36 square feet   **I.** $36\frac{1}{4}$ square feet

1. A and B; if you divide 6 by a number less than 1, the quotient is greater than 6.

2. F and G; if you multiply a number greater than 5 and a number greater than 6, the product must be greater than 30.

Eliminating Answers

This strategy alerts students to the fact that multiple-choice questions often have one or more answer choices that can be quickly discarded because they are unreasonable.

Resources

PRENTICE HALL ASSESSMENT SYSTEM

Test-Taking Strategies With Transparencies
- Transparency 6
- Practice master, p. 5

Teaching Notes

Emphasize to students that by eliminating unreasonable answers, they can greatly improve their chances on a multiple-choice test question, particularly when they are unsure of the best answer. On tests that do not penalize incorrect answers, eliminating unreasonable answers to a question right away can improve students' chances when they have time left only to make a sensible guess.

Test-Taking Strategies With Transparencies

Chapter 5: Eliminating Answers

Exercises

Identify the answer choices you can immediately eliminate. Cross the choices out and explain why you eliminated them. Then solve the problem.

1. Sandra is making 4 batches of cookies, so she will need to use 4 times the amount of flour the recipe calls for. The recipe calls for $3\frac{1}{4}$ cups of flour. How much flour does Sandra need?

   A. 12 cups   B. $1\frac{1}{4}$ cups   C. 13 cups   D. 17 cups

   Since $1\frac{1}{4}$ is less than the original amount, you can immediately eliminate choice B. $4 \times 3 = 12$, so you can eliminate choice A since it would not take into account the extra $\frac{1}{4}$ cup. 17 is too large since 4 times 4 is only 16 and $3\frac{1}{4}$ is less than 4. So, you can rule out choice D. The answer is C.

2. Alice's grandmother made a quilt that is $9\frac{1}{2}$ feet wide and $12\frac{5}{8}$ feet long. Alice plans to make a quilt that is half as wide and half as long. What will be the dimensions of Alice's quilt?

   F. $4\frac{3}{4}$ ft wide by $6\frac{5}{16}$ ft long   G. $4\frac{5}{8}$ ft wide by $6\frac{3}{8}$ ft long
   H. 4 ft wide by 6 ft long   I. $18\frac{1}{4}$ ft wide by $24\frac{5}{8}$ ft long

   Since Alice's quilt will be half the size, you can eliminate choice I; the numbers are almost twice the original numbers. Since 4 is less than half of 9, you can eliminate choice H. The correct answer must be either choice F or G.

3. There are 95 different kinds of butterflies in a zoo. There are $\frac{4}{5}$ as many different kinds of beetles as butterflies at the zoo. How many different kinds of beetles are at the zoo?

   A. 76 beetles   B. 50 beetles   C. 120 beetles   D. 75 beetles

   Eliminate choice B; since $\frac{4}{5}$ is nearly equal to 1, 50 is too small. Eliminate choice C; $\frac{4}{5}$ is a fraction less than one, and the answer cannot be larger than the original number. The answer is A.

Student Edition
Extra Practice, Ch. 5, p. 646
English/Spanish Glossary, p. 669
Table of Symbols, p. 666

 Reaching All Students
Reading and Math Literacy 5D
Spanish Reading and Math
  Literacy 5D

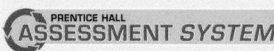 **ASSESSMENT SYSTEM**

Test Preparation
• Chapter 5 practice in test
  formats

 www.PHSchool.com
Student Site
• Self-grading vocabulary test

PH SuccessNet Teacher Center
• Resources

 Plus **iTEXT**

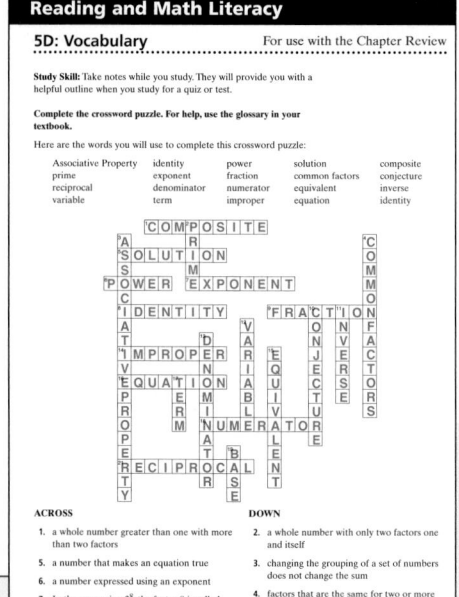

Spanish Reading and Math Literacy

Reading and Math Literacy

5D: Vocabulary   For use with the Chapter Review

Study Skill: Take notes while you study. They will provide you with a helpful outline when you study for a quiz or test.

Complete the crossword puzzle. For help, use the glossary in your textbook.

Here are the words you will use to complete this crossword puzzle:

Associative Property   identity   power   solution   composite
prime   exponent   fraction   common factors   conjecture
reciprocal   denominator numerator   equivalent   inverse
variable   term   improper   equation   identity

(crossword puzzle grid)

ACROSS
1. a whole number greater than one with more than two factors
5. a number that makes an equation true
6. a number expressed using an exponent
7. In the expression 3^8, the factor 8 is called the ___

DOWN
2. a whole number with only two factors one and itself
3. changing the grouping of a set of numbers does not change the sum
4. factors that are the same for two or more numbers

260

 **Chapter 5**

Chapter Review

 **Take It to the NET**
Online vocabulary quiz
at **www.PHSchool.com**
Web Code: aaa-0551

Vocabulary

reciprocal (p. 230)

Skills and Concepts

5-1 and 5-2 Objectives
▼ To multiply two fractions
▼ To multiply fractions by whole numbers
▼ To estimate products of mixed numbers
▼ To multiply mixed numbers

To multiply fractions, multiply the numerators and then multiply the denominators.

To multiply with mixed numbers, first write the mixed numbers as improper fractions. Then multiply the fractions.

Estimate each product.

1. $3\frac{1}{3} \times 4\frac{1}{8}$ 12
2. $5\frac{2}{3} \cdot 1\frac{5}{6}$ 12
3. $8\frac{3}{8} \times 9\frac{11}{15}$ 80
4. $7\frac{10}{23} \cdot 12\frac{3}{16}$ 84

Find each product.

5. $\frac{1}{2} \cdot \frac{3}{5}$ $\frac{3}{10}$
6. $\frac{12}{13} \times \frac{1}{18}$ $\frac{2}{39}$
7. $\frac{7}{9} \cdot \frac{18}{35}$ $\frac{2}{5}$
8. $\frac{5}{8} \times 24$ 15

9. $25 \cdot \frac{7}{10}$ $17\frac{1}{2}$
10. $5\frac{1}{6} \times \frac{3}{4}$ $3\frac{7}{8}$
11. $3\frac{1}{3} \times 2\frac{2}{25}$ $6\frac{14}{15}$
12. $4\frac{5}{11} \cdot 4\frac{9}{14}$ $20\frac{15}{22}$

13. **Dessert** A recipe for fruit salad calls for $\frac{2}{3}$ cup peaches. How many cups of peaches do you need to make $\frac{1}{2}$ of the original recipe? $\frac{1}{3}$ c

5-3 and 5-4 Objectives
▼ To divide whole numbers by fractions
▼ To divide fractions by fractions
▼ To estimate quotients of mixed numbers
▼ To divide mixed numbers

Two numbers are **reciprocals** if their product is 1. The numbers $\frac{2}{3}$ and $\frac{3}{2}$ are reciprocals, as are $\frac{1}{5}$ and 5. To divide by a fraction, multiply by the reciprocal of the fraction.

To divide mixed numbers, first write the numbers as improper fractions. Then multiply by the reciprocal of the divisor.

Estimate each quotient.

14. $2\frac{1}{5} \div 2\frac{1}{3}$ 1
15. $8\frac{2}{3} \div 3\frac{2}{11}$ 3
16. $12\frac{2}{7} \div 3\frac{5}{9}$ 3
17. $13\frac{1}{2} \div 7\frac{5}{16}$ 2

Find each quotient.

18. $8 \div \frac{1}{2}$ 16
19. $4 \div \frac{12}{17}$ $5\frac{2}{3}$
20. $\frac{3}{11} \div \frac{3}{5}$ $\frac{5}{11}$
21. $\frac{5}{6} \div \frac{15}{16}$ $\frac{8}{9}$

22. $\frac{4}{7} \div \frac{2}{5}$ $1\frac{3}{7}$
23. $\frac{18}{25} \div 9$ $\frac{2}{25}$
24. $3\frac{3}{4} \div 1\frac{13}{15}$ $2\frac{1}{112}$
25. $4\frac{1}{7} \div 1\frac{1}{3}$ $3\frac{3}{28}$

5-5 Objective

▼ To solve fraction equations

To solve equations in which a variable is multiplied by a fraction, multiply both sides of the equation by the reciprocal of the fraction.

If the variable is multiplied by a mixed number, write the mixed number as an improper fraction. Then solve.

Solve each equation.

26. $\frac{m}{6} = 16$ 96   **27.** $\frac{2}{5}x = 10$ 25   **28.** $\frac{3}{8}k = \frac{3}{4}$ 2   **29.** $\frac{6}{7}y = \frac{9}{14}$ $\frac{3}{4}$

30. $\frac{5}{6}z = 3\frac{1}{3}$ 4   **31.** $\frac{4}{5}w = 1\frac{3}{5}$ 2   **32.** $\frac{2}{3}x = 4\frac{4}{5}$ $7\frac{1}{5}$ **33.** $5a = 1\frac{3}{10}$ $\frac{13}{50}$

5-6 Objective

▼ To solve problems by solving a simpler problem

Solving a similar, simpler problem can help you see how to solve a more complicated problem.

Solve the problem by first solving a simpler problem.

 34. Alarms A fire alarm rings 20 times. It pauses for 1 second between rings. Each ring is 3 seconds long. How long does the ringing last? 79 s

5-7 and 5-8 Objectives

▼ To choose an appropriate unit of measurement

▼ To change units of measurement

▼ To compute with units

When trying to decide what unit of measurement to use, first decide whether you are measuring length, weight, or capacity. Then choose the unit in that category that best describes what you are measuring.

These conversions can help you change measurements.

Length	Weight	Capacity
12 inches = 1 foot	16 ounces = 1 pound	8 fluid ounces = 1 cup
3 feet = 1 yard	2,000 pounds = 1 ton	2 cups = 1 pint
5,280 feet = 1 mile		2 pints = 1 quart
		4 quarts = 1 gallon

Choose an appropriate unit for each measurement.

35. weight of a car tons

36. the capacity of a can of soda fluid ounces

Complete each statement.

37. 880 in. = ■ ft $73\frac{1}{3}$ **38.** $2\frac{1}{2}$ gal = ■ c 40   **39.** 12,000 lb = ■ t 6

Use <, =, or > to complete each statement.

40. 3 yd ═ 9 ft (=)

41. 1,800 lb ═ $\frac{3}{4}$ t (>)

42. 68 fl oz ═ 2 qt (>)

Alternative Assessment Form C

Alternative Assessment   **Form C**
Chapter 5

CHILI NIGHT

Your family moved recently. Before the move you used to help your parents out by making dinner every Wednesday night. One of your favorite dishes to prepare was chili, which you made by adding water and several fresh ingredients to Montana Martha's Chili Mix. Now, however, you live in a part of the country where Montana Martha's Chili Mix is not sold. But you have a plan to change that. Your first step was asking 240 people in your new town how often they eat chili. The circle graph shows the results of your survey.

Show all of your work on a separate sheet of paper.

1. How many of the 240 people in your survey said they never eat chili?

2. Of the people who said they eat chili often, $\frac{3}{4}$ said they would be interested in trying Montana Martha's Chili Mix. What fraction of the survey group is this?

You think that grocery store managers will be more likely to carry Montana Martha's Chili Mix if you give them a sample of chili made from it. You have two packages left. You need to make a lot of chili to give away, but you want to save some of the mix to make a small batch for yourself.

3. You decide to use $1\frac{1}{2}$ packages of mix to make a large batch of chili for store managers to taste. The basic recipe calls for adding $\frac{2}{3}$ cup of water to each package. How much water will you need for $1\frac{1}{2}$ packages of mix?

Chapter 5 **Chapter Test**

Take It to the NET
Online chapter test at
www.PHSchool.com
Web Code: aaa-0552

Estimate each product.

1. $4\frac{2}{3} \times 1\frac{2}{7}$ **5**

2. $5\frac{3}{4} \cdot 7\frac{4}{9}$ **42**

3. $2\frac{1}{2} \cdot \frac{11}{19}$ **3**

4. $9\frac{1}{8} \times 2\frac{5}{6}$ **27**

Find each product.

5. $\frac{3}{8}$ of 32 **12**

6. $\frac{5}{6} \cdot \frac{12}{25}$ **$\frac{2}{5}$**

7. $\frac{7}{9} \cdot 5\frac{4}{7}$ **$4\frac{1}{3}$**

8. $3\frac{1}{3} \times 2\frac{3}{4}$ **$9\frac{1}{6}$**

9. **Cabin Design** A log cabin has walls made up of 12 logs lying horizontally on top of one another. If each log is $\frac{3}{4}$ foot thick, how tall is each wall? **9 ft**

10. Jolene weighs 96 pounds. Jolene's father weighs $1\frac{7}{8}$ times as much as she does. How much does her father weigh? **180 lb**

Find each quotient.

11. $15 \div \frac{9}{11}$ **$18\frac{1}{3}$**

12. $\frac{2}{5} \div \frac{8}{25}$ **$1\frac{1}{4}$**

13. $\frac{5}{7} \div 25$ **$\frac{1}{35}$**

14. $6\frac{3}{4} \div 4\frac{1}{2}$ **$1\frac{1}{2}$**

Estimate each quotient.

15. $10\frac{4}{17} \div 4\frac{5}{9}$ **2**

16. $30\frac{2}{7} \div 15\frac{1}{10}$ **2**

17. **Encyclopedias** A set of encyclopedias fills a shelf. Each volume is $1\frac{1}{4}$ inches wide and the shelf is $27\frac{1}{2}$ inches long. How many volumes are in the set of encyclopedias? **22 volumes**

Solve for *x*.

18. $\frac{1}{3}x = 5$ **15**

19. $\frac{2}{3}x = \frac{7}{24}$ **$\frac{7}{16}$**

20. $\frac{1}{3}x = 3\frac{1}{7}$ **$9\frac{3}{7}$**

21. $\frac{x}{3} = 8$ **24**

22. How many miles are in 63,360 inches? **1 mi**

23. How many gallons are in $36\frac{1}{2}$ quarts? **$9\frac{1}{8}$ gal**

24. Instead of walking from school to the grocery store, Scott walked 2 miles to the video store. His walk was $\frac{5}{6}$ of the distance to the grocery store. How far from school is the grocery store? **$2\frac{2}{5}$ mi**

25. **a.** What is the area of the square? Use the formula area = side × side. **$1\frac{7}{9}$ ft^2**

$1\frac{1}{3}$ ft

$1\frac{1}{3}$ ft

   b. How many squares with sides of length 2 inches will fill the square? **64 squares**

26. There are $1\frac{1}{3}$ times as many women as there are men at a party. If there are 18 men, how many people are at the party? **42 people**

Complete each statement.

27. $5\frac{3}{4}$ ft = ■ yd **$1\frac{11}{12}$**

28. 150 lb = ■ oz **2,400**

Use <, =, or > to complete each statement.

29. 15 qt ■ $3\frac{1}{2}$ gal **>**

30. 16 fl oz ■ 1 pt **=**

31. **Writing in Math** Explain how you can use the Distributive Property to find $7\frac{2}{5} \times 5$. **See margin.**

32. **Give an appropriate unit of measurement for each object.** See margin.
   a. weight of an airplane
   b. length of a soccer field
   c. amount of water in a bathtub
   d. amount of mouthwash in one mouthful
   e. weight of a mouse
   f. length of a person's foot

31. Answers may vary.
   Sample: Multiply:
   $5 \times 7 = 35$ and
   $5 \times \frac{2}{5} = 2$;
   $35 + 2 = 37$.

32. Answers may vary.
   Samples are given.
   a. tons
   b. yards
   c. gallons
   d. fluid ounces
   e. ounces
   f. inches

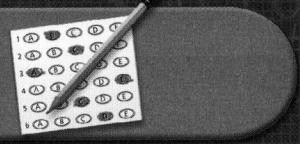

Test Prep

 **Test Prep**

Students must be able to extract information from reading passages, answer multiple-choice questions, and construct responses in order to be successful in current state and national assessments.

Resources

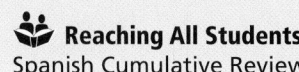 **Teaching Resources**
Cumulative Review

 **Reaching All Students**
Spanish Cumulative Review

 **ASSESSMENT SYSTEM**

Test Preparation
• Ch. 5 standardized test prep

Assessment Resources
• Cumulative Review

Computer Test Generator CD
• Standardized test prep

 **www.PHSchool.com**
• Standardized test prep
• Resources

Plus iTEXT

Reading Comprehension Read each passage and answer the questions that follow.

> **In the Dough** Here is a recipe for making modeling dough.
>
> 1 cup flour $1\frac{1}{2}$ teaspoons cream of tartar
> $\frac{1}{2}$ cup salt   1 tablespoon vegetable oil
> 1 cup water   a few drops of food coloring
>
> Heat vegetable oil in a pan. Then add the other ingredients. Stir constantly. Let the dough cool. Store in an airtight container.

1. How many cups of flour, salt, and water does the recipe call for? **C**

   A. $1\frac{1}{2}$ cups   **B.** 2 cups
   C. $2\frac{1}{2}$ cups   **D.** $2\frac{3}{4}$ cups

2. Suppose you only have enough flour to make half a batch of dough. How much salt would you need? **F**

   F. $\frac{1}{4}$ cup   **G.** $\frac{1}{2}$ cup   **H.** $\frac{3}{4}$ cup   **I.** 1 cup

3. Suppose you only have 1 teaspoon cream of tartar. By what fraction will you need to multiply the other ingredients in order to make dough with the same consistency? **C**

   A. $\frac{1}{3}$ **B.** $\frac{1}{2}$ **C.** $\frac{2}{3}$ **D.** $\frac{3}{4}$

4. What fraction of a cup of cream of tartar does the recipe call for? (There are 48 teaspoons in 1 cup.) **F**

   F. $\frac{1}{32}$ **G.** $\frac{1}{16}$ **H.** $\frac{1}{3}$ **I.** $\frac{1}{2}$

> **Video Value** Carlos, Lisa, and Lenny found a box of used computer games at a yard sale. Carlos wanted four of the games, Lisa wanted two of them, and Lenny wanted the other six. The price for the box of computer games was $18. They plan to split the cost according to how many games each person wanted.

5. What fraction of the computer games did Lisa pick? **A**

   A. $\frac{1}{6}$ **B.** $\frac{1}{4}$ **C.** $\frac{1}{3}$ **D.** $\frac{2}{3}$

6. How much should Lenny pay? **H**

   F. $4   **G.** $6   **H.** $9   **I.** $12

7. How much should Lisa pay? **A**

   A. $3   **B.** $4   **C.** $6   **D.** $8

8. What fraction of the computer games did Lenny and Carlos pick together? **H**

   F. $\frac{2}{3}$ **G.** $\frac{3}{4}$ **H.** $\frac{5}{6}$ **I.** $\frac{7}{8}$

Cumulative Review

Cumulative Review
Chapters 1–5

Multiple Choice. Choose the letter of the best answer.

1. What is the decimal for fifty-seven thousandths?
   A. 5.7
   B. 0.57
   C. 0.057
   D. 0.0057

2. List the decimals 2.35, 3.02, 2.53, 2.45, 2.44 from greatest to least.
   F. 3.02, 2.53, 2.45, 2.44, 2.35
   G. 2.35, 2.45, 2.44, 2.53, 3.02
   H. 2.35, 2.44, 2.45, 2.53, 3.02
   I. 3.02, 2.35, 2.45, 2.44, 2.53

3. Find the sum 1.72 + 0.38 + 1.10.
   A. 1.20
   B. 2.02
   C. 3.20
   D. 2.23

4. You have $15 to go to the mall. You want to buy a CD for $8.99, a card for $3.60, and a snack for $1.75. How much change will you get?
   F. none
   G. $.66
   H. $.75
   I. $15 is not enough

5. Find the product 1.82 × 0.4.
   A. 1.728
   B. 1.0728
   C. 0.728
   D. 0.0728

6. Five notebooks cost $4.65. What is the price for two notebooks?
   F. $.93
   G. $2.32
   H. $1.50
   I. $1.86

7. Solve 12z = 144.
   A. 12
   B. 72
   C. 132
   D. 1,728

8. Which is the prime factorization tree of 60?
   F. 60 / 4, 15
   G. 60 / 2, 30
   H. 60 / 4, 15 / 2, 2
   I. 60 / 2, 30 / 2, 15 / 3, 5

9. What is the GCF of 180 and 700?
   A. 5
   B. 15
   C. 10
   D. 20

Swimming to Win

Swimming to Win

Students will use data from these two pages to answer the questions posed here in Put It All Together.

Activating Prior Knowledge

Have students share any experiences they have had diving, swimming the breaststroke or butterfly stroke, and turning. Invite them to compare the difficulty of each activity. Ask swimmers to identify and describe other competitive swimming strokes.

Teaching Notes

Have volunteers read aloud the data about swimming. Ask students to suggest all the ways they can think of to use fractions to describe swimming events and swim meets.

History Connection

Have students work in groups to research the history of swimming as a competitive sport. Guide them to divide the task to focus on different aspects of the sports: strokes, key Olympic records and events, bathing suit styles and trends, training and preparation techniques, and so on. Have groups make their presentations to the class.

Applying Mixed Numbers Suppose you want to build a set of shelves to hold the trophies and photographs for your school's swim team. Knowing how to work with fractions and mixed numbers can help you design and build shelves.

Put It All Together

1. Suppose you are building a trophy case $36\frac{3}{4}$ inches tall with three evenly spaced shelves, each $\frac{3}{4}$ inch thick. Let h represent the height of each shelf. Calculate h.

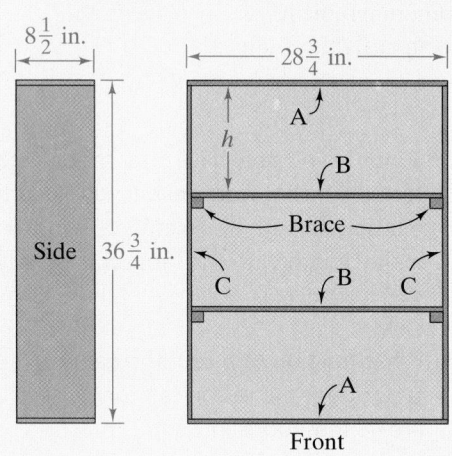

Side $36\frac{3}{4}$ in. — $8\frac{1}{2}$ in.

$28\frac{3}{4}$ in. — A, B, Brace, C, B, C, A

Front

2. Calculate the lengths of each of the boards needed to build the trophy case, including the top and bottom (A), the shelves (B), and the sides (C). Sketch each piece with its dimensions labeled.

3. **a.** The lumberyard sells boards that are 8 feet long and boards that are 10 feet long. How many 8-foot boards would you need to buy? How many 10-foot boards? Draw a diagram to support your answers.

   b. The price of the lumber is $3.25 per foot. How much would the lumber for the project cost?

Off the Block

To power your dive off the starting block, grip the block with your hands and toes and put your weight on your back foot. Next, pull hard with your arms and push with your feet.

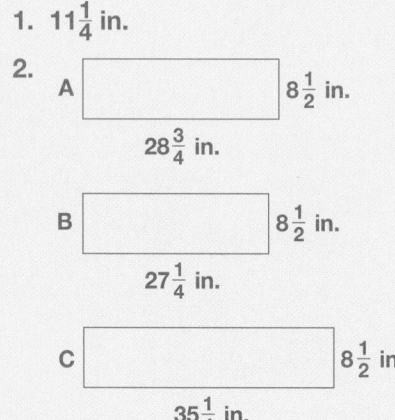

1. $11\frac{1}{4}$ in.

2.
   A — $8\frac{1}{2}$ in. — $28\frac{3}{4}$ in.

   B — $8\frac{1}{2}$ in. — $27\frac{1}{4}$ in.

   C — $8\frac{1}{2}$ in. — $35\frac{1}{4}$ in.

3a. Answers may vary. Sample: two 8-foot boards cut as shown

96 in.

C	A	B	
$35\frac{1}{4}$ in.	$28\frac{3}{4}$ in.	$27\frac{1}{4}$ in.	$4\frac{3}{4}$ in.

b. $52

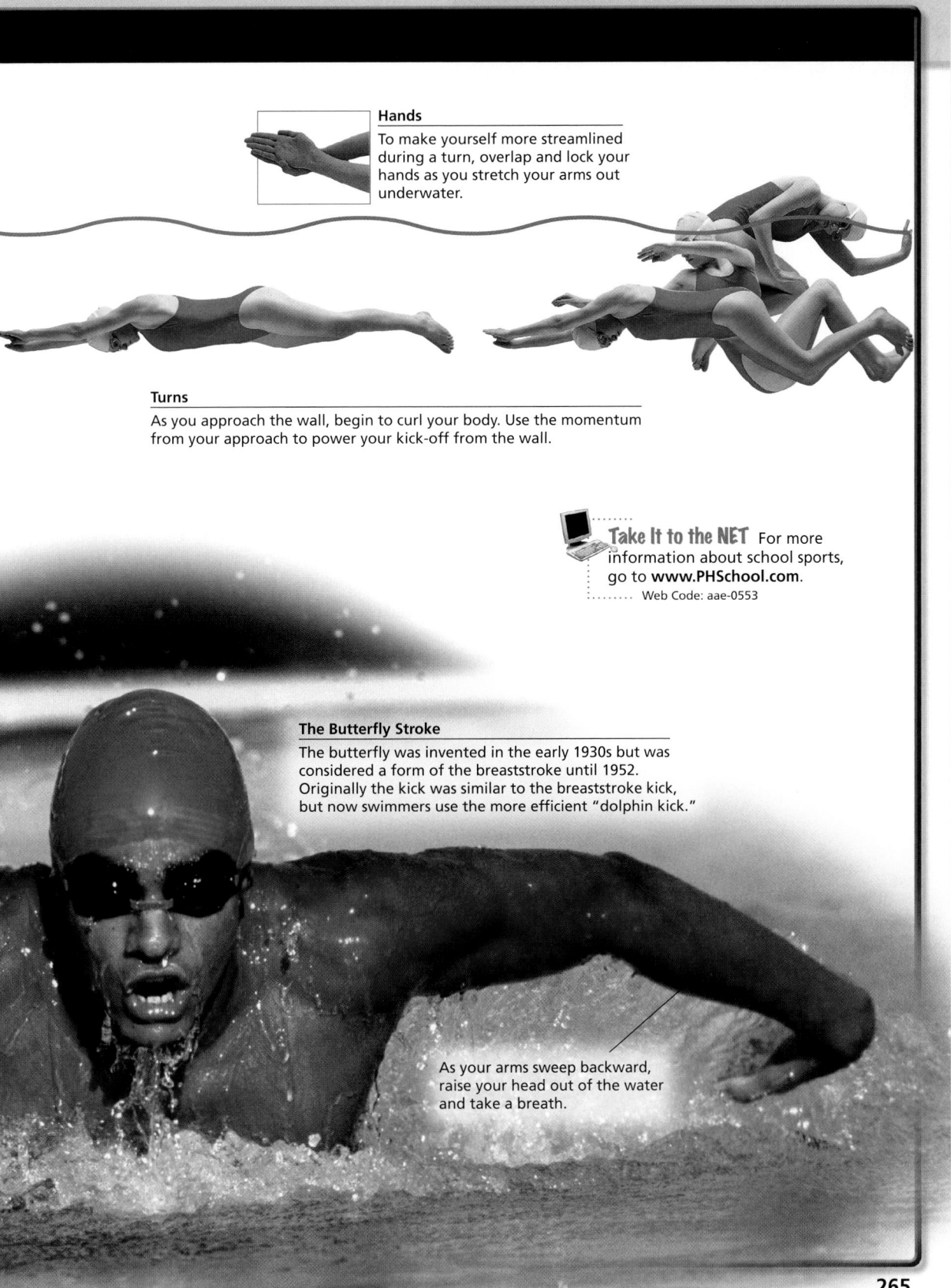

Hands

To make yourself more streamlined during a turn, overlap and lock your hands as you stretch your arms out underwater.

Turns

As you approach the wall, begin to curl your body. Use the momentum from your approach to power your kick-off from the wall.

Take It to the NET For more information about school sports, go to **www.PHSchool.com**.

Web Code: aae-0553

The Butterfly Stroke

The butterfly was invented in the early 1930s but was considered a form of the breaststroke until 1952. Originally the kick was similar to the breaststroke kick, but now swimmers use the more efficient "dolphin kick."

As your arms sweep backward, raise your head out of the water and take a breath.

265

Put It All Together

Have students share their experiences measuring and building shelves. Ask them to identify any components of the process not included here. Then have students work in pairs to answer the questions.

Inclusion Learners
Help students read the diagram and visualize what this shelf looks like. Guide them to understand that a shelf has height, width, and depth, and that the wood itself has thickness. Ask:
- *How deep is this book shelf?* $8\frac{1}{2}$ inches
- *How wide is it?* $28\frac{3}{4}$ inches wide, or $27\frac{1}{4}$ inches of interior space per shelf

Have students identify some books in the classroom that would fit on this shelf.

Exercise 2 Ask students to find the maximum height of a book that can fit on one of these shelves. $11\frac{1}{4}$ in. high

Exercise 3 Discuss with students that experienced carpenters know to buy more lumber than they need to account for errors. Have students keep this in mind as they justify their answers.

CHAPTER 6 Ratios, Proportions, and Percents

Chapter at a Glance

6-1
Ratios
pp. 269–272

Objectives
1. Writing Ratios

New Vocabulary
ratio, equal ratios

NCTM Standards
1, 6, 7, 8, 9, 10

Local Standards

6-2
Unit Rates
pp. 273–276

Objectives
1. Finding a Unit Rate
2. Using Unit Rates

New Vocabulary
rate, unit rate, unit price

NCTM Standards
1, 3, 4, 6, 7, 8, 9, 10

Local Standards

6-3 Algebra
Understanding Proportions
pp. 278–282

Objectives
1. Testing Ratios
2. Completing Proportions

New Vocabulary
proportion

NCTM Standards
1, 2, 6, 7, 8, 9, 10

Local Standards

6-4 Algebra
Using Cross Products
pp. 283–287

Objectives
1. Identifying Proportions
2. Solving Proportions

New Vocabulary
cross products

NCTM Standards
1, 2, 6, 7, 8, 9, 10

Local Standards

6-5
Scale Drawings
pp. 288–292

Objectives
1. Finding the Scale
2. Finding Actual Dimensions

New Vocabulary
scale

Optional Materials
metric rulers

NCTM Standards
1, 2, 3, 4, 6, 7, 8, 9, 10

Local Standards

✔ **Checkpoint Quiz 1**

6-6
Percents, Fractions, and Decimals
pp. 294–298

Objectives
1. Writing Percents as Decimals and Fractions
2. Writing Decimals and Fractions as Percents

New Vocabulary
percent

NCTM Standards
1, 3, 6, 7, 8, 9, 10

Local Standards

6-7 Algebra
Finding a Percent of a Number
pp. 299–302

Objectives
1. Using Proportions With Percents
2. Using Decimals With Percents

NCTM Standards
1, 2, 3, 6, 7, 8, 9, 10

Local Standards

6-8
Estimating With Percents
pp. 303–306

Objectives
1. Estimating With Percents

NCTM Standards
1, 6, 7, 8, 9, 10

Local Standards

✔ **Checkpoint Quiz 2**

6-9 Problem Solving
Write an Equation
pp. 307–309

Objectives
1. Solving Problems by Writing an Equation

NCTM Standards
1, 2, 3, 6, 7, 8, 9, 10

Local Standards

Reaching All Students

Reading and Math Literacy

📖 Reading Math

Reading a Math Lesson
p. 277

Reading Math hints,
pp. 289, 294

Understanding Vocabulary,
p. 312

✏ Writing in Math

Daily Writing Practice,
pp. 271, 275, 281, 286, 291, 297, 301, 305, 308, 314

Above Level

🅒 Challenge exercises

pp. 272, 276, 281, 287, 291, 297, 302, 305, 309

⬤ Extension

Percents Under 1% or Over 100%, p. 310

Hands-On and Technology

🔍 Investigations

Using Proportional Reasoning, p. 278

Identifying Proportions, p. 283

Enlarging a Design, p. 288

Modeling Percents, p. 293

Activities and Projects

📖 Real-World Snapshots

Applying Proportions
pp. 316–317

📁 Chapter Project

Planet of the Stars, p. 638

Test Prep

📝 Daily Test Prep

pp. 272, 276, 282, 287, 292, 298, 302, 306, 309

📝 Test-Taking Strategies

Work Backward, p. 311

📝 Test Prep

Cumulative Review
(Chapters 1–6), p. 315

Chapter Assessment

✔ Checkpoint Quiz

pp. 292, 306

⬤ Chapter Review

pp. 312–313

⬤ Chapter Test

p. 314

Pacing Options

This chart suggests pacing only for the core lessons and their parts. It is provided as a possible guide. It will help you determine how much time you have in your schedule to cover the additional features and assessment, as described at the left.

Day	Traditional 45-minute class periods	Block 90-minute class periods
1	6-1 ▽	6-1 ▽ 6-2 ▽ ▽
2	6-2 ▽	6-3 ▽ ▽ 6-4 ▽ ▽
3	6-2 ▽	6-5 ▽ ▽ 6-6 ▽ ▽
4	6-3 ▽	6-7 ▽ ▽ 6-8 ▽
5	6-3 ▽	6-9 ▽
6	6-4 ▽	
7	6-4 ▽	
8	6-5 ▽	
9	6-5 ▽	
10	6-6 ▽	
11	6-6 ▽	
12	6-7 ▽	
13	6-7 ▽	
14	6-8 ▽	
15	6-9 ▽	

NCTM STANDARDS 2000

1 Number and Operations	6 Problem Solving
2 Algebra	7 Reasoning and Proof
3 Geometry	8 Communication
4 Measurement	9 Connections
5 Data Analysis and Probability	10 Representation

Math Background

Skills Trace

BEFORE Chapter 6
Grade 5 presented fractions, decimals, and percents.

DURING Chapter 6
Course 1 introduces ratios, proportions, and percents with applications such as scale drawings.

AFTER Chapter 6
Throughout this course students apply proportional reasoning to solve problems.

6-1 Ratios

Math Understandings
- A ratio compares two similar measures by means of division.
- All ratios can be written in fraction form.
- Equal ratios can be generated using multiplication or division, just as with fractions.
- The order of the numbers in a ratio is extremely important.

A **ratio** is a comparison of two numbers by division. Each number in a ratio is called a *term*. Each of the following ratios are read "six to two."

Three Ways to Write a Ratio		
In Words	With a Symbol	As a Fraction
6 to 2	6 : 2	$\frac{6}{2}$

Two ratios that name the same number are **equal ratios.** You can find equal ratios by multiplying or dividing each term of a ratio by the same nonzero number.

Example: Write two different equal ratios to $\frac{4}{6}$.

$$\frac{4}{6} = \frac{4 \div 2}{6 \div 2} = \frac{2}{3} \qquad \frac{4}{6} = \frac{4 \times 3}{6 \times 3} = \frac{12}{18}$$

6-2 Unit Rates

Math Understandings
- Rates and unit rates are special types of ratios.
- You can easily make price comparisons for products of different package sizes by finding the unit price for each.

A **rate** is a ratio that compares two quantities measured in different units. The rate for one unit of a given quantity is called the **unit rate.** A unit rate that gives the cost per unit, such as $1.29 per lb, is a **unit price.**

Example: Find the unit rate for 370 heart beats in 5 minutes.

$$\frac{\text{beats}}{\text{min}} = \frac{370 \text{ heart beats}}{5 \text{ min}}$$
$$= 74 \text{ beats per min}$$

6-3 6-4 Understanding Proportions Using Cross Products

Math Understandings
- In any true proportion, the product of the means equals the product of the extremes. These are called cross products.

A **proportion** is an equation stating that two ratios are equal. You can use the Multiplication Property of Equality to show an important property of proportions.

$$\frac{3}{4} = \frac{15}{20}$$
$$4 \times 20 \times \frac{3}{4} = 4 \times 20 \times \frac{15}{20} \leftarrow \textit{Multiply each side by 4 and 20.}$$
$$4 \times 20 \times \frac{3}{4} = 4 \times 20 \times \frac{15}{20} \leftarrow \textit{Divide by common factors.}$$
$$20 \times 3 = 4 \times 15$$
$$60 = 60$$

The products 20×3 and 4×15 are called **cross products.** You can find the cross products of two ratios by multiplying the denominator of each ratio by the numerator of the other ratio.

Example: Solve $\frac{x}{32} = \frac{2}{8}$.

$$8x = 32 \cdot 2 \rightarrow x = \frac{64}{8}, \text{ or } 8$$

6-5 Scale Drawings

Math Understandings
• Maps, models, and scale drawings have corresponding quantities that vary proportionally.

A **scale** is the ratio that compares a length in a drawing or model to the length in the original object. The scale of the original envelope to the enlarged envelope is 1 to 3 or $\frac{1}{3}$.

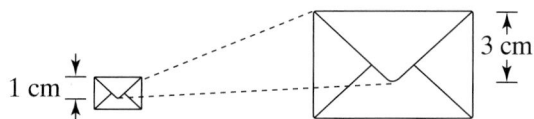

6-6 Percents, Fractions, and Decimals

Math Understandings
• You can represent a percent in different but related ways, such as a ratio, a fraction, and a decimal.
• You can rewrite a decimal that names hundredths directly as the equivalent percent.

A **percent** is a ratio that compares a number to 100. You can write any percent as a decimal. When you write a percent as a fraction, write the fraction in simplest form. To write a decimal as a percent, you multiply by 100, or move the decimal point two places to the right. When the denominator of a fraction is a factor of 100, you can use equal ratios to convert the fraction to an equivalent fraction with denominator of 100 and then to a percent. When the denominator of a fraction is not a factor of 100, convert the fraction to a decimal by dividing, and then write the decimal as a percent.

Examples: $36\% = 0.36 = \frac{36}{100} = \frac{9}{25}$
$\frac{40}{75} = 0.533333\ldots = 53.\overline{3}\%$

6-7 Finding a Percent of a Number

Math Understandings
• Knowing the fraction equivalent of common percents can help you use mental math to calculate with them.

You can find a given percent of a number by rewriting the percent as either a decimal or a fraction and then multiplying.

Example: Find 36% of 112. $0.36 \times 112 = 40.32$

When you estimate with percents, it is often helpful to know the fraction equivalents of common percents shown below.

Percent	10%	20%	25%	50%	75%
Fraction	$\frac{1}{10}$	$\frac{1}{5}$	$\frac{1}{4}$	$\frac{1}{2}$	$\frac{3}{4}$
Decimal	0.1	0.2	0.25	0.5	0.75

6-8 Estimating With Percents

Math Understandings
• You can estimate percents in daily transactions such as paying sales tax and figuring the tip on a restaurant bill.

Example: Estimate a 15% tip of $14.

First find 10% of $14 ($1.40). Then add half of that amount ($.70) which is 5%. A 15% tip of $14 is $1.40 × $.70, or $2.10.

6-9 Write an Equation

Writing an equation is a way to organize the information needed to solve a problem.

Additional Professional Development Opportunities

Professional Development

Chapter 6 Math Background notes: pp. 270, 274, 279, 284, 289, 295, 300, 304, 307

SkyLight
Professional Development

Additional resources available from SkyLight Professional Development:

On-site courses, workshops, summer institutes. Online courses and chat rooms. Videocassettes and books. Visit www.skylightedu.com.

 # Ongoing Assessment and Intervention

The *Prentice Hall Mathematics* program provides many options for assessment in the Student Edition, Teacher's Edition, and teaching resources. From these options you may choose instructional materials that are appropriate for your students and that support your district's curriculum requirements.

Daily Assessment

 Instant Check System™ in Chapter 6

Allows students to check their own learning before, during, and after each lesson.

Diagnosing Readiness before the chapter (p. 268)

Check Skills You'll Need exercises in each lesson (pp. 269, 273, 278, 283, 288, 294, 299, 303, 307)

Check Understanding questions with each Example (pp. 269, 270, 273, 274, 279, 284, 285, 289, 290, 294, 295, 296, 299, 300, 303, 304, 307)

Checkpoint Quiz (pp. 292, 306)

Formal Assessment

Assessment in the Student Text and in Additional Resources

Assess student progress throughout the Course 1 textbook and with blackline masters and CD-ROM.

Student Edition
- Chapter 6 Review, with Vocabulary, Skills, and Concepts Review, pp. 312–313
- Chapter 6 Test, p. 314

Assessment Resources
- Checkpoint Quizzes 1 & 2
- Chapter Test, forms A & B
- Chapter Alternative Assessment

Spanish versions available.

Computer Test Generator CD-ROM
- Instant Chapter Tests™—pre-made tests with items that vary every time you print.
- Online Testing allows you to give tests online and receive progress reports.
- Prepare students by making tests based on standardized test objectives.

Algebra Readiness Tests
- Includes Basic Skills Tests and Concept-Readiness Tests.
- Assess understanding of skills and concepts needed for success in algebra.

Intervention

 Skills Intervention Kit

 **Online Intervention**
Integrated within the iText, this online intervention system includes diagnostic tests and prescribed remediation, plus reports to track student mastery.

A *complete* system for the student who is struggling with course-level work

Eight intervention units cover core skills and allow you to:
- **Diagnose** students' gaps in basic skills
- **Prescribe** an individualized course of study
- **Monitor** student progress

Includes print workbooks, tutorial CD-ROM, teacher editions, progress folders, and more. *Available in Spanish.*

How to Use with Chapter 6

6-1	Ratio, Proportion, and Percent, Skills 1–2
6-2	Ratio, Proportion, and Percent, Skill 3
6-3	Ratio, Proportion, and Percent, Skill 4
6-4	Ratio, Proportion, and Percent, Skills 5–6
6-5	Ratio, Proportion, and Percent, Skill 9
6-6	Ratio, Proportion, and Percent, Skills 10–11
6-7	Ratio, Proportion, and Percent, Skills 12–13
6-8	Ratio, Proportion, and Percent, Skill 14
6-9	Ratio, Proportion, and Percent, Skill 7

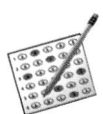

Standardized Test Preparation

The *Prentice Hall Mathematics* program integrates preparation for high-stakes standardized tests in every lesson of the Student Edition and continues this support in the Prentice Hall Assessment System.

Test Prep

In Student Text, Chapter 6

Teaches students strategies and gives them practice with all the test item formats they will encounter on high-stakes tests.

Test Prep exercises in each lesson (pp. 272, 276, 282, 287, 292, 298, 302, 306, 309)

Test-Taking Strategies (Work Backward, p. 311)

Test Prep Cumulative Review (Chapters 1–6), p. 315

A three-step approach to preparing students for high stakes, national, and state exams.

1 Diagnose & Prescribe

Content Diagnostic Tests
- Diagnose strengths and weaknesses with ongoing benchmark tests.
- Prescribe individualized reteaching opportunities.

2 Review & Reteach

Skills and Concepts Review
- Provides reteaching worksheets with instruction and practice for each skill.
- Includes course prerequisite skills.

3 Practice & Assess

Standardized Test Preparation
- Features practice for national standardized exams.
- Includes practice tests for NAEP, SAT10, ITBS, and Terra Nova.

Test-Taking Strategies with Transparencies
- Support the Test-Taking Strategies pages in the Student Edition.
- Provide a transparency and a worksheet for each strategy.

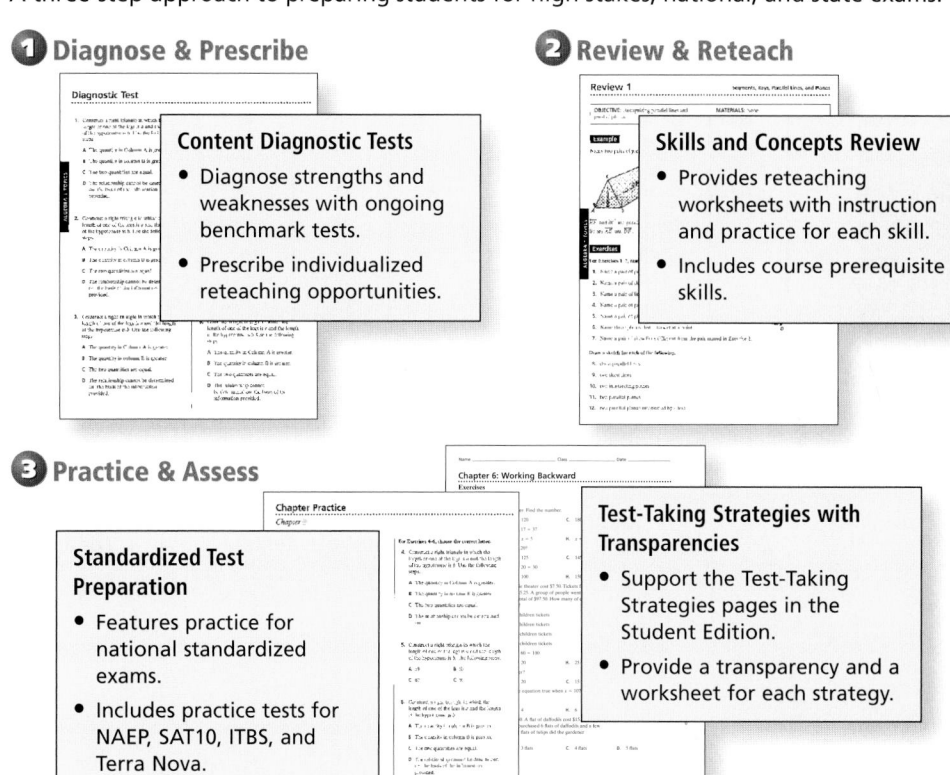

Correlation to Standardized Tests

Lesson		NAEP	Terra Nova		ITBS	SAT10	Local Test
			CAT6	CTBS			
6-1	Ratios	N4a, N4b	■			■	
6-2	Unit Rates	N4c	■				
6-3	Understanding Proportions	N4b, N4c	■			■	
6-4	Using Cross Products	N4b, N4c	■			■	
6-5	Scale Drawings	N4c, M1k, M2f	■	■		■	
6-6	Percents, Fractions, and Decimals	N1d, N1i	■	■			
6-7	Finding a Percent of a Number	N4d	■	■			
6-8	Estimating With Percents	N4d		■			
6-9	Problem Solving: Write an Equation	A4c					

NAEP National Assessment of Educational Progress
CAT6/Terra Nova California Achievement Test, 6th Ed.

CTBS/Terra Nova Comprehensive Test of Basic Skills
ITBS Iowa Test of Basic Skills, Form M.

SAT10 Stanford Achievement Test, 10th Ed.

Program Resources

	Resources in Grab & Go™ Files				Resources for Reaching All Students				Spanish Resources			Presentation Assistant Plus! Transparencies					Prentice Hall Presentation Pro CD-ROM
	Practice	Reteach	Enrich	Checkpt Quiz	Reading & Math Literacy	Technology Activities	Hands-On Activities	Guided Problem Solving	Practice	Reading & Math Literacy	Checkpt Quiz	Skills Check	Problem of the Day	Additional Examples	Answers to Exercises	Lesson Quiz	
6-1	■	■	■		■		■	■	■	■		■	■	■	■	■	■
6-2	■	■	■					■	■	■		■	■	■	■	■	■
6-3	■	■	■					■	■	■		■	■	■	■	■	■
6-4	■	■	■			■		■	■	■		■	■	■	■	■	■
6-5	■	■	■	■	■	■	■	■	■	■	■	■	■	■	■	■	■
6-6	■	■	■				■	■	■	■		■	■	■	■	■	■
6-7	■	■	■				■	■	■	■		■	■	■	■	■	■
6-8	■	■	■	■	■		■	■	■	■	■	■	■	■	■	■	■
6-9	■	■	■					■	■			■	■	■	■	■	■
For the Chapter	Chapter Projects, Chapter Tests, Alternative Assessment, Cumulative Review, Cumulative Assessment				On web site only: Home Activities, Interdisciplinary Activities, Algebra Readiness Puzzles				Spanish Chapter Tests, Alternative Assessment, Cumulative Review, Cumulative Assessment			Classroom Aid Transparencies					

Also available for use with the chapter:

 *See page 266F.*

- Practice Workbook
- Solution Key
- MathNotes folder

- For teacher support and access to student Web materials, use the Web Code aak-5500.
- For additional online and technology resources, *see below.*

 # Technology

 Online and on CD-ROM

Complete Interactive Student Text online and on CD-ROM—with instant feedback assessment, tutorial help, dynamic activities, instructional and real-world videos, audio, and additional practice.

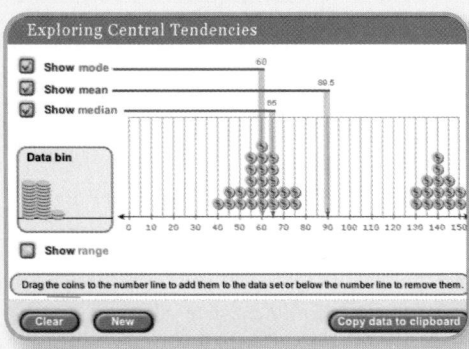

www.PHSchool.com For Students

Use Web codes for easy access to online activities, chapter projects, self-grading lesson quizzes, chapter tests, vocabulary quizzes, updated data sources, graphing calculator procedures, and more.

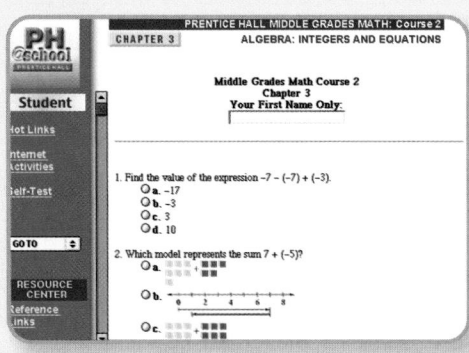

PH SuccessNet For Teachers

Online lesson planning with built-in state correlations, all the teaching resources, complete reference library, your own calendar and Teacher Web page, professional development, and more.

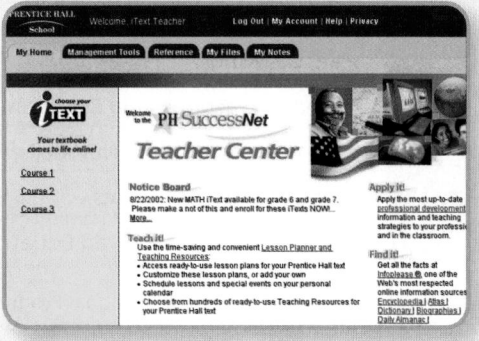

Presentation Assistant Plus!

The *Prentice Hall Presentation Assistant Plus!* provides you with the material you need to teach a lesson from beginning to end. Two easy-to-use formats—Transparencies and PowerPoint®—allow you to present a lesson the way you are most comfortable.

 ## Transparencies

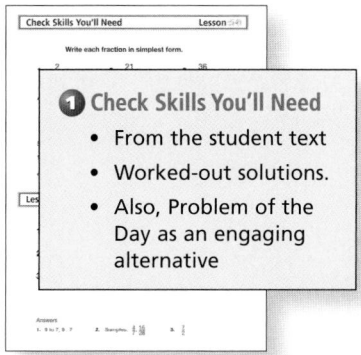

❶ Check Skills You'll Need
- From the student text
- Worked-out solutions.
- Also, Problem of the Day as an engaging alternative

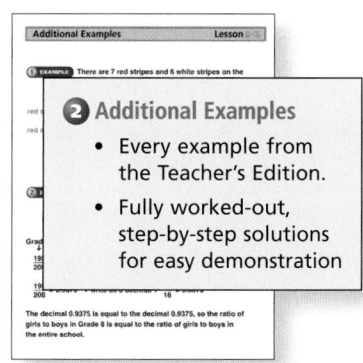

❷ Additional Examples
- Every example from the Teacher's Edition.
- Fully worked-out, step-by-step solutions for easy demonstration

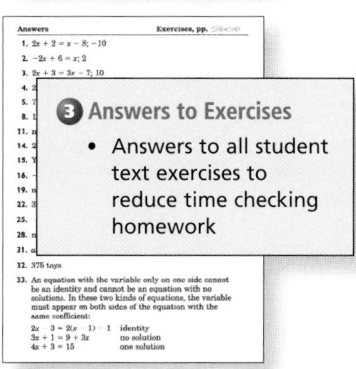

❸ Answers to Exercises
- Answers to all student text exercises to reduce time checking homework

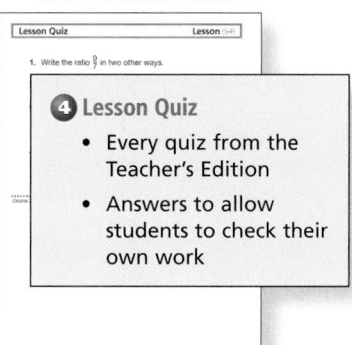

❹ Lesson Quiz
- Every quiz from the Teacher's Edition
- Answers to allow students to check their own work

 **PowerPoint** Throughout the Teacher's Edition, this symbol indicates material that is available in the Presentation Assistant Plus!

PowerPoint ## Prentice Hall Presentation Pro CD-ROM

- Includes all Transparencies.
- Conveniently organized by lesson so you can easily ❶ Introduce, ❷ Teach, ❸ Check Homework, and ❹ Assess each lesson.
- Animated examples allow step-by-step instruction at your own pace.
- Easy to edit so you can create custom presentations.

Teaching Chapter 6 Using Presentation Assistant Plus!

	❶ Introduce	❷ Teach	❸ Check Homework	❹ Assess
	Check Skills You'll Need	Additional Examples	Student Edition Answers	Lesson Quiz
6-1	p. 47	p. 76	✔	p. 47
6-2	p. 48	p. 77	✔	p. 48
6-3	p. 49	p. 78	✔	p. 49
6-4	p. 50	pp. 79–80	✔	p. 50
6-5	p. 51	pp. 81–82	✔	p. 51
6-6	p. 52	pp. 83–84	✔	p. 52
6-7	p. 53	p. 85	✔	p. 53
6-8	p. 54	pp. 86–87	✔	p. 54
6-9	p. 55	p. 89	✔	p. 55

 ### Prentice Hall Presentation Pro

CD-ROM with dynamic PowerPoint® presentations for every lesson. Helps you introduce and develop concepts, check homework, and assess progress. Part of Presentation Assistant Plus! *(See above.)*

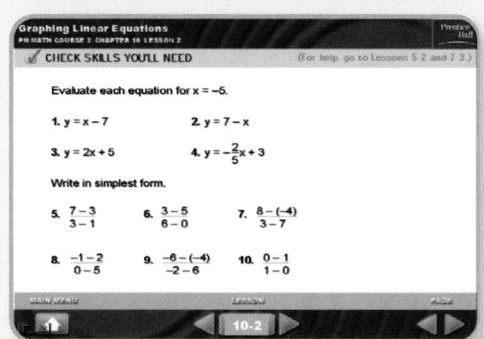

 ### Computer Test Generator

CD-ROM to create practice sheets and tests for course objectives and standardized tests. Includes Instant Chapter Tests™, online testing, and student reports. Part of the PH Assessment System. *(See page 266F.)*

 ### Resource Pro® with Planning Express®

CD-ROM with a lesson planning tool that allows you to import state and local objectives. Includes electronic versions of all the teaching resources.

Chapter Resources

Reading and Math Support

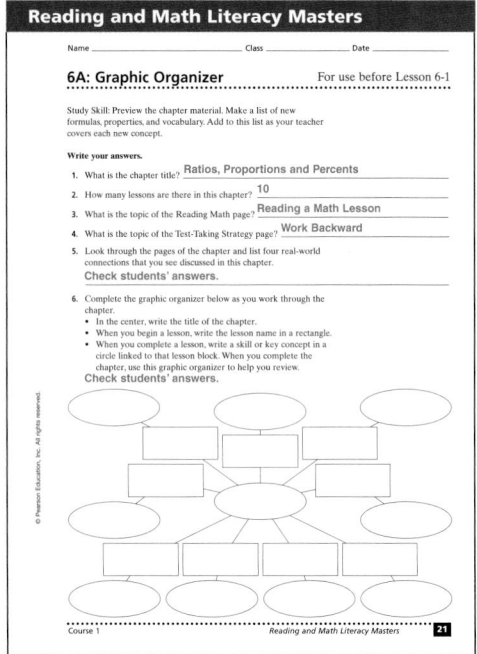

Available in Spanish

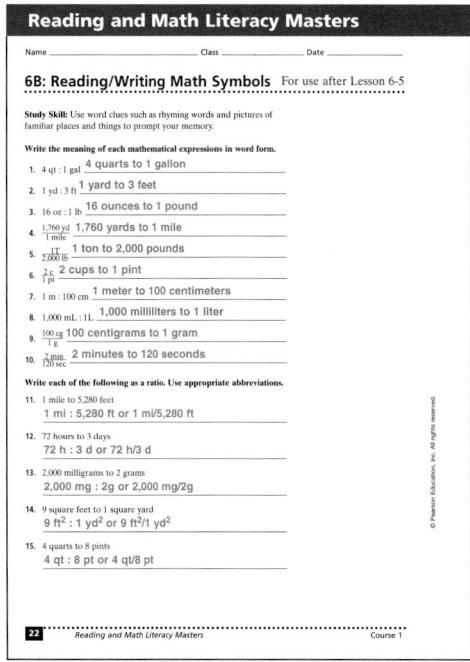

Available in Spanish

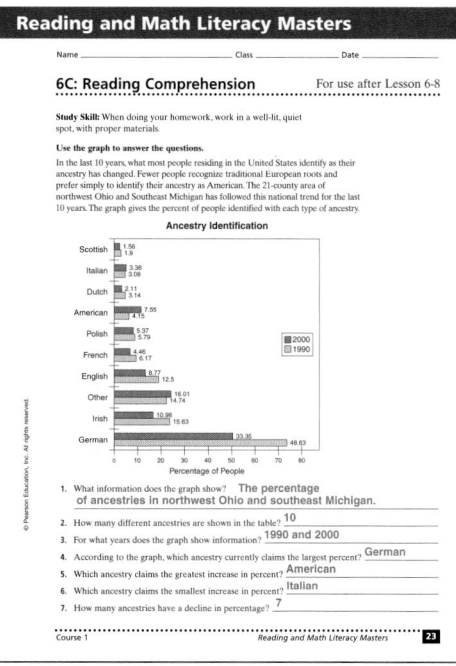

Available in Spanish

Problem Solving

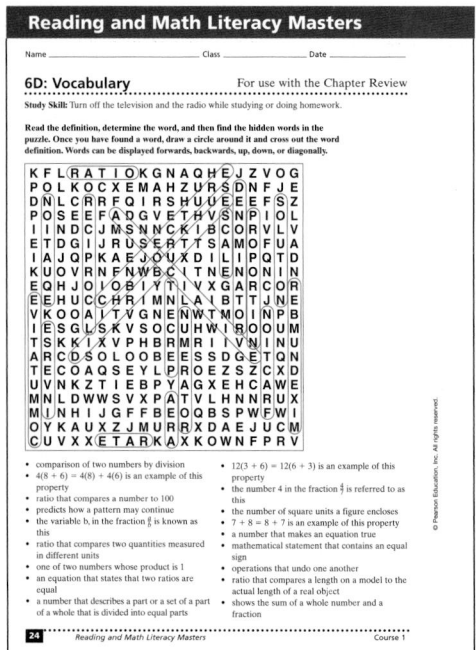

Available in Spanish

Guided Problem Solving Masters

Name _____ Class _____ Date _____

6-3 • Guided Problem Solving

GPS Student Page 281, Exercise 24:

Yogurt A flavor of frozen yogurt has 64 Calories in 2 ounces. How many Calories are in 5 ounces?

Read and Understand

1. Circle the information you will need to solve.

2. Will 5 ounces have more or less Calories than 2 ounces?
   more

Plan and Solve

3. Write a ratio comparing 64 Calories and 2 ounces.
   $\frac{64}{2}$

4. Write a ratio comparing an unknown amount of Calories and 5 ounces.
   $\frac{x}{5}$

5. Write a proportion using the two ratios from Steps 3 and 4.
   $\frac{64}{2} = \frac{x}{5}$

6. Find the value that completes the proportion.
   160 Calories

Look Back and Check

7. Explain how to check your answer.
   $\frac{64}{2} = \frac{160}{5} = 32$

Solve Another Problem

8. 12 cans of chicken noodle soup contain 48 servings. How many servings do 8 cans of soup contain?
   $\frac{12}{48} = \frac{8}{x}$; $x = 32$; 32 servings

Guided Problem Solving Masters

Name _____ Class _____ Date _____

6-4 • Guided Problem Solving

GPS Student Page 286, Exercise 26:

Printing Your friend is having a poster printed from a photograph that is 4 inches wide by 6 inches tall. If the poster is 22 inches wide, how tall will the poster be if it is proportional to the photograph?

Read and Understand

1. Circle the information you will need to solve.

2. What does it mean to be *proportional*?
   The two ratios on either side of the proportion
   are equal.

Plan and Solve

3. Write a ratio comparing 4 inches and 6 inches. $\frac{4}{6}$

4. Write a ratio comparing 22 inches and an unknown length. $\frac{22}{x}$

5. Write a proportion using the two ratios from Steps 3 and 4. $\frac{4}{6} = \frac{22}{x}$

6. Use cross products to find the value that completes the proportion. 33

7. How tall will the poster be? 33 inches

Look Back and Check

8. How can you check your answer? Does your answer check?
   $\frac{4}{6} = \frac{22}{33} = \frac{2}{3}$; yes

Solve Another Problem

9. You need to have a picture enlarged for a birthday party. The original picture is 3 inches high by 5 inches wide. You need the enlarged picture to be 15 inches wide. How long should the picture be if it is going to be proportional to the original picture?
   $\frac{3}{5} = \frac{x}{15}$; $x = 9$; 9 inches

Guided Problem Solving Masters

Name _____ Class _____ Date _____

6-5 • Guided Problem Solving

GPS Student Page 291, Exercise 19a:

Maps Suppose you redraw the map at the right using a scale of 0.5 centimeter : 1 centimeter. Does your drawing enlarge or reduce the size of the map? Explain how you know.

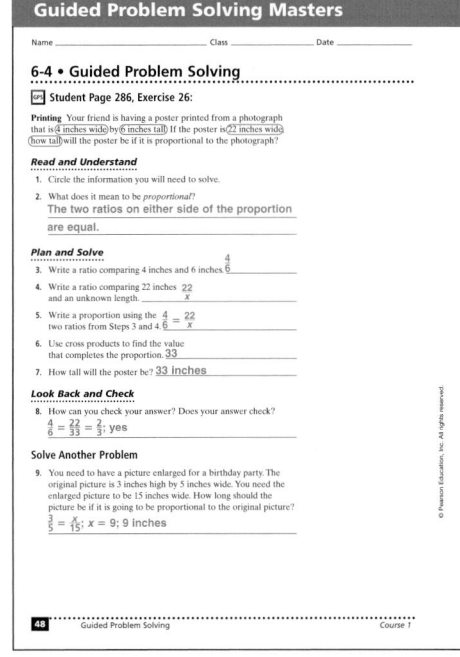

Read and Understand

1. What are you being asked to do?
   Determine if your drawing will enlarge or
   reduce the size of the map.

2. What is a scale?
   The ratio that compares a length in a drawing
   or model to the length in the original object.

3. What scale are you going to use to redraw the map?
   0.5 centimeter : 1 centimeter

Plan and Solve

4. Does *0.5 centimeter* refer to the original map or the new map?
   original map

5. Does *1 centimeter* refer to the original map or the new map?
   new map

6. A length of 0.5 centimeter on the original map will be how long on your map?
   1 centimeter

7. Does your drawing enlarge or reduce the size of the map?
   enlarge

Look Back and Check

8. If your drawing is going to reduce the size of the map, give an example of a scale that would achieve this.
   1 centimeter = 0.5 centimeter

Solve Another Problem

9. You are going to redraw a painting exactly as it is in the original. What is the scale?
   1 : 1

Guided Problem Solving Masters

Name _____ Class _____ Date _____

6-6 • Guided Problem Solving

GPS Student Page 297, Exercise 44:

Biology Ninety-nine percent of all kinds of plants and animals that have ever lived are now extinct. Write ninety-nine percent as a fraction and as a decimal.

Read and Understand

1. What percent of plants and animals are extinct?
   99%

2. A percent is a ratio of a number to what other number?
   100

Plan and Solve

3. Ninety-nine percent means 99 out of what number?
   100

4. Write this number as a fraction.
   $\frac{99}{100}$

5. Which decimal place is the hundredths place?
   two places to the right of the decimal

6. Write ninety-nine percent as a decimal.
   0.99

Look Back and Check

7. Explain how you can check your answer.
   Divide 99 by 100 and see if the answer
   equals 0.99.

Solve Another Problem

8. Sixty-one percent of a school's students participate in extra-curricular activities. Write this number as a fraction and a decimal.
   $\frac{61}{100}$; 0.61

Guided Problem Solving Masters

Name _____ Class _____ Date _____

6-7 • Guided Problem Solving

GPS Student Page 301, Exercise 19a:

Vision In the United States, about 46% of the population wear glasses or contact lenses.

a. In a group of 85 people, how many people would you expect to wear glasses or contact lenses?

Read and Understand

1. Circle the information you will need to solve.

2. What are you being asked to do?
   Find the number of people out of 85 who
   would wear glasses or lenses.

3. What method can you use to solve this problem?
   Write and solve a proportion.

Plan and Solve

4. Write 46% as a ratio. $\frac{46}{100}$

5. Write a ratio comparing the unknown out of 85 people. $\frac{x}{85}$

6. Write a proportion using the two ratios from Steps 4 and 5. $\frac{46}{100} = \frac{x}{85}$

7. Solve the proportion for the unknown. $x = 39.1$

8. How many people would you expect to wear glasses or contact lenses? 39 people

Look Back and Check

9. How can you check your answer? Does your answer check?
   Divide 39 by 85 or approximately 0.46; yes

Solve Another Problem

10. 77 percent of all band members received either an A or B on the last test. If this trend continues throughout the entire school of 1,260 students, how many students do you expect to receive A's or B's?
    970 students

Guided Problem Solving Masters

Name _____ Class _____ Date _____

6-8 • Guided Problem Solving

GPS Student Page 305, Exercise 26:

Jobs Micah received the following tips. Estimate the value of each.

a. 20% of $14.20   b. 10% of $24.75

c. 15% of $19.70   d. Which tip was the greatest value?

Read and Understand

1. What is the easiest way to find 10% of an amount?
   Move the decimal point to the left one place.

Plan and Solve

2. Estimate 10% of $24.75. $2.48

3. What is the relationship between 10% and 20%? 20% is 10% doubled.

4. How do you use 10% in order to find 20%?
   Find 10% first and then double the answer.

5. Estimate 20% of $14.20 $1.42 × 2 = $2.84

6. What is the relationship between 10%, 20%, and 15%?
   15% is halfway between 10% and 20%.

7. How can you use 10% and 20% of an amount to find 15% of an amount?
   Find 10% and 20%, then find the number that
   is halfway between the two numbers.

8. Estimate 15% of $19.70.
   $1.97 ≈ $2; $3.94 ≈ $4; halfway between $2
   and $4 is $3

Look Back and Check

9. Which tip was the greatest value? Explain.
   15% of $19.70; compare $2.84, $2.48, and $3.

Solve Another Problem

10. Find 15% of $24.80 and determine if it is more or less than 20% of $22.40.
    $3.72; $4.48; it is less.

Activities and Projects

Guided Problem Solving Masters

Name _____ Class _____ Date _____

6-9 • Guided Problem Solving

Student Page 308, Exercise 13:

Population According to the U.S. Census Bureau, the population of Illinois was 12,419,293 in the year 2000. Of the population, 26% was younger than 18 years of age. To the nearest hundred thousand, how many individuals in Illinois were *not* younger than 18 in the year 2000?

Read and Understand

1. What are you being asked to find?
   Find how many individuals in Illinois were not younger than 18 in the year 2000.

Plan and Solve

2. What percent of the population was younger than 18 years old?
   26%

3. What percent of the population was *not* younger than 18 years old? 74%

4. Which operation will you use to solve the problem? multiplication

5. Write an expression to find how many individuals in Illinois were *not* younger than 18 in the year 2000. $0.74 \times 12{,}419{,}293$

6. How many individuals in Illinois were *not* younger than 18 in the year 2000? 9,190,277 people

7. To the nearest hundred thousand, how many individuals in Illinois were *not* younger than 18 in the year 2000? 9,200,000 people

Look Back and Check

8. Can you think of another way to solve this problem?
   Find 26% of 12,419,293. Subtract that value from 12,419,293.

Solve Another Problem

9. It rained 15% of the days over a period of 32 days. How many days did it *not* rain?
   $0.85 \times 32 = 27$ days

Hands-On Activities

Name _____ Class _____ Date _____

Activity 20: Fractions, Decimals, Percents

Materials needed: counters; paper

Work in groups of 4 students.

1. In each group, one student should have 100 counters, one should have 50 counters, one should have 20 counters, and one should have 5 counters.

2. Each group member should remove the number of counters necessary to model $\frac{1}{5}$ of his or her counters.

3. **a.** How many counters did each group member remove?
   b. Copy and complete the table below.

Number of Counters	To model $\frac{1}{5}$, remove ___ counters.
1. 100 counters	
2. 50 counters	
3. 20 counters	
4. 5 counters	

   c. Use the information in the table to write the fractions equivalent to $\frac{1}{5}$.

4. The term *percent* means "per hundred." How can you use the models above to determine the percent equivalent to $\frac{1}{5}$? Write the percent.

5. Have the group member with 100 counters count out 20 counters. This represents 0.20 of the counters. How does the model compare or differ from the model of 20% or $\frac{1}{5}$? Explain.

6. Have each group member use their counters to model the following fraction, decimal, and percent. Copy and complete the table.

Number of Counters	To model 60%, remove ___ counters.	To model $\frac{2}{5}$, remove ___ counters.	To model 0.40, remove ___ counters.
1. 100 counters			
2. 50 counters			
3. 20 counters			
4. 5 counters			

7. Use your counters and the table to help you to write the equivalent fractions, decimals, and percents that correspond to 60%, to $\frac{2}{5}$, and 0.40.

Hands-On Activities

Name _____ Class _____ Date _____

Activity 21: Percent Sense

Materials needed: decimal squares, counter hundredths chart (see Activity 1), counters, graph paper

Work with a partner.

1. Put any number of counters on the squares of the counter hundredths chart. Then, your partner writes a percent to show what part of the chart is covered. Draw and label your work on decimal squares. A sample is done for you.

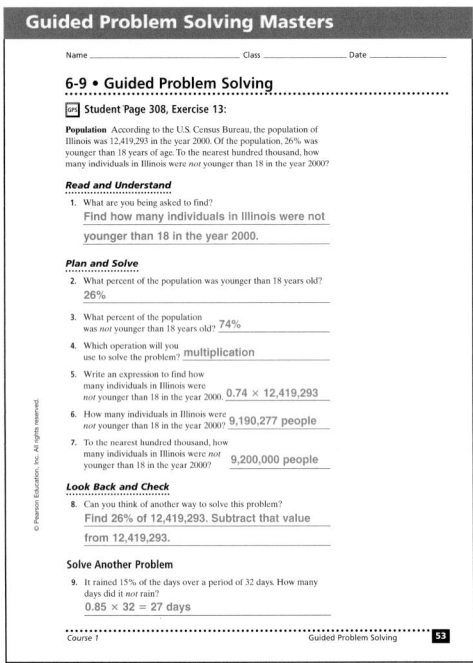

20%

2. Draw a model like this with ten equal sections to solve each problem below. Each section equals 10%. Label the sections from 10% to 100% from top to bottom along the left side of the model. Write $0 at the top of the right side of the model and the money amount at the bottom of the model.

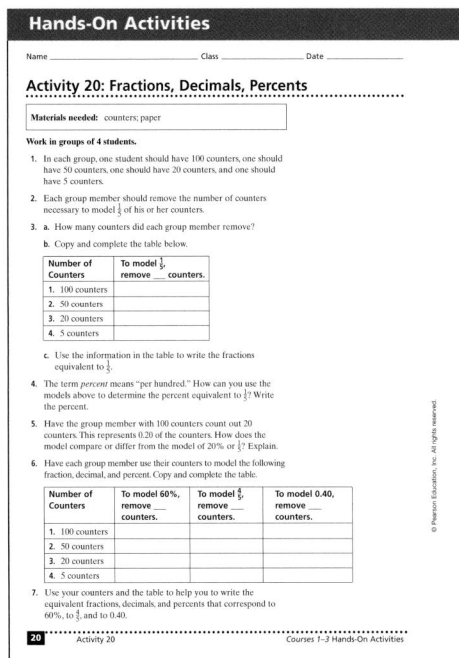

Use this model to find the percents in the problems below.

a. 40% of $5
b. 75% of $90
c. 80 percent of $200
d. 20 percent of $450

Sample pages; see p. G for complete list.

Hands-On Activities

Name _____ Class _____ Date _____

Activity 31: Measuring Area

Materials needed: 1 yard stick and 1 meter stick

Work in groups of 3–4 students

1. Assign roles (measure, record, check) to the members of your group. Then measure the length and width of your classroom floor. Record the dimensions in both feet and meters in a table like the one below.

floor length	feet	meters
floor width	feet	meters
desktop length	feet	meters
desktop width	feet	meters
floor area	square feet	square meters
desktop area	square feet	square meters
total desktop area	square feet	square meters

2. Exchange roles in your group. Measure the length and width of a student desktop. Record the dimensions in both feet and meters.

3. Use the formula for the area of a rectangle (area = length × width) to calculate the area of the classroom floor. Round to the nearest tenth.

4. Use the same area formula to calculate the area of one student desktop to the nearest tenth.

5. Find the total area of all the student desktops in the classroom. (Number of desktops × desktop area = total desktop area)

6. Which area is greater, total desktop area or total floor area? Explain.

7. Do you think the ratio of total student desktop area to floor area will be greater than or less than one? Why?

8. Do you think the ratio of total student desktop area to floor area in square feet will be equal to the same ratio in square meters? Explain?

9. **a.** Write fractions to show the ratio of total student desktop area to floor area in square feet and square meters.
   b. Do these two ratios form a proportion? How do they compare?
   c. Write a conclusion about using different units of measure to write area ratios.

Technology Activities

Name _____ Class _____ Date _____

Proportions   Activity 11

Use your graphing calculator to do this activity.

Example: Solve for the variable in $\frac{8}{32} = \frac{20}{x}$.

① You know that cross products are equal in a proportion. Use pencil and paper to write an equation.
$$\frac{8}{32} = \frac{20}{x}$$
$$x(32) = 20 \cdot 8$$

② Use your calculator to find $20 \cdot 8$. Press 20 × 8 ENTER. The result is 160.

③ $\frac{32x}{32} = \frac{160}{32}$ To solve for x, divide both sides of the equation by 32.
$x = 5$ Press 160 ÷ 32 ENTER. The result is 5.

④ You can use a unique feature of your calculator to check whether 5 is the correct solution to the proportion. Substitute 5 for the variable in the original proportion.
$$\frac{8}{32} = \frac{20}{5}$$

⑤ To check the proportion, enter 5 × 8 ► . Then press 2nd [TEXT] and select = , then select **Done**, and press ENTER. Now enter 20 × 32 and press ENTER. The calculator window shows a 1, which indicates that the statement you entered, $\frac{8}{32} = \frac{20}{5}$, is true.

Since the equation is true, the proportion is true. Your solution of 5 is correct. If the calculator window shows a 0 for the equation, this would indicate that the equation is not true, and the ratios do not form a proportion.

Exercises

Solve for the variable.

1. $\frac{5}{x} = \frac{75}{10}$
2. $\frac{28}{55} = \frac{196}{x}$
3. $\frac{43}{50} = \frac{559}{y}$

4. $\frac{39}{y} = \frac{819}{1{,}092}$
5. $\frac{g}{17} = \frac{86}{731}$
6. $\frac{63}{89} = \frac{x}{4{,}539}$

7. $\frac{9}{16} = \frac{2{,}088}{d}$
8. $\frac{6{,}408}{n} = \frac{534}{716}$
9. $\frac{2}{k} = \frac{138}{121{,}233}$

Technology Activities

Name _____ Class _____ Date _____

Scale Drawings   Activity 12

Use your geometry software to do this activity.

Example: Rectangle $ABCD$ has vertices $A(1, -3)$, $B(7, -3)$, $C(1, -7)$, $D(7, -7)$. Rectangle $EFGH$ is a scale drawing of rectangle $ABCD$. Rectangle $EFGH$ has vertices $E(-5, 3)$, $F(-2, 3)$, $G(-2, 1)$, and $H(-5, 1)$. What is the scale of the drawing?

① Pull down the **Graph** menu and select **Show Grid**.

② Pull down the **Graph** menu again and see if there is a check mark next to **Snap Points**. If there is no check mark, select **Snap Points**.

③ Use the **Point Tool** to plot and label these points: $A(1, -3)$, $B(7, -3)$, $C(1, -7)$, $D(7, -7)$, $E(-5, 3)$, $F(-2, 3)$, $G(-2, 1)$, and $H(-5, 1)$. Label them with the **Text Tool**.

④ Highlight only points A, B, C, and D. Pull down the **Construct** menu and select **Segments**. This should form rectangle $ABCD$.

⑤ Highlight only points E, F, G, and H. Pull down the **Construct** menu and select **Segments**. This should form rectangle $EFGH$.

⑥ Highlight $\overline{EF}$ and $\overline{AB}$ in that order. Pull down the **Measure** menu and select **Ratio**. The ratio of the measurement of $\overline{EF}$ to $\overline{AB}$ is displayed in the top left-hand corner of the screen as $\frac{m\overline{EF}}{m\overline{AB}} = 0.50$. The ratio of $\overline{EF}$ to $\overline{AB}$ is 0.50, or $\frac{1}{2}$.

⑦ Repeat this procedure for the other corresponding segments. You will find that the ratio of all segments of rectangle $EFGH$ to the corresponding segments of rectangle $ABCD$ are $\frac{1}{2}$. (*Note:* They may not be exact, because of slight measurement differences.)

⑧ As you can see from the ratios calculated by the program, the scale of the drawing of rectangle $EFGH$ to rectangle $ABCD$ is $\frac{1}{2}$.

Exercise

Find the scale of the drawing.

Rectangle $WXYZ$ has vertices $W(-1, 9)$, $X(-1, -9)$, $Y(-13, -9)$, $Z(-13, 9)$. Rectangle $RSTQ$ is a scale drawing of rectangle $WXYZ$. Rectangle $QRST$ has vertices $Q(1, 5)$, $R(5, 5)$, $S(5, -1)$, and $T(1, -1)$. What is the scale of the drawing?

266K

Name _____ Class _____ Date _____

Chapter 6 Project: Planet of the Stars
Make a Scale Model

Beginning the Chapter

When you look up at the stars in the sky, you may not think about how far away they are. Stars appear a lot closer than they really are. The same is true of planets. The huge distances between planets make it impossible for books to show how vast our solar system really is.

In this chapter, you will make scale models of two planets. You will compare sizes and distances from the sun and calculate the ratios involved in your scale model.

Activities

Activity 1: Writing Ratios Check students' work.

Your class's solar system model will be based on a 2-millimeter diameter for Pluto. For each of your two assigned planets, write the ratio of the planet's real diameter to the real diameter of Pluto. (Use the table below.) How many times bigger than Pluto is each of your assigned planets?

Body	Diameter (mi)	Mean Distance from Sun (millions of miles)
Sun	865,120	—
Mercury	3,030	36.0
Venus	7,520	67.2
Earth	7,926	93.0
Mars	4,216	141.7
Jupiter	88,724	483.9
Saturn	74,560	885.0
Uranus	31,600	1,781.6
Neptune	30,600	2,790.2
Pluto	1,860	3,670.7

Activity 2: Calculating

You know three pieces of data: the diameter of Pluto, the diameters of your assigned planets, and the scale diameter of Pluto. Use proportions to find the scale-model diameters of your planets. Then make two-dimensional drawings of the planets.

Name _____ Class _____ Date _____

Chapter 6 Project: Planet of the Stars (continued)

Activity 3: Analyzing Data

Use ratios, proportions, and the data in the table to find the scale distances from the sun to your two assigned planets.

Finishing the Project

Imagine you are an architect. Eventually, you will design a livable environment on your chosen planets. First, you must create a scale model of your planets to help decide on a location for a city. Convince your classmates that your calculations from the sun are correct and that your model is to scale.

Reflect and Revise

Meet with other students who also chose one of your planets and compare data. Compare any differences that you find and revise your calculations if necessary.
Is your model neat and legible?
Is it attractive but informative?
Could your scale model be improved?
If necessary, revise parts of your project.

Extending the Project

Use the Internet to find large solar system models created throughout the United States and the world, such as in Kansas and Austria. Research the methods used to create the models and give an opinion as to the accuracy of each model you discover. Write a report explaining your findings. Be sure to include the location of the models and the types of materials used to create them.

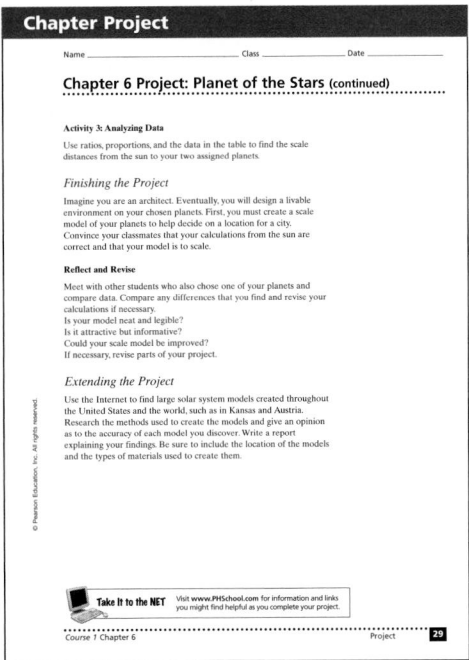

Take It to the NET Visit www.PHSchool.com for information and links you might find helpful as you complete your project.

Name _____ Class _____ Date _____

Chapter Project Manager
Chapter 6: Planet of the Stars

Getting Started

Read about the project. As you work on it, you will need several sheets of paper. If available, a spreadsheet program also can be used. Keep all your work for the project in a folder, along with this Project Manager.

Checklist	Suggestions
☐ Activity 1: writing ratios	☐ Practice writing ratios based on other scale models, i.e. maps.
☐ Activity 2: calculating	☐ Calculate ratios and proportions using miniature cars and buildings.
☐ Activity 3: analyzing data	☐ Check students' calculations of the scale models used for practice.

Scoring Rubric

3 You correctly write ratios for planet diameters and distances to the sun. All scaled dimensions are accurate. You neatly show your calculations are correct and draw your two assigned planets to scale. You use distances familiar to your classmates to describe where in your model your planets would be relative to the sun.

2 You correctly write all ratios, and most of your calculations are correct. You draw your two assigned planets to scale, and you calculate the distances from the sun to these planets. Your work is neat and easy to follow.

1 Your ratios are not correctly written, many of your calculations are inaccurate, or your drawings or explanations are incomplete or not organized.

0 You do not complete the project, or you leave out a large part of the required work.

Your Evaluation of the Project Evaluate your work based on the Scoring Rubric.

Teacher's Evaluation of Project

Transparencies

Name _____ Class _____ Date _____

Chapter Project Teacher Notes
Chapter 6 Project: Planet of the Stars

About the Project The Chapter Project allows students to apply their knowledge of ratios, proportions, and percents.

Introducing the Project

Ask students:
- *Have you ever made a scale model without using a kit? If so, of what?*
- *What did you do to plan out your scale model?*
- *How can you make sure your scale model will look like the real object?*

Activity 1: Writing Ratios

Allow students to use calculators to find the equal ratios. Have students create a table similar to the one in the project to record their data.

Activity 2: Calculating

Have students set up their proportions first using words. Then have them put the numbers in and use calculations to solve.

Activity 3: Analyzing Data

Allow students to use calculators to check their proportions. Encourage them to first write an equation to solve for the unknown scale distance.

Finishing the Project

Project Day You may wish to plan a project day in which students share their completed projects. Encourage students to explain their processes as well as their projects.

Project Notebook Have students review their project work and bring their notebooks up to date.

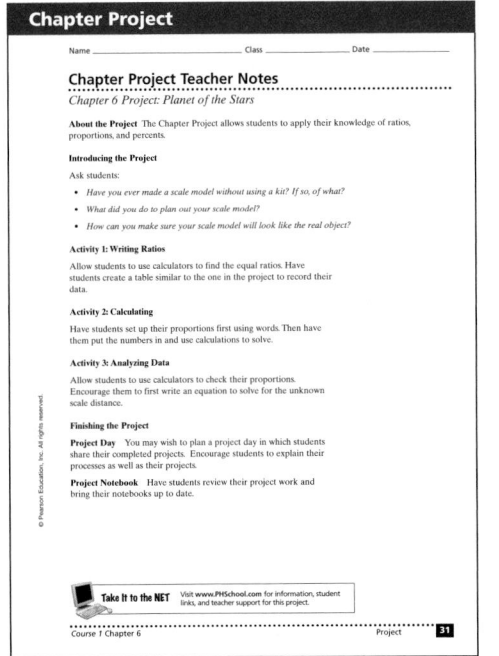

Take It to the NET Visit www.PHSchool.com for information, student links, and teacher support for this project.

| Problem of the Day | Lesson 6-1 |

Use graph paper to find $\frac{1}{2} \times \frac{4}{7}$ and $\frac{3}{4} \times \frac{2}{3}$.

Answers

$\frac{4}{14}$ or $\frac{2}{7}$; $\frac{6}{12}$ or $\frac{1}{2}$

| Problem of the Day | Lesson 6-2 |

Write <, >, or = to make each statement true.

a. $\frac{3}{4} \times 4$? $\frac{3}{7} \times 7$ b. $3 - \frac{3}{4}$? $3 \times \frac{3}{4}$

c. $\frac{1}{3} \times \frac{1}{3}$? $\frac{1}{3}$ d. $\frac{7}{5} \times \frac{4}{3}$? $\frac{5}{7} \times \frac{3}{4}$

Answers

a. =   b. =   c. <   d. >

| Problem of the Day | Lesson 6-3 |

Jeff went to the store with $25.00. If he spent $10.00, what fraction of his money does he have left?

Answer

$\frac{3}{5}$

| Problem of the Day | Lesson 6-4 |

Write an expression that represents this situation: Aretha sang for a number of minutes, then she sang for 8 more minutes.

Answer

$n + 8$

| Problem of the Day | Lesson 6-5 |

What is the prime factorization of 320?

Answer

$2 \times 2 \times 2 \times 2 \times 2 \times 2 \times 5$

| Problem of the Day | Lesson 6-6 |

Find the prime common factors of 52 and 78.

Answer

2, 13

Problem of the Day

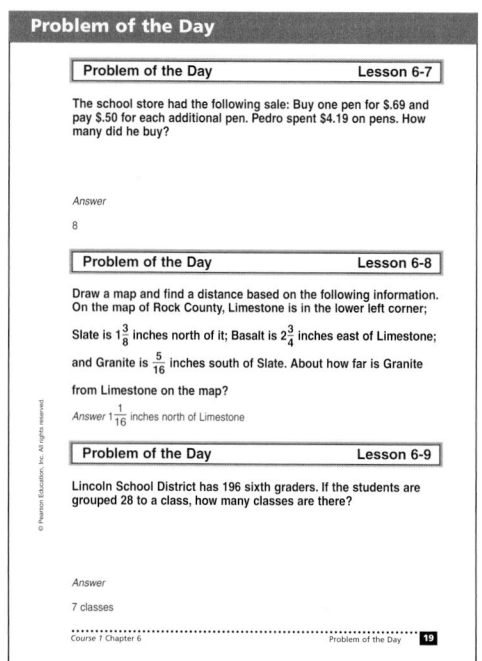

Problem of the Day — Lesson 6-7

The school store had the following sale: Buy one pen for $.69 and pay $.50 for each additional pen. Pedro spent $4.19 on pens. How many did he buy?

Answer

8

Problem of the Day — Lesson 6-8

Draw a map and find a distance based on the following information. On the map of Rock County, Limestone is in the lower left corner; Slate is $1\frac{3}{8}$ inches north of it; Basalt is $2\frac{3}{4}$ inches east of Limestone; and Granite is $\frac{5}{16}$ inches south of Slate. About how far is Granite from Limestone on the map?

Answer $1\frac{1}{16}$ inches north of Limestone

Problem of the Day — Lesson 6-9

Lincoln School District has 196 sixth graders. If the students are grouped 28 to a class, how many classes are there?

Answer

7 classes

Course 1 Chapter 6 — Problem of the Day — **19**

Check Skills You'll Need

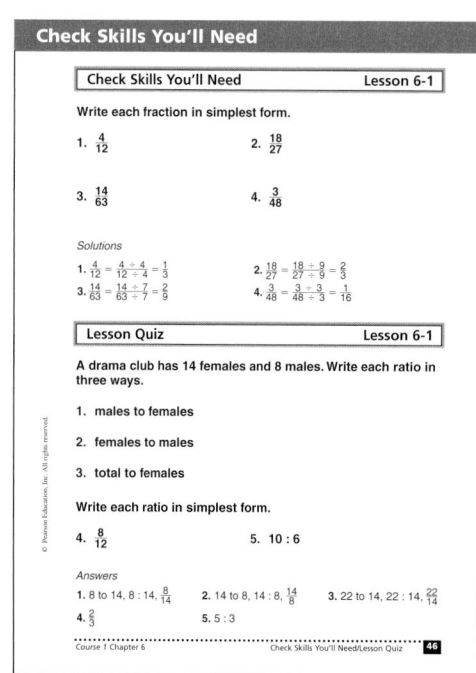

Check Skills You'll Need — Lesson 6-1

Write each fraction in simplest form.

1. $\frac{4}{12}$ 2. $\frac{18}{27}$

3. $\frac{14}{63}$ 4. $\frac{3}{48}$

Solutions

1. $\frac{4}{12} = \frac{4 \div 4}{12 \div 4} = \frac{1}{3}$ 2. $\frac{18}{27} = \frac{18 \div 9}{27 \div 9} = \frac{2}{3}$

3. $\frac{14}{63} = \frac{14 \div 7}{63 \div 7} = \frac{2}{9}$ 4. $\frac{3}{48} = \frac{3 \div 3}{48 \div 3} = \frac{1}{16}$

Lesson Quiz — Lesson 6-1

A drama club has 14 females and 8 males. Write each ratio in three ways.

1. males to females

2. females to males

3. total to females

Write each ratio in simplest form.

4. $\frac{8}{12}$ 5. $10:6$

Answers

1. 8 to 14, 8 : 14, $\frac{8}{14}$ 2. 14 to 8, 14 : 8, $\frac{14}{8}$ 3. 22 to 14, 22 : 14, $\frac{22}{14}$

4. $\frac{2}{3}$ 5. 5 : 3

Course 1 Chapter 6 — Check Skills You'll Need/Lesson Quiz — **46**

Sample page; see p. G for complete list.

Additional Examples

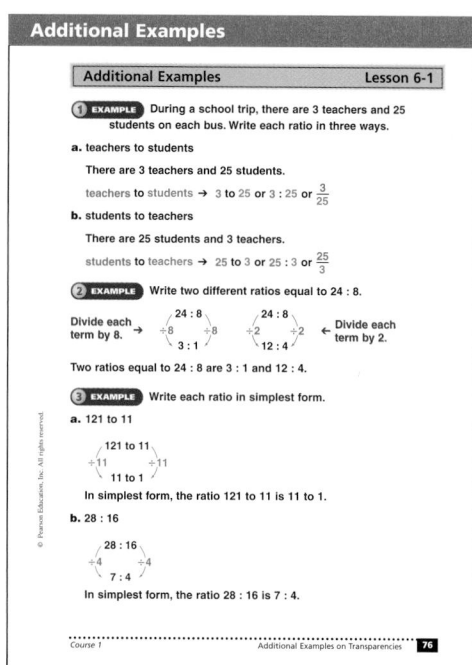

Additional Examples — Lesson 6-1

① **EXAMPLE** During a school trip, there are 3 teachers and 25 students on each bus. Write each ratio in three ways.

a. teachers to students

There are 3 teachers and 25 students.

teachers to students → 3 to 25 or 3 : 25 or $\frac{3}{25}$

b. students to teachers

There are 25 students and 3 teachers.

students to teachers → 25 to 3 or 25 : 3 or $\frac{25}{3}$

② **EXAMPLE** Write two different ratios equal to 24 : 8.

Divide each term by 8. → 24 : 8 → 3 : 1 (÷8, ÷8)   24 : 8 → 12 : 4 (÷2, ÷2) ← Divide each term by 2.

Two ratios equal to 24 : 8 are 3 : 1 and 12 : 4.

③ **EXAMPLE** Write each ratio in simplest form.

a. 121 to 11

121 to 11 → 11 to 1 (÷11, ÷11)

In simplest form, the ratio 121 to 11 is 11 to 1.

b. 28 : 16

28 : 16 → 7 : 4 (÷4, ÷4)

In simplest form, the ratio 28 : 16 is 7 : 4.

Course 1 — Additional Examples on Transparencies — **76**

Sample page; see p. G for complete list.

Classroom Aid

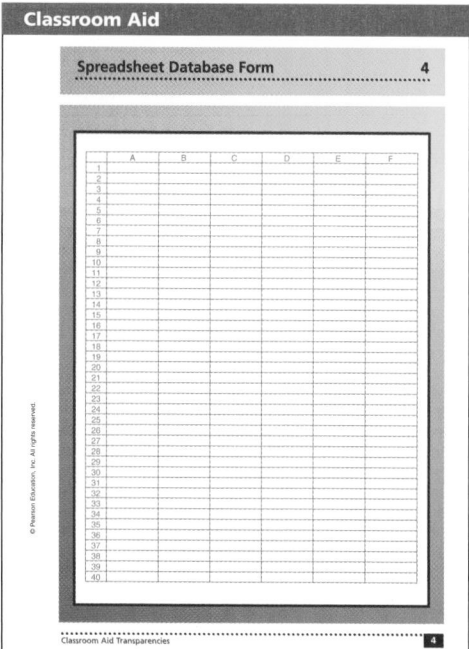

Spreadsheet Database Form — 4

Classroom Aid Transparencies — **4**

Sample page.

Student Edition Answers

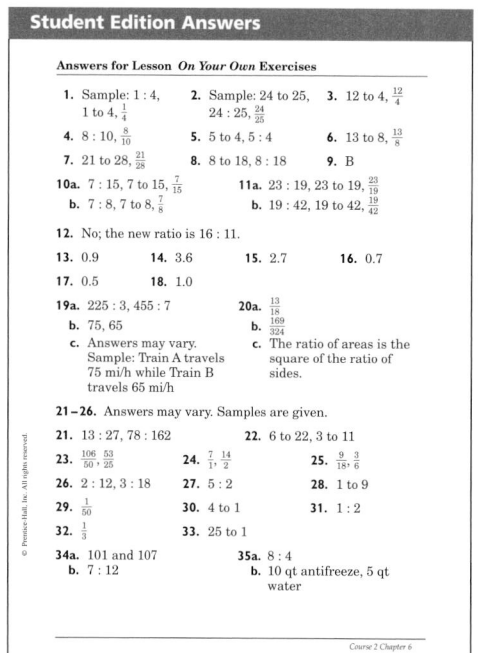

Answers for Lesson *On Your Own* Exercises

1. Sample: 1 : 4, 1 to 4, $\frac{1}{4}$ 2. Sample: 24 to 25, 24 : 25, $\frac{24}{25}$ 3. 12 to 4, $\frac{12}{4}$

4. 8 : 10, $\frac{8}{10}$ 5. 5 to 4, 5 : 4   6. 13 to 8, $\frac{13}{8}$

7. 21 to 28, $\frac{21}{28}$ 8. 8 to 18, 8 : 18   9. B

10a. 7 : 15, 7 to 15, $\frac{7}{15}$ 11a. 23 : 19, 23 to 19, $\frac{23}{19}$

b. 7 : 8, 7 to 8, $\frac{7}{8}$ b. 19 : 42, 19 to 42, $\frac{19}{42}$

12. No; the new ratio is 16 : 11.

13. 0.9   14. 3.6   15. 2.7   16. 0.7

17. 0.5   18. 1.0

19a. 225 : 3, 455 : 7   20a. $\frac{13}{18}$

b. 75, 65   b. $\frac{169}{324}$

c. Answers may vary. Sample: Train A travels 75 mi/h while Train B travels 65 mi/h   c. The ratio of areas is the square of the ratio of sides.

21–26. Answers may vary. Samples are given.

21. 13 : 27, 78 : 162   22. 6 to 22, 3 to 11

23. $\frac{106}{50}$, $\frac{53}{25}$ 24. $\frac{7}{1}$, $\frac{14}{2}$ 25. $\frac{9}{18}$, $\frac{3}{6}$

26. 2 : 12, 3 : 18   27. 5 : 2   28. 1 to 9

29. $\frac{1}{50}$ 30. 4 to 1   31. 1 : 2

32. $\frac{1}{3}$ 33. 25 to 1

34a. 101 and 107   35a. 8 : 4

b. 7 : 12   b. 10 qt antifreeze, 5 qt water

Course 2 Chapter 6

Sample page; see p. H for complete list.

Lesson Quiz

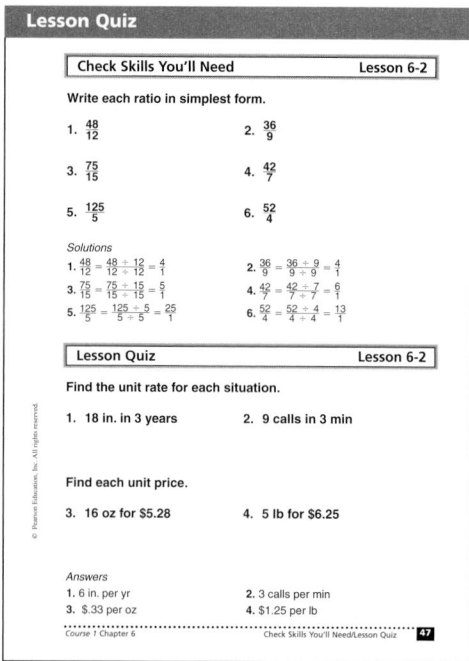

Check Skills You'll Need — Lesson 6-2

Write each ratio in simplest form.

1. $\frac{48}{12}$ 2. $\frac{36}{9}$

3. $\frac{75}{15}$ 4. $\frac{42}{7}$

5. $\frac{125}{5}$ 6. $\frac{52}{4}$

Solutions

1. $\frac{48}{12} = \frac{48 \div 12}{12 \div 12} = \frac{4}{1}$ 2. $\frac{36}{9} = \frac{36 \div 9}{9 \div 9} = \frac{4}{1}$

3. $\frac{75}{15} = \frac{75 \div 15}{15 \div 15} = \frac{5}{1}$ 4. $\frac{42}{7} = \frac{42 \div 7}{7 \div 7} = \frac{6}{1}$

5. $\frac{125}{5} = \frac{125 \div 5}{5 \div 5} = \frac{25}{1}$ 6. $\frac{52}{4} = \frac{52 \div 4}{4 \div 4} = \frac{13}{1}$

Lesson Quiz — Lesson 6-2

Find the unit rate for each situation.

1. 18 in. in 3 years   2. 9 calls in 3 min

Find each unit price.

3. 16 oz for $5.28   4. 5 lb for $6.25

Answers

1. 6 in. per yr   2. 3 calls per min
3. $.33 per oz   4. $1.25 per lb

Course 1 Chapter 6 — Check Skills You'll Need/Lesson Quiz — **47**

Sample page; see p. H for complete list.

266M

Assessment

Checkpoint Quizzes

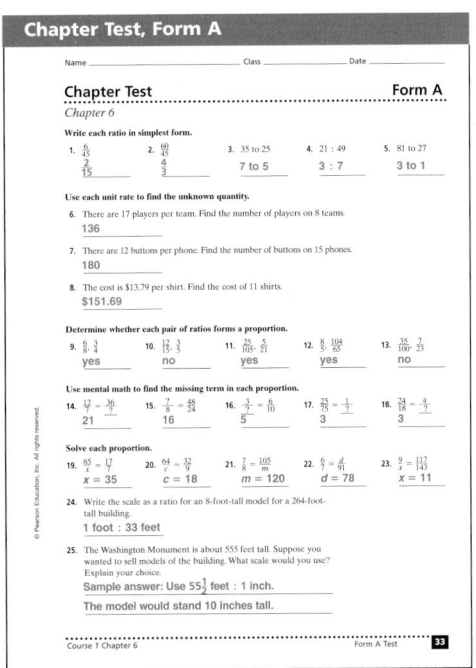

Available in Spanish

Chapter Test, Form A

Available in Spanish

Chapter Test, Form A

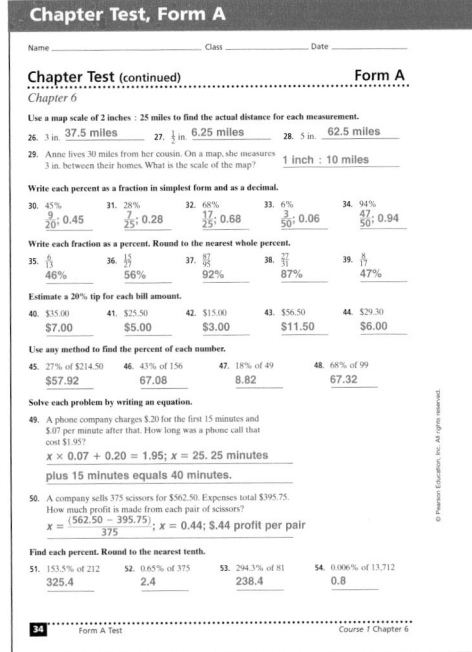

Available in Spanish

Chapter Test, Form B

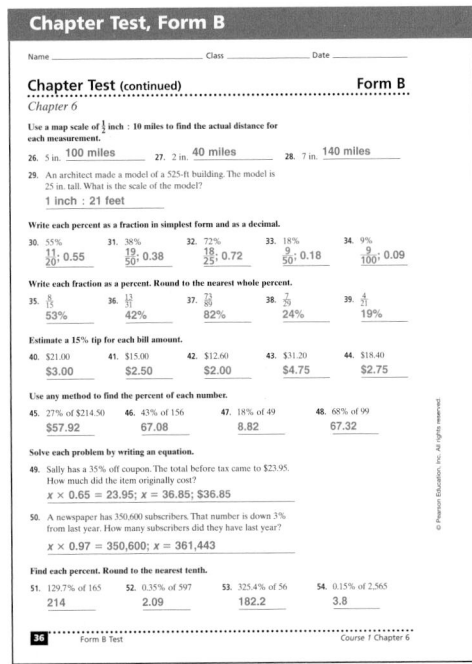

Available in Spanish

Chapter Test, Form B

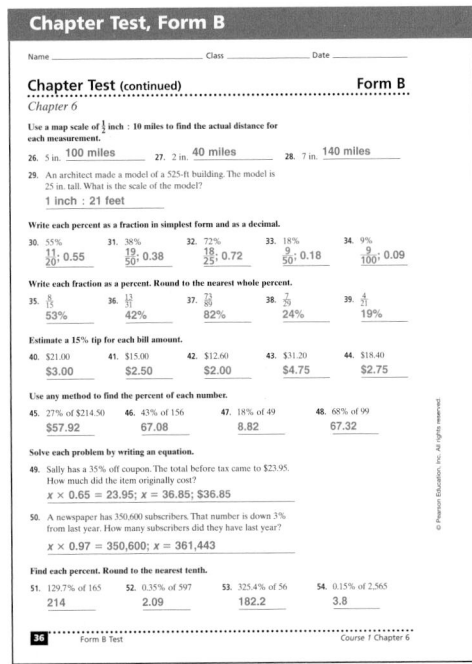

Available in Spanish

Alternative Assessment

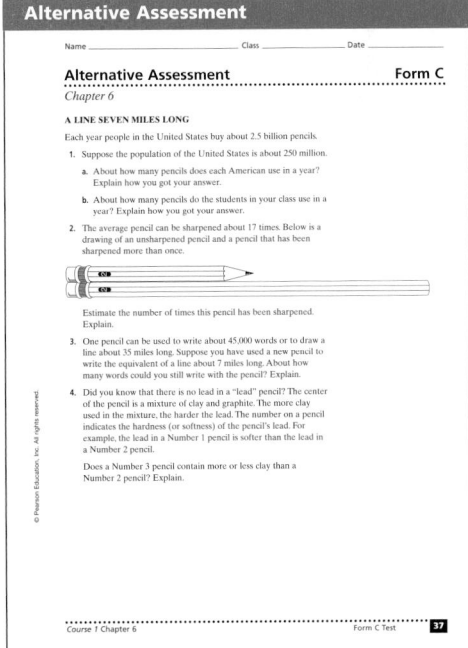

Available in Spanish

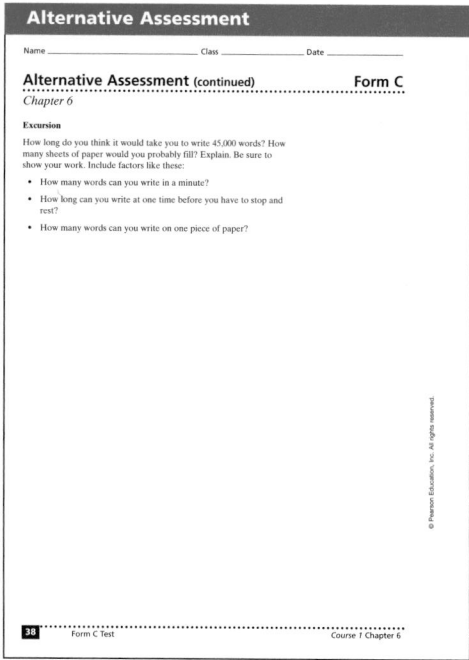

Available in Spanish

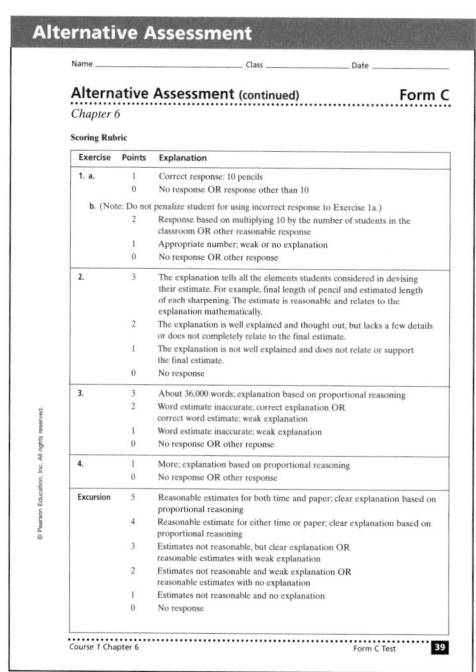

Available in Spanish

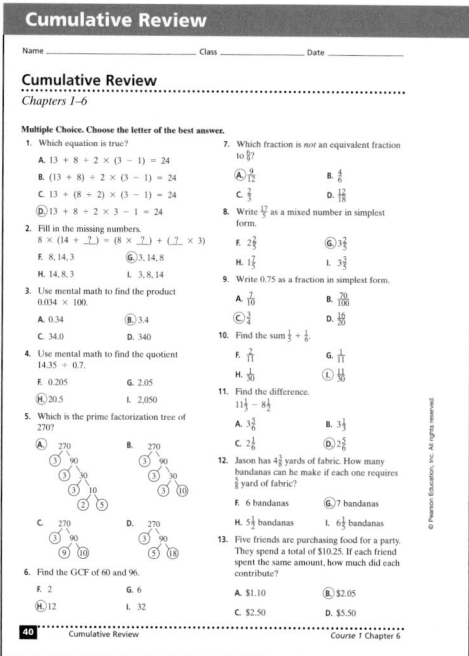

Available in Spanish

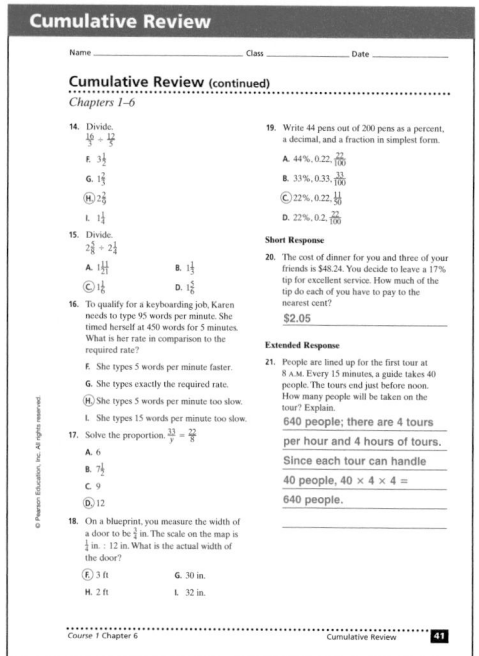

Available in Spanish

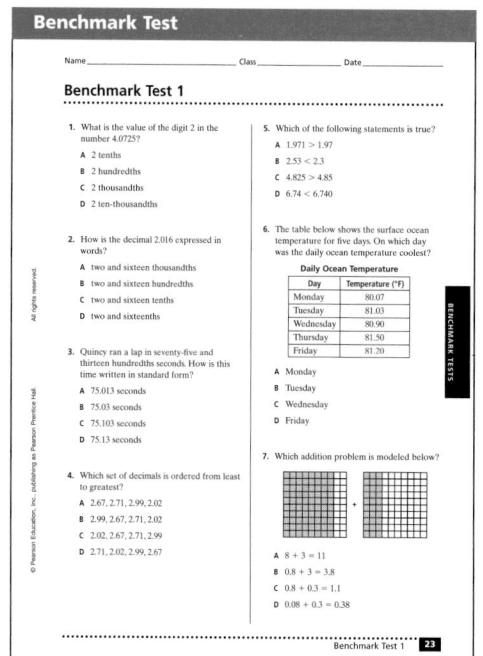

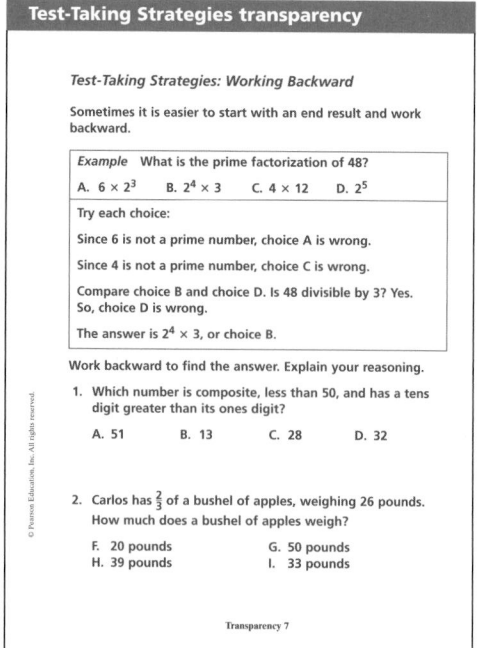

On PH Website

Test-Taking Strategies worksheet

Name ______________ Class ______________ Date ______________

Chapter 6: Working Backward

Exercises

Solve by working backward.

1. 72 is 40% of some number. Find the number.
   A. 28 B. 120 Ⓒ 180 D. 240
2. Solve the equation. $4x + 17 = 37$
   F. $x = 3$ Ⓖ $x = 5$ H. $x = 7$ I. $x = 10$
3. 75% of what number is 120?
   A. 110 B. 125 C. 145 Ⓓ 160
4. Solve the equation. $\frac{1}{2}x - 20 = 30$
   F. 50 Ⓖ 100 H. 150 I. 200
5. Adult tickets at the movie theater cost $7.50. Tickets for children under 12 years old cost $5.25. A group of people went to the movies and they paid a total of $97.50. How many of each type of ticket did the group buy?
   A. 8 adult tickets and 6 children tickets
   B. 6 adult tickets and 8 children tickets
   Ⓒ 6 adult tickets and 10 children tickets
   D. 4 adult tickets and 12 children tickets
6. Solve the equation. $4y + 60 = 100$
   Ⓕ 10 G. 20 H. 25 I. 40
7. 15% of 25 is what number?
   A. 21.25 B. 20 C. 15 Ⓓ 3.75
8. For what value of g is the equation true when $x = 10$?
   $\frac{g}{2}(x + 2) = 24$
   F. 2 Ⓖ 4 H. 6 I. 10
9. A flat of tulips cost $11.50. A flat of daffodils cost $15.25. A gardener paid $126 and purchased 6 flats of daffodils and a few flats of tulips. How many flats of tulips did the gardener purchase?
   A. 2 flats Ⓑ 3 flats C. 4 flats D. 5 flats

6 Course 1 Test-Taking Strategies

Home Activities

in math class ...

We have been learning about ratio, proportion, and percent. Here is a list of some of the skills and concepts we have studied.

- What is a ratio?
- Equal ratios
- What is a rate?
- What is a proportion?
- Solving proportions using cross products
- Solving proportions using unit rates
- What is a percent?
- Estimating percents
- Connecting percents to fractions and decimals
- Finding a percent of a number

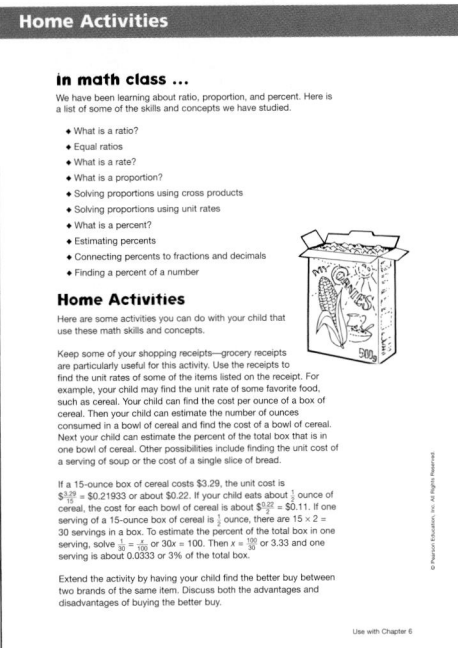

Home Activities

Here are some activities you can do with your child that use these math skills and concepts.

Keep some of your shopping receipts—grocery receipts are particularly useful for this activity. Use the receipts to find the unit rates of some of the items listed on the receipt. For example, your child may find the unit rate of some favorite food, such as cereal. Your child can find the cost per ounce of a box of cereal. Then your child can estimate the number of ounces consumed in a bowl of cereal and find the cost of a bowl of cereal. Next your child can estimate the percent of the total box that is in one bowl of cereal. Other possibilities include finding the unit cost of a serving of soup or the cost of a single slice of bread.

If a 15-ounce box of cereal costs $3.29, the unit cost is $\$\frac{3.29}{15} = \$0.21933$ or about $0.22. If your child eats about $\frac{1}{2}$ ounce of cereal, the cost for each bowl of cereal is about $\$\frac{0.22}{2} = \$0.11$. If one serving of a 15-ounce box of cereal is $\frac{1}{2}$ ounce, there are $15 \times 2 = 30$ servings in a box. To estimate the percent of the total box in one serving, solve $\frac{1}{30} = \frac{x}{100}$ or $30x = 100$. Then $x = \frac{100}{30}$ or 3.33 and one serving is about 0.0333 or 3% of the total box.

Extend the activity by having your child find the better buy between two brands of the same item. Discuss both the advantages and disadvantages of buying the better buy.

Use with Chapter 6

Available in Spanish; Web Code: aak-5500

Interdisciplinary Activities

Name ______________ ***Math and Social Studies***

SCRAPING THE SKY

Use proportions to build scale models of buildings.

Skyscrapers are the world's tallest buildings. They are mainly built for office space, but they can also be used for apartments, stores, hotels, restaurants, athletic clubs, and other facilities. Skyscrapers symbolize a city's growth and prosperity. In a developing city, space for buildings becomes harder and harder to find. Land also becomes very expensive. For these reasons, buildings must be built taller, rather than wider. The result is the skyscraper.

By the 1920s, New York City was the skyscraper capital of the world. Almost 200 skyscrapers were built in the city between 1902 and 1929. One of the oldest and most famous skyscrapers in New York is the Flatiron Building. It got its name because it is shaped like a clothes iron. Completed in 1903, it is 21 stories tall, short by today's standards but tall for its time.

Three developments made the construction of skyscrapers possible: (1) the quality of steel improved. Steel is a hard, rust-resistant metal made of iron combined with other substances. (2) The structural steel frame was designed. Steel frames support the walls and floors of buildings much as your skeleton supports your body. (3) The development of the elevator increased access to the tall buildings. Before the elevator, buildings could not be taller than the number of stairs people could climb.

Competition among builders produced taller and taller skyscrapers. New York's Empire State Building was finished in 1931 and was the world's tallest skyscraper. It has 102 stories and measures 1,250 feet from the sidewalk to the roof. The Empire State Building kept its title until the 1970s when it was replaced by the World Trade Center in New York City. Today the tallest building in the world is the Petronas Towers in Kuala Lumpur, Malayasia.

Architects often create scale models of skyscrapers. A scale model is a small version of an object. The model's dimensions are proportional to the full-size object. One reason scale models are made is to see how the finished building will look. Architects may also create scale models of a section of a city to determine how a new skyscraper will fit in. At other times, architects build a scale model and then test it to see how the building will respond to such things as wind. Before the construction of the Worldwide Plaza, a 45-story skyscraper in New York City, a scale model was built to test its strength. The model was placed in a wind tunnel at the University of Western Ontario. A wind tunnel is a device in which air is made to move at various speeds, as wind does. Winds hit the model just as they would hit the skyscraper on the New York street on which it was to be built. By studying the results of the test, architects could modify the design to produce a building that moved neither too much nor too little when winds blew on it.

In addition to using proportions to build scale models, architects use proportions to draw building plans, or blueprints. For example, $\frac{1}{4}$ inch on a blueprint might represent 1 foot of an actual building. So an 8-foot-tall door would appear as a 2-inch-tall drawing on the blueprint.

Use with Chapter 6

Available in Spanish; Web Code: aak-5500

Interdisciplinary Activities

Name ______________ ***Math and Social Studies***

1. What advances in technology made the skyscraper possible?
2. a. The scale model of Worldwide Plaza was 1:500. What does this ratio mean?
   b. If the building was 800 feet tall, including structures built on the roof, how tall was the scale model?
3. Complete the following table. Round all decimals to the tenths place. An example has been provided to help you get started.
4. Make a scale model of a building. You might choose a famous building or a building in your community. Working in small groups, find the dimensions. The building can be any size, from a shed to an office building. Using the dimensions, set up proportions for making a scale model of the building. Use a scale that will allow you to build a model that will fit on a table and will not be too tall for you to reach its top. Use materials of your choice for the model, but try to make the model look as much like the real building as possible.
5. a. Who, besides architects, must understand proportions so buildings can be constructed correctly? Explain your answer.
   b. What kinds of scale models have you played with or constructed? About what was the scale of each model?

Name and Location of Skyscraper	Height from Sidewalk to Roof (feet)	Total Height of Building Including *Structures Built on Roof (feet)	Ratio of Height of Structures on Roof to Height of Building from Sidewalk to Roof	Total Height of a 1:500 Model (feet)
Sears Tower, Chicago, Illinois	1454	1707	253:1454	3.4
Empire State Building, New York, New York	1250	1454		
John Hancock Center, Chicago, Illinois	1127	1476		
Bank of China, Hong Kong	1001	1309		

*Structures include such objects as television antennas, spires, and statues.

Use with Chapter 6

Available in Spanish; Web Code: aak-5500

Algebra Readiness Puzzles

Name ______________ Class ______________ Date ______________

Proportion Tic-Tac-Toe **Puzzle 6**

Ratio, Proportions, and Percents

Determine whether the two ratios are in proportion. If they are, place an X in the square. If not, place an O in the square. Be sure to mark the tic-tac-toes!

$\frac{2}{3} \square \frac{6}{9}$	$\frac{3}{7} \square \frac{6}{13}$	$\frac{25}{75} \square \frac{4}{6}$
$\frac{1}{3} \square \frac{24}{72}$	$\frac{8}{7} \square \frac{49}{56}$	$\frac{7}{10} \square \frac{28}{40}$
$\frac{6}{35} \square \frac{18}{105}$	$\frac{16}{30} \square \frac{8}{15}$	$\frac{18}{5} \square \frac{9}{2}$

$\frac{5}{6} \square \frac{15}{18}$	$\frac{51}{17} \square \frac{3}{1}$	$\frac{13}{75} \square \frac{50}{200}$
$\frac{42}{72} \square \frac{13}{21}$	$\frac{96}{15} \square \frac{33}{5}$	$\frac{5}{12} \square \frac{25}{60}$
$\frac{63}{26} \square \frac{7}{3}$	$\frac{87}{30} \square \frac{29}{10}$	$\frac{16}{80} \square \frac{1}{5}$

$\frac{3}{8} \square \frac{33}{88}$	$\frac{20}{36} \square \frac{15}{27}$	$\frac{12}{54} \square \frac{81}{18}$
$\frac{20}{32} \square \frac{8}{12}$	$\frac{4}{64} \square \frac{1}{16}$	$\frac{28}{4} \square \frac{49}{8}$
$\frac{15}{33} \square \frac{5}{3}$	$\frac{9}{10} \square \frac{15}{16}$	$\frac{12}{21} \square \frac{16}{28}$

$\frac{9}{40} \square \frac{30}{150}$	$\frac{2}{5} \square \frac{8}{20}$	$\frac{6}{14} \square \frac{9}{21}$
$\frac{31}{62} \square \frac{27}{54}$	$\frac{18}{16} \square \frac{42}{32}$	$\frac{76}{12} \square \frac{228}{36}$
$\frac{40}{24} \square \frac{8}{5}$	$\frac{55}{40} \square \frac{8}{6}$	$\frac{121}{66} \square \frac{11}{6}$

6 Algebra Readiness Puzzles © Pearson Education, Inc.

Web Code: aak-5500

Algebra Readiness Puzzles

Name ______________ Class ______________ Date ______________

Ratio and Proportion **Puzzle 56**

A **ratio** is a comparison of two numbers.
A ratio can be written three ways.

2 spoonfuls to 3 cupfuls
2 to 3
2:3
$\frac{2}{3}$

Write each ratio in two other ways.

1. 8:3 $\frac{8}{3}$ ______
2. $\frac{4}{11}$ ______ ______
3. 2 to 5 ______ ______
4. $\frac{9}{10}$ ______ ______
5. 6:10 ______ ______
6. 5 to 1 ______ ______

A statement that two ratios are equal is called a **proportion.** $\frac{1}{2} = \frac{2}{4}$ is a proportion.

7. Complete the table to show several ratios that are equal to the ratio of 1 to 6.

ratio of 1 to 6	1	2	3		5	
	6			24		36

Write three proportions for each of the following ratios.

8. $\frac{1}{8} =$ ______ 9. $\frac{7}{10} =$ ______ 10. $\frac{4}{5} =$ ______ 11. $\frac{6}{13} =$ ______

$\frac{1}{8} =$ ______ $\frac{7}{10} =$ ______ $\frac{4}{5} =$ ______ $\frac{6}{13} =$ ______

$\frac{1}{8} =$ ______ $\frac{7}{10} =$ ______ $\frac{4}{5} =$ ______ $\frac{6}{13} =$ ______

56 Algebra Readiness Puzzles © Pearson Education, Inc.

Web Code: aak-5500

CHAPTER 6

Ratios, Proportions, and Percents

Chapter 6 Overview

In this chapter students extend their study of numbers and numerical relationships to work with the concepts of ratio and proportion and with related applications such as scale drawings. They then explore the relationship between fractions, decimals, and percents, find percents of numbers, and estimate percents.

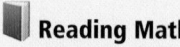 **Reading Math**
- Reading a Math Lesson, p. 277
- **Vocabulary:** A complete list, plus exercises, in the Chapter Review, p. 312
- **Illustrated Glossary:** Examples for each vocabulary term, plus definitions in English and Spanish, on p. 669

 **Test-Taking Strategies**
Working Backward, p. 311

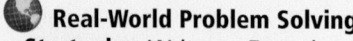 **Real-World Problem Solving**
- **Strategies:** Write an Equation, pp. 307–310
- **Real-World Snapshots:** Prehistoric Giants, pp. 316–317
- **Chapter Project:** Planet of the Stars, p. 638

www.PHSchool.com
Internet support includes:
- Self-grading Vocabulary and Chapter 6 Tests
- Activity Masters
- Chapter Project support
- Chapter Planner
- Ch. 6 Resources

Plus *iTEXT*

Key Vocabulary

- cross products (p. 283)
- equal ratios (p. 270)
- percent (p. 294)
- proportion (p. 278)
- rate (p. 273)
- ratio (p. 269)
- scale (p. 288)
- unit price (p. 274)
- unit rate (p. 273)

Ratios, Proportions, and Percents

Real-World Snapshots

Evidence of dinosaurs has been found throughout the world. These dinosaur tracks were discovered in the Painted Desert near Cameron, Arizona. The heights of dinosaurs and other animals are usually proportional to the lengths of their tracks.

Data File Animal Tracks

Animal	Track	Track Size (inches)	Animal Height (feet)
Beaver		7	2 to $3\frac{3}{5}$
Grizzly bear		12	$5\frac{3}{5}$ to $9\frac{1}{5}$
Moose		$6\frac{1}{4}$	$7\frac{9}{10}$ to $10\frac{1}{5}$
Norway rat		$\frac{5}{8}$	$\frac{3}{10}$ to 1
Striped skunk		$1\frac{1}{2}$	$\frac{9}{10}$ to $1\frac{1}{5}$

SOURCE: *Mammals of the World*

You will use the data above in this chapter:

- p. 271   Lesson 6-1   • p. 286   Lesson 6-4
- p. 291   Lesson 6-5   • p. 301   Lesson 6-7

Real-World Snapshots On pages 316 and 317, you will solve problems involving scale drawings of dinosaurs.

Teaching Notes

Activating Prior Knowledge
In this chapter students build on and extend their knowledge of simplifying and computing with fractions as they work with ratios and proportions. They also draw upon their understanding of percents and of the relationship between fractions, decimals, and percents. Ask questions such as:
- What is $\frac{10}{35}$ in simplest form? $\frac{2}{7}$
- What is $\frac{6}{10}$ in simplest form? $\frac{3}{5}$
- Which is greater: $\frac{3}{4}$ of 24 or $\frac{8}{10}$ of 24? Explain. Sample: $\frac{8}{10}$ of 24 because $\frac{8}{10}$ is greater than $\frac{3}{4}$.

Real-World Snapshots
The data here will be used throughout the chapter. Have a volunteer read the opening sentences. Focus students on the data in the chart and ask:
- What animal has the greatest track size? grizzly bear
- How many of the track sizes are greater than 6 inches? 3
- What are the possible heights of a Norway rat? between $\frac{3}{10}$ in. and 1 in.

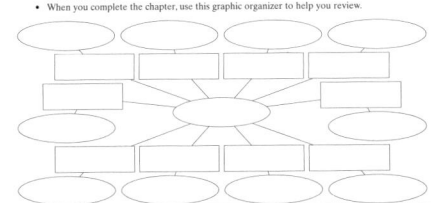

Available in Spanish

Chapter 6:
Ratios, Proportions, and Percents

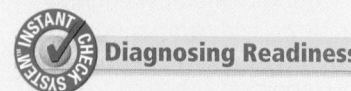 **Diagnosing Readiness**

Students will find answers to these exercises in the back of their textbooks.

Prescribing Intervention
For intervention, direct students to:

Solving Equations by Multiplying or Dividing
Lesson 2-7: Examples 1, 3. Extra Practice, p. 643.

Simplifying Fractions
Lesson 3-4: Example 2. Extra Practice, p. 644.

Comparing Fractions
Lesson 3-7: Example 1. Extra Practice, p. 644.

Multiplying and Dividing Fractions
Lesson 5-1: Example 2. Lesson 5-3: Example 3. Extra Practice, p. 646.

Chapter 6 Preview

Where You've Been

- In Chapter 1, you learned to multiply, compare, order, and estimate with decimals.

- In Chapter 3, you learned to write decimals as fractions and fractions as decimals, and to simplify fractions using prime factorization.

Where You're Going

- In Chapter 6, you will write ratios, use unit rates, recognize and solve proportions, and use a scale to determine actual dimensions.

- You will find and estimate percents.

- Applying what you learn, you will use a map to find distances. You will also use proportions to enlarge photo sizes.

Muralists use proportions to enlarge their sketches to create paintings.

iTEXT Instant self-check online and on CD-ROM

Diagnosing Readiness ? **For help, go to the lesson in green.**

Solving Equations by Multiplying or Dividing (Lesson 2-7)

Solve for n.

1. $n \div 3 = 6$ 18
2. $5n = 35$ 7
3. $n \div 8 = 6$ 48
4. $n \div 11 = 12$ 132

5. $3 \times n = 72$ 24
6. $\frac{n}{7} = 6$ 42
7. $6n = 54$ 9
8. $n \times 4 = 64$ 16

Simplifying Fractions (Lesson 3-4)

Write each fraction in simplest form.

9. $\frac{10}{25}$ $\frac{2}{5}$
10. $\frac{20}{44}$ $\frac{5}{11}$
11. $\frac{34}{51}$ $\frac{2}{3}$
12. $\frac{27}{81}$ $\frac{1}{3}$

Comparing Fractions (Lesson 3-7)

Compare. Use <, =, or >.

13. $\frac{7}{9} \boxed{>} \frac{3}{4}$
14. $\frac{2}{3} \boxed{>} \frac{3}{5}$
15. $\frac{12}{15} \boxed{<} \frac{12}{9}$
16. $\frac{24}{48} \boxed{=} \frac{1}{2}$

Multiplying and Dividing Fractions (Lessons 5-1 and 5-3)

Find the product or quotient.

 **17.** $\frac{4}{7} \times \frac{2}{3}$ $\frac{8}{21}$
18. $\frac{12}{14} \times \frac{7}{12}$ $\frac{1}{2}$
19. $\frac{7}{9} \div \frac{1}{5}$ $3\frac{8}{9}$
20. $\frac{11}{12} \div \frac{2}{9}$ $4\frac{1}{8}$

What You'll Learn

 OBJECTIVE 1 To write ratios

. . . And Why

To compare amounts in a recipe, as in Example 1

 **Check Skills You'll Need**   ? For help, go to Lesson 3-4.

Write each fraction in simplest form.

1. $\frac{4}{12}$ $\frac{1}{3}$ 2. $\frac{18}{27}$ $\frac{2}{3}$ 3. $\frac{14}{63}$ $\frac{2}{9}$ 4. $\frac{3}{48}$ $\frac{1}{16}$

New Vocabulary   • ratio   • equal ratios

Lesson Preview

 PowerPoint

✔ **Check Skills You'll Need**

Writing Fractions in Simplest Form
Lesson 3-4: Example 2. Extra Practice, p. 644.

Lesson Resources

📁 **Teaching Resources**
Practice, Reteaching, Enrichment

👥 **Reaching All Students**
Practice Workbook 6-1
Spanish Practice Workbook 6-1
Guided Problem Solving 6-1
Hands-On Activities 31

⏱ **Presentation Assistant Plus!**
Transparencies
• Check Skills You'll Need 6-1
• Problem of the Day 6-1
• Additional Examples 6-1
• Student Edition Answers 6-1
• Lesson Quiz 6-1
PH Presentation Pro CD-ROM 6-1

PRENTICE HALL ASSESSMENT SYSTEM

Computer Test Generator CD

💻 **Technology**
Resource Pro® CD-ROM
Computer Test Generator CD
PH Presentation Pro CD-ROM

💻 **www.PHSchool.com**
Student Site
• Teacher Web Code: aak-5500
• Self-grading Lesson Quiz

PH SuccessNet Teacher Center
• Lesson Planner
• Resources

Plus **iTEXT**

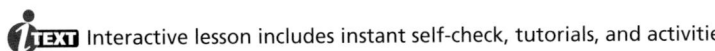 **iTEXT** Interactive lesson includes instant self-check, tutorials, and activities.

OBJECTIVE 1   **Writing Ratios**

A recipe for 6 cups of party mix calls for 4 cups of cereal and 2 cups of pretzels. You can compare amounts like these using ratios. A **ratio** is a comparison of two numbers by division. Each number in a ratio is called a *term*.

The table below shows three ways to write the ratio of cups of party mix to cups of pretzels. All three ratios are read "six to two."

Statement	Ways to Write a Ratio		
	In Words	With a Symbol	As a Fraction
6 cups party mix to 2 cups pretzels	6 to 2	6 : 2	$\frac{6}{2}$

PARTY MIX
Makes 6 cups
4 cups cereal
2 cups pretzels
3 tbsp Worcestershire sauce

① **EXAMPLE**   **Three Ways to Write a Ratio**   🌐 Real World

Recipes Use the party-mix recipe at the left. Write each ratio in three ways.

a. amount of cereal to amount of pretzels

The recipe calls for 4 cups of cereal and 2 cups of pretzels.

cereal to pretzels →   4 to 2   or   4 : 2   or $\frac{4}{2}$

b. amount of cereal to amount of party mix

The recipe calls for 4 cups of cereal and makes 6 cups of party mix.

cereal to party mix →   4 to 6   or   4 : 6   or $\frac{4}{6}$

 **Check Understanding** ① Use the recipe in Example 1. Write each ratio in three ways.

a. pretzels to cereal
2 to 4, 2 : 4, $\frac{2}{4}$

b. pretzels to party mix
2 to 6, 2 : 6, $\frac{2}{6}$

6-1   Ratios   **269**

Ongoing Assessment and Intervention

Before the Lesson	During the Lesson	After the Lesson
Diagnose prerequisite skills using: • Check Skills You'll Need	**Monitor progress using:** • Check Understanding • Additional Examples • Test Prep	**Assess knowledge using:** • Lesson Quiz • Computer Test Generator CD

Math Background

A *ratio* is a comparison of two quantities. A ratio can be expressed in three different ways: *a* to *b*, *a* : *b*, and $\frac{a}{b}$. Two ratios that name the same number are *equal ratios*. You can find equal ratios by multiplying both quantities of the ratio by the same non-zero number. Using equal ratios, you can write ratios in simplest form.

Teaching Notes

1 EXAMPLE Error Prevention

Emphasize that the order of the numbers is critical in a ratio.

Tactile Learners
Give different quantities of two coins or colored counters to groups of students. Each group writes as many ratios as possible that compare the different coins or colored counters. **six ratios for each group are possible**

2 EXAMPLE Teaching Tip

Ask: *How many equal ratios can you write for $\frac{4}{6}$?* **infinitely many**

PowerPoint

Additional Examples

1 During a school trip, there are 3 teachers and 25 students on each bus. Write each ratio in three ways.

   a. teachers to students
   3 to 25 or 3 : 25 or $\frac{3}{25}$

   b. students to teachers
   25 to 3 or 25 : 3 or $\frac{25}{3}$

2 Write two different ratios equal to 24 : 8. **Sample: 3 : 1 and 12 : 4**

3 Write each ratio in simplest form.

   a. 121 to 11 **11 to 1**

   b. 28 : 16 **7 : 4**

Closure

• *What is a ratio?* **A comparison of two quantities by division.**
• *What are equal ratios?* **Sample: Two ratios that name the same quantity.**

270

Two ratios that name the same number are **equal ratios.** You can find equal ratios by multiplying or dividing each term of a ratio by the same nonzero number.

2 EXAMPLE **Writing Equal Ratios**

Write two different ratios equal to $\frac{4}{6}$.

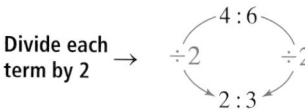

Divide each term by 2 →

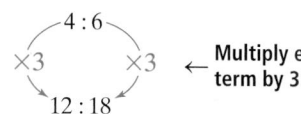

← Multiply each term by 3.

Two ratios equal to 4:6 are 2:3 and 12:18.

2a–c. Answers may vary. Samples are given.

✓ **Check Understanding** 2 Write two different ratios equal to each ratio.

   a. $\frac{10}{35}$ **$\frac{2}{7}, \frac{4}{14}$**

   b. 12:3 **4:1, 8:2**

   c. 8 to 22 **4 to 11, 12 to 33**

   d. Number Sense Use the definition of ratio to explain why $\frac{9}{5}$ is a ratio but $1\frac{4}{5}$ is not a ratio. **9 to 5 is a comparison of two numbers by division. $1\frac{4}{5}$ is not a comparison of two numbers.**

Just as with fractions, you can write ratios in simplest form. Divide the terms of the ratio by their greatest common factor (GCF).

? Need Help?
For help finding the greatest common factor (GFC), go to Lesson 3-3.

3 EXAMPLE **Ratios in Simplest Form**

Write the ratio of bats to balls in simplest form.

There are 8 bats and 12 balls, so the ratio of bats to balls is 8 to 12.

$$\frac{8}{12} = \frac{2}{3}$$

÷ 4 (top), ÷ 4 (bottom)   ← Write the ratio in simplest form.

In simplest form, the ratio of bats to balls is 2 to 3.

✓ **Check Understanding** 3 Write each ratio in simplest form.

   a. 4:20 **1:5**

   b. 50 to 45 **10 to 9**

   c. $\frac{39}{3}$ **$\frac{13}{1}$**

   d. Suppose you use 3 cups of popcorn kernels to make 24 quarts of popcorn. Write the ratio of kernels to the amount of popcorn the kernels can make in simplest form. **1 to 8**

Reaching All Students

Below Level Help students understand that they can form equivalent fractions by multiplying or dividing a fraction by fractional forms of 1, such as $\frac{5}{5}$.

$$\frac{3}{4} \times \frac{5}{5} = \frac{15}{20} \qquad \frac{15}{20} \div \frac{5}{5} = \frac{3}{4}$$

Advanced Learners Students complete the table below to find ratios equivalent to 40 : 60.

40	20	8	4	12	5
60	30	12	6	18	7.5

Inclusion
See note on page 271.
Tactile Learners
See note on page 270.

 For more practice, see *Extra Practice.*

3. Practice

A Practice by Example

Example 1
(page 269)

A drama club sells 35 student tickets, 24 adult tickets, and 11 senior citizen tickets. Write each ratio in three ways.

35 to 24, 35:24, $\frac{35}{24}$ 24 to 11, 24:11, $\frac{24}{11}$

1. student tickets to adult tickets   **2.** adult tickets to senior citizen tickets

3. senior citizen tickets to total number of tickets   11 to 70, 11:70, $\frac{11}{70}$

Example 2
(page 270)

Write two different ratios equal to each ratio.   4–7. Answers may vary. Samples are given.

4. 6 to 18   **5.** $\frac{4}{14}$ $\frac{2}{7}$, $\frac{16}{56}$ **6.** 8:10   **7.** $\frac{30}{40}$ $\frac{3}{4}$, $\frac{6}{8}$
3 to 9, 18 to 54   4:5, 16:20

Example 3
(page 270)

Write each ratio in simplest form.

8. $\frac{6}{15}$ $\frac{2}{5}$ **9.** 40:30 4:3   21 to 25
10. 42 to 50   **11.** $\frac{14}{42}$ $\frac{1}{3}$

12. 9 to 81 1 to 9   **13.** 75:15 5:1   **14.** 8:36 2:9   **15.** 18 to 12
3 to 2

B Apply Your Skills

Find the value that makes the ratios equal.

2   700   20
16. 6 to 9, ■ to 3   **17.** 10:1, ■:70   **18.** $\frac{■}{20}$, $\frac{50}{50}$

45
19. 32:90, 16:■   **20.** $\frac{18}{3}$, $\frac{54}{■}$ 9   **21.** ■ to 25, 9 to 5
45

22. $\frac{72}{24}$, $\frac{■}{6}$ 18   **23.** ■ to 96, 4 to 6   **24.** 50:150, 75:■
64   225

25. Writing in Math Explain the steps you would use to rewrite 48:56 as 6:7. Divide the terms of the original ratio by their GCF, 8.

26. Data File, p. 267 Write the ratio of a beaver's track size to a grizzly bear's track size.   7 to 12

 27. Cats and Dogs The average adult cat has 30 teeth. The average adult dog has 42 teeth. Write the ratio of cat's teeth to dog's teeth in simplest form.   5:7

Use the picture. Write each ratio in three ways.
6:5, 6 to 5, $\frac{6}{5}$ 4:2, 4 to 2, $\frac{4}{2}$
28. cups to bowls   **29.** coasters to blue cups

30. coasters to cups   **31.** yellow cups to blue bowls
4:6, 4 to 6, $\frac{4}{6}$ 2:3, 2 to 3, $\frac{2}{3}$

32. coasters to total number of items
4:15, 4 to 15, $\frac{4}{15}$

33. Open-Ended Write a ratio of the number of vowels to the number of consonants in your first name.
Check students' work.

Assignment Guide

1 Objective 1
A B Core 1–33
C Extension 34–39

Test Prep 40–43
Mixed Review 44–48

Inclusion
Exercises 16–24 Have students write each ratio in fraction form. Then students should first find the number that they need to multiply or divide by.

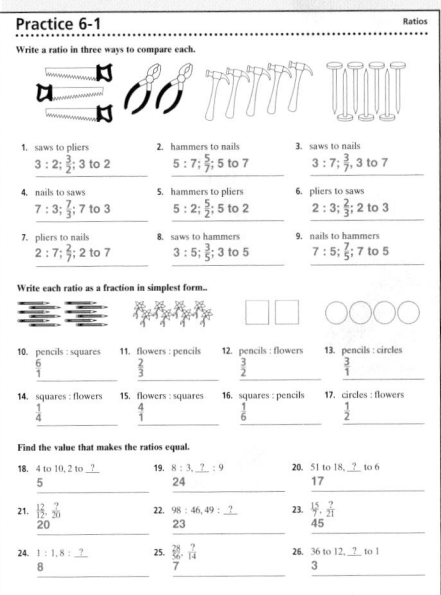

GPS Use the Guided Problem Solving worksheet with Exercise 27.

Lesson Quiz 6-1

A drama club has 14 females and 8 males. Write each ratio in three ways.

1. males to females 8 to 14, 8 : 14, $\frac{8}{14}$

2. females to males 14 to 8, 14 : 8, $\frac{14}{8}$

3. total to females 22 to 14, 22 : 14, $\frac{22}{14}$

Write each ratio in simplest form.

4. $\frac{8}{12}$ $\frac{2}{3}$ **5.** 10 : 6 5 : 3

Alternative Assessment

Each student in a pair writes five different ratios in words. Partners exchange papers and write each ratio three ways. They then write each ratio in simplest form and write a second equal ratio.

Test Prep

Resources

For additional practice with a variety of test item formats:
• Test Prep, p. 315
• Test-Taking Strategies, p. 311
• Test-Taking Strategies With Transparencies

Enrichment 6-1   Ratios
Critical Thinking

The ratios below describe a set of polygons. Use the ratios to find the number of polygons in the set. All ratios are written in lowest terms.

• Right triangles to obtuse triangles is 2 to 3.
  Obtuse triangles to scalene triangles is 6 : 5.
• Triangles to rectangles is $\frac{4}{5}$.
• Rhombuses to trapezoids is 3 : 5.
• Quadrilaterals to triangles is $\frac{4}{3}$.

1. List the order in which you will find the number of polygons in the set. Explain. **Sample answers are given.**

a. First	right triangle	b. Second	obtuse triangle
c. Third	scalene triangle	d. Fourth	rectangle
e. Fifth	rhombus	f. Sixth	trapezoid

It is easiest to find how many of each type of triangle, then use those quantities to find the number of rectangles and other quadrilaterals.

2. What is the fewest number of polygons that can be in the set?

a. Right triangles	4	b. Obtuse triangles	6
c. Scalene triangles	5	d. Triangles	15
e. Rectangles	12	f. Rhombuses	3
g. Trapezoids	5	h. Quadrilaterals	20

3. Show the number of polygons in another set that has the same ratios. **Sample answers are given.**

a. Right triangles	8	b. Obtuse triangles	12
c. Scalene triangles	10	d. Triangles	30
e. Rectangles	24	f. Rhombuses	6
g. Trapezoids	10	h. Quadrilaterals	40

C Challenge   **Write each comparison in simplest form.** (*Hint:* Use the GCF.)

34. 15 : 10 : 5   **35.** 32 : 20 : 8   **36.** 18 : 30 : 57   **37.** 8x : 16x : 4x
   3 : 2 : 1   8 : 5 : 2   6 : 10 : 19   2 : 4 : 1

38. Stretch Your Thinking For the figure at the left, which three toothpicks should you remove so that exactly three squares remain?
See margin.

39. Each digit from 1 through 9 is used once on the left side of this pair of equal ratios. Complete with the missing digits. $\frac{9,876}{12,345}$

$$\frac{9,\blacksquare 76}{\blacksquare 2,34\blacksquare} = \frac{4}{5}$$

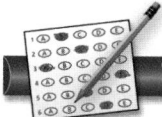

Test Prep

Reading Comprehension   Read the passage, then write each ratio described below in simplest form.

Sign on the Dotted Line

Autographs from famous people are sometimes worth big money. Stephen King's autograph is worth $60. Nomar Garciaparra's autograph is worth $35. Denzel Washington's autograph is worth $25, and Albert Einstein's autograph is worth $900.

Button Gwinnett signed the Declaration of Independence, and his autograph recently sold for $85,000.

Take It to the NET
Online lesson quiz at
www.PHSchool.com
Web Code: aaa-0601

Multiple Choice

                                                                     5 : 7
40. the price of Denzel Washington's autograph to Nomar Garciaparra's

41. the price of Stephen King's autograph to Albert Einstein's 2 : 30

42. the price of Denzel Washington's autograph to Button Gwinnett's 1 : 3,400

43. A bookstore sells 24 paperbacks, 6 hardcovers, 38 magazines, and 5 calendars. What is the ratio of magazines sold to paperbacks sold?
   A. 24 : 38   **B.** 19 to 31   **C.** $\frac{19}{12}$ **D.** 12 : 24   C

Mixed Review

Lesson 5-1   **Write each product in simplest form.**

44. $\frac{2}{5} \times \frac{3}{7}$ $\frac{6}{35}$ **45.** $\frac{3}{4} \times \frac{5}{8}$ $\frac{15}{32}$ **46.** $\frac{1}{6}$ of $\frac{3}{5}$ $\frac{1}{10}$ **47.** $\frac{3}{16} \cdot \frac{16}{21}$ $\frac{1}{7}$

Lesson 4-8   **48.** A square garden is enclosed by a fence that has 9 posts on each side. How many posts are there in all? **32 posts**

38.

Unit Rates

What You'll Learn

OBJECTIVE 1 To find unit rates

OBJECTIVE 2 To use unit rates

...And Why

To compare unit prices, as in Example 3

✔ **Check Skills You'll Need**

? For help, go to Lesson 6-1.

Write each ratio in simplest form.

1. $\frac{48}{12}$ $\frac{4}{1}$

2. $\frac{36}{9}$ $\frac{4}{1}$

3. $\frac{75}{15}$ $\frac{5}{1}$

4. $\frac{42}{7}$ $\frac{6}{1}$

5. $\frac{125}{5}$ $\frac{25}{1}$

6. $\frac{52}{4}$ $\frac{13}{1}$

New Vocabulary • rate • unit rate • unit price

Lesson Preview

PowerPoint

✔ **Check Skills You'll Need**
Writing Ratios in Simplest Form
Lesson 6-1: Example 3. Extra Practice, p. 647.

Lesson Resources

Teaching Resources
Practice, Reteaching, Enrichment

Reaching All Students
Practice Workbook 6-2
Spanish Practice Workbook 6-2
Guided Problem Solving 6-2

Presentation Assistant Plus!
Transparencies
• Check Skills You'll Need 6-2
• Problem of the Day 6-2
• Additional Examples 6-2
• Student Edition Answers 6-2
• Lesson Quiz 6-2
PH Presentation Pro CD-ROM 6-2

PRENTICE HALL ASSESSMENT SYSTEM
Computer Test Generator CD

Technology
Resource Pro® CD-ROM
Computer Test Generator CD
PH Presentation Pro CD-ROM

www.PHSchool.com
Student Site
• Teacher Web Code: aak-5500
• Self-grading Lesson Quiz

PH SuccessNet Teacher Center
• Lesson Planner
• Resources

Plus **iTEXT**

OBJECTIVE 1 **Finding a Unit Rate**

iTEXT Interactive lesson includes instant self-check, tutorials, and activities.

A **rate** is a ratio that compares two quantities measured in different units. The rate $\frac{150 \text{ heartbeats}}{2 \text{ minutes}}$ compares heartbeats to minutes. The rate for one unit of a given quantity is called the **unit rate**. A unit rate has the denominator 1.

$$\frac{150 \text{ heartbeats}}{2 \text{ minutes}} \rightarrow 150 \div 2 = 75$$

The unit rate is 75 heartbeats per minute.

Suppose a box of wheat crackers holds 6 servings and has a total of 420 Calories. You want to find the number of Calories in 1 serving.

6 servings → [box] ← 420 Calories

1 serving → ← ■ Calories

The model shows that
total Calories ÷ **number of servings** = **Calories per serving.**

1 EXAMPLE Finding a Unit Rate

Find the unit rate for 420 Calories in 6 servings.

Calories → $\frac{420}{6} = 70$ ← **Divide the first quantity by the second quantity.**
servings →

The unit rate is $\frac{70 \text{ Calories}}{1 \text{ serving}}$, or 70 Calories per serving.

✔ **Check Understanding** 1 Find the unit rate for each situation.

a. 66 pages read in 2 hours
33 pages per hour

b. $2.37 for 3 pounds of grapes
$.79 per pound

c. **Reasoning** Which of the following rates, $\frac{36 \text{ inches}}{3 \text{ feet}}$ or $\frac{12 \text{ inches}}{1 \text{ foot}}$, is a unit rate? Explain how you know. $\frac{12 \text{ inches}}{1 \text{ foot}}$; it is the number of inches in 1 foot.

Ongoing Assessment and Intervention

Before the Lesson
Diagnose prerequisite skills using:
• Check Skills You'll Need

During the Lesson
Monitor progress using:
• Check Understanding
• Additional Examples
• Test Prep

After the Lesson
Assess knowledge using:
• Lesson Quiz
• Computer Test Generator CD

Math Background

Professional Development

A *rate* is a special type of ratio that compares two quantities with different units of measure. Speed is a rate that is commonly expressed as a *unit rate*, a rate that compares something to one unit, such as 55 mi/h (miles per "one" hour). You can compare the costs of two sizes of the same product by comparing each cost per unit, or *unit price*.

Teaching Notes

English Learners

In the definition of a rate, "a ratio that compares two quantities measured in different units," *units* refer to measures such as miles or seconds. In "unit rate," *unit* refers to the second quantity in the rate as *one* unit of a given quantity.

2 EXAMPLE Alternative Method

Show students how multiplying both numerator and denominator by 8 is really multiplication by 1.

$$\frac{25 \text{ mi}}{1 \text{ gal}} \cdot \frac{8}{8} = \frac{25 \text{ mi} \cdot 8}{1 \text{ gal} \cdot 8} = \frac{200 \text{ mi}}{8 \text{ gal}}$$

PowerPoint
Additional Examples

1. Find the unit rate for typing 145 words in 5 minutes. **29 words per min**

2. Apples cost $1.49 for 1 pound. How much do 5 pounds of apples cost? **$7.45**

3. The same brand of pretzels comes in two sizes: a 10-ounce bag for $.99, and an 18-ounce bag for $1.49. Which size is a better buy? Round each unit price to the nearest cent. **10-oz: $.10, 18-oz: $.08; The 18-oz bag is a better buy.**

Closure

- *What is a rate?* **Sample: A rate is a ratio that compares quantities of different units.**

- *How can you compare the cost of two items that are different sizes?* **Sample: Find the unit price for each item. The lesser unit price is the better buy.**

You can use unit rates to solve problems.

2 EXAMPLE Using a Unit Rate  Real World

Travel A car travels 25 miles on 1 gallon of gas. How far can the car travel on 8 gallons of gas?

Write the unit rate as a ratio. Then find an equal ratio.

$$\frac{25 \text{ miles}}{1 \text{ gallon}} \overset{\times 8}{\underset{\times 8}{=}} \frac{200 \text{ miles}}{8 \text{ gallons}} \quad \leftarrow \text{Multiply each term by 8.}$$

The car can travel 200 miles on 8 gallons of gas.

✓ **Check Understanding** 2 Write the unit rate as a ratio. Then find an equal ratio. $\frac{\$5.25}{1 \text{ hour}} = \frac{\$26.25}{5 \text{ hours}}$
  a. You earn $5.25 in 1 hour. How much do you earn in 5 hours?
  b. You type 25 words in 1 minute. How many words can you type in 10 minutes? $\frac{25 \text{ words}}{1 \text{ minute}} = \frac{250 \text{ words}}{10 \text{ minutes}}$

A unit rate that gives the cost per unit is a **unit price.** Unit prices help you compare costs.

3 EXAMPLE Comparing Unit Prices  Real World

Comparison Shopping Two sizes of sports drink bottles are shown. Which size is the better buy? Round each unit price to the nearest cent.

Divide to find the unit price for each size.

$$\frac{\text{price} \rightarrow}{\text{size} \rightarrow} \frac{\$1.20}{24 \text{ oz}} = \$.05 \text{ per fluid ounce}$$

$$\frac{\text{price} \rightarrow}{\text{size} \rightarrow} \frac{\$1.29}{32 \text{ oz}} \approx \$.04 \text{ per fluid ounce}$$

The better buy costs less per fluid ounce. Since $.04 is less than $.05, the 32-ounce bottle is the better buy.

✓ **Check Understanding** 3 Find each unit price. Round to the nearest cent. Then determine the better buy.
  a. yogurt: 6 ounces for $.68   **$.11 per ounce; $.09 per ounce;**
          32 ounces for $2.89   **the 32-ounce container**
  b. phone call: 3 minutes for $.42   **$.14 per minute; $.09 per minute;**
          15 minutes for $1.35   **the 15 minutes for $1.35.**
  c. **Reasoning** Explain how unit pricing helps you compare costs in a grocery store. **Answers may vary. Sample: It helps to find the less expensive item.**

👥 Reaching All Students

| Below Level Have students make a table of Calories for each serving size for the model on page 273. | Advanced Learners One office space costs $143,500 and has 1,825 sq ft. Another office space is $129,799 and has 1,625 sq ft. Which looks like a better buy? **1,825 sq ft office is slightly less per sq ft** | English Learners See note on page 274. Alternative Method See note on page 274. |

Serving	1	2	3	4	5	6
Calories	70	140	210	280	350	420

 **EXERCISES**

🔎 For more practice, see *Extra Practice*.

3. Practice

Assignment Guide

1 Objective 1
Ⓐ Ⓑ Core 1–5, 20
Ⓒ Extension 21–23

2 Objective 2
Ⓐ Ⓑ Core 6–19
Ⓒ Extension 24

Test Prep 25–30
Mixed Review 31–39

Technology Tip
Exercises 10–13 You might allow students to use a calculator to perform the unit rate divisions.

Ⓐ **Practice by Example**

Example 1
(page 273)

Find the unit rate for each situation. Exercise 1 has been started for you.

70 heartbeats per minute

1. 210 heartbeats in 3 minutes: $\frac{210 \text{ heartbeats}}{3 \text{ minutes}} \rightarrow 210 \div 3 = \blacksquare$

2. 92 desks in 4 classrooms
   23 desks per classroom

3. $19.50 for 3 T-shirts
   $6.50 per T-shirt

4. 45 miles in 5 hours
   9 miles per hour

5. $29.85 for 3 presents
   $9.95 per present

Example 2
(page 274)

Write the unit rate as a ratio. Then find an equal ratio.

6. The cost is $6.75 for 1 item. Find the cost of 8 items. $\frac{\$6.75}{1} = \frac{\$54.00}{8 \text{ items}}$

7. $\frac{3 \text{ feet}}{1 \text{ yard}} = \frac{45 \text{ feet}}{15 \text{ yards}}$

7. There are 3 feet in 1 yard. Find the number of feet in 15 yards.

8. $\frac{9 \text{ players}}{1 \text{ team}} = \frac{63 \text{ players}}{7 \text{ teams}}$

8. There are 9 players per team. Find the number of players on 7 teams.

9. $\frac{45 \text{ students}}{1 \text{ bus}} = \frac{225 \text{ students}}{5 \text{ buses}}$

9. There are 45 students per bus. Find the number of students on 5 buses.

Example 3
(page 274)

🛒 **Comparison Shopping** **Find each unit price. Round to the nearest cent. Then determine the better buy.**

$.95 per bagel; $.80 per bagel; 5 for $4.00

10. crackers: 16 ounces for $2.39
    20 ounces for $3.19
    $.15 per oz; $.16 per oz; 16 oz for $2.39

11. bagels: 3 for $2.85
    5 for $4.00

12. juice: 48 fluid ounces for $2.07
    32 fluid ounces for $1.64
    $.04 per fl oz; $.05 per fl oz; 48 fl oz for $2.07

13. apples: 3 pounds for $1.89
    1 pound for $.79
    $.63 per lb; $.79 per lb; 3 lb for $1.89

Ⓑ **Apply Your Skills**

For Exercises 14–18, tell which unit rate is greater.

$44.55 in 9 hours

14. Carlos earns $44.55 in 9 hours. Maggie earns $51 in 12 hours.

15. Dylan reads 60 pages in 2 hours. Terry reads 99 pages in 3 hours.
    99 pages in 3 hours

16. Damian types 110 words in 5 minutes. Heather types 208 words in 8 minutes. **208 words in 8 min**

17. Janelle bikes 18 miles in 2 hours. Nicole bikes 33 miles in 3 hours.
    33 mi in 3 hours

18. Tanya scores 81 points in 9 games. Todd scores 132 points in 12 games.
    132 points in 12 games

19. **Jump Rope** Crystal jumps 255 times in 3 minutes. The United States
    GPS record for 11-year-olds is 864 jumps in 3 minutes.
    a. Find Crystal's unit rate for jumps per minute. **85 jumps per min**
    b. Find the record-holder's unit rate for jumps per minute. **See left.**
    c. How many more times did the record-holder jump per minute?
       203 times

19. 288 jumps per min

20. **Writing in Math** Explain how a car's speed is an example of a unit rate. **Answers may vary. Sample: A car's speed is given in miles per hour.**

 GPS **Use the Guided Problem Solving worksheet with Exercise 19.**

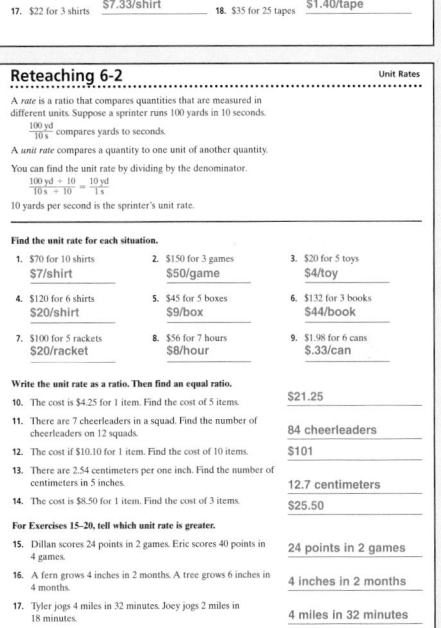

Practice 6-2 — Unit Rates

Find the unit rate for each situation.
1. 44 breaths in 2 minutes — 22 breaths per minute
2. 72 players on 9 teams — 8 players per team
3. 60 miles in 2 hours — 30 miles per hour
4. 15 pages in 30 minutes — ½ page per minute
5. 48 questions in 4 quizzes — 12 questions per quiz
6. $3 for 4 packages — $.75 per package

Write the unit rate as a ratio. Then find an equal ratio.
7. There are 12 inches in a foot. Find the number of inches in 6 feet. $\frac{12 \text{ in.}}{1 \text{ ft.}} = \frac{72 \text{ in.}}{6 \text{ ft.}}$
8. The cost is $8.50 for 1 shirt. Find the cost of 4 shirts. $\frac{\$8.50}{1 \text{ shirt}} = \frac{\$34}{4 \text{ shirts}}$
9. There are 365 days in a year. Find the number of days in 3 years. $\frac{365 \text{ days}}{1 \text{ year}} = \frac{1{,}095 \text{ days}}{3 \text{ years}}$
10. There are 6 cans per box. Find the number of cans in 11 boxes. $\frac{6 \text{ cans}}{1 \text{ box}} = \frac{66 \text{ cans}}{11 \text{ boxes}}$
11. There are 5 students in a group. Find the number of students in 5 groups. $\frac{5 \text{ students}}{1 \text{ group}} = \frac{25 \text{ students}}{5 \text{ groups}}$
12. There are 70 pages in a notebook. Find the number of pages in 8 notebooks. $\frac{70 \text{ pages}}{1 \text{ notebook}} = \frac{560 \text{ pages}}{8 \text{ notebooks}}$

Find each unit price.
13. $5 for 10 pounds — $.50/pound
14. 40 ounces for $12 — $.30/ounce
15. $6 for 10 pens — $.60/pen
16. $60 for 5 books — $12/book
17. $22 for 3 shirts — $7.33/shirt
18. $35 for 25 tapes — $1.40/tape

Reteaching 6-2 — Unit Rates

A *rate* is a ratio that compares quantities that are measured in different units. Suppose a sprinter runs 100 yards in 10 seconds.
$\frac{100 \text{ yd}}{10 \text{ s}}$ compares yards to seconds.
A *unit rate* compares a quantity to one unit of another quantity.
You can find the unit rate by dividing by the denominator.
$\frac{100 \text{ yd} \div 10}{10 \text{ s} \div 10} = \frac{10 \text{ yd}}{1 \text{ s}}$
10 yards per second is the sprinter's unit rate.

Find the unit rate for each situation.
1. $70 for 10 shirts — $7/shirt
2. $150 for 3 games — $50/game
3. $20 for 5 toys — $4/toy
4. $120 for 6 shirts — $20/shirt
5. $45 for 5 boxes — $9/box
6. $132 for 3 books — $44/book
7. $100 for 5 rackets — $20/racket
8. $56 for 7 hours — $8/hour
9. $1.98 for 6 cans — $.33/can

Write the unit rate as a ratio. Then find an equal ratio.
10. The cost is $4.25 for 1 item. Find the cost of 5 items. — $21.25
11. There are 7 cheerleaders in a squad. Find the number of cheerleaders on 12 squads. — 84 cheerleaders
12. The cost if $10.10 for 1 item. Find the cost of 10 items. — $101
13. There are 2.54 centimeters per one inch. Find the number of centimeters in 5 inches. — 12.7 centimeters
14. The cost is $8.50 for 1 item. Find the cost of 3 items. — $25.50

For Exercises 15–20, tell which unit rate is greater.
15. Dillan scores 24 points in 2 games. Eric scores 40 points in 4 games. — 24 points in 2 games
16. A fern grows 4 inches in 2 months. A tree grows 6 inches in 4 months. — 4 inches in 2 months
17. Tyler jogs 4 miles in 32 minutes. Joey jogs 2 miles in 18 minutes. — 4 miles in 32 minutes
18. Dixie drinks 2 cups of water in 5 minutes. Dale drinks 10 cups of water in 12 minutes. — 10 cups in 12 minutes

275

Lesson Quiz 6-2

Find the unit rate for each situation.

1. 18 in. in 3 years 6 in. per yr

2. 9 calls in 3 min 3 calls per min

Find each unit price.

3. 16 oz for $5.28 $.33 per oz

4. 5 lb for $6.25 $1.25 per lb

Alternative Assessment

Each student in a pair writes the size and cost for two different quantities of the same product. Partners exchange papers and find each unit price to determine the better buy.

Test Prep

Resources

For additional practice with a variety of test item formats:
• Test Prep, p. 315
• Test-Taking Strategies, p. 311
• Test-Taking Strategies With Transparencies

Exercise 28 Encourage students to use mental math to eliminate answer choices.

276

Challenge **Air Travel** A commercial airplane flies 2,750 miles in 5 hours. Find each unit rate. Round your answer to the nearest tenth if necessary.

21. miles per hour
550 mi per h

22. miles per minute
9.2 mi per min

23. miles per second
0.2 mi per sec

24. Stretch Your Thinking Tina is two inches taller than Jay. Tim is 5 inches shorter than Cole. Cole is 1 inch shorter than Tina. Who is shortest?
Tim

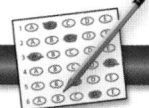
Test Prep

Multiple Choice

25. You earn $4.75 per hour babysitting. How much will you earn in 4 hours? C
  A. $17   **B.** $18   **C.** $19   **D.** $20

26. There are 54 students and 18 computers. What is the unit rate of students to computers? G
  F. $\frac{6 \text{ students}}{2 \text{ computers}}$ **G.** $\frac{3 \text{ students}}{1 \text{ computer}}$ **H.** $\frac{5 \text{ students}}{1 \text{ computer}}$ **I.** $\frac{1 \text{ student}}{5 \text{ computers}}$

Take It to the NET
Online lesson quiz at
www.PHSchool.com
Web Code: aaa-0602

27. Which of these is a unit rate? C
  A. $\frac{3 \text{ pages}}{5 \text{ minutes}}$ **B.** $\frac{2 \text{ miles}}{8 \text{ minutes}}$ **C.** $\frac{\$2.00}{1 \text{ pound}}$ **D.** $\frac{80 \text{ miles}}{90 \text{ hours}}$

28. Which is the best buy? I
  F. $6.59 for 6 muffins   **G.** $2.00 for 2 muffins
  H. $7.20 for 8 muffins   **I.** $3.00 for 4 muffins

29. The cost for 2 pounds of fish is $7.98. Which of the following is true? B
  A. 1 pound for $2.99   **B.** 3 pounds for $11.97
  C. 4 pounds for $19.96   **D.** 5 pounds for $23.95

Short Response

30. A car travels 279.9 miles on 9.8 gallons of gasoline. **(a)** Estimate the car's miles per gallon. **(b)** Explain how you found your estimate.
See margin.

Mixed Review

Lesson 5-4   **Find each quotient.**

31. $2\frac{1}{5} \div 1\frac{5}{6}$ $\frac{6}{5}$ **32.** $6\frac{1}{2} \div 2\frac{1}{6}$ 3   **33.** $5\frac{1}{8} \div 2\frac{1}{2}$ $2\frac{1}{20}$

34. $4\frac{2}{3} \div 1\frac{3}{4}$ $2\frac{2}{3}$ **35.** $6\frac{1}{4} \div 2\frac{1}{2}$ $2\frac{1}{2}$ **36.** $2\frac{2}{5} \div 7\frac{1}{5}$ $\frac{1}{3}$

Lesson 5-1   **Find each product.**

37. $\frac{1}{7} \times \frac{1}{2}$ $\frac{1}{14}$ **38.** $\frac{2}{5} \times \frac{4}{5}$ $\frac{8}{25}$ **39.** $\frac{10}{11} \cdot \frac{5}{6}$ $\frac{25}{33}$

30. [2] a. about 28 mi per gal

b. The car travels about 280 miles on about 10 gallons of gasoline. The unit rate is about $\frac{280 \text{ miles}}{10 \text{ gallons}} = 28$ miles per gallon.

[1] answers one part only

Reading a Math Lesson

When you read a math lesson, keep the purpose in mind. Here are some strategies you can use to help you understand the important ideas of a math lesson.

Focus Before you read a lesson:
- Read the objective headings in the red bars. These headings let you know what topics will be covered.
- Write questions for each objective heading. Ask for information you think is important.

Read When you read a new section:
- Try to answer your questions.
- Ask yourself how the ideas connect with earlier ideas in the book.
- If necessary, read the lesson or section again.

Reflect After you read a section:
- Make up your own example. Explain it to a friend, or write out the explanation.

EXAMPLE

Write questions for the objective headings of Lesson 6-2.

- What is a unit rate?
- How *do* I find a unit rate?
- How are ratios and rates alike? How are they different?

1. Answers may vary. Sample: A unit rate is a rate for one unit of a quantity. To find a unit rate divide the first quantity by the second so the denominator is 1. A ratio compares two quantities. A rate is a ratio that compares two quantities measured in different units. A unit rate is a rate whose denominator is 1.

EXERCISES

1. Answer the questions that were posed for Lesson 6-2 in the example.

2. Look ahead to Lesson 6-3. The title is "Understanding Proportions." The objective headings are "Testing Ratios" and "Completing Proportions." **2a–c. See margin.**
   a. Write a question for each objective heading.
   b. Read Lesson 6-3. Answer your questions.
   c. How does this lesson relate to any earlier lessons in the book?

Reading Math

2a–c. Answers may vary. Samples are given.

2a. How can you tell if two ratios form a proportion? How do you complete a proportion?

b. Two ratios form a proportion if they are equal. You can sometimes complete a proportion by finding unit rates.

c. Two rates form a proportion if two fractions are equal.

Reading Math

Reading a Math Lesson

Textbooks provide helpful clues and features students can use to find the information the lessons contain. This feature presents strategies students can apply to use the tools given in their texts to gain a better understanding of the key ideas in each lesson.

Teaching Notes

Teaching Tip
Inform students that their textbook has been designed to guide them through the lessons in a systematic, logical way. Emphasize the importance of taking a proactive approach to the lessons—asking questions, connecting ideas presented to those from earlier lessons and to their everyday lives, and preparing themselves to explain key ideas to classmates. Then have a volunteer read aloud the three sets of general hints provided. Discuss each strategy. For the Reflect set of strategies, ask: *What is an advantage of making up an example?* **Sample: to more fully understand the concept(s) behind the example given**

Tactile Learners
To help students focus on key parts of lessons, have them (1) bracket sections with fingers as they read, (2) mask all but the portions of the page they are reading, or (3) make use of self-stick notes to highlight key sections, or to remind them of questions to ask or parts to reread.

Exercises
Assign the exercises. Then have students share their answers and strategies.

1. Plan

Lesson Preview

✓ **Check Skills You'll Need**

Comparing Fractions With Unlike Denominators
Lesson 3-7: Example 1. Extra Practice, p. 644.

Lesson Resources

 Teaching Resources
Practice, Reteaching, Enrichment

 Reaching All Students
Practice Workbook 6-3
Spanish Practice Workbook 6-3
Guided Problem Solving 6-3

 Presentation Assistant Plus!
Transparencies
• Check Skills You'll Need 6-3
• Problem of the Day 6-3
• Additional Examples 6-3
• Student Edition Answers 6-3
• Lesson Quiz 6-3
PH Presentation Pro CD-ROM 6-3

Computer Test Generator CD

 Technology
Resource Pro® CD-ROM
Computer Test Generator CD
PH Presentation Pro CD-ROM

 www.PHSchool.com
Student Site
• Teacher Web Code: aak-5500
• Algebra Readiness Puzzle 56
• Self-grading Lesson Quiz

PH SuccessNet Teacher Center
• Lesson Planner
• Resources

Plus

6-3 Understanding Proportions

What You'll Learn

OBJECTIVE 1 To test ratios

OBJECTIVE 2 To complete proportions

...And Why

To find driving distances, as in Example 2

✓ **Check Skills You'll Need**

? For help, go to Lesson 3-7.

Compare each pair of fractions using <, =, or >.

1. $\frac{3}{5} \; \boxed{<} \; \frac{7}{9}$

2. $\frac{1}{3} \; \boxed{=} \; \frac{5}{15}$

3. $\frac{4}{9} \; \boxed{<} \; \frac{2}{3}$

4. $\frac{14}{35} \; \boxed{<} \; \frac{14}{25}$

5. $\frac{8}{48} \; \boxed{>} \; \frac{1}{8}$

6. $\frac{36}{42} \; \boxed{=} \; \frac{18}{21}$

New Vocabulary
• proportion

 Interactive lesson includes instant self-check, tutorials, and activities.

OBJECTIVE 1 Testing Ratios

Investigation: Using Proportional Reasoning

Suppose you make lemonade by adding a powdered mix to water. The more powdered mix you add, the stronger the lemonade will be.

1. Order these glasses of lemonade from strongest to weakest.
   A. 8 ounces of water 1 scoop of mix
   B. 8 ounces of water 2 scoops of mix
   C. 8 ounces of water $1\frac{1}{2}$ scoops of mix
   B, C, A

2. Order these glasses of lemonade from strongest to weakest.
   A. 8 ounces of water 1 scoop of mix
   B. 9 ounces of water 1 scoop of mix
   C. 10 ounces of water 1 scoop of mix
   A, B, C

3. Two of the three glasses below have the same strength. Find them, and explain how you know they have the same strength.
   A. 8 ounces of water 1 scoop of mix
   B. 10 ounces of water 1 scoop of mix
   C. 16 ounces of water 2 scoops of mix
   A and C; they have the same unit rate.

Real-World Connection
You can change the strength of lemonade by adjusting the ratio of water to powdered mix.

When two ratios are equal, you can write them as a proportion.

Key Concepts | **Proportions**

A **proportion** is an equation stating that two ratios are equal.

Examples:
$\frac{1}{2} = \frac{4}{8}$; $\frac{27}{18} = \frac{9}{6}$

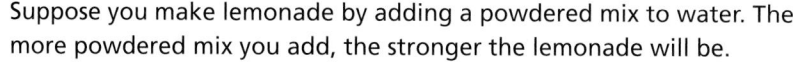 **Ongoing Assessment and Intervention**

Before the Lesson
Diagnose prerequisite skills using:
• Check Skills You'll Need

During the Lesson
Monitor progress using:
• Check Understanding
• Additional Examples
• Test Prep

After the Lesson
Assess knowledge using:
• Lesson Quiz
• Computer Test Generator CD

A way to show that two ratios can form a proportion is to show that the ratios are equivalent.

① EXAMPLE   Recognizing Proportions

Do the ratios in each pair form a proportion?

a. $\dfrac{9}{10}, \dfrac{27}{30}$

b. $\dfrac{72}{81}, \dfrac{7}{9}$

$$\overset{\times 3}{\underset{\times 3}{\dfrac{9}{10} \overset{?}{=} \dfrac{27}{30}}}$$

$$\dfrac{72}{81} \overset{?}{=} \dfrac{7}{9} \quad \leftarrow \begin{array}{l} 72 \div 9 = 8, \\ \text{not } 7 \end{array}$$

$$\dfrac{9}{10} = \dfrac{27}{30} \quad \leftarrow \textbf{Compare ratios.} \rightarrow \quad \dfrac{72}{81} \ne \dfrac{7}{9}$$

$\dfrac{9}{10}$ and $\dfrac{27}{30}$ form a proportion.

$\dfrac{72}{81}$ and $\dfrac{7}{9}$ do *not* form a proportion.

✔ **Check Understanding** ① Do the ratios in each pair form a proportion?

a. $\dfrac{2}{5}, \dfrac{8}{20}$ yes

b. $\dfrac{12}{52}, \dfrac{4}{14}$ no

c. $\dfrac{8}{5}, \dfrac{36}{20}$ no

OBJECTIVE

② Completing Proportions

You can sometimes use a unit rate to complete a proportion.

② EXAMPLE   Completing a Proportion   🌐 Real World

Cars A hybrid car can travel 260 miles using 5 gallons of gas. How many miles can the car travel using 8 gallons of gas?

Write a proportion that compares miles driven to gallons of gas used.

$$\begin{array}{c} \text{miles} \rightarrow \\ \text{gallons} \rightarrow \end{array} \dfrac{260}{5} = \dfrac{\blacksquare}{8} \begin{array}{l} \leftarrow \text{miles} \\ \leftarrow \text{gallons} \end{array}$$

The denominators 5 and 8 are not easy to relate by multiplication, so find a unit rate for 260 miles and 5 gallons.

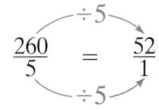

$$\overset{\div 5}{\underset{\div 5}{\dfrac{260}{5} = \dfrac{52}{1}}} \quad \leftarrow \begin{array}{l} \textbf{Find an equivalent fraction} \\ \textbf{with denominator 1.} \end{array}$$

52 miles per gallon × 8 gallons = 416 miles

The car can travel 416 miles using 8 gallons of gas.

✔ **Check Understanding** ② Find the value that completes each proportion.

a. $\dfrac{12}{4} = \dfrac{\blacksquare}{5}$ 15

b. $\dfrac{3}{9} = \dfrac{2}{\blacksquare}$ 6

Real-World 🌐 Connection

A hybrid car uses both gas and electricity for fuel. Hybrids were introduced to the U.S. in 1999.

👫 Reaching All Students

Below Level Have students make a list of ratios that are equal to $\frac{1}{2}$. Sample: $\frac{2}{4}$, $\frac{3}{6}, \frac{10}{20}$ Ask students what math symbol could be used between any two ratios on the list. =

Advanced Learners Have students solve the following proportion for the missing numbers.

$$\dfrac{1}{33} = \dfrac{24.5}{\blacksquare} = \dfrac{\blacksquare}{198}$$
808.5   6

English Learners
See note on page 279.
Inclusion
See note on page 280.

Math Background

A *proportion* is an equation stating that two ratios are equal. You can verify that two ratios form a proportion by writing each ratio in simplest form and checking that they are the same. You can complete a proportion by using unit rates to find the missing quantity.

Teaching Notes

Investigation (Optional)
Circulate and assist students by asking questions such as:
• *In Step 1, what quantity changes from glass A to B to C?* the amount of powdered mix
• *In Step 2, what quantity changes from glass A to B to C?* the amount of water
• *In Step 3, how can you compare different amounts of water and powdered mix?* find a ratio for each glass

Make sure students use the same relationship between the water and the powdered mix when they find and compare ratios.

① EXAMPLE Alternative Method

Students can write each ratio as a decimal by performing the long division and comparing quotients. This method is helpful when fractions are difficult to simplify or when they use a calculator.

English Learners
Explain that the word *proportion* in everyday use refers to a harmonious relationship of one part to another (or to the whole). In mathematics, a *proportion* refers specifically to the equality of two ratios. Students may recognize that *portion* means "amount," so that *proportion* indicates "equal amounts."

PowerPoint

🖥 Additional Examples

① Do the ratios in each pair form a proportion?
a. $\dfrac{6}{14}, \dfrac{42}{77}$ no **b.** $\dfrac{3}{13}, \dfrac{9}{39}$ yes

② Leslie biked 45 mi in 5 h. How far could she bike in 3 hours? 27 mi

279

More Than One Way

A package of 50 blank CDs is $25. However, the store ran out of 50-packs. The manager agrees to sell you packages of 12 at the same unit price. How much should a 12-pack of CDs cost?

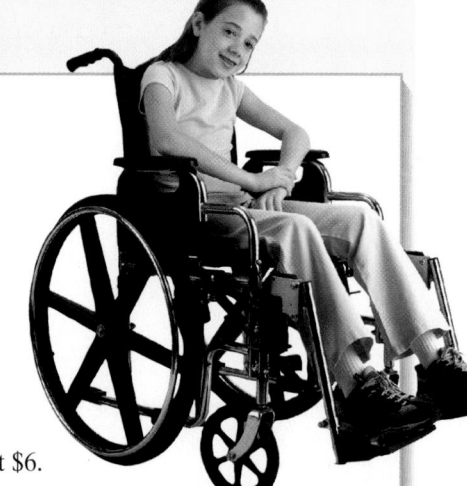

Jessica's Method

First I'll set up a proportion.

$$\frac{50 \text{ CDs}}{\$25} = \frac{12 \text{ CDs}}{\blacksquare \text{ dollars}}$$

In the first ratio, I can divide 50 by 2 to get 25. I'll do the same thing to the second ratio.

$$\div 2 \quad \frac{50}{\$25} = \frac{12}{\$6} \quad \div 2$$

A pack of 12 blank CDs should cost $6.

Michael's Method

I know that $25 is the cost of a 50-pack of blank CDs. I'll find the unit rate for the cost of one CD.

$$\$25 \div 50 = \$.50$$

Each CD costs $.50. I'll multiply to find the price of 12 CDs.

$$12 \times \$.50 = \$6$$

A pack of 12 blank CDs should cost $6.

Choose a Method

An ad says "3 videos for $18." At the same rate, how much will 5 videos cost? Describe your method, and explain why you chose it. **See margin.**

EXERCISES

? For more practice, see *Extra Practice*.

A Practice by Example

Do the ratios in each pair form a proportion?

Example 1
(page 279)

1. $\frac{1}{2}$, $\frac{50}{100}$ yes **2.** $\frac{10}{20}$, $\frac{30}{40}$ no **3.** $\frac{4}{12}$, $\frac{6}{8}$ no **4.** $\frac{42}{6}$, $\frac{504}{72}$ yes

5. $\frac{9}{11}$, $\frac{63}{77}$ yes **6.** $\frac{72}{27}$, $\frac{8}{3}$ yes **7.** $\frac{16}{27}$, $\frac{4}{9}$ no **8.** $\frac{3}{2}$, $\frac{22}{16}$ no

Example 2
(page 279)

Find the value that completes each proportion.

9. $\frac{7}{35} = \frac{21}{\blacksquare}$ 105   **10.** $\frac{12}{4} = \frac{\blacksquare}{28}$ 84   **11.** $\frac{57}{\blacksquare} = \frac{19}{38}$ 114   **12.** $\frac{2}{4} = \frac{\blacksquare}{52}$ 26

13. $\frac{\blacksquare}{20} = \frac{11}{55}$ 4   **14.** $\frac{8}{32} = \frac{\blacksquare}{40}$ 10   **15.** $\frac{\blacksquare}{190} = \frac{3}{114}$ 5   **16.** $\frac{38}{\blacksquare} = \frac{2}{6}$ 114

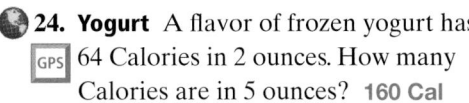 **17. Earth Science** A glacier moves about 12 inches every 36 hours. About how far does the glacier move in 90 hours? **30 in.**

B **Apply Your Skills**

Do the ratios in each pair form a proportion?

18. $\frac{93}{60}, \frac{62}{40}$ yes   **19.** $\frac{18}{9}, \frac{6}{3}$ yes   **20.** $\frac{10}{15}, \frac{3}{5}$ no   **21.** $\frac{10}{16}, \frac{5}{8}$ yes   **22.** $\frac{24}{54}, \frac{8}{18}$ yes

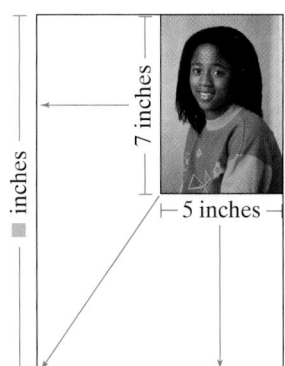

23. Photos A photo 5 inches wide and 7 inches long is enlarged. The new photo is 10 inches wide. What is the length of the enlarged photo? **14 in.**

24. Yogurt A flavor of frozen yogurt has GPS 64 Calories in 2 ounces. How many Calories are in 5 ounces? **160 Cal**

25. Gas Mileage A car can travel 54 miles on 3 gallons of gas. How far can the car travel on 8 gallons of gas? **144 mi**

26. Architecture Blueprints like the one at the left represent actual dimensions. In a blueprint, suppose 1 inch represents 3 feet. The kitchen in the blueprint is 6 inches long and 4.75 inches wide. What are the kitchen's actual dimensions? **18 ft long × 14.25 ft wide**

Real-World Connection

Careers Architects create blueprints when designing buildings or bridges.

Find the value of each variable.

27. $\frac{42}{g} = \frac{7}{10}$ 60   **28.** $\frac{25}{6} = \frac{d}{30}$ 125   **29.** $\frac{z}{12} = \frac{56}{4}$ 168   **30.** $\frac{60.5}{6} = \frac{f}{3}$ 30.25

31. Writing in Math Explain why the ratios $\frac{\$.37}{1 \text{ stamp}}$ and $\frac{\$1.85}{5 \text{ stamps}}$ form a proportion. **Answers may vary.**
Sample: The fractions are equivalent when simplified.

C **Challenge**

32. Babysitting Suppose you charge $7 to babysit for 2 hours. Last night you earned $17.50. How long did you babysit? **5 h**

33. Solve the first proportion for y. Use that value of y to solve the second proportion for x.

$$\frac{y}{15} = \frac{54}{30} \qquad \frac{y}{9} = \frac{x}{5}$$ **y = 27, x = 15**

34. Stretch Your Thinking Change two operations in the expression below to make the value of the expression equal to 27.

$$7 + 7 + 7 + 7 + 7 + 7$$

Answers may vary. Sample: 7 + 7 + 7 + 7 − 7 ÷ 7

6-3 Understanding Proportions   **281**

GPS Use the Guided Problem Solving worksheet with Exercise 24.

Assignment Guide

 **Objective 1**
   A **B** Core 1–8, 18–22, 31
   C Extension 34

 **Objective 2**
   A **B** Core 9–17, 23–30
   C Extension 32–33

Test Prep 35–38
Mixed Review 39–45

Error Prevention!

Exercises 23–26 Have students first set up their proportions using words.

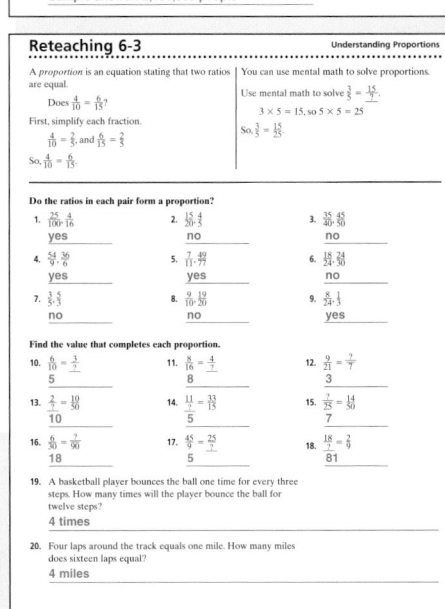

4. Assess

PowerPoint Lesson Quiz 6-3

Determine whether each pair of ratios forms a proportion.

1. $\frac{5}{35}$, $\frac{20}{140}$ yes

2. $\frac{24}{72}$, $\frac{1}{3}$ yes

Find the value that completes each proportion.

3. $\frac{6}{7} = \frac{\blacksquare}{84}$ 72

4. $\frac{26}{65} = \frac{2}{\blacksquare}$ 5

Alternative Assessment

Each student in a partner writes five pairs of ratios, similar to those in Exercises 1–8. Partners exchange papers and determine whether each pair of ratios forms a proportion. If the ratios in each pair do not, have students rewrite one ratio in each pair so that the pairs form a proportion.

Test Prep

Resources

For additional practice with a variety of test item formats:
• Test Prep, p. 315
• Test-Taking Strategies, p. 311
• Test-Taking Strategies With Transparencies

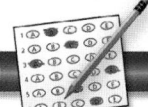

Multiple Choice

35. What value makes $\frac{\blacksquare}{12} = \frac{6}{18}$ true? B

   A. 2   B. 4   C. 5   D. 9

Take It to the NET
Online lesson quiz at **www.PHSchool.com**
Web Code: aaa-0603

36. If 2 ounces of cheese has 230 Calories, how many Calories are in 5 ounces of cheese? H

   F. 500   G. 550   H. 575   I. 615

37. Which pair of ratios do NOT form a proportion? B

   A. $\frac{4}{32}$ and $\frac{1}{8}$ B. $\frac{9}{4}$ and $\frac{3}{2}$ C. $\frac{16}{80}$ and $\frac{1}{5}$ D. $\frac{21}{42}$ and $\frac{9}{18}$

Short Response

38. Youth soccer teams in Hopkinton have 22 players and 3 coaches each. How many coaches are needed for 198 players? **(a)** Write a proportion to find the number of coaches. **(b)** Solve your proportion. See margin.

Mixed Review

Lesson 5-8   **Complete each statement.**

39. $80 \text{ oz} = \blacksquare \text{ lb}$
    5

40. $2 \text{ mi} = \blacksquare \text{ ft}$
    10,560

41. $3 \text{ pt} = \blacksquare \text{ c}$
    6

Lesson 4-5   **Find each difference.**

42. $7\frac{1}{2} - 6\frac{1}{4}$
    $1\frac{1}{4}$

43. $7\frac{2}{9} - 5\frac{1}{3}$
    $1\frac{8}{9}$

44. $4\frac{1}{4} - 1\frac{1}{2}$
    $2\frac{3}{4}$

45. $9\frac{1}{6} - 4\frac{2}{3}$
    $4\frac{1}{2}$

Math at Work

Help-Desk Technician

Do you enjoy helping your family and friends with their computer-related questions? If so, a career as a help-desk technician might be for you. Help-desk technicians provide computer support to people who have hardware and software questions. Help-desk technicians are valued by companies that make computer products because they understand customers' questions and concerns.

Help-desk technicians must be able to apply logical reasoning and problem-solving skills in order to assist their customers.

Take It to the NET
For more information about help-desk technicians, go to **www.PHSchool.com**.
Web Code: aab-2031

38. [2] a. $\frac{22}{3} = \frac{198}{x}$

    b. 27 coaches

    [1] correct proportion with incorrect answer

Enrichment 6-3
Understanding Proportions
Critical Thinking

"Why didn't Molly turn in her homework last night?"

Match each fraction or unit rate in Column I to its equivalent in Column II to find the answer.

COLUMN I	COLUMN II
1. 6 to 18	k. $\frac{41}{8}$
2. 350 ounces for $14	i. $\frac{174}{232}$
3. 32 to 20	t. $\frac{7}{16}$
4. $\frac{105}{240}$	c. 43
5. 369 to 72	o. $\frac{167}{25}$
6. 731 miles in 17 hours	g. $\frac{384}{240}$
7. $648 for 54 books	s. 12
8. $\frac{855}{125}$	p. 25

She ate too much $\underset{2}{p}\ \underset{1}{i}$ and $\underset{3}{g}\ \underset{8}{o}\ \underset{4}{t}\ \underset{7}{s}\ \underset{1}{i}\ \underset{6}{c}\ \underset{5}{k}$

"Which animal has the largest brain in proportion to its size?"

Circle the letter of the correct answer to each exercise. Then unscramble the circled letters to find the answer to the question.

9. A newborn baby's heart beats about 7 times every 3 seconds. At this rate, how many times does a baby's heart beat in 60 seconds?

   R. 21 times   S. 420 times   T. 140 times

10. Ammonia consists of a 1 : 3 ratio of nitrogen and hydrogen atoms. If a sample of ammonia contains 250 nitrogen atoms, how much hydrogen is present?

   E. 84 atoms   A. 750 atoms   O. 253 atoms

11. Four quarts of water weighs about 8 pounds. About how much does two quarts of water weigh?

   N. 4 lb   M. 16 lb   P. 32 lb

The animal with the largest brain in proportion to its size is the $\underset{}{a}\ \underset{}{n}\ \underset{}{t}$

282

6-4 Using Cross Products

What You'll Learn

 OBJECTIVE 1 To identify proportions

 OBJECTIVE 2 To solve proportions

. . . And Why

To find the cost of school supplies, as in Example 3

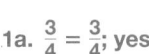 **Check Skills You'll Need**

 For help, go to Lesson 6-3.

Complete each proportion.

1. $\frac{5}{8} = \frac{\blacksquare}{16}$ 10

2. $\frac{4}{12} = \frac{2}{\blacksquare}$ 6

3. $\frac{3}{\blacksquare} = \frac{15}{35}$ 7

4. $\frac{6}{18} = \frac{4}{\blacksquare}$ 12

5. $\frac{9}{12} = \frac{\blacksquare}{144}$ 108

6. $\frac{\blacksquare}{60} = \frac{14}{15}$ 56

New Vocabulary • cross products

---

1. Plan

Lesson Preview

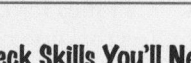 **Check Skills You'll Need**

Completing a Proportion
Lesson 6-3: Example 2. Extra Practice, p. 647.

Lesson Resources

 **Teaching Resources**
Practice, Reteaching, Enrichment

 **Reaching All Students**
Practice Workbook 6-4
Spanish Practice Workbook 6-4
Guided Problem Solving 6-4
Technology Activities II

Presentation Assistant Plus!
Transparencies
• Check Skills You'll Need 6-4
• Problem of the Day 6-4
• Additional Examples 6-4
• Student Edition Answers 6-4
• Lesson Quiz 6-4
PH Presentation Pro CD-ROM 6-4

ASSESSMENT SYSTEM

Computer Test Generator CD

 **Technology**
Resource Pro® CD-ROM
Computer Test Generator CD
PH Presentation Pro CD-ROM

 **www.PHSchool.com**
Student Site
• Teacher Web Code: aak-5500
• Algebra Readiness Puzzles 6, 57
• Self-grading Lesson Quiz

PH SuccessNet Teacher Center
• Lesson Planner
• Resources

Plus **iTEXT**

OBJECTIVE

1 Using Cross Products to Identify Proportions

iTEXT Interactive lesson includes instant self-check, tutorials, and activities.

Investigation: Identifying Proportions

1a. $\frac{3}{4} = \frac{3}{4}$; yes

b. $\frac{2}{3} \neq \frac{3}{5}$; no

c. $\frac{3}{8} = \frac{3}{8}$; yes

d. $\frac{1}{3} \neq \frac{2}{5}$; no

1. Simplify each ratio. Which pairs of ratios form proportions?

a. $\frac{15}{20} \stackrel{?}{=} \frac{12}{16}$ b. $\frac{8}{12} \stackrel{?}{=} \frac{9}{15}$ c. $\frac{6}{16} \stackrel{?}{=} \frac{9}{24}$ d. $\frac{5}{15} \stackrel{?}{=} \frac{4}{10}$

2. For each pair of ratios above, find the products of the blue numbers. Then find the products of the red numbers.
240, 240; 108, 120; 144, 144; 60, 50

3. a. What do you notice about the products for the pairs of ratios that form proportions? **They are equal.**

b. What do you notice about the products for the pairs of ratios that do not form proportions? **They are not equal.**

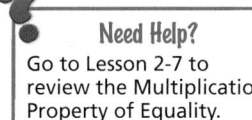 **Need Help?**
Go to Lesson 2-7 to review the Multiplication Property of Equality.

You can use the Multiplication Property of Equality to show an important property of proportions.

$$\frac{3}{4} = \frac{15}{20}$$ ← Start with a proportion.

$$\frac{3}{4} \times \frac{4}{1} \times \frac{20}{1} = \frac{15}{20} \times \frac{4}{1} \times \frac{20}{1}$$ ← Multiply each side by the values in the denominators.

$$\frac{3}{{}_1 4} \times \frac{4^1}{1} \times \frac{20}{1} = \frac{15}{{}_1 20} \times \frac{4}{1} \times \frac{20^1}{1}$$ ← Divide the common factors.

$$(3 \times 20) = (15 \times 4)$$ ← Multiply and divide by 1.

$$60 = 60$$ ← The products are equal.

The products 20×3 and 4×15 are called *cross products.*

Ongoing Assessment and Intervention

Before the Lesson	During the Lesson	After the Lesson
Diagnose prerequisite skills using:	Monitor progress using:	Assess knowledge using:
• Check Skills You'll Need	• Check Understanding • Additional Examples • Test Prep	• Lesson Quiz • Computer Test Generator CD

Math Background

In the proportion $\frac{a}{b} = \frac{c}{d}$, ad and bc are called *cross products*. If the cross products of two ratios are equal, then the ratios form a proportion. The converse of this statement is also true: If two ratios form a proportion, then their cross products are equal. This means you can use cross products to solve for the missing value in a proportion.

Teaching Notes

Investigation (Optional)
Make sure students multiply each pair of red and blue numbers accurately to obtain the correct conclusion—that the red and blue products are equal for proportions.

② EXAMPLE Visual Learners

Draw ovals around each pair of cross products in a proportion to form a large "X." Explain that this makes a multiplication symbol and suggests the name "cross products."

③ EXAMPLE Inclusion

Ask: *How many numbers do you need to solve the proportion using cross products?* **3 numbers**

PowerPoint
Additional Examples

① Does each pair of ratios form a proportion?
 a. $\frac{9}{10}, \frac{18}{30}$ **no**
 b. $\frac{9}{27}, \frac{7}{21}$ **yes**

② Solve $\frac{14}{26} = \frac{21}{n}$. **39**

③ Janet earned $31.50 for 5 hours of work. How much does she earn for 7 hours of work at the same rate of pay? **$44.10**

Closure

- *How can you use cross products to identify proportions?* **Sample: Given a pair of ratios, find the cross products; if they are equal the ratios form a proportion.**

- *How can you use cross products to solve a proportion?* **Sample: Write the cross products. Isolate the variable and simplify.**

284

You can find the **cross products** of two ratios by multiplying the denominator of each ratio by the numerator of the other ratio. The cross products of a proportion are *always* equal.

$$\frac{3}{4} = \frac{15}{20} \qquad \leftarrow \text{Start with a proportion.}$$

$$3 \times 20 = 4 \times 15 \qquad \leftarrow \begin{array}{l}\text{Multiply the numerator of each ratio by the}\\ \text{denominator of the other ratio.}\end{array}$$

$$60 = 60 \qquad \leftarrow \text{The cross products are equal.}$$

① EXAMPLE Using Cross Products

Does each pair of ratios form a proportion?

a. $\frac{3}{9}, \frac{6}{18}$ b. $\frac{10}{7}, \frac{30}{14}$

$\frac{3}{9} \overset{?}{=} \frac{6}{18}$ ← Write a possible proportion. → $\frac{10}{7} \overset{?}{=} \frac{30}{14}$

$3 \times 18 \overset{?}{=} 9 \times 6$ ← Write the cross products. → $10 \times 14 \overset{?}{=} 7 \times 30$

$54 = 54$ ← Multiply. → $140 \neq 210$

The ratios $\frac{3}{9}$ and $\frac{6}{18}$ form a proportion.

The ratios $\frac{10}{7}$ and $\frac{30}{14}$ do *not* form a proportion.

✔ **Check Understanding** ① Do the ratios $\frac{2}{4}$ and $\frac{8}{16}$ form a proportion? Explain.
Yes; the cross products are equal.

OBJECTIVE
② Solving Proportions

To solve a proportion that contains a variable, you find the value of the variable that makes the equation true.

② EXAMPLE Solving Proportions Using Cross Products

Solve $\frac{x}{9} = \frac{4}{6}$.

$$\frac{x}{9} = \frac{4}{6} \qquad \leftarrow \text{Start with the proportion.}$$

$$x \cdot 6 = 9 \cdot 4 \qquad \leftarrow \text{Write the cross products.}$$

$$6x = 36 \qquad \leftarrow \text{Multiply.}$$

$$\frac{6x}{6} = \frac{36}{6} \qquad \leftarrow \text{Divide each side by 6.}$$

$$x = 6 \qquad \leftarrow \text{Simplify.}$$

✔ **Check Understanding** ② Solve each proportion.
 a. $\frac{6}{8} = \frac{n}{20}$ **15** b. $\frac{9}{12} = \frac{3}{x}$ **4** c. $\frac{2}{8} = \frac{t}{20}$ **5**

👥 Reaching All Students

| Below Level As students write each cross product, have them say "top value times bottom value" and "bottom value times top value." Also have students use a different color to write each pair of cross products. | Advanced Learners Explain whether the following equation is a proportion. $$\frac{\$.25}{1\text{ lb cabbage}} \overset{?}{=} \frac{3\text{ lb cabbage}}{\$.75}$$ No; the units do not correspond because $\$.25 \times \$.75 \neq 3 \times 1$. | Inclusion See note on page 284. Visual Learners See note on page 284. |

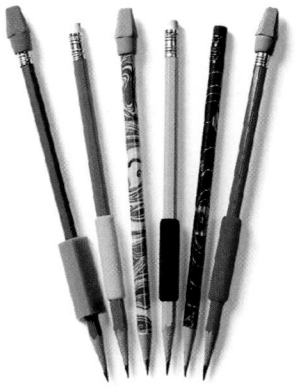

3 EXAMPLE <u>Real-World</u> <u>Problem Solving</u>

School Supplies A student buys 6 drawing pencils for $3.90. How much will the student have to pay for 10 pencils?

Write a proportion that compares that number of pencils to their cost. Let c = the cost of the pencils.

$$\text{pencils} \rightarrow \frac{6}{3.90} = \frac{10}{c} \leftarrow \text{pencils} \atop \text{cost (\$)} \rightarrow \qquad \leftarrow \text{cost (\$)} \qquad \leftarrow \textbf{Write a proportion.}$$

$$6 \cdot c = 3.90 \cdot 10 \qquad \leftarrow \textbf{Write the cross products.}$$

$$6c = 39 \qquad \leftarrow \textbf{Multiply.}$$

$$\frac{6c}{6} = \frac{39}{6} \qquad \leftarrow \textbf{Divide each side by 6.}$$

$$c = 6.5 \qquad \leftarrow \textbf{Simplify.}$$

○ The student will have to pay $6.50 for 10 drawing pencils.

✓ Check Understanding **3** **a.** If 5 notebooks cost $7.50, how much do 3 notebooks cost? **$4.50**
b. Estimation If 7 pens cost $5.53, about how much will 4 pens cost? **about $3.20**

EXERCISES

 For more practice, see *Extra Practice.*

A Practice by Example

Does each pair of ratios form a proportion? Exercise 1 has been started for you.

Example 1
(page 284)

1. $\frac{3}{18}, \frac{1}{6} \rightarrow \frac{3}{18} \overset{?}{=} \frac{1}{6} \rightarrow 3 \times 6 \overset{?}{=} \boxed{18} \times \boxed{1} \rightarrow$? **yes**

2. $\frac{4}{12}, \frac{3}{9}$ **yes** **3.** $\frac{32}{80}, \frac{4}{10}$ **yes** **4.** $\frac{5}{7}, \frac{8}{10}$ **no** **5.** $\frac{6}{2}, \frac{8}{5}$ **no**

Example 2
(page 284)

Solve each proportion.

6. $\frac{10}{3} = \frac{c}{12}$ **40** **7.** $\frac{12}{n} = \frac{4}{21}$ **63** **8.** $\frac{3}{11} = \frac{15}{a}$ **55** **9.** $\frac{16}{27} = \frac{4}{m}$ **6.75**

10. $\frac{h}{2} = \frac{3}{16}$ **0.375** **11.** $\frac{25}{4} = \frac{p}{8}$ **50** **12.** $\frac{9}{28} = \frac{18}{t}$ **56** **13.** $\frac{k}{17} = \frac{20}{68}$ **5**

Example 3
(page 285)

Write and solve a proportion for each exercise.

 14. Groceries Three quarts of milk cost $2.97. How much will 7 quarts of milk cost? **$6.93**

15. Cooking A recipe for 10 ounces of fondue requires 8 ounces of cheese. How much cheese is needed to make 36 ounces of fondue? **28.8 oz**

6-4 Using Cross Products **285**

GPS Use the Guided Problem Solving worksheet with Exercise 26.

---

3. Practice

Assignment Guide

1 Objective 1
Ⓐ Ⓑ Core 1–5, 16–18, 33–35
Ⓒ Extension 39

2 Objective 2
Ⓐ Ⓑ Core 6–15, 19–32
Ⓒ Extension 36–38

Test Prep 40–43
Mixed Review 44–48

Error Prevention!

Exercises 1–13 Some students may copy the proportions incorrectly.

Practice 6-4 Using Cross Products

Does each pair of ratios form a proportion?

1. $\frac{14}{21}, \frac{8}{12}$ yes   2. $\frac{12}{18}, \frac{16}{24}$ yes
3. $\frac{24}{25}, \frac{12}{15}$ no   4. $\frac{28}{42}, \frac{20}{30}$ yes
5. $\frac{16}{10}, \frac{19}{45}$ no   6. $\frac{50}{8}, \frac{155}{25}$ no
7. $\frac{9}{10}, \frac{40.5}{45}$ yes   8. $\frac{85}{90}, \frac{45}{50}$ no

Solve each proportion.

9. $\frac{9}{7} = \frac{27}{x}$ 10. $\frac{17}{12} = \frac{34}{y}$
  21   24
11. $\frac{6}{a} = \frac{36}{54}$ 12. $\frac{63}{21} = \frac{9}{75}$
  9   3
13. $\frac{31}{c} = \frac{93}{15}$ 14. $\frac{14}{35} = \frac{m}{5}$
  5   2
15. $\frac{12}{9} = \frac{4}{w}$ 16. $\frac{46}{y} = \frac{23}{26}$
  9   26

Write and solve a proportion for each problem.

17. It costs $15 to buy 5 packs of baseball cards. How much will it cost to buy 25 packs of baseball cards?
  $75
18. There are 35 children and 6 adults at a preschool. To keep the same child to adult ratio, how many adults are needed for 140 children?
  24 adults
19. Sam is making dinner for four people. The recipe calls for 15 ounces of steak. How much steak will he need if he makes dinner for 10 people?
  37.5 ounces
20. Brenda is selling magazines. Two subscriptions sell for $15.99. How much will 8 subscriptions cost?
  $63.96
21. A baseball player made 14 errors in 156 games this year. About how many errors would you expect the player to make in 350 games?
  about 31 errors

Reteaching 6-4 Using Cross Products

If two ratios are equal, they form a *proportion*.
$\frac{1}{5} = \frac{2}{10}$
Equal ratios have equal cross products.
$\frac{1}{5} \diagdown \frac{2}{10} \quad \begin{array}{l} 5 \times 2 = 10 \\ 1 \times 10 = 10 \end{array}$
Equal cross products also show that a proportion is true.
$\frac{1}{5} \diagdown \frac{3}{6} \quad \begin{array}{l} 6 \times 3 = 18 \\ 1 \times 18 = 18 \end{array}$
The cross products are equal, so the ratios are equal and form a proportion.

You can find the missing term in a proportion by using cross products.
Solve $\frac{4}{n} = \frac{12}{n}$.
① Write the cross products. $4 \times n = 7 \times 12$
② Simplify. $4n = 84$
③ Divide by 4. $\frac{4n}{4} = \frac{84}{4}$
④ Simplify. $n = 21$

Does each pair of ratios form a proportion?

1. $\frac{4}{7}, \frac{8}{14}$ 2. $\frac{5}{2}, \frac{10}{4}$ 3. $\frac{6}{9}, \frac{3}{5}$ 4. $\frac{15}{9}, \frac{10}{7}$
  yes   yes   no   yes
5. $\frac{15}{45}, \frac{25}{60}$ 6. $\frac{12}{16}, \frac{15}{20}$ 7. $\frac{9}{10}, \frac{19}{20}$ 8. $\frac{32}{12}, \frac{8}{3}$
  no   yes   no   yes
9. $\frac{50}{8}, \frac{1}{4}$ 10. $\frac{4}{9}, \frac{14}{21}$ 11. $\frac{40}{50}, \frac{8}{10}$ 12. $\frac{5}{15}, \frac{9}{27}$
  no   no   yes   yes

Solve each proportion.

13. $\frac{9}{8} = \frac{2}{10}$ 14. $\frac{9}{n} = \frac{27}{3}$ 15. $\frac{30}{6} = \frac{a}{9}$ 16. $\frac{42}{12} = \frac{x}{4}$
  $n = 1$ $n = 1$ $a = 45$ $x = 14$
17. $\frac{t}{24} = \frac{3}{8}$ 18. $\frac{10}{r} = \frac{15}{18}$ 19. $\frac{18}{32} = \frac{27}{m}$ 20. $\frac{48}{30} = \frac{32}{e}$
  $t = 9$ $r = 24$ $m = 48$ $e = 20$
21. $\frac{5}{6} = \frac{6}{h}$ 22. $\frac{90}{24} = \frac{16}{w}$ 23. $\frac{11}{14} = \frac{33}{y}$ 24. $\frac{90}{25} = \frac{3}{x}$
  $h = 30$ $w = 30$ $y = 42$ $x = 18$
25. $\frac{10}{9} = \frac{6}{t}$ 26. $\frac{9}{a} = \frac{3}{5}$ 27. $\frac{6}{2} = \frac{16}{b}$ 28. $\frac{12}{18} = \frac{2}{n}$
  $t = 3$ $a = 15$ $b = 8$ $n = 3$

285

Does each pair of ratios form a proportion?

16. $\frac{93}{6}, \frac{62}{4}$ yes   **17.** $\frac{25}{6}, \frac{4}{30}$ no   **18.** $\frac{7}{2}, \frac{77}{22}$ yes

Solve each proportion.

19. $\frac{b}{9} = \frac{3}{27}$ 1   **20.** $\frac{96}{144} = \frac{n}{12}$ 8   **21.** $\frac{7}{5} = \frac{63}{w}$ 45

22. $\frac{25}{6} = \frac{d}{30}$ 125   **23.** $\frac{72}{c} = \frac{8}{3}$ 27   **24.** $\frac{42}{g} = \frac{7}{10}$ 60

Real-World 🌐 Connection

The carvings of Washington, Jefferson, Roosevelt, and Lincoln are 80 times larger than life-size.

🌐 **25. Sculpture** The carvings at Mount Rushmore National Memorial in South Dakota are each 60 feet from chin to forehead.
   a. If the typical distance from a man's chin to the top of his head is 9 inches, and the typical distance between the pupils of his eyes is 2.5 inches, what is the approximate distance between the pupils in the carving of George Washington's head? **16.7 ft**
   b. Reasoning Do you need to convert feet to inches or inches to feet before you solve this proportion? Explain. **No; the ratios need only to have the same units in corresponding places in the proportion.**

🌐 **26. Printing** Your friend is having a poster printed from a photograph that is 4 inches wide by 6 inches tall. If the poster is 22 inches wide, how tall will the poster be if it is proportional to the photograph? **33 in.**

🌐 **27. Schools** There are 221 students and 13 teachers at Hampton School. To keep the same student-to-teacher ratio, how many teachers are needed for 272 students? **16 teachers**

🌐 **28. Basketball** Darrin makes 3 free throws for every 5 he attempts. If he attempts 80 free throws in a season, how many is he expected to make?
   48 free throws

Solve each proportion. Round to the nearest hundredth if necessary.

29. $\frac{5,280 \text{ feet}}{1.609 \text{ kilometers}} = \frac{f}{10 \text{ kilometers}}$ **32,815.41 ft**   **30.** $\frac{c}{100 \text{ inches}} = \frac{30.48 \text{ centimeters}}{12 \text{ inches}}$ **254 cm**

31. $\frac{168 \text{ hours}}{7 \text{ days}} = \frac{h}{365 \text{ days}}$ **8,760 h**   **32.** $\frac{907.18 \text{ kilograms}}{2.000 \text{ pounds}} = \frac{2 \text{ kilograms}}{p}$ **4.41 lb**

33. Writing in Math Explain how you can determine if the ratios $\frac{45}{50}$ and $\frac{18}{20}$ form a proportion. **Answers may vary. Sample: See if the product of 45 and 20 equals the product of 50 and 18.**

34. a. Data File, p. 267 Write the ratio of the beaver's maximum height to the moose's maximum height. Then write the ratio of the beaver's track size to the moose's track size. $3\frac{3}{5}$ ft to $10\frac{1}{5}$ ft, 7 in. to $6\frac{1}{4}$ in.
   b. Does the ratio of their maximum heights form a proportion with the ratio of their track sizes? Explain.
   No; the cross products are not equal.

🌐 **35. Crafts** In 10 hours, a weaver makes 4 baskets. In 48 hours, another weaver makes 18 baskets. Are they working at the same pace? Explain.
   No; the unit rates are different.

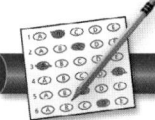

C **Challenge** **Solve each proportion.**

36. $\frac{7}{9} = \frac{3.5}{r}$ 4.5

37. $\frac{t}{15} = \frac{6.75}{2.25}$ 45

38. $\frac{2}{5} = \frac{a}{2}$ 0.8

39. Stretch Your Thinking Solve for x and y: $\frac{x}{3} = \frac{8}{12} = \frac{14}{y}$.

$x = 2, y = 21$

Test Prep

Multiple Choice

40. A basketball team's wins to losses ratio is 4 to 3. What record could the team have? **C**

   A. 12 wins and 10 losses
   B. 16 wins and 9 losses
   C. 16 wins and 12 losses
   D. 30 wins and 40 losses

41. Matt can type 216 words in 6 minutes. Lya can type 128 words in 4 minutes. Which statement is true? **F**

   F. Matt can type faster than Lya.
   G. Lya can type faster than Matt.
   H. Matt can type 88 more words than Lya during a 20-minute time period.
   I. Matt and Lya working at the same time need 10 minutes to type 344 words.

Take It to the NET
Online lesson quiz at
www.PHSchool.com
Web Code: aaa-0604

42. Which ratio forms a proportion with $\frac{16}{64}$? **A**

   A. $\frac{1}{4}$
   B. $\frac{4}{8}$
   C. $\frac{14}{48}$
   D. $\frac{64}{16}$

Extended Response

43. A cable television channel charges $21 for 6 movies. A movie store charges $22.50 for 10 DVD rentals. **a–c. See margin.**

   a. Find the unit rate for the cable offer and the DVD offer.
   b. How much do you save per movie if you choose the DVD offer?
   c. Reasoning Do the ratios of cost to number of movies form a proportion? Explain.

Mixed Review

Lesson 5-3   **Find each quotient.**

44. $4 \div \frac{4}{5}$ 5

45. $\frac{4}{5} \div 4$ $\frac{1}{5}$

46. $\frac{4}{5} \div \frac{1}{5}$ 4

47. $\frac{4}{5} \div 5$ $\frac{4}{25}$

Lesson 2-4

48. You have sweaters that are white, blue, green, and yellow. You have pants that are blue, black, and tan. How many combinations of pants and sweaters do you have? **12**

43. **[4] a.** cable: $3.50 per movie; store: $2.25 per DVD
   b. $1.25
   c. The ratios do not form a proportion because they are not equal.

   [3] appropriate methods, but with one computational error
   [2] a. and b. correct, but c. incorrect
   [1] one part correct

---

4. Assess

PowerPoint Lesson Quiz 6-4

Solve each proportion.

1. $\frac{10}{7} = \frac{a}{56}$ $a = 80$

2. $\frac{b}{3} = \frac{6}{18}$ $b = 1$

3. $\frac{15}{c} = \frac{75}{100}$ $c = 20$

4. $\frac{16}{30} = \frac{8}{d}$ $d = 15$

Alternative Assessment

Each partner writes four pairs of ratios. Partners exchange papers and use cross products to find whether each pair forms a proportion. Each partner then writes two proportions similar to those in Exercises 6–13. They exchange papers and solve each proportion.

Test Prep

Resources
For additional practice with a variety of test item formats:
• Test Prep, p. 315
• Test-Taking Strategies, p. 311
• Test-Taking Strategies With Transparencies

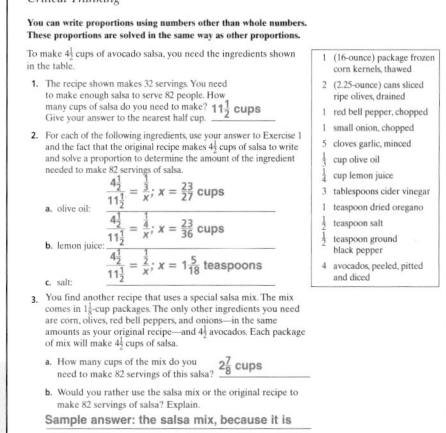

287

6-5

Lesson Preview

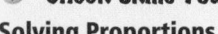 **Check Skills You'll Need**

Solving Proportions
Lesson 6-4: Example 2. Extra Practice, p. 647.

Lesson Resources

Optional Materials
• metric rulers

 **Teaching Resources**
Practice, Reteaching, Enrichment Checkpoint Quiz 1

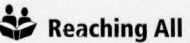 **Reaching All Students**
Practice Workbook 6-5
Spanish Practice Workbook 6-5
Reading and Math Literacy 6B
Spanish Reading and Math
  Literacy 6B
Spanish Checkpoint Quiz 1
Guided Problem Solving 6-5
Technology Activities 12
Hands-On Activities 22

Presentation Assistant Plus!
Transparencies
• Check Skills You'll Need 6-5
• Problem of the Day 6-5
• Additional Examples 6-5
• Student Edition Answers 6-5
• Lesson Quiz 6-5
• Classroom Aid 9
PH Presentation Pro CD-ROM 6-5

 **ASSESSMENT SYSTEM**

Checkpoint Quiz 1
Computer Test Generator CD

 Technology
Resource Pro® CD-ROM
Computer Test Generator CD
PH Presentation Pro CD-ROM

 **www.PHSchool.com**
Student Site
• Teacher Web Code: aak-5500
• Self-grading Lesson Quiz

PH SuccessNet Teacher Center
• Lesson Planner
• Resources

Plus **iTEXT**

288

6-5 Scale Drawings

What You'll Learn

OBJECTIVE 1 To find the scale of a drawing

OBJECTIVE 2 To find actual dimensions

...And Why

To find map distances, as in Example 2

Check Skills You'll Need

? For help, go to Lesson 6-4.

Solve each proportion.

1. $\dfrac{6}{30} = \dfrac{4}{x}$ **20**

2. $\dfrac{15}{21} = \dfrac{y}{35}$ **25**

3. $\dfrac{5}{z} = \dfrac{145}{174}$ **6**

4. $\dfrac{5}{m} = \dfrac{12.5}{5}$ **2**

5. $\dfrac{n}{16} = \dfrac{4.5}{72}$ **1**

6. $\dfrac{49}{t} = \dfrac{4.2}{9}$ **105**

New Vocabulary • scale

 Interactive lesson includes instant self-check, tutorials, and activities.

OBJECTIVE 1 **Finding the Scale of a Drawing**

Investigation: Enlarging a Design

1. Use a metric ruler to find the length of the sides of a green and gold square in each design. **0.8 cm, 1.6 cm**

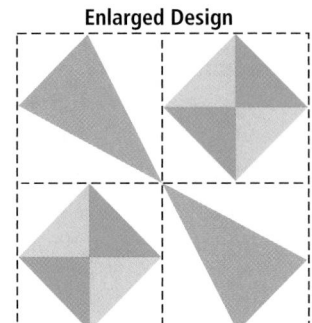

Original Design   Enlarged Design

2. Find the ratio of the length of a side in the enlarged design to the length in the original design. **2 to 1**

3. Enlarge the original design using a ratio of 3 centimeters (new design) to 1 centimeter (original design). **Check students' work.**

A **scale** is the ratio that compares a length in a drawing or model to the length in the original object. You write a scale in simplest form.

The scale of the original design to the enlarged design above is 1 to 2 or $\frac{1}{2}$.

288 **Chapter 6** Ratios, Proportions, and Percents

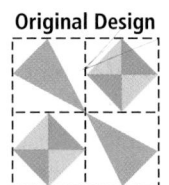 **Ongoing Assessment and Intervention**

Before the Lesson	During the Lesson	After the Lesson
Diagnose prerequisite skills using: • Check Skills You'll Need	Monitor progress using: • Check Understanding • Additional Examples • Test Prep	Assess knowledge using: • Lesson Quiz • Computer Test Generator CD • Chapter Checkpoint 1 (p. 292)

3 cm

① EXAMPLE Finding the Scale of a Drawing

In the drawing, the height of the goat is 3 centimeters. The actual height of the goat is 90 centimeters. What is the scale of the drawing?

drawing height → $\dfrac{3 \text{ centimeters}}{90 \text{ centimeters}} = \dfrac{1}{30}$ ← **Divide each measure by the GCF, 3.**
actual height →

● The scale is 1 centimeter to 30 centimeters, or 1 : 30.

✓ **Check Understanding** ① The length of a drawing of an object is 6 inches. The length of the actual object is 84 inches. What is the scale of the drawing? **1 in. : 14 in.**

OBJECTIVE

2 **Finding Actual Dimensions**

Mapmakers and architects make scale drawings. They apply the same scale ratio to each length in an object to create a drawing that is smaller than actual size. You can use the scale to calculate actual distances.

② EXAMPLE Finding Distances on a Map 🌎 Real World

Maps Use the map and scale above to find the actual distance from Winfield to Auburn.

Step 1 Use a metric ruler to measure the distance from Winfield to Auburn on the map. The distance is 6 centimeters.

Step 2 Write the scale as a ratio: $\dfrac{1 \text{ centimeter}}{20 \text{ miles}}$.

Step 3 Find the number of miles represented by 6 centimeters.

Let $y =$ the actual distance from Winfield to Auburn.

$\dfrac{1 \text{ cm}}{20 \text{ mi}} = \dfrac{6 \text{ cm}}{y \text{ mi}}$ ← map distances
                    ← actual distances

$1y = 20 \cdot 6$ ← **Write the cross products.**

$y = 120$ ← **Multiply.**

● The actual distance from Winfield to Auburn is about 120 miles.

✓ **Check Understanding** ② Find the actual distance from Winfield to Montgomery. **about 100 mi**

📖 **Reading Math**

The scale on a map sometimes uses "=" to indicate the ratio:
1 cm = 20 mi.

👥 **Reaching All Students**

Below Level Review the GCF (greatest common factor) and simplifying fractions by using the factors of the numerator and denominator. $\dfrac{10}{25} = \dfrac{2 \cdot 5}{5 \cdot 5} = \dfrac{2}{5}$	**Advanced Learners** What happens to the volume of a scale model when you double each of its three-dimensions? **The volume (and corresponding weight) is** $2 \cdot 2 \cdot 2$, **or 8 times larger.**	**English Learners** See notes on pages 289 and 291. **Alternative Method** See note on page 290.

---

2. Teach

 Professional Development

Math Background

A *scale drawing* is an enlarged or reduced drawing of an object. The *scale* in a map or drawing is the ratio that compares a length of the drawing to the length in the original object. Scales are given in simplest form and include the corresponding units, such as 1 inch : 5 miles.

Teaching Notes

Investigation (Optional)
Show examples of an image enlarged by a photocopier. Ask students how they would describe the change. **Every dimension in the original has been increased proportionally.**

English Learners
The word *scale* may confuse students who think of musical scales or weighing scales. A map or model scale is a ratio that compares two numbers, a length on the model to the corresponding length on the original object.

① EXAMPLE Error Prevention

Point out that both units in the scale are in centimeters. Clarify that a scale must include units, but the units can be the same. Also point out that the length of the drawing comes first in the scale ratio.

② EXAMPLE Visual Learners

Ask: *Why is it likely that the distance you drive on a road is longer than the distance calculated from the map?* **Sample: The distance calculated from the map is for a straight line. Roads are seldom perfectly straight.**

📽 PowerPoint
Additional Examples

① The length of a drawing of a kitten is 3 cm. The actual length of the kitten is 27 cm. What is the scale of the drawing? **1 cm : 9 cm**

② Use a map scale of 1 in. : 20 mi to find the actual distance of 3.4 in. **68 mi**

289

③ EXAMPLE  Real-World 🌐 Problem Solving

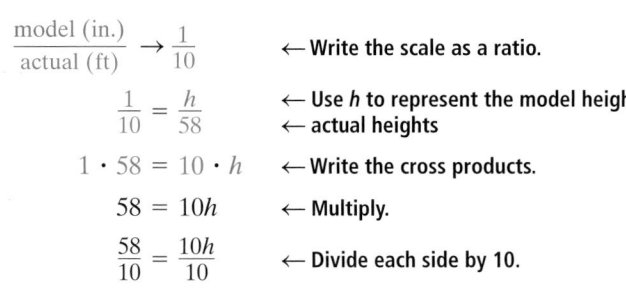

Real-World 🌐 Connection
The White House contains 132 rooms on 6 floors.

Architecture Gwen uses a scale of 1 inch : 10 feet to build a model of the White House. The White House is 58 feet tall. How tall will her model be?

$$\frac{\text{model (in.)}}{\text{actual (ft)}} \rightarrow \frac{1}{10} \qquad \leftarrow \text{Write the scale as a ratio.}$$

$$\frac{1}{10} = \frac{h}{58} \qquad \begin{array}{l}\leftarrow \text{Use } h \text{ to represent the model height.} \\ \leftarrow \text{actual heights}\end{array}$$

$$1 \cdot 58 = 10 \cdot h \qquad \leftarrow \text{Write the cross products.}$$

$$58 = 10h \qquad \leftarrow \text{Multiply.}$$

$$\frac{58}{10} = \frac{10h}{10} \qquad \leftarrow \text{Divide each side by 10.}$$

$$5.8 = h \qquad \leftarrow\text{Simplify.}$$

Gwen's model will be 5.8 inches tall.

✔ Check Understanding ③ The White House is 170 feet long. How long will Gwen's model be? **17 in.**

EXERCISES

? For more practice, see *Extra Practice.*

Ⓐ Practice by Example

Write each scale as a ratio. Exercise 1 has been started for you.

Example 1
(page 289)

1. a 4-foot-tall model of a 100-foot-tall building $\rightarrow \dfrac{4 \text{ feet}}{100 \text{ feet}} = \dfrac{1}{\blacksquare\,25}$ **1 : 25**

2. a 10-inch-long drawing of a 40-inch-long table
1 : 4

3. a 15-foot-long model of a 300-foot-long fence
1 : 20

🌐 **4. Architecture** The height of a wall in a blueprint is 3 inches. The actual wall is 96 inches high. Find the scale of the blueprint. **1 : 32**

Example 2
(page 289)

🌐 **Geography Find the actual distance between each pair of cities. Use a metric ruler to measure. Round to the nearest mile.**

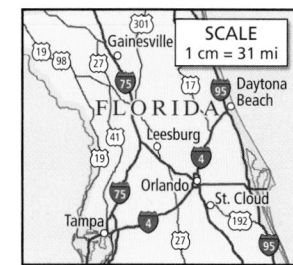

5–8. Answers may vary. Samples are given:

5. Gainesville to Leesburg **47 mi**

6. Gainesville to Orlando **71 mi**

7. Tampa to Daytona Beach **87 mi**

8. St. Cloud to Daytona Beach **47 mi**

Example 3
(page 290)

Suppose you are making a model of each item. Use a scale of 1 inch : 9 inches to find the length or height of your model.

9. A chair is 36 inches tall. *4 in.*

10. A whale is 468 inches long. *52 in.*

11. A lizard is 12 inches long. *1⅓ in.*

12. A stop sign is 117 inches tall. *13 in.*

B **Apply Your Skills**   🌐 **Map Scales** **Use a map scale of 1 centimeter : 100 kilometers. How many centimeters on the map represent each actual distance?**

13. 125 kilometers *1.25 cm*

14. 80 kilometers *0.8 cm*

15. 4,000 kilometers *40 cm*

16. 170 kilometers *1.7 cm*

17. 800 kilometers *8 cm*

18. 2,500 kilometers *25 cm*

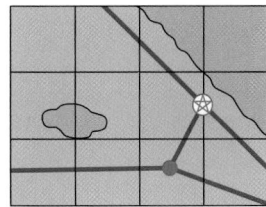

🌐 19. **a.** **Maps** Suppose you redraw the map at the left using a scale of 0.5 centimeter : 1 centimeter. Does your drawing enlarge or reduce the size of the map? Explain how you know.

b. Redraw the map using the scale of 0.5 centimeter : 1 centimeter. *a–b. See margin.*

20. **Data File, p. 267** The drawing of each track in the table has been scaled to fit the table.

a. Write the scale of a Norway rat's track. *½ in. : ⅝ in., or 4 in. : 5 in.*

b. Draw a full-size moose track. *Check students' work.*

🌐 21. **Toy Design** From head to tail, the length of a *Tyrannosaurus rex* was about 40 feet. You want to design a toy of this dinosaur with a scale of 1 inch : 8 feet. How long is your toy? *5 in.*

22. Approximate; most maps give distance from town line to town line and miles are rounded to the nearest whole number.

22. **Writing in Math** When you find actual distances on a map, would you expect to get exact or approximate answers? Explain. *See left.*

C **Challenge**   🌐 **Model Cars** **The table below shows toy car measurements and actual car measurements. Copy and complete the table. Use the ratio** $\frac{\text{length of toy car}}{\text{length of real car}}$.

Part	Toy Size	Actual Size	
Car	3 in.	120 in.	
23. Door handle	■	5 in.	0.125 in.
24. Headlight	■	8 in.	0.2 in.
25. Front bumper	0.18 ft	■	7.2 ft
26. Rear window	■	4.5 ft	1.35 in.

27. Answers may vary.
Sample: 001
             333
             777
           + 000
           ⎯⎯⎯⎯⎯
           1,111

27. **Stretch Your Thinking** In the problem at the right, replace five of the digits with zeros so that the sum is 1,111. *See left.*

```
    111
    333
    777
  + 999
  ⎯⎯⎯⎯
  1,111
```

19a. **Reduce; the map is 4 cm wide and 3 cm high. For each centimeter on the map, I would draw 0.5 centimeter on my drawing. My drawing would measure 2 cm wide and 1.5 cm high.**

b.

GPS Use the Guided Problem Solving worksheet with Exercise 19a.

3. Practice

Assignment Guide

1 **Objective 1**
  Ⓐ Ⓑ Core 1–4, 20
  Ⓒ Extension 27

2 **Objective 2**
  Ⓐ Ⓑ Core 5–19, 21–22
  Ⓒ Extension 23–26

Test Prep 28–30
Mixed Review 31–38

English Learners
Exercise 19 Make sure students understand the terms *enlarge* and *reduce*.

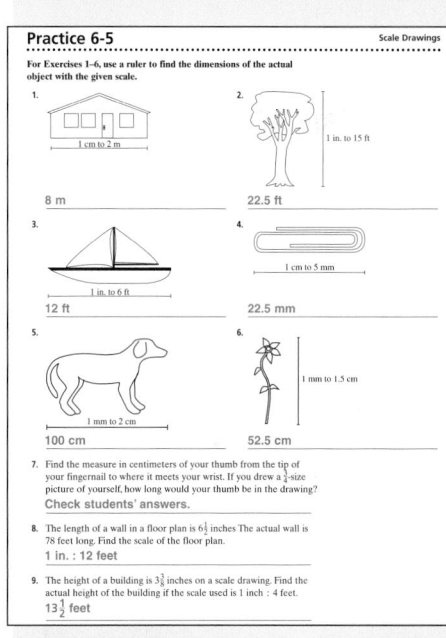

Practice 6-5 — Scale Drawings

For Exercises 1–6, use a ruler to find the dimensions of the actual object with the given scale.

7. Find the measure in centimeters of your thumb from the tip of your fingernail to where it meets your wrist. If you drew a ¼-size picture of yourself, how long would your thumb be in the drawing? **Check students' answers.**

8. The length of a wall in a floor plan is 6½ inches The actual wall is 78 feet long. Find the scale of the floor plan. **1 in. : 12 feet**

9. The height of a building is 3⅜ inches on a scale drawing. Find the actual height of the building if the scale used is 1 inch : 4 feet. **13½ feet**

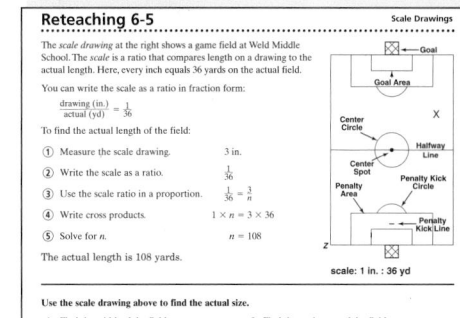

Reteaching 6-5 — Scale Drawings

Lesson Quiz 6-5

Use a scale of 1 cm : 50 km to find each actual distance.

1. 4.2 cm   **2.** 0.8 cm
   210 km   40 km

3. Use a scale of 1 in. = 8 ft to find the model length of a 14 ft automobile. **1.75 in.**

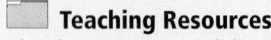
Chapter Checkpoint

To check understanding of Lessons 6-1 to 6-5:

Checkpoint Quiz 1 (p. 292)

Teaching Resources
Checkpoint Quiz 1 (also in Prentice Hall Assessment System)

Reaching All Students
Reading and Math Literacy 6B

Spanish versions available

Test Prep

Resources
For additional practice with a variety of test item formats:
• Test Prep, p. 315
• Test-Taking Strategies, p. 311
• Test-Taking Strategies With Transparencies

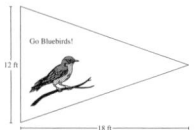

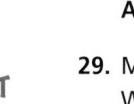
Test Prep

Multiple Choice

28. A scale model of an airplane is 7.5 inches long. The scale used to make the model is 1 inch : 5 feet. How long is the original airplane? **D**
   A. 1.5 inches   **B.** 5 feet   **C.** 37.5 inches   **D.** 37.5 feet

Take It to the NET
Online lesson quiz at
www.PHSchool.com
Web Code: aaa-0605

29. Measure the boat. The scale is 1 cm : 3 m. What is a reasonable length for the actual boat?
   F. 2.5 centimeters   **G.** 7.5 centimeters
   H. 2.5 meters   **I.** 7.5 meters

Short Response

30. Aaron is building a model train set. The rails of his model's track are 1.5 inches apart. The actual train's rails are 57 inches apart. The actual locomotive is 76 feet long. How long should Aaron's locomotive be? Write and solve a proportion to find the model's length. **See margin.**

Mixed Review

Lesson 5-4   **Estimate each quotient.**

31. $10 \div 4\frac{3}{4}$ **2**   **32.** $7\frac{3}{4} \div 2\frac{1}{8}$ **4**   **33.** $13\frac{1}{2} \div 6\frac{6}{7}$ **2**   **34.** $99\frac{4}{5} \div 19\frac{5}{8}$ **5**

Lesson 5-1   **Find each product.**

35. $\frac{5}{16}$ of 32 **10**   **36.** $\frac{3}{4} \times 10$ **$7\frac{1}{2}$**   **37.** $\frac{9}{10} \cdot 55$ **$49\frac{1}{2}$**   **38.** $\frac{4}{5}$ of 100 **80**

Checkpoint Quiz 1   **Lessons 6-1 through 6-5**

TEXT Instant self-check quiz online and on CD-ROM

1. Write 18:40 in two other ways. **18 to 40, $\frac{18}{40}$**

2. A cereal box is \$.19 per ounce. How much does a 15-ounce box cost? **\$2.85**

3. Two movie tickets cost \$7. What is the cost of five tickets? **\$17.50**

Do the ratios in each pair form a proportion?

4. $\frac{6}{45}, \frac{2}{18}$ **no**   **5.** $\frac{4}{7}, \frac{30}{42}$ **no**   **6.** $\frac{8}{12}, \frac{30}{45}$ **yes**

Solve each proportion.

7. $\frac{21}{36} = \frac{7}{n}$ **12**   **8.** $\frac{54}{c} = \frac{9}{13}$ **78**   **9.** $\frac{x}{18} = \frac{\$6.30}{7}$ **\$16.20**

10. A beverage cup is 6 inches tall. The beverage cup on a restaurant billboard is 18 feet tall. Write the scale as a ratio in simplest form. **3 ft : 1 in.**

Alternative Assessment

Provide pairs of students with a meter stick and graph paper. Partners work together to make a scale drawing of the dimensions of the classroom, putting in doors and windows as necessary. Remind them to choose an appropriate scale. Have pairs share their scale drawings with the class.

30. [2] $\frac{1.5 \text{ in.}}{57 \text{ in.}} = \frac{x}{76 \text{ ft}}$
   $1.5 \times 76 = 57x$
   $114 = 57x$
   $2 = x$
   2 ft

[1] correct answer with no work shown or one minor computational error

 **Investigation**

Modeling Percents

For Use With Lesson 6-6

In Lesson 6-6, you will learn about *percents*, which are ratios that compare numbers to 100. You can model percents with 10-by-10 grids because each grid has 100 squares. The portion of the grid that represents the percent is shaded. You can use the symbol % to write percents.

EXAMPLE Using a Percent Model

What percent of the grid is shaded?

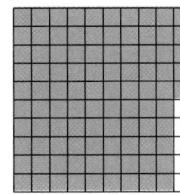

amount shaded → $\frac{95 \text{ squares}}{100 \text{ squares}}$ ← Use a fraction to represent the shaded portion of the grid.
the whole →

$\frac{95}{100} = 95\%$ ← Write the numerator of the fraction followed by %.

95% of the grid is shaded.

EXERCISES

What percent of each grid is shaded?

1.
41%
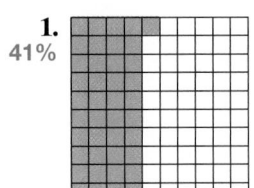

2.
32%
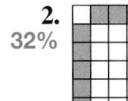

3.
52%
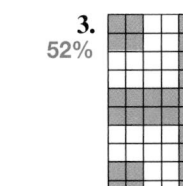

4. a. What percent of the grid at the right is shaded? **18%**
  b. What percent of the grid at the right is *not* shaded?
  c. **Writing in Math** Explain how you found your **82%** answer to part (b). **Subtract 18% from 100%.**

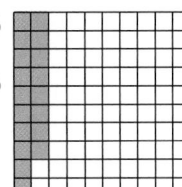

Use a 10-by-10 square grid to model each percent.

5–8. See margin.

5. 5%   **6.** 100%   **7.** 75%   **8.** 37%

Investigation Modeling Percents **293**

5.

6.
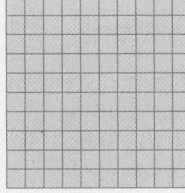

7.
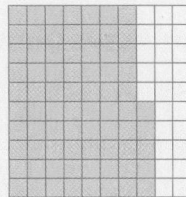

8.
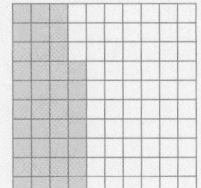

293

Investigation

Modeling Percents

This investigation explores percents that are presented in Lesson 6-6. Like fractions, percents can be modeled as parts of a whole using a 10-by-10 grid model.

Optional Materials

• graph paper
• Classroom Aid 2, 10

Teaching Notes

Begin by asking students to define *percent*. **a ratio that compares a number to 100** Then have a volunteer read aloud the opening paragraph as the other students read it to themselves. Before working the Example, ask: *How many small squares are in the square grid model?* **100**

Inclusion

Some students may assume the percent relates the number of shaded squares to the number of unshaded squares. Help them see the comparison is with the total number of squares, which is 100.

Error Prevention!

Exercises 1–3 Watch for students who incorrectly write their answers as decimals, either with or without the percent symbol, %.

Exercise 4 Elicit the fact that students can subtract the percent of shaded from 100% to obtain the percent not shaded.

Exercises 5–8 Elicit the fact that there are many possible models for each given percent. Have students work in small groups to draw the models. You might want to provide copies of blank grids for each student to use. Group members should check each other's models.

Lesson Preview

 Check Skills You'll Need

Writing Fractions in Simplest Form
Lesson 3-4: Example 2. Extra Practice, p. 644.

Lesson Resources

 Teaching Resources
Practice, Reteaching, Enrichment

 Reaching All Students
Practice Workbook 6-6
Spanish Practice Workbook 6-6
Guided Problem Solving 6-6
Hands-On Activities 20

 Presentation Assistant Plus!
Transparencies
• Check Skills You'll Need 6-6
• Problem of the Day 6-6
• Additional Examples 6-6
• Student Edition Answers 6-6
• Lesson Quiz 6-6
• Classroom Aid 2, 10, 11
PH Presentation Pro CD-ROM 6-6

 **ASSESSMENT SYSTEM**

Computer Test Generator CD

 Technology
Resource Pro® CD-ROM
Computer Test Generator CD
PH Presentation Pro CD-ROM

 www.PHSchool.com
Student Site
• Teacher Web Code: aak-5500
• Algebra Readiness Puzzle 58
• Self-grading Lesson Quiz

PH SuccessNet Teacher Center
• Lesson Planner
• Resources

 *Plus* **iTEXT**

6-6 Percents, Fractions, and Decimals

What You'll Learn

 OBJECTIVE 1 To write percents as decimals and fractions

 OBJECTIVE 2 To write decimals and fractions as percents

. . . And Why

To describe survey data with percents, as in Example 5

 Check Skills You'll Need

Write each fraction in simplest form.

1. $\frac{48}{200}$ $\frac{6}{25}$ 2. $\frac{50}{125}$ $\frac{2}{5}$

3. $\frac{39}{52}$ $\frac{3}{4}$ 4. $\frac{28}{84}$ $\frac{1}{3}$

5. What fraction is modeled at the right? Write the fraction with a denominator of 100. $\frac{79}{100}$

? For help, go to Lesson 3-4.

New Vocabulary   • percent

 OBJECTIVE 1

Writing Percents as Decimals and Fractions

iTEXT Interactive lesson includes instant self-check, tutorials, and activities.

 Reading Math
Read 49% as "49 percent."

A **percent** is a ratio that compares a number to 100. The symbol for percent is %. If 49 out of 100 students are girls, you can say that 49% of the students are girls. You can write any percent as a decimal.

---

1 EXAMPLE Writing Percents as Decimals

Write each percent as a decimal.

a. 36%   **b.** 5%

$36\% = \frac{36}{100}$ ← Write each percent as a fraction with a → $5\% = \frac{5}{100}$
denominator of 100.

$= 0.36$ ← Divide. → $= 0.05$

✓ **Check Understanding 1** Write each percent as a decimal.
a. 18% **0.18**   **b.** 2% **0.02**   **c.** 25% **0.25**

When writing percents as fractions, write the fractions in simplest form.

---

2 EXAMPLE Writing Percents as Fractions

Write 36% as a fraction in simplest form.

$36\% = \frac{36}{100}$ ← Write the percent as a fraction with a denominator of 100.

$= \frac{9}{25}$ ← Write the fraction in simplest form.

---

294   **Chapter 6**   Ratios, Proportions, and Percents

Ongoing Assessment and Intervention

Before the Lesson	During the Lesson	After the Lesson
Diagnose prerequisite skills using:	Monitor progress using:	Assess knowledge using:
• Check Skills You'll Need	• Check Understanding	• Lesson Quiz
	• Additional Examples	• Computer Test Generator CD
	• Test Prep	

✓ **Check Understanding** (2) Write each percent as a fraction in simplest form.

  a. 4% $\frac{1}{25}$ **b.** 55% $\frac{11}{20}$ **c.** 75% $\frac{3}{4}$

  d. Mental Math Write 20% as a fraction in simplest form. $\frac{1}{5}$

OBJECTIVE

2 **Writing Decimals and Fractions as Percents**

To write a percent as a decimal, as in Example 1, you divide by 100. To write a decimal as a percent, you multiply by 100. Remember that multiplying by 100 is the same as moving the decimal point two places to the right.

(3) EXAMPLE **Writing Decimals as Percents**

Write each decimal as a percent.

  a. 0.43   0.43 $\longrightarrow$ 43%   ← Move each decimal point two
  b. 0.07   0.07 $\longrightarrow$ 7%   places to the right.

✓ **Check Understanding** (3) Write each decimal as a percent.

  a. 0.52 52%   **b.** 0.05 5%   **c.** 0.5 50%

  d. Reasoning Explain how you could write 72% as a decimal by moving a decimal point. **Move the decimal point two places to the left.**

When the denominator of a fraction is a factor of 100, you can use equal ratios to convert the fraction to a percent.

Real-World Connection

Careers Primary care physicians see the same patients on a regular basis.

(4) EXAMPLE **Writing Fractions as Percents**   **Real World**

Doctors According to a news article, 6 of every 25 doctors in the United States are women. As a fraction, *6 of every 25* is written $\frac{6}{25}$. Write $\frac{6}{25}$ as a percent.

$$\frac{6}{25} \overset{\times 4}{\underset{\times 4}{=}} \frac{24}{100}$$ ← Find the fraction with denominator 100 that is equal to $\frac{6}{25}$.

$$\frac{24}{100} = 24\%$$ ← Write using a percent symbol.

Twenty-four percent of the doctors in the United States are women.

✓ **Check Understanding** (4) **a.** The same article also stated that 1 of every 20 neurosurgeons in the United States is a woman. Write the fraction $\frac{1}{20}$ as a percent. **5%**

  b. Number Sense List all possible denominators that are factors of 100. **1, 2, 4, 5, 10, 20, 25, 50, 100**

👥 **Reaching All Students**

Below Level Make sure students understand that $x\%$ is $\frac{x}{100}$. Ask: *Why can you write 36% as $\frac{36}{100}$?* Sample: Percent is a comparison to 100, so 36% is 36 to 100, or $\frac{36}{100}$.	**Advanced Learners** What percent is 50% of 60% of a number? **30%** If you increase the original price of an item by 25%, by what percent do you need to reduce the new price to obtain the original price? **20%**	**Inclusion** See note on page 295. **Diversity** See note on page 296.

---

2. Teach

Math Background

A *percent* is a ratio that compares a number to 100. Percents, fractions, and decimals can all represent parts of a whole. You can convert between percents, fractions, and decimals by using the definition of percent as $\frac{part}{whole} = \frac{percent}{100}$.

To write a percent as a fraction, write it with a denominator of 100 and simplify. For example, 5% = $\frac{5}{100}$, or $\frac{1}{20}$. To write a percent as a decimal, write it as a fraction and then divide. So 5% = $\frac{5}{100}$ = 0.05.

To write a decimal as a percent, move the decimal point two places to the right and write the percent sign. For example, 0.33 becomes 33%. To convert a fraction to a percent, divide the numerator by the denominator and convert the resulting decimal to a percent.

Teaching Notes

(3) EXAMPLE Teaching Tip

Explain that when the decimal point moves two places to the right it is the same as multiplying by 100. When the percent sign is inserted, it is the same as dividing by 100. Multiplying by 100 and then dividing by 100 does not change the value.

(4) EXAMPLE Inclusion

Have students list the factors of 100. **1, 2, 4, 5, 10, 20, 25, 50, 100**

PowerPoint

 **Additional Examples**

(1) Write each percent as a decimal.

  a. 87% **0.87**

  b. 9% **0.09**

(2) Write 4% as a fraction in simplest form. $\frac{1}{25}$

(3) Write each decimal as a percent.

  a. 0.16 **16%**

  b. 0.03 **3%**

(4) Write $\frac{7}{20}$ as a percent. **35%**

295

Diversity

Ask a volunteer to explain what a survey is and why they are conducted.

⑤ EXAMPLE Teaching Tip

Ask: *When is it preferable to use a calculator to convert a fraction to a percent?* Sample: when the denominator of the fraction is not a factor of 100

Error Prevention!

Watch for students who incorrectly move the decimal point to the left instead of to the right when they convert decimals to percents.

Tactile Learners

Have students create posters of common percents and their fraction and decimal equivalents, as shown in Lesson 6-7 on page 300. Refer to the posters, as appropriate, to demonstrate how memorizing these facts can be helpful.

PowerPoint
Additional Examples

⑤ Write each fraction as a percent. Round to the nearest whole percent.

a. $\frac{8}{11}$ 73%

b. $\frac{2}{9}$ 22%

Closure

• *How do you write a percent as a fraction?* Sample: Write the percent with a denominator of 100 and simplify.
• *How do you write a decimal as a percent?* Sample: Move the decimal point two places to the right and add the percent sign.
• *How do you write a fraction as a percent?* Sample: Write the fraction with a denominator of 100 and rewrite the fraction $\frac{x}{100}$ as $x\%$. If the denominator of the fraction is not a factor of 100, divide the numerator by the denominator to obtain a decimal and convert it to a percent.

Sometimes the denominator of a fraction is not a factor of 100. In this case, convert the fraction to a decimal. Then write the decimal as a percent.

⑤ EXAMPLE Percents with Repeating Decimals  Real World

Surveys The makers of Grin toothpaste took the survey shown at the right. What percent of the 75 people surveyed say they prefer Grin toothpaste over Brand X?

What Brand of Toothpaste Do You Prefer?	
Grin	40
Brand X	30
No preference	5

Out of 75 people surveyed, 40 prefer Grin.

$\frac{40}{75}$ ← Write a fraction to represent 40 of 75.

40 ÷ 75 = 0.533333333 ← Use a calculator.

0.533333333 ← Move the decimal point two places to the right.

≈ 53.$\overline{3}$% ← Write as a percent.

About 53% of the people surveyed prefer Grin toothpaste.

✓ **Check Understanding** ⑤ Refer to the survey above. What percent of the people surveyed say they have no preference? about 7%

EXERCISES

For more practice, see *Extra Practice*.

A Practice by Example

Write each percent as a decimal.

Example 1
(page 294)

1. 15% 0.15 **2.** 22% 0.22 **3.** 82% 0.82 **4.** 63% 0.63 **5.** 10% 0.1

6. 40% 0.4 **7.** 3% 0.03 **8.** 7% 0.07 **9.** 12% 0.12 **10.** 100% 1

Write each percent as a fraction in simplest form.

Example 2
(page 294)

11. 70% $\frac{7}{10}$ **12.** 88% $\frac{22}{25}$ **13.** 5% $\frac{1}{20}$ **14.** 33% $\frac{33}{100}$ **15.** 14% $\frac{7}{50}$

16. 15% $\frac{3}{20}$ **17.** 75% $\frac{3}{4}$ **18.** 18% $\frac{9}{50}$ **19.** 2% $\frac{1}{50}$ **20.** 42% $\frac{21}{50}$

Examples 3, 4
(page 295)

Write each decimal or fraction as a percent.

21. 0.17 17% **22.** 0.08 8% **23.** 0.98 98% **24.** 0.22 22% **25.** 0.44 44%

26. $\frac{19}{20}$ 95% **27.** $\frac{27}{50}$ 54% **28.** $\frac{1}{4}$ 25% **29.** $\frac{19}{25}$ 76% **30.** $\frac{7}{25}$ 28%

🌐 **31. School Play** Three of every five students who tried out for the school play made the cast list. Write the fraction $\frac{3}{5}$ as a percent. 60%

Example 5
(page 296)

Write each fraction as a percent. Round to the nearest whole percent.

32. $\frac{1}{6}$
about 17%

33. $\frac{4}{15}$
about 27%

34. $\frac{7}{9}$
about 78%

35. $\frac{15}{24}$
about 63%

36. $\frac{14}{45}$
about 31%

37. Quality Control A shipment of 30 radios is packed incorrectly. Two of the radios arrive damaged. What percent is damaged? about 7%

3. Practice

Assignment Guide

1 Objective 1
Ⓐ Ⓑ Core 1–20, 44, 57
Ⓒ Extension 62

2 Objective 2
Ⓐ Ⓑ Core 21–43, 45–56, 58
Ⓒ Extension 59–61

Test Prep 63–66
Mixed Review 67–72

Ⓑ Apply Your Skills

Copy and complete the table below. Write each fraction in simplest form.

	38.	**39.**	**40.**	**41.**	**42.**	**43.**
Fraction	$\frac{11}{50}$	$\frac{39}{50}$	$\frac{22}{25}$	▦ $\frac{9}{20}$	▦ $\frac{21}{50}$	$\frac{4}{5}$
Decimal	▦0.22	0.78	▦0.88	0.45	▦0.42	▦ 0.8
Percent	22%	▦78%	▦88%	▦45%	42%	▦80%

44. Biology Ninety-nine percent of all kinds of plants and animals that have ever lived are now extinct. Write ninety-nine percent as a fraction and as a decimal. $\frac{99}{100}$, 0.99

45. Geography About $\frac{7}{10}$ of Earth's surface is covered by water. Write $\frac{7}{10}$ as a decimal and as a percent. 0.7, 70%

Write each decimal or fraction as a percent. Round to the nearest percent if necessary.

about 38%   about 83%   about 36%   about 57%

46. $\frac{3}{8}$ **47.** $\frac{5}{6}$ **48.** $\frac{4}{11}$ **49.** $\frac{9}{20}$ 45%   **50.** $\frac{17}{30}$

51. $0.\overline{5}$ **52.** $0.\overline{3}$ **53.** $0.\overline{45}$ **54.** $0.\overline{60}$ **55.** 0.7
about 56%   about 33%   about 45%   about 61%   70%

Real-World Connection

The paradise parrot once lived in Australia. It has been extinct since the early 1900s.

56. Fuel Gauge Use the fuel gauge at the right to estimate how full the fuel tank is. $\frac{3}{4}$

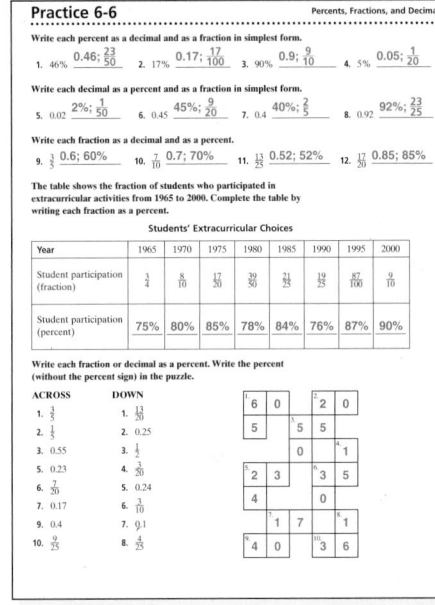

57. Suppose you answer 29 questions correctly on a 40-question test. What percent of the questions are correct? 72.5%

58. Writing in Math Explain how to write a decimal as a percent.
See margin.

Ⓒ Challenge

Number Sense Use the whole numbers 1 through 100 and find the percent of numbers in each category.

59. multiples of 3
33%

60. odd numbers
50%

61. prime numbers
25%

62. Stretch Your Thinking When a three-digit number is divided by the sum of the digits of the number, the quotient is 26. What is the least number for which this is true? 234

6-6 Percents, Fractions, and Decimals **297**

Use the Guided Problem Solving worksheet with Exercise 44.

58. Answers may vary. Sample: Move the decimal point two places to the right. Round to the nearest whole number. Add a percent sign.

Error Prevention!

Exercises 51–54 Review bar notation that indicates all digits under the bar are repeated.

Practice 6-6 — Percents, Fractions, and Decimals

Write each percent as a decimal and as a fraction in simplest form.

1. 46% — $0.46; \frac{23}{50}$ 2. 17% — $0.17; \frac{17}{100}$ 3. 90% — $0.9; \frac{9}{10}$ 4. 5% — $0.05; \frac{1}{20}$

Write each decimal as a percent and as a fraction in simplest form.

5. 0.02 — $2\%; \frac{1}{50}$ 6. 0.45 — $45\%; \frac{9}{20}$ 7. 0.4 — $40\%; \frac{2}{5}$ 8. 0.92 — $92\%; \frac{23}{25}$

Write each fraction as a decimal and as a percent.

9. $\frac{3}{5}$ 0.6; 60%   10. $\frac{7}{10}$ 0.7; 70%   11. $\frac{13}{25}$ 0.52; 52%   12. $\frac{17}{20}$ 0.85; 85%

The table shows the fraction of students who participated in extracurricular activities from 1965 to 2000. Complete the table by writing each fraction as a percent.

Students' Extracurricular Choices

Year	1965	1970	1975	1980	1985	1990	1995	2000
Student participation (fraction)	$\frac{3}{4}$	$\frac{8}{10}$	$\frac{17}{20}$	$\frac{39}{50}$	$\frac{21}{25}$	$\frac{19}{25}$	$\frac{87}{100}$	$\frac{9}{10}$
Student participation (percent)	75%	80%	85%	78%	84%	76%	87%	90%

Write each fraction or decimal as a percent. Write the percent (without the percent sign) in the puzzle.

ACROSS
1. $\frac{3}{5}$ 2. $\frac{1}{5}$ 3. 0.55   5. 0.23   6. $\frac{7}{10}$ 7. 0.17   9. 0.4   10. $\frac{9}{25}$

DOWN
1. $\frac{13}{20}$ 2. 0.25   3. $\frac{1}{2}$ 4. $\frac{9}{20}$ 5. 0.24   6. $\frac{3}{10}$ 7. 0.1   8. $\frac{4}{25}$

Reteaching 6-6 — Percents, Fractions, and Decimals

- To write a percent as a fraction in simplest form, first write a fraction with a denominator of 100. Then simplify.
$74\% = \frac{74}{100} = \frac{37}{50}$
- To write a percent as a decimal, first write a fraction with a denominator of 100. Then write the decimal.
$74\% = \frac{74}{100} = 0.74$
- To write a decimal as a percent, move the decimal point two places to the right.
$0.23 = 23\%$

Here are two ways to write a fraction as a percent.
- Write an equivalent fraction with a denominator of 100, then write the percent.
$\frac{3}{20} = \frac{15}{100} = 15\%$
- Divide the numerator by the denominator.
$\frac{3}{8} = \frac{0.375}{8)3.000} = 37.5\%$
Move the decimal point two places to the right.
So, $\frac{3}{8} = 37.5\%$.

Write each percent as a decimal and as a fraction in simplest form.

1. 30% — $0.30, \frac{3}{10}$ 2. 14% — $0.14, \frac{7}{50}$ 3. 16% — $0.16, \frac{4}{25}$ 4. 5% — $0.05, \frac{1}{20}$
5. 92% — $0.92, \frac{23}{25}$ 6. 80% — $0.80, \frac{4}{5}$ 7. 21% — $0.21, \frac{21}{100}$ 8. 38% — $0.38, \frac{19}{50}$

Write each fraction or decimal as a percent.

9. $\frac{17}{25}$ 68%   10. 0.85 85%   11. 0.16 16%   12. $\frac{5}{40}$ 12.5%
13. $\frac{7}{200}$ 3.5%   14. $\frac{1}{10}$ 10%   15. 0.64 64%   16. 0.008 0.8%
17. $\frac{9}{20}$ 45%   18. $\frac{6}{15}$ 40%   19. 0.32 32%   20. 0.07 7%
21. $\frac{13}{100}$ 13%   22. $\frac{45}{50}$ 90%   23. 0.010 1%   24. 0.60 60%

297

4. Assess

Write each percent as a decimal and as a fraction in simplest form.

1. 60% 0.60; $\frac{3}{5}$

2. 38% 0.38; $\frac{19}{50}$

Write each decimal or fraction as a percent.

3. 0.05 5%   4. $\frac{3}{20}$ 15%

Alternative Assessment

Each student in a pair writes several percents. Partners exchange papers and write each other's percents as decimals and fractions in simplest form. Next, partners write several fractions and decimals, exchange papers, and write each other's fractions and decimals as percents. Have students round to the nearest whole percent.

Test Prep

Resources

For additional practice with a variety of test item formats:
• Test Prep, p. 315
• Test-Taking Strategies, p. 311
• Test-Taking Strategies With Transparencies

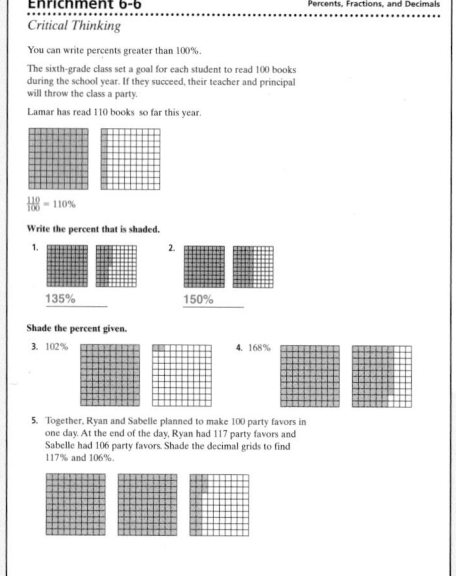

Multiple Choice Use the graph at the right.

63. Which decimal is equivalent to the percent of lunch bags that contain cake? **A**
    A. 0.06   B. 0.10
    C. 0.16   D. 0.60

64. Which of the following can you NOT conclude from the graph? **I**
    F. About one fourth of lunch bags contain fruit.
    G. About 12% of lunch bags contain a sandwich.
    H. Fruit is in more than twice as many lunch bags as cookies.
    I. More students take fruit than all other items combined.

65. In what percent of lunch bags are you likely to find fruit? **C**
    A. 4.5%   B. 13%
    C. 23%   D. 90%

66. [2] a. yes
    b. $\frac{32}{45} = 0.71$
    $0.71 > 0.7$
    [1] correct answer with error in justification

Take It to the NET
Online lesson quiz at
www.PHSchool.com
Web Code: aaa-0606

Short Response

66. Suppose you answer 32 questions correctly on a 45-question test.
    a. If the passing grade is 70%, did you pass? **a–b. See above left.**
    b. Justify your answer.

What's in Lunch Bags?

Mixed Review

Lesson 5-5

67. (**Algebra**) A package of soy nuts weighs $\frac{3}{8}$ pound and costs $1.65.
    a. Write an equation to determine the cost of 1 pound of soy nuts. Then solve and check your equation.
    b. Explain how you could estimate the cost of 1 pound without solving an equation. **a–b. See margin.**

Lesson 5-2 **Estimate each product.**

68. $2\frac{3}{4} \times 5\frac{1}{4}$ 15   69. $6\frac{1}{8} \times 3\frac{3}{8}$ 18   70. $4\frac{5}{8} \times 2\frac{2}{3}$ 15   71. $3\frac{1}{2} \cdot 5\frac{1}{3}$ 20

72. Estimate the area of a floor that measures 11 feet 10 inches by 9 feet 2 inches. 108 ft²

298 Chapter 6 Ratios, Proportions, and Percents

---

67. **Answers may vary. Samples are given.**
    a. Let x = cost of 1 lb of nuts. An equation is
    $\frac{\frac{3}{8}}{1.65} = \frac{1}{x}$; $4.40.
    b. 1 lb is about three times $\frac{3}{8}$ lb, and $1.65 is about $1.50. So 1 lb of nuts costs about 3($1.50) or $4.50.

6-7 Finding a Percent of a Number

What You'll Learn

 OBJECTIVE 1 To use proportions with percents

 OBJECTIVE 2 To use decimals with percents

...And Why

To find a part of a whole, as in Example 1

✔ Check Skills You'll Need

? For help, go to Lesson 6-4.

Solve each proportion.

1. $\frac{x}{42} = \frac{3}{7}$ **18**

2. $\frac{m}{12} = \frac{6}{9}$ **8**

3. $\frac{6}{45} = \frac{2}{n}$ **15**

4. $\frac{54}{c} = \frac{9}{13}$ **78**

5. $\frac{8}{10} = \frac{68}{y}$ **85**

6. $\frac{92}{100} = \frac{q}{250}$ **230**

7. Explain how you would solve the proportion $\frac{39}{100} = \frac{x}{40}$. *See margin.*

OBJECTIVE

 **i TEXT** Interactive lesson includes instant self-check, tutorials, and activities.

1 Using Proportions With Percents

A Little League team won 80% of the 30 games it played. You can write a proportion to find how many games the team won. This model is helpful in setting up a proportion to find 80% of 30.

part whole

0   n   30

0%   80% 100%

$\frac{n}{30} = \frac{80}{100}$ ← The part *n* corresponds to 80 in the diagram.
← The whole 30 corresponds to 100.

Real-World Connection

Over 3 million players participate in Little League Baseball.

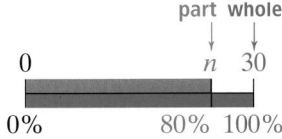

 1 EXAMPLE Using a Proportion   **Real World**

Baseball A Little League team played 30 games and won 80% of its games. Use a proportion to find the number of games the team wins.

Let *n* represent the number of wins.

$\frac{n}{30} = \frac{80}{100}$ ← part
← whole

$100 \times n = 80 \times 30$ ← **Write the cross products.**

$100n = 2,400$ ← **Multiply.**

$n = 24$ ← **Divide each side by 100.**

● The team won 24 games.

✔ Check Understanding 1 Brendan has read 60% of a novel that has 80 pages. Use a proportion to find the number of pages Brendan has read. **48**

6-7 Finding a Percent of a Number **299**

 Ongoing Assessment and Intervention

Before the Lesson	During the Lesson	After the Lesson
Diagnose prerequisite skills using:	**Monitor progress using:**	**Assess knowledge using:**
• Check Skills You'll Need	• Check Understanding • Additional Examples • Test Prep	• Lesson Quiz • Computer Test Generator CD

Lesson Preview

 PowerPoint

✔ **Check Skills You'll Need**

Solving Proportions
Lesson 6-4: Example 2. Extra Practice, p. 647.

Lesson Resources

 Teaching Resources
Practice, Reteaching, Enrichment

Reaching All Students
Practice Workbook 6-7
Spanish Practice Workbook 6-7
Guided Problem Solving 6-7
Hands-On Activities 21

Presentation Assistant Plus!
Transparencies
• Check Skills You'll Need 6-7
• Problem of the Day 6-7
• Additional Examples 6-7
• Student Edition Answers 6-7
• Lesson Quiz 6-7
PH Presentation Pro CD-ROM 6-7

PRENTICE HALL ASSESSMENT SYSTEM

Computer Test Generator CD

 Technology
Resource Pro® CD-ROM
Computer Test Generator CD
PH Presentation Pro CD-ROM

 www.PHSchool.com
Student Site
• Teacher Web Code: aak-5500
• Self-grading Lesson Quiz

PH SuccessNet Teacher Center
• Lesson Planner
• Resources

Plus  **i TEXT**

Check Skills You'll Need

7. Answers may vary. Sample: Use cross products.
$39 \times 40 = 100 \times x$;
$1,560 = 100x$. Divide both sides by 100. The solution is 15.6.

Math Background

You can find a percent of a number, such as 25% of 60, by performing the multiplication $0.25 \cdot 60$, or $\frac{1}{4} \cdot 60$. You can often use mental math to solve the fractional form. You can also set up the proportion $\frac{percent}{100} = \frac{part}{whole}$ to solve percent problems.

Teaching Notes

1 EXAMPLE Alternative Method

Some students find using the definition of percent helps them set up the correct proportion. Students write $\frac{percent}{100} = \frac{part}{whole}$ and substitute the given numbers for each term. The remaining term in the proportion becomes the variable.

2 EXAMPLE Error Prevention

Watch for students who do not write the percent as a decimal before they multiply.

3 EXAMPLE Inclusion

Review the fraction equivalents for common percents such as 10%, 20%, 25%, 50%, and 75%.

PowerPoint

Additional Examples

1. Use a proportion to find 60% of 45. 27; $\frac{n}{45} = \frac{60}{100}$

2. Find 88% of 250. 220

3. Use mental math to find 75% of 84. 63

Closure

How can you use a proportion to find a part of a whole? **Sample:** Set up a proportion using the $\frac{percent}{100} = \frac{part}{whole}$. Substitute for the percent and the whole; solve for the unknown part using cross products.

300

OBJECTIVE 2 Using Decimals With Percents

You can find a percent of a number by using a decimal.

2 EXAMPLE Using a Decimal

Find 22% of 288.

$22\% = 0.22$ ← Write 22% as a decimal.

$0.22 \times 288 = 63.36$ ← Multiply.

So, 22% of 288 is 63.36.

✔ **Check Understanding 2** Find each answer.
  a. 12% of 91 **10.92**
  b. 18% of 121 **21.78**

The percents in the table below are commonly found in real-world situations. You can change these to decimals or percents and then use mental math to calculate with them.

Test-Prep Tip
Memorizing the table at the right can help you find percents quickly on tests.

Equivalent Expressions for Mental Math

Percent	10%	20%	25%	50%	75%	80%
Fraction	$\frac{1}{10}$	$\frac{1}{5}$	$\frac{1}{4}$	$\frac{1}{2}$	$\frac{3}{4}$	$\frac{4}{5}$
Decimal	0.1	0.2	0.25	0.5	0.75	0.8

3 EXAMPLE Using Mental Math Real World

Surveys Suppose 25% of 80 students in a survey said they have vacationed in Florida. Find the number of students who have vacationed in Florida.

What you think

25% is equivalent to $\frac{1}{4}$; $\frac{1}{4} \times 80 = 20$. Twenty students have vacationed in Florida.

Why it works

$25\% = \frac{25}{100}$

$= \frac{1}{4}$ ← Write 25% as a fraction in simplest form.

$\frac{1}{4} \times 80 = \frac{1}{4} \times \frac{80}{1}$ ← Multiply 80 by $\frac{1}{4}$. Rewrite 80 as $\frac{80}{1}$.

$= \frac{80}{4}$ ← Simplify.

$= 20$ ← Divide.

✔ **Check Understanding 3** Use mental math to find each of the following.
  a. 10% of 56 **5.6**
  b. 75% of 12 **9**
  c. 50% of 36 **18**

👥 Reaching All Students

Below Level Have students make a horizontal bar model for Check Understanding 1 to help them set up their proportions correctly.	**Advanced Learners** Have students find their favorite sports team's number of wins and games played. They calculate the percent of wins and find the number of games they might win for the entire season.	**Inclusion** See note on page 300. **Alternative Method** See note on page 300.

 For more practice, see *Extra Practice.*

A Practice by Example

Example 1
(page 299)

Find each answer. Exercise 1 has been started for you.

1. 18% of 40 → $\frac{18}{100} = \frac{n}{40}$ **7.2**

2. 42% of 70 **29.4**

3. 8% of 210 **16.8**

4. 70% of 185 **129.5**

5. 11% of 600 **66**

6. 15% of 90 **13.5**

7. 65% of 240 **156**

Example 2
(page 300)

Find each answer.

8. 7% of 50 **3.5**

9. 18% of 170 **30.6**

10. 44% of 165 **72.6**

11. 43% of 61 **26.23**

12. 55% of 91 **50.05**

13. 30% of 490 **147**

Example 3
(page 300)

Find each answer using mental math.

14. 20% of 180 **36**

15. 80% of 40 **32**

16. 75% of 480 **360**

17. 25% of 50 **12.5**

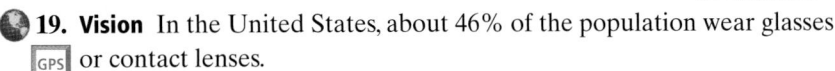

18. Dance Suppose 50% of the 178 dancers at a school for the performing arts prefer modern dance. How many dancers prefer modern dance? **89 dancers**

B Apply Your Skills

19. Vision In the United States, about 46% of the population wear glasses or contact lenses.
  a. In a group of 85 people, how many people would you expect to wear glasses or contact lenses? **about 39 people**
  b. Writing in Math Explain how you found your answer to part (a).
  c. Open-Ended How many people in your classroom would you expect to wear glasses or contact lenses? **b–c. See margin.**

20. Data File, p. 267 Which animal's track is 10% of the length of the moose track? **Norway rat**

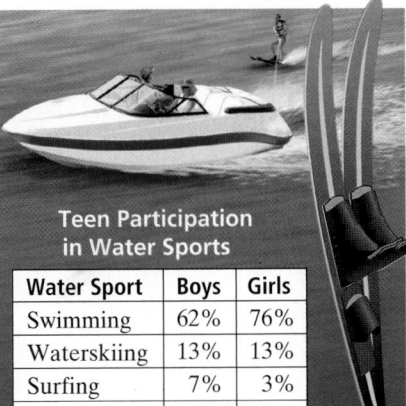

Teen Participation in Water Sports

Water Sport	Boys	Girls
Swimming	62%	76%
Waterskiing	13%	13%
Surfing	7%	3%
Sailboarding	4%	2%

Recreation Use the survey at the left. Suppose 200 boys and 200 girls were surveyed. Find the number of boys or girls who participated in each water sport.

21. girls in swimming **152**

22. boys in waterskiing **26**

23. boys in surfing **14**

24. girls in surfing **6**

25. girls in sailboarding **4**

26. boys in swimming **124**

Money *Simple interest* on a bank account is found by multiplying the original investment (*I*), the yearly interest rate (*r*), and the time in years (*t*). Find the simple interest of each below.

27. $I = \$500, r = 1\%, t = 2$ **$10**

28. $I = \$1,000, r = 3\%, t = 4$ **$120**

29. $I = \$895, r = 5\%, t = 2$ **$89.50**

30. $I = \$4,500, r = 2\%, t = 3$ **$270**

6-7 Finding a Percent of a Number **301**

Practice 6-7

Finding a Percent of a Number

Find each answer.

1. 15% of 20 __3__	**2.** 40% of 80 __32__	**3.** 20% of 45 __9__	**4.** 18% of 70 __12.6__
5. 90% of 120 __108__	**6.** 65% of 700 __455__	**7.** 25% of 84 __21__	**8.** 63% of 80 __50.4__
9. 60% of 50 __30__	**10.** 45% of 90 __40.5__	**11.** 12% of 94 __11.28__	**12.** 15% of 52 __7.8__
13. 37% of 80 __29.6__	**14.** 25% of 16 __4__	**15.** 63% of 800 __504__	**16.** 72% of 950 __684__
17. 55% of 250 __137.5__	**18.** 18% of 420 __75.6__	**19.** 33% of 140 __46.2__	**20.** 53% of 400 __212__

Solve each problem.

21. Teri used 60% of 20 gallons of paint. How much did she use? **12 gallons**

22. The Badgers won 75% of their 32 games this year. How many games did they win? **24 games**

23. Vivian earned $540 last month. She saved 30% of this money. How much did she save? **$162**

24. A survey of the students at Lakeside School yielded the results shown below. There are 1,400 students enrolled at Lakeside. Complete the table for the number of students in each activity.

How Lakeside Students Spend Their Time on Saturday

Activity	Percent of Students	Number of Students
Baby-sitting	22%	308
Sports	26%	364
Job	15%	210
At home	10%	140
Tutoring	10%	140
Other	17%	238

Reteaching 6-7

Finding a Percent of a Number

You can find 70% of 90 using different methods.

Use mental math.

① Write the percent as a fraction in simplest form.

$70\% = \frac{70}{100} = \frac{7}{10}$

② Multiply by the fraction.

$\frac{7}{10} \times \frac{90}{1} = \frac{630}{10} = 63$

70% of 90 = 63.

Use a proportion.

① Write a proportion.

$\frac{70}{100} = \frac{c}{90}$

② Write cross products and simplify.

$100 \times c = 70 \times 90$
$100c = 6,300$

③ Solve.

$c = \frac{6,300}{100}$
$c = 63$

70% of 90 = 63.

Find each answer using mental math.

1. 45% of 60 __27__	**2.** 60% of 160 __96__	**3.** 15% of 220 __33__
4. 90% of 80 __72__	**5.** 35% of 60 __21__	**6.** 70% of 350 __245__

Find each answer using a proportion.

7. 40% of 60 __24__	**8.** 85% of 300 __255__	**9.** 15% of 160 __24__
10. 22% of 500 __110__	**11.** 37% of 400 __148__	**12.** 68% of 250 __170__

Find each answer.

13. 25% of 100 __25__	**14.** 70% of 70 __49__	**15.** 10% of 70 __7__
16. 75% of 40 __30__	**17.** 80% of 50 __40__	**18.** 12% of 60 __7.2__
19. 24% of 80 __19.2__	**20.** 45% of 90 __40.5__	**21.** 60% of 72 __43.2__
22. 55% of 120 __66__	**23.** 95% of 180 __171__	**24.** 16% of 80 __12.8__

Assignment Guide

1 **Objective 1**
  A **B** Core 1–7, 19–20
  C Extension 35

2 **Objective 2**
  A **B** Core 8–18, 21–33
  C Extension 34

Test Prep 36–39
Mixed Review 40–51

19b. **Answers may vary. Sample: I used the equation** $x = 0.46 \times 85$ **since it is easy to multiply a whole number by a decimal. I rounded because I can't have a fraction of a person.**

c. **Check students' work.**

GPS Use the Guided Problem Solving worksheet with Exercise 19a.

PowerPoint **Lesson Quiz 6-7**

Find each answer.

1. 40% of 295 **118**

2. 65% of 340 **221**

3. 18% of 150 **27**

Alternative Assessment

One student in a pair writes five percents on separate slips of paper while the partner does the same with whole numbers greater than 20. Students place the slips facedown in two stacks. Together they draw a percent and a whole number from each stack. Then they work together to find the percent of the number.

Test Prep

Resources
A sheet of blank grids is available in the *Test-Taking Strategies With Transparencies* booklet. Give copies of this sheet to students so they can practice filling in grids.

For additional practice with a variety of test item formats:
• Test Prep, p. 315
• Test-Taking Strategies, p. 311
• Test-Taking Strategies With Transparencies

Enrichment 6-7   Finding a Percent of a Number

Critical Thinking

Use what you know about finding percents and writing equations to find multiple percents of a number.

1. What is 25% of 40% of 45?
   a. What is 40% of 45? **18**
   b. What is 25% of your answer to part (a)? **4.5**
2. a. What is 25% of 45? **11.25**
   b. What is 40% of your answer to part (a)? **4.5**
3. a. What is 25% of 40%? **10%**
   b. What is 45 multiplied by your answer to part (a)? **4.5**
   Sample answers: Exercises 4–7
4. Compare how you found the answers to Exercises 1, 2, and 3. What are the similarities? What are the differences?
   They have same factors and same products. The order in which the factors are multiplied differs.
5. How can you use this observation to mentally solve percent problems such as 50% of 140% of 200?
   Use factors that are easy to compute mentally, such as 50% of 200 (100). Then find 140% of 100 (140).
6. If 50% of 120% of 30% of a number is 108, what is the number? Show how you found your answer.
   50% of 120% is 60%; 30% of 60% is 18%;
   $0.18 \cdot x = 108; x = 600$
7. If 40% of 60% of 25% of a number is 54, what is the number? Show how you found your answer.
   25% of 60% is 15%; 40% of 15% is 6%;
   $0.06 \cdot x = 54; x = 900$
8. A ski shop sells a pair of skis for $210. For a winter sale, the skis are 30% off. Two weeks later, the shop has a clearance sale and sells the skis for 20% off the sale price. What is the clearance price of the skis?
   $117.60

---

34. Store B has the better rate; $\frac{2}{3} \approx 67\%$ and $67\% > 60\%$

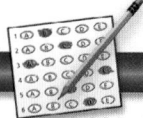 **Challenge**

35. Answers may vary. Sample: The first store; sale price for store 1 was $20 and store 2 was $21.

📟 **You can use a calculator to find percents. Some calculators have a percent key. If yours does not, then enter your percent as a decimal.**

SAMPLE   Find 58% of 165.

58 **%** **✕** 165 **═** 95.7   OR   0.58 **✕** 165 **═** 95.7

31. Find 33% of 31.
10.23

32. Find 91% of 234.
212.94

33. Find 12% of 88.
10.56

34. Store A is selling all books and posters at 60% off the marked price. Store B is selling the same items at $\frac{2}{3}$ off. Which store is offering the greatest discount rate? Explain your thinking. **See above left.**

35. Stretch Your Thinking Identical sweatshirts are being sold in two different stores. In the first store, the sale price is 20% off the regular price of $25. In the second store, the sale price is 30% off the regular price of $30. Which sweatshirt is the better buy? Explain. **See left.**

 **Test Prep**

Gridded Response

Use the table below for Exercises 36–39. Estimate, to the nearest whole number, the number of letters to expect in each passage.

Frequency of Vowels in Written Passages

Letter	A	E	I	O	U
Frequency	8%	13%	6%	8%	3%

💻 **Take It to the NET**
Online lesson quiz at
www.PHSchool.com
Web Code: aaa-0607

36. number of E's in a passage of 300 letters **39**

37. number of A's in a passage of 1,400 letters **112**

38. number of U's in a passage of 235 letters **about 7**

39. number of I's in a passage of 695 letters **about 42**

⚪ **Mixed Review**

Lesson 6-1   **Write each ratio in simplest form.**

40. $\frac{10}{45}$ $\frac{2}{9}$

41. $36:90$ **2:5**

42. 18 to 21 **6 to 7**

43. $\frac{100}{150}$ $\frac{2}{3}$

44. $24:40$ **3:5**

45. $\frac{55}{30}$ $\frac{11}{6}$

46. $336:36$ **28:3**

47. 729 to 540 **27 to 20**

Lesson 3-5   **Write each improper fraction as a mixed number.**

48. $\frac{23}{4}$ $5\frac{3}{4}$

49. $\frac{15}{6}$ $2\frac{1}{2}$

50. $\frac{32}{12}$ $2\frac{2}{3}$

51. $\frac{42}{5}$ $8\frac{2}{5}$

Estimating With Percents

What You'll Learn

 OBJECTIVE 1 To estimate with percents

...And Why

To estimate a tip, as in Example 2

 Check Skills You'll Need

? For help, go to Lesson 5-1.

Find each product.

1. $\frac{1}{8}$ of 240   30

2. $\frac{3}{4}$ of 160   120

3. $\frac{4}{5}$ of 2,500   2,000

4. $\frac{2}{7}$ of 1,400   400

OBJECTIVE

1 **Estimating With Percents**

 **iTEXT** Interactive lesson includes instant self-check, tutorials, and activities.

When you go shopping, you want to know if you have enough money to purchase an item. You can use mental math to estimate prices.

1 **EXAMPLE** **Estimating Sales Tax** 🌐 **Real World**

Sales Tax Suppose you buy the scarf at the left. The sales tax rate is 6%. Estimate the sales tax and the total cost.

Method 1

The scarf costs about $15.

6% of 15 = 0.06 × 15   ← **Write 6% as 0.06.**

= 0.90   ← **Multiply to find the tax.**

15 + 0.90 = 15.90   ← **Find the sum of the price and the tax.**

The cost of the scarf, including tax, is about $15.90.

Method 2

The scarf costs about $15. The sales tax rate is 6%, or 6 cents for every dollar.

$15 × 6 cents/dollar = 90¢, or $.90.

$15 + $.90 = $15.90

The cost of the scarf, including tax, is about $15.90.

1b. Answers may vary. Sample: High estimate; I may estimate too low and not have enough money.

 **Check Understanding** **1** **a.** Using a 5% sales tax rate, estimate the sales tax and total cost for the hat shown above.   **about $10.50**

b. **Reasoning** When estimating tax, would it be better to round a price like $34.48 up to $35, or down to $34? Explain your choice.   **See above left.**

Ongoing Assessment and Intervention

Before the Lesson
Diagnose prerequisite skills using:
• Check Skills You'll Need

During the Lesson
Monitor progress using:
• Check Understanding
• Additional Examples
• Test Prep

After the Lesson
Assess knowledge using:
• Lesson Quiz
• Computer Test Generator CD
• Chapter Checkpoint 2 (p. 306)

Lesson Preview

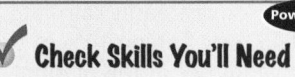 **PowerPoint**

✔ **Check Skills You'll Need**

Multiplying Fractions by Whole Numbers
Lesson 5-1: Example 3. Extra Practice, p. 646.

Lesson Resources

📁 **Teaching Resources**
Practice, Reteaching, Enrichment
Checkpoint Quiz 2

👥 **Reaching All Students**
Practice Workbook 6-8
Spanish Practice Workbook 6-8
Reading and Math Literacy 6C
Spanish Reading and Math
  Literacy 6C
Spanish Checkpoint Quiz 2
Guided Problem Solving 6-8

🕐 **Presentation Assistant Plus!**
Transparencies
• Check Skills You'll Need 6-8
• Problem of the Day 6-8
• Additional Examples 6-8
• Student Edition Answers 6-8
• Lesson Quiz 6-8
PH Presentation Pro CD-ROM 6-8

 PRENTICE HALL ASSESSMENT SYSTEM

Checkpoint Quiz 2
Computer Test Generator CD

 Technology
Resource Pro® CD-ROM
Computer Test Generator CD
PH Presentation Pro CD-ROM

 **www.PHSchool.com**
Student Site
• Teacher Web Code: aak-5500
• Self-grading Lesson Quiz

PH SuccessNet Teacher Center
• Lesson Planner
• Resources

Plus **iTEXT**

Math Background

We commonly estimate percents to calculate dollar amounts for discounted merchandise, sales tax, and tips. You can easily calculate tips of 15% by finding 10% of the bill and adding $\frac{1}{2}$ of this amount (5%).

Teaching Notes

③ EXAMPLE Alternative Method

Some students may find it easier to work with fractions such as:

$60\% \times \$90 \rightarrow \frac{60}{100} \times \frac{90}{1} = 54.$

Error Prevention!

The boots in Example 3 are not 40% *of* the original price but 40% *off.* 40% *off* the regular price is 60% *of* the regular price.

English Learners

Have students create a receipt that lists and illustrates each vocabulary term: *regular price, sale price, sales tax,* and *total cost.*

PowerPoint

Additional Examples

1 Using a 5% sales tax, estimate the sales tax and the total cost for a pair of sneakers that costs $34.99. sales tax: $1.75; total cost: about $36.75

2 Estimate a 15% tip for a bill of $29.34. about $4.50

3 A jacket is on sale for 20% off the regular price of $49.95. Estimate the sale price of the jacket. about $40

Closure

• *How do you find the total cost of an item with sales tax?* Sample: Find and add the sales tax to the cost of the item.

• *How do you estimate a 15% tip for a bill?* Sample: Find 10% by moving the decimal one place to the left. Then add to it half of this amount, which is 5%.

---

② EXAMPLE Estimating a Tip  Real World

Dining Out Suppose you and two friends eat at a restaurant. Estimate a 15% tip for a bill of $26.22.

What you think

The bill is about $26.
I can break apart 15% into 10% and 5%.
Since 10% of $26 is $2.60, 5% is half of $2.60, or $1.30.
A 15% tip is about $2.60 + $1.30, or $3.90.

Why it works

$$15\% \times \$26 = (10\% + 5\%) \times \$26 \qquad \leftarrow \text{Replace 15\% with 10\% + 5\%.}$$
$$= (10\% \times \$26) + (5\% \times \$26) \quad \leftarrow \text{Distributive Property}$$
$$= \$2.60 + (5\% \times \$26) \qquad \leftarrow \text{Find 10\% } \times \text{ \$26.}$$
$$= \$2.60 + \left(\frac{1}{2} \times 10\% \times \$26\right) \quad \leftarrow \text{Replace 5\% with } \frac{1}{2} \times \text{10\%.}$$
$$= \$2.60 + \$1.30 \qquad \leftarrow \text{Simplify inside the parentheses.}$$
$$= \$3.90 \qquad \leftarrow \text{Add.}$$

✓ **Check Understanding** ② Estimate a 15% tip for a bill of $41.63. about $6

③ EXAMPLE Estimating a Sale Price  Real World

 $57.95

Sales The regular price for a pair of hiking boots is $57.95. The store is having a 30% off sale. Estimate the sale price.

What you think

The regular price of the boots is about $60. If the price is 30% off, you pay 100% − 30%, or 70% of the regular price.

70% of $60 = $42

The sale price is about $42.

Why it works

The sale price is 30% off the regular cost.

$$30\% \times \$60 = 0.3 \times \$60 \quad \leftarrow \text{Write 30\% as 0.3.}$$
$$= \$18 \qquad \leftarrow \text{Simplify.}$$

Subtract the amount off the regular price to find the sale price.

$60 − $18 = $42

✓ **Check Understanding** ③ **a.** A baseball glove is on sale for 40% off the original price of $40.19. Estimate the sale price of the glove. about $24

b. Number Sense Is the estimated sale price of the boots in Example 3 a high estimate or a low estimate? Explain how you know. High estimate; the original price was rounded up.

304 Chapter 6 Ratios, Proportions, and Percents

👥 Reaching All Students

| Below Level Have students practice finding 15% tips using three steps such as: 10% of $24 = $2.40; 5% of 24 = $\frac{1}{2}$ of $2.40 = $1.20; $2.40 + $1.20 = $3.60, a 15% tip. | Advanced Learners Give at least two different ways to estimate a 7.5% sales tax. Sample: Find 15% and divide by 2; or find 10% and then 5% and choose a value between them. | English Learners See note on page 304. Diversity See note on page 305. |

A Practice by Example

Example 1
(page 303)

Using a sales tax rate of 7%, estimate the sales tax and total cost for each item.

$1.96, $29.96
1. a board game that costs $27.60

$9.10, $139.10
2. a bicycle that costs $129

3. a dictionary that costs $14.59
$1.05, $16.05

4. a DVD that costs $19.95
$1.40, $21.40

Example 2
(page 304)

Estimate a 15% tip for each bill amount.

5. $41.90 $6.30   6. $8.60 $1.35   7. $79.10 $12   8. $40.60 $6

Example 3
(page 304)

Estimate the sale price of each item.

$24
9. 40% off a necklace for $42

$400
10. 50% off a sofa for $789

11. 70% off a shirt for $16.99
$5.10

12. 90% off a jacket for $68
$7

B Apply Your Skills

Sales Tax Use the sales tax rate table.
Estimate the sales tax and total cost of each item below in each state. 13–18. **Answers may vary. See margin for samples.**

13. in-line skates: $75   14. calculator: $18.50

15. erasers: $.79   16. birthday card: $2.99

17. sneakers: $64.45   18. diary: $5.29

State Sales Tax

State	Tax
Florida	6%
Georgia	4%
Massachusetts	5%
Tennessee	7%

SOURCE: *The World Almanac*

Estimate each amount.

19. 50% of 89 45   20. 12% of 302 30   21. 30% of 295 90

22. 1.2% of 490 5   23. 25% of 59 15   24. 90% of 49 45

25. I could round to $4.50 and multiply by 4; I could round to $4.50 and multiply by 3.

25. **Writing in Math** Suppose 5% tax on a restaurant bill is $4.36. Explain how you can use this to find a 20% tip and a 15% tip. See left.
26a–c. Answers may vary. Samples are given.

26. **Jobs** Micah received the following tips. Estimate the value of each.
GPS
a. 20% of $14.20 $2.80   b. 10% of $24.75 $2.50   c. 15% of $19.70
d. Which tip was the greatest value? 15% of $19.70 $3.00

C Challenge

27. By the age of 2, a child's height is usually about 50% of his or her full adult height. Estimate the adult height of a 2-year-old whose height is 2 feet 9 inches. 5 ft 6 in.

28. **Stretch Your Thinking** What is the least number that has factors of 1, 2, 3, 4, 5, 6, 7, and 8? 840

13. Florida: $4.80, $84.80
Georgia: $3.20, $83.20
Massachusetts: $4.00, $84.00
Tennessee: $5.60, $85.60

14. Florida: $1.14, $20.14
Georgia: $.76, $19.76
Massachusetts: $.95,

$19.95
Tennessee: $1.33, $20.33

15. Florida: $.05, $.85
Georgia: $.03, $.83
Massachusetts: $.04, $.84
Tennessee: $.06, $.86

GPS Use the Guided Problem Solving worksheet with Exercise 26.

16–18. See back of book.

Assignment Guide

1 Objective 1
A B Core 1–26
C Extension 27–28

Test Prep 29–32
Mixed Review 33–41

Diversity
Exercises 5–8 Some students may be unfamiliar with tips. Explain that the word *tip* may be an acronym for <u>T</u>o <u>I</u>nsure <u>P</u>romptness. Tips are generally not set amounts like sales tax but are determined by the tip giver.

Practice 6-8   Estimating With Percents

Estimate each amount.

1. 81% of 60   48   2. 20% of 490   100

3. 48% of 97   50   4. 72% of 80   56

5. 18% of 90   18   6. 21% of 80   16

7. 39% of 200   80   8. 81% of 150   120

9. 68% of 250   175   10. 73% of 99   75

Solve each problem.

11. Mr. Andropolis wants to leave the waitress a 12% tip. Estimate the tip he should leave if the family's bill is $32.46.
Sample answer: $3.50

12. Michael receives a 9.8% raise. He currently earns $1,789.46 per month. Estimate the amount by which his monthly earnings will increase.
Sample answer: $180

13. Estimate the sales tax and final cost of a book that costs $12.95 with a sales tax of 6%.
Sample answer: $.78 tax; $13.78 total

14. A real estate agent receives a 9% commission for every house sold. Suppose she sold a house for $112,000. Estimate her commission.
Sample answer: $11,200

15. A jacket costs $94.95. It is on sale for 30% off. Estimate the sale price.
Sample answer: $66.50

Reteaching 6-8   Estimating With Percents

You can estimate a percent of a number using mental math.

Example: Estimate 19% of $83.

① Round to convenient numbers.
20% of 80

② Find 10% of 80.
10% of 80 = 8.

③ 20% of 80 is 2 times as much.
20% of 80 is 2 × 8, or 16.

19% of 83 is about 16.

Estimate each amount.

1. 50% of 41   20   2. 20% of 99   20   3. 10% of 73   7

4. 40% of 59   24   5. 1% of 94   1   6. 5% of 313   15

7. 70% of 498 350   8. 15% of 172   25   9. 25% of 154 38

10. 90% of 81   72   11. 30% of 60   18   12. 15% of 401 60

13. 40% of 23   9   14. 20% of 178   36   15. 75% of 21   15

16. 25% of 216 50   17. 50% of 77   40   18. 15% of 39   6

19. 3% of 887   27   20. 70% of 419 280   21. 80% of 69   56

22. A baseball glove is on sale for 75% off the original price of $96.25. Estimate the sale price of the glove.
$24

4. Assess

1. Estimate the sale price of a $397 camera on sale for 30% off. **sale price is about $280**

2. Using a 6% sales tax, estimate the sales tax and total cost of a $48.95 DVD. **sales tax is about $3; total cost is about $52**

3. Estimate a 15% tip for a bill of $51.23. **about $7.50**

Chapter Checkpoint

To check understanding of Lessons 6-6 to 6-8:

Checkpoint Quiz 2 (p. 306)

📁 **Teaching Resources**
Checkpoint Quiz 2 (also in Prentice Hall Assessment System)

👥 **Reaching All Students**
Reading and Math Literacy 6C

Spanish versions available

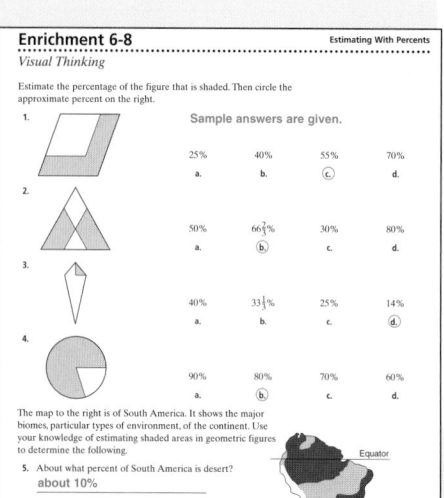

Enrichment 6-8 Estimating With Percents
Visual Thinking

Estimate the percentage of the figure that is shaded. Then circle the approximate percent on the right.

Sample answers are given.

1.
25% 40% 55% 70%
a. b. c. d.

2.
50% 66⅔% 30% 80%
a. b. c. d.

3.
40% 33⅓% 25% 14%
a. b. c. d.

4.
90% 80% 70% 60%
a. b. c. d.

The map to the right is of South America. It shows the major biomes, particular types of environment, of the continent. Use your knowledge of estimating shaded areas in geometric figures to determine the following.

5. About what percent of South America is desert? **about 10%**

6. About what percent of South America is rainforest? **about 33%**

7. About what percent of the South America rainforest is above the equator? **about 33%**

306

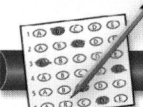
Test Prep

Multiple Choice

29. Which is the best estimate of 20% of 128? **D**
   A. 2,600   **B.** 260   **C.** 130   **D.** 26

30. Kate estimates 15% of a bill and leaves a $3 tip. What is the amount of the bill? **H**
   F. $.20   **G.** $.45   **H.** $20.00   **I.** $45.00

31. Which value is greatest? **C**
   A. 25% of 81   **B.** 40% of 63   **C.** 70% of 49   **D.** 85% of 35

Extended Response

Take It to the NET
Online lesson quiz at
www.PHSchool.com
Web Code: aaa-0608

32. Alabama has a 4% sales tax. Mississippi has a 7% sales tax. In Alabama, you can buy a camera on sale for $72.72. In Mississippi, you can buy the same camera for 20% off the regular price of $89.99.
   (a) At which store would you pay less for a new camera?
   (b) Explain your reasoning. **a–b. See back of book.**

Mixed Review

Lesson 5-6
Solve the problem by first solving a simpler problem.

33. Benito's digital watch beeps every 30 minutes. How many times does it beep in the month of May? **1,488 times**

Lesson 4-7
How many minutes are in each amount of time?

34. 1 h 15 min   35. 2 h 10 min   36. 5 h 45 min   37. 6 h 20 min
   75 min   **130 min**   **345 min**   **380 min**

Lesson 3-2
Use prime factorization to find the LCM of each set of numbers.

38. 12, 40 **120**   39. 18, 60 **180**   40. 8, 24, 36 **72**   41. 9, 30, 40 **360**

Checkpoint Quiz 2   Lessons 6-6 through 6-8

 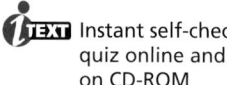
Instant self-check quiz online and on CD-ROM

1. Write 74% as a decimal and as a fraction in simplest form. **0.74, $\frac{37}{50}$**

2. Write $\frac{21}{25}$ as a percent. **84%**

3. Using a sales tax rate of 5%, estimate the sales tax and total cost for a calendar that costs $14.95. **tax: $.75; $15.75**

Find each percent.

4. 44% of 250 **110**   5. 25% of 72 **18**

306 Chapter 6 Ratios, Proportions, and Percents

Alternative Assessment

Each student in a pair writes several bill amounts. Partners exchange papers and find a 7% sales tax and the total cost for each bill amount. Partners then estimate a 15% tip for each total amount.

Test Prep

Resources
For additional practice with a variety of test item formats:
- Test Prep, p. 315
- Test-Taking Strategies, p. 311
- Test-Taking Strategies With Transparencies

6-9 Write an Equation

What You'll Learn

OBJECTIVE 1 To solve problems by writing an equation

. . . And Why

To find the regular price of an item, as in Example 1

 Check Skills You'll Need

? For help, go to Lesson 2-7.

Solve for x.

1. $9x = 45$ 5

2. $x \div 15 = 6$ 90

3. $12x = 54$ 4.5

4. $\frac{x}{8} = 7.25$ 58

5. $5.5x = 121$ 22

6. $2.25x = 450$ 200

OBJECTIVE 1

iTEXT Interactive lesson includes instant self-check, tutorials, and activities.

Solving Problems by Writing an Equation

When to Use This Strategy Writing an equation is a way to organize the information needed to solve a problem.

1 EXAMPLE   Real-World  Problem Solving

Discount A bicycle is on sale for $139.93. This is 30% off the regular price. What is the regular price of the bicycle?

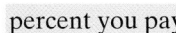 **Read and Understand** The sale price of the bicycle, $139.93, is 30% off the regular price. You need to find the regular price.

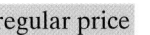 **Plan and Solve** You will pay 100% − 30%, or 70% of the regular price.

Words	percent you pay	times	regular price	equals	sale price

Let r = the regular price.

Equation	70%	×	r	=	$139.93

$0.7r = 139.93$ ← **Write 70% as a decimal.**

$\frac{0.7r}{0.7} = \frac{139.93}{0.7}$ ← **Divide each side by 0.7 to find r.**

$r = \$199.90$ ← **Simplify.**

The regular price of the bicycle is $199.90.

  Real-World Connection

The Tour de France is an annual 3,300-kilometer bicycle race. Lance Armstrong won in 1999, 2000, 2001, 2002, and 2003.

Look Back and Check The regular price is about $200. The sale price is about 70% of $200, or $140. This is close to the sale price, $139.93.

Check Understanding ① A sleeping bag is on sale for $29.97. This is 25% off the original price. What is the regular price of the sleeping bag? $39.96

6-9 Write an Equation   **307**

 **Ongoing Assessment and Intervention**

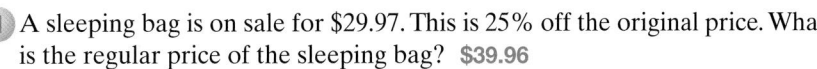

Before the Lesson
Diagnose prerequisite skills using:
• Check Skills You'll Need

During the Lesson
Monitor progress using:
• Check Understanding
• Additional Examples
• Test Prep

After the Lesson
Assess knowledge using:
• Lesson Quiz
• Computer Test Generator CD

6-9

1. Plan

Lesson Preview

 PowerPoint

✓ **Check Skills You'll Need**

Solving Equations by Multiplying or Dividing
Lesson 2-7: Examples 1, 3. Extra Practice, p. 643.

Lesson Resources

Teaching Support includes:
Practice, Reteaching, Enrichment Assessment, Reading & Literacy, Activities, Transparencies, Technology, CD-ROMs, Spanish, and More

See pp. 266G–266H for a complete list of resources for this lesson.

 • www.PHSchool.com
• Teacher Web Code: aak-5500

Plus **iTEXT**

2. Teach

 **Professional Development**

Math Background

Real-world problems often require multiple solution steps. Writing an equation is often helpful. The most challenging step is finding a word relationship that can be translated into an equation with numbers, symbols, and a variable.

PowerPoint

Additional Examples

① Solve by writing an equation. Soccer shoes are on sale for $67.97. The sale is for 15% off the regular price. What is the regular price of the shoes?
$p \cdot 85\% = 67.97$; $79.97

① EXAMPLE Alternative Method

You can write the equation using "30% off" as shown below.

$r - 0.3r = 139.93$
$(1 - 0.3)r = 139.93$
$0.7r = 139.93$
$r = 199.90$

307

How can you use write an equation to solve word problems?
Sample: Identify the key information in the problem. Make a word relationship between the given information. Translate the words into numbers, symbols, and one variable. Solve the equation for the variable.

3. Practice

Assignment Guide

 **Objective 1**
Ⓐ Ⓑ **Core** 1–15
Ⓒ **Extension** 16–17

Test Prep 18–21
Mixed Review 22–28

Error Prevention!

Remind students that a percent needs to be changed to a decimal before they do any calculations.

4. Assess

 **Lesson Quiz 6-9**

1. Solve by writing an equation. Terrell earns a 4% commission on sales of electronics. On Monday he earned $100 in commission. What was the amount of Terrell's sales on Monday?
$s \cdot 4\% = 100; \$2,500$ sales

Alternative Assessment

Each student in a pair writes a problem similar to Exercises 1–4 that can be solved by writing an equation. Partners exchange problems and solve them.

Test Prep

Resources
For additional practice with a variety of test item formats:
• Test Prep, p. 315
• Test-Taking Strategies, p. 311
• Test-Taking Strategies With Transparencies

308

EXERCISES

❓ For more practice, see *Extra Practice*.

Ⓐ **Practice by Example**

Solve each problem by writing an equation.

Example 1
(page 307)

1. **Media** A magazine has 5,580,000 subscribers this year. This number is down 7% from last year. How many subscribers were there last year? **6,000,000 subscribers**

2. A "light" popcorn has 120 Calories per serving. This is 25% fewer Calories than a serving of the regular popcorn. How many Calories does each serving of the regular popcorn have? **160 Cal**

3. The sign at the entrance of a store reads, "30% off all winter apparel! Discount reflected at the register." The price tag of a coat is missing. The register rings up a price before tax of $55.93. What was the regular price of the coat? **$79.90**

4. A boat is on sale for 15% off. Its sale price is $1,700. What is the regular price of the boat? **$2000**

? Need Help?
• Reread the problem.
• Identify the key facts and details.
• Tell the problem in your own words.
• Try a different strategy.
• Check your work.

Ⓑ **Apply Your Skills**

Choose a strategy to solve each problem.

5. **Sales** What is the regular price of the snowboard at the right? The sale price is 20% off the regular price. **$15.93**

Using the sale price that is given, find the regular price for each item at a 20%-off sale.

6. kite: $16 **$20**   7. yo-yo: $12 **$15**

8. radio: $13.72 **$17.15**   9. puzzle: $10.60 **$13.25**

10. stationery: $7.56 **$9.45**   11. CD: $11.96 **$14.95**

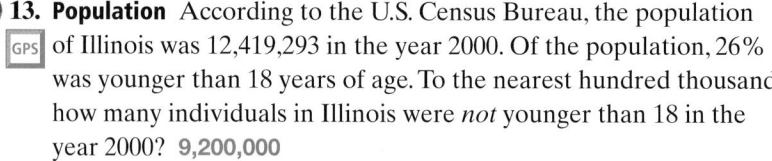
Sale Price $12.74

Strategies

Draw a Diagram
Make a Graph
Make an Organized List
Make a Table and Look for a Pattern
Simulate a Problem
Solve a Simpler Problem
Try, Check, and Revise
Use Logical Reasoning
Work Backward
Write an Equation

---

12. **Sales** The regular price of a mountain bike is $175.
   a. What is the price of the bike with a 10% discount? **$157.50**
   b. What is the price of the bike with the 10% discount followed by a 2% discount for paying in cash? **$154.35**
   c. **Writing in Math** Is a 10% discount followed by a 2% discount the same as a 12% discount? Explain. See below left.

13. **Population** According to the U.S. Census Bureau, the population of Illinois was 12,419,293 in the year 2000. Of the population, 26% was younger than 18 years of age. To the nearest hundred thousand, how many individuals in Illinois were *not* younger than 18 in the year 2000? **9,200,000**

c. No; if you take off 2% after first taking off 10%, you take 2% off a smaller amount, so the total discount is less than 12%.

👥 **Reaching All Students**

Below Level Have students find the percent of the original price they would pay for the following percents off.	**Advanced Learners** *Can 25% of something be greater than 50% of something else? Explain.* **Yes; it depends on the quantities of each "something." 25% of 8 is 2 while 50% of 2 is 1, and 2 > 1.**	**Alternative Method** See note on page 307. **Error Prevention** See note on page 308.
20% off **80%** 30% off **70%**		
40% off **60%** 22% off **78%**		

14. Pennies The height of 16 pennies is shown at the right. How tall is a stack of 50 pennies? **7.5 cm**

15. With 1,000,018,176 pennies, you could make five blocks of pennies, each the size of a school bus. Combined, the five blocks would weigh 3,125 tons. How much would two bus-sized blocks of pennies weigh? **1,250 t**

C Challenge **16. Depreciation** Each year a car's value is about 85% the previous year's value. Suppose you buy a new car this year for $15,500.
  a. What will be the value of the car after 1 year? 2 years? 5 years?
  b. Will the value of the car ever be zero? Explain. **a–b. See margin.**

17. Stretch Your Thinking How can you cut a bagel into eight equal pieces with just three cuts? **See margin.**

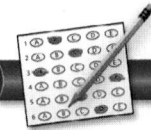

Test Prep

Multiple Choice

18. A pair of sandals is on sale for 65% off the regular price of $8.99. What is the sale price? **A**
  A. $3.15 **B.** $4.05 **C.** $5.84 **D.** $14.84

19. A restaurant bill is $15.50. What is the total cost with a 15% tip? **H**
  F. $2.33 **G.** $15.65 **H.** $17.83 **I.** $18.00

Take It to the NET
Online lesson quiz at
www.PHSchool.com
Web Code: aaa-0609

20. What is the solution of $24x = 120$? **C**
  A. 30 **B.** 20 **C.** 5 **D.** $\frac{4}{3}$

Short Response

21. Earrings at Store A are on sale for 25% off. Earrings at Store B are "Buy 3, Get 1 Free." The least expensive item is the free one. Suppose the regular prices of the earrings you like are $4.65, $5.75, $4.35, and $5.25 at each store. **(a)** At which store do you get a better bargain? **(b)** Explain your reasoning. **See margin.**

Mixed Review

Lesson 6-3 Do the ratios in each pair form a proportion?

22. $\frac{8}{5}, \frac{11}{7}$ no **23.** $\frac{45}{81}, \frac{5}{9}$ yes **24.** $\frac{3}{23}, \frac{6}{50}$ no

Lesson 5-5 **Algebra** Solve each equation. Check the solution.

25. $\frac{a}{4} = 11$ 44 **26.** $\frac{b}{12} = 3$ 36 **27.** $\frac{1}{4}c = 5$ 20 **28.** $\frac{2}{3}d = 6$ 9

6-9 Write an Equation **309**

16a. $13,175; $11,198.75, $6,877.43

b. No; the value will never be zero because any number minus 15% of that number will always leave 85%.

17. Slice it in half from the side. Then make two cuts from the top to slice those halves into quarters.

 GPS Use the Guided Problem Solving worksheet with Exercise 13.

21. [2] $4.65 + $5.75 + $4.35 + $5.25 = $20, $0.75 × $20 = $15, $20 − $4.35 = $15.65; store A is the better bargain.

[1] correct answer with no work shown **309**

Percents Under 1% or Over 100%

This Extension of Lesson 6-9 introduces percents that are less than 1% or greater than 100%.

Optional Materials

• Classroom Aid 10

Teaching Notes

Begin by describing this situation: If the price of an item doubles, it costs 200% of its original price. So, percents can be greater than 100%. Ask: *How can you represent 200% using a 10-by-10 grid model?* Completely shade two grid models. Percents can also be less than 1%. Such percents can be expressed as fractions less than $\frac{1}{100}$, such as $\frac{1}{200}$, or as 0.5%. Ask: *How can you represent 0.5% using a 10-by-10 grid model?* Shade half of one small square.

Inclusion

Review converting percents to decimals and decimals to percents. To help students who confuse which way to move the decimal point, have them think of the percent sign as ÷ 100. When they remove the %, the decimal point moves left. When they insert the %, the decimal point moves right.

2 EXAMPLE Error Prevention

Encourage students to check their answers for reasonableness. Ask: *Is 150% of 60 going to be greater than or less than 60?* greater than

Diversity

Have a volunteer explain what is meant by suggested daily value (SDV). If possible, display a vitamin box or bottle that shows SDV values.

Exercises

Watch for students who incorrectly write answers that still have the percent symbol, %.

For Use With Lesson 6-9

Percents, like the ones modeled at the right, can be less than 1% or greater than 100%. Any fraction less than $\frac{1}{100}$ is less than 1%. Any fraction greater than $\frac{100}{100}$ is greater than 100%.

The examples below show you how to work with these percents.

0.5%

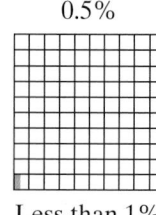

Less than 1%

105%

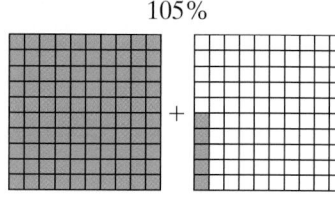

Greater than 100%

1 EXAMPLE   Writing a Percent as a Decimal or Fraction

Write 0.4% as a decimal and as a fraction in simplest form.

000.4 ⟵ Move the decimal point two places to the left.

0.004

$0.4\% = \frac{0.4}{100}$ ⟵ Write the percent as a fraction.

$= \frac{4}{1,000}$ ⟵ Rewrite the fraction without a decimal.

$= \frac{1}{250}$ ⟵ Write the fraction in simplest form.

As a decimal, 0.4% is 0.004. As a fraction, 0.4% is $\frac{1}{250}$.

2 EXAMPLE   Finding a Percent of a Number    Real World

Nutrition A vitamin supplement provides 150% of the Suggested Daily Value (SDV) of vitamin C. The SDV is 60 milligrams. How many milligrams of vitamin C are in the vitamin supplement?

150% of 60 = 1.50 × 60 ⟵ Move the decimal point two places to the left.

= 90

The vitamin supplement contains 90 milligrams of vitamin C.

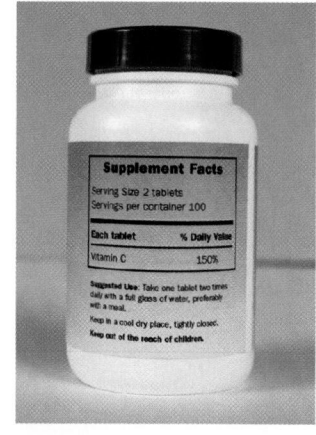

EXERCISES

Write each percent as a decimal and as a fraction in simplest form.

1. 0.2% 0.002, $\frac{1}{500}$

2. 0.75% 0.0075, $\frac{3}{400}$

3. 110% 1.1, $\frac{11}{10}$

4. 250% 2.5, $\frac{5}{2}$

Find each percent.

5. 400% of 5 20

6. 150% of 18 27

7. 0.5% of 300 1.5

8. 0.25% of 12 0.03

Test-Taking Strategies

Work Backward

The problem-solving strategy **work backward** is useful when taking multiple-choice tests. Work backward by testing each choice in the original problem. You will eventually find the correct answer.

 **EXAMPLE**

A fruit stand is selling 8 bananas for $1.00. At this rate, how much will 20 bananas cost?
A. $1.50   **B.** $2.00   **C.** $2.50   **D.** $3.00

Use mental math to test the choices that are easy to use.

$2.00 is twice $1.00. Twice 8 is only 16, so choice B is not the answer.

$3.00 is three times $1.00. Three times 8 is 24, so choice D is not the answer.

Since 20 is between 16 and 24, the cost must be between $2.00 and $3.00. The answer is C.

EXERCISES

1. In the example, how much do 6 bananas cost? C
   A. $.25   **B.** $.50   **C.** $.75   **D.** $1.00

2. The telephone company charged Omar for an overseas phone call. The rate was $2.40 for the first minute and $.55 for each additional minute. His bill was $6.80. For how many additional minutes was Omar charged? G
   F. 7   **G.** 8   **H.** 9   **I.** 10

3. At the copy center, it costs $4.00 to print 100 copies. At this rate, how much will 450 copies cost? B
   A. $16.00   **B.** $18.00   **C.** $20.00   **D.** $22.00

4. What method should NOT be used to find 88% of 40? I
   F. 0.88×40 **G.** $\frac{88}{100} \times 40$ **H.** $\frac{n}{40} = \frac{88}{100}$ **I.** $\frac{40}{n} = \frac{88}{100}$

5. Anjeli collected 15 postcards. Some of the cards cost $.79 and some cost $1.19. She spent a total of $14.25. How many postcards of each price did she buy? C
   A. 5 for $.79 each, 10 for $1.19 each
   B. 6 for $.79 each, 9 for $1.19 each
   C. 9 for $.79 each, 6 for $1.19 each
   D. 10 for $.79 each, 5 for $1.19 each

6. 40% of what number is 236? H
   F. 5.9   **G.** 94.4   **H.** 590   **I.** 9,440

Test-Taking Strategies

Work Backward

In general, students can use the work backward strategy effectively when they know a solution but need to find out information that led to that solution. This feature guides students to work backward to solve multiple-choice questions.

Resources

PRENTICE HALL
ASSESSMENT *SYSTEM*

Test-Taking Strategies With Transparencies
• Transparency 7
• Practice master, p. 6

Teaching Notes

EXAMPLE Teaching Tip

Guide students to stop checking each answer choice once their substitution results in the desired result.

Exercise 6 Ask: *How can you use number sense to eliminate three answer choices immediately?*
Sample: The answer must be greater than 236, which eliminates choices F and G; choice I is far too great a number—the answer should be somewhat more than twice 236, not 40 times 236.

Test-Taking Strategies With Transparencies

Chapter 6: Working Backward

Exercises

Solve by working backward.

1. 72 is 40% of some number. Find the number.
   A. 28   B. 120   C. 180   D. 240

2. Solve the equation. $4x + 17 = 37$
   F. $x = 3$ G. $x = 5$ H. $x = 7$ I. $x = 10$

3. 75% of what number is 120?
   A. 110   B. 125   C. 145   D. 160

4. Solve the equation. $\frac{1}{2}x - 20 = 30$
   F. 50   G. 100   H. 150   I. 200

5. Adult tickets at the movie theater cost $7.50. Tickets for children under 12 years old cost $5.25. A group of people went to the movies and they paid a total of $97.50. How many of each type of ticket did the group buy?
   A. 8 adult tickets and 6 children tickets
   B. 6 adult tickets and 8 children tickets
   C. 6 adult tickets and 10 children tickets
   D. 4 adult tickets and 12 children tickets

6. Solve the equation. $4y + 60 = 100$
   F. 10   G. 20   H. 25   I. 40

7. 15% of 25 is what number?
   A. 21.25   B. 20   C. 15   D. 3.75

8. For what value of g is the equation true when $x = 10$?
   $\frac{g}{2}(x + 2) = 24$
   F. 2   G. 4   H. 6   I. 10

9. A flat of tulips cost $11.50. A flat of daffodils cost $15.25. A gardener paid $126 and purchased 6 flats of daffodils and a few flats of tulips. How many flats of tulips did the gardener purchase?
   A. 2 flats   B. 3 flats   C. 4 flats   D. 5 flats

311

Vocabulary

cross products (p. 283)   proportion (p. 278)   scale (p. 288)
equal ratios (p. 270)   rate (p. 273)   unit price (p. 274)
percent (p. 294)   ratio (p. 269)   unit rate (p. 273)

 **Reading Math:**
Understanding
Vocabulary

Choose the vocabulary term from the column on the right that best completes the sentence.

1. The _E_ _?_ on a map may tell you 1 inch = 250 miles.

2. Two equal ratios can be written as a _B_ _?_ .

3. You can use a _D_ _?_ to compare a part to a part.

4. An example of a _C_ _?_ is 25 miles per hour.

5. You can use a _A_ _?_ to compare a number to 100.

A. percent
B. proportion
C. rate
D. ratio
E. scale
F. unit price

Take It to the NET
Online vocabulary quiz
at www.PHSchool.com
Web Code: aaj-0651

Skills and Concepts

6-1 Objective
▼ To write ratios

6. 15 to 23, 15:23, $\frac{15}{23}$

7. 15 to 8, 15:8, $\frac{15}{8}$

8. 23 to 8, 23:8, $\frac{23}{8}$

9. 15 to 46, 15:46, $\frac{15}{46}$

A **ratio** compares two quantities by division. To write a ratio in simplest form, divide both numbers by their GCF. **Equal ratios** name the same number.

A jar contains 8 tacks, 15 bolts, and 23 nails. Write each ratio in three ways.

6. bolts to nails   **7.** bolts to tacks   **8.** nails to tacks   **9.** bolts to total
6–9. See left.

Write each ratio in simplest form.

10. 8 to 32
1 to 4

11. $\frac{18}{30}$ $\frac{3}{5}$

12. 24 ft : 8 yd
3 ft : 1 yd

13. $\frac{45 \text{ boys}}{54 \text{ girls}}$ $\frac{5}{6}$

6-2 Objectives
▼ To find unit rates
▼ To use unit rates

A **rate** is a ratio that compares quantities measured in different units. A **unit rate** has a denominator of 1. To find a unit rate, divide the numerator by the denominator. A **unit price** gives the cost per unit.

14. You run 1 mile in 8 minutes. How long does it take to run 5 miles? 40 min

15. You earn $400 in 32 hours. How much do you earn in 1 hour? $12.50

🌐 **16. Bread** A loaf of bread costs $3.09 for 32 ounces or $1.40 for 24 ounces. Find each unit price and then determine the better buy. $1.40 for 24 oz

6-3 and 6-4 Objectives

▼ To test ratios

▼ To complete proportions

▼ To identify proportions

▼ To solve proportions

A **proportion** is an equation stating that two ratios are equal.

Do the ratios in each pair form a proportion?

17. $\frac{2}{5}, \frac{1}{3}$ no **18.** $\frac{6}{16}, \frac{21}{56}$ yes **19.** $\frac{15}{9}, \frac{5}{3}$ yes **20.** $\frac{3}{8}, \frac{9}{16}$ no

21. There are 944 marbles in a bag. If 3 out of 8 marbles are yellow, how many marbles are yellow? **354**

6-5 Objectives

▼ To find the scale of a drawing

▼ To find dimensions

A **scale** is a ratio that compares a length on a model to an actual length.

🌐 **Ships** The *S.S. United States,* a passenger ship built in an American shipyard, is 990 feet long. Find the length of a model with the given scale.

22. 1 foot : 10 feet **99 ft** **23.** 3 inches : 20 feet **148.5 in.** **24.** 2 inches : 15 feet **11 ft or 132 in.**

6-6 and 6-7 Objectives

▼ To write percents as decimals and fractions

▼ To write decimals and fractions as percents

▼ To use proportions with percents

▼ To use decimals with percents

A **percent** is a ratio that compares a number to 100.

Write each percent as a fraction in simplest form and as a decimal.

25. 30% $\frac{3}{10}$, 0.3 **26.** 25% $\frac{1}{4}$, 0.25 **27.** 56% $\frac{14}{25}$, 0.56 **28.** 12% $\frac{3}{25}$; 0.12

29. There are 200 students in your class, and 30% of them joined the school band. How many students in your class joined the band? **60**

30. If 3 out of 5 children enjoy swimming, what percent like to swim? **60%**

6-8 Objective

▼ To estimate with percents

You can use mental math to estimate percents.
31–34. Answers may vary. Samples given.

Estimate each amount.

31. 20% of 48 **10** **32.** 6% of $19.99 **$1.20** **33.** 15% of $38.56 **$6**

34. A game costs $18.95 and the sales tax is 7%. Estimate the total cost. **$21.40**

6-9 Objective

▼ To solve problems by writing an equation

You can write an equation to solve a problem.

🌐 **35. Jobs** You work every Monday, Friday, and Saturday for 4 hours each day. If you earn $7 per hour, how many weeks will it take to save $252? **3 weeks**

36. Suppose you buy six comic books with the same price. You hand the clerk $20 and receive $3.50 in change. How much does each book cost? **$2.75**

Quarter 2 Test – Form B

Quarter 2 Test – Form A

Quarter 2 Test   **Form A**
Chapters 4–6

1. Round $11\frac{7}{9}$ to the nearest whole number.

2. Estimate $7\frac{4}{5} + 9\frac{1}{15}$ by first rounding to the nearest whole number.

3. Add. Write your answer in simplest form.
$\frac{9}{20} + \frac{7}{20} - \frac{9}{20}$

4. Explain how you would add the fractions $\frac{1}{2}$ and $\frac{3}{4}$.

5. Sean rode his bicycle $4\frac{1}{4}$ miles on Saturday and $5\frac{7}{8}$ on Sunday. How many miles did he ride during the weekend?

6. Add. Write your answer in simplest form. $11\frac{1}{2} + 3\frac{4}{5}$

7. There are two boards leaning against the wall. The first board is $3\frac{5}{8}$ meters long and the second is $4\frac{1}{4}$ meters long. How much longer is the second board?

8. What is the first step in solving the equation $x + 1\frac{5}{6} = 5$?

9. Solve the equation. Write your answer in simplest form.
$x - 3\frac{1}{12} = 6\frac{5}{12}$

10. Find the elapsed time from 8:35 A.M. to 10:15 A.M.

11. To celebrate its opening day, a carnival gives free admission to every 25th person. The carnival expects 600 people per hour. About how many people will enter free in a 16-hour day?

12. Which product is NOT equal to the others? $\frac{1}{2} \cdot \frac{8}{5}, \frac{5}{4} \cdot \frac{16}{25}, 2 \cdot \frac{1}{2}, \frac{1}{4} \cdot \frac{4}{1}$

13. A chocolate pie has a total of about 2,200 calories. The pie is divided into 8 equal slices. Write an expression using a fraction to calculate the number of calories in each slice. Then calculate the number of calories in each slice.

14. Find the product. Write your answer as a mixed number in simplest form. $5\frac{1}{4} \cdot 2\frac{3}{8}$

15. What is the reciprocal of 16?

16. Find the quotient. Write your answer as a mixed number in simplest form. $\frac{11}{5} \div \frac{8}{24}$

Alternative Assessment Form C

Alternative Assessment   **Form C**
Chapter 6

A LINE SEVEN MILES LONG

Each year people in the United States buy about 2.5 billion pencils.

1. Suppose the population of the United States is about 250 million.
   a. About how many pencils does each American use in a year? Explain how you got your answer.
   b. About how many pencils do the students in your class use in a year? Explain how you got your answer.

2. The average pencil can be sharpened about 17 times. Below is a drawing of an unsharpened pencil and a pencil that has been sharpened more than once.

   Estimate the number of times this pencil has been sharpened. Explain.

3. One pencil can be used to write about 45,000 words or to draw a line about 35 miles long. Suppose you have used a new pencil to write the equivalent of a line about 7 miles long. About how many words could you still write with the pencil? Explain.

4. Did you know that there is no lead in a "lead" pencil? The center of the pencil is a mixture of clay and graphite. The more clay used in the mixture, the harder the lead. The number on a pencil indicates the hardness (or softness) of the pencil's lead. For example, the lead in a Number 1 pencil is softer than the lead in a Number 2 pencil.

   Does a Number 3 pencil contain more or less clay than a Number 2 pencil? Explain.

 Chapter **6**

Chapter Test

 Take It to the NET
Online chapter test at
www.PHSchool.com
Web Code: aaa-0652

You have 3 nickels, 11 dimes, and 5 quarters in your pocket. Write each ratio in three ways.

1. nickels to quarters
3 to 5, 3:5, $\frac{3}{5}$

2. dimes to nickels
11 to 3, 11:3, $\frac{11}{3}$

3. dimes to total coins
11 to 19, 11:19, $\frac{11}{19}$

4. quarters to dimes
5 to 11, 5:11, $\frac{5}{11}$

5. Find the ratio of the shaded region to the unshaded region in simplest form. Use the figure below. **2 to 3**

Write three ratios equal to each ratio.

6. 3 to 2   **7.** $\frac{3}{18}$ **8.** 6:8
6–8. See margin.

🌍 **9. Cars** A car can go 28 miles per gallon of gas. How far can it travel with 8 gallons of gas? **224 mi**

10. A 6-ounce juice costs $.96. An 8-ounce juice costs $1.12. Which juice is the better buy? **the 8-oz jar**

Do the ratios in each pair form a proportion?

11. $\frac{5}{3}$, $\frac{15}{9}$
yes

12. $\frac{3}{4}$, $\frac{4}{5}$
no

13. $\frac{8}{12}$, $\frac{12}{18}$
yes

Solve each proportion.

14. $\frac{4}{5} = \frac{x}{25}$
20

15. $\frac{6}{4} = \frac{9}{m}$
6

16. $\frac{a}{25} = \frac{3}{10}$
7.5

🌍 **17. Groceries** A grocery store sells 6 pounds of apples for $4. How much will 8 pounds of apples cost? Round your answer to the nearest cent. **$5.33**

18. Writing in Math The ratio of girls to boys in a class is 5 to 6. Can there be 15 boys in the class? Explain why or why not.
No; 15 is not a multiple of 6.

🌐 **Maps** Use a map scale of 1 inch : 30 miles to find each actual distance.

19. 3 inches
90 mi

20. 6 inches
180 mi

21. 0.5 inches
15 mi

22. A scale model of a tiger is 1.5 feet long. If the actual length is 9 feet, what scale is used? $\frac{1}{6}$

Write each percent as a decimal and a fraction.

23. 25%
0.25, $\frac{1}{4}$

24. 6%
0.06, $\frac{3}{50}$

25. 98%
0.98, $\frac{49}{50}$

Write each decimal or fraction as a percent. If necessary, round to the nearest percent.

26. 0.48   48%   **27.** 0.02   2%   **28.** $\frac{1}{10}$ 10%

29. $\frac{3}{15}$ 20%   **30.** $\frac{5}{6}$ 83%   **31.** $0.\overline{9}$ 100%

Find each percent.

32. 5% of 200   **33.** 80% of 8   **34.** 2% of 50
10   6.4   1

35. Suppose 86% of 50 people at a law firm like their job. How many people like their job?
43 people

Estimate a 15% tip for each bill amount.
36–38. Answers may vary. Samples are given.

36. $32.04   **37.** $48.76   **38.** $12.83
$4.80 $7.50 $1.95

🌍 **39. Sales Tax** Suppose you buy a DVD for $12.98. The sales tax is 7%. Estimate the total cost.
$13.91

🌍 **40. Sales** A pair of sneakers is on sale for 25% off the regular price. The regular price is $89.96. What is the sale price? **$67.47**

🌍 **41. Sales** A dress is on sale for $32.88. This is 40% off of the regular price. Find the regular price. **$54.80**

6–8. Answers may vary. Samples are given.

6. 6 to 4, 9 to 6, 12 to 8

7. $\frac{1}{6}$, $\frac{2}{12}$, $\frac{5}{30}$

8. 3 : 4, 9 : 12, 15 : 20

13. **[2]** 17 days; multiply 68 by $\frac{1}{4}$ OR equivalent method
[1] correct answer with no reason

14. **[4]** About $25; use $20 for the cost, find the 5% tax. Use that result to calculate the 20% tip by multiplying the tax by 4 OR equivalent method

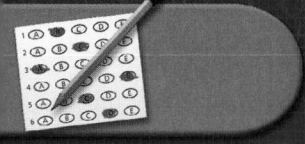

Multiple Choice

Choose the correct letter.

1. Find the product of $\frac{2}{9}$ and $\frac{5}{7}$. **A**

   A. $\frac{10}{63}$ **B.** $\frac{5}{31}$

   C. $\frac{14}{45}$ **D.** $3\frac{3}{14}$

2. Which could you use to describe how to find $1\frac{3}{4}$ divided by $\frac{1}{2}$? **I**

   F. Multiply $\frac{1}{2}$ and $\frac{7}{4}$.   **G.** Multiply $\frac{1}{2}$ and $\frac{4}{7}$.

   H. Multiply $\frac{4}{7}$ and 2.   **I.** Multiply $\frac{7}{4}$ and 2.

3. You bought a 12-count variety pack of dried fruit. Each bag of dried fruit contains c ounces. How many ounces of dried fruit did you buy? **D**

   A. $c \div 12$ **B.** $12 \div c$

   C. $c + 12$ **D.** $12c$

4. Which statement is false? **I**

   F. $\frac{8}{10} = \frac{32}{40}$ **G.** $\frac{1}{3} = \frac{12}{36}$

   H. $\frac{24}{42} = \frac{28}{49}$ **I.** $\frac{13}{14} = \frac{169}{196}$

5. Which decimal represents the portion of the model that is NOT shaded? **D**

   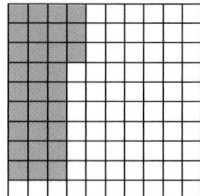

   A. 0.3   **B.** 0.33   **C.** 0.67   **D.** 0.7

6. Which of the following numbers is divisible by 2, 3, 5, 9, and 10? **F**

   F. 1,350   **G.** 1,010

   H. 945   **I.** 120

7. Choose an appropriate unit for measuring the length of a driveway. **B**

   A. inches   **B.** feet   **C.** miles   **D.** tons

8. Solve $x - \frac{1}{10} = \frac{1}{2}$. **I**

   F. $\frac{1}{10}$ **G.** $\frac{1}{6}$ **H.** $\frac{2}{5}$ **I.** $\frac{3}{5}$

9. At a car dealer, $\frac{2}{5}$ of the vehicles sold during the year were minivans. What percent of the vehicles sold were minivans? **D**

   A. 2.5%   **B.** 20%   **C.** 25%   **D.** 40%

Gridded Response

10. A bank teller spends about 8 minutes helping each customer. How long does the teller spend with 7 customers? **56**

11. Solve $\frac{k}{9} = \frac{2}{5}$ for k. Write your answer as an improper fraction. $\frac{18}{5}$

12. Find the product of $7\frac{5}{6}$ and $2\frac{1}{2}$. Write your answer as a decimal rounded to the nearest hundredth. **19.58**

Short Response

13. Summer vacation is 68 days long and $\frac{3}{4}$ of vacation has gone by. How many days are left? Explain how you found your answer. *See margin.*

Extended Response

14. Your dinner bill comes to $19.68. Estimate your total cost for dinner with a 5% tax and a 20% tip on the original bill. Justify your reasoning. *See margin.*

15. A customer service agent gets a phone call about every 12 minutes in a 7-hour work day. How many calls does she get in a 5-day work week? Explain how you found your answer. *See margin.*

Item	1	2	3	4	5	6	7	8	9	10	11	12	13	14	15
Lesson	5-1	5-4	2-3	6-2	1-1	3-1	5-7	4-6	6-6	6-2	6-3	5-2	6-5	6-7	5-8

14. **[3]** minor computation error and correct reasoning   **[2]** correct answer, but significant computational error   **[1]** correct answer with no reason

15. See back of book.

Cumulative Review

Cumulative Review
Chapters 1–6

Multiple Choice. Choose the letter of the best answer.

1. Which equation is true?
   A. $13 + 8 + 2 \times (3 - 1) = 24$
   B. $(13 + 8) + 2 \times (3 - 1) = 24$
   C. $13 + (8 + 2) \times (3 - 1) = 24$
   D. $13 + 8 + 2 \times 3 - 1 = 24$

2. Fill in the missing numbers.
   $8 \times (14 + \underline{?}) = (8 \times \underline{?}) + (\underline{?} \times 3)$
   F. 8, 14, 3   G. 3, 14, 8
   H. 14, 8, 3   I. 3, 8, 14

3. Use mental math to find the product 0.034×100.
   A. 0.34   B. 3.4
   C. 34.0   D. 340

4. Use mental math to find the quotient $14.35 \div 0.7$.
   F. 0.205   G. 2.05
   H. 20.5   I. 2,050

5. Which is the prime factorization tree of 270?

6. Find the GCF of 60 and 96.
   F. 2   G. 6
   H. 12   I. 32

7. Which fraction is *not* an equivalent fraction to $\frac{6}{7}$?
   A. $\frac{9}{12}$ B. $\frac{6}{8}$
   C. $\frac{3}{7}$ D. $\frac{12}{16}$

8. Write $\frac{17}{5}$ as a mixed number in simplest form.
   F. $2\frac{2}{5}$ G. $3\frac{2}{5}$
   H. $1\frac{2}{5}$ I. $3\frac{2}{5}$

9. Write 0.75 as a fraction in simplest form.
   A. $\frac{7}{10}$ B. $\frac{70}{100}$
   C. $\frac{3}{4}$ D. $\frac{16}{20}$

10. Find the sum $\frac{1}{2} + \frac{1}{6}$.
    F. $\frac{7}{12}$ G. $\frac{2}{11}$
    H. $\frac{1}{30}$ I. $\frac{11}{30}$

11. Find the difference. $11\frac{1}{3} - 8\frac{3}{4}$
    A. $3\frac{5}{6}$ B. $3\frac{1}{4}$
    C. $2\frac{1}{6}$ D. $2\frac{5}{8}$

12. Jason has $4\frac{2}{3}$ yards of fabric. How many bandanas can he make if each one requires $\frac{2}{3}$ yard of fabric?
    F. 6 bandanas   G. 7 bandanas
    H. $5\frac{1}{2}$ bandanas   I. $6\frac{1}{4}$ bandanas

13. Five friends are purchasing food for a party. They spend a total of $10.25. If each friend spent the same amount, how much did each contribute?
    A. $1.10   B. $2.05
    C. $2.50   D. $5.50

Prehistoric Giants

Students will use data from these two pages to answer the questions posed here in Put It All Together.

Activating Prior Knowledge

Have students read the data and look at the pictures on these pages. Some students may know a great deal about dinosaurs. Invite them to share knowledge they have about some of the extraordinary characteristics of dinosaurs, such as how fast they moved, what colors they might have been, how much and what they ate, where the most fossilized remains have been discovered, and so on.

Teaching Notes

To introduce the activity, ask:
- *About how many people tall is the dinosaur?* **8 people**
- *How tall would the dinosaur be if the person shown is 5 ft tall?* **40 ft tall**
- *How tall would the dinosaur be if the person shown is 6 ft tall?* **48 ft tall**
- *What is the ratio of heights of the person shown to the dinosaur?* **Sample: 1 to 8**

History Connection

Have interested students use proportional reasoning to make a time line of the history of life on Earth, beginning with the earliest sea creatures and continuing to include dinosaurs, early mammals, humans, and key events in human history. Invite students to post and explain their time lines, which should emphasize visually how very short the span of human existence on Earth appears when shown alongside the span of other life forms.

Real-World Snapshots

Prehistoric Giants

Applying Proportions Dinosaurs first appeared on Earth about 230 million years ago and died out about 65 million years ago. Today, scientists study dinosaur remains to learn more about them. For example, scientists can calculate the size of a dinosaur by measuring bones they have found. Then they use proportions to estimate the dimensions of other bones.

Fossilized Bones
Skeletons of animals that die in soft earth or mud can become fossils. Over time, the skeleton sinks and mud covers it. The mud turns to stone, preserving the skeleton.

Put It All Together

Data File Use the information on these two pages and on page 267 to answer these questions.

Materials centimeter ruler, poster board

1. Copy the table.
   a. Measure the dinosaur in the photo. Complete the first column of the table.
   b. Measure the height of one of the people in the photo. Then measure your own height (in centimeters). Use the measurements to estimate the scale of the photo.
   c. Use your scale to estimate the actual dimensions of the dinosaur. Complete the second column of the table.

2. a. **Open-Ended** Choose a large object such as your family's car, your bicycle, your bed, or a desk in your classroom. Measure at least four different parts of the object in centimeters.
   b. Choose a scale that will allow a drawing of both the dinosaur and your object to fit on (and cover as much as possible of) the poster board. Write the scale in a corner of the poster board.
   c. Calculate the poster dimensions for the dinosaur and the object. Complete the third column of your table.
   d. Use the dimensions from part (c) to draw the dinosaur and the object on the poster board.

3. **Research** Choose an animal from the table on page 267. Find out what the animal looks like. Calculate its size using the scale for your poster. If possible, add a drawing of it to your poster.

Dinosaur Measurements (centimeters)

Body Part	Math Book Length	Actual Length	Poster Length
Height	■	■	■
Leg	■	■	■
Foot	■	■	■
Neck	■	■	■

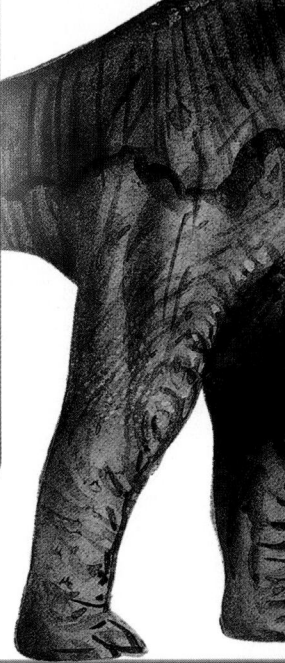

316

1a. **Answers may vary.**
Sample: 22.2 cm, 5.7 cm, 2.2 cm, 15.1 cm

b. **Answers may vary.**
Sample: 2.8 cm; 145.6 cm; scale 1:52.

c. **Answers may vary.**
Sample: 1154.4 cm, 296.4 cm, 114.4 cm, 785.2 cm

2a. **Check students' work.**

b. **Answers may vary.**

c-d. **Check students' work.**

3. **Check students' work.**

Sue and Sue

In 1990, fossil hunter Sue Hendrickson discovered Sue, a Tyrannosaurus rex fossil that is nearly 90% complete. Here she poses with a reconstructed back foot.

How Tall Is That?

A brachiosaurus was about the height of eight middle school students.

Compsognathus

Compsognathus was one of the smallest dinosaurs, about the size of a turkey.

Digging Up Dinosaurs

A paleontologist carefully chisels fossils from rock.

Take It to the NET For more information about dinosaurs, go to **www.PHSchool.com**.
Web Code: aae-0653

Put It All Together

Have students work in pairs to answer the questions and make the posters. Students may have an easier time if they use measuring tape instead of a ruler to measure their heights. Guide students to understand that they will find and record the length of the dinosaur as it appears on the page, the dinosaur's actual length, and the length it will be in their poster. Have students share and discuss their choices.

Inclusion

As needed, provide help with the concepts of ratio and proportion, and with how to apply these concepts to choose and use a sensible scale. Also, if necessary, provide students with benchmarks to help them better understand the size of centimeters and meters.

Exercise 2 Expect that students may need a period of trial and error in the process of choosing an appropriate scale for their posters.

Humor Connection

Have students design and draw to scale common items designed for dinosaur use. They can, for example, design sunglasses, toothbrushes, sleeping bags, slippers, hats, or gloves.

317

Celebration

Students apply their number sense and common sense to plan a celebration.

Resources

📁 **Teaching Resources**
Chapter 1 Project Support with Project Manager, Student Activities, Teacher Notes

Teaching Notes

Activating Prior Knowledge
Have students share experiences planning parties. Then ask:
• *What things will you consider to help you plan your celebration?* Sample: how many guests; what foods, entertainment, and decorations to have; what these things cost; how many people will share the costs

Careers
Event planning and fundraising are careers that might interest students. Discuss what skills these careers require.

Stepping Stones

Students apply their knowledge of geometrical patterns to construct a model of a fort.

Resources

📁 **Teaching Resources**
Chapter 2 Project Support with Project Manager, Student Activities, Teacher Notes

Teaching Notes

Activating Prior Knowledge
Discuss the kinds of patterns that might emerge when students build their forts. Ask:
• *How will you record the patterns?* Sample: using tables

Social Studies Connection
Invite volunteers to research the architecture of the Maya and compare Mayan structures with those of the Egyptians or Greeks.

T318

Chapter Projects

Suppose your class is planning to honor someone special in the community or to congratulate a winning team. You need to decide when and where you will hold the event, how you will decorate, and what entertainment and refreshments you will provide. You may also need to decide how to raise funds for the celebration.

Chapter **1** Decimals

Plan a Celebration Your chapter project is to plan a celebration. You must decide how much it will cost and how much money each member of the class must raise. Your plan should include a list of supplies for the event and their costs.

💻 **Take It to the NET** Go to **www.PHSchool.com** for information to help you complete your project.
Web Code: aad-0161

Think about a historic building, such as one of the ancient pyramids or the Eiffel Tower. How many pieces of stone do you think were needed for the bottom of a pyramid compared to a layer near the top? Many buildings use mathematical patterns in their designs.

Chapter **2** Patterns and Variables

Building a Fort For this project, you will build a model of a simple fort. You will record the amounts of materials needed for each layer. You will look for patterns and write equations to describe the patterns.

💻 **Take It to the NET** Go to **www.PHSchool.com** for information to help you complete your project.
Web Code: aad-0261

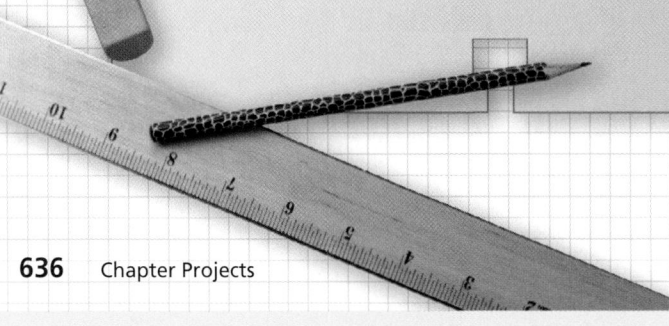

HOME COURT ADVANTAGE

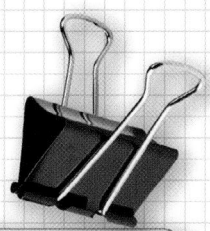

In Malcolm's daydream, he floats in the air on the way to a slam dunk. In reality, he tosses pieces of paper into a wastebasket. He makes some shots, and he misses others.

Compare Basketball Statistics Your project will be to record and compare baskets attempted and baskets made by the players on your own imaginary basketball team. You can shoot baskets with a real basketball on a real court, or you can toss pieces of paper into a wastebasket.

Take It to the NET Go to **www.PHSchool.com** for information to help you complete your project.
Web Code: aad-0361

SEEing is Believing

Have you ever conducted a science experiment? Scientists perform experiments to prove if an idea is correct or incorrect. You can prove if something is correct or not in math class, too.

Design a Demonstration You will learn ways to add fractions and mixed numbers with unlike denominators, but can you prove these techniques really work? Your goal is to prove that they do by giving several demonstrations.

Take It to the NET Go to **www.PHSchool.com** for information to help you complete your project.
Web Code: aad-0461

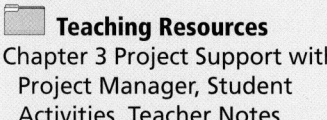

Home Court Advantage

Students apply their knowledge of comparing fractions to making a basket in basketball.

Resources

📁 **Teaching Resources**
Chapter 3 Project Support with Project Manager, Student Activities, Teacher Notes

Teaching Notes

Activating Prior Knowledge
Initiate a discussion on free-throw statistics. Ask:
• *How can you tell if your "shooting" improves over time?* Sample: Shoot in regular sets of 5 or 10; record your results as fractions and compare them.

Physical Education Connection
Have students discuss free-throw statistics for both men and women pro players.

Seeing is Believing

Students apply their knowledge of adding fractions to prove that an adding technique works.

Resources

📁 **Teaching Resources**
Chapter 4 Project Support with Project Manager, Student Activities, Teacher Notes

Teaching Notes

Activating Prior Knowledge
Discuss the idea of carefully designing an experiment and recording the results. Then ask:
• *How can you use models to add fractions with different denominators?* Sample: use fraction models that demonstrate renaming

Inclusion
Discuss and demonstrate that "renaming" a fraction as an equivalent fraction with a different denominator does not change the value of that fraction.

T319

Crack It and Cook It

Students apply their knowledge of multiplying fractions and mixed numbers to adjust a recipe.

Resources

 Teaching Resources
Chapter 5 Project Support with Project Manager, Student Activities, Teacher Notes

Teaching Notes

Activating Prior Knowledge
Discuss how cooks adjust the amounts of ingredients in recipes to make enough of the dish to feed different numbers of diners. Ask:
- *How would you have to adjust the amounts of the ingredients of a dish that serves 4 in order to serve 12?* multiply the quantity of each ingredient by 3

Careers
Discuss mathematical skills that a chef might need. For example, estimating cooking time, amounts of ingredients; working with money amounts, percents, and so on.

Planet of the Stars

Students apply their knowledge of ratios to make scale models of two planets.

Resources

 Teaching Resources
Chapter 6 Project Support with Project Manager, Student Activities, Teacher Notes

Teaching Notes

Activating Prior Knowledge
Talk about models of the solar system that students have seen in planetariums or museums. Ask:
- *How do you think the builders of these models chose the scale to use?* Sample: the size of the space available or the size they want the models to be.

T320

Chapter 5 *Multiplying and Dividing Fractions*

Eating a hearty breakfast is a great way to start any day! You are probably familiar with pouring a bowl of cereal, making toast, or maybe even scrambling eggs. But have you ever made an omelet? An omelet recipe can be pretty simple—eggs, water, and maybe some salt or pepper. However, you can add other ingredients to this basic recipe to suit your taste. A cheese omelet is delicious. So is a bacon-and-tomato omelet. You might also add mushrooms, onions, and peppers.

Create a Recipe Put on your chef's hat. In this chapter project, you will write and name your own recipe for an omelet. Your final project will be a recipe that can feed everyone in your class.

 **Take It to the NET** Go to **www.PHSchool.com** for information to help you complete your project.
Web Code: aad-0561

Chapter 6 *Ratios, Proportions, and Percents*

When you look up at the stars in the sky, you may not think about how far away they are. Stars appear a lot closer than they really are. The same is true of planets. The huge distances between planets make it impossible for books to show how vast our solar system really is.

Make a Scale Model In this chapter project, you will make scale models of two planets. You will compare their sizes and distances from the sun and calculate the ratios involved in your scale model.

 Take It to the NET Go to **www.PHSchool.com** for information to help you complete your project.
Web Code: aad-0661

Chapter 7 *Data and Graphs*

RING!!! The last bell of the day has rung. You and your classmates will soon head in different directions. Some of your classmates are on the same team or in the same club as you. Some of them are not. Do you know how much time your classmates spend on their favorite activities? You could guess the answers to the last question, but a more accurate method of finding the answers would be to collect real data.

Conduct a Survey For this chapter project, you will survey 25 of your friends and classmates. You can choose the survey subject, such as how much time your classmates spend on sports. You will organize and graph the data. Then you will present your findings to your class.

Take It to the NET Go to **www.PHSchool.com** for information to help you complete your project.
Web Code: aad-0761

Puzzling Pictures

Chapter 8 *Tools of Geometry*

Do you remember putting together simple puzzles when you were younger? Puzzles designed for young children are often made of wood and have large pieces. The pieces have straight sides so that the child can put the puzzle together easily.

Create a Puzzle Think about one of your favorite pictures. How would it look as a puzzle? Your project is to make an attractive but challenging puzzle for your classmates. Include as many geometric shapes as you can.

Take It to the NET Go to **www.PHSchool.com** for information to help you complete your project.
Web Code: aad-0861

Chapter Projects **639**

On Your Own Time

Students apply their knowledge of data collection and graphing to conduct a survey and present their results.

Resources

Teaching Resources
Chapter 7 Project Support with Project Manager, Student Activities, Teacher Notes

Teaching Notes

Activating Prior Knowledge
Discuss the different graphs and the kinds of data each displays. Then ask:
• *Which graph would be appropriate to show students' findings?* Sample: bar graphs

Careers
Have students brainstorm a list of jobs in which gathering, organizing, displaying, and interpreting data play a key role. Sample: marketing director, baseball manager

Puzzling Pictures

Students apply their knowledge of geometric shapes to make a puzzle.

Resources

Teaching Resources
Chapter 8 Project Support with Project Manager, Student Activities, Teacher Notes

Teaching Notes

Activating Prior Knowledge
Discuss how solving jigsaw puzzles can help make one. Ask:
• *What math concepts can help you make your puzzle?* Sample: congruent and similar figures, slides, flips, turns, tessellations

Inclusion
Have students begin by dividing their puzzle into rectangles. They can then sub-divide the rectangles into other, smaller shapes.

T321

Go Fish

Students apply their knowledge of geometry and measurement to design a class aquarium.

Resources

Teaching Resources
Chapter 9 Project Support with Project Manager, Student Activities, Teacher Notes

Teaching Notes

Activating Prior Knowledge
Invite students to share their experiences setting up and caring for a fish tank. Ask:
* *What considerations must you keep in mind when planning your proposed aquarium?* Sample: number of fish desired, what plants and objects you want

Science Connection
Have students visit a pet store to learn more about aquariums and differences types of fish.

The Time of Your Life

Students apply their knowledge of measurement to create time lines that show key events in their lives.

Resources

Teaching Resources
Chapter 10 Project Support with Project Manager, Student Activities, Teacher Notes

Teaching Notes

Activating Prior Knowledge
Have students discuss what kinds of events belong on a time line of their lives. Then ask:
* *What might be your first step in setting up a time line of your life?* Sample: choose time intervals

Diversity
Have students who are not comfortable displaying personal data make a time line for a day in a pet's life.

T322

Go Fish

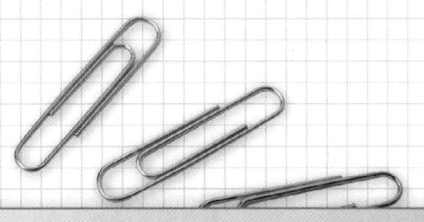

Have you ever spent time gazing into an aquarium full of fish? You can get lost in thought as you look through the glass watching the fish. Many people enjoy having an aquarium because they feel peaceful while observing nature in this miniature form.

Design an Aquarium In this chapter project, you will design an aquarium for your classroom. You should consider how many fish you want in the aquarium. Also consider the size of each type of fish that you plan to place in the aquarium. As part of your final project, you will create a drawing of your proposed aquarium.

Take It to the NET Go to **www.PHSchool.com** for information to help you complete your project.
Web Code: aad-0961

The TIME of your life

Do you know an older person who has lived an interesting life? That person could probably tell you a lot of stories about his or her life. You can tell stories about your life, too. You may not have lived as long, but there have been important events in your past, and there will be others in your future.

Draw a Time Line Your project will be to build a time line of your life—past, present, and future. Think about the time lines you have seen in your social studies classes. You will have a chance to apply math skills such as ratios, measurements, scale drawings, and integers.

Take It to the NET Go to **www.PHSchool.com** for information to help you complete your project.
Web Code: aad-1061

NOW PLAYING

Chapter 11 *Exploring Probability*

Suppose you and a friend have to choose among three movies, and you can't make up your mind. Should you flip a coin? You'd probably agree that assigning "heads" to one movie, "tails" to the second, and "lands on edge" to the third would not give the third movie much of a chance. What should you do?

Design a Three-Choice System Your project will be to design a device or system that is equally fair to three different outcomes. You will test your system to make sure each outcome can be expected one third of the time over a large number of trials.

Take It to the NET Go to **www.PHSchool.com** for information to help you complete your project.
Web Code: aad-1161

WORKING for a Cause

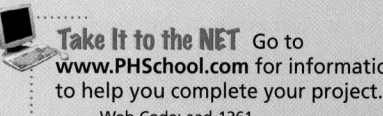

Chapter 12 *Equations and Inequalities*

Have you ever participated in a fundraiser? Schools and sports clubs often use fundraisers as a way to pay for such things as equipment, trips, and camps. You have probably purchased candy bars, magazines, or wrapping paper to help a friend raise money.

Plan a Fundraiser In this chapter project, you will plan a fundraiser. You will choose a cause or charity, decide how much money you would like to raise, and determine the type of event to hold or the type of product to sell. As part of your final project, you will present a fundraising plan to your class.

Take It to the NET Go to **www.PHSchool.com** for information to help you complete your project.
Web Code: aad-1261

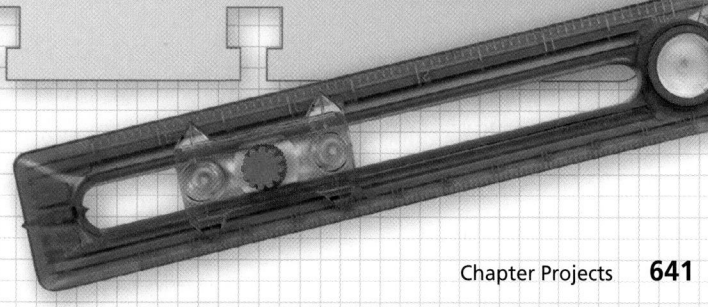

Now Playing

Students apply their understanding of probability to design a fair way to choose among three movies.

Resources

📁 **Teaching Resources**
Chapter 11 Project Support with Project Manager, Student Activities, Teacher Notes

Teaching Notes

Activating Prior Knowledge
Discuss the idea of equally likely outcomes with students. Ask:
• *How could you use a six-sided number cube to give each of the three movies the same chance of being chosen?*
Sample: Assign 1–2 for one movie, 3–4 for another, and 5–6 for the third.

Physical Education Connection
Have students talk about how the idea of equal outcomes applies in the sports world.

Working for a Cause

Students apply their knowledge of operations with money to come up with a fundraising plan.

Resources

📁 **Teaching Resources**
Chapter 12 Project Support with Project Manager, Student Activities, Teacher Notes

Teaching Notes

Activating Prior Knowledge
Discuss fundraising by focusing on who does it and how they do it. Invite students to share their experiences raising money. Ask:
• *What must you consider when you plan how to raise money for a charity?* Sample: how much money is needed, where to find interested contributors, how to motivate them to contribute, how to keep track of and safeguard the money

T323

Chapter 1

Extra Practice

Margin answers:

1. eight hundred fifty-four

2. ten thousand, fifty-nine

3. seven thousand, three hundred two

4. one million, two hundred five thousand, eight hundred seven

5. twenty-six hundredths

6. three thousand four hundred eighty-one ten thousandths

7. seventy-two and fifty-three thousandths

8. six hundred ninety-one and four tenths

● **Lesson 1-1 and Lesson 1-2** Write each number in words. 1–8. See margin.

1. 854   **2.** 10,059   **3.** 7,302   **4.** 1,205,807

5. 0.26   **6.** 0.3481   **7.** 72.053   **8.** 691.4

Write each number in standard form.

9. two hundred sixteen   216   **10.** two hundred twenty-two thousandths   0.222

● **Lesson 1-3** Order each set of decimals from least to greatest.

11. 0.2, 0.4, 0.7
0.2, 0.4, 0.7

12. 0.2, 0.02, 0.202, 0.002
0.002, 0.02, 0.2, 0.202

13. 6.25, 6.05, 6.2, 6.025
6.025, 6.05, 6.2, 6.25

● **Lesson 1-4** Use rounding, front-end estimation, or compatible numbers to estimate.

14. 5.32×2.01
about 10

15. $15.348 - 7.92$
about 7

16. $22.961 \div 3.6$
about 6

17. $728.6 + 36.09$
about 770

● **Lesson 1-5** First estimate and then find each sum or difference.

18. $1.14 + 9.3$ 10; 10.44   **19.** $3.541 + 1.333$ 5; 4.874   **20.** $5.45 - 2.8$ 2; 2.65   **21.** $4.11 - 2.621$ 1; 1.489

● **Lesson 1-6** Use a Problem-Solving Plan to solve the problem.

22. A bag of popcorn costs $2.35. A coupon will save you $2.00 on 4 bags. How much will 5 bags cost before tax if you use the coupon? $9.75

● **Lesson 1-7** Find each product.

23. 1.8×4.302 7.7436   **24.** $0.29(0.43)$ 0.1247   **25.** $7.4(930)$ 6,882   **26.** $0.617 \cdot 0.09$ 0.05553

● **Lesson 1-8** Use mental math to find each product or quotient.

27. $3.85 \times 1,000$ 3,850   **28.** $100 \cdot 2.7$ 270   **29.** $93.1 \div 10$ 9.31   **30.** $105 \div 1,000$ 0.105

● **Lesson 1-9** Find each quotient. Identify each as a terminating or repeating decimal.

31. $8 \div 9$
$0.\overline{8}$; repeating

32. $23 \div 25$
0.92; terminating

33. $348 \div 60$
5.8; terminating

34. $11 \div 16$
0.6875; terminating

● **Lesson 1-10** Find the value of each expression.

35. $2 + 6 \times 3 + 1$ 21   **36.** $(14 + 44) \div 2$ 29   **37.** $3 + 64 \div 4 - 10$ 9   **38.** $144 + 56 \div 4$ 158

Extra Practice

● **Lesson 2-1** Write the next three terms and write a rule for each number pattern.   1–4. See margin.

  1. $1, 4, 16, 64, \ldots$ **2.** $2, 6, 18, 54, \ldots$ **3.** $7, 11, 15, 19, \ldots$ **4.** $80, 74, 68, 62, \ldots$

● **Lesson 2-2** Evaluate each expression for $n = 9$.

  5. $n - 7$ 2   **6.** $3n - 5$ 22   **7.** $22 - 2n$ 4   **8.** $4n \div 6$ 6

● **Lesson 2-3** Write an expression for each word phrase.

  9. 1 less than b $b - 1$ **10.** p times 2 $2p$ **11.** 4 more than b $b + 4$ **12.** n divided by 2 $n \div 2$

● **Lesson 2-4** Use the strategy *Make a Table and Look for a Pattern*.

  13. For $3.00, Audrey buys a sandwich and milk for lunch. Suppose the amount she spends for lunch increases $.10 each day. What will Audrey pay for lunch on the sixth day? $3.50

● **Lesson 2-5** Tell whether each equation is true or false.

  14. $65 = 10 + 85$ false   **15.** $8 \times 6 = 48$ true   **16.** $1 \times 9.8 = 9.8$ true   **17.** $9 = 24 \div 3$ false

  Use mental math to solve each equation.

  18. $20 = y + 1$ 19   **19.** $t - 10 = 24$ 34   **20.** $a \div 3 = 3$ 9   **21.** $178 = 10b$ 17.8

● **Lessons 2-6 and 2-7** Solve each equation. Then check the solution.

  22. $b + 4 = 7.7$ 3.7   **23.** $c + 3.5 = 7.5$ 4   **24.** $n - 1.7 = 8$ 9.7   **25.** $8.4 = s - 0.2$ 8.6

  26. $15t = 600$ 40   **27.** $62 = 2b$ 31   **28.** $x \div 5 = 2.5$ 12.5   **29.** $a \div 0.05 = 140$ 7

● **Lesson 2-8** Write each number in expanded form using powers of 10.   30–33. See margin.

  30. 9,450   **31.** 72,003   **32.** 300,026   **33.** 8,120,432

  Simplify each expression.

  34. $7 + 5^2$ 32   **35.** $(6 - 2)^3 \times 3$ 192   **36.** 8^3 512   **37.** $9^2 + 2^2$ 85

● **Lesson 2-9** Use the Distributive Property to simplify each expression.

  38. 7×78 546   **39.** 3×19 57   **40.** 6×66 396   **41.** 4×47 188

Extra Practice

Extra Practice

1. 256; 1,024; 4,096; the first term is 1. Multiply each term by 4.

2. 162; 486; 1,458; the first term is 2. Multiply each term by 3.

3. 23, 27, 31; the first term is 7. Add 4 to each term.

4. 56, 50, 44; the first term is 80. Subtract 6 from each term.

30. $9 \times 10^3 + 4 \times 10^2 + 5 \times 10^1 + 0 \times 1$

31. $7 \times 10^4 + 2 \times 10^3 + 0 \times 10^2 + 0 \times 10^1 + 3 \times 1$

32. $3 \times 10^5 + 0 \times 10^4 + 0 \times 10^3 + 0 \times 10^2 + 2 \times 10^1 + 6 \times 1$

33. $8 \times 10^6 + 1 \times 10^5 + 2 \times 10^4 + 0 \times 10^3 + 4 \times 10^2 + 3 \times 10^1 + 2 \times 1$

● **Lesson 3-1** Test each number for divisibility by 2, 3, 5, 9, or 10.

1. 324 2, 3, 9   **2.** 2,685 3, 5   **3.** 540   **4.** 114 2, 3   **5.** 31 none   **6.** 981 3, 9

2, 3, 5, 9, 10

● **Lesson 3-2** Tell whether each number is prime or composite.

7. 24   **8.** 49   **9.** 7   **10.** 81   **11.** 37   **12.** 29

composite   composite   prime   composite   prime   prime

● **Lesson 3-3** Find the GCF of each set of numbers.

13. 10, 30 10   **14.** 15, 18 3   **15.** 25, 35 5   **16.** 28, 36 4   **17.** 45, 72 9   **18.** 8, 12, 20 4

● **Lesson 3-4** Write each fraction in simplest form.

19. $\frac{6}{60}$ $\frac{1}{10}$ **20.** $\frac{3}{5}$ $\frac{3}{5}$ **21.** $\frac{27}{36}$ $\frac{3}{4}$ **22.** $\frac{40}{50}$ $\frac{4}{5}$ **23.** $\frac{3}{4}$ $\frac{3}{4}$ **24.** $\frac{42}{70}$ $\frac{3}{5}$

● **Lesson 3-5** Write each mixed number as an improper fraction. Write each improper fraction as a mixed number in simplest form.

25. $1\frac{7}{8}$ $\frac{15}{8}$ **26.** $2\frac{3}{5}$ $\frac{13}{5}$ **27.** $11\frac{1}{9}$ $\frac{100}{9}$ **28.** $\frac{25}{7}$ $3\frac{4}{7}$ **29.** $\frac{39}{12}$ $3\frac{1}{4}$ **30.** $\frac{12}{5}$ $2\frac{2}{5}$

● **Lesson 3-6** Find the LCM of each set of numbers.

31. 4, 8 8   **32.** 6, 14 42   **33.** 15, 25 75   **34.** 20, 36 180   **35.** 3, 4, 12 12   **36.** 8, 10, 15

120

● **Lesson 3-7** Order each set of numbers from least to greatest.

37. $\frac{4}{7}, \frac{4}{5}, \frac{4}{9}$ **38.** $\frac{6}{16}, \frac{7}{16}, \frac{5}{16}$ **39.** $\frac{2}{3}, \frac{5}{6}, \frac{7}{12}$ **40.** $\frac{3}{4}, \frac{4}{6}, \frac{7}{9}$ **41.** $2\frac{3}{4}, 2\frac{1}{8}, 2\frac{1}{2}$ **42.** $\frac{5}{8}, \frac{3}{5}, \frac{9}{20}$

$\frac{4}{9}, \frac{4}{7}, \frac{4}{5}$ $\frac{5}{16}, \frac{6}{16}, \frac{7}{16}$ $\frac{7}{12}, \frac{2}{3}, \frac{5}{6}$ $\frac{4}{6}, \frac{3}{4}, \frac{7}{9}$ $2\frac{1}{8}, 2\frac{1}{2}, 2\frac{3}{4}$ $\frac{9}{20}, \frac{3}{5}, \frac{5}{8}$

● **Lesson 3-8** Write each decimal as a fraction or mixed number in simplest form.

43. 1.25 $1\frac{1}{4}$ **44.** 0.02 $\frac{1}{50}$ **45.** 0.32 $\frac{8}{25}$ **46.** 3.45 $3\frac{9}{20}$ **47.** 0.175 $\frac{7}{40}$ **48.** 2.16 $2\frac{4}{25}$

Write each fraction or mixed number as a decimal. Use a bar to indicate repeating digits.

49. $\frac{2}{3}$ $0.\bar{6}$ **50.** $\frac{2}{5}$ 0.4   **51.** $\frac{1}{4}$ 0.25   **52.** $7\frac{5}{12}$ $7.41\bar{6}$ **53.** $4\frac{2}{3}$ $4.\bar{6}$ **54.** $\frac{13}{8}$ 1.625

● **Lesson 3-9** Use the strategy *Try, Check, and Revise* to solve the problem.

55. Reed pays $.40 for tolls twice a day. He must use exact change. How many quarters, nickels, and dimes does he need for five days?
Answers may vary. Sample: 10 quarters, 10 nickels, and 10 dimes

Chapter 4

Extra Practice

● **Lesson 4-1** Estimate each sum or difference. Use the benchmarks 0, $\frac{1}{2}$, or 1.

1. $\frac{2}{3} + \frac{1}{8}$ about $\frac{1}{2}$
2. $\frac{3}{5} + \frac{4}{7}$ about 1
3. $\frac{5}{6} - \frac{3}{8}$ about $\frac{1}{2}$
4. $\frac{3}{8} - \frac{5}{12}$ about 0

Estimate each sum or difference.

5. $12\frac{3}{4} - 7\frac{4}{9}$ about 6
6. $5\frac{7}{9} + 9\frac{3}{5}$ about 16
7. $2\frac{1}{3} - 1\frac{6}{7}$ about 0
8. $6\frac{3}{10} + 4\frac{5}{8}$ about 11

● **Lessons 4-2 and 4-3** Find each sum or difference.

9. $\frac{5}{8} + \frac{1}{8}$ $\frac{3}{4}$
10. $\frac{4}{5} - \frac{2}{5}$ $\frac{2}{5}$
11. $\frac{11}{12} + \frac{5}{12}$ $1\frac{1}{3}$
12. $\frac{7}{8} - \frac{3}{8}$ $\frac{1}{2}$
13. $\frac{5}{6} + \frac{2}{3}$ $1\frac{1}{2}$
14. $\frac{7}{8} - \frac{3}{4}$ $\frac{1}{8}$
15. $\frac{3}{5} + \frac{5}{8}$ $1\frac{9}{40}$
16. $\frac{3}{8} - \frac{1}{12}$ $\frac{7}{24}$

● **Lesson 4-4** Find each sum.

17. $6\frac{2}{3} + 1\frac{1}{2}$ $8\frac{1}{6}$
18. $5\frac{7}{8} + 1\frac{3}{4}$ $7\frac{5}{8}$
19. $8\frac{1}{4} + 3\frac{1}{3}$ $11\frac{7}{12}$
20. $7\frac{3}{10} + 3\frac{1}{4}$ $10\frac{11}{20}$

● **Lesson 4-5** Find each difference.

21. $7\frac{3}{8} - 1\frac{2}{3}$ $5\frac{17}{24}$
22. $11\frac{1}{6} - 2\frac{3}{4}$ $8\frac{5}{12}$
23. $7\frac{5}{6} - 2\frac{1}{10}$ $5\frac{11}{15}$
24. $6\frac{1}{3} - 2\frac{1}{4}$ $4\frac{1}{12}$

● **Lesson 4-6** Solve each equation.

25. $x + 6\frac{4}{9} = 8\frac{1}{9}$ $1\frac{2}{3}$
26. $y + 2\frac{3}{8} = 8\frac{1}{5}$ $5\frac{33}{40}$
27. $a + 9 = 12\frac{7}{9}$ $3\frac{7}{9}$
28. $4\frac{5}{7} = b - 3\frac{1}{2}$ $8\frac{3}{14}$
29. $c - 11\frac{2}{3} = 15$ $26\frac{2}{3}$
30. $n + 4\frac{1}{2} = 5$ $\frac{1}{2}$
31. $m - 5\frac{3}{4} = 10\frac{1}{2}$ $16\frac{1}{4}$
32. $p - 8\frac{1}{3} = 9\frac{1}{4}$ $17\frac{7}{12}$

● **Lesson 4-7** Find the elapsed time between each pair of times.

33. from 3:45 P.M. to 5:15 P.M. 1 h 30 min
34. from 8:10 P.M. to 11:55 P.M. 3 h 45 min
35. from 11:45 A.M. to 6:23 P.M. 6 h 38 min
35. from 4:05 A.M. to 4:10 P.M. 12 h 5 min
37. from 3:25 P.M. to 5:02 P.M. 1 h 37 min
38. from 8:10 A.M. to 11:55 A.M. 3 h 45 min

● **Lesson 4-8** Use the strategy *Draw a Diagram* to solve the problem.

39. All pies at a bakery are the same size. Apple pies are cut into eight equal pieces. Custard pies are cut into six equal pieces. Two slices of apple pie and three slices of custard pie are placed in a pie tin for a carry-out order. What fraction of the pie tin is filled? $\frac{3}{4}$ of the tin

● **Lesson 5-1** Find each product.

1. $\frac{1}{2}$ of $\frac{2}{3}$ $\frac{1}{3}$

2. $\frac{1}{3}$ of $\frac{1}{5}$ $\frac{1}{15}$

3. $\frac{7}{8} \times \frac{3}{4}$ $\frac{21}{32}$

4. $\frac{7}{6} \times 42$ 49

● **Lesson 5-2** Find each product.

5. $7\frac{1}{2} \times 2\frac{2}{3}$ 20

6. $6\frac{2}{3} \times 7\frac{1}{5}$ 48

7. $5\frac{5}{8} \times 2\frac{1}{3}$ $13\frac{1}{8}$

8. $12\frac{1}{4} \times 6\frac{2}{7}$ 77

● **Lesson 5-3** Find each quotient.

9. $2 \div \frac{4}{5}$ $2\frac{1}{2}$

10. $\frac{2}{3} \div \frac{2}{5}$ $1\frac{2}{3}$

11. $\frac{1}{4} \div \frac{1}{5}$ $1\frac{1}{4}$

12. $\frac{4}{11} \div 8$ $\frac{1}{22}$

● **Lesson 5-4** Estimate each quotient.

13. $12 \div 3\frac{1}{5}$ 4

14. $7\frac{3}{7} \div 1\frac{2}{5}$ 7

15. $41\frac{8}{10} \div 6\frac{1}{3}$ 7

16. $36\frac{2}{7} \div 4\frac{3}{9}$ 9

Find each quotient.

17. $2\frac{1}{4} \div \frac{2}{3}$ $3\frac{3}{8}$

18. $4\frac{1}{2} \div 3\frac{1}{3}$ $1\frac{7}{20}$

19. $2\frac{2}{5} \div \frac{2}{25}$ 30

20. $5\frac{2}{3} \div 1\frac{1}{2}$ $3\frac{7}{9}$

● **Lesson 5-5** Solve each equation. Check the solution.

21. $\frac{x}{4} = 8$ 32

22. $\frac{a}{3} = 9$ 27

23. $\frac{c}{7} = 24$ 168

24. $\frac{m}{2} = 14$ 28

25. $\frac{r}{4} = 3.5$ 14

26. $\frac{t}{12} = 3$ 36

27. $\frac{1}{3}y = 15$ 45

28. $\frac{3}{4}w = 12$ 16

● **Lesson 5-6** Use the strategy *Solve a Simpler Problem* to solve the problem.

29. You want to make a quilt that is 75 inches long and 50 inches wide. How many $6\frac{1}{4}$-inch squares do you need? **96 squares**

● **Lesson 5-7** Choose an appropriate unit for each measurement.

30. capacity of a bathtub **gallons**

31. weight of a school bus **tons**

32. width of a computer monitor **inches**

33. weight of a pair of jeans **ounces**

34. your height **feet**

35. capacity of a water pitcher **quarts**

● **Lesson 5-8** Complete each statement.

36. 4 ft = ■ yd $1\frac{1}{3}$

37. 48 oz = ■ lb 3

38. 32 qt = ■ gal 8

39. 8,000 lb = ■ t 4

40. 10 lb = ■ oz 160

41. ■ ft = 60 in. 5

42. 64 c = ■ pt 32

43. 9 mi = ■ ft 47,520

Chapter 6 Extra Practice

● **Lesson 6-1 Write two different ratios equal to each ratio.**   1-5. Answers may vary.

1. $\frac{30}{60}$ $\frac{1}{2}, \frac{4}{8}$

2. $5:15$ $1:3, 10:30$

3. 13 to 52
1 to 4, 26 to 104

4. $7:77$
$1:11, 14:154$

5. 18 to 72
1 to 4, 9 to 36

● **Lesson 6-2 Find each unit price. Round to the nearest cent. Then determine the better buy.**

6. cereal: 12 ounces for $2.99
16 ounces for $3.59
$.25 per ounce; $.22 per ounce; 16 ounces for $3.59

7. rice: 8 ounces for $1.95
12 ounces for $2.99
$.24 per ounce; $.25 per ounce; 8 ounces for $1.95

● **Lesson 6-3 Do the ratios in each pair form a proportion?**

8. $\frac{6}{30}, \frac{3}{15}$ yes

9. $\frac{9}{12}, \frac{12}{9}$ no

10. $\frac{13}{3}, \frac{26}{6}$ yes

11. $\frac{5}{225}, \frac{2}{95}$ no

12. $\frac{64}{130}, \frac{5}{10}$ no

● **Lesson 6-4 Solve each proportion.**

13. $\frac{a}{50} = \frac{3}{75}$ 2

14. $\frac{18}{b} = \frac{3}{10}$ 60

15. $\frac{51}{17} = \frac{c}{3}$ 9

16. $\frac{2}{16} = \frac{d}{24}$ 3

17. $\frac{3}{45} = \frac{4}{g}$ 60

● **Lesson 6-5 Find each actual distance. Use a map scale of 1 centimeter : 100 kilometers.**

18. 3.5 cm 350 km

19. 1.3 cm 130 km

20. 0.7 cm 70 km

21. 5 cm 500 km

● **Lesson 6-6 Write each percent as a decimal and as a fraction in simplest form.**

22. 42%
$0.42; \frac{21}{50}$

23. 96%
$0.96; \frac{24}{25}$

24. 80%
$0.8; \frac{4}{5}$

25. 1%
$0.01; \frac{1}{100}$

26. 87%
$0.87; \frac{87}{100}$

27. 88%
$0.88; \frac{22}{25}$

Write each decimal or fraction as a percent.

28. 0.18 18%

29. 0.32 32%

30. 0.05 5%

31. $\frac{1}{4}$ 25%

32. $\frac{3}{4}$ 75%

33. $\frac{5}{8}$ 62.5%

● **Lesson 6-7 Find each answer.**

34. 20% of 80 16

35. 15% of 22.5 3.375

36. 50% of 86 43

37. 90% of 100 90

● **Lesson 6-8 Estimate a 15% tip for each bill amount.**   38–43. Answers may vary. Samples are given.

38. $34.90
about $5.25

39. $9.54
about $1.50

40. $17.50
about $2.70

41. $24.80
about $3.75

42. $15.21
about $2.25

43. $42.36
about $6.30

● **Lesson 6-9 Use the strategy _Write an Equation_ to solve the problem.**

44. Kennedy Middle School has 550 students. If the number of students increases by 8 percent, how many students will there be? 594 students

1. mean: 21.875
median: 22.5
mode: 22

2. mean: 12.483
median: 12.5
mode: none

3. mean: 44.875
median: 43.5
mode: 29

4.

Books Read	Tally	Frequency
1	|||	3
2	||	3
3	||	2
4	||||	4

```
                X
    X   X       X
    X   X   X   X
    X   X   X   X
    1   2   3   4
```

5.

wpm	Tally	Frequency
35	||||	4
40	|||	3
45		0
50		0
55	||	2
60		0
65	||	2
70	|	1

```
 X
 X  X
 X  X            X         X
 X  X        X       X  X  X
35 40  45  50  55  60  65  70
```

7. hours of reading per year per person; type of reading material

11b. The United States received 25 silver medals during the 2000 Summer Olympics.

13.
```
6 | 9
7 | 2 4 7 8
8 | 5 6 9
9 | 1
```
Key: 7|2 means 72

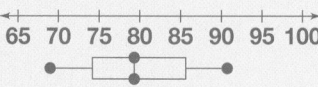
```
65 70 75 80 85 90 95 100
```

Chapter 7 Extra Practice

● **Lesson 7-1 Find the mean, median, and mode of each data set.** 1–3. See margin.

  1. 23, 26, 22, 25, 22, 28, 22, 10   **2.** 14.2, 11.3, 12.0, 11.1, 13.0, 13.3   **3.** 36, 42, 58, 29, 45, 63, 57, 29

● **Lesson 7-2 Make a frequency table and a line plot for each set of data.** 4–5. See margin.

  4. books read each month:
  3, 1, 4, 2, 4, 1, 3, 2, 4, 4, 2, 1

  5. words typed per minute:
  65, 35, 40, 65, 40, 40, 55, 35, 35, 70, 35, 55

● **Lesson 7-3 Use the strategy *Make an Organized List* to solve the problem.**

  6. How many ways can you make $1 using any combination of quarters, nickels, and dimes? **29 ways**

● **Lesson 7-4 Use the bar graph for Exercises 7–8.**

  7. What information is given on each axis? **See margin.**

  8. What is the average yearly reading time for books? **about 100 hours**

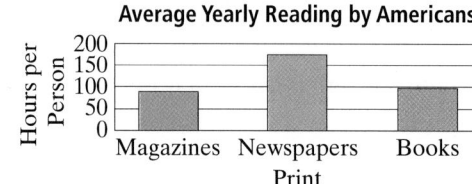

Average Yearly Reading by Americans

● **Lesson 7-5 Use the circle graph for Exercises 9–10.**

  9. What item accounts for the most money in Malinda's budget? **rent**

  10. About what percent of her budget does Malinda use for rent? **25%**

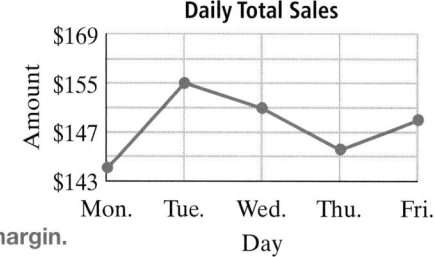

Malinda's Budget

● **Lesson 7-6 The spreadsheet below shows the number of medals the United States won during the 2000 Summer Olympics.**

  11. a. What is the value in C2? **25**
     b. What does this number mean? See margin.
  12. Write the formula for cell E2.
     = B2 + C2 + D2

	A	B	C	D	E	
1	Country	Gold	Silver	Bronze	Total	
2	United States	39	25	33	■	

● **Lesson 7-7 Make a stem-and-leaf plot and a box-and-whisker plot for the set of data below.**

  13. test scores (percents): 86, 74, 72, 89, 69, 85, 78, 91, 77 See margin.

● **Lesson 7-8 Use the line graph at the right.**

  14. Explain why the graph is misleading.
  The intervals on the vertical scale are not the same.
  15. Use the data to draw a graph that is not misleading. **See margin.**

Daily Total Sales

15.
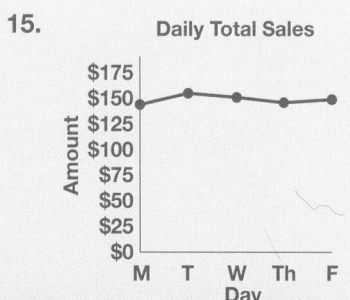
Daily Total Sales

25.
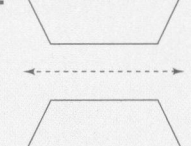

● **Lessons 8-1 and 8-2** Use the diagram at the right for Exercises 1–8.
Name each of the following. 1–2. **Answers may vary.**

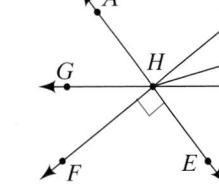

1. three collinear points
   Sample: *G, H, D.*

2. six rays
   Sample: $\overrightarrow{HA}$, $\overrightarrow{HB}$,
   $\overrightarrow{HC}$, $\overrightarrow{HD}$, $\overrightarrow{HE}$, $\overrightarrow{HF}$

3. two perpendicular lines
   $\overleftrightarrow{AE}$ and $\overleftrightarrow{FB}$

Use a protractor to measure each angle. Classify each angle as *acute, right,*
obtuse, **or** *straight.*

4. ∠*BHF* straight 5. ∠*FHC* obtuse 6. ∠*FHA* right   7. ∠*CHD* acute 8. ∠*AHC*
                                                                           obtuse

● **Lesson 8-3** Find the complement and the supplement of each angle measure.

9. 28°
   complement: 62°
   supplement: 152°

10. 13.5°
    complement: 76.5°
    supplement: 166.5°

11. 56.3°
    complement: 33.7°
    supplement: 123.7°

12. 79°
    complement: 11°
    supplement: 101°

13. 85°
    complement: 5°
    supplement: 95°

● **Lesson 8-4** Classify each triangle with the given side lengths by its sides.

14. 7 inches, 9 inches, 7 inches
    isosceles

15. 3 feet, 3 feet, 3 feet
    equilateral

16. 18 yards, 16 yards, 5 yards
    scalene

● **Lesson 8-5** Classify each statement as *true* or *false.*

17. All octagons have eight sides.
    true

18. All rhombuses are squares.
    false

19. All squares are rectangles.
    true

● **Lesson 8-6** Use the strategy of *Use Logical Reasoning* to solve the problem.

20. You have four pairs of pants, six T-shirts, and five vests. How many
    different outfits of pants, T-shirt, and vest can you wear? 120 outfits

● **Lesson 8-7** Each pair of figures appears to be *similar.* Confirm your answer
by finding whether corresponding sides are proportional.

21.
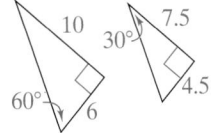
similar

22.
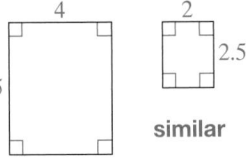
similar

23.
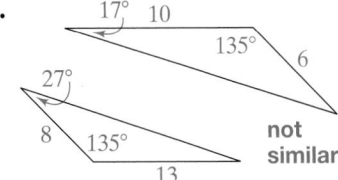
not
similar

● **Lesson 8-8** Trace the figure at the right.

24. Draw all lines of symmetry in the figure.

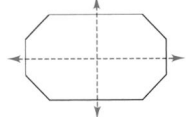

● **Lesson 8-9** Copy the figure at the right on graph paper.

25. Draw its reflection over the given line of reflection.
    See margin.

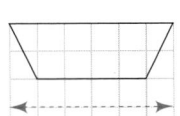

● **Lesson 9-1 Choose an appropriate metric unit of measure.**

    1. capacity of a shampoo bottle mL **2.** mass of a television kg   **3.** length of your shoe cm

● **Lesson 9-2 Complete each statement.**

    4. 35 mm = ■ cm   **5.** 10.8 km = ■ m   **6.** ■ L = 2,400 mL   **7.** 1,008 g = ■ kg
       3.5   10,800   2.4   1.008

● **Lesson 9-3 Estimate the area of each figure. Each square represents
1 square centimeter.**

    8. 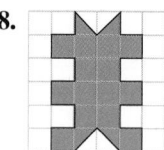 about 16 cm²   **9.**  about 18 cm²   **10.** 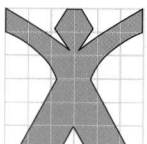 about 16 cm²

● **Lessons 9-3 and 9-4 Find the area of each figure.**

    11.  5.5 ft **52.25 ft²**
          9.5 ft

    12. 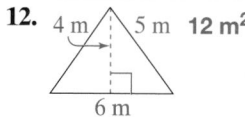 4 m / 5 m **12 m²**
          6 m

    13. **144 cm²**   18 cm
    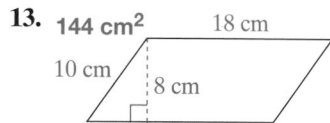 10 cm 8 cm

● **Lessons 9-5 and 9-6 Find the circumference and the area of a circle with
the given diameter *d* or radius *r*. Use 3.14 for *π* and round to the nearest
whole number.**

    14. $d = 26$ yards   **15.** $d = 10.6$ feet   **16.** $r = 30$ inches   **17.** $r = 11$ miles   **18.** $d = 8.5$ meters

       82 yd; 531 yd²   33 ft; 88 ft²   188 in.; 2,826 in.²   69 mi; 380 mi²   27 m; 57 m²

● **Lesson 9-7 Name each figure.**

    19. 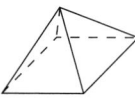   **20.** 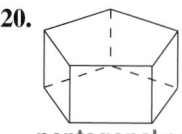   **21.**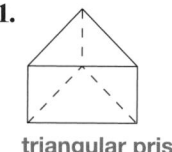

      rectangular pyramid   pentagonal prism   triangular prism

● **Lessons 9-8 and 9-9 Find the surface area and the volume of each
rectangular prism with the given dimensions.**

    22. $\ell = 10$ ft, $w = 5$ ft, $h = 8$ ft   **23.** $\ell = 12$ m, $w = 16$ m, $h = 12$ m
      340 ft²; 400 ft³   1,056 m²; 2,304 m³

● **Lesson 9-10 Use the strategy *Work Backward* to solve this problem.**

    24. If you multiply a number by 6 and then subtract 5, the result is 13. What
is the number? 3

● **Lesson 10-1** Order from least to greatest.

1. 3, −1, 0, −2
−2, −1, 0, 3

2. 4, −8, −5, 2
−8, −5, 2, 4

3. −6, 8, 7, −8
−8, −6, 7, 8

4. −1, −8, 0, 1
−8, −1, 0, 1

● **Lesson 10-2** Find each sum.

5. −3 + (−1) −4   **6.** −14 + 28 14   **7.** −72 + (−53)
−125

8. −101 + 121 20   **9.** 65 + (−5) 60

● **Lesson 10-3** Find each difference.

10. −3 − 1 −4   **11.** 4 − 8 −4   **12.** 31 − (−52) 83   **13.** −27 − (−27) 0   **14.** 19 − (−18) 37

● **Lessons 10-4 and 10-5** Find each product or quotient.

15. −8 × 5 −40   **16.** −4 × (−9) 36   **17.** 1 × (−12) −12   **18.** 93 ÷ (−3) −31

19. −68 ÷ 4 −17   **20.** −5 ÷ (−2) 2.5   **21.** 154 ÷ (−11) −14   **22.** −54 ÷ 9 −6

● **Lesson 10-6** Use the coordinate grid at the right for Exercises 23–30.
Find the coordinates of each point.

23. A (2, 3)   **24.** B (3, −3)   **25.** C (−3, −1)   **26.** D (−3, 3)

Name the point with the given coordinates.

27. (4, 2) G   **28.** (2, −2) I   **29.** (−4, 1) H   **30.** (−2, −4) J

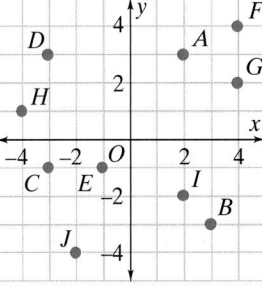

● **Lesson 10-7** Look at the data for Snazzy Stuff. Find the profit or loss for each month.

31. January $5,002   **32.** March $1,263   **33.** May −$86

34. Draw a line graph based on the profits and losses for Snazzy Stuff.
See margin.

● **Lesson 10-8** Make a table and graph each function.

35. Kilometers are a function of meters. See margin.

36. Yards are a function of feet. See margin.

Snazzy Stuff

Month	Income	Expenses
Jan.	$9,002	−$4,000
Feb.	$8,410	−$5,113
Mar.	$7,596	−$6,333
Apr.	$7,523	−$7,641
May	$7,941	−$8,027
June	$8,569	−$6,299

● **Lesson 10-9** Use the strategy *Make a Graph* to solve this problem.

37. A health bar charges $1.76 for a 16-ounce shake and $2.20 for a 20-ounce shake. What should the health bar charge for a 24-ounce shake?
Answers may vary. $2.64

34.

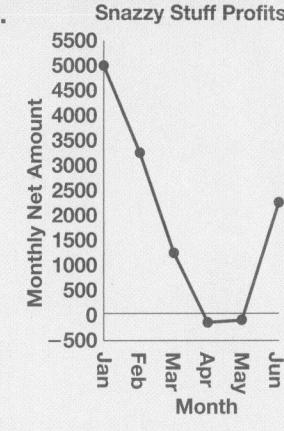

Snazzy Stuff Profits

35.

m	1,000	1,500	2,000	2,500
km	1	1.5	2	2.5

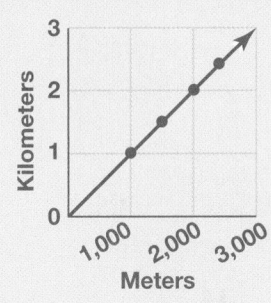

36.

Ft	3	6	9	12
Yd	1	2	3	4

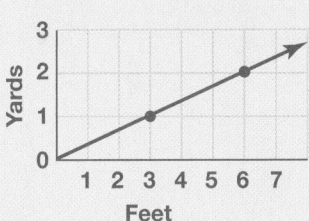

T333

17.

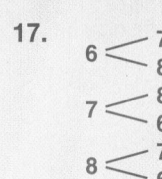

18.

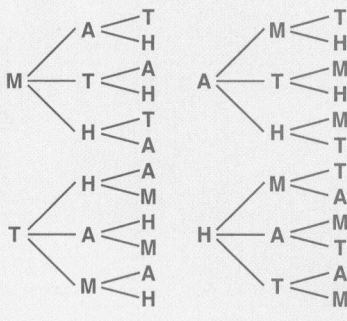

● **Lesson 11-1 A jar contains 2 red, 4 yellow, 3 green, and 5 blue marbles. You select a marble without looking. Find each probability.**

1. P(yellow) $\frac{2}{7}$ **2.** P(green) $\frac{3}{14}$ **3.** P(red or blue) $\frac{1}{2}$ **4.** P(red, green, or blue) $\frac{5}{7}$

● **Lesson 11-2 Find the experimental probability that each person wins.**

5. Yelena won 168 of 196 games. $\frac{6}{7}$

6. Chang played a game 43 times and did not lose a game. **100%**

● **Lesson 11-3 The probability of winning a game is 80%. How many times should you expect to win if you play the following number of times?**

7. 4 **3**   **8.** 10 **8**   **9.** 30 **24**   **10.** 55 **44**   **11.** 125 **100**   **12.** 520 **416**

Write and solve a proportion to make the prediction.

13. In a school of 2,037 students, 500 were asked to name their favorite fruit. Apples were named by 325 students. Predict how many of the 2,037 students would name apples as their favorite fruit. **1,324 students**

● **Lesson 11-4 Use the strategy *Simulate a Problem* to solve the problem.**

14. The forecast calls for a $\frac{2}{3}$ chance of rain for each of the next three days. Find the experimental probability that it rains on two of the three days. Use three number cubes. Let 1, 2, 3, and 4 represent rain. **Check students' work.**

● **Lesson 11-5 Use the counting principle.**

15. You flip a coin six times. Find P(three tails). $\frac{1}{8}$

16. You roll a number cube two times. Find P(two odds). $\frac{1}{4}$

● **Lesson 11-6 Draw a tree diagram to find the permutations. Use each item exactly once.** **17–18. See margins for diagrams.**

17. the numbers 6, 7, 8 **6**   **18.** the letters M, A, T, H **24**

● **Lesson 11-7 A bag contains 2 red, 6 blue, and 2 green marbles. Marbles are drawn twice with replacement. Find the probability of each compound event.**

19. blue, then red $\frac{3}{25}$ **20.** both blue $\frac{9}{25}$ **21.** both not green $\frac{16}{25}$

● **Lesson 12-1** Solve each equation.

1. $2a + 8 = 26$ 9

2. $3c + 2.5 = 29.5$ 9

3. $5b - 13 = 17$ 6

4. $7.5d - 7 = 53$ 8

5. $4e - 1 = -93$ −23

6. $\frac{f}{8} + 6 = 8$ 16

7. $2 + 8g = 34$ 4

8. $-4 + \frac{h}{4} = 4$ 32

● **Lesson 12-2** Write an inequality for each graph.

9.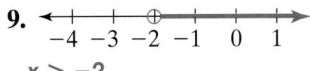
$x > -2$

10.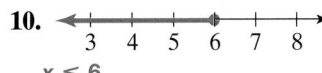
$x \le 6$

11.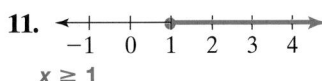
$x \ge 1$

Write an inequality to represent each situation. Then graph the inequality. 12–14. See margin for graphs.

12. The temperature stayed below 0°. $d < 0$

13. You must bring at least \$5 to cover the cost of lunch. $c \ge 5$

14. The paintings for display can be a maximum of 12 inches wide. $p \le 12$

● **Lesson 12-3** Solve each inequality.

15. $m + 8 < 14$
$m < 6$

16. $n - 16 \ge 3$
$n \ge 19$

17. $p + 9 \le -5$
$p \le -14$

18. $q - 8 > 7$
$q > 15$

● **Lesson 12-4** Use the strategy *Draw a Diagram* or *Write an Equation* to solve each problem. Explain why you chose the method you did.

19. There are 120 bicycles in a parade. Thirty-five percent of them have streamers. How many bicycles have streamers? 42; check students' explanations.

20. Your fabric is 10 feet by 8 feet. You want small strips that are 6 inches long and 4 inches wide. How many strips can you cut from the fabric?
480; check students' explanations.

● **Lesson 12-5** Find each square root.

21. $\sqrt{49}$ 7

22. $\sqrt{81}$ 9

23. $\sqrt{169}$ 13

24. $\sqrt{484}$ 22

25. $\sqrt{625}$ 25

26. $\sqrt{900}$ 30

Tell which two consecutive whole numbers the square root is between.

27. $\sqrt{3}$
1, 2

28. $\sqrt{11}$
3, 4

29. $\sqrt{17}$
4, 5

30. $\sqrt{29}$
5, 6

31. $\sqrt{51}$
7, 8

32. $\sqrt{92}$
9, 10

● **Lesson 12-6** Find the missing side length of each right triangle.

33. $a = 16, b = 30, c = $ ▨
34

34. $a = 21, b = $ ▨$, c = 35$
28

35. $a = $ ▨$, b = 9, c = 15$
12

12.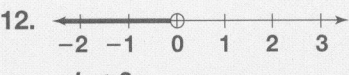
$d < 0$

14.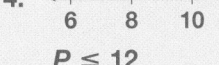
$P \le 12$

13.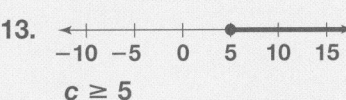
$c \ge 5$

T335

 # Skills Handbook

Place Value of Whole Numbers

The digits in a whole number are grouped into periods. A period has three digits, and each period has a name. Each digit in a whole number has both a place and a value.

Billions Period			Millions Period			Thousands Period			Ones Period		
Hundred billions	Ten billions	Billions	Hundred millions	Ten millions	Millions	Hundred thousands	Ten thousands	Thousands	Hundreds	Tens	Ones
9	5	1	6	3	7	0	4	1	1	8	2

The digit 5 is in the ten billions place. So, its value is 5 ten billions, or 50 billion.

EXAMPLE

a. In what place is the digit 7?

millions

b. What is the value of the digit 7?

7 million

EXERCISES

Use the chart above. Write the place of each digit.

1. the digit 3 ten millions

2. the digit 4 ten thousands

3. the digit 6 hundred millions

4. the digit 8 tens

5. the digit 9 hundred billions

6. the digit 0 hundred thousands

Use the chart above. Write the value of each digit.

7. the digit 3 3 ten million

8. the digit 4 4 ten thousand

9. the digit 6 6 hundred million

10. the digit 8 8 ten

11. the digit 9 9 hundred billion

12. the digit 0 0 hundred thousand

Write the value of the digit 6 in each number.

13. 633
6 hundred

14. 761,523
6 ten thousand

15. 163,500,000
6 ten million

16. 165,417
6 ten thousand

17. 265
6 ten

18. 4,396
6 one

19. 618,920
6 hundred thousand

20. 204,602
6 hundred

21. 162,450,000,000
6 ten billion

22. 7,682
6 hundred

23. 358,026,113
6 thousand

24. 76,030,100
6 million

25. 642,379
6 hundred thousand

26. 16,403
6 thousand

27. 45,060
6 ten

28. 401,601,001
6 hundred thousand

Rounding Whole Numbers

Number lines can help you round numbers. On a number line, 5 is halfway between 0 and 10, 50 is halfway between 0 and 100, and 500 is halfway between 1 and 1,000. The accepted method of rounding is to round 5 up to 10, 50 up to 100, and 500 up to 1,000.

 **EXAMPLE**

Round 2,462 to the nearest ten.

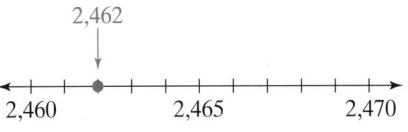

2,462 is closer to 2,460 than to 2,470.

2,462 rounded to the nearest ten is 2,460.

2 **EXAMPLE**

Round 247,451 to the nearest hundred.

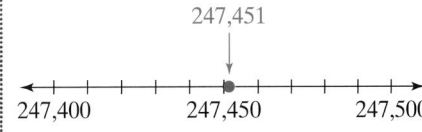

247,451 is closer to 247,500 than to 247,400.

247,451 rounded to the nearest hundred is 247,500.

EXERCISES

Round each number to the nearest ten.

1. 65 **70**
2. 832 **830**
3. 4,437 **4,440**
4. 21,024 **21,020**
5. 3,545 **3,550**

Round each number to the nearest hundred.

6. 889 **900**
7. 344 **300**
8. 2,861 **2,900**
9. 1,138 **1,100**
10. 50,549 **50,500**

11. 6,411 **6,400**
12. 88,894 **88,900**
13. 13,735 **13,700**
14. 17,459 **17,500**
15. 6,059 **6,100**

Round each number to the nearest thousand.

16. 2,400 **2,000**
17. 16,218 **16,000**
18. 7,430 **7,000**
19. 89,375 **89,000**
20. 9,821 **10,000**

21. 15,631 **16,000**
22. 76,900 **77,000**
23. 163,875 **164,000**
24. 38,295 **38,000**
25. 102,359 **102,000**

26. Describe a situation in which it is helpful to round data. **Check students' work.**

27. Explain how to round number 17 in the exercises above to the nearest ten thousand. **Check students' work.**

28. Suppose you round 31 to the nearest hundred. Is 0 a reasonable response? Explain your answer. **Answers may vary. Sample: Yes; 31 is closer to 0 than it is to 100.**

Adding Whole Numbers

When you add, line up the digits in the correct columns. Begin by adding the ones. You may need to regroup from one column to the next.

① EXAMPLE

Add 463 + 58.

Step 1

$$\begin{array}{r} {\scriptstyle 1} \\ 463 \\ + 58 \\ \hline 1 \end{array}$$

Step 2

$$\begin{array}{r} {\scriptstyle 11} \\ 463 \\ + 58 \\ \hline 21 \end{array}$$

Step 3

$$\begin{array}{r} {\scriptstyle 11} \\ 463 \\ + 58 \\ \hline 521 \end{array}$$

② EXAMPLE

Find each sum.

a. 962 + 120

$$\begin{array}{r} 962 \\ + 120 \\ \hline 1{,}082 \end{array}$$

b. 25 + 9 + 143

$$\begin{array}{r} {\scriptstyle 1} \\ 25 \\ 9 \\ + 143 \\ \hline 177 \end{array}$$

c. 3,887 + 1,201

$$\begin{array}{r} {\scriptstyle 1} \\ 3{,}887 \\ + 1{,}201 \\ \hline 5{,}088 \end{array}$$

EXERCISES

Find each sum.

1. $\begin{array}{r} 45 \\ + 31 \\ \hline 76 \end{array}$
2. $\begin{array}{r} 56 \\ + 80 \\ \hline 136 \end{array}$
3. $\begin{array}{r} 25 \\ + 16 \\ \hline 41 \end{array}$
4. $\begin{array}{r} 43 \\ + 29 \\ \hline 72 \end{array}$
5. $\begin{array}{r} 66 \\ + 78 \\ \hline 144 \end{array}$
6. $\begin{array}{r} 87 \\ + 35 \\ \hline 122 \end{array}$

7. $\begin{array}{r} 81 \\ + 312 \\ \hline 393 \end{array}$
8. $\begin{array}{r} 406 \\ + 123 \\ \hline 529 \end{array}$
9. $\begin{array}{r} 207 \\ + 72 \\ \hline 279 \end{array}$
10. $\begin{array}{r} 480 \\ + 365 \\ \hline 845 \end{array}$
11. $\begin{array}{r} 217 \\ + 347 \\ \hline 564 \end{array}$
12. $\begin{array}{r} 675 \\ + 329 \\ \hline 1{,}004 \end{array}$

13. $\begin{array}{r} 2{,}051 \\ + 843 \\ \hline 2{,}894 \end{array}$
14. $\begin{array}{r} 786 \\ + 4{,}109 \\ \hline 4{,}895 \end{array}$
15. $\begin{array}{r} 5{,}227 \\ + 1{,}527 \\ \hline 6{,}754 \end{array}$
16. $\begin{array}{r} 3{,}104 \\ + 2{,}698 \\ \hline 5{,}802 \end{array}$
17. $\begin{array}{r} 5{,}337 \\ + 1{,}812 \\ \hline 7{,}149 \end{array}$
18. $\begin{array}{r} 4{,}282 \\ + 7{,}518 \\ \hline 11{,}800 \end{array}$

19. 78 + 56 **134**
20. 35 + 96 **131**
21. 105 + 71 **176**
22. 29 + 342 **371**
23. 654 + 103 **757**

24. 286 + 42 **328**
25. 55 + 77 **132**
26. 242 + 83 **325**
27. 32 + 68 **100**
28. 108 + 13 **121**

29. 589 + 318 **907**
30. 642 + 975 **1,617**
31. 2,308 + 451 **2,759**
32. 976 + 4,035 **5,011**

33. 8,228 + 1,024
  9,252
34. 5,417 + 2,391
  7,808
35. 6,470 + 9,828
  16,298
36. 7,121 + 5,359
  12,480

Subtracting Whole Numbers

When you subtract, line up the digits in the correct columns. Begin by subtracting the ones. Rename if the bottom digit is greater than the top digit. You may need to rename more than once.

1 EXAMPLE

Subtract 725 − 86.

Step 1

$$\begin{array}{r} 115 \\ 72\cancel{5} \\ -\ 86 \\ \hline 9 \end{array}$$

Step 2

$$\begin{array}{r} 11 \\ 6\,\cancel{1}\,15 \\ 72\cancel{5} \\ -\ 86 \\ \hline 39 \end{array}$$

Step 3

$$\begin{array}{r} 11 \\ 6\,\cancel{1}\,15 \\ 72\cancel{5} \\ -\ 86 \\ \hline 639 \end{array}$$

2 EXAMPLE

Find each difference.

a. 602 − 174

$$\begin{array}{r} 9 \\ 5\,10\,12 \\ 6\,0\,2 \\ -\ 1\,7\,4 \\ \hline 4\,2\,8 \end{array}$$

b. 625 − 273

$$\begin{array}{r} 5\ 12 \\ 625 \\ -\ 273 \\ \hline 352 \end{array}$$

c. 5,002 − 1,247

$$\begin{array}{r} 9\ \ 9 \\ 4\,10\,10\,12 \\ 5{,}002 \\ -\ 1{,}247 \\ \hline 3{,}755 \end{array}$$

EXERCISES

Find each difference.

1. $\begin{array}{r}81\\-37\\\hline 44\end{array}$	**2.** $\begin{array}{r}59\\-23\\\hline 36\end{array}$	**3.** $\begin{array}{r}41\\-19\\\hline 22\end{array}$	**4.** $\begin{array}{r}83\\-25\\\hline 58\end{array}$

5. $\begin{array}{r}99\\-78\\\hline 21\end{array}$ **6.** $\begin{array}{r}87\\-31\\\hline 56\end{array}$

7. $\begin{array}{r}707\\-361\\\hline 346\end{array}$ **8.** $\begin{array}{r}680\\-47\\\hline 633\end{array}$ **9.** $\begin{array}{r}240\\-63\\\hline 177\end{array}$ **10.** $\begin{array}{r}881\\-391\\\hline 490\end{array}$ **11.** $\begin{array}{r}517\\-287\\\hline 230\end{array}$ **12.** $\begin{array}{r}973\\-529\\\hline 444\end{array}$

13. $\begin{array}{r}7{,}411\\-583\\\hline 6{,}828\end{array}$ **14.** $\begin{array}{r}3{,}789\\-809\\\hline 2{,}980\end{array}$ **15.** $\begin{array}{r}6{,}508\\-2{,}147\\\hline 4{,}361\end{array}$ **16.** $\begin{array}{r}8{,}000\\-5{,}274\\\hline 2{,}726\end{array}$ **17.** $\begin{array}{r}3{,}003\\-1{,}998\\\hline 1{,}005\end{array}$ **18.** $\begin{array}{r}8{,}282\\-4{,}118\\\hline 4{,}164\end{array}$

19. 78 − 19 59   **20.** 231 − 99 132   **21.** 901 − 65 836   **22.** 629 − 382 247   **23.** 918 − 133 785

24. 800 − 435 365   **25.** 403 − 122 281   **26.** 973 − 228 745   **27.** 721 − 119 602   **28.** 522 − 146 376

29. 642 − 223 419   **30.** 427 − 193 234   **31.** 444 − 345 99   **32.** 988 − 489 499   **33.** 601 − 425 176

Multiplying Whole Numbers

When you multiply by a one-digit number, multiply the one-digit number by each digit in the other number.

 **EXAMPLE**

Multiply 294 × 7.

Step 1 Multiply 7 by the ones digit.

$$\begin{array}{r} {\scriptstyle 2} \\ 294 \\ \times7 \\ \hline 8 \end{array}$$

Step 2 Multiply 7 by the tens digit.

$$\begin{array}{r} {\scriptstyle 62} \\ 294 \\ \times7 \\ \hline 58 \end{array}$$

Step 3 Multiply 7 by the hundreds digit.

$$\begin{array}{r} {\scriptstyle 62} \\ 294 \\ \times7 \\ \hline 2{,}058 \end{array}$$

When you multiply by a two-digit number, first multiply by the ones. Then multiply by the tens. Add the products. Remember, 0 times any number is equal to 0.

 **EXAMPLE**

Multiply 48 × 327.

Step 1 Multiply the ones.

$$\begin{array}{r} {\scriptstyle 25} \\ 327 \\ \times48 \\ \hline 2{,}616 \end{array}$$

Step 2 Multiply the tens.

$$\begin{array}{r} {\scriptstyle 12} \\ 327 \\ \times48 \\ \hline 2616 \\ +1308 \\ \hline \end{array}$$

Step 3 Add the products.

$$\begin{array}{r} 327 \\ \times48 \\ \hline 2616 \\ +1308 \\ \hline 15{,}696 \end{array}$$

EXERCISES

Find each product.

1. $\begin{array}{r} 81 \\ \times3 \\ \hline 243 \end{array}$

2. $\begin{array}{r} 47 \\ \times2 \\ \hline 94 \end{array}$

3. $\begin{array}{r} 58 \\ \times6 \\ \hline 348 \end{array}$

4. $\begin{array}{r} 678 \\ \times5 \\ \hline 3{,}390 \end{array}$

5. $\begin{array}{r} 412 \\ \times7 \\ \hline 2{,}884 \end{array}$

6. $\begin{array}{r} 326 \\ \times4 \\ \hline 1{,}304 \end{array}$

7. 7 × 45 315
8. 62 × 3 186
9. 213 × 4 852
10. 8 × 177 1,416
11. 673 × 9 6,057

12. 5 × 41 205
13. 3 × 82 246
14. 94 × 6   564
15. 63 × 4   252
16. 58 × 3   174

17. $\begin{array}{r} 25 \\ \times46 \\ \hline 1{,}150 \end{array}$

18. $\begin{array}{r} 62 \\ \times88 \\ \hline 5{,}456 \end{array}$

19. $\begin{array}{r} 808 \\ \times60 \\ \hline 48{,}480 \end{array}$

20. $\begin{array}{r} 409 \\ \times70 \\ \hline 28{,}630 \end{array}$

21. $\begin{array}{r} 915 \\ \times27 \\ \hline 24{,}705 \end{array}$

22. $\begin{array}{r} 312 \\ \times53 \\ \hline 16{,}536 \end{array}$

23. 415 × 76 31,540
24. 500 × 80 40,000
25. 320 × 47 15,040
26. 562 × 18 10,116
27. 946 × 37 35,002

28. 76 × 103 7,828
29. 32 × 558 17,856
30. 371 × 84 31,164
31. 505 × 40 20,200
32. 620 × 19 11,780

658   Skills Handbook

Multiplying and Dividing Whole Numbers by 10, 100, and 1,000

Basic facts and patterns can help you when multiplying and dividing whole numbers by 10, 100, and 1,000.

$8 \times 1 = 8$	$5,000 \div 1 = 5,000$
$8 \times 10 = 80$	$5,000 \div 10 = 500$
$8 \times 100 = 800$	$5,000 \div 100 = 50$
$8 \times 1,000 = 8,000$	$5,000 \div 1,000 = 5$

Count the number of ending zeros.

The product will have this many zeros.

Count the zeros in the divisor.

If possible, remove this many zeros from the dividend. This number will be the quotient.

 **EXAMPLE**

Multiply or divide.

a. $77 \times 1,000$
   $77,000$ ← Insert three zeros.

b. $430 \div 10$
   43 ← Remove one zero.

EXERCISES

Multiply.

1. 85×10
850
2. 85×100
8,500
3. $85 \times 1,000$
85,000
4. $420 \times 1,000$
420,000
5. 420×100
42,000

6. 420×10
4,200
7. 603×100
60,300
8. 97×10
970
9. 31×100
3,100
10. 10×17
170

11. 100×56
5,600
12. $1,000 \times 4$
4,000
13. 13×10
130
14. 68×100
6,800
15. $19 \times 1,000$
19,000

Divide.

16. $3,200 \div 10$
320
17. $3,200 \div 100$
32
18. $32,000 \div 1,000$
32
19. $8,000 \div 100$
80
20. $8,000 \div 10$
800

21. $170 \div 10$
17
22. $45,000 \div 1,000$
45
23. $9,300 \div 10$
930
24. $90 \div 10$
9
25. $6,100 \div 100$
61

26. $7,900 \div 100$
79
27. $2,400 \div 10$
240
28. $240 \div 10$
24
29. $78,000 \div 1,000$
78
30. $9,900 \div 10$
990

Multiply or divide.

31. 76×100
7,600
32. $52 \times 1,000$
52,000
33. $370 \div 10$
37
34. 505×10
5,050
35. $6,200 \div 100$
62

36. $340 \div 10$
34
37. $14,000 \div 1,000$
14
38. 253×100
25,300
39. $3,700 \div 10$
370
40. 418×10
4,180

Dividing Whole Numbers

Division is the opposite of multiplication. So, you multiply the divisor by your estimate for each digit in the quotient. Then subtract. You repeat this step until you have a remainder that is less than the divisor.

EXAMPLE

Divide $23\overline{)1{,}178}$.

Step 1 Estimate the quotient.

$1{,}178 \div 23$ ← The dividend is 1,178. The divisor is 23.

$\downarrow \qquad \downarrow$

$1{,}200 \div 20 = 60$ ← Round 1,178 to the nearest hundred. Round 23 to the nearest ten.

Step 2

$$\begin{array}{r} 6 \\ 23\overline{)1178} \\ -\,138 \end{array}$$
← Try 6 tens.

← $6 \times 23 = 138$
You cannot subtract, so 6 tens is too much.

Step 3

$$\begin{array}{r} 5 \\ 23\overline{)1178} \\ -\,115 \\ \hline 2 \end{array}$$
← Try 5 tens.

← $5 \times 23 = 115$

← Subtract.

Step 4

$$\begin{array}{r} 51 \text{ R5} \\ 23\overline{)1178} \\ -\,115\downarrow \\ \hline 28 \\ -\,23 \\ \hline 5 \end{array}$$

← Bring down 8.

← $1 \times 23 = 23$

← Subtract. The remainder is 5.

Step 5 Check your answer.

First compare your answer to the estimate. Since 51 R5 is close to 60, the answer is reasonable.

Then find $51 \times 23 + 5$.

EXERCISES

Find each quotient. Check your answer.

1. $9\overline{)659}$ 73 R2
2. $9\overline{)376}$ 41 R7
3. $3\overline{)280}$ 93 R1
4. $8\overline{)541}$ 67 R5
5. $8\overline{)232}$ 29

6. $1{,}058 \div 5$
211 R3
7. $3{,}591 \div 3$
1,197
8. $5{,}072 \div 7$
724 R4
9. $1{,}718 \div 4$
429 R2
10. $3{,}767 \div 6$
627 R5

11. $3{,}872 \div 17$
227 R13
12. $19\overline{)1{,}373}$
72 R5
13. $27\overline{)1{,}853}$
68 R17
14. $4{,}195 \div 59$
71 R6
15. $41\overline{)4{,}038}$
98 R20

16. $2{,}612 \div 31$
84 R8
17. $34\overline{)1{,}609}$
47 R11
18. $1{,}937 \div 40$
48 R17
19. $54\overline{)1{,}350}$
25
20. $1{,}824 \div 32$
57

21. **Writing in Math** Describe how to estimate a quotient. Use the words *dividend* and *divisor* in your description. Check students' work.

Zeros in Quotients

When you divide, after you bring down a digit you must write a digit in the quotient. In this example, the second digit in the quotient is 0.

Skills Handbook

EXAMPLE

Find $19\overline{)5{,}823}$.

Step 1

Estimate the quotient.
$5{,}823 \div 19$
  ↓   ↓
$5{,}800 \div 20 = 290$

Step 2

$$
\begin{array}{r}
3 \\
19\overline{)5{,}823} \\
-\,57 \\
\hline
1
\end{array}
$$

Step 3

$$
\begin{array}{r}
30 \\
19\overline{)5{,}823} \\
-\,57 \\
\hline
12 \\
-\,0 \\
\hline
12
\end{array}
$$

Step 4

$$
\begin{array}{r}
306\ \text{R}9 \\
19\overline{)5{,}823} \\
-\,57 \\
\hline
12 \\
-\,0 \\
\hline
123 \\
-\,114 \\
\hline
9
\end{array}
$$

Step 5

Check your answer.
Since 306 is close to 290,
the answer is reasonable.
Find $306 \times 19 + 9$.

EXERCISES

Find each quotient.

1. $7\overline{)212}$ 30 R2

2. $9\overline{)367}$ 40 R7

3. $3\overline{)271}$ 90 R1

4. $8\overline{)485}$ 60 R5

5. $6\overline{)483}$ 80 R3

6. $34\overline{)1{,}371}$
   40 R11

7. $19\overline{)1{,}335}$
   70 R5

8. $62\overline{)1{,}881}$
   30 R21

9. $54\overline{)1{,}094}$
   20 R14

10. $41\overline{)3{,}710}$
    90 R20

11. $282 \div 4$ 70 R2

12. $143 \div 7$ 20 R3

13. $181 \div 3$ 60 R1

14. $400 \div 8$ 50

15. $365 \div 9$ 40 R5

16. $1{,}008 \div 5$
    201 R3

17. $3{,}018 \div 6$
    503

18. $4{,}939 \div 7$
    705 R4

19. $1{,}682 \div 4$
    420 R2

20. $3{,}647 \div 6$
    607 R5

21. $2{,}488 \div 31$
    80 R8

22. $3{,}372 \div 67$
    50 R22

23. $1{,}937 \div 48$
    40 R17

24. $4{,}165 \div 59$
    70 R35

25. $1{,}686 \div 82$
    20 R46

Reading Thermometer Scales

The thermometer at the right shows temperature in degrees Celsius (°C) and degrees Fahrenheit (°F).

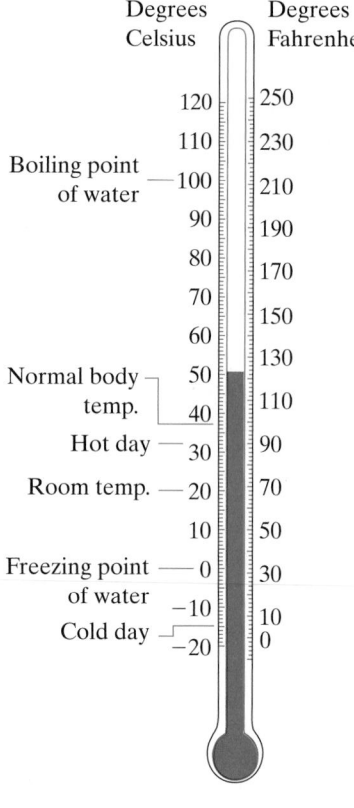

① EXAMPLE

How do you read point *A* on the Celsius thermometer below?

Each 1-degree interval is divided into 10 smaller intervals of 0.1 degree each. The reading at point *A* is 36.2°C.

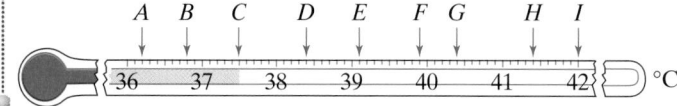

② EXAMPLE

How do you read point *V* on the Fahrenheit thermometer below?

Each 1-degree interval is divided into 5 smaller intervals. Since 10 ÷ 5 = 2, each smaller interval represents 0.2 degree. Count by 0.2, beginning with 98.0. The reading at point *V* is 98.6°F.

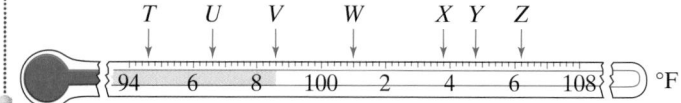

EXERCISES

Use the thermometers above to write the temperature reading for each point. Tell whether the reading is in degrees Celsius (°C) or degrees Fahrenheit (°F).

1. *B* 36.8°C   **2.** *C* 37.5°C   **3.** *D* 38.4°C   **4.** *T* 94.6°F   **5.** *U* 96.6°F   **6.** *Z* 106.2°F

Use the thermometers above to name the point that relates to each temperature reading.

7. 40.4°C *G*   **8.** 42.0°C *I*   **9.** 39.9°C *F*   **10.** 104.8°F *Y*   **11.** 101°F *W*   **12.** 103.8°F *X*

Roman Numerals

The ancient Romans used letters to represent numerals. The table below shows the value of each Roman numeral.

I	V	X	L	C	D	M
1	5	10	50	100	500	1,000

Here are the Roman numerals from 1 to 10.

1	2	3	4	5	6	7	8	9	10
I	II	III	IV	V	VI	VII	VIII	IX	X

Roman numerals are read in groups from left to right.

If the value of the second numeral is the same as or less than the first numeral, add the values. The Roman numerals II, III, VI, VII, and VIII are examples in which you use addition.

If the value of the second numeral is greater than the first numeral, subtract the values. The Roman numerals IV and IX are examples in which you use subtraction.

 EXAMPLE

Find the value of each Roman numeral.

a. CD

$500 - 100$

400

b. MXXVI

$1,000 + 10 + 10 + 5 + 1$

$1,026$

c. XCIV

$(100 - 10) + (5 - 1)$

$90 + 4 = 94$

EXERCISES

Find the value of each Roman numeral.

1. XI 11
2. DIII 503
3. XCV 95
4. CMX 910
5. XXIX 29

6. DLIX 559
7. MLVI 1,056
8. LX 60
9. CDIV 404
10. DCV 605

Write each number as a Roman numeral.

11. 15
XV
12. 35
XXXV
13. 1,632
MDCXXXII
14. 222
CCXXII
15. 159
CLIX

16. 67
LXVII
17. 92
XCII
18. 403
CDIII
19. 1,990
MCMXC
20. 64
LXIV

Estimating Lengths Using Nonstandard Units

Jan wanted to find a way to estimate lengths when she did not have any measuring tools. She measured her hand in several ways, the length of her foot and the length of her walking stride. Then she used these "natural units" as measuring tools.

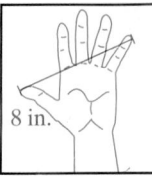

Span

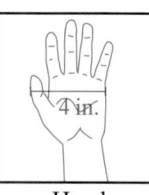

Finger width

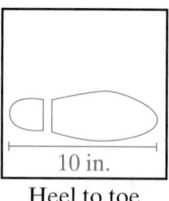

Hand

Heel to toe

10 in.

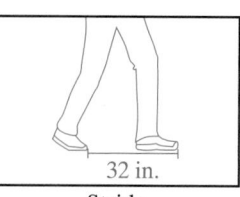

Stride

32 in.

EXAMPLE

Jan used strides to measure the length of her room. She counted about 5 strides. What is the approximate length of the room?

1 stride ≈ 32 in.	← Write the relationship between strides and inches.
5 × 1 stride ≈ 5 × 32 in.	← Multiply both sides by 5.
5 strides ≈ 160 in.	← Change strides to inches.
160 in. ≈ (160 ÷ 12) ft	← Change inches to feet.
160 in. ≈ 13 ft	

The approximate length of the room is 13 feet.

EXERCISES

Measure your "finger width," "hand," "span," and "heel to toe." Use these natural units to find the indicated measure for each object. Then give the approximate measure in inches, feet, or yards. 1–9. Answers may vary.

1. thickness of a math book
2. height of a chair
3. height of a door
4. length of an eraser
5. height of your desk
6. length of a new pencil
7. distance across a room
8. thickness of a door
9. length of a chalkboard

10. **Open-Ended** Measure your stride. Then measure something such as a hallway in strides, and approximate the length in feet or yards. Tell what distance you measured. **Check students' work.**

Tables

Table 1 Measures

Metric	United States Customary
Length	**Length**
10 millimeters (mm) = 1 centimeter (cm)	12 inches (in.) = 1 foot (ft)
100 cm = 1 meter (m)	36 in. = 1 yard (yd)
1,000 mm = 1 meter	3 ft = 1 yard
1,000 m = 1 kilometer (km)	5,280 ft = 1 mile (mi)
	1,760 yd = 1 mile
Area	**Area**
100 square millimeters (mm^2) =	144 square inches (in.^{2}) =
1 square centimeter (cm^2)	1 square foot (ft^2)
10,000 cm^2 = 1 square meter (m^2)	9 ft^2 = 1 square yard (yd^2)
	4,840 yd^2 = 1 acre
Volume	**Volume**
1,000 cubic millimeters (mm^3) =	1,728 cubic inches (in.^{3}) =
1 cubic centimeter (cm^3)	1 cubic foot (ft^3)
1,000,000 cm^3 = 1 cubic meter (m^3)	27 ft^3 = 1 cubic yard (yd^3)
Mass	**Mass**
1,000 milligrams (mg) = 1 gram (g)	16 ounces (oz) = 1 pound (lb)
1,000 g = 1 kilogram (kg)	2,000 lb = 1 ton (t)
Liquid Capacity	**Liquid Capacity**
1,000 milliliters (mL) = 1 liter (L)	8 fluid ounces (fl oz) = 1 cup (c)
1,000 L = 1 kiloliter (kL)	2 c = 1 pint (pt)
	2 pt = 1 quart (qt)
	4 qt = 1 gallon (gal)

Time

60 seconds (s) = 1 minute (min)
60 min = 1 hour (h)
24 h = 1 day
7 days = 1 week (wk)
365 days ≈ 52 wk ≈ 1 year (yr)

Table 2 📖 Reading Math Symbols

+	plus (addition)	p. 5
=	is equal to	p. 6
>	is greater than	p. 6
<	is less than	p. 6
−	minus (subtraction)	p. 17
×, ·	times (multiplication)	p. 19
≈	is approximately equal to	p. 19
÷, $\sqrt{\ }$	divide (division)	p. 20
( )	parentheses for grouping	p. 25
. . .	and so on	p. 44
°	degree(s)	p. 79
≠	is not equal to	p. 84
$\overset{?}{=}$	Is the statement true?	p. 84
3^4	3 to the power 4	p. 99
$\frac{1}{4}$	reciprocal of 4	p. 230
3 : 5	ratio of 3 to 5	p. 269
%	percent	p. 293
*	multiply (in a spreadsheet formula)	p. 348
$\overline{AB}$	segment AB	p. 373
$\overrightarrow{AB}$	ray AB	p. 373
$\overleftrightarrow{AB}$	line AB	p. 373
$\angle ABC$	angle with sides BA and BC	p. 379
$\angle A$	angle with vertex A	p. 379
⦜	right angle (90°)	p. 380

P	perimeter	p. 441
ℓ	length	p. 441
w	width	p. 441
A	area	p. 441
s	side	p. 442
b	base	p. 446
h	height	p. 446
C	circumference	p. 453
d	diameter	p. 453
π	pi; ≈ 3.14	p. 453
r	radius	p. 453
S.A.	surface area	p. 469
V	volume	p. 472
B	area of base	p. 472
-6	opposite of 6	p. 491
$|5|$	absolute value of 5	p. 492
$(2, 3)$	ordered pair with x-coordinate 2 and y-coordinate 3	p. 518
P(event)	probability of the event	p. 548
!	factorial	p. 576
≥	is greater than or equal to	p. 601
≤	is less than or equal to	p. 601
$\sqrt{9}$	square root of 9	p. 616

Formulas and Properties

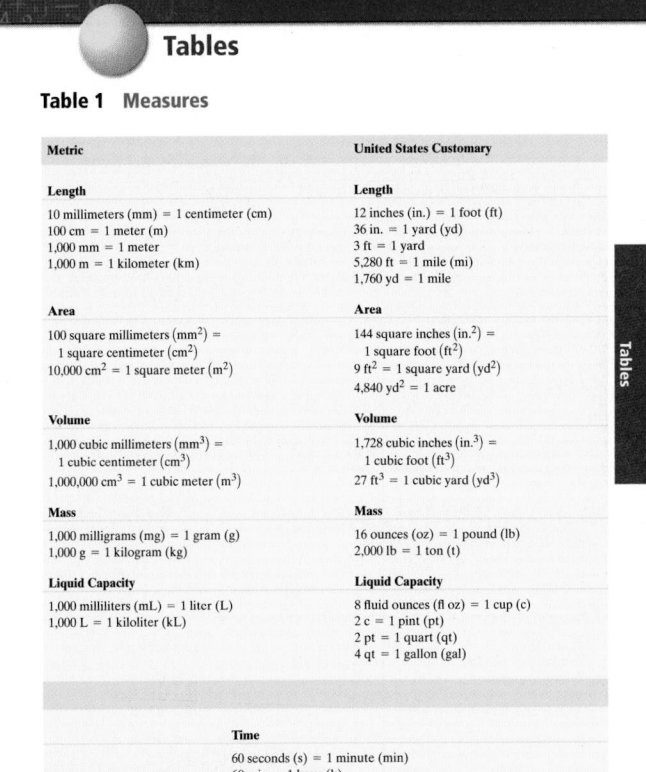

Rectangle
$P = 2\ell + 2w$, or $P = 2(\ell + w)$
$A = \ell \times w$

Square
$P = s + s + s + s$, or $P = 4s$
$A = s \times s$, or $A = s^2$

Triangle
$A = \frac{1}{2}b \times h$

Parallelogram
$A = b \times h$

Circle
$C = 2\pi r$, or $C = \pi d$
$A = \pi r^2$

Pythagorean Theorem
$a^2 + b^2 = c^2$

Rectangular Prism
$V = B \times h$, or $V = \ell \times w \times h$
Surface Area (S.A.) =
$2(\ell \times w) + 2(\ell \times h) + 2(w \times h)$

Cylinder
$V = B \times h$, or $V = \pi r^2 \times h$
Surface Area (S.A.) =
$2\pi r^2 + C \times h$

Properties of Numbers

Unless otherwise stated, the variables $a, b, c,$ and d used in these properties can be replaced with any number represented on a number line.

Associative Properties
Addition $\quad (a + b) + c = a + (b + c)$
Multiplication $\quad (a \cdot b) \cdot c = a \cdot (b \cdot c)$

Commutative Properties
Addition $\quad a + b = b + a$
Multiplication $\quad a \cdot b = b \cdot a$

Identity Properties
Addition $\quad a + 0 = a$ and $0 + a = a$
Multiplication $\quad a \cdot 1 = a$ and $1 \cdot a = a$

Inverse Properties
Addition
$a + (-a) = 0$ and $-a + a = 0$
Multiplication
$a \cdot \frac{1}{a} = 1$ and $\frac{1}{a} \cdot a = 1$ $(a \neq 0)$

Distributive Properties
$a(b + c) = ab + ac$
$a(b - c) = ab - ac$

Cross Products Property
If $\frac{a}{c} = \frac{b}{d}$, then $ad = bc$ $(c \neq 0, d \neq 0)$.

Zero-Product Property
If $ab = 0$, then $a = 0$ or $b = 0$.

Properties of Equality
Addition $\quad$ If $a = b$, then $a + c = b + c$.
Subtraction $\quad$ If $a = b$, then $a - c = b - c$.
Multiplication $\quad$ If $a = b$, then $a \cdot c = b \cdot c$.
Division $\quad$ If $a = b$, and $c \neq 0$, then $\frac{a}{c} = \frac{b}{c}$.
Substitution $\quad$ If $a = b$, then b can replace a in any expression.

Reflexive $\quad a = a$
Symmetric $\quad$ If $a = b$, then $b = a$.
Transitive $\quad$ If $a = b$ and $b = c$, then $a = c$.

Properties of Inequality
Addition $\quad$ If $a > b$, then $a + c > b + c$.
$\qquad\qquad$ If $a < b$, then $a + c < b + c$.
Subtraction $\quad$ If $a > b$, then $a - c > b - c$.
$\qquad\qquad$ If $a < b$, then $a - c < b - c$.

Multiplication
If $a > b$ and c is positive, then $ac > bc$.
If $a < b$ and c is positive, then $ac < bc$.
Division
If $a > b$ and c is positive, then $\frac{a}{c} > \frac{b}{c}$.
If $a < b$ and c is positive, then $\frac{a}{c} < \frac{b}{c}$.

Note: The Properties of Inequality apply also to ≤ and ≥.

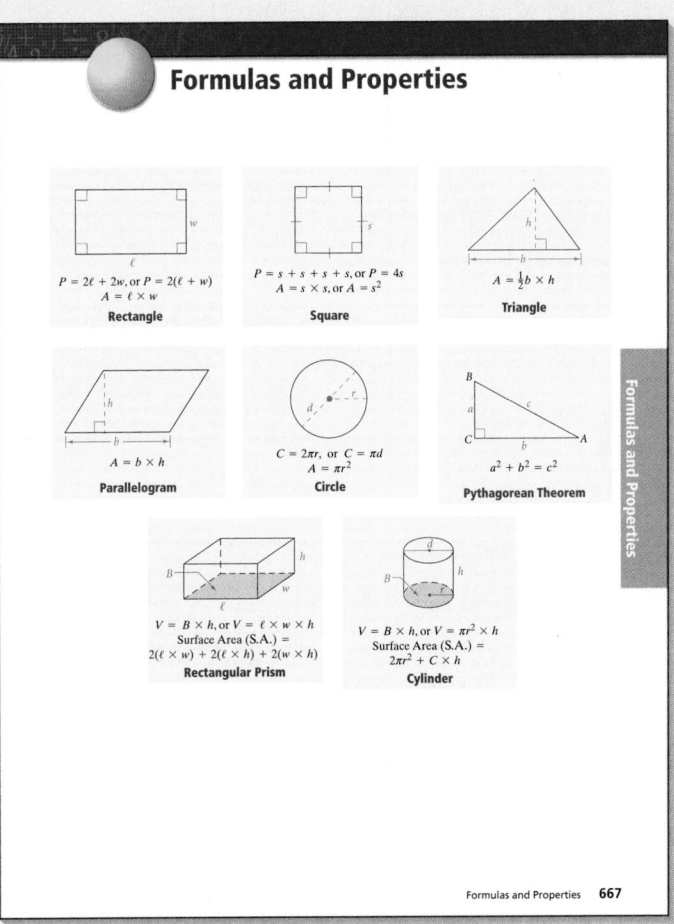

English/Spanish Illustrated Glossary

A

Absolute value (p. 492)   The absolute value of a number is its distance from 0 on a number line.

Valor absoluto (p. 492)   El valor absoluto de un número es su distancia del 0 en una recta numérica.

-7 is 7 units from 0, so $|-7| = 7$.

Acute angle (p. 380)   An acute angle is an angle with a measure between 0° and 90°.

Ángulo agudo (p. 380)   Un ángulo agudo es un ángulo que mide entre 0° y 90°.

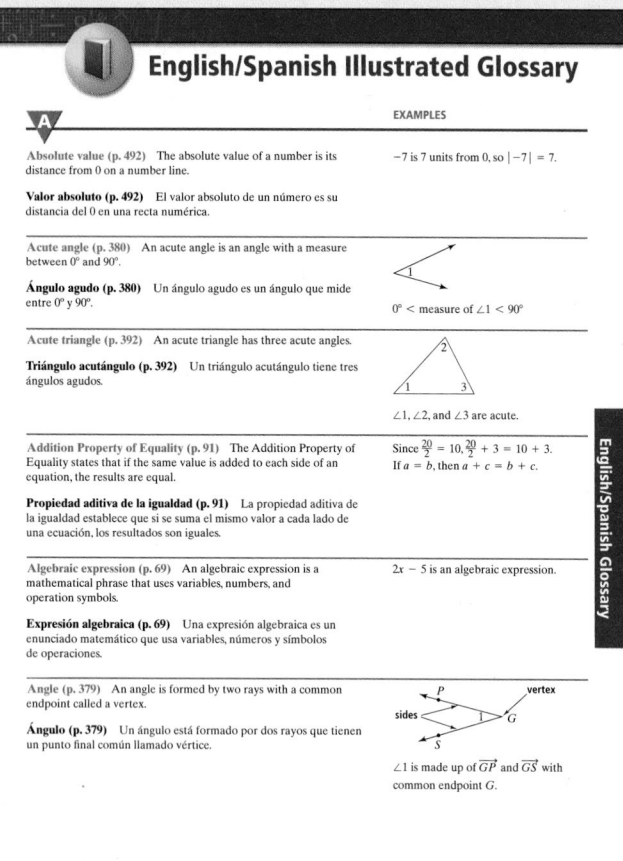

$0° <$ measure of $\angle 1 < 90°$

Acute triangle (p. 392)   An acute triangle has three acute angles.

Triángulo acutángulo (p. 392)   Un triángulo acutángulo tiene tres ángulos agudos.

$\angle 1, \angle 2,$ and $\angle 3$ are acute.

Addition Property of Equality (p. 91)   The Addition Property of Equality states that if the same value is added to each side of an equation, the results are equal.

Propiedad aditiva de la igualdad (p. 91)   La propiedad aditiva de la igualdad establece que si se suma el mismo valor a cada lado de una ecuación, los resultados son iguales.

Since $\frac{20}{2} = 10, \frac{20}{2} + 3 = 10 + 3$.
If $a = b$, then $a + c = b + c$.

Algebraic expression (p. 69)   An algebraic expression is a mathematical phrase that uses variables, numbers, and operation symbols.

Expresión algebraica (p. 69)   Una expresión algebraica es un enunciado matemático que usa variables, números y símbolos de operaciones.

$2x - 5$ is an algebraic expression.

Angle (p. 379)   An angle is formed by two rays with a common endpoint called a vertex.

Ángulo (p. 379)   Un ángulo está formado por dos rayos que tienen un punto final común llamado vértice.

$\angle 1$ is made up of $\overrightarrow{GP}$ and $\overrightarrow{GS}$ with common endpoint G.

Angle bisector (p. 385)   An angle bisector is a ray that divides an angle into angles of equal measure.

Bisectriz de un ángulo (p. 385)   La bisectriz de un ángulo es un rayo que divide un ángulo en ángulos de igual medida.

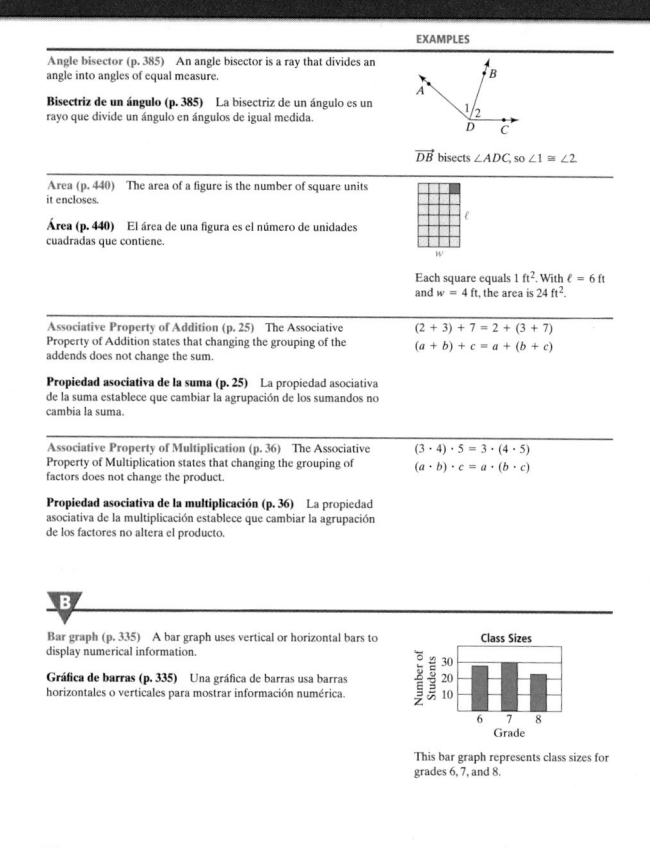

$\overrightarrow{DB}$ bisects $\angle ADC$, so $\angle 1 \cong \angle 2$.

Area (p. 440)   The area of a figure is the number of square units it encloses.

Área (p. 440)   El área de una figura es el número de unidades cuadradas que contiene.

Each square equals 1 ft². With $\ell = 6$ ft and $w = 4$ ft, the area is 24 ft².

Associative Property of Addition (p. 25)   The Associative Property of Addition states that changing the grouping of the addends does not change the sum.

Propiedad asociativa de la suma (p. 25)   La propiedad asociativa de la suma establece que cambiar la agrupación de los sumandos no cambia la suma.

$(2 + 3) + 7 = 2 + (3 + 7)$
$(a + b) + c = a + (b + c)$

Associative Property of Multiplication (p. 36)   The Associative Property of Multiplication states that changing the grouping of factors does not change the product.

Propiedad asociativa de la multiplicación (p. 36)   La propiedad asociativa de la multiplicación establece que cambiar la agrupación de los factores no altera el producto.

$(3 \cdot 4) \cdot 5 = 3 \cdot (4 \cdot 5)$
$(a \cdot b) \cdot c = a \cdot (b \cdot c)$

B

Bar graph (p. 335)   A bar graph uses vertical or horizontal bars to display numerical information.

Gráfica de barras (p. 335)   Una gráfica de barras usa barras horizontales o verticales para mostrar información numérica.

This bar graph represents class sizes for grades 6, 7, and 8.

Base (p. 99)   When a number is written in exponential form, the number that is used as a factor is the base.

Base (p. 99)   Cuando un número se escribe en forma exponencial, el número que se usa como factor es la base.

$5^4 = 5 \times 5 \times 5 \times 5$
↑— base

Bases of two-dimensional figures (pp. 446, 447)   See *Parallelogram*, *Triangle*, and *Trapezoid*.

Bases de figuras bidimensionales (pp. 446, 447)   Ver *Parallelogram*, *Triangle* y *Trapezoid*.

Benchmark (p. 171)   A benchmark is a convenient number used to replace fractions that are less than 1.

Punto de referencia (p. 171)   Un punto de referencia es un número conveniente que se usa para reemplazar fracciones menores que 1.

Using benchmarks, you would estimate $\frac{5}{6} + \frac{4}{9}$ as $1 + \frac{1}{2}$.

Box-and-whisker plot (p. 356)   A box-and-whisker plot is a graph that summarizes a data set using five key values. There is a box in the middle and "whiskers" at either side. The quartile values show how each fourth of the data is distributed.

Gráfica de caja y brazos (p. 356)   Una gráfica de caja y brazos es un diagrama que resume un conjunto de datos usando cinco valores clave. Hay una caja en el centro y extensiones a cada lado. Los valores cuartiles muestran cómo se distribuye cada cuarto de los datos.

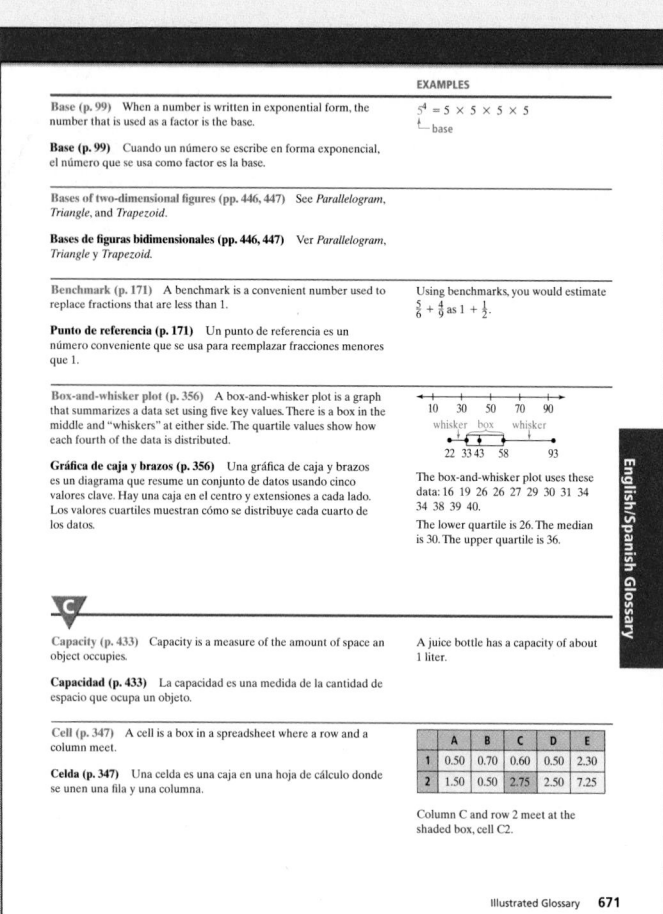

The box-and-whisker plot uses these data: 16 19 26 26 27 29 30 31 34 34 38 39 40.
The lower quartile is 26. The median is 30. The upper quartile is 36.

C

Capacity (p. 433)   Capacity is a measure of the amount of space an object occupies.

Capacidad (p. 433)   La capacidad es una medida de la cantidad de espacio que ocupa un objeto.

A juice bottle has a capacity of about 1 liter.

Cell (p. 347)   A cell is a box in a spreadsheet where a row and a column meet.

Celda (p. 347)   Una celda es una caja en una hoja de cálculo donde se unen una fila y una columna.

	A	B	C	D	E
1	0.50	0.70	0.60	0.50	2.30
2	1.50	0.50	2.75	2.50	7.25

Column C and row 2 meet at the shaded box, cell C2.

Center of a circle (p. 452)   A circle is named by its center.

Centro de un círculo (p. 452)   Un círculo es denominado por su centro.

Circle O

Center of rotation (p. 416)   The center of rotation is a fixed point about which a figure is rotated.

Centro de rotación (p. 416)   El centro de rotación es un punto fijo alrededor del cual rota una figura.

center of rotation

Chord (p. 452)   A chord is a segment that has both endpoints on a circle.

Cuerda (p. 452)   Una cuerda es un segmento que tiene ambos extremos sobre un círculo.

$\overline{CB}$ is a chord of circle O.

Circle (p. 452)   A circle is the set of points in a plane that are all the same distance from a given point called the center.

Círculo (p. 452)   Un círculo es el conjunto de puntos de un plano que están a la misma distancia de un punto dado llamado centro.

Circle graph (p. 342)   A circle graph is a graph of data where a circle represents the whole.

Gráfica circular (p. 342)   Una gráfica circular es una gráfica de datos donde un círculo representa el todo.

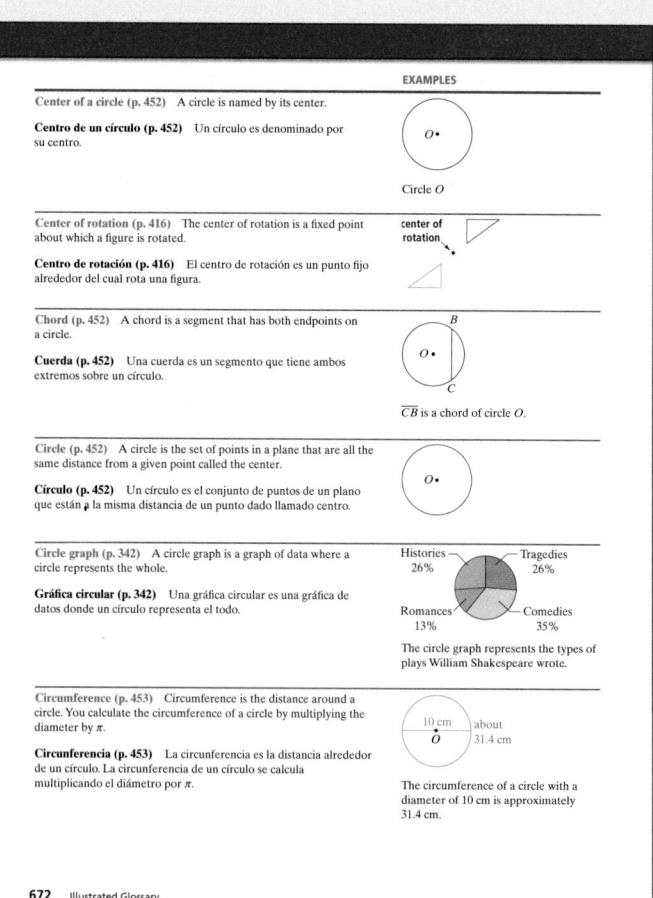

The circle graph represents the types of plays William Shakespeare wrote.

Circumference (p. 453)   Circumference is the distance around a circle. You calculate the circumference of a circle by multiplying the diameter by π.

Circunferencia (p. 453)   La circunferencia es la distancia alrededor de un círculo. La circunferencia de un círculo se calcula multiplicando el diámetro por π.

The circumference of a circle with a diameter of 10 cm is approximately 31.4 cm.

T348

Collinear (p. 374) Points on the same line are collinear.

Colineal (p. 374) Los puntos que están en la misma recta son colineales.

B C R S

Points B, C, R, and S are collinear.

Common factor (p. 128) A factor that two or more numbers share is a common factor.

Factor común (p. 128) Un número que es factor de dos o más números, es un factor común.

4 is a common factor of 8 and 20.

Common multiple (p. 143) A multiple shared by two or more numbers is a common multiple.

Múltiplo común (p. 143) Un número que es múltiplo de dos o más números, es un múltiplo común.

12 is a common multiple of 4 and 6.

Commutative Property of Addition (p. 25) The Commutative Property of Addition states that changing the order of the addends does not change the sum.

Propiedad conmutativa de la suma (p. 25) La propiedad conmutativa de la suma establece que al cambiar el orden de los sumandos no se altera la suma.

$3 + 1 = 1 + 3$
$a + b = b + a$

Commutative Property of Multiplication (p. 36) The Commutative Property of Multiplication states that changing the order of the factors does not change the product.

Propiedad conmutativa de la multiplicación (p. 36) La propiedad conmutativa de la multiplicación establece que al cambiar el orden de los factores no se altera el producto.

$6 \cdot 3 = 3 \cdot 6$
$a \cdot b = b \cdot a$

Compass (p. 384) A compass is a geometric tool used to draw circles or arcs.

Compás (p. 384) Un compás es una herramienta que se usa en geometría para dibujar círculos o arcos.

Compatible numbers (p. 20) Compatible numbers are numbers that are easy to compute mentally.

Números compatibles (p. 20) Los números compatibles son números con los que se puede calcular mentalmente con facilidad.

Estimate $151 \div 14.6$.
$151 \approx 150, 14.6 \approx 15$
$150 \div 15 = 10$
$151 \div 14.6 \approx 10$

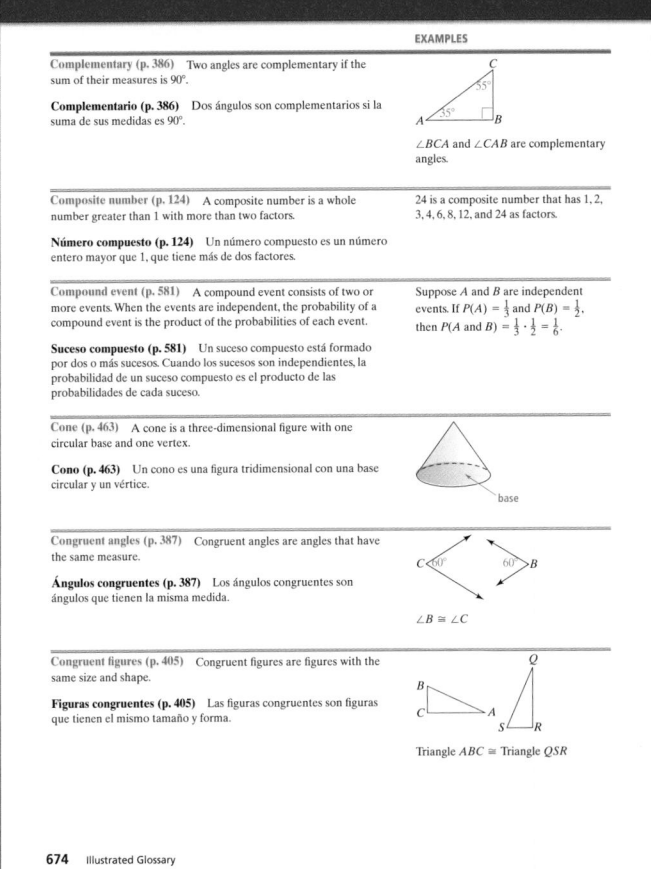

Complementary (p. 386) Two angles are complementary if the sum of their measures is 90°.

Complementario (p. 386) Dos ángulos son complementarios si la suma de sus medidas es 90°.

∠BCA and ∠CAB are complementary angles.

Composite number (p. 124) A composite number is a whole number greater than 1 with more than two factors.

Número compuesto (p. 124) Un número compuesto es un número entero mayor que 1, que tiene más de dos factores.

24 is a composite number that has 1, 2, 3, 4, 6, 8, 12, and 24 as factors.

Compound event (p. 581) A compound event consists of two or more events. When the events are independent, the probability of a compound event is the product of the probabilities of each event.

Suceso compuesto (p. 581) Un suceso compuesto está formado por dos o más sucesos. Cuando los sucesos son independientes, la probabilidad de un suceso compuesto es el producto de las probabilidades de cada suceso.

Suppose A and B are independent events. If $P(A) = \frac{1}{3}$ and $P(B) = \frac{1}{2}$, then $P(A \text{ and } B) = \frac{1}{3} \cdot \frac{1}{2} = \frac{1}{6}$.

Cone (p. 463) A cone is a three-dimensional figure with one circular base and one vertex.

Cono (p. 463) Un cono es una figura tridimensional con una base circular y un vértice.

base

Congruent angles (p. 387) Congruent angles are angles that have the same measure.

Ángulos congruentes (p. 387) Los ángulos congruentes son ángulos que tienen la misma medida.

∠B ≅ ∠C

Congruent figures (p. 405) Congruent figures are figures with the same size and shape.

Figuras congruentes (p. 405) Las figuras congruentes son figuras que tienen el mismo tamaño y forma.

Triangle ABC ≅ Triangle QSR

Congruent segments (p. 393) Segments that have the same length are congruent segments.

Segmentos congruentes (p. 393) Los segmentos que tienen la misma longitud son segmentos congruentes.

$\overline{AB}$ is congruent to $\overline{WX}$.

Conjecture (p. 64) A conjecture is a prediction that suggests what can be expected to happen.

Conjetura (p. 64) Una conjetura es una predicción que sugiere lo que se puede esperar que ocurra.

Every clover has three leaves.

Coordinate plane (p. 518) A coordinate plane is formed by a horizontal number line called the x-axis and a vertical number line called the y-axis.

Plano de coordenadas (p. 518) Un plano de coordenadas está formado por una recta numérica horizontal llamada eje de x y por una recta numérica vertical llamada eje de y.

Corresponding parts (p. 405) The matching parts of similar figures are called corresponding parts.

Partes correspondientes (p. 405) Las partes que coinciden de figuras semejantes se llaman partes correspondientes.

$\overline{BC}$ and $\overline{YZ}$ are corresponding sides.
∠A and ∠X are corresponding angles.

Counting principle (p. 569) If there are m ways of making one choice from a first situation and n ways of making a choice from a second situation, then there are $m \times n$ ways to make the first choice followed by the second.

Principio de conteo (p. 569) Si hay m maneras de hacer una elección para una primera situación y n maneras de hacer una elección para una segunda situación, entonces hay $m \times n$ maneras de hacer la primera elección seguida de la segunda.

Toss a coin and roll a standard number cube. The total number of possible outcomes is $2 \times 6 = 12$.

Cross products (p. 284) For two ratios, the cross products are found by multiplying the denominator of one ratio by the numerator of the other ratio.

Productos cruzados (p. 284) En dos razones, los productos cruzados se hallan al multiplicar el denominador de una razón por el numerador de la otra razón.

In the proportion $\frac{2}{5} = \frac{10}{25}$, the cross products are $2 \cdot 25$ and $5 \cdot 10$.

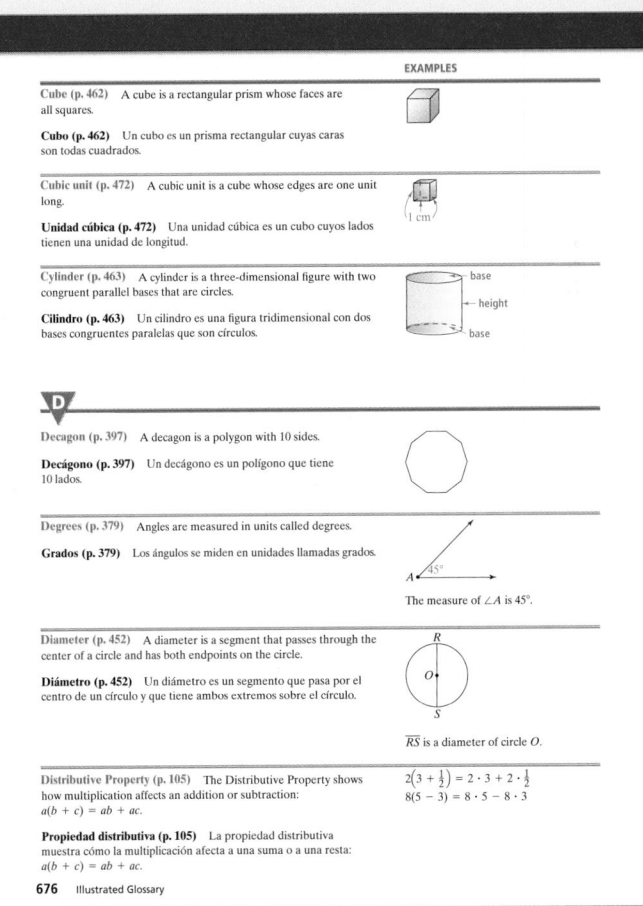

Cube (p. 462) A cube is a rectangular prism whose faces are all squares.

Cubo (p. 462) Un cubo es un prisma rectangular cuyas caras son todas cuadradas.

Cubic unit (p. 472) A cubic unit is a cube whose edges are one unit long.

Unidad cúbica (p. 472) Una unidad cúbica es un cubo cuyos lados tienen una unidad de longitud.

1 cm

Cylinder (p. 463) A cylinder is a three-dimensional figure with two congruent parallel bases that are circles.

Cilindro (p. 463) Un cilindro es una figura tridimensional con dos bases congruentes paralelas que son círculos.

base
height
base

D

Decagon (p. 397) A decagon is a polygon with 10 sides.

Decágono (p. 397) Un decágono es un polígono que tiene 10 lados.

Degrees (p. 379) Angles are measured in units called degrees.

Grados (p. 379) Los ángulos se miden en unidades llamadas grados.

The measure of ∠A is 45°.

Diameter (p. 452) A diameter is a segment that passes through the center of a circle and has both endpoints on the circle.

Diámetro (p. 452) Un diámetro es un segmento que pasa por el centro de un círculo y que tiene ambos extremos sobre el círculo.

$\overline{RS}$ is a diameter of circle O.

Distributive Property (p. 105) The Distributive Property shows how multiplication affects an addition or subtraction:
$a(b + c) = ab + ac$.

Propiedad distributiva (p. 105) La propiedad distributiva muestra cómo la multiplicación afecta a una suma o a una resta:
$a(b + c) = ab + ac$.

$2\left(3 + \frac{1}{2}\right) = 2 \cdot 3 + 2 \cdot \frac{1}{2}$
$8(5 - 3) = 8 \cdot 5 - 8 \cdot 3$

T349

Divisible (p. 119)   A whole number is divisible by a second whole number if the first number can be divided by the second number with a remainder of 0.

Divisible (p. 119)   Un número entero es divisible por un segundo número entero si el primer número se puede dividir por el segundo número y el residuo es 0.

16 is divisible by 1, 2, 4, 8, and 16.

Division Property of Equality (p. 95)   The Division Property of Equality states that if both sides of an equation are divided by the same nonzero number, the results are equal.

Propiedad de división de la igualdad (p. 95)   La propiedad de división de la igualdad establece que si ambos lados de una ecuación se dividen por el mismo número distinto de cero, los resultados son iguales.

Since $3(2) = 6, 3(2) \div 2 = 6 \div 2$.
If $a = b$ and $c \neq 0$, then $\frac{a}{c} = \frac{b}{c}$.

Double bar graph (p. 340)   A double bar graph is a graph that uses bars to compare two sets of data.

Gráfica de doble barra (p. 340)   Una gráfica de doble barra es una gráfica que usa barras para comparar dos conjuntos de datos.

Average Class Enrollment

This double bar graph shows class size for grades 6, 7, and 8 for boys and girls.

Double line graph (p. 340)   A double line graph is a graph that compares changes over time for two sets of data.

Gráfica de doble línea (p. 340)   Una gráfica de doble línea es una gráfica que compara los cambios de dos conjuntos de datos a través del tiempo.

This double line graph represents seasonal air conditioner and snowblower sales for a large department store chain.

E

Edge (p. 462)   An edge is a segment formed by the intersection of two faces of a three-dimensional figure.

Arista (p. 462)   Una arista es un segmento formado por la intersección de dos caras de una figura tridimensional.

edge

Elapsed time (p. 202)   The time between two events is elapsed time.

Tiempo transcurrido (p. 202)   El tiempo que hay entre dos sucesos es el tiempo transcurrido.

The elapsed time between 8:10 A.M. and 8:45 A.M. is 35 minutes.

Equal ratios (p. 270)   Equal ratios name the same number. Equal ratios written as fractions are equivalent fractions.

Razones iguales (p. 270)   Las razones iguales indican el mismo número. Las razones iguales escritas como fracciones son fracciones equivalentes.

The ratios $\frac{4}{7}$ and $\frac{8}{14}$ are equal.

Equally likely outcomes (p. 547)   Equally likely outcomes are outcomes that have the same chance of occurring.

Resultados igualmente probables (p. 547)   Los resultados igualmente probables son resultados que tienen la misma posibilidad de ocurrir.

When a number cube is rolled once, the outcomes 1, 2, 3, 4, 5, and 6 are all equally likely outcomes.

Equation (p. 84)   An equation is a mathematical sentence with an equal sign.

Ecuación (p. 84)   Una ecuación es una oración matemática con un signo igual.

$27 \div 9 = 3$ and $x + 10 = 8$ are examples of equations.

Equilateral triangle (p. 393)   An equilateral triangle is a triangle with three congruent sides.

Triángulo equilátero (p. 393)   Un triángulo equilátero es un triángulo que tiene tres lados congruentes.

$\overline{SL} \cong \overline{LW} \cong \overline{WS}$

Equivalent fractions (p. 134)   Equivalent fractions are fractions that name the same amount.

Fracciones equivalentes (p. 134)   Las fracciones equivalentes son fracciones que indican la misma cantidad.

$\frac{1}{2}$ and $\frac{25}{50}$ are equivalent fractions.

Evaluating algebraic expressions (p. 69)   To evaluate an algebraic expression, replace each variable with a number. Then follow the order of operations.

Evaluación de una expresión algebraica (p. 69)   Para evaluar una expresión algebraica se reemplaza cada variable con un número. Luego se sigue el orden de las operaciones.

To evaluate the expression $3x + 2$ for $x = 4$, substitute 4 for x.
$3x + 2 = 3(4) + 2 = 14$

Even number (p. 120)   An even number is any whole number that ends with a 0, 2, 4, 6, or 8.

Número par (p. 120)   Un número par es cualquier número entero que termina en 0, 2, 4, 6 u 8.

20 and 534 are even numbers.

Event (p. 547)   A collection of possible outcomes is an event.

Suceso (p. 547)   Un suceso es un grupo de resultados posibles.

In a game that includes tossing a coin and rolling a standard number cube, "heads and a 2" is an event.

Expanded form (p. 9)   The expanded form of a number is the sum that shows the place and value of each digit. See also *Standard form.*

Forma desarrollada (p. 9)   La forma desarrollada de un número es la suma que muestra el lugar y valor de cada dígito. Ver también *Standard form.*

4.85 can be written in expanded form as $4 + 0.8 + 0.05$.

Experimental probability (p. 553)   For a series of trials, the experimental probability of an event is the ratio of the number of times an event occurs to the total number of trials.
$P(\text{event}) = \frac{\text{number of times an event occurs}}{\text{total number of trials}}$

Probabilidad experimental (p. 553)   En una serie de pruebas, la probabilidad experimental de un suceso es la razón del número de veces que ocurre un suceso al número total de pruebas.
$P(\text{suceso}) = \frac{\text{número de veces que ocurre un suceso}}{\text{número de pruebas}}$

A basketball player makes 15 baskets in 28 attempts. The experimental probability that the player makes a basket is $\frac{15}{28} \approx 54\%$.

Exponent (p. 99)   An exponent tells how many times a number, or base, is used as a factor.

Exponente (p. 99)   Un exponente dice cuántas veces se usa como factor un número o base.

exponent
$3^4 = 3 \times 3 \times 3 \times 3$
Read 3^4 as *three to the fourth power.*

Expression (p. 48)   An expression is a mathematical phrase containing numbers and operation symbols.

Expresión (p. 48)   Una expresión es un enunciado matemático que contiene números y símbolos de operaciones.

The expression $24 - 6 \div 3$ contains two operations.

Exterior angles (p. 387)   The angles outside two lines that are crossed by a transversal are called exterior angles.

Ángulos exteriores (p. 387)   Los ángulos que están fuera de las dos rectas cruzadas por una secante se llaman ángulos exteriores.

Angles 1, 2, 7, and 8 are exterior angles.

F

Face (p. 462)   A face is a flat, polygon-shaped surface of a three-dimensional figure.

Cara (p. 462)   Una cara es una superficie plana de una figura tridimensional que tiene la forma de un polígono.

face

Factor (p. 123)   A factor is a whole number that divides another whole number with a remainder of 0.

Divisor (p. 123)   Un divisor es un número entero que divide a otro número entero y el residuo es 0.

1, 2, 3, 4, 6, 9, 12, 18, and 36 are factors of 36.

Factor tree (p. 124)   A factor tree is a diagram that shows how a composite number breaks down into its prime factors.

Árbol de factores (p. 124)   Un árbol de factores es un diagrama que muestra cómo se descompone un número compuesto en sus factores primos.

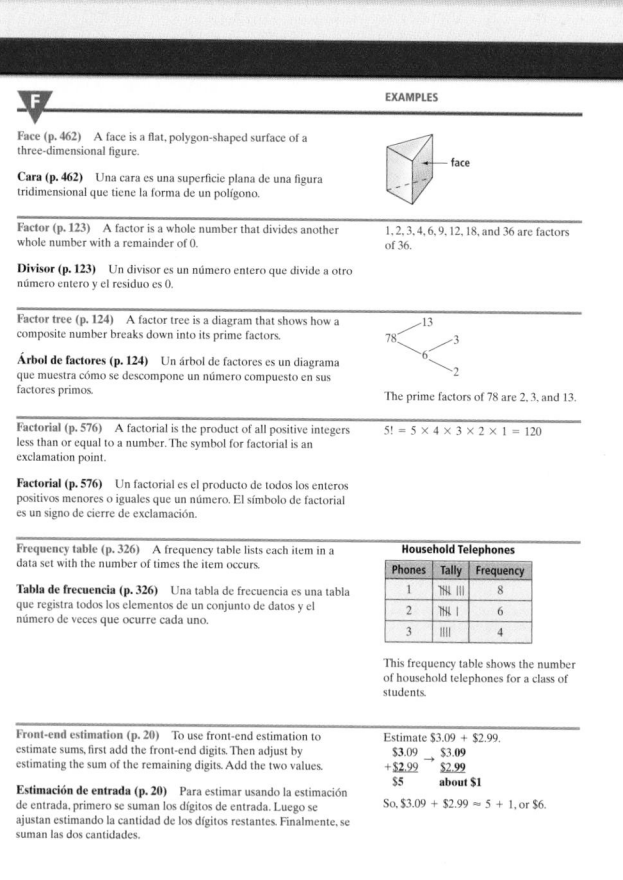

The prime factors of 78 are 2, 3, and 13.

Factorial (p. 576)   A factorial is the product of all positive integers less than or equal to a number. The symbol for factorial is an exclamation point.

Factorial (p. 576)   Un factorial es el producto de todos los enteros positivos menores o iguales que un número. El símbolo de factorial es un signo de cierre de exclamación.

$5! = 5 \times 4 \times 3 \times 2 \times 1 = 120$

Frequency table (p. 326)   A frequency table lists each item in a data set with the number of times the item occurs.

Tabla de frecuencia (p. 326)   Una tabla de frecuencia es una tabla que registra todos los elementos de un conjunto de datos y el número de veces que ocurre cada uno.

Household Telephones

Phones	Tally	Frequency
1	卌 III	8
2	卌 I	6
3	IIII	4

This frequency table shows the number of household telephones for a class of students.

Front-end estimation (p. 20)   To use front-end estimation to estimate sums, first add the front-end digits. Then adjust by estimating the sum of the remaining digits. Add the two values.

Estimación de entrada (p. 20)   Para estimar usando la estimación de entrada, primero se suman los dígitos de entrada. Luego se ajustan estimando la cantidad de los dígitos restantes. Finalmente, se suman las dos cantidades.

Estimate $3.09 + 2.99.
$\begin{array}{ll} \$3.09 & \$3.09 \\ +\$2.99 & \underline{\$2.99} \\ \$5 & \text{about } \$1 \end{array}$
So, $3.09 + 2.99 \approx 5 + 1$, or $6.

Function (p. 527) A function is a relationship that assigns exactly one output value for each input value.

Función (p. 527) Una función es una relación que asigna exactamente un valor resultante a cada valor inicial.

Earned income *i* is a function of the number of hours worked *h*. If you earn $6 per hour, then your income can be expressed by the function $i = 6h$.

G

Gram (p. 432) The standard unit of mass in the metric system is the gram.

Gramo (p. 432) La unidad de masa estándar en el sistema métrico es el gramo.

A paper clip has the mass of about 1 gram.

Graph of a function (p. 528) The graph of a function is the graph of all the points whose coordinates are solutions of the equation.

Gráfica de una función (p. 528) La gráfica de una función es la gráfica de todos los puntos cuyas coordenadas son soluciones a la ecuación.

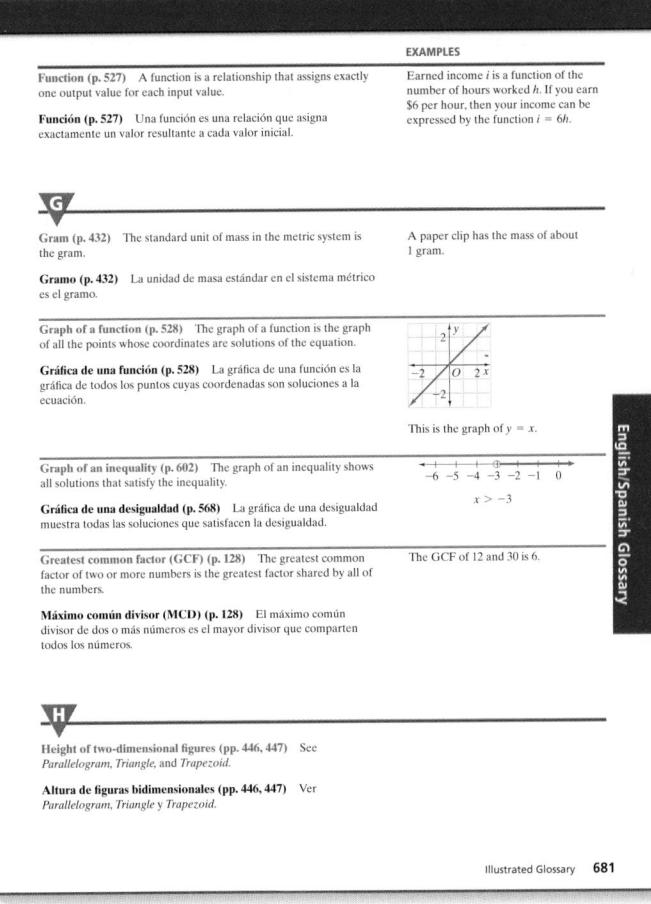

This is the graph of $y = x$.

Graph of an inequality (p. 602) The graph of an inequality shows all solutions that satisfy the inequality.

Gráfica de una desigualdad (p. 568) La gráfica de una desigualdad muestra todas las soluciones que satisfacen la desigualdad.

$x > -3$

Greatest common factor (GCF) (p. 128) The greatest common factor of two or more numbers is the greatest factor shared by all of the numbers.

Máximo común divisor (MCD) (p. 128) El máximo común divisor de dos o más números es el mayor divisor que comparten todos los números.

The GCF of 12 and 30 is 6.

H

Height of two-dimensional figures (pp. 446, 447) See *Parallelogram, Triangle,* and *Trapezoid.*

Altura de figuras bidimensionales (pp. 446, 447) Ver *Parallelogram, Triangle y Trapezoid.*

Hexagon (p. 397) A hexagon is a polygon with six sides.

Hexágono (p. 397) Un hexágono es un polígono que tiene seis lados.

Histogram (p. 336) A histogram is a bar graph with no spaces between the bars. The height of each bar shows the frequency of data within that interval.

Histograma (p. 336) Un histograma es una gráfica de barras sin espacio entre las barras. La altura de cada barra muestra la frecuencia de los datos dentro del intervalo.

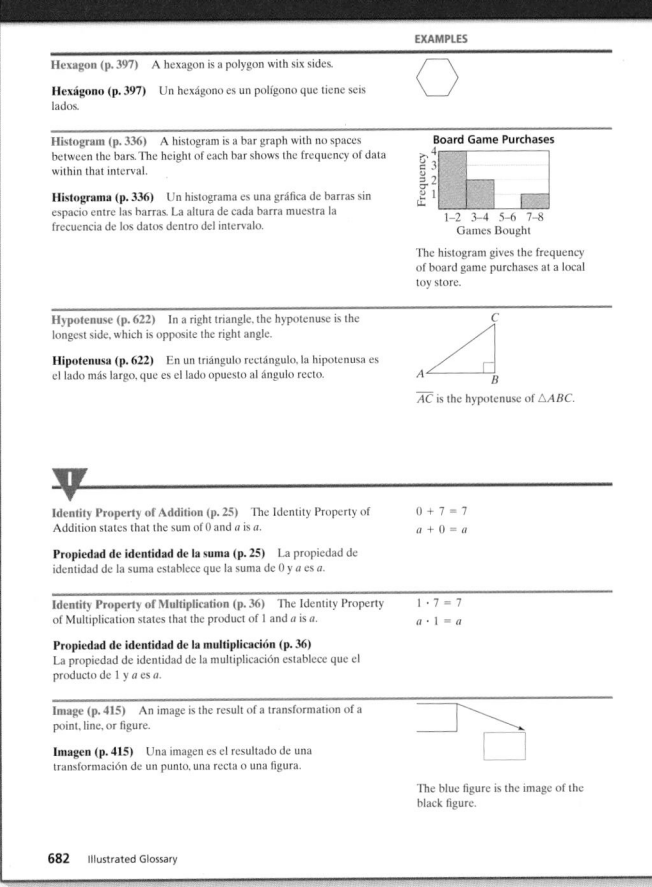

The histogram gives the frequency of board game purchases at a local toy store.

Hypotenuse (p. 622) In a right triangle, the hypotenuse is the longest side, which is opposite the right angle.

Hipotenusa (p. 622) En un triángulo rectángulo, la hipotenusa es el lado más largo, que es el lado opuesto al ángulo recto.

$\overline{AC}$ is the hypotenuse of $\triangle ABC$.

I

Identity Property of Addition (p. 25) The Identity Property of Addition states that the sum of 0 and *a* is *a*.

Propiedad de identidad de la suma (p. 25) La propiedad de identidad de la suma establece que la suma de 0 y *a* es *a*.

$0 + 7 = 7$
$a + 0 = a$

Identity Property of Multiplication (p. 36) The Identity Property of Multiplication states that the product of 1 and *a* is *a*.

Propiedad de identidad de la multiplicación (p. 36) La propiedad de identidad de la multiplicación establece que el producto de 1 y *a* es *a*.

$1 \cdot 7 = 7$
$a \cdot 1 = a$

Image (p. 415) An image is the result of a transformation of a point, line, or figure.

Imagen (p. 415) Una imagen es el resultado de una transformación de un punto, una recta o una figura.

The blue figure is the image of the black figure.

Improper fraction (p. 139) An improper fraction has a numerator that is greater than or equal to its denominator.

Fracción impropia (p. 139) Una fracción impropia tiene un numerador mayor o igual que su denominador.

$\frac{24}{15}$ and $\frac{16}{16}$ are improper fractions.

Independent events (p. 580) Two events are independent events if the occurrence of one event does not affect the probability of the occurrence of the other.

Sucesos independientes (p. 580) Dos sucesos son independientes si el acontecimiento de uno no afecta la probabilidad de que el otro suceso ocurra.

Suppose you draw two marbles, one after the other, from a bag. If you replace the first marble before drawing the second marble, the events are independent.

Inequality (p. 601) An inequality is a mathematical sentence that contains $<, >, \leq, \geq,$ or $\neq$.

Desigualdad (p. 601) Una desigualdad es una oración matemática que contiene los signos $<, >, \leq, \geq$ o $\neq$.

$x < -5$
$x > 8$
$x \leq 1$
$x \geq -11$
$x \neq 3$

Integers (p. 491) Integers are the set of positive whole numbers, their opposites, and 0.

Enteros (p. 491) Los enteros son el conjunto de números enteros positivos, sus opuestos y el 0.

$\ldots -3, -2, -1, 0, 1, 2, 3, \ldots$

Interior angles (p. 387) The angles between two lines that are crossed by a transversal are called interior angles.

Ángulos interiores (p. 387) Los ángulos que están entre dos rectas, cruzadas por una secante se llaman ángulos interiores.

Angles 3, 4, 5, and 6 are interior angles.

Intersecting lines (p. 374) Intersecting lines lie in the same plane and have exactly one point in common.

Rectas que se intersectan (p. 374) Las rectas que se intersectan están en el mismo plano y tienen exactamente un punto en común.

Inverse operations (p. 90) Inverse operations are operations that undo each other.

Operaciones inversas (p. 90) Las operaciones inversas son las operaciones que se anulan entre ellas.

Addition and subtraction are inverse operations.

Isosceles triangle (p. 393) An isosceles triangle is a triangle with at least two congruent sides.

Triángulo isósceles (p. 393) Un triángulo isósceles es un triángulo que tiene al menos dos lados congruentes.

$\overline{LM} \cong \overline{LB}$

L

Least common denominator (LCD) (p. 148) The least common denominator of two or more fractions is the least common multiple (LCM) of their denominators.

Mínimo común denominador (mcd) (p. 148) El mínimo común denominador de dos o más fracciones es el mínimo común múltiplo (mcm) de sus denominadores.

The LCD of the fractions $\frac{3}{8}$ and $\frac{7}{10}$ is 40.

Least common multiple (LCM) (p. 143) The least common multiple of two numbers is the smallest number that is a multiple of both numbers.

Mínimo común múltiplo (mcm) (p. 143) El mínimo común múltiplo de dos números es el menor número que es múltiplo de ambos números.

The LCM of 15 and 6 is 30.

Legs of a right triangle (p. 622) The legs of a right triangle are the two shorter sides of the triangle.

Catetos de un triángulo rectángulo (p. 622) Los catetos de un triángulo rectángulo son los dos lados más cortos del triángulo.

$\overline{AB}$ and $\overline{BC}$ are the legs of triangle ABC.

Line (p. 373) A line is a series of points that extends in two opposite directions without end.

Recta (p. 373) Una recta es una serie de puntos que se extiende indefinidamente en dos direcciones opuestas.

$\overleftrightarrow{CG}$ is shown.

Line graph (p. 336) A line graph is a graph that uses a series of line segments to show changes in data. Typically, a line graph shows changes over time.

Gráfica lineal (p. 336) Una gráfica lineal es una gráfica que usa una serie de segmentos de recta para mostrar cambios en los datos. Típicamente, una gráfica lineal muestra cambios a través del tiempo.

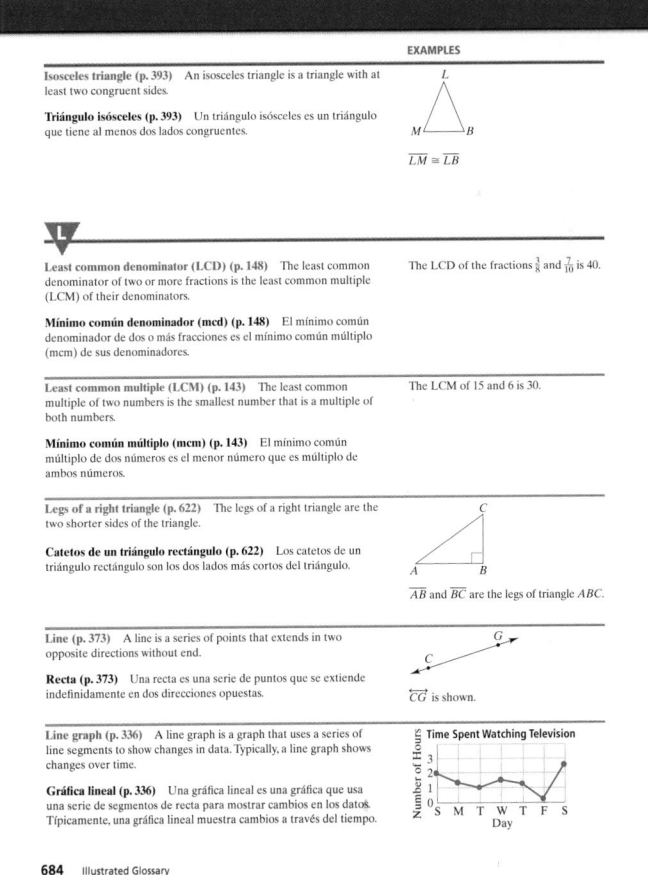

Page 685 (top-left)

Line of reflection (p. 416)   A line of reflection is a line over which a figure is reflected.

Eje de reflexión (p. 416)   Un eje de reflexión es una recta sobre la cual se refleja una figura.

line of reflection

Figure B is a reflection of Figure A.

Line of symmetry (p. 410)   A line of symmetry divides a figure into mirror images.

Eje de simetría (p. 410)   Un eje de simetría divide una figura en imágenes reflejas.

line of symmetry

Line plot (p. 327)   A line plot is a graph that shows the shape of a data set by stacking X's above each data value on a number line.

Diagrama de puntos (p. 327)   Un diagrama de puntos es una gráfica que muestra la forma de un conjunto de datos agrupando X sobre cada valor de una recta numérica.

Pets Owned by Students

```
            x
            x
x       x   x
x   x   x   x
x   x   x   x   x
0   1   2   3   4
```

The line plot shows the number of pets owned by each of 12 students.

Liter (p. 433)   The liter (L) is the standard unit of capacity in the metric system.

Litro (p. 433)   El litro (L) es la unidad de capacidad estándar en el sistema métrico.

A pitcher holds about 2 liters of juice.

M

Mass (p. 432)   Mass is a measure of the amount of matter in an object.

Masa (p. 432)   La masa es la medida de la cantidad de materia en un objeto.

A brick has a greater mass than a feather.

Mean (p. 322)   The mean of a set of data values is the sum of the data divided by the number of data items.

Media (p. 322)   La media de un conjunto de valores de datos es la suma de los datos dividida por el número de datos.

The mean temperature (°F) for the set of temperatures 44, 52, 48, 55, 61, and 67 is
$\frac{44 + 52 + 48 + 55 + 61 + 67}{6} = 54.5°F.$

English/Spanish Glossary

Page 686 (top-right)

Median (p. 323)   The median of a data set is the middle value when the data are arranged in numerical order. When there is an even number of data values, the median is the mean of the two middle values.

Mediana (p. 323)   La mediana de un conjunto de datos es el valor del medio cuando los datos están organizados en orden numérico. Cuando hay un número par de valores de datos, la mediana es la media de los dos valores del medio.

A set of temperatures (°F) arranged in order are 44, 48, 52, 55, and 58. The median temperature is 52°F because it is the middle number in the set of data.

Meter (p. 431)   The meter (m) is the standard unit of length in the metric system.

Metro (p. 431)   El metro (m) es la unidad de longitud estándar en el sistema métrico.

A doorknob is about 1 meter from the floor.

Metric system (p. 431)   The metric system of measurement is a decimal system. Prefixes indicate the relative size of units.

Sistema métrico (p. 431)   El sistema métrico de medidas es un sistema decimal. Los prefijos indican el tamaño relativo de las unidades.

1 kilogram = 1,000 grams
1 centimeter = $\frac{1}{100}$ meter
1 milliliter = $\frac{1}{1,000}$ liter

Midpoint (p. 384)   The midpoint of a segment is the point that divides the segment into two segments of equal length.

Punto medio (p. 384)   El punto medio de un segmento es el punto que divide el segmento en dos segmentos de igual longitud.

X M Y

$XM = YM$. M is the midpoint of $\overline{XY}$.

Mixed number (p. 139)   A mixed number is the sum of a whole number and a fraction.

Número mixto (p. 139)   Un número mixto es la suma de un número entero y una fracción.

$3\frac{11}{16}$ is a mixed number. $3\frac{11}{16} = 3 + \frac{11}{16}$.

Mode (p. 323)   The mode of a data set is the item that occurs with the greatest frequency.

Moda (p. 323)   La moda de un conjunto de datos es el dato que sucede con mayor frecuencia.

The mode of the set of prices $2.50, $2.75, $3.60, $2.75, and $3.70 is $2.75.

Multiple (p. 143)   A multiple of a number is the product of the number and any nonzero whole number.

Múltiplo (p. 143)   Un múltiplo de un número es el producto de ese número y cualquier número entero diferente de cero.

The number 39 is a multiple of 13.

Page 687 (bottom-left)

Multiplication Property of Equality (p. 96)   The Multiplication Property of Equality states that if each side of an equation is multiplied by the same number, the results are equal.

Propiedad multiplicativa de la igualdad (p. 96)   La propiedad multiplicativa de la igualdad establece que si cada lado de una ecuación se multiplica por el mismo número, los resultados son iguales.

Since $\frac{12}{2} = 6, \frac{12}{2} \cdot 2 = 6 \cdot 2.$
If $a = b$, then $a \cdot c = b \cdot c.$

N

Net (p. 464)   A net is a two-dimensional pattern that can be folded to form a three-dimensional figure.

Plantilla (p. 464)   Una plantilla es un patrón bidimensional que se puede doblar para formar una figura tridimensional.

These are nets for a cube.

Numerical expression (p. 68)   A numerical expression is an expression with only numbers and operation symbols.

Expresión numérica (p. 68)   Una expresión numérica es una expresión que tiene sólo números y símbolos de operaciones.

$2(5 + 7) - 14$ is a numerical expression.

O

Obtuse angle (p. 380)   An obtuse angle is an angle with a measure greater than 90° and less than 180°.

Ángulo obtuso (p. 380)   Un ángulo obtuso es un ángulo que mide más de 90° y menos de 180°.

Obtuse triangle (p. 392)   An obtuse triangle is a triangle with one obtuse angle.

Triángulo obtusángulo (p. 392)   Un triángulo obtusángulo es un triángulo que tiene un ángulo obtuso.

N J X

The measure of $\angle J$ is between 90° and 180°. Triangle NJX is an obtuse triangle.

Octagon (p. 397)   An octagon is a polygon with eight sides.

Octágono (p. 397)   Un octágono es un polígono que tiene ocho lados.

English/Spanish Glossary

Page 688 (bottom-right)

Odd number (p. 120)   An odd number is a whole number that ends with a 1, 3, 5, 7, or 9.

Número impar (p. 120)   Un número impar es un número entero que termina en 1, 3, 5, 7 ó 9.

43 and 687 are odd numbers.

Odds (p. 552)   When outcomes are equally likely, odds are expressed as the following ratios.
odds *in favor of* an event = number of favorable outcomes : number of unfavorable outcomes
odds *against* an event = number of unfavorable outcomes : number of favorable outcomes

Posibilidades (p. 552)   Cuando los resultados son igualmente posibles, las posibilidades se expresan como las siguientes razones.
posibilidades *en favor* de un suceso = número de resultados favorables : número de resultados desfavorables
posibilidades *en contra* de un suceso = número de resultados desfavorables : número de resultados favorables

You roll a standard number cube. The odds in favor of getting a 4 are $\frac{1}{5}$. The odds against getting a 4 are $\frac{4}{5}$.

Open sentence (p. 85)   An open sentence is an equation with one or more variables.

Proposición abierta (p. 85)   Una proposición abierta es una ecuación con una o más variables.

$b - 7 = 12$

Opposites (p. 491)   Opposites are two numbers that are the same distance from 0 on a number line, but in opposite directions.

Opuestos (p. 491)   Opuestos son dos números que están a la misma distancia del 0 en una recta numérica, pero en direcciones opuestas.

17 and −17 are opposites.

Ordered pair (p. 518)   An ordered pair identifies the location of a point. The *x*-coordinate shows a point's position left or right of the *y*-axis. The *y*-coordinate shows a point's position up or down from the *x*-axis.

Par ordenado (p. 518)   Un par ordenado identifica la ubicación de un punto. La coordenada *x* muestra la posición de un punto a la izquierda o derecha del eje de *y*. La coordenada *y* muestra la posición de un punto arriba o abajo del eje de *x*.

The *x*-coordinate of the point $(-2, 1)$ is −2, and the *y*-coordinate is 1.

Order of operations (pp. 48, 100)
1. Work inside grouping symbols.
2. Do all work with exponents.
3. Multiply and divide in order from left to right.
4. Add and subtract in order from left to right.

$$2^3(7-4) = 2^3 \cdot 3 = 8 \cdot 3 = 24$$

Orden de las operaciones (pp. 48, 100)
1. Trabaja dentro de los signos de agrupación.
2. Trabaja con los exponentes.
3. Multiplica y divide en orden de izquierda a derecha.
4. Suma y resta en orden de izquierda a derecha.

Origin (p. 518) The origin is the point of intersection of the x- and y-axes on a coordinate plane.

Origen (p. 518) El origen es el punto de intersección de los ejes de x y de y en un plano de coordenadas.

The ordered pair that describes the origin is $(0, 0)$.

Outcome (p. 547) An outcome is any of the possible results that can occur in an experiment.

Resultado (p. 547) Un resultado es cualquiera de los posibles desenlaces que pueden ocurrir en un experimento.

The outcomes of rolling a standard number cube are 1, 2, 3, 4, 5, and 6.

Outlier (p. 322) An outlier is a data item that is much greater or less than the other items in a data set.

Valor extremo (p. 322) Un valor extremo es un dato que es mucho más alto o más bajo que los demás datos de un conjunto de datos.

An outlier in the data set 6, 7, 9, 10, 11, 12, 14, and 52 is 52.

P

Parallel lines (p. 374) Parallel lines are lines in the same plane that never intersect.

Rectas paralelas (p. 378) Las rectas paralelas son rectas en el mismo plano que nunca se intersectan.

$\overleftrightarrow{EF}$ is parallel to $\overleftrightarrow{HI}$.

Parallelogram (p. 398) A parallelogram is a quadrilateral with both pairs of opposite sides parallel.

Paralelogramo (p. 398) Un paralelogramo es un cuadrilátero cuyos pares de lados opuestos son paralelos.

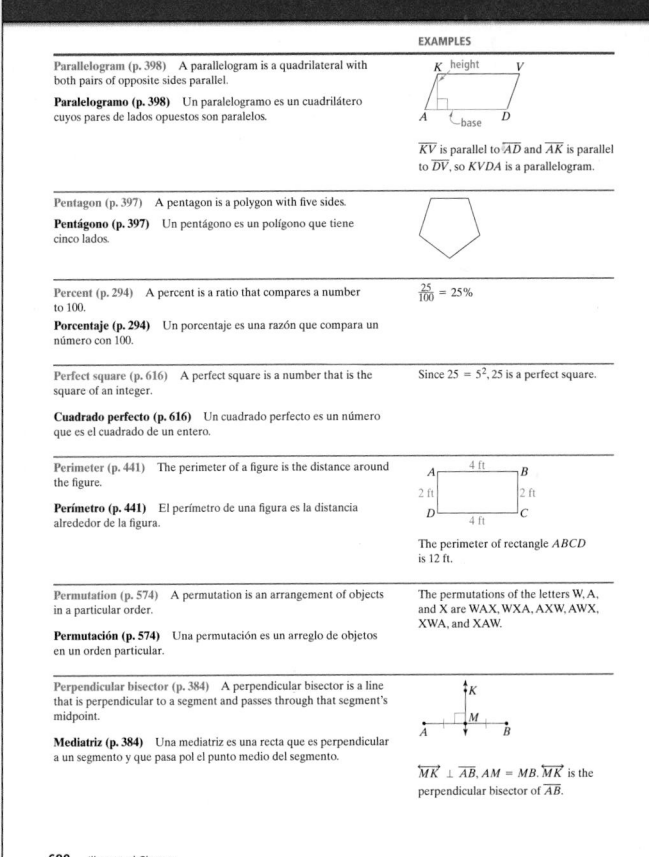

$\overline{KV}$ is parallel to $\overline{AD}$ and $\overline{AK}$ is parallel to $\overline{DV}$, so $KVDA$ is a parallelogram.

Pentagon (p. 397) A pentagon is a polygon with five sides.

Pentágono (p. 397) Un pentágono es un polígono que tiene cinco lados.

Percent (p. 294) A percent is a ratio that compares a number to 100.

Porcentaje (p. 294) Un porcentaje es una razón que compara un número con 100.

$$\frac{25}{100} = 25\%$$

Perfect square (p. 616) A perfect square is a number that is the square of an integer.

Cuadrado perfecto (p. 616) Un cuadrado perfecto es un número que es el cuadrado de un entero.

Since $25 = 5^2$, 25 is a perfect square.

Perimeter (p. 441) The perimeter of a figure is the distance around the figure.

Perímetro (p. 441) El perímetro de una figura es la distancia alrededor de la figura.

The perimeter of rectangle $ABCD$ is 12 ft.

Permutation (p. 574) A permutation is an arrangement of objects in a particular order.

Permutación (p. 574) Una permutación es un arreglo de objetos en un orden particular.

The permutations of the letters W, A, and X are WAX, WXA, AXW, AWX, XWA, and XAW.

Perpendicular bisector (p. 384) A perpendicular bisector is a line that is perpendicular to a segment and passes through that segment's midpoint.

Mediatriz (p. 384) Una mediatriz es una recta que es perpendicular a un segmento y que pasa por el punto medio del segmento.

$\overleftrightarrow{MK} \perp \overline{AB}$, $AM = MB$. $\overleftrightarrow{MK}$ is the perpendicular bisector of $\overline{AB}$.

Perpendicular lines (p. 380) Perpendicular lines intersect to form right angles.

Rectas perpendiculares (p. 380) Las rectas perpendiculares se intersectan para formar ángulos rectos.

$\overleftrightarrow{RS}$ is perpendicular to $\overleftrightarrow{DE}$.

Pi (p. 453) Pi (π) is the ratio of the circumference C of any circle to its diameter d.

Pi (p. 453) Pi (π) es la razón de la circunferencia C de cualquier círculo a su diámetro d.

$\pi = \frac{C}{d}$

Place value (p. 5) The place value tells you the value of a digit based on its place in a particular number.

Valor posicional (p. 5) El valor posicional indica el valor de un dígito, basándose en el lugar que ocupa en un número en particular.

In 26, the 6 represents 6 ones, or 6.
In 604, The 6 represents 6 hundreds, or 600.

Plane (p. 374) A plane is a flat surface with no thickness that extends without end in all directions on the surface.

Plano (p. 374) Un plano es una superficie plana que no tiene grosor, que se extiende indefinidamente en todas las direcciones sobre la superficie.

$DEFG$ is a plane.

Point (p. 373) A point is a location that has no size.

Punto (p. 373) Un punto es una ubicación que no tiene tamaño.

A is a point.

Polygon (p. 397) A polygon is a closed figure formed by three or more line segments that do not cross.

Polígono (p. 397) Un polígono es una figura cerrada que está formada por tres o más segmentos de recta que no se cruzan.

Population (p. 559) A population is a group of objects or people about which information is wanted.

Población (p. 559) Una población es un grupo de objectos o personas sobre el que se busca información.

In a survey regarding the hobbies of teenagers, the population would be all people ages 13 through 19.

Power (p. 100) A power is a number that can be expressed using an exponent.

Potencia (p. 100) Una potencia es un número que se puede expresar usando un exponente.

3^4, 5^2, and 2^{10} are powers.

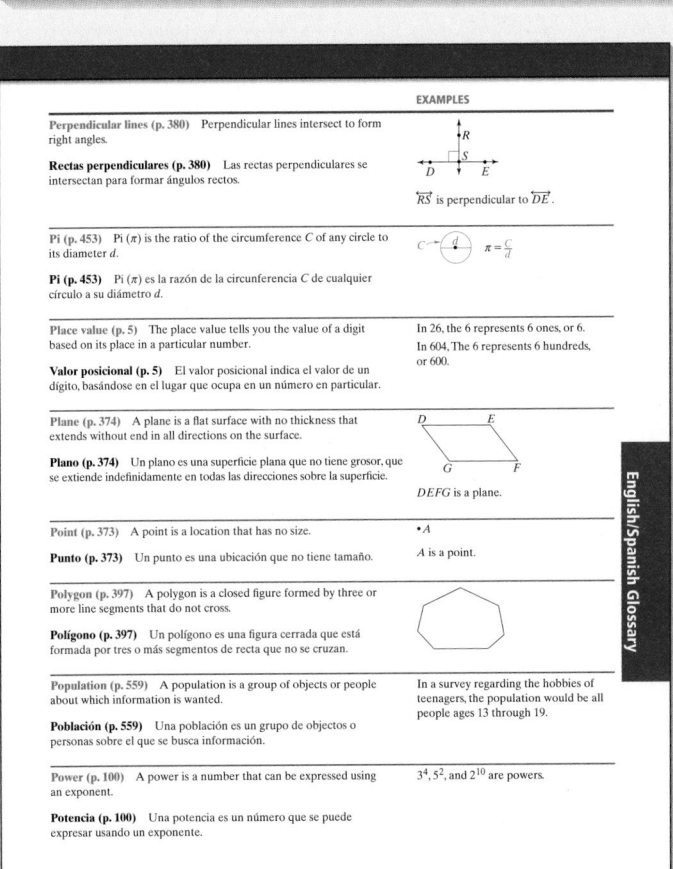

Prime factorization (p. 124) Writing a composite number as the product of prime numbers is the prime factorization of the number.

Factorización en primos (p. 124) Escribir un número compuesto como el producto de sus factores primos es la factorización en primos del número.

The prime factorization of 12 is $2 \cdot 2 \cdot 3$, or $2^2 \cdot 3$.

Prime number (p. 124) A prime number is a whole number with exactly two factors, 1 and the number itself.

Número primo (p. 124) Un número primo es un entero que tiene exactamente dos factores, 1 y el mismo número.

13 is a prime number because its only factors are 1 and 13.

Prism (p. 462) A prism is a three-dimensional figure with two parallel and congruent faces that are polygons. These faces are called bases. A prism is named for the shape of its base.

Prisma (p. 462) Un prisma es una figura tridimensional que tiene dos caras paralelas y congruentes que son polígonos. Estas caras se llaman bases. Un prisma recibe su nombre por la forma de su base.

Rectangular Prism   Triangular Prism

Probability of an event (p. 547) When outcomes are equally likely, the probability of an event is given by this formula:
$$P(\text{event}) = \frac{\text{number of favorable outcomes}}{\text{total number of possible outcomes}}$$
See *Experimental probability*.

Probabilidad de un suceso (p. 547) Cuando los resultados son igualmente posibles, la probabilidad de un suceso se da por esta fórmula:
$$P(\text{suceso}) = \frac{\text{número favorable de resultados}}{\text{número total de resultados posibles}}$$
Ver *Probabilidad experimental*.

Proper fraction (p. 139) A proper fraction has a numerator that is less than its denominator.

Fracción propia (p. 139) Una fracción propia tiene un numerador que es menos que su denominador.

$\frac{3}{8}$ and $\frac{11}{12}$ are proper fractions.

Proportion (p. 278) A proportion is an equation stating that two ratios are equal.

Proporción (p. 278) Una proporción es una ecuación que establece que dos razones son iguales.

$\frac{3}{12} = \frac{9}{36}$ is a proportion.

Pyramid (p. 463)   A pyramid is a three-dimensional figure with triangular faces that meet at a vertex. Its base is a polygon. A pyramid is named for the shape of its base.

Pirámide (p. 463)   Una pirámide es una figura tridimensional que tiene caras triangulares que coinciden en un vértice. Su base es un polígono. Una pirámide recibe su nombre por la forma de su base.

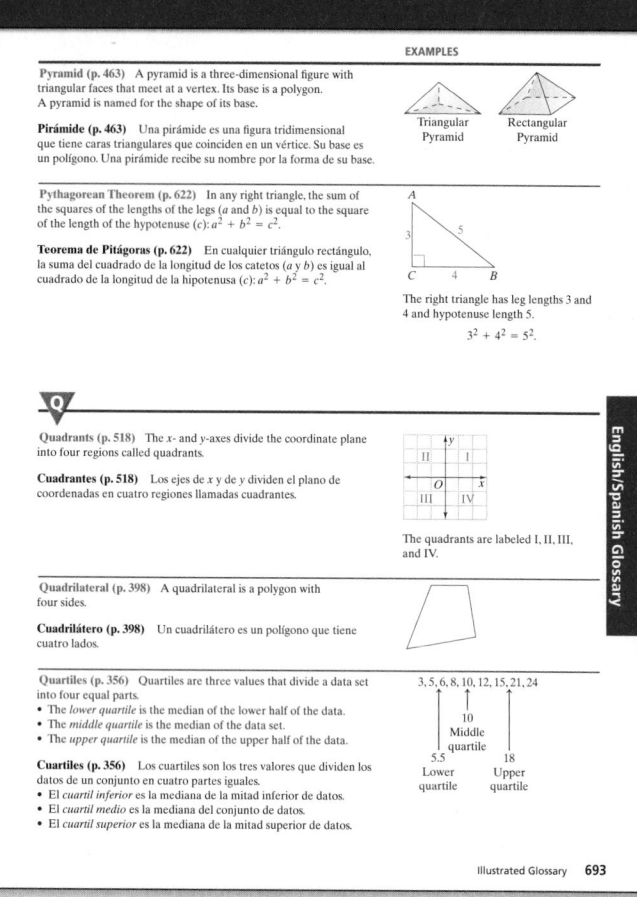

Triangular Pyramid   Rectangular Pyramid

Pythagorean Theorem (p. 622)   In any right triangle, the sum of the squares of the lengths of the legs (a and b) is equal to the square of the length of the hypotenuse (c): $a^2 + b^2 = c^2$.

Teorema de Pitágoras (p. 622)   En cualquier triángulo rectángulo, la suma del cuadrado de la longitud de los catetos (a y b) es igual al cuadrado de la longitud de la hipotenusa (c): $a^2 + b^2 = c^2$.

The right triangle has leg lengths 3 and 4 and hypotenuse length 5.

$$3^2 + 4^2 = 5^2.$$

Q

Quadrants (p. 518)   The x- and y-axes divide the coordinate plane into four regions called quadrants.

Cuadrantes (p. 518)   Los ejes de x y de y dividen el plano de coordenadas en cuatro regiones llamadas cuadrantes.

The quadrants are labeled I, II, III, and IV.

Quadrilateral (p. 398)   A quadrilateral is a polygon with four sides.

Cuadrilátero (p. 398)   Un cuadrilátero es un polígono que tiene cuatro lados.

Quartiles (p. 356)   Quartiles are three values that divide a data set into four equal parts.
• The *lower quartile* is the median of the lower half of the data.
• The *middle quartile* is the median of the data set.
• The *upper quartile* is the median of the upper half of the data.

Cuartiles (p. 356)   Los cuartiles son los tres valores que dividen los datos de un conjunto en cuatro partes iguales.
• El *cuartil inferior* es la mediana de la mitad inferior de datos.
• El *cuartil medio* es la mediana del conjunto de datos.
• El *cuartil superior* es la mediana de la mitad superior de datos.

3, 5, 6, 8, 10, 12, 15, 21, 24

10 Middle quartile

5.5 Lower quartile   18 Upper quartile

R

Radius (p. 452)   A radius of a circle is a segment that connects the center to the circle.

Radio (p. 452)   Un radio de un círculo es un segmento que conecta el centro con el círculo.

$\overline{OA}$ is a radius of circle O.

Range (p. 327)   The range of a data set is the difference between the greatest and the least values.

Rango (p. 327)   El rango de un conjunto de datos es la diferencia entre los valores mayor y menor.

Data set: 62, 109, 234, 35, 96, 49, 201
Range: $201 - 35 = 166$

Rate (p. 273)   A rate is a ratio that compares two quantities measured in different units.

Tasa (p. 273)   Una tasa es una razón que compara dos cantidades medidas en diferentes unidades.

Suppose you read 116 words in 1 minute. Your reading rate is $\frac{116 \text{ words}}{1 \text{ minute}}$.

Ratio (p. 269)   A ratio is a comparison of two quantities by division.

Razón (p. 269)   Una razón es una comparación de dos cantidades mediante la división.

There are three ways to write a ratio: 9 to 10, 9 : 10, and $\frac{9}{10}$.

Rational number (p. 617)   A rational number is any number that can be written as a quotient of two integers where the denominator is not 0.

Número racional (p. 617)   Un número racional es cualquier número que puede ser escrito como cociente de dos enteros, donde el denominador es diferente de 0.

$\frac{1}{3}$, -5, 6.4, $0.666\ldots$, $-2\frac{4}{5}$, 0, and $\frac{7}{3}$ are rational numbers.

Ray (p. 373)   A ray is part of a line. It has one endpoint and all the points of the line on one side of the endpoint.

Rayo (p. 373)   Un rayo es parte de una recta. Tiene un extremo y todos los puntos de la recta a un lado del extremo.

endpoint of $\overrightarrow{CG}$

$\overrightarrow{CG}$ represents a ray.

Reciprocal (p. 230)   Two numbers are reciprocals if their product is 1.

Recíproco (p. 230)   Dos números son recíprocos si su producto es 1.

The numbers $\frac{4}{9}$ and $\frac{9}{4}$ are reciprocals.

Rectangle (p. 398)   A rectangle is a parallelogram with four right angles.

Rectángulo (p. 398)   Un rectángulo es un paralelogramo que tiene cuatro ángulos rectos.

Reflection (p. 416)   A reflection, or flip, is a transformation that flips a figure over a line of reflection.

Reflección (p. 416)   Una reflección es una transformación que voltea una figura sobre un eje de reflexión.

line of reflection

Figure B is a reflection of Figure A.

Repeating decimal (p. 44)   A repeating decimal is a decimal that repeats the same digits without end. The repeating block can be one digit or more than one digit.

Decimal periódico (p. 44)   Un decimal periódico es un decimal que repite los mismos dígitos interminablemente. El bloque que se repite puede ser un dígito o más de un dígito.

$0.888\ldots = 0.\overline{8}$
$0.272727\ldots = 0.\overline{27}$

Rhombus (p. 398)   A rhombus is a parallelogram with four congruent sides.

Rombo (p. 398)   Un rombo es un paralelogramo que tiene cuatro lados congruentes.

Right angle (p. 380)   A right angle is an angle with a measure of 90°.

Ángulo recto (p. 380)   Un ángulo recto es un ángulo que mide 90°.

$m\angle D = 90°$

Right triangle (p. 392)   A right triangle is a triangle with one right angle.

Triángulo rectángulo (p. 392)   Un triángulo rectángulo es un triángulo que tiene un ángulo recto.

$\triangle ABC$ is a right triangle since $\angle B$ is a right angle.

Rotation (p. 416)   A rotation is a transformation that turns a figure about a fixed point called the center of rotation.

Rotación (p. 416)   Una rotación es una transformación que gira una figura sobre un punto fijo llamado centro de rotación.

center of rotation

The blue triangle is a rotation of the black triangle.

S

Sample (p. 559)   A sample is a part of a population. You use a sample to make predictions about a population.

Muestra (p. 559)   Una muestra es una parte de una población. Se usa una muestra para hacer predicciones acerca de una población.

Suppose 50 students out of the 700 students at a school are surveyed. The 50 students represent a sample population.

Scale (p. 288)   A scale is the ratio that compares a length in a drawing to the corresponding length in the actual object.

Escala (p. 288)   Una escala es la razón que compara la longitud en un dibujo con la longitud correspondiente en el objeto real.

A 25-mile road is 1 inch long on a map. The scale can be written three ways: 1 inch : 25 miles, $\frac{1 \text{ inch}}{25 \text{ miles}}$, 1 inch = 25 miles.

Scale drawing (p. 289)   A scale drawing is an enlarged or reduced drawing of an object that is similar to the actual object.

Dibujo a escala (p. 289)   Un dibujo a escala es un dibujo aumentado o reducido de un objeto que es semejante al objeto real.

Maps and floor plans are scale drawings.

Scalene triangle (p. 393)   A scalene triangle is a triangle with no congruent sides.

Triángulo escaleno (p. 393)   Un triángulo escaleno es un triángulo cuyos lados no son congruentes.

Scientific notation (p. 104)   A number in scientific notation is written as the product of two factors. The first factor is a number greater than or equal to 1 and less than 10; the second factor is a power of 10.

Notación científica (p. 104)   Un número en notación científica se escribe como el producto de dos factores. El primer factor es un número mayor o igual a 1 y menor que 10; el segundo factor es una potencia de 10.

37,000,000 is written as 3.7×10^7 in scientific notation.

Segment (p. 373)   A segment is part of a line. It has two endpoints and all the points of the line between the endpoints.

Segmento (p. 373)   Un segmento es parte de una línea. Tiene dos extremos y todos los puntos de la recta entre los puntos extremos.

endpoints of $\overline{EF}$

$\overline{EF}$ is a segment.

Similar figures (p. 406)   Two figures are similar if their corresponding angles have the same measure and the lengths of their corresponding sides are proportional. The symbol ~ means "is similar to."

Figuras semejantes (p. 406)   Dos figuras son semejantes si sus ángulos correspondientes tienen la misma medida y las longitudes de sus lados correspondientes son proporcionales. El símbolo ~ significa "es semejante a."

$\triangle ABC \sim \triangle RTS$

English/Spanish Glossary

T354

Simplest form (p. 135) A fraction is in simplest form when the numerator and denominator have no common factors other than 1.

The simplest form of $\frac{3}{9}$ is $\frac{1}{3}$.

Mínima expresión (p. 135) Una fracción está en su mínima expresión cuando el numerador y el denominador no tienen otro factor común más que el uno.

Simulation (p. 563) A simulation of a real-world situation is a model used to find experimental probabilities.

A baseball team has equal chances of winning or losing the next game. You can use a coin to simulate the outcome.

Simulación (p. 563) Una simulación de una situación real es un modelo que se usa para hallar probabilidades experimentales.

Skew lines (p. 374) Skew lines are neither parallel nor intersecting. They lie in different planes.

Rectas cruzadas (p. 374) Las rectas cruzadas no son paralelas ni se intersecan. Están en planos diferentes.

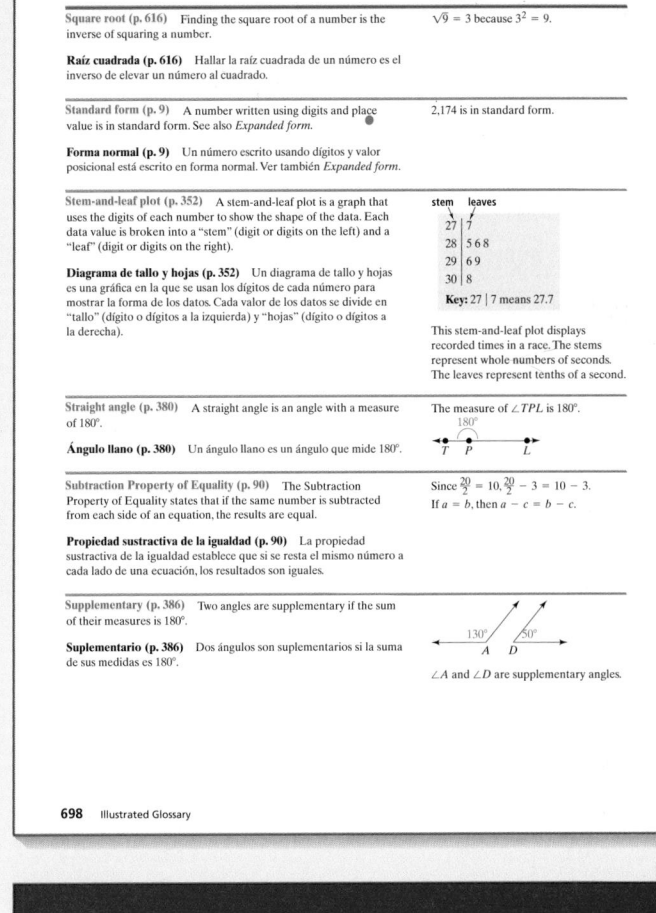

$\overleftrightarrow{MT}$ and $\overleftrightarrow{QR}$ are skew lines.

Solution (pp. 85, 602) A solution is any value or values that makes an equation or inequality true.

4 is the solution of $x + 5 = 9$.
7 is a solution of $x < 15$.

Solución (pp. 85, 602) Una solución es cualquier valor o valores que hacen que una ecuación o una desigualdad sea verdadera.

Sphere (p. 463) A sphere is the set of all points in space that are the same distance from a center point.

Esfera (p. 463) Una esfera es el conjunto de todos los puntos en el espacio que están a la misma distancia de un punto central.

Spreadsheet (p. 347) A spreadsheet is a tool used for organizing and analyzing data. Spreadsheets are arranged in numbered rows and lettered columns.

	A	B	C	D	E
1	0.50	0.70	0.60	0.50	2.30
2	1.50	0.50	2.75	2.50	7.25

Column C and row 2 meet at cell C2.

Hoja de cálculo (p. 347) Una hoja de cálculo es una herramienta que se usa para organizar y analizar datos. Las hojas de cálculo se organizan en filas numeradas y columnas en orden alfabético.

Square (p. 398) A square is a parallelogram with four right angles and four congruent sides.

Cuadrado (p. 398) Una cuadrado es un paralelógramo que tiene cuatro ángulos rectos y cuatro lados congruentes.

$QRST$ is a square. $\angle Q$, $\angle R$, $\angle S$, and $\angle T$ are right angles, and $\overline{QR} \cong \overline{RS} \cong \overline{ST} \cong \overline{QT}$.

Square root (p. 616) Finding the square root of a number is the inverse of squaring a number.

$\sqrt{9} = 3$ because $3^2 = 9$.

Raíz cuadrada (p. 616) Hallar la raíz cuadrada de un número es el inverso de elevar un número al cuadrado.

Standard form (p. 9) A number written using digits and place value is in standard form. See also *Expanded form.*

2,174 is in standard form.

Forma normal (p. 9) Un número escrito usando dígitos y valor posicional está escrito en forma normal. Ver también *Expanded form.*

Stem-and-leaf plot (p. 352) A stem-and-leaf plot is a graph that uses the digits of each number to show the shape of the data. Each data value is broken into a "stem" (digit or digits on the left) and a "leaf" (digit or digits on the right).

stem	leaves
27	7
28	5 6 8
29	6 9
30	8

Key: 27 | 7 means 27.7

Diagrama de tallo y hojas (p. 352) Un diagrama de tallo y hojas es una gráfica en la que se usan los dígitos de cada número para mostrar la forma de los datos. Cada valor de los datos se divide en "tallo" (dígito o dígitos a la izquierda) y "hojas" (dígito o dígitos a la derecha).

This stem-and-leaf plot displays recorded times in a race. The stems represent whole numbers of seconds. The leaves represent tenths of a second.

Straight angle (p. 380) A straight angle is an angle with a measure of 180°.

The measure of $\angle TPL$ is 180°.

Ángulo llano (p. 380) Un ángulo llano es un ángulo que mide 180°.

Subtraction Property of Equality (p. 90) The Subtraction Property of Equality states that if the same number is subtracted from each side of an equation, the results are equal.

Since $\frac{20}{2} = 10$, $\frac{20}{2} - 3 = 10 - 3$.
If $a = b$, then $a - c = b - c$.

Propiedad sustractiva de la igualdad (p. 90) La propiedad sustractiva de la igualdad establece que si se resta el mismo número a cada lado de una ecuación, los resultados son iguales.

Supplementary (p. 386) Two angles are supplementary if the sum of their measures is 180°.

Suplementario (p. 386) Dos ángulos son suplementarios si la suma de sus medidas es 180°.

$\angle A$ and $\angle D$ are supplementary angles.

Surface area of a three-dimensional figure (p. 468) The surface area of a three-dimensional figure is the sum of the areas of all the surfaces.

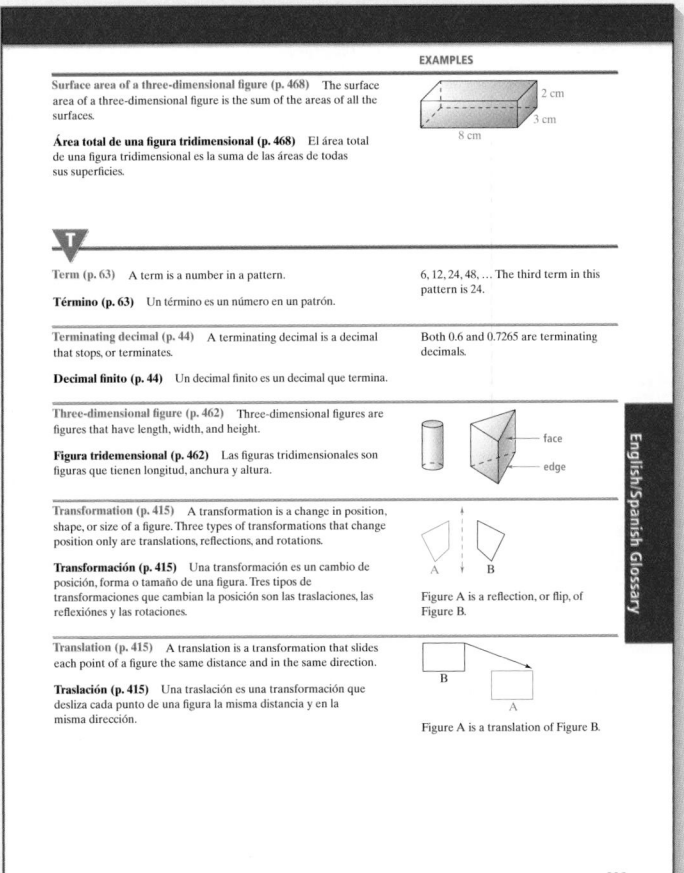

Área total de una figura tridimensional (p. 468) El área total de una figura tridimensional es la suma de las áreas de todas sus superficies.

T

Term (p. 63) A term is a number in a pattern.

6, 12, 24, 48, ... The third term in this pattern is 24.

Término (p. 63) Un término es un número en un patrón.

Terminating decimal (p. 44) A terminating decimal is a decimal that stops, or terminates.

Both 0.6 and 0.7265 are terminating decimals.

Decimal finito (p. 44) Un decimal finito es un decimal que termina.

Three-dimensional figure (p. 462) Three-dimensional figures are figures that have length, width, and height.

Figura tridimensional (p. 462) Las figuras tridimensionales son figuras que tienen longitud, anchura y altura.

Transformation (p. 415) A transformation is a change in position, shape, or size of a figure. Three types of transformations that change position only are translations, reflections, and rotations.

Transformación (p. 415) Una transformación es un cambio de posición, forma o tamaño de una figura. Tres tipos de transformaciones que cambian la posición son las traslaciones, las reflexiones y las rotaciones.

Figure A is a reflection, or flip, of Figure B.

Translation (p. 415) A translation is a transformation that slides each point of a figure the same distance and in the same direction.

Traslación (p. 415) Una traslación es una transformación que desliza cada punto de una figura la misma distancia y en la misma dirección.

Figure A is a translation of Figure B.

Transversal (p. 387) A line that intersects two or more lines is called a transversal.

Secante (p. 387) Una recta que interseca a dos o más rectas se llama secante.

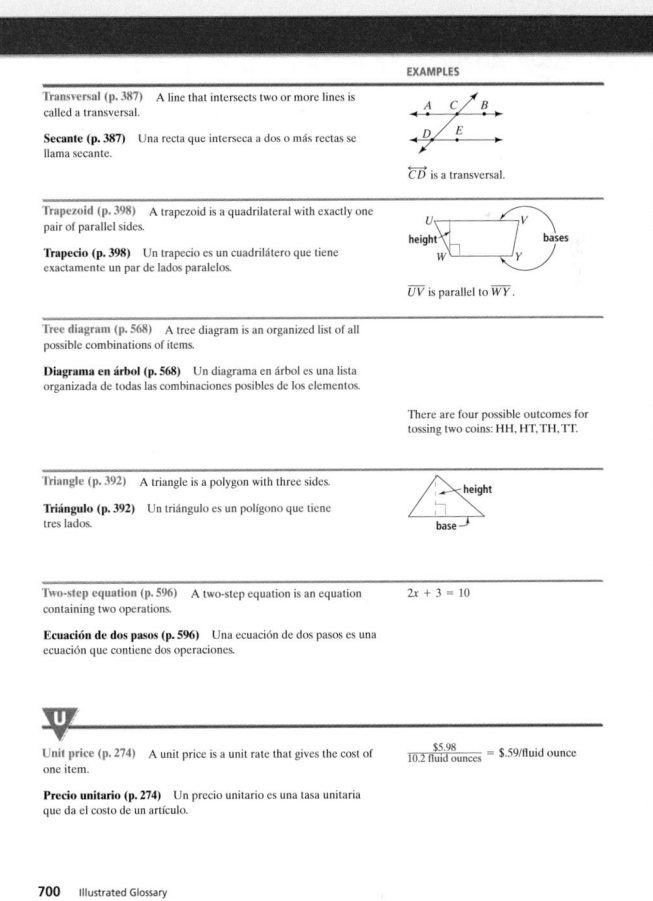

$\overleftrightarrow{CD}$ is a transversal.

Trapezoid (p. 398) A trapezoid is a quadrilateral with exactly one pair of parallel sides.

Trapecio (p. 398) Un trapecio es un cuadrilátero que tiene exactamente un par de lados paralelos.

$\overline{UV}$ is parallel to $\overline{WY}$.

Tree diagram (p. 568) A tree diagram is an organized list of all possible combinations of items.

Diagrama en árbol (p. 568) Un diagrama en árbol es una lista organizada de todas las combinaciones posibles de los elementos.

There are four possible outcomes for tossing two coins: HH, HT, TH, TT.

Triangle (p. 392) A triangle is a polygon with three sides.

Triángulo (p. 392) Un triángulo es un polígono que tiene tres lados.

Two-step equation (p. 596) A two-step equation is an equation containing two operations.

$2x + 3 = 10$

Ecuación de dos pasos (p. 596) Una ecuación de dos pasos es una ecuación que contiene dos operaciones.

U

Unit price (p. 274) A unit price is a unit rate that gives the cost of one item.

$\frac{\$5.98}{10.2 \text{ fluid ounces}} = \$.59/\text{fluid ounce}$

Precio unitario (p. 274) Un precio unitario es una tasa unitaria que da el costo de un artículo.

English/Spanish Glossary

T355

Unit rate (p. 273) The rate for one unit of a given quantity is called the unit rate.

Tasa unitaria (p. 273) La tasa para una unidad de una cantidad dada se llama tasa unitaria.

If you drive 130 miles in 2 hours, your unit rate is $\frac{65 \text{ miles}}{1 \text{ hour}}$ or 65 mi/h.

V

Variable (p. 69) A variable is a letter that stands for a number. The value of an algebraic expression varies, or changes, depending upon the value given to the variable.

Variable (p. 69) Una variable es una letra que representa un número. El valor de una expresión algebraica varía, o cambia, dependiendo del valor que se le dé a la variable.

x is a variable in the equation $9 + x = 7$.

Vertex of an angle (p. 379) The vertex of an angle is the point of intersection of two sides of an angle or figure.

Vértice de un ángulo (p. 379) El vértice de un ángulo es el punto de intersección de dos lados de un ángulo o figura.

vertex

Vertical angles (p. 387) Vertical angles are formed by two intersecting lines. Vertical angles have equal measures.

Ángulos verticales (p. 387) Los ángulos verticales están formados por dos rectas que se intersecan. Los ángulos verticales tienen la misma medida.

$\angle 1$ and $\angle 2$ are vertical angles, as are $\angle 3$ and $\angle 4$.

Volume (p. 472) The volume of a three-dimensional figure is the number of cubic units needed to fill the space inside the figure.

Volumen (p. 472) El volumen de una figura tridimensional es el número de unidades cúbicas que se necesitan para llenar el espacio dentro de la figura.

each cube = 1 in.³

The volume of the rectangular prism is 36 in.³.

X

x-axis (p. 518) The x-axis is the horizontal number line that, together with the y-axis, forms the coordinate plane.

Eje de x (p. 518) El eje de x es la recta numérica horizontal que, junto con el eje de y, forma el plano de coordenadas.

---

x-coordinate (p. 518) The x-coordinate is the first number in an ordered pair. It tells the number of horizontal units a point is from 0.

Coordenada x (p. 518) La coordenada x es el primer número en un par ordenado. Indica el número de unidades horizontales a las que un punto está del cero.

The x-coordinate is −2 for the ordered pair (−2, 1). The x-coordinate is 2 units to the left of the y-axis.

Y

y-axis (p. 518) The y-axis is the vertical number line that, together with the x-axis, forms the coordinate plane.

Eje de y (p. 518) El eje de y es la recta numérica vertical que, junto con el eje de x, forma el plano de coordenadas.

y-coordinate (p. 518) The y-coordinate is the second number in an ordered pair. It tells the number of vertical units a point is from 0.

Coordenada y (p. 518) La coordenada y es el segundo número en un par ordenado. Indica el número de unidades verticales a las que un punto está del cero.

The y-coordinate is 1 for the ordered pair (−2, 1). The y-coordinate is 1 unit up from the x-axis.

Z

Zero pair (p. 496) The pairing of one "+" chip with one "−" chip is called a zero pair.

Par cero (p. 496) El emparejamiento de una ficha "+" con una ficha "−" se llama par cero.

⊕ ⊖ ← a zero pair

Answers to Instant Check System™

Chapter 1

Diagnosing Readiness p. 4

1. 310 **2.** 7,530 **3.** 40 **4.** 60 **5.** 700 **6.** 1,990 **7.** 175 **8.** 145 **9.** 14,192 **10.** 3,027 **11.** 10,000 **12.** 1,392 **13.** 747 **14.** 4,544 **15.** 43,700 **16.** 25,000 **17.** 462 **18.** 1,856 **19.** 5 **20.** 17 **21.** 72 **22.** 32 **23.** 13 **24.** 73

Lesson 1-1 pp. 5–6

Check Skills You'll Need 1. 2 tens **2.** 2 ones **3.** 2 thousand **4.** 2 hundred million

Check Understanding 1. twenty-six billion, two hundred thirty-six million, eight hundred forty-six thousand eighty dollars **2a.** < **b.** 9,789; 9,897; 9,987

Lesson 1-2 pp. 9–10

Check Skills You'll Need 1. twenty-eight **2.** eight thousand, six hundred seventy-two **3.** six hundred twelve thousand, nine hundred eighty **4.** fifty-eight million, twenty-six thousand, one hundred thirteen

Check Understanding 1a. 3 + 0.1 + 0.04 + 0.001 + 0.0006 **b.** 0.8 + 0.06 + 0.005 **c.** 30 + 7 + 0.5 **d.** No; the zero in 6.207 is covered when you write "+ 0.007." **2a.** sixteen thousand, seven hundred two and three tenths **b.** one thousand six hundred seventy and two hundred thirty-four thousandths **c.** one and sixty-seven thousand twenty-three hundred-thousandths **3a.** 9.587 **b.** the 5, since 0.5 > 0.007

Lesson 1-3 pp. 13–17

Check Skills You'll Need 1. > **2.** > **3.** > **4.** > **5.** digits on the left

Check Understanding

1.
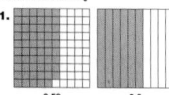
0.59   0.6

0.6 is greater.

2.

1.09 1.3   1.76 1.91
            1.67 1.87

3a. < **b.** > **c.** = **d.** Answers may vary. Sample: Compare the digits starting with the highest place values. The ones and tenths digits are the same. The hundredths digit in 1.697 is greater than the hundredths digit in 1.679. So, 1.697 > 1.679. **4a.** 2.076, 2.6, 2.76 **b.** 3.059, 3.46, 3.64

Checkpoint Quiz 1 1. six trillion, eighty billion, four hundred five thousand and thirty-one hundredths **2.** 10 + 2 + 0.03 + 0.005 **3.** 400.7 **4.** < **5.** 8.0, 8.05, 8.7, 9, 9.31

Lesson 1-4 pp. 19–21

Check Skills You'll Need 1. 50 **2.** 65,330 **3.** 132,800 **4.** 30,910,000 **5.** 6,000 **6.** 15,345,000

Check Understanding 1a. about 32 **b.** about 3 **c.** about 112 **2a.** because 28 is divisible by 4 **b.** about 250 **3a.** about 2; 1.8 **b.** about 8; 7.53 **c.** about 0.3; 0.27 **d.** Answers may vary. Sample: Aligning the decimal points aligns all the places correctly. **4a.** about 91; 91.2 **b.** about 32; 31.68 **c.** about 77; 77.084

Lesson 1-5 pp. 25–27

Check Skills You'll Need 1. 9 **2.** 10 **3.** 5 **4.** 1.5 **5.** 6.3

Check Understanding 1. about 6; 6.16 **2a.** 13.9 **b.** 94 **c.** 9.4 **3a.** about 2; 1.8 **b.** about 8; 7.53 **c.** about 0.3; 0.27 **d.** Answers may vary. Sample: Aligning the decimal points aligns all the places correctly. **4a.** about 91; 91.2 **b.** about 32; 31.68 **c.** about 77; 77.084

Lesson 1-6 pp. 30–31

Check Skills You'll Need 1. 62 **2.** 57 **3.** 24 **4.** 82 **5.** 77 **6.** 3,815

Check Understanding 1. 0.16 s

Lesson 1-7 pp. 35–39

Check Skills You'll Need 1. 147 **2.** 816 **3.** 21,607 **4.** 42,340

Check Understanding 1a. 0.78 **b.** 21.85 **2a.** 0.06 **b.** 0.126 **c.** It is less than either factor. **3a.** 7.464 **b.** 57.984 **4a.** 23 **b.** 310 **c.** 333

Checkpoint Quiz 2

1–4. Answers may vary. Samples are given. **1.** 29 **2.** 60 **3.** 15 **4.** 8 **5.** 7.32 **6.** 8.26 **7.** 32.76 **8.** 1.42 **9.** 1.65 lb **10.** Answers may vary. Sample: 8 · 13.1 · 0.5 = 8 · 0.5 · 13.1 Comm. Prop. of Add. = (8 · 0.5) · 13.1 Assoc. Prop. of Add. = 4 · 13.1 = 52.4 Assoc. Prop. of Add.; 8(0.5) = 4 and 4(13.1) = 52.4

Lesson 1-8 pp. 40–41

Check Skills You'll Need 1. 360 **2.** 3,600 **3.** 36,000 **4.** 470 **5.** 47 **6.** 4.7

Check Understanding 1a. 342 **b.** 2.35 **c.** 55,200 **2a.** 5.342 **b.** 0.0235 **c.** 0.0552 **d.** Sample: To divide by 10,000, move the decimal point in the dividend four places to the left; 0.00073.

Lesson 1-9 pp. 43–45

Check Skills You'll Need 1. 5 **2.** 32 **3.** 101 **4.** 27 **5.** yes **6.** no **7.** yes **8.** yes

Check Understanding 1a. 1.52 **b.** 48.2 **c.** 0.144 **2a.** 0.6; repeating **b.** 0.25; terminating **c.** 0.18; repeating **3a.**

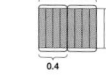
0.8
0.4

b.
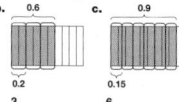
0.6   0.9
0.2   0.15
3   6

d. the number of groups **4a.** 6.2 **b.** 108 **c.** 30.5

Lesson 1-10 pp. 48–49

Check Skills You'll Need 1. = **2.** > **3.** > **4.** > **5.** < **6.** <

Check Understanding 1a. 8 **b.** 11.7 **c.** 16 **d.** I would add before multiplying if the addition of two numbers is done within parentheses and the multiplication is done outside of the parentheses. **2.** $46.85

Chapter 2

Diagnosing Readiness p. 62

1. about 50 **2.** about 7 **3.** about 52 **4.** about 42; 42.15 **5.** about 9; 9.5 **6.** about 5; 5.1 **7.** 379 **8.** 3,040 **9.** 1.57 **10.** 26.5 **11.** 39 **12.** 17.2

Lesson 2-1 pp. 63–65

Check Skills You'll Need 1. 0.0105, 0.105, 10.5 **2.** 3.1, 3.31, 3.331 **3.** 9.06, 9.09, 9.6 **4.** 0.602, 20.06, 26.0 **5.** 100.01, 100.1, 101.0 **6.** 0.35, 0.4, 0.99

Check Understanding 1a. 41, 51 **b.** 24, 16 **c.** 57, 64 **d.** 22 tiles **2a.** 90, 75, 60, 45, 30, 15 **b.** 1, 3, 9, 27, 81, 243 **c.** 17, 36, 55, 74, 93, 112 **3a.** 2,401, 16,807, 117,649; the first term is 1; multiply each term by 7 to get the next term. **b.** 6.4, 5.2, 4; the first term is 10.0; subtract 1.2 from a term to get the next term. **c.** 32, 16, 8; the first term is 256; divide each term by 2 to get the next term.

Lesson 2-2 pp. 68–70

Check Skills You'll Need 1. 32 **2.** 19 **3.** 44.1 **4.** 4

Check Understanding 1a.

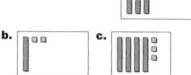

b. **c.**

2a. 36 **b.** 5 **c.** 28 **d.** x was replaced by 7; 7 was multiplied by 4; 28 was subtracted from 56. **3.** $255

Lesson 2-3 pp. 74–78

Check Skills You'll Need 1. 10 **2.** 1 **3.** 15 **4.** 30 **5.** 48 **6.** 11

Check Understanding 1a. 5 ÷ y **b.** 6z **c.** m + 3.4 **2.** h + 2 **3.** Answers may vary. Samples are given. **a.** n ÷ 2 **b.** n + 4 **4a.** b + 28 **b.** 41

Checkpoint Quiz 1 1. 1,296; 7,776; 46,656; the first term is 1; multiply a term by 6 to get the next term. **2.** 225, 210, 195; the first term is 285; subtract 15 from a term to get the next term. **3.** 0.005, 0.0005, 0.00005; the first term is 50; divide a term by 10 to get the next term. **4.** 56 **5.** 9 **6.** 10.5 **7.** 17 − d **8.** ae **9.** 14 ÷ q **10a.** 5q + 3 **b.** 63

T356

Answers to Instant Check System™

Chapter 1

Diagnosing Readiness p. 4

1. 310 **2.** 7,530 **3.** 40 **4.** 60 **5.** 700 **6.** 1,990 **7.** 175 **8.** 145 **9.** 14,192 **10.** 3,027 **11.** 10,000 **12.** 1,392 **13.** 747 **14.** 4,544 **15.** 43,700 **16.** 25,000 **17.** 462 **18.** 1,856 **19.** 5 **20.** 17 **21.** 72 **22.** 32 **23.** 13 **24.** 73

Lesson 1-1 pp. 5–6

Check Skills You'll Need **1.** 2 tens **2.** 2 ones **3.** 2 thousand **4.** 2 hundred million

Check Understanding **1.** twenty-six billion, two hundred thirty-six million, eight hundred forty-six thousand eighty dollars **2a.** < **b.** 9,789; 9,897; 9,987

Lesson 1-2 pp. 9–10

Check Skills You'll Need **1.** twenty-eight **2.** eight thousand, six hundred seventy-two **3.** six hundred twelve thousand, nine hundred eighty **4.** fifty-eight million, twenty-six thousand, one hundred thirteen

Check Understanding **1a.** 3 + 0.1 + 0.04 + 0.001 + 0.0006 **b.** 0.8 + 0.06 + 0.005 **c.** 30 + 7 + 0.5 **d.** No; the zero in 6.207 is covered when you write "+ 0.007." **2a.** sixteen thousand, seven hundred two and three tenths **b.** one thousand six hundred seventy and two hundred thirty-four thousandths **c.** one and sixty-seven thousand twenty-three hundred-thousandths **3a.** 9.587 **b.** the 5, since 0.5 > 0.007

Lesson 1-3 pp. 13–17

Check Skills You'll Need **1.** > **2.** > **3.** > **4.** > **5.** digits on the left

Check Understanding

1.

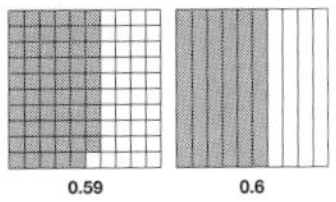

0.6 is greater.

2.

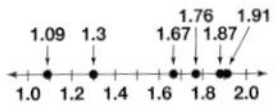

3a. < **b.** > **c.** = **d.** Answers may vary. Sample: Compare the digits starting with the highest place values. The ones and tenths digits are the same. The hundredths digit in 1.697 is greater than the hundredths digit in 1.679. So, 1.697 > 1.679. **4a.** 2.076, 2.6, 2.76 **b.** 3.059, 3.46, 3.64

Checkpoint Quiz 1 **1.** six trillion, eighty billion, four hundred five and thirty-one hundredths **2.** 10 + 2 + 0.03 + 0.005 **3.** 400.7 **4.** < **5.** 8.0, 8.05, 8.7, 9, 9.31

Lesson 1-4 pp. 19–21

Check Skills You'll Need **1.** 50 **2.** 65,330 **3.** 132,800 **4.** 30,910,000 **5.** 6,000 **6.** 15,345,000

Check Understanding **1a.** about 32 **b.** about 3 **c.** about 112 **2a.** because 28 is divisible by 4 **b.** about 250 **3a.** about $22 **b.** About $6; front-end estimation always includes the cents, so the estimates are higher and less likely to leave you short of money.

Lesson 1-5 pp. 25–27

Check Skills You'll Need **1.** 9 **2.** 10 **3.** 5 **4.** 1 **5.** 3 **6.** 3

Check Understanding **1.** about 6; 6.16 **2a.** 13.9 **b.** 94 **c.** 9.4 **3a.** about 2; 1.8 **b.** about 8; 7.53 **c.** about 0.3; 0.27 **d.** Answers may vary. Sample: Aligning the decimal points aligns all the places correctly. **4a.** about 91; 91.2 **b.** about 32; 31.68 **c.** about 77; 77.084

Lesson 1-6 pp. 30–31

Check Skills You'll Need **1.** 62 **2.** 57 **3.** 24 **4.** 82 **5.** 77 **6.** 3,815

Check Understanding **1.** 0.16 s

Lesson 1-7 pp. 35–39

Check Skills You'll Need **1.** 147 **2.** 816 **3.** 21,607 **4.** 42,340

Check Understanding **1a.** 0.78 **b.** 21.85 **2a.** 0.06 **b.** 0.126 **c.** It is less than either factor. **3a.** 7.464 **b.** 57.984 **4a.** 23 **b.** 310 **c.** 333

Checkpoint Quiz 2

1–4. Answers may vary. Samples are given. **1.** 29 **2.** 60 **3.** 15 **4.** 8 **5.** 7.32 **6.** 8.26 **7.** 32.76 **8.** 1.42 **9.** 1.65 lb **10.** Answers may vary. Sample: 8 · 13.1 · 0.5 = 8 · 0.5 · 13.1 Comm. Prop. of Add. = (8 · 0.5) · 13.1 Assoc. Prop. of Add. = 4 · 13.1 = 52.4 Assoc. Prop. of Add.; 8(0.5) = 4 and 4(13.1) = 52.4

Lesson 1-8 pp. 40–41

Check Skills You'll Need **1.** 360 **2.** 3,600 **3.** 36,000 **4.** 470 **5.** 47 **6.** 4.7

Check Understanding **1a.** 342 **b.** 2.35 **c.** 55,200 **2a.** 5.342 **b.** 0.0235 **c.** 0.0552 **d.** Sample: To divide by 10,000, move the decimal point in the dividend four places to the left; 0.00073.

Lesson 1-9 pp. 43–45

Check Skills You'll Need **1.** 5 **2.** 32 **3.** 101 **4.** 27 **5.** yes **6.** no **7.** yes **8.** yes

Check Understanding **1a.** 1.52 **b.** 48.2 **c.** 0.144 **2a.** $0.\overline{6}$; repeating **b.** 0.25; terminating **c.** $0.\overline{18}$; repeating **3a.**

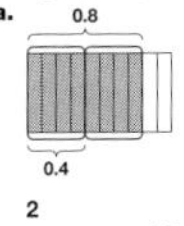

b.

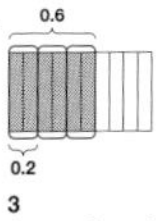

c.

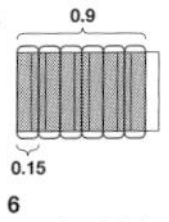

d. the number of groups **4a.** 6.2 **b.** 108 **c.** 30.5

Lesson 1-10 pp. 48–49

Check Skills You'll Need **1.** = **2.** > **3.** > **4.** > **5.** < **6.** <

Check Understanding **1a.** 8 **b.** 11.7 **c.** 16 **d.** I would add before multiplying if the addition of two numbers is done within parentheses and the multiplication is done outside of the parentheses. **2.** $46.85

Chapter 2

Diagnosing Readiness p. 62

1. about 50 **2.** about 7 **3.** about 52 **4.** about 42; 42.15 **5.** about 9; 9.5 **6.** about 5; 5.1 **7.** 379 **8.** 3,040 **9.** 1.57 **10.** 26.5 **11.** 39 **12.** 17.2

Lesson 2-1 pp. 63–65

Check Skills You'll Need **1.** 0.0105, 0.105, 10.5 **2.** 3.1, 3.31, 3.331 **3.** 9.06, 9.09, 9.6 **4.** 0.602, 20.06, 26.0 **5.** 100.01, 100.1, 101.0 **6.** 0.35, 0.4, 0.99

Check Understanding **1a.** 41, 51 **b.** 24, 16 **c.** 57, 64 **d.** 22 tiles **2a.** 90, 75, 60, 45, 30, 15 **b.** 1, 3, 9, 27, 81, 243 **c.** 17, 36, 55, 74, 93, 112 **3a.** 2,401, 16,807, 117,649; the first term is 1; multiply each term by 7 to get the next term. **b.** 6.4, 5.2, 4; the first term is 10.0; subtract 1.2 from a term to get the next term. **c.** 32, 16, 8; the first term is 256; divide each term by 2 to get the next term.

Lesson 2-2 pp. 68–70

Check Skills You'll Need **1.** 32 **2.** 19 **3.** 44.1 **4.** 4

Check Understanding **1a.**

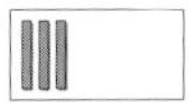

b.

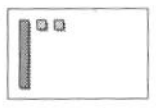

c.

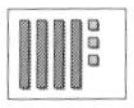

2a. 36 **b.** 5 **c.** 28 **d.** *x* was replaced by 7; 7 was multiplied by 4; 28 was subtracted from 56. **3.** $255

Lesson 2-3 pp. 74–78

Check Skills You'll Need **1.** 10 **2.** 1 **3.** 15 **4.** 30 **5.** 48 **6.** 11

Check Understanding **1a.** $5 \div y$ **b.** $6z$ **c.** $m + 3.4$ **2.** $h + 2$ **3.** Answers may vary. Samples are given. **a.** $n \div 2$ **b.** $n + 4$ **4a.** $b + 28$ **b.** 41

Checkpoint Quiz 1 **1.** 1,296; 7,776; 46,656; the first term is 1; multiply a term by 6 to get the next term. **2.** 225, 210, 195; the first term is 285; subtract 15 from a term to get the next term. **3.** 0.005, 0.0005, 0.00005; the first term is 50; divide a term by 10 to get the next term. **4.** 56 **5.** 9 **6.** 10.5 **7.** $17 - d$ **8.** ae **9.** $14 \div q$ **10a.** $5q + 3$ **b.** 63

Lesson 2-4 p. 80

Check Skills You'll Need **1.** 256; 1,024; 4,096 **2.** 35, 42, 49 **3.** 112, 224, 448 **4.** 52, 43, 34 **5.** 6.1, 7.2, 8.3 **6.** 5; 2.5; 1.25

Check Understanding **1.** No; for 10 tables, there are 64 seats, but for 20 tables there are 124 seats (not 128).

Lesson 2-5 pp. 84–86

Check Skills You'll Need **1.** about 6 **2.** about 4 **3.** about 2 **4.** about 16 **5.** about 24 **6.** about 5

Check Understanding **1a.** true **b.** false **c.** false **2a.** 9 **b.** 80 **c.** 1.2 **3a–d.** Answers may vary. Samples are given. **3a.** about 29 **b.** about 6 **c.** about 18

Lesson 2-6 pp. 90–92

Check Skills You'll Need **1.** 9 **2.** 1 **3.** 70 **4.** 2 **5.** 9 **6.** 3

Check Understanding **1.** 4.8 **2.** 9.8 lb **3a.** 81 **b.** 55 **c.** 6.4 **4.** t = temperature at 7:00 P.M., $t - 9 = 54$; 63°F

Lesson 2-7 pp. 95–98

Check Skills You'll Need **1–6.** Answers may vary. Samples are given. **1.** 7 **2.** 6 **3.** 16 **4.** 3 **5.** 8 **6.** 32

Check Understanding **1a.** 4 **b.** 2.7 **c.** 40 **2.** Equations may vary. Sample: $.35c = 302.75$; 865 cards **3a.** 200 **b.** 15 **c.** 1.58

Checkpoint Quiz 2 **1.** 13 **2.** 18.2 **3.** 2.2 **4.** 14.4 **5.** 10.8 **6.** 20 **7.** 8.4 **8.** 7 **9.** 5 **10.** x = change received; $x + 5.73 = 10.00$; $4.27

Lesson 2-8 pp. 99–101

Check Skills You'll Need **1.** 25 **2.** 0 **3.** 19.2 **4.** 10,000 **5.** 1 **6.** 2

Check Understanding **1a.** 3.94^2; 3.94; 2 **b.** 7^4; 7; 4 **c.** x^3; x; 3 **d.** No; 5^4 means 5 × 5 × 5 × 5, which is 625. 5 × 4 is 20. **2a.** $5 \times 10^4 + 5 \times 10^3 + 6 \times 10^2 + 0 \times 10^1 + 7 \times 1$ **b.** $3 \times 10^5 + 8 \times 10^4 + 0 \times 10^3 + 2 \times 10^2 + 5 \times 10^1 + 4 \times 1$ **3a.** 100,000 **b.** 19,683 **c.** 1.331 **d.** No; 2^5 means 2 × 2 × 2 × 2 × 2, which is 32; 5^2 means 5 × 5, which is 25. **4a.** 6 **b.** 112 **c.** 14

Lesson 2-9 pp. 105–106

Check Skills You'll Need **1.** 13.4 **2.** 17.3 **3.** 23.3 **4.** 16.5

Check Understanding **1a.** 3 × (40 + 2) = (3 × 40) + (3 × 2) = 120 + 6 = 126 **1b.** 5 × (70 − 2) = (5 × 70) − (5 × 2) = 350 − 10 = 340 **2.** $14

Chapter 3

Diagnosing Readiness p. 118

1. four tenths **2.** thirty-seven hundredths **3.** one and eight tenths **4.** two hundred five thousandths **5.** twenty and eighty-eight hundredths **6.** one hundred fifty thousandths **7.** 4.02, 4.2, 4.21 **8.** 0.033, 0.3, 0.33 **9.** 6.032, 6.203, 6.302 **10.** 0.8 **11.** 0.55 **12.** 19 **13.** 36.3 **14.** 132 **15.** 53 **16.** 3^3 **17.** 5^2 **18.** 2^6

Lesson 3-1 pp. 119–120

Check Skills You'll Need **1.** 49 **2.** 41 **3.** 41.5 **4.** 145 **5.** 41 **6.** 50

Check Understanding **1a.** no **b.** yes **c.** 54 = 9 × 6 = 9 × (2 × 3) **2a.** 2, 5, and 10 **b.** 5 **c.** none **d.** 2 **3a.** no **b.** yes **c.** yes **4a.** yes **b.** no **c.** yes **d.** If the sum of the digits is divisible by 9, the sum is divisible by 3, since 9 is divisible by 3.

Lesson 3-2 pp. 123–124

Check Skills You'll Need **1.** 2, 3, 5, 9, and 10 **2.** none **3.** 5 **4.** 2, 5, and 10 **5.** 2, 5, and 10 **6.** 2

Check Understanding **1.** 1, 2, 3, 6, 7, 14, 21, 42 **2a.** composite; 39 = 3 × 13 **b.** Prime; it has only two factors, 1 and 47. **c.** composite; 63 = 3 × 21 or 63 = 7 × 9 **3a.** $2^2 \times 3^2$ **b.** 5^3

Lesson 3-3 pp. 128–131

Check Skills You'll Need **1.** $3^2 \times 5$ **2.** 3 × 7 **3.** $3^2 \times 11$ **4.** 3 × 31 **5.** 3 × 13 **6.** 2^7 **7.** 21 is not prime.

Check Understanding **1a.** factors of 6: 1, 2, 3, 6; factors of 21: 1, 3, 7, 21; GCF of 6 and 21: 3 **b.** factors of 18: 1, 2, 3, 6, 9, 18; factors of 49: 1, 7, 49; GCF of 18; and 49: 1 **c.** factors of 14: 1, 2, 7, 14; factors of 28: 1, 2, 4, 7, 14, 28; GCF of 14 and 28: 14 **d.** three from the set of 18 and five from the set of 30

2a.

```
2)24  54    GCF = 6
3)12  27
   4   9
```

b.

```
3)18  27  36    GCF = 9
3) 6   9  12
   2   3   4
```


3a. GCF = 4

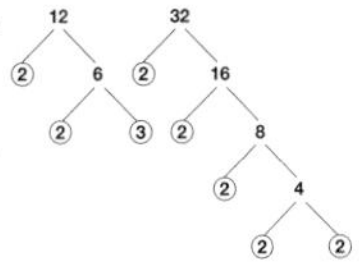

12 = 2 × 2 × 3
32 = 2 × 2 × 2 × 2 × 2

b. GCF = 6

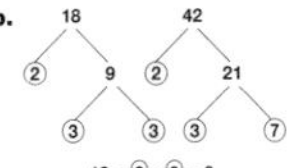

18 = 2 × 3 × 3
42 = 2 × 3 × 7

Checkpoint Quiz 1 **1.** 3, 5 **2.** 2 **3.** 2, 3, 5, 10 **4.** $2^4 \times 3$ **5.** $2^4 \times 5$ **6.** $2^3 \times 5^3$ **7.** 5 **8.** 24 **9.** 3 **10.** 1, 2, 3, 6

Lesson 3-4 pp. 134–135

Check Skills You'll Need **1.** 4 **2.** 5 **3.** 6 **4.** 1 **5.** 4 **6.** 7

Check Understanding **1a–c.** Answers may vary. Samples are given. **1a.** $\frac{2}{5}, \frac{8}{20}, \frac{12}{30}$ **b.** $\frac{10}{16}, \frac{15}{24}, \frac{25}{40}$ **c.** $\frac{1}{3}, \frac{4}{12}, \frac{6}{18}$ **2a.** $\frac{3}{4}$ **b.** $\frac{2}{7}$ **c.** $\frac{1}{5}$ **3a.** $\frac{7}{20}$ **b.** dog food and bird food; 42 + 18 = 60, and $\frac{60}{120} = \frac{1}{2}$

Lesson 3-5 pp. 139–140

Check Skills You'll Need **1.** $\frac{1}{3}$ **2.** $\frac{2}{3}$ **3.** $\frac{5}{16}$ **4.** $\frac{1}{17}$ **5.** $\frac{9}{10}$ **6.** There are 60 minutes in an hour, so compare 35 to 60 by using the fraction $\frac{35}{60}$. In simplest form, $\frac{35}{60}$ is $\frac{7}{12}$.

Check Understanding **1.** $\frac{25}{7}$ **2.** whole units **3a.** $4\frac{4}{9}$ **b.** $5\frac{1}{3}$ **c.** $5\frac{3}{4}$ **d.** $1\frac{2}{3}$

Lesson 3-6 pp. 143–144

Check Skills You'll Need **1.** $2^4 \times 5$ **2.** 2^5 **3.** 5 × 19 **4.** $2^2 \times 5^3$ **5.** $2^4 \times 13$ **6.** 5^4

Check Understanding **1a.** 60 **b.** 12, 24, 36, 48, 60 **2.** 350

Lesson 3-7 pp. 148–152

Check Skills You'll Need **1–9.** Answers may vary. Samples are given. **1.** $\frac{6}{14}, \frac{15}{35}$ **2.** $\frac{1}{3}, \frac{21}{63}$ **3.** $\frac{1}{5}, \frac{2}{10}$ **4.** $\frac{4}{6}, \frac{20}{30}$ **5.** $\frac{5}{6}, \frac{20}{24}$ **6.** $\frac{1}{6}, \frac{5}{30}$ **7.** $\frac{3}{4}, \frac{12}{16}$ **8.** $\frac{4}{10}, \frac{120}{300}$ **9.** $\frac{16}{10}, \frac{24}{15}$

Check Understanding **1a.** < **b.** = **c.** > **d.** 40 min, 36 min; $\frac{2}{3}$ **2a.** < **b.** > **c.** = **d.** Yes; $\frac{7}{8} = \frac{28}{32}$ and $\frac{28}{32} > \frac{27}{32}$. So $6\frac{7}{8} > 6\frac{27}{32}$. **3.** $2\frac{2}{3}, 2\frac{4}{5}, 2\frac{5}{6}$

Checkpoint Quiz 2 **1.** $\frac{2}{3}$ **2.** $\frac{3}{4}$ **3.** $\frac{1}{4}$ **4.** $\frac{16}{5}$ **5.** $1\frac{5}{8}$ **6.** 60 **7.** $\frac{1}{8}, \frac{3}{16}, \frac{1}{3}$ **8.** < **9.** > **10.** >

Lesson 3-8 pp. 153–154

Check Skills You'll Need **1.** 1.5; terminating **2.** $0.\overline{6}$; repeating **3.** 1.6; terminating **4.** 0.375; terminating **5.** 0.3; terminating **6.** 0.24; terminating **7.** 0.24; terminating **8.** 0.2; terminating **9.** 3.2; terminating

Check Understanding **1a.** $\frac{3}{5}$ **b.** $\frac{7}{20}$ **c.** $5\frac{2}{25}$ **d.** $7\frac{81}{200}$ **e.** Using the digits to the right of the decimal point, the number you say first tells you the numerator, and the number that is read with "-th" at the end tells you the denominator. **2a.** 0.45 **b.** The mixed number $2\frac{3}{4}$ is equal to the whole number 2 plus the decimal equivalent of $\frac{3}{4}$. To find the decimal equivalent of $\frac{3}{4}$, divide the numerator 3 by the denominator 4. Add the quotient 0.75 to the whole number 2 to get 2.75. **3a.** $0.\overline{6}$ **b.** $0.1\overline{6}$ **c.** $0.\overline{5}$ **d.** $1.\overline{3}$ **e.** when the numerator is not divisible by 3

Lesson 3-9 pp. 157–158

Check Skills You'll Need **1.** 10, 12, 14 **2.** 32, 64, 128 **3.** 54, 162, 486 **4.** 85, 80, 75 **5.** 21, 26, 31 **6.** 9, 11, 13

Check Understanding **1.** 20 adult tickets

Chapter 4

Diagnosing Readiness p.170

1. 2.59 **2.** 1.99 **3.** 6.22 **4.** $\frac{1}{2}$ **5.** $\frac{2}{5}$ **6.** $\frac{3}{4}$ **7.** $9\frac{2}{3}$ **8.** $5\frac{1}{4}$ **9.** $7\frac{1}{2}$ **10.** $\frac{26}{3}$ **11.** $\frac{23}{3}$ **12.** $\frac{151}{9}$ **13.** 72 **14.** 80 **15.** 210

Lesson 4-1 pp. 171–172

Check Skills You'll Need **1.** > **2.** < **3.** = **4.** < **5.** > **6.** <

Check Understanding **1a.** $1\frac{1}{2}$ **b.** 1 **2.** 5 hours

Lesson 4-2 pp. 175–176

Check Skills You'll Need **1.** $\frac{1}{4}$ **2.** $\frac{1}{3}$ **3.** $\frac{4}{5}$ **4.** $\frac{4}{5}$ **5.** $\frac{2}{3}$ **6.** $\frac{3}{4}$ **7.** $\frac{5}{6}$ **8.** $\frac{3}{7}$ **9.** $\frac{3}{7}$

Check Understanding **1a.** $\frac{5}{6}$ **b.** $\frac{3}{5}$ **2a.** $1\frac{1}{8}$ **b.** $1\frac{2}{5}$ **c.** Answers may vary. Sample: If the numerator and denominator have a common factor, the answer is not in simplest form. **3a.** $\frac{1}{5}$ **b.** $\frac{1}{2}$ **c.** $\frac{1}{3}$ yard

Lesson 4-3 pp. 180–184

Check Skills You'll Need **1.** 18 **2.** 36 **3.** 120 **4.** 240 **5.** 150 **6.** 60 **7.** 24. Explanations may vary. Sample: List multiples of 8: 8; 16; 24. List multiples of 12: 12; 24. The LCM is 24.

Check Understanding **1.** $\frac{7}{10}$ **2.** $1\frac{5}{12}$ h **3.** $\frac{1}{8}$ **4.** $\frac{1}{10}$ yd

Checkpoint Quiz 1 **1.** $1\frac{1}{2}$ **2.** 1 **3.** $1\frac{1}{5}$ **4.** $\frac{1}{2}$ **5.** $1\frac{1}{4}$ **6.** $\frac{17}{30}$ **7.** $\frac{1}{2}$ **8.** $\frac{7}{10}$ **9.** $\frac{11}{18}$ of the class **10.** $1\frac{1}{6}$ c

Lesson 4-4 pp. 185–187

Check Skills You'll Need **1.** $4\frac{1}{2}$ **2.** $3\frac{1}{3}$ **3.** $1\frac{1}{3}$ **4.** $2\frac{1}{2}$ **5.** $1\frac{3}{4}$ **6.** $2\frac{1}{2}$ **7.** $2\frac{2}{5}$. Explanations may vary. Sample: Divide 36 by 15. The quotient 2 is the integer of the mixed number. The remainder 6 is the numerator, and 15 is the denominator: $2\frac{6}{15}$. Reduce to $2\frac{2}{5}$.

Check Understanding **1.** Answers may vary. Sample: It doesn't matter because addition is commutative. **2a.** $5\frac{7}{12}$ h **b.** $2\frac{1}{3} + 3\frac{1}{4} \approx 2 + 3$, or 5 **3a.** $9\frac{3}{4}$ **b.** $19\frac{1}{8}$ **c.** $21\frac{4}{15}$ **4.** No; you need $3\frac{1}{4}$ c of milk, but you have only 3 c.

Lesson 4-5 pp. 190–192

Check Skills You'll Need **1.** $1\frac{1}{2}$ **2.** $2\frac{2}{3}$ **3.** $4\frac{3}{5}$ **4.** $2\frac{1}{2}$ **5.** $2\frac{1}{2}$ **6.** $2\frac{2}{5}$ **7.** Divide 24 by 10. The quotient 2 is the integer of the mixed number. The remainder 4 is the numerator, and 10 is the denominator: $2\frac{4}{10}$. Reduce to $2\frac{2}{5}$.

Check Understanding **1a.** $\frac{11}{16}$ in. **b.** Yes; answers may vary. Sample: 32 is a common multiple of 8 and 4, so it is also a common denominator. **2a.** $1\frac{1}{3}$ **b.** $5\frac{3}{4}$ **3.** Answers may vary. Sample: If the benchmark of the first fraction is less than the benchmark of the second fraction, then rename before subtracting.

Lesson 4-6 pp. 196–197

Check Skills You'll Need **1.** 26 **2.** 268 **3.** 3.8 **4.** 18.9 **5.** 0 **6.** 14.2

Check Understanding **1a.** $3\frac{2}{3}$ **b.** $11\frac{1}{4}$ **c.** $2\frac{3}{4}$ **2a.** $\frac{7}{12}$ **b.** $\frac{1}{4}$ **3.** $1\frac{3}{4}$ in.

Lesson 4-7 pp. 201–205

Check Skills You'll Need **1.** $\frac{16}{60}$ **2.** $\frac{15}{60}$ **3.** $\frac{12}{60}$ **4.** $\frac{20}{60}$ **5.** $\frac{40}{60}$ **6.** $\frac{35}{60}$

Check Understanding **1.** 31 days **2.** 47 min **3a.** 9 h 15 min **b.** Answers may vary. Sample: Adding 12 hours makes both times the hours elapsed since midnight, so they can be subtracted. **4.** 5:20 P.M.

Checkpoint Quiz 2 **1.** $5\frac{5}{8}$ **2.** $4\frac{3}{4}$ **3.** $14\frac{5}{6}$ **4.** $5\frac{8}{9}$ **5.** $\frac{1}{2}$ **6.** $1\frac{2}{9}$ **7.** $\frac{3}{10}$ **8.** $\frac{2}{15}$ **9.** 6 h 47 min **10.** 9 h 43 min

Lesson 4-8 pp. 206–207

Check Skills You'll Need **1–6.** Answers may vary. Samples are given. **1.** 6 **2.** 10 **3.** 11 **4.** 2 **5.** 19 **6.** 2

Check Understanding **1.** 35 mats

Chapter 5

Diagnosing Readiness p. 218

1. 4 **2.** 5 **3.** 12 **4.** 112 **5.** 100 **6.** 5 **7.** 54 **8.** 0.6 **9.** 3 **10.** 12 **11.** 7 **12.** 3 **13.** 20 **14.** 6 **15.** 21 **16.** $\frac{3}{7}$ **17.** $\frac{2}{3}$ **18.** $\frac{1}{3}$ **19.** $\frac{3}{8}$ **20.** $\frac{1}{4}$ **21.** $\frac{3}{7}$ **22.** $\frac{2}{3}$ **23.** $\frac{7}{8}$ **24.** $\frac{3}{7}$

Lesson 5-1 pp. 219–221

Check Skills You'll Need **1.** $\frac{1}{2}$ **2.** $\frac{3}{5}$ **3.** $\frac{2}{3}$ **4.** $\frac{9}{10}$ **5.** $\frac{3}{4}$ **6.** $\frac{3}{4}$ **7.** Answers may vary. Sample: Yes; the GCF of 9 and 16 is 1.

Check Understanding **1.** 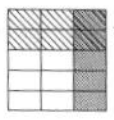 $\frac{2}{15}$ **2a.** $\frac{3}{20}$ **b.** $\frac{10}{63}$

c. When you add $\frac{3}{8}$ and $\frac{5}{8}$ you add numerators and keep the same denominator. When you multiply the fractions, you multiply numerators and multiply denominators. **3a.** $\frac{28}{5} = 5\frac{3}{5}$ **b.** $\frac{40}{3} = 13\frac{1}{3}$ **4.** $4\frac{1}{2}$ mi

Lesson 5-2 pp. 224–226

Check Skills You'll Need **1.** 2 **2.** 13 **3.** 30 **4.** 8 **5.** 6 **6.** 6

Check Understanding **1a.** 36 **b.** 56 **c.** 143 **d.** The actual product is greater than $80 \cdot \frac{1}{8}$, since $82\frac{5}{7} > 80$. So the actual product is greater than 10. $83 \cdot 0$ would give an estimate of 0, which is not realistic. **2a.** $3\frac{7}{16}$ **b.** $27\frac{1}{2}$ **c.** 18 **3.** $2\frac{5}{8}$ mi

Lesson 5-3 pp. 230–232

Check Skills You'll Need **1.** 6 **2.** 4 **3.** $\frac{1}{5}$ **4.** 1 **5.** $\frac{1}{7}$ **6.** $\frac{4}{11}$

Check Understanding **1a.** $\frac{4}{3}$ or $1\frac{1}{3}$ **b.** $\frac{1}{7}$ **c.** $\frac{7}{8}$ **2a.** $10\frac{2}{3}$ **b.** $31\frac{1}{2}$ **c.** $10\frac{1}{2}$ **3a.** $\frac{3}{4}$ **b.** $\frac{3}{4}$ **c.** $\frac{4}{5}$ **d.** Answers may vary. Sample: $\frac{2}{3}$ is between $\frac{1}{2}$ and 1. There are 2 fourths in $\frac{1}{2}$, and 4 fourths in 1. So there must be between 2 and 4 fourths in $\frac{2}{3}$. **4a.** $\frac{1}{32}$ **b.** $\frac{1}{150}$ **c.** Answers may vary. Sample: $\frac{1}{5}$ of the original piece, or $\frac{1}{6}$ yd.

Lesson 5-4 pp. 236–240

Check Skills You'll Need **1.** 28 **2.** $23\frac{1}{3}$ **3.** $\frac{7}{24}$ **4.** $\frac{1}{6}$ **5.** $\frac{15}{16}$ **6.** $2\frac{8}{11}$ **7.** When you divide by a fraction, find its reciprocal and multiply by it.

Check Understanding **1a.** about 7 **b.** about 5 **c.** about 10 **d.** Answers may vary. Sample: about 10 **2.** $1\frac{1}{4}$ c **3a.** 6 **b.** $2\frac{1}{20}$ **c.** $3\frac{1}{2}$ **d.** When you divide a number by a greater number, the quotient is less than 1.

Checkpoint Quiz 1 **1.** 15 **2.** $23\frac{5}{8}$ **3.** 64 **4.** $\frac{1}{6}$ **5.** $1\frac{11}{21}$ **6.** $\frac{3}{5}$ **7.** $16\frac{1}{3}$ **8.** $2\frac{7}{30}$ **9.** 39 ft **10.** 24 cookies

Lesson 5-5 pp. 242–243

Check Skills You'll Need **1.** $\frac{7}{30}$ **2.** $\frac{3}{11}$ **3.** $\frac{2}{5}$

Check Understanding **1a.** 30 **b.** 72 **2a.** 20 **b.** 25 **c.** 48 **3.** 10 boards

Lesson 5-6 pp. 246–247

Check Skills You'll Need **1.** $1\frac{1}{2}$ **2.** $\frac{10}{27}$ **3.** 10 **4.** $\frac{25}{36}$ **5.** $6\frac{2}{5}$ **6.** $\frac{11}{12}$

Check Understanding **1.** 408 cards

Lesson 5-7 pp. 250–253

Check Skills You'll Need **1.** > **2.** > **3.** > **4.** > **5.** < **6.** =

Check Understanding
1–3. Answers may vary. Samples are given. **1a.** Inches; pencils are shorter than a foot. **b.** Feet or yards; adult whales are longer than humans. **c.** Inches are a short unit of measure. Inches are too small to measure a walking distance. **2a.** Pounds; a refrigerator weighs less than a grand piano. **b.** Ounces; an ice cube weighs about the same as a slice of bread. **3a.** Gallons; a tanker truck holds more gasoline than can fit in a small bucket. **b.** Fluid ounces or cups; a serving of yogurt is less than a pint. **c.** Gallons; a bathtub can hold a few small buckets of water. **d.** Fluid ounces; a bottle of cough syrup holds less than a pint.

Checkpoint Quiz 2 **1.** $10\frac{1}{2}$ **2.** $\frac{2}{5}$ **3.** mile **4.** pound **5.** 51 markers

Lesson 5-8 pp. 254–255

Check Skills You'll Need **1.** $25\frac{1}{2}$ **2.** $10\frac{1}{2}$ **3.** 24 **4.** $\frac{55}{78}$ **5.** $\frac{3}{8}$ **6.** $\frac{20}{27}$ **7.**

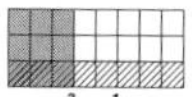

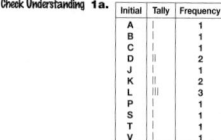

$\frac{3}{24} = \frac{1}{8}$

Check Understanding **1a.** $3\frac{3}{4}$ **b.** $4\frac{25}{36}$ **c.** $2\frac{1}{2}$ yd **2a.** $6\frac{1}{2}$ **b.** 4,500 **3.** 8 lb 1 oz

Chapter 6

Diagnosing Readiness p. 268

1. 18 **2.** 7 **3.** 48 **4.** 132 **5.** 24 **6.** 42 **7.** 9 **8.** 16 **9.** $\frac{2}{5}$ **10.** $\frac{5}{11}$ **11.** $\frac{2}{3}$ **12.** $\frac{1}{3}$ **13.** > **14.** > **15.** < **16.** = **17.** $\frac{8}{21}$ **18.** $\frac{1}{2}$ **19.** $3\frac{8}{9}$ **20.** $4\frac{1}{8}$

Lesson 6-1 pp. 269–270

Check Skills You'll Need **1.** $\frac{1}{3}$ **2.** $\frac{2}{3}$ **3.** $\frac{2}{9}$ **4.** $\frac{1}{16}$

Check Understanding **1a.** 2 to 4, 2 : 4, $\frac{2}{4}$ **b.** 2 to 6, 2 : 6, $\frac{2}{6}$ **2a–c.** Answers may vary. Samples are given. **2a.** $\frac{2}{7}$, $\frac{4}{14}$ **b.** 4 : 1, 8 : 2 **c.** 4 to 11, 12 to 33 **d.** 9 to 5 is a comparison of two numbers by division. $1\frac{4}{5}$ is not a comparison of two numbers.

3a. 1 : 5 **b.** 10 to 9 **c.** $\frac{13}{1}$ **d.** 1 to 8

Lesson 6-2 pp. 273–274

Check Skills You'll Need **1.** $\frac{4}{1}$ **2.** $\frac{4}{1}$ **3.** $\frac{5}{1}$ **4.** $\frac{6}{1}$ **5.** $\frac{25}{1}$ **6.** $\frac{13}{1}$

Check Understanding **1a.** 33 pages per hour **b.** \$.79 per pound **c.** $\frac{12 \text{ inches}}{1 \text{ foot}}$; it is the number of inches in 1 foot. **2a.** $\frac{\$5.25}{1 \text{ hour}} = \frac{\$26.25}{5 \text{ hours}}$ **b.** $\frac{25 \text{ words}}{1 \text{ minute}} = \frac{250 \text{ words}}{10 \text{ minutes}}$ **3a.** \$.11 per ounce; \$.09 per ounce; the 32-ounce container **b.** \$.14 per minute; \$.09 per minute; the 15 minutes for \$1.35 **c.** Answers may vary. Sample: It helps find the less expensive item.

Lesson 6-3 pp. 278–280

Check Skills You'll Need **1.** < **2.** = **3.** < **4.** < **5.** > **6.** =

Check Understanding **1a.** yes **b.** no **c.** no **2a.** 15 **b.** 6

Lesson 6-4 pp. 283–285

Check Skills You'll Need **1.** 10 **2.** 6 **3.** 7 **4.** 12 **5.** 108 **6.** 56

Check Understanding **1.** Yes; the cross products are equal. **2a.** 15 **b.** 4 **c.** 5 **3a.** \$4.50 **b.** about \$3.20

Lesson 6-5 pp. 288–292

Check Skills You'll Need **1.** 20 **2.** 25 **3.** 6 **4.** 2 **5.** 1 **6.** 105

Check Understanding **1.** 1 in. : 14 in. **2.** about 100 mi **3.** 17 in.

Checkpoint Quiz 1 **1.** 18 to 40, $\frac{18}{40}$ **2.** \$2.85 **3.** \$17.50 **4.** no **5.** no **6.** yes **7.** 12 **8.** 78 **9.** \$16.20 **10.** 1 in. : 3 ft

Lesson 6-6 pp. 294–296

Check Skills You'll Need **1.** $\frac{6}{25}$ **2.** $\frac{2}{5}$ **3.** $\frac{3}{4}$ **4.** $\frac{1}{3}$ **5.** $\frac{79}{100}$

Check Understanding 1a. 0.18 **b.** 0.02 **c.** 0.25 2a. $\frac{1}{25}$ **b.** $\frac{11}{20}$ **c.** $\frac{3}{4}$ **d.** $\frac{1}{5}$ 3a. 52% **b.** 5% **c.** 50% **d.** Move the decimal point two places to the left. **4a.** 5% **b.** 1, 2, 4, 5, 10, 20, 25, 50, 100 **5.** about 7%

Lesson 6-7 pp. 299–300

Check Skills You'll Need **1.** 18 **2.** 8 **3.** 15 **4.** 78 **5.** 85 **6.** 230 **7.** Answers may vary. Sample: Use cross products. $39 \times 40 = 100 \times x$; $1{,}560 = 100x$. Divide both sides by 100. The solution is 15.6.

Check Understanding **1.** 48 **2a.** 10.92 **b.** 21.78 **3a.** 5.6 **b.** 9 **c.** 18

Lesson 6-8 pp. 303–306

Check Skills You'll Need **1.** 30 **2.** 120 **3.** 2,000 **4.** 400

Check Understanding **1a.** about \$10.50 **b.** Answers may vary. Sample: High estimate; I may estimate too low and not have enough money. **2.** about \$6 **3a.** about \$24 **b.** High estimate; the original price was rounded up but the percent was kept at 40%.

Checkpoint Quiz 2 **1.** 0.74, $\frac{37}{50}$ **2.** 84% **3.** tax: \$0.75; \$15.75 **4.** 110 **5.** 18

Lesson 6-9 p. 307

Check Skills You'll Need **1.** 5 **2.** 90 **3.** 4.5 **4.** 58 **5.** 22 **6.** 200

Check Understanding **1.** \$39.96

Chapter 7

Diagnosing Readiness p. 320

1. 0.12, 0.13, 0.21, 0.35, 0.45 **2.** 44, 45.01, 45.1, 46.01 **3.** 99.9, 100.80, 102, 124.32, 133 **4.** 0.22, 0.99, 2.5, 4.9, 7.04 **5.** 63.1 **6.** 423.9 **7.** 105.82 **8.** 25.87 **9.** 20.21 **10.** 1.06 **11.** 1.8 **12.** 14.203 **13.** 22.6 **14.** 4.03

Lesson 7-1 pp. 322–323

Check Skills You'll Need **1.** 27.5 **2.** 42.58 **3.** 59.35 **4.** 5.9 **5.** 8.55 **6.** 3.09

Check Understanding **1a.** 3.5 **b.** 22.4 **c.** 20 **d.** 57 **e.** 45; the new mean is much less. **2a.** 88 **b.** 27.5 **3.** apple

Lesson 7-2 pp. 326–327

Check Skills You'll Need **1.** blue and green **2.** 5.2; 5; 4 **3.** 2; 1.25; 0

Instant Check System™ Answers

Check Understanding **1a.**

Initial	Tally	Frequency
A	|	1
B	|	1
C	|	1
D	||	2
J	|	1
K	||	2
L	|||	3
P	|	1
S	|	1
T	|	1
V	|	1

mode: L

b. The data items are letters, not numbers.

2. 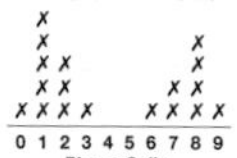
Number of Phone Calls
0 1 2 3 4 5 6 7 8 9
Phone Calls

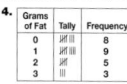

3a. 32 **b.** 0.17 **c.** No; explanations may vary. Sample: Add 10 to all data in the first set. The range stays the same, but the median increases by 10.

Lesson 7-3 pp. 331–333

Check Skills You'll Need **1.** 35, 42, 49 **2.** 13, 16, 19 **3.** 52, 43, 34 **4.** 324, 972, 2,916

Check Understanding **1.** day 8

Checkpoint Quiz 1 **1.** 30; 30; 30; 26 **2.** 21 **3.** 21

4.

Grams of Fat	Tally	Frequency
0	~~||||~~ |||	8
1	~~||||~~ ||||	9
2	~~||||~~	5
3	|||	3

5. 10 ways

Lesson 7-4 pp. 335–337

Check Skills You'll Need

1. 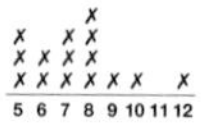
5 6 7 8 9 10 11 12

2. 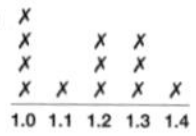
1.0 1.1 1.2 1.3 1.4

3. 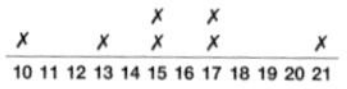
10 11 12 13 14 15 16 17 18 19 20 21

Check Understanding **1.** 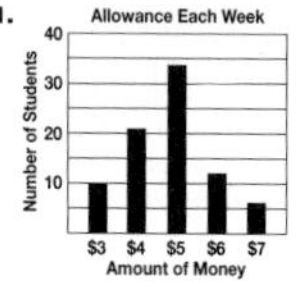
Allowance Each Week
Number of Students
40
30
20
10
$3 $4 $5 $6 $7
Amount of Money

2. 12–15 hours **3.** 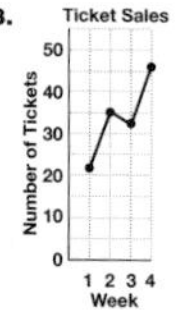
Ticket Sales
Number of Tickets
50
40
30
20
10
0
1 2 3 4
Week

Lesson 7-5 pp. 341–343

Check Skills You'll Need **1.** 98 **2.** 104 **3.** 96 **4.** 88 **5.** 615 **6.** 136

Check Understanding **1a.** 39% are processed **b.** 87%

2. 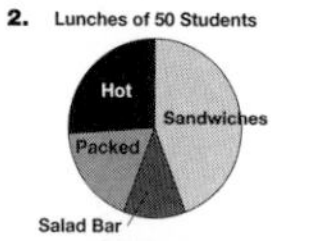
Lunches of 50 Students
Hot
Sandwiches
Packed
Salad Bar

Lesson 7-6 pp. 347–350

Check Skills You'll Need **1.** $5x$ **2.** $b - 7$ **3.** $52 - x$ **4.** $\frac{a}{9}$ **5.** xy **6.** $\frac{a}{b}$

Check Understanding **1a.** 30; the third country CD is 30 min long. **b.** A2, B2, C2, D2; the length (in minutes) of each of the three rock/pop CDs **2a.** =B2+B3+B4 **b.** =D2+D3+D4

Checkpoint Quiz 2 **1.** =B2+B3+B4+B5 **2.** \$800

3. Money Raised By Fundraisers

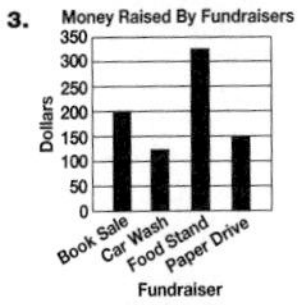

Money Raised By Fundraisers
Dollars
350
300
250
200
150
100
50
0
Book Sale
Car Wash
Food Stand
Paper Drive
Fundraiser

4. Money Raised by Fundraisers

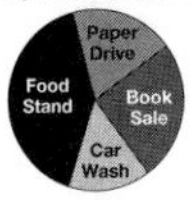

Paper Drive
Food Stand
Book Sale
Car Wash

5.

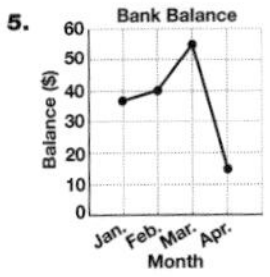

Bank Balance
Balance ($)
60
50
40
30
20
10
0
Jan.
Feb.
Mar.
Apr.
Month

Lesson 7-7 pp. 352–353

Check Skills You'll Need **1.** 32 **2.** 15 **3.** 212 **4.** 5.2

Check Understanding **1a.** 3 **b.** 35

c. Answers may vary. Sample: A stem-and-leaf plot groups the data so that it is easier to find the median and mode.

2.

12	1 3 4 5 5 6 7
13	0 2 3 6 7 8 8
14	0 1 4 5
15	0 5
16	
17	
18	1

Key: 12|3 means 123

Lesson 7-8 pp. 358–359

Check Skills You'll Need **1.** 55.5 **2.** 13.5 **3.** 131 **4.** 63.7 **5.** The data set in Exercise 4, which has outliers.

Check Understanding **1.**

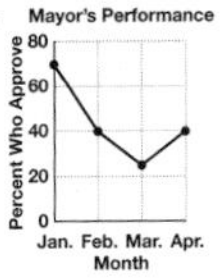

Mayor's Performance
Percent Who Approve
80
60
40
20
0
Jan.
Feb.
Mar.
Apr.
Month

2a. two times taller **b.** 3 cars

c.

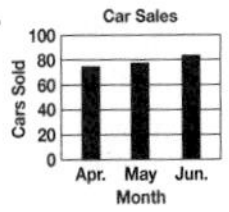

Car Sales
Cars Sold
100
80
60
40
20
0
Apr.
May
Jun.
Month

3a. $950,000

b. Median; the mode is the least data value. It occurs only twice, so its value is really too low to give a good idea of what a typical data value is.

Chapter 8

Diagnosing Readiness p. 372

1. 9 **2.** 9 **3.** 4 **4.** 10 **5.** 1.27 **6.** 59.5 **7.** 27.1 **8.** 17.5 **9.** 33.3 **10.** 12.07 **11.** Yes **12.** No **13.** No **14.** Yes **15.** No **16.** Yes

Lesson 8-1 pp. 373–375

Check Skills You'll Need **1.** $2\frac{13}{16}$ in. **2.** 2 in. **3.** $3\frac{3}{8}$ in. or $3\frac{6}{16}$ in.

Check Understanding **1a.** Answers may vary. Sample: $\overleftrightarrow{VP}$, $\overleftrightarrow{MV}$ **b.** $\overline{VM}$, $\overline{VP}$, $\overline{MP}$ **c.** Answers may vary. Samples are given. $\overrightarrow{VM}$ is a ray that has vertex V and contains M. $\overrightarrow{MV}$ is a ray that has vertex M and contains V. **2.** Answers may vary. Samples are given. **a.** Q, T, and M **b.** N, Q, and M **3.** Answers may vary. Samples are given. **a.** NE 3rd St. and NE 2nd St. **b.** NE 4th St. and N Miami Ave. **c.** No; all lines on the map represent streets in the same plane.

Lesson 8-2 pp. 379–381

Check Skills You'll Need **1.** Answers may vary. Samples are given. $\overleftrightarrow{AC}$, $\overleftrightarrow{BE}$, $\overleftrightarrow{DB}$ **2.** No; they do not lie on the same line.

Check Understanding **1a.** 125° **b.** greater **2a.** Answers may vary. Sample: 60° **b.** acute

Lesson 8-3 pp. 386–390

Check Skills You'll Need **1–4.** Check students' work.

Check Understanding **1.** 37° **2.** 35° **3a.** ∠3 and ∠6 **b.** Answers may vary. Sample: ∠6 and ∠5

Checkpoint Quiz 1 **1–10.** Answers may vary. Samples are given. **1.** $\overleftrightarrow{LM}$ and $\overleftrightarrow{KN}$ **2.** $\overrightarrow{JP}$ and $\overrightarrow{NK}$ **3.** ∠PJM **4.** ∠PJK **5.** ∠PJN **6.** ∠LJM **7.** ∠KJL and ∠MJN **8.** ∠KJL **9.** ∠PJK and ∠KJL **10.** ∠LJN and ∠NJM

Lesson 8-4 pp. 392–394

Check Skills You'll Need **1.** acute **2.** obtuse **3.** acute **4.** obtuse **5.** right **6.** acute **7.** obtuse **8.** straight

Check Understanding **1a.** right triangle **b.** acute triangle **2.** 50° 3a. isosceles **b.** scalene **4.** isoceles right triangle

Lesson 8-5 pp. 397–398

Check Skills You'll Need **1–3.** Answers may vary. Samples are given. **1.** $\overline{DC}$ and $\overline{FG}$ **2.** $\overline{CB}$ and $\overline{GH}$ **3.** $\overline{FG}$ and $\overline{BC}$

Check Understanding **1a.** quadrilateral **b.** hexagon **c.** octagon **2a.** parallelogram, rectangle **b.** Rectangle; answers may vary. Sample: A rectangle has four right angles and two pairs of parallel lines. **c.** Yes; every square has 4 congruent sides.

Lesson 8-6 pp. 401–402

Check Skills You'll Need **1.**

<table>
<tr><td>0</td><td>1</td><td>2</td><td>3</td><td>4</td></tr>
<tr><td>|||</td><td>|||</td><td>|||</td><td>|||</td><td>|</td></tr>
</table>

2.

<table>
<tr><td>75</td><td>|</td></tr>
<tr><td>80</td><td>|||</td></tr>
<tr><td>82</td><td>|</td></tr>
<tr><td>85</td><td>||</td></tr>
<tr><td>90</td><td>|||</td></tr>
<tr><td>100</td><td>||</td></tr>
</table>

3.

<table>
<tr><td>80</td><td>||</td></tr>
<tr><td>82</td><td>||</td></tr>
<tr><td>85</td><td>|</td></tr>
<tr><td>87</td><td>||</td></tr>
<tr><td>88</td><td>||</td></tr>
<tr><td>89</td><td>|</td></tr>
</table>

Check Understanding **1.**

	a.	b.	c.	d.
a.	T	H	A	T
b.	H	E	X	A
c.	A	X	E	S
d.	T	A	S	K

2. Janna was born in Jamaica. Georgine was born in France. Tanika was born in Peru.

Lesson 8-7 pp. 405–407

Check Skills You'll Need **1.** scalene **2.** isosceles **3.** scalene

Check Understanding **1a.** no **b.** yes **2a.** yes **b.** no **3.** Congruent and similar; all of their sides and angles are congruent.

Lesson 8-8 pp. 410–414

Check Skills You'll Need **1.** yes **2.** yes

Check Understanding **1.** No; if you fold the figure along the line, the two parts do not match.

2a. 1

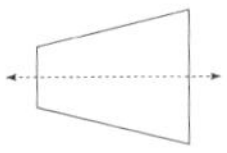

b. 4

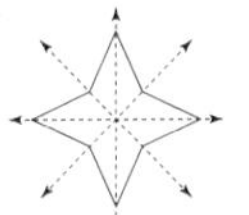

c. Infinitely many; any line that goes through the center of a circle is a line of symmetry.

Checkpoint Quiz 2 **1.** obtuse **2.** right **3.** acute **4.** isosceles **5.** scalene **6.** equilateral **7.** 4 m **8.** Fred is the teacher. Matt is the writer. Alison is the artist. **9.** B, D, and E **10.** B and E

Lesson 8-9 pp. 415–417

Check Skills You'll Need **1.**

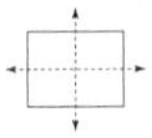

2.

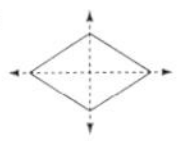

3.

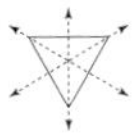

Check Understanding **1.** no

2a.

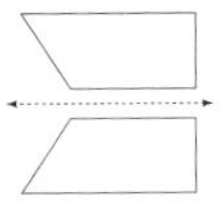

b.

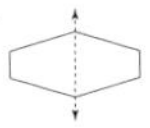

3a. no **b.** yes **c.** no

Chapter 9

Diagnosing Readiness p. 430

1. pounds **2.** gallons **3.** miles **4.** inches **5.** 144 **6.** $3\frac{5}{6}$ **7.** $3\frac{5}{8}$ **8.** $2\frac{1}{4}$ **9.** 26 **10.** $1\frac{1}{2}$ **11.** > **12.** < **13.** > **14.** < **15.** < **16.** = **17.** rhombus **18.** isosceles triangle **19.** trapezoid

Lesson 9-1 pp. 431–433

Check Skills You'll Need **1.** ounces **2.** pounds **3.** Feet; yards would also be appropriate. **4.** Pints; cups or fluid ounces would also be appropriate.

Check Understanding **1.** meter **2a.** 20 mm or 2 cm **b.** 36 mm or 3.6 cm **c.** 79 mm or 7.9 cm **3a.** kilograms **b.** kilograms **c.** grams **d.** milligrams **4a.** liters **b.** kiloliters **c.** milliliters

Lesson 9-2 pp. 436–437

Check Skills You'll Need **1.** 3,900 **2.** 53 **3.** 574 **4.** 0.07 **5.** 1.43 **6.** 980

Check Understanding **1a.** 150 mm **b.** 837,000 m **c.** 5 m is greater; 1 m = 1,000 mm, but 5 m = 5,000 mm. **2a.** 0.005 m **b.** 7.5 cm **c.** 60 km **3a.** 0.015 **b.** 0.386 **c.** 0.082

Lesson 9-3 pp. 440–443

Check Skills You'll Need **1.** 16 **2.** 36 **3.** 81 **4.** 29.16 **5.** 2.56 **6.** 100

Check Understanding **1.** Answers may vary. Sample: about 144 square miles **2.** P = 26 ft, A = 40 ft^2 **3a.** 49 $in.^2$ **b.** 36 ft^2

Lesson 9-4 pp. 446–448

Check Skills You'll Need **1.** quadrilateral, trapezoid; trapezoid **2.** quadrilateral, parallelogram; parallelogram **3.** quadrilateral, rectangle, rhombus, square; square

Check Understanding **1a.** 70 m^2 **b.** 519 ft^2 **2a.** 259.5 m^2 **b.** The area would double. **3a.** 16m^2 **b.** Answers may vary. Sample:

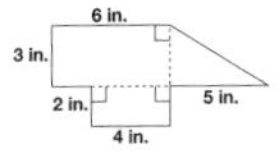

6 in.
3 in.
2 in.
5 in.
4 in.

Checkpoint Quiz 1 **1.** 0.062 L **2.** 4,300 g **3.** 1.78 m **4.** 72.25 cm^2 **5.** 18 mi^2

Lesson 9-5 pp. 452–453

Check Skills You'll Need **1.** 6.28 **2.** 25.12 **3.** 157 **4.** 219.8 **5.** 37.68 **6.** 62.8

Check Understanding **1.** $\overline{AC}$, $\overline{BD}$ **2a.** 4 cm **b.** 20 in. **3.** 18 cm

Lesson 9-6 pp. 456–457

Check Skills You'll Need **1.** 49 **2.** 25 **3.** 16 **4.** 100 **5.** 18 **6.** 144

Check Understanding **1a.** 452.16 km^2 **b.** 28.26 $in.^2$ **c.** 50.24 yd^2 **2a.** 1,386 m^2 **b.** 616 cm^2 **c.** 38.5 mi^2 **d.** 154 $in.^2$

Lesson 9-7 pp. 462–464

Check Skills You'll Need **1.** hexagon **2.** quadrilateral **3.** triangle

Check Understanding **1a.** pentagonal prism **b.** rectangular prism **c.** triangular prism **d.** rectangle **2a.** rectangular prism **b.** Answers may vary. Sample: They both have a circle as a base. But a cylinder has two bases, a cone has one.

Lesson 9-8 pp. 467–469

Check Skills You'll Need **1.** 200.96 m^2 **2.** 12.56 yd^2 **3.** 5,024 mm^2

Check Understanding **1.** Answers may vary. Sample:

2a. 1,728 m^2 **b.** 336 $in.^2$

3a. The areas of the top and bottom of the can are πr^2. The area around the can is the product of the height of the can and the distance around the can. The distance around the can is the circumference of the can, so the area around the can is Ch. **b.** 96.6 $in.^2$

Lesson 9-9 pp. 472–476

Check Skills You'll Need **1.** 8 yd^2 **2.** 500 km^2

Check Understanding **1a.** 12 $units^3$ **b.** 36 $units^3$ **c.** The volume would double. **2.** 560 m^3 **3.** 452 $in.^3$

Checkpoint Quiz 2 **1.** triangular pyramid **2.** cone **3.** pentagonal pyramid **4.** hexagonal prism **5.** 62 cm^2 **6.** 30 cm^3 **7.** 31.4 m **8.** 78.5 m^2 **9.** 314.0 m^2 **10.** 392.5 m^3

Lesson 9-10 pp. 477–478

Check Skills You'll Need **1.** 36 **2.** 7 **3.** 9 **4.** 68 **5.** 105 **6.** 14

Check Understanding **1.** 21 pencils

Chapter 10

Diagnosing Readiness p. 490

1. 39 **2.** 31 **3.** 100 **4.** 79 **5.** 31 **6.** 118 **7.** 6 **8.** 66 **9.** 4 **10.** 72 **11.** 15 **12.** 252 **13.** < **14.** > **15.** = **16.** $\frac{1}{12}, \frac{1}{8}, \frac{1}{3}$ **17.** $\frac{4}{9}, \frac{7}{12}, \frac{5}{6}$ **18.** $\frac{1}{4}, \frac{1}{2}, \frac{6}{7}$

Lesson 10-1 pp. 491–493

Check Skills You'll Need **1.** > **2.** = **3.** > **4.** $\frac{4}{3}, \frac{14}{9}, \frac{8}{5}$ **5.** $\frac{1}{4}, \frac{2}{5}, \frac{3}{6}$ **6.** $\frac{3}{8}, \frac{6}{15}, \frac{4}{5}$

Check Understanding **1.** −8 **2.** 5 **3a.** 1 **b.** 7 **c.** 9 **4a.** > **b.** < **5.** −50 , −25 , 75, 100

Lesson 10-2 pp. 497–499

Check Skills You'll Need **1.** 15 **2.** 12 **3.** 8 **4.** 8 **5.** Answers may vary. Sample: No; absolute value is the distance the number is from zero on a number line.

Check Understanding **1a.** −4 **b.** 12 **c.** −9 **d.** negative **2a.** 16 **b.** −21 **3a.** 3 **b.** 3 **4a.** −3 **b.** −7 **c.** 9 **d.** If the integer with the greatest absolute value is negative, then the sum will be negative. **5.** 2 ft

Lesson 10-3 pp. 503–505

Check Skills You'll Need **1.** 17 **2.** 31 **3.** 7 **4.** 0 **5.** 158 **6.** 180 **7.** about 38

Check Understanding **1a.** 3 **b.** 5 **c.** 8 **d.** It is the same as adding the opposite. **2a.** 12 **b.** −4 **c.** −8 **d.** If the first number is larger than the second number, the difference will be positive; the difference will be negative if either the second number is larger OR they are both negative and the second number has a smaller absolute value. **3.** 622 ft **4a.** −6 **b.** 10

Lesson 10-4 pp. 509–511

Check Skills You'll Need **1.** −8 **2.** 64 **3.** −28 **4.** −90 **5.** 162 **6.** −46

Check Understanding **1a.** −12 **b.** 12 **c.** −12 **2a.** −42 **b.** 27 **c.** −15 **3.** −20

Lesson 10-5 pp. 513–516

Check Skills You'll Need **1.** 576 **2.** 8 **3.** 252 **4.** 6 **5.** 540 **6.** 3

Check Understanding **1a.** −4 **b.** 18 **2a.** z = −6 **b.** u = −28 **3.** −4

Checkpoint Quiz 1 **1.** −3 **2.** −2 **3.** −12 **4.** −6 **5.** −12 **6.** −36 **7.** −16 **8.** −7 **9.** 7 **10.** −20

Lesson 10-6 pp. 518–519

Check Skills You'll Need **1.**

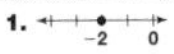

-2
0

2.

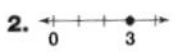

0
3

3.

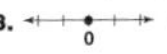

0

4.

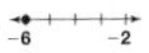

-6
-2

5.

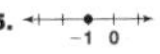

-1
0

6.

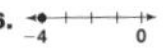

-4
0

Check Understanding **1a.** C(1, 3) **b.** D(−2, −3) **c.** E(2, −2) **2a–c.**

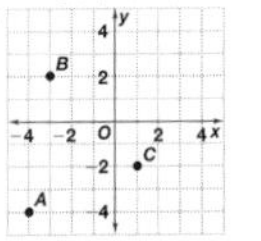

y
4
B
2
-4
-2
O
2
4
x
-2
C
A
-4

3a. City Hall **b.** (3, −1)

Lesson 10-7 pp. 523–524

Check Skills You'll Need **1.** 38 **2.** 9 **3.** −13 **4.** −28 **5.** −14 **6.** −6 **7.** −31 **8.** −59 **9.** 26

Check Understanding **1a.** −$2,886 **b.** $821 **c.** −$1,529 **d.** −$337 **2.** March, April, June, July, August, November, December

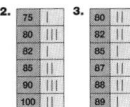

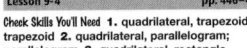

Lesson 10-8   pp. 527–532

Check Skills You'll Need 1. 11 2. 12 3. 6 4. 18 5. 14 6. 50 7. 76 8. 33

Check Understanding

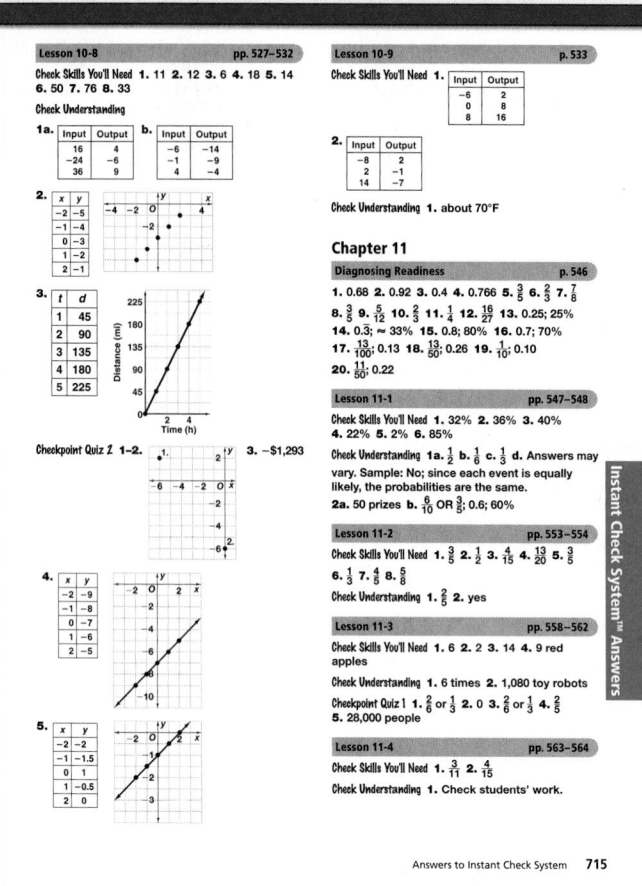

1a. Input/Output b. Input/Output

2. table; graph

3. table t/d; graph

Checkpoint Quiz 1 1–2. graph 3. −$1,293

4. table; graph

5. table; graph

Lesson 10-9   p. 533

Check Skills You'll Need 1. Input/Output

2. Input/Output

Check Understanding 1. about 70°F

Chapter 11

Diagnosing Readiness   p. 546

1. 0.68 2. 0.92 3. 0.4 4. 0.766 5. $\frac{3}{5}$ 6. $\frac{2}{3}$ 7. $\frac{7}{8}$ 8. $\frac{3}{5}$ 9. $\frac{5}{12}$ 10. $\frac{2}{3}$ 11. $\frac{1}{4}$ 12. $\frac{16}{27}$ 13. 0.25; 25% 14. 0.3; ≈ 33% 15. 0.8; 80% 16. 0.7; 70% 17. $\frac{13}{100}$; 0.13 18. $\frac{13}{50}$; 0.26 19. $\frac{1}{10}$; 0.10 20. $\frac{11}{50}$; 0.22

Lesson 11-1   pp. 547–548

Check Skills You'll Need 1. 32% 2. 36% 3. 40% 4. 22% 5. 2% 6. 85%

Check Understanding 1a. $\frac{1}{2}$ b. $\frac{1}{6}$ c. $\frac{1}{3}$ d. Answers may vary. Sample: No; since each event is equally likely, the probabilities are the same. 2a. 50 prizes b. $\frac{6}{10}$ OR $\frac{3}{5}$; 0.6; 60%

Lesson 11-2   pp. 553–554

Check Skills You'll Need 1. $\frac{3}{5}$ 2. $\frac{1}{2}$ 3. $\frac{4}{15}$ 4. $\frac{13}{20}$ 5. $\frac{3}{5}$ 6. $\frac{1}{3}$ 7. $\frac{4}{5}$ 8. $\frac{5}{8}$

Check Understanding 1. $\frac{2}{5}$ 2. yes

Lesson 11-3   pp. 558–562

Check Skills You'll Need 1. 6 2. 3 3. 14 4. 9 red apples

Check Understanding 1. 6 times 2. 1,080 toy robots

Checkpoint Quiz 1 1. $\frac{2}{6}$ or $\frac{1}{3}$ 2. 0 3. $\frac{2}{6}$ or $\frac{1}{3}$ 4. $\frac{2}{5}$ 5. 28,000 people

Lesson 11-4   pp. 563–564

Check Skills You'll Need 1. $\frac{3}{11}$ 2. $\frac{4}{15}$

Check Understanding 1. Check students' work.

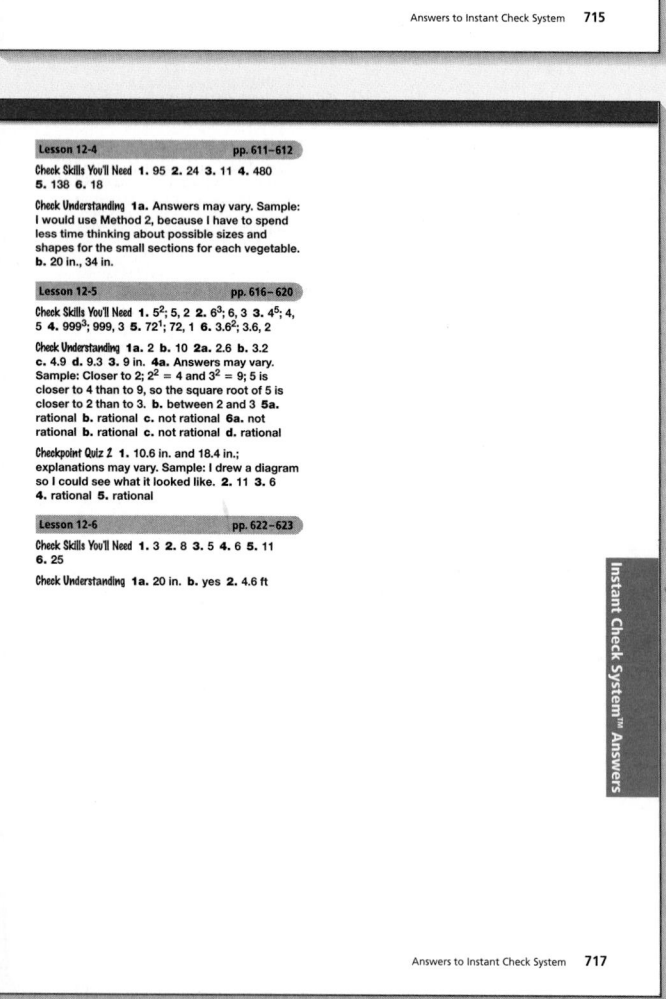

Lesson 11-5   pp. 568–570

Check Skills You'll Need 1. $\frac{1}{6}$ 2. $\frac{1}{3}$ 3. 1 4. $\frac{1}{2}$ 5. 0 6. $\frac{1}{2}$

Check Understanding 1a. $\frac{1}{12}$ b. They have the same number of favorable outcomes (1) and the same number of possible outcomes (12), so their probabilities are the same. 2. 48 different dessert specials 3. On a tree diagram, write M for a male name and F for a female name. Make one column for president and the other for treasurer. Then count the number of the 12 outcomes that are FF.

2.

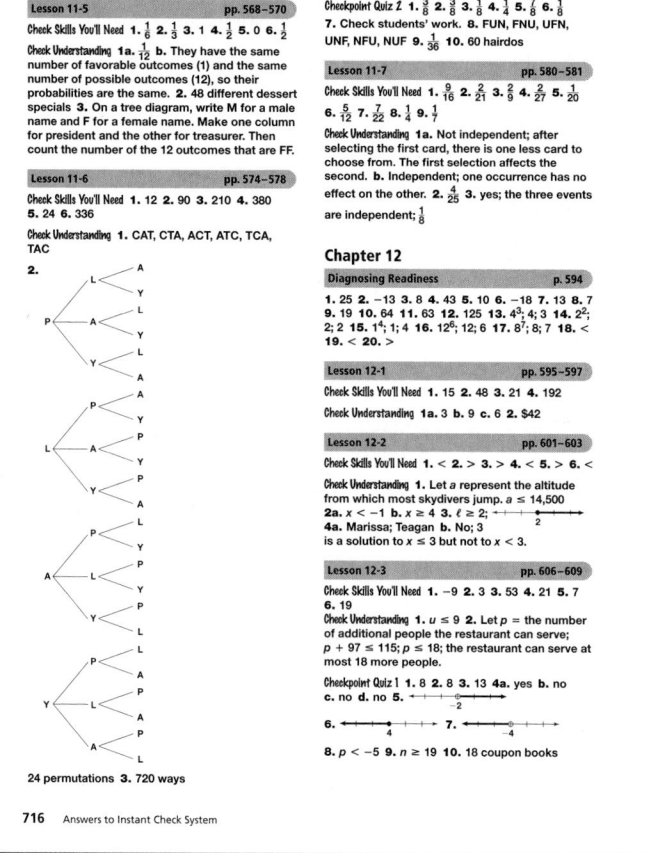

24 permutations 3. 720 ways

Lesson 11-6   pp. 574–578

Check Skills You'll Need 1. 12 2. 90 3. 210 4. 380 5. 24 6. 336

Check Understanding 1. CAT, CTA, ACT, ATC, TCA, TAC

Checkpoint Quiz 2 1. $\frac{3}{8}$ 2. $\frac{3}{8}$ 3. $\frac{1}{4}$ 4. $\frac{5}{8}$ 6. $\frac{1}{8}$
7. Check students' work. 8. FUN, FNU, UFN, UNF, NFU, NUF 9. $\frac{1}{36}$ 10. 60 hairdos

Lesson 11-7   pp. 580–581

Check Skills You'll Need 1. $\frac{9}{16}$ 2. $\frac{2}{21}$ 3. $\frac{2}{5}$ 4. $\frac{2}{27}$ 5. $\frac{1}{20}$ 6. $\frac{5}{12}$ 7. $\frac{7}{22}$ 8. $\frac{1}{4}$ 9. $\frac{1}{7}$

Check Understanding 1a. Not independent; after selecting the first card, there is one less card to choose from. The first selection affects the second. b. Independent; one occurrence has no effect on the other. 2. $\frac{2}{25}$ 3. yes; the three events are independent; $\frac{1}{8}$

Chapter 12

Diagnosing Readiness   p. 594

1. 25 2. −13 3. 8 4. 43 5. 10 6. −18 7. 13 8. 7 9. 19 10. 64 11. 63 12. 125 13. 4^3; 4; 3 14. 2^2; 2; 2 15. 1^4; 1; 4 16. 12^6; 12; 6 17. 8^7; 8; 7 18. < 19. < 20. >

Lesson 12-1   pp. 595–597

Check Skills You'll Need 1. 15 2. 48 3. 21 4. 192

Check Understanding 1a. 3 b. 9 c. 6 2. $42

Lesson 12-2   pp. 601–603

Check Skills You'll Need 1. < 2. > 3. > 4. < 5. > 6. <

Check Understanding 1. Let a represent the altitude from which most skydivers jump. $a \le 14{,}500$ 2a. $x < -1$ b. $x \ge 4$ 3. $\ell \ge 2$; (number line) 4a. Marissa; Teagan b. No; 3 is a solution to $x \le 3$ but not to $x < 3$.

Lesson 12-3   pp. 606–609

Check Skills You'll Need 1. −9 2. 3 3. 53 4. 21 5. 7 6. 19

Check Understanding 1. $u \le 9$ 2. Let p = the number of additional people the restaurant can serve; $p + 97 \le 115$; $p \le 18$; the restaurant can serve at most 18 more people.

Checkpoint Quiz 1 1. 8 2. 8 3. 13 4a. yes b. no c. no d. no 5. (number line)

6. (number line) 7. (number line)

8. $p < -5$ 9. $n \ge 19$ 10. 18 coupon books

Lesson 12-4   pp. 611–612

Check Skills You'll Need 1. 95 2. 24 3. 11 4. 480 5. 138 6. 18

Check Understanding 1a. Answers may vary. Sample: I would use Method 2, because I have to spend less time thinking about possible sizes and shapes for the small sections for each vegetable. b. 20 in., 34 in.

Lesson 12-5   pp. 616–620

Check Skills You'll Need 1. 5^2; 5, 2 2. 6^3; 6, 3 3. 4^5; 4, 5 4. 999^3; 999, 3 5. 72^1; 72, 1 6. 3.6^2; 3.6, 2

Check Understanding 1a. 2 b. 10 2a. 2.6 b. 3.2 c. 4.9 d. 9.3 3. 9 in. 4a. Answers may vary. Sample: Closer to 2; $2^2 = 4$ and $3^2 = 9$; 5 is closer to 4 than to 9, so the square root of 5 is closer to 2 than to 3. b. between 2 and 3 5a. rational b. rational c. not rational 6a. not rational b. rational c. not rational d. rational

Checkpoint Quiz 1 1. 10.6 in. and 18.4 in.; explanations may vary. Sample: I drew a diagram so I could see what it looked like. 2. 11 3. 6 4. rational 5. rational

Lesson 12-6   pp. 622–623

Check Skills You'll Need 1. 3 2. 8 3. 5 4. 6 5. 11 6. 25

Check Understanding 1a. 20 in. b. yes 2. 4.6 ft

Selected Answers

Chapter 1

Lesson 1-1   pp. 6–7

EXERCISES 1. 25; twenty-five **3.** 508,310; five hundred eight thousand, three hundred ten **7.** < **9.** > **13.** 51,472; 51,572; 54,172; 57,142 **15.** 17,414; 17,444; 17,671; 18,242 **17.** 4 ten thousands or 40,000 **19.** 4 thousands or 4,000
25.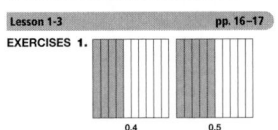
27. Braeburn, Empire, Idared, York, McIntosh **29.** >, **31.** <, < **37.** 390 **39.** 2,129

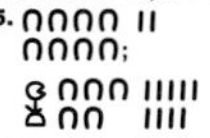

Lesson 1-2   pp. 10–12

EXERCISES 1. 500 + 30 + 0.3 + 0.04 **3.** 0.2 + 0.03 **9.** two and three tenths **11.** nine and five tenths **17.** 40.009 **19.** 0.0012 **21.** 8 + 0.2; eight and two tenths **23.** 90 + 1 + 0.09 + 0.001; ninety-one and ninety-one thousandths **25.** 0.20 **27.** 0.25 **29.** The value of each 2 is 10 times greater than the value of the 2 to its right. **31.** 4 tenths, or 0.4 **33.** 4 ten-thousandths, or 0.0004 **35.** $.006 **37.** $.053 **39.** 0.618 **47.** <

Lesson 1-3   pp. 16–17

EXERCISES 1.

0.53 is greater.

3.
0.2 is greater.

5.
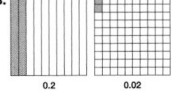

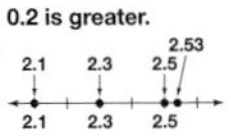

7.
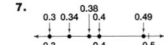

9. > **11.** > **15.** 13.7, 17.1, 17.7 **17.** 9.02, 9.024, 9.2, 9.209 **23.** 0.6595, 0.6095, 0.62 **25.** Alia; 11.88 < 11.9 **33.** 125 **35.** 10,136

Lesson 1-4   pp. 21–23

EXERCISES 1. about 37 **3.** about 34 **9.** about 600 **11.** about 270 **17.** about $15 **19.** about $48 **21.** about 9 **23.** about 3.1 oz **25.** about 1.9 oz **27.** 70 **29.** 2.320 **41a.** about $9 **b.** Compatible numbers make the division easy to compute mentally. **43.** about 24 **45.** about 15 **53.** < **55.** > **57.** 0.23 **59.** 0.0038

Lesson 1-5   pp. 27–29

EXERCISES 1. about 4; **3.** about 9; 8.771 **7.** 9.7 **9.** 12.37 **13.** about 5; 5.69 **21.** 2.72 m **23.** $270.15 **27.** > **29.** = **31.** 0; Ident. Prop. of Add. **33.** 7.5; Comm. Prop. of Add.
41a. No; the value of the number he drew is 32,009. **b.** 
37. 1; total U.S. energy supply **39.** hydroelectric **51.** 21,000 **53.** 0.1

Lesson 1-6   pp. 32–33

EXERCISES 1. $26 **3.** 6:25 **5.** 16 min **7.** 12 teams **9a.** 6 cuts **b.** 27 pieces **c.** 2 pieces; there is one side of the wooden block initially without paint. 8 pieces of that side have painted sides; 1 does not. There is also a piece in the center that doesn't get painted. **17.** 1.76 **19.** 1.71 **21.** tens **23.** hundreds

Lesson 1-7   pp. 37–39

EXERCISES 1. 0.072 **3.** 173.6 **9.** 0.14 **11.** 0.15 **17.** 1,035 **19.** 14.4 **25.** $3.55 **27.** 2.8 **29.** 190 **35.** $50.00 **37.** 68.28 **39.** 56.414 **45.** 58.5 mi **47.** 483.48 million mi **49.** Incorrect; the decimal point should move left one place. **51.** Incorrect; addition was used instead of multiplication. **59.** < **61.** >

Lesson 1-8   pp. 41–42

EXERCISES 1. 62 **3.** 92.5 **7.** 12.29 **9.** 1.617 **13.** < **15.** < **17.** about 2.75 mi/h **19.** False; 300 ÷ 100 ≠ 300 × 0.1. **21.** true

Lesson 1-9   pp. 45–47

EXERCISES 1. 25.25 **3.** 7.2 **9.** $3.18 **11.** 0.54; repeating **13.** 0.76; terminating
19.
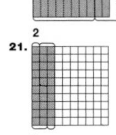
21.
23. 73.75 **25.** 3.31 **29.** 0.8 **31.** 0.05 **33.** 20.30 **35.** 8.12 **37.** $4.95 **39.** 5; terminating **41.** 0.2; terminating **45.** 29.4 mi/gal **53.** 0.22675 **55.** 46.48

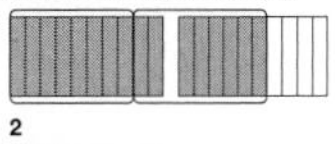

Lesson 1-10   pp. 49–51

EXERCISES 1. 12 **3.** 60 **7.** 28.6 **9.** 7.7 **11a.** 1 × $45 + 3 × $.95 + 2 × $.65 **b.** $4.60 **13.** 10 × 3 **15.** 9 ÷ 3 **17.** 2 **19.** 10 **21.** = **23.** > **27.** C **29.** (11 − 7) ÷ 2 = 2 **31.** (7 − 2) × 2 − 1 = 9 **45.** 280 **47.** 0.00462

Chapter Review   pp. 54–55

1. Ident. Prop. of Add. **2.** expression **3.** standard form **4.** repeating decimal **5.** Assoc. Prop. of Add. **6.** 6,004,030 **7.** 6.043 **8.** five hundred twenty-five and four tenths; 500 + 20 + 5 + 0.5 **9.** five million, twenty-five; 5,000,000 + 20 + 5 **10.** five thousand, two hundred fifty-five ten-thousandths; 0.5 + 0.02 + 0.005 + 0.0005 **11.** five and twenty-five thousandths; 5 + 0.02 + 0.005 **12.** > **13.** < **14.** < **15.** > **16.** 0.06; 0.14; 0.4; 0.52 **17.** 23; 23.03; 23.2; 23.25 **18.** 9.04; 9.2; 9.24; 9.4

19–22. Answers may vary. Samples are given. **19.** about 357 **20.** about 1 **21.** about 3 **22.** about 6 **23.** 3.4 **24.** 0.17 **25.** 3.867 **26.** 7.4 **27.** $.48 **28.** 35.4 **29.** 2.02 **30.** 480 **31.** 9.18 **32.** 3.4 **33.** 0.9 **34.** 0.98127 **35.** 37 **36.** 0 **37.** 44.4

Chapter 2

Lesson 2-1   pp. 65–67

EXERCISES 1. 18, 22 **3.** 81, 243 **5.** 7, 11, 15, 19, 23, 27, ... **7.** 625; 3,125; 15,625; the first term is 1; multiply a term by 5 to get the next term. **9.** 6,000; 600; 60; the first term is 6,000,000, divide a term by 10 to get the next term. **11a.** 4:51, 5:51 **b.** 3:17, 4:02, 4:47, 5:32 **13.** 6 **15.** 1,200 **19.** 189
21. 216 **29.**
37. about 3; 3.2 **39.** about 49; 49.21

Lesson 2-2   pp. 71–72

EXERCISES 1.
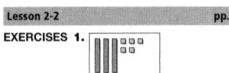
3.
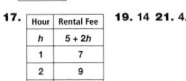
9. 20 **11.** 13
17.

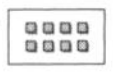

Hour	Rental Fee
h	5 + 2h
1	7
2	9
3	11

19. 14 **21.** 4.8
29. 2006 + 12x **31.**

x	x + 6
1	7
4	10
7	13

33.

x	100 − x
20	80
35	65
50	50

45. 9, 3 **47.** 29.16 **49.** 0.0374

Lesson 2-3   pp. 76–78

EXERCISES 1. k − 34 **3.** 50 + d **7.** 10 + 8h **9.** n − 3 **11.** n + 2 **13a.** y − 20 **b.** 7 years **15.** 11n **17a.** 10w **b.** 70 feet **19.** 3j + 12 **29.** 5.441 **31.** 3.149 **33.** about 380

Lesson 2-4   pp. 81–82

EXERCISES 1. 62 seats **3a.** 11 fence posts **b.** 10 fence posts **5.** 35 cars **7.** 9 pairs **9.** 132 in. **17.** 12c **19.** 4.5 + n **23.** 3 **25.** 32

Lesson 2-5   pp. 86–88

EXERCISES 1. false **3.** false **7.** 2 **9.** 0 **15.** 15 straps **23.** true **25.** yes **29.** 20 lb **31.** False; 1 more than a number can never be equal to the number. **33.** True; (100 − 2) simplifies to 98. 98n = 98n **35.** 100 **37.** 500 **39.** No; 2x = 3x is true if x = 0. **55.** 324, 972, 2,916 **57.** 60 **59.** 16

Lesson 2-6   pp. 92–94

EXERCISES 1. 26 **3.** 52 **11.** s = sale price of the jeans; s + 4.99 = 29.97; s = $24.98 **13.** 11.4 **15.** 48 **21.** m = height of male giraffe; m − 3.2 = 14.1; 17.3 feet **23.** 8.2 **25.** 1.5 **29.** No; using estimation, about 60 + about 30 = about 90, and 90 is not at all close to 31.8. **31.** Let c = approximate area of Cape Cod National Seashore; c + 14,101 = 57,627; 43,526 acres **41.** 37; 40; 43; 46; 49 **43.** 0 **45.** 24

Lesson 2-7   pp. 97–98

EXERCISES 1. 20 **3.** 1.7 **11.** 32,000,000 square miles **13.** 441 **15.** 51,772 **21.** $2.99 per video **23.** 0.4096 **25.** 900 **29.** The teammate could not have scored half the goals because half of 41 is 20.5. It is impossible to score half of a goal. **41.** = **43.** 0.18

Lesson 2-8   pp. 101–103

EXERCISES 1. 3^2; 3; 2 **3.** 9^3; 9; 3 **11.** 8 × 10^4 + 3 × 10^3 + 7 × 10^2 + 9 × 10^1 + 2 × 1 **13.** 6 × 10^4 + 0 × 10^3 + 2 × 10^2 + 5 × 10^1 + 1 × 1 **17.** 64 **19.** 15,625 **29.** 54,872 **31.** 60 **35.** 3 **37.** 3 **39a.** 10,000; 10^5; 100,000 **b.** The exponent tells the number of 0's in standard form. **c.** 10^7; 10,000,000; 10^8; 100,000,000 **41.** 3 × 10^7 + 5 × 10^6 **43.** 27; 64; 125; 216 **45.** 2 **47.** 10^5 **49.** 80 **51.** 12 **61.** 1,123 **63.** 880 **67.** < **69.** =

Lesson 2-9   pp. 107–108

EXERCISES 1. (4 × 10) + (4 × 8) = 40 + 32 = 72 **3.** 8(20 + 8) = 8 × 20 + 8 × 8 = 160 + 64 = 224 **7.** $27.00 **9.** 8.7 **11.** 9.5 **15.** 265 mi **17.** One way to find the total area is to find the area of each rectangle and then add the areas: (6.8 × 2.5) + (2 × 2.5). Another way to find the total area is to multiply the total length of the rectangle by its width: (6.8 + 2) × 2.5. **25.** false **27.** 32, 64

Chapter Review   pp. 110–111

1. term **2.** algebraic expression OR equation **3.** base **4.** variable **5.** exponent **6.** 162; 486; 1,458; the first term is 2; multiply a term by 3 to get the next term. **7.** 55, 67, 79; the first term is 7; add 12 to a term to get the next term. **8.** 112, 224, 448; the first term is 7; multiply a term by 2 to get the next term. **9.** 8 **10.** 49 **11.** 42 **12.** x ÷ 12 **13.** 2b **14.** h + k **15.** 28 laps **16.** false **17.** true **18.** false **19.** 5 **20.** 8.1 **21.** 3.7 **22.** 5,640 **23.** 7 **24.** 1,010 **25.** 56 **26.** 128 **27.** 6.06 **28.** 1.4 **29.** 0.9 **30.** 60.8 **31.** 128 **32.** 40 **33.** 14 **34.** 15 **35.** 7(20 + 8) = 140 + 56 = 196 **36.** 5(3 + 0.4) = 15 + 2.0 = 17 **37.** (10 + 1)57 = 570 + 57 = 627 **38.** $19.00

Chapter 3

Lesson 3-1   pp. 121–122

EXERCISES 1. yes **3.** yes **7.** 2, 5, and 10 **9.** 2 **13.** yes **15.** yes **19.** no **21.** yes **25.** Yes; since 1 + 1 + 4 = 6 and 6 is divisible by 3, 114 is divisible by 3. **27.** 3 and 9 **29.** 2 **35.** 4 **37.** 4 **39.** 2, 3, 4, 5, 6, and 10 **41a.** 30, 36, 42, 48 **b.** All are divisible by 2 and 3. **c.** Any number that is divisible by both 2 and 3 is also divisible by 6. **49.** 45 **51.** 16.2 **55.** 1 **57.** 11.5

Lesson 3-2   pp. 125–126

EXERCISES 1. 1, 2, 4, 8 **3.** 1, 2, 3, 6, 9, 18 **9.** composite; 55 = 5 × 11 **11.** Prime; the only factors are 1 and 83. **17.** 2^5 **19.** 5^2 × 3 **25.** 1,001 **27.** 1 × 36; 2 × 18; 3 × 12; 4 × 9; 6 × 6 **29.** composite; 3^3 × 5 **31.** composite; 2 × 3 × 5 × 7 **45.** 50 **47.** > **49.** <

Lesson 3-3   pp. 129–131

EXERCISES 1. factors of 14: 1, 2, 7, 14; factors of 35: 1, 5, 7, 35; GCF of 14 and 35: 7 **3.** factors of 26: 1, 2, 13, 26; factors of 34: 1, 2, 17, 34; GCF of 26 and 34: 2 **7.**
```
  2) 10   18         GCF = 2
       5    9
```
9. GCF = 1
13.
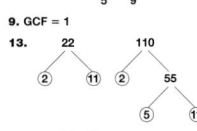
GCF = 22

15. 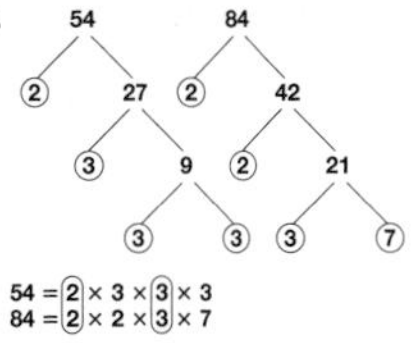
```
        54              84
      2      27       2       42
           3    9           2     21
              3   3             3     7
```
$54 = 2 \times 3 \times 3 \times 3$
$84 = 2 \times 2 \times 3 \times 7$
GCF = 6 **21.** 140 **23.** 25 **27.** Brand B with 12 cards and Brand C with 15 cards because 12 and 15 are divisible by 3. **29.** 4 **31.** 10 **33.** 48; 1, 2, 3, 4, 6, 8, 12, 16, 24, 48 **39a.** 3 × $1.25 + $1.50 **b.** $5.25 **41.** nine tenths **43.** eighty hundredths

Lesson 3-4   pp. 136–137

EXERCISES 9. $\frac{2}{3}$ **11.** $\frac{1}{2}$ **17.** $\frac{5}{8}$ **19.** no; $\frac{1}{2}$ **21.** no; $\frac{5}{7}$ **31.** The first engineer is recording time in minutes. The second engineer is recording fractions of an hour. **33.** Divide the numerator and the denominator by their GCF. **35.** $\frac{8}{12}, \frac{3}{2}$; no **37.** $\frac{1}{2}$ **47.** 3 **49.** 150 **51.** 0.9 **53.** 20

Lesson 3-5   pp. 141–142

EXERCISES 1. $\frac{23}{6}$ **3.** $\frac{23}{9}$ **13.** $5\frac{2}{3}$ **15.** $2\frac{1}{4}$ **21.** $\frac{33}{7}$ **23.** $21\frac{1}{6}$ **29.** $1\frac{13}{16}$ in.; $1\frac{3}{4}$ in. **31.** $\frac{33}{7}$; $16\frac{1}{2}$ **33.** $\frac{106}{4}$; $26\frac{1}{2}$ **37.** $8\frac{1}{3}$ melons; 9 melons **45.** false **47.** 26 **49.** 6

Lesson 3-6   pp. 145–146

EXERCISES 1. 36 **3.** 60 **9.** 48 **11.** 72 **17.** 120th customer **19.** 84 **21.** 315 **29a.** 15 days **b.** If Monday is day 1, then the first both items are picked up on a Sunday will be on day 91. **31a.** 2, 4, 5 **b.** 40 **33.** 2x **45.** 0.3, 0.37, 0.49, 0.51, 0.6 **47.** 5^3; 5, 3 **49.** 7^3; 7, 3

Lesson 3-7   pp. 150–152

EXERCISES 1. < **3.** > **11.** < **13.** > **17.** $\frac{2}{3}, \frac{3}{4}, \frac{5}{6}$ **19.** $\frac{1}{8}, \frac{7}{40}, \frac{1}{2}$ **23.** the cherry-flavored drink **25a.** $\frac{1}{2}, \frac{1}{4}, \frac{1}{4}, \frac{1}{8}$ **b.** 
c. Yes; the note symbol that is "open" has the greatest value, and for the other symbols, the more flags there are, the less the value of the note. **27.** <; the numerators are equal, so the fraction with the lesser denominator is greater. **29.** > **31.** > **33.** true **35.** true **37.** In fractions with the same numerators, the fraction with the greater denominator is the lesser fraction. **47.** $\frac{17}{3}$ **49.** $\frac{36}{21}$, or $\frac{12}{7}$ **51.** $\frac{3}{8}$ **53.** $\frac{3}{11}$

Lesson 3-8   pp. 155–156

EXERCISES 1. $\frac{3}{10}$ **3.** $\frac{3}{4}$ **13.** 0.4 **15.** 0.375 **25.** 1.25 **27.** Write 0.125 as $\frac{125}{1,000}$. Divide numerator and denominator by 125 to express the fraction in simplest form as $\frac{1}{8}$. **29.** greater than **31.** equal to **33.** $4\frac{3}{4}$ lb, 4.75 lb **35.** 0.8, 0.87, $\frac{7}{8}$ **37.** $6.625, $8.50 **49.** 126 **51.** $20.\overline{3}$ **53.** 180 miles

Lesson 3-9   pp. 158–160

EXERCISES 1. 48 juices **3.** 11 years old and 16 years old **5.** 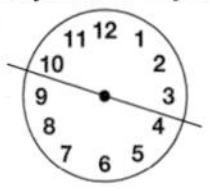
7. 12:20 P.M. **9.** 24 sweatshirts **19.** = **21.** = **25.** 0.32 **27.** 10.5 **31.** p − 3

Chapter Review   pp. 162–163

1. B **2.** D **3.** A **4.** C **5.** E **6.** 3 and 9 **7.** 3, 5, and 9 **8.** 2, 3, and 9 **9.** 2, 3, 5, 9, and 10 **10.** 2^2 × 7 **11.** 51 = 3 × 17 **12.** 2^2 × 5^2 **13.** 2 × 5^3 **14.** 2 **15.** 2 **16.** 5 **17.** 8 **18.** no; $\frac{1}{2}$ **19.** no; $\frac{2}{3}, \frac{6}{8}, \frac{1}{12}$ **20.** yes; $\frac{2}{6}, \frac{6}{18}$ **21.** yes; $\frac{4}{18}, \frac{2}{9}$ **22.** $\frac{14}{3}$ **23.** $\frac{41}{5}$ **24.** $4\frac{1}{3}$ **25.** $9\frac{2}{5}$ **26.** 10 **27.** 18 **28.** 132 **29.** 140 **30.** $\frac{1}{4}, \frac{1}{6}, \frac{1}{2}$ **31.** $2\frac{4}{15}, 2\frac{3}{13}, \frac{5}{2}$ **32.** $\frac{5}{16}, \frac{7}{20}, \frac{17}{40}$ **33.** 0.1875 **34.** 6.2083 **35.** $\frac{3}{5}$ **36.** $4\frac{13}{25}$ **37.** 76 chicken dinners **38.** two 36-exposure rolls, five 24-exposure rolls

Chapter 4

Lesson 4-1   pp. 173–174

EXERCISES 1. $\frac{1}{2}$ **3.** $1\frac{1}{2}$ **7.** 10 **9.** 5 **13.** about 4 ft **15.** $\frac{1}{2}$ **17.** $\frac{1}{2}$ **23.** about $3\frac{1}{2}$ in. **33.** 0.047 **35.** 0.006 **39.** 20h **41.** s + 12

Lesson 4-2 pp. 177–178

EXERCISES **1.** $\frac{1}{2}$ **3.** $\frac{2}{3}$ **9.** $\frac{2}{3}$ **11.** $\frac{1}{5}$ **17.** $\frac{1}{2}$ in. **19.** $\frac{2}{6}+\frac{3}{6}=\frac{5}{6}$ **21.** $\frac{1}{10}$ **23.** $\frac{9}{20}$ **25.** $\frac{4}{5}$ **43.** 5

Lesson 4-3 pp. 182–184

EXERCISES **1.** $\frac{9}{10}$ **3.** $\frac{1}{2}$ **7.** $1\frac{23}{40}$ mi **9.** $\frac{1}{4}$ **11.** $\frac{9}{16}$ **15.** $\frac{5}{12}$ c **17.** $\frac{11}{15}$ **19.** $\frac{3}{10}$ **25a.** $1\frac{1}{2}$ in. **b.** $1\frac{7}{40}$ in. **27.** $\frac{9}{20}$ mi per min **29.** $\frac{1}{8}$ **43.** 11 **45.** 30 **47.** 16 **49.** 49 **51.** 720

Lesson 4-4 pp. 187–189

EXERCISES **1.** $3\frac{1}{6}$ **3.** $4\frac{6}{7}$ **5.** $4\frac{1}{4}$ lb **7.** $11\frac{1}{6}$ **9.** $4\frac{3}{8}$ **13.** $21\frac{1}{8}$ min **15.** > **17.** < **21.** $4\frac{1}{8}$ in. **23.** $10\frac{23}{24}$ **25.** 13 yd **31.** C **33.** B

Lesson 4-5 pp. 192–194

EXERCISES **1.** $2\frac{3}{8}$ **3.** $1\frac{3}{8}$ **9.** $1\frac{1}{6}$ h **11.** $3\frac{3}{8}$ **13.** $6\frac{7}{10}$ **17.** $1\frac{15}{16}$ in. **19.** $\frac{5}{6}$ **21.** $2\frac{1}{2}$ **29.** 6 in. **31.** 1 ft $5\frac{1}{2}$ in. **41.** $1\frac{1}{2}$ **43.** $\frac{4}{5}$ **47.** $\frac{2}{7}$ **49.** 2

Lesson 4-6 pp. 198–199

EXERCISES **1.** $3\frac{2}{5}$ **3.** $7\frac{1}{5}$ **7.** $1\frac{5}{42}$ **9.** $1\frac{17}{24}$ **13.** Sample: Let b = amount of book read; $b=\frac{1}{3}+\frac{1}{4}$; $\frac{7}{12}$ of the book. **15.** $\frac{1}{4}$ **17.** $3\frac{17}{25}$ **21.** $g=\frac{3}{10}+\frac{1}{2}$; $g=\frac{4}{5}$ mi **23.** $r=1-\frac{2}{5}-\frac{1}{3}$; $r=\frac{4}{15}$ **33.** $\frac{1}{4}$ **35.** $\frac{11}{12}$ **37.** $\frac{3}{10}, \frac{1}{2}, \frac{4}{7}, \frac{2}{3}$ **39.** $\frac{0}{5}, \frac{2}{11}, \frac{5}{9}, \frac{8}{7}$

Lesson 4-7 pp. 203–205

EXERCISES **1.** 90 min **3.** 482 min **7.** 1 h 10 min **9.** 5 h 46 min **13.** 9 h 47 min **15.** 29 min **17.** 1:00 P.M. **19.** 11:00 A.M. **31.** 36 **33.** 3.8

Lesson 4-8 pp. 207–208

EXERCISES **5.** 18 lights **9.** 80 gifts **17.** $3\frac{1}{2}$ **19.** $13\frac{15}{16}$ **21.** $7\frac{7}{10}$

Chapter Review pp. 210–211

1. benchmark **2.** elapsed time **3–10.** Answers may vary. Samples are given. **3.** $1\frac{1}{2}$ **4.** 0 **5.** 1 **6.** 0 **7.** 14 **8.** 10 **9.** 15 **10.** 6 **11.** about 6 c **12.** $1\frac{2}{5}$ **13.** $\frac{1}{2}$ **14.** $\frac{3}{5}$ **15.** $\frac{5}{9}$ **16.** $\frac{7}{8}$ **17.** $\frac{1}{2}$ **18.** $\frac{1}{8}$ **19.** $1\frac{7}{30}$ **20.** $\frac{13}{15}$ mi **21.** $7\frac{1}{8}$ **22.** $17\frac{1}{3}$ **23.** $6\frac{1}{2}$ **24.** about $59\frac{7}{12}$ in. **25.** $\frac{3}{7}$ **26.** $\frac{1}{8}$ **27.** $1\frac{1}{9}$

28. $3\frac{1}{3}$ **29.** $11\frac{1}{18}$ **30.** $6\frac{2}{5}$ **31.** 3 h 41 min **32.** 8 h 48 min **33.** 8:10 P.M. **34.** 180 cards **35.** 24 plants

Chapter 5

Lesson 5-1 pp. 222–223

EXERCISES

1. 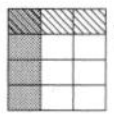 $\frac{1}{12}$

3. 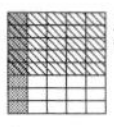 $\frac{5}{40}=\frac{1}{8}$

5. $\frac{3}{16}$ **7.** $\frac{11}{16}$ **15.** 22 **17.** $16\frac{1}{3}$ **21.** 11 **23.** 5 **29.** In the first and third fractions, divide the denominator and numerator by the common factor 3. In the second and third fractions, divide numerator and denominator by the common factor 4. You get $\frac{2}{{}_1 3}\cdot\frac{4^1}{5}\cdot\frac{3^1}{4_1}$ or $\frac{2}{1}\cdot\frac{1}{5}\cdot\frac{1}{1}$. **31.** 10 **33.** $\frac{3}{5}$ **35.** $\frac{3}{10}$ **43.** $1\frac{1}{6}$ **45.** $\frac{8}{45}$ **51.** composite **53.** prime

Lesson 5-2 pp. 226–228

EXERCISES **1.** 4 **3.** 60 **7.** 65 **9.** $10\frac{1}{2}$ **17.** 5 in. by 5 in. **19.** 48 **21.** 18 **23.** No; the carpenter needs $6\times 3\frac{1}{2}=21$ ft of wood and two 10-ft boards are only 20 ft. **25.** 6 in. **27.** $104\frac{13}{15}$ **29.** $49\frac{5}{6}$ **39.** $7\frac{3}{5}$ **41.** $7\frac{5}{8}$ **45.** 30 **47.** 100

Lesson 5-3 pp. 232–234

EXERCISES **1.** $\frac{5}{2}$, or $2\frac{1}{2}$ **3.** $\frac{1}{11}$ **7.** $6\frac{2}{3}$ **9.** $11\frac{2}{3}$ **13.** $2\frac{2}{3}$ **15.** $7\frac{1}{3}$ **21.** $\frac{1}{4}$ **23.** $\frac{11}{12}$ **25.** $\frac{3}{16}$ t **27.** $\frac{10}{11}$ **29.** $\frac{11}{27}$ **35.** about $4\frac{1}{2}$ times more **37.** 36 **39.** $\frac{5}{12}$ **45.** 64 pieces **47.** 3 **49.** 2 **61.** 20 **63.** 15 **65.** 2, 3 **67.** 5

Lesson 5-4 pp. 238–240

EXERCISES **1.** 10 **3.** 11 **7.** 9 points **9.** $\frac{19}{20}$ **11.** $\frac{13}{16}$ ft **13.** 4 **15.** $2\frac{2}{9}$ **19.** $\frac{5}{14}$ **21.** $\frac{2}{9}$ **29.** about 24 strips **31.** 70 **33.** 5 **35.** 30 books **37.** $\frac{4}{11}$ **39.** $\frac{5}{18}$ **41.** $1\frac{1}{15}$ **43.** $2\frac{7}{9}$ **45a.** 80; 800; 80,000

b. As a gets larger, $8\div\frac{1}{a}$ also gets larger. **47.** $1\frac{1}{25}$ **49.** $\frac{7}{8}$ **61.** 9 **63.** 20 **65.** $2^4\times 3^2$ **67.** $2^2\times 3\times 23$

Lesson 5-5 pp. 244–245

EXERCISES **1.** 36 **3.** 324 **11.** 15 **13.** 24 **17.** $7\frac{1}{2}\times p=3$; $\frac{2}{5}$ lb **19.** 20 **21.** $\frac{4}{7}$ **27.** k is greater than 11, because if it were 11 or less, multiplying it by $\frac{3}{5}$ would give a product less than 11. **29.** $\frac{8}{5}k=12$; $7\frac{1}{2}$ mi **31.** about 300 mi **41.** $2\frac{1}{4}$ **43.** $21\frac{8}{9}$ **45.** $\frac{9}{100}$

Lesson 5-6 pp. 247–249

EXERCISES **1.** 7 classes **3.** 18 cuts **5.** 48 brownies **7a.** 1 in. **b.** 70 in. **11.** \$79.20 **21.** $2\frac{1}{2}$ **23.** $\frac{20}{21}$ **27.** 6 **29.** 4

Lesson 5-7 pp. 252–253

EXERCISES **1–12.** Answers may vary. Samples are given. **1.** Feet; lots are usually measured in feet. **3.** Inches; a license plate is a little longer than a foot-ruler. **5.** Pounds; one orange weighs less than a pound, so a bag of oranges would weigh more. **7.** Pounds; a bowling ball weighs more than a loaf of bread. **9.** Fluid ounces; a sample-size bottle of shampoo holds less than a cup. **11.** Gallon; lawnmowers usually hold about 1 gallon of gas. **13.** > **15.** < **17.** about $13\frac{1}{3}$ times as heavy **27.** $1\frac{1}{3}$ **29.** 1 h 59 min

Lesson 5-8 pp. 256–257

EXERCISES **1.** 96 **3.** 66 **7.** about $\frac{1}{2}$ t **9.** 6 ft 7 in. **11.** 1 lb 1 oz **13.** = **15.** < **21.** 15 **23.** 68 **27.** $1\frac{8}{9}$, or about 2 yd **35.** $5\frac{3}{14}$ **37.** $1\frac{7}{18}$ **39.** $5\frac{2}{3}$ **41.** $12\frac{3}{4}$

Chapter Review pp. 260–261

1. 12 **2.** 12 **3.** 80 **4.** 84 **5.** $\frac{3}{10}$ **6.** $\frac{2}{39}$ **7.** $\frac{2}{5}$ **8.** 15 **9.** $17\frac{1}{2}$ **10.** $3\frac{7}{8}$ **11.** $6\frac{14}{15}$ **12.** $20\frac{15}{22}$ **13.** $\frac{1}{3}$ c **14.** 1 **15.** 3 **16.** 3 **17.** 2 **18.** 16 **19.** $5\frac{2}{3}$ **20.** $\frac{5}{11}$ **21.** $\frac{8}{9}$ **22.** $1\frac{3}{7}$ **23.** $\frac{2}{25}$ **24.** $2\frac{1}{112}$ **25.** $3\frac{3}{28}$ **26.** 96 **27.** 25 **28.** 2 **29.** $\frac{3}{4}$ **30.** 4 **31.** 2 **32.** $7\frac{1}{5}$ **33.** $\frac{13}{50}$ **34.** 79 s **35.** tons **36.** fluid ounces **37.** $73\frac{1}{3}$ **38.** 40 **39.** 6 **40.** = **41.** > **42.** >

Chapter 6

Lesson 6-1 pp. 271–272

EXERCISES 1. 35 to 24, 35 : 24, $\frac{35}{24}$ **3.** 11 to 70, 11 : 70, $\frac{11}{70}$ **9.** 4 : 3 **11.** $\frac{1}{3}$ **17.** 700. **19.** 45 **25.** Divide the terms of the original ratio by their GCF, 8. **27.** 5 : 7 **29.** 4 : 2, $\frac{4}{2}$, 4 to 2 **31.** 2 : 3, $\frac{2}{3}$, 2 to 3 **45.** $\frac{15}{32}$ **47.** $\frac{1}{7}$

Lesson 6-2 pp. 275–276

EXERCISES **1.** 70 heartbeats per minute **3.** \$6.50 per T-shirt **7.** $\frac{3\text{ feet}}{1\text{ yard}}=\frac{45\text{ feet}}{15\text{ yards}}$ **9.** $\frac{45\text{ students}}{1\text{ bus}}=\frac{225\text{ students}}{5\text{ buses}}$ **11.** \$.95 per bagel; \$.80 per bagel; 5 for \$4.00 **13.** \$.63 per lb; \$.79 per lb; 3 lb for \$1.89 **15.** 99 pages in 3 hours **17.** 33 mi in 3 hours **19a.** 85 jumps per min **b.** 288 jumps per min **c.** 203 times **31.** $1\frac{1}{5}$ **33.** $2\frac{1}{20}$ **37.** $\frac{1}{14}$ **39.** $\frac{25}{33}$

Lesson 6-3 pp. 280–282

EXERCISES **1.** yes **3.** no **9.** 105 **11.** 114 **17.** 30 in. **19.** yes **21.** yes **23.** 14 in. **25.** 144 mi **27.** 60 **29.** 168 **39.** 5 **41.** 6 **43.** $1\frac{8}{9}$ **45.** $4\frac{1}{2}$

Lesson 6-4 pp. 285–287

EXERCISES **1.** yes **3.** yes **7.** 63 **9.** 6.75 **15.** 28.8 oz **17.** no **19.** 1 **21.** 45 **25a.** about 16.7 ft **b.** No; the ratios need only to have the same units in corresponding places in the proportion. **27.** 16 teachers **29.** 32,815.41 ft **31.** 8,760 h **35.** No; the unit rates are different. **45.** $\frac{1}{5}$ **47.** $\frac{4}{25}$

Lesson 6-5 pp. 290–292

EXERCISES **1.** 1 : 25 **3.** 1 : 20 **9.** 4 in. **11.** $1\frac{1}{3}$ in. **13.** 1.25 cm **15.** 40 cm **19a.** Reduce; the map is 4 cm wide and 3 cm high. For each centimeter on the map, I would draw 0.5 centimeter on my drawing. My drawing would measure 2 cm wide and 1.5 cm high. **b.** 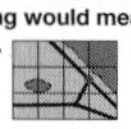 **21.** 5 in. **31.** 2 **33.** 2 **35.** 10 **37.** $49\frac{1}{2}$

Lesson 6-6 pp. 296–298

EXERCISES **1.** 0.15 **3.** 0.82 **11.** $\frac{7}{10}$ **13.** $\frac{1}{20}$

21. 17% **23.** 98% **31.** 60% **33.** about 27% **35.** about 63% **37.** about 7% **45.** 0.7, 70% **47.** about 83% **49.** 45% **57.** 72.5% **69.** 18 **71.** 20

Lesson 6-7 pp. 301–302

EXERCISES **1.** 7.2 **3.** 16.8 **9.** 30.6 **11.** 26.23 **15.** 32 **17.** 12.5 **21.** 152 **23.** 14 **27.** \$10 **29.** \$89.50 **41.** 2 : 5 **43.** $\frac{2}{3}$ **49.** $2\frac{1}{2}$ **51.** $8\frac{2}{5}$

Lesson 6-8 pp. 305–306

EXERCISES **1.** \$1.96, \$29.96 **3.** \$1.05, \$16.05 **5.** \$6.30 **7.** \$12 **9.** \$24 **11.** \$5.10 **13.** Florida: \$4.80, \$84.80; Georgia: \$3.20, \$83.20; Massachusetts: \$4.00, \$84.00; Tennessee: \$5.60, \$85.60 **15.** Florida: \$.05, \$.85; Georgia: \$.03, \$.83; Massachusetts: \$.04, \$.84; Tennessee: \$.06, \$.86 **19.** 45 **21.** 90 **25.** I could round to \$4.50 and multiply by 4; I could round to \$4.50 and multiply by 3. **33.** 1,488 times **35.** 130 min **37.** 380 min **39.** 180 **41.** 360

Lesson 6-9 pp. 308–309

EXERCISES **1.** 6,000,000 subscribers **3.** \$79.90 **5.** \$15.93 **7.** \$15 **9.** \$13.25 **13.** 9,200,000 **15.** 1,250 t **23.** yes **25.** 44 **27.** 20

Chapter Review pp. 312–313

1. E **2.** B **3.** D **4.** C **5.** A **6.** 15 to 23, 15 : 23, $\frac{15}{23}$ **7.** 15 to 8, 15 : 8, $\frac{15}{8}$ **8.** 23 to 8, 23 : 8, $\frac{23}{8}$ **9.** 15 to 46, 15 : 46, $\frac{15}{46}$ **10.** 1 to 4 **11.** $\frac{3}{5}$ **12.** 3 ft : 1 yd **13.** $\frac{5}{6}$ **14.** 40 min **15.** \$12.50 **16.** \$1.40 for 24 oz **17.** no **18.** yes **19.** yes **20.** no **21.** 354 **22.** 99 ft **23.** 148.5 in. **24.** 11 ft or 132 in. **25.** $\frac{3}{10}$, 0.3 **26.** $\frac{1}{4}$, 0.25 **27.** $\frac{14}{25}$; 0.56 **28.** $\frac{3}{25}$; 0.12 **29.** 60 **30.** 60% **31–34.** Answers may vary. Samples are given. **31.** 10 **32.** \$1.20 **33.** \$6 **34.** \$21.40 **35.** 3 weeks **36.** \$2.75

Chapter 7

Lesson 7-1 pp. 324–325

EXERCISES **1.** 10 **3.** 2 **7.** 0.5 **9.** 20.7 **11.** 8 **13.** 94 **15.** \$2.09 **17.** 13; 13; no mode **19.** Increase; decrease; stay the same; explanations may vary. Sample: If a new value is added to a data set, and if the value is greater than/less than/equal to the mean of the original data set, the new mean will increase/decrease/stay the same. **21.** 240 **27.** 0.55; 55% **29.** 0.02; 2% **31.** 160 **33.** 30

Lesson 7-2 pp. 328–330

EXERCISES **1.**

Number of Days	Tally	Frequency
28	|	1
30	||||	4
31	卌 ||	7

3. 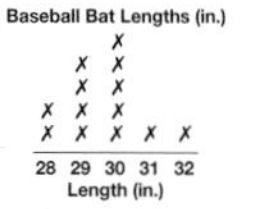

5. 43,612 square miles **7.** 1.7 m

9a.

Letter	Tally	Frequency
a	|||	3
b	|	1
c	||	2
d	|	1
e	|	1
f	|	1
g	卌 ||	7
h	||	2
i	|||	3
l	卌 卌 |	11
n	||||	4
o	卌 |	6
p	|	1
r	||||	4
s	|	1
t	|	1
w	||||	4
y	卌	5

b. Use the mode, L; the data are not numbers, therefore the mode is the best way to represent the data. **11.** frequency of letter grades in science **13.** 11 students

15. 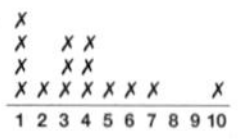

17a. 1, 1 **b.** Answers may vary. Sample: No; the mean is not a whole number. **c.** 27 siblings **19.** 6,622 meters **27.** 500 km **29.** 830 km **31.** $\frac{3}{10}$ **33.** $\frac{2}{9}$

Lesson 7-3 pp. 332–333

EXERCISES **1.** 12 ways **3.** 43 **5a.** \$1, \$3, \$7, \$15, \$31, \$63 **b.** Answers may vary. Sample: The total saved will be \$1 less than twice the amount saved that week. **13.** 1 lb **15.** 8 oz **17.** $\frac{1}{16}$ **19.** $\frac{4}{5}$

Lesson 7-4 pp. 337–339

EXERCISES **1.** 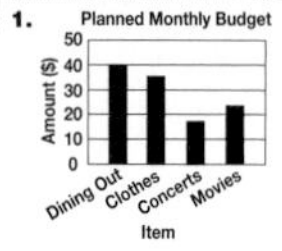

3. 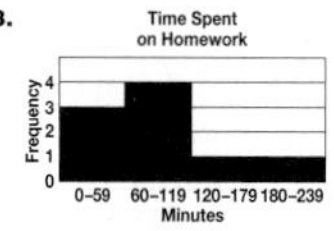

5. 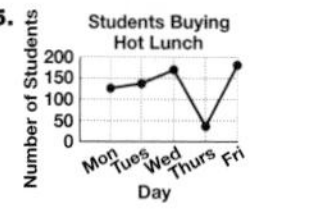

7a. 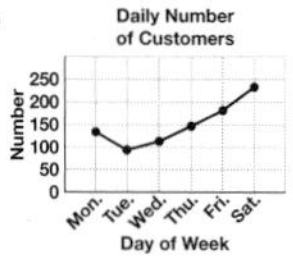

b. The daily number of customers increases, starting on Wednesday.

9a. 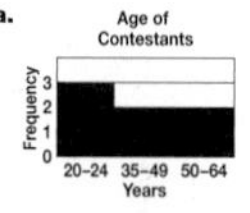

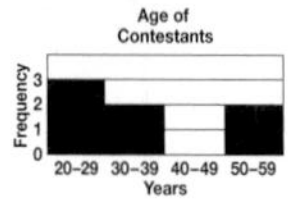

b. 4 intervals; the second histogram shows that there are no contestants in the interval 40–49.

Lesson 7-5 pp. 343–345

EXERCISES **1.** tennis **3.** tennis, volleyball, basketball, baseball, soccer

5. 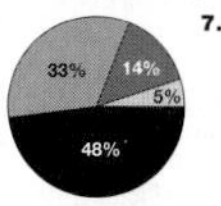

7. 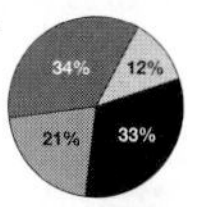

11. 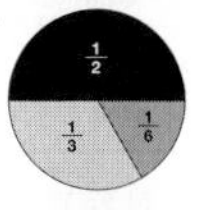

13. 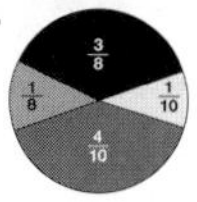

15a. 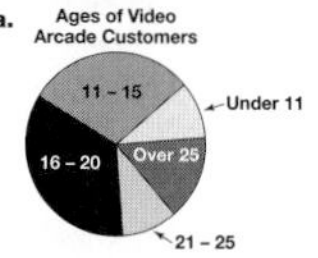

b. 60% **c.** No; explanations may vary. Sample: You can find only the percent of customers 11 to 15 years old. **17.** 24% **23.** 12 **25.** 164 **27.** 30 **29.** 5

Lesson 7-6 pp. 348–350

EXERCISES **1.** C2, C3, C4, C5 **3.** B5, C5, D5, E5, F5 **5.** 100 **7.** 95 **9.** =B4+C4+D4 **11.** =C2−B2; 5 **13.** =D5*7 or =E2+E3+E4 **21.** 4.5 **23.** $\frac{5}{6}$ c; equations may vary. Sample: $\frac{2}{3}+w=1\frac{1}{2}$

Lesson 7-7 pp. 353–355

EXERCISES **1.** 8 seconds **3.** none

5. Heights of Tomato Plants (inches)

2 | 6 7 9
3 | 0 1 3 3 5 6 6
4 | 0 1

Key: 2|6 means 26 in.

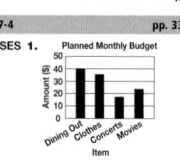

Page 726

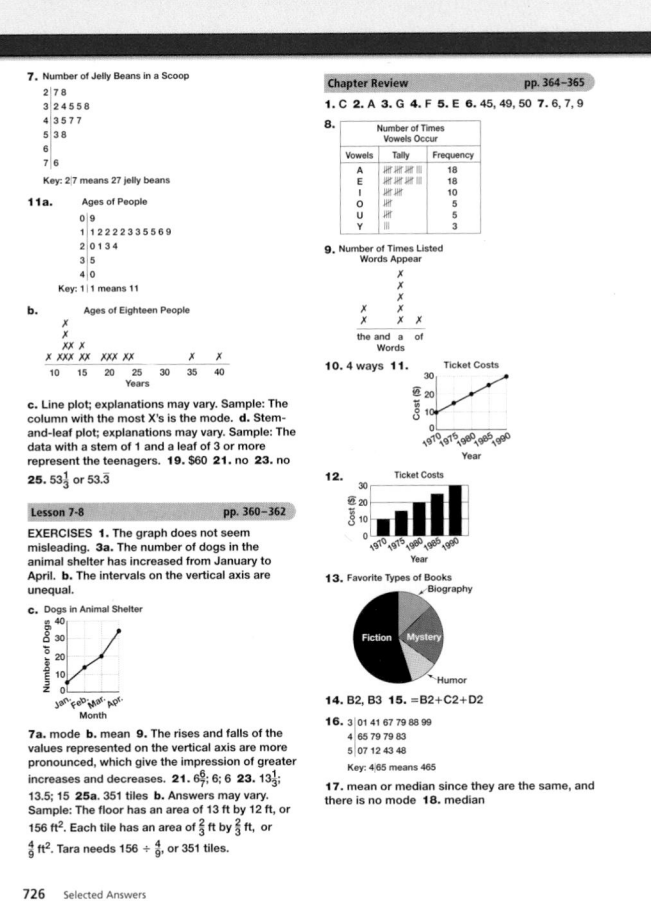

7. Number of Jelly Beans in a Scoop
```
2 | 7 8
3 | 2 4 5 5 8
4 | 3 5 7 7
5 | 3 8
6 |
7 | 6
```
Key: 2|7 means 27 jelly beans

11a. Ages of People
```
0 | 9
1 | 1 2 2 2 2 3 5 5 5 6 9
2 | 0 1 3 4
3 | 5
4 | 0
```
Key: 1|1 means 11

b. Ages of Eighteen People

c. Line plot; explanations may vary. Sample: The column with the most X's is the mode. d. Stem-and-leaf plot; explanations may vary. Sample: The data with a stem of 1 and a leaf of 3 or more represent the teenagers. 19. $60 21. no 23. no 25. $53\frac{1}{3}$ or $53.\overline{3}$

Lesson 7-8   pp. 360–362
EXERCISES 1. The graph does not seem misleading. 3a. The number of dogs in the animal shelter has increased from January to April. b. The intervals on the vertical axis are unequal.
c. Dogs in Animal Shelter

7a. mode b. mean 9. The rises and falls of the values represented on the vertical axis are more pronounced, which give the impression of greater increases and decreases. 21. $6\frac{9}{0}$; 6; 6 23. $13\frac{1}{3}$; 13.5; 15 25a. 351 tiles b. Answers may vary. Sample: The floor has an area of 13 ft by 12 ft, or 156 ft². Each tile has an area of $\frac{2}{3}$ ft by $\frac{2}{3}$ ft, or $\frac{4}{9}$ ft². Tara needs $156 \div \frac{4}{9}$, or 351 tiles.

Chapter Review   pp. 364–365
1. C 2. A 3. G 4. F 5. E 6. 45, 49, 50 7. 6, 7, 9

8.

Number of Times Vowels Occur		
Vowels	Tally	Frequency
A		18
E		18
I		10
O		5
U		5
Y		3

9. Number of Times Listed Words Appear

the and a of Words

10. 4 ways 11. Ticket Costs

12. Ticket Costs

13. Favorite Types of Books

14. B2, B3 15. =B2+C2+D2
16.
```
3 | 01 41 67 79 88 99
4 | 65 79 79 83
5 | 07 12 43 48
```
Key: 4|65 means 465

17. mean or median since they are the same, and there is no mode 18. median

Page 727

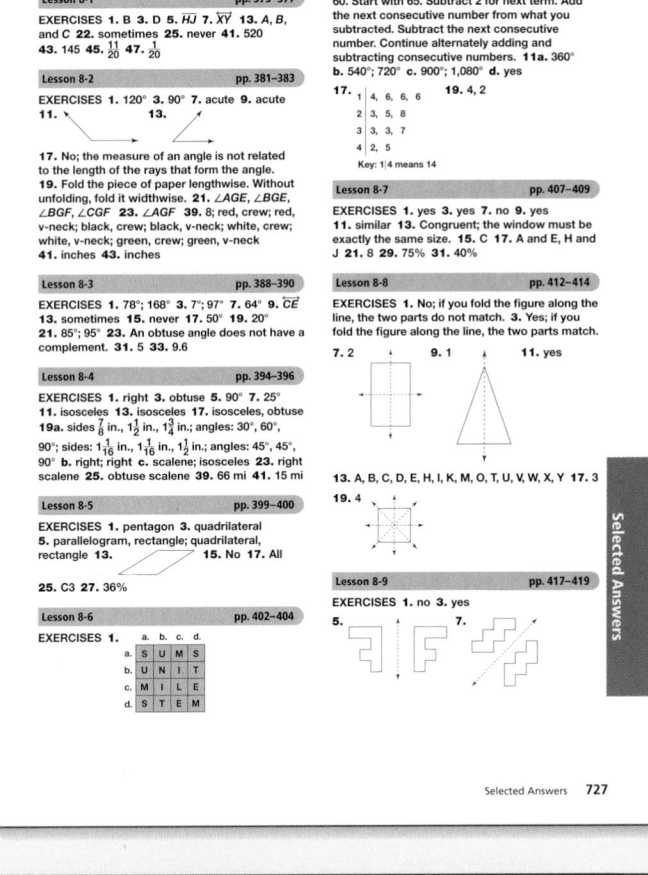

Chapter 8

Lesson 8-1   pp. 375–377
EXERCISES 1. B 3. D 5. $\overrightarrow{HJ}$ 7. $\overleftrightarrow{XY}$ 13. A, B, and C 22. sometimes 25. never 41. 520 43. 145 45. $\frac{11}{20}$ 47. $\frac{1}{20}$

Lesson 8-2   pp. 381–383
EXERCISES 1. 120° 3. 90° 7. acute 9. acute
11. 13.
17. No; the measure of an angle is not related to the length of the rays that form the angle. 19. Fold the piece of paper lengthwise. Without unfolding, fold it widthwise. 21. ∠AGE, ∠BGE, ∠BGF, ∠CGF 23. ∠AGF 39. 8; red, crew; red, v-neck; black, crew; black, v-neck; white, crew; white, v-neck; green, crew; green, v-neck 41. inches 43. inches

Lesson 8-3   pp. 388–390
EXERCISES 1. 78°; 168° 3. 7°; 97° 7. 64° 9. $\overleftrightarrow{CE}$ 13. sometimes 15. never 17. 50° 19. 20° 21. 85°; 95° 23. An obtuse angle does not have a complement. 31. 5 33. 9.6

Lesson 8-4   pp. 394–396
EXERCISES 1. right 3. obtuse 5. 90° 7. 25° 11. isosceles 13. isosceles 17. isosceles, obtuse 19a. sides $\frac{7}{8}$ in., $1\frac{1}{2}$ in., $1\frac{3}{4}$ in.; angles: 30°, 60°, 90°; sides: $1\frac{1}{16}$ in., $1\frac{1}{16}$ in., $1\frac{1}{2}$ in.; angles: 45°, 45°, 90° b. right; right c. scalene; isosceles 23. right scalene 25. obtuse scalene 39. 66 mi 41. 15 mi

Lesson 8-5   pp. 399–400
EXERCISES 1. pentagon 3. quadrilateral 5. parallelogram, rectangle; quadrilateral, rectangle 13. 15. No 17. All 25. C3 27. 36%

Lesson 8-6   pp. 402–404
EXERCISES 1.

	a.	b.	c.	d.
a.	S	U	M	S
b.	U	N	I	T
c.	M	I	L	E
d.	S	T	E	M

3. Amy has a green bike. Bill has a red bike. Chuck has a blue bike. 5. Sue 7. 49 cards 9. 68, 60. Start with 65. Subtract 2 for next term. Add the next consecutive number from what you subtracted. Subtract the next consecutive number. Continue alternately adding and subtracting consecutive numbers. 11a. 360° b. 540°; 720°; 900°; 1,080° d. yes

17.
```
1 | 4, 6, 6, 6
2 | 3, 5, 8
3 |
4 | 2, 5
```
Key: 1|4 means 14

19. 4, 2

Lesson 8-7   pp. 407–409
EXERCISES 1. yes 3. yes 7. no 9. yes 11. similar 13. Congruent; the window must be exactly the same size. 15. C 17. A and E, H and J 21. 8 29. 75% 31. 40%

Lesson 8-8   pp. 412–414
EXERCISES 1. No; if you fold the figure along the line, the two parts do not match. 3. Yes; if you fold the figure along the line, the two parts match.
7. 2 9. 1 11. yes
13. A, B, C, D, E, H, I, K, M, O, T, U, V, W, X, Y 17. 3
19. 4

Lesson 8-9   pp. 417–419
EXERCISES 1. no 3. yes
5. 7.

Page 728

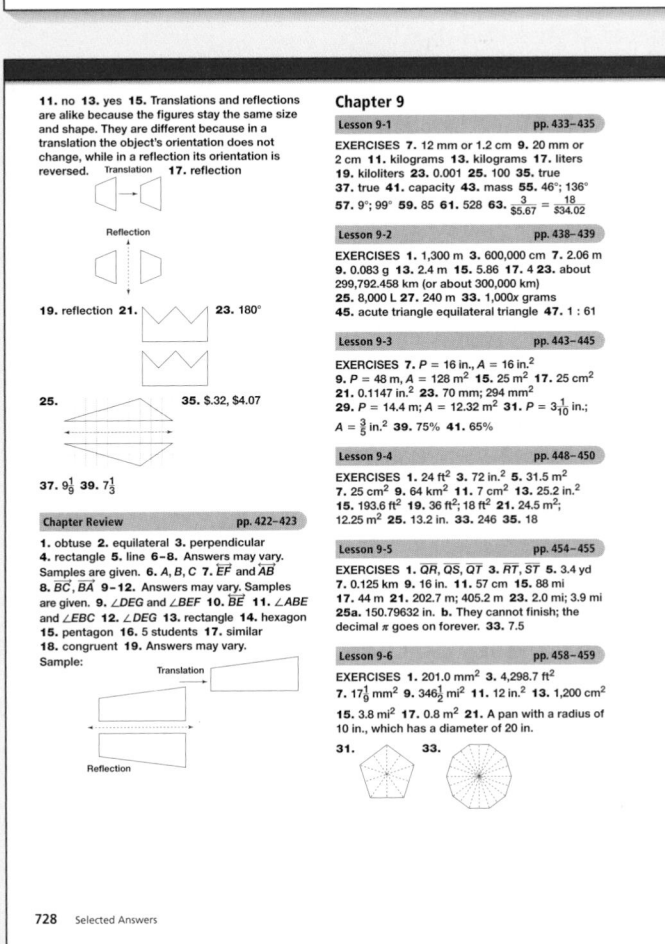

11. no 13. yes 15. Translations and reflections are alike because the figures stay the same size and shape. They are different because in a translation the object's orientation does not change, while in a reflection its orientation is reversed.

Translation   17. reflection

Reflection

19. reflection 21. 23. 180°

25. 35. $.32, $4.07

37. $9\frac{5}{9}$ 39. $7\frac{1}{3}$

Chapter Review   pp. 422–423
1. obtuse 2. equilateral 3. perpendicular 4. rectangle 5. line 6–8. Answers may vary. Samples are given. 6. A, B, C 7. $\overleftrightarrow{EF}$ and $\overleftrightarrow{AB}$ 8. $\overrightarrow{BC}$, $\overrightarrow{BA}$ 9–12. Answers may vary. Samples are given. 9. ∠DEG and ∠BEF 10. $\overrightarrow{BE}$ 11. ∠ABE and ∠EBC 12. ∠DEG 13. rectangle 14. hexagon 15. pentagon 16. 5 students 17. similar 18. congruent 19. Answers may vary. Sample:

Translation

Reflection

Chapter 9

Lesson 9-1   pp. 433–435
EXERCISES 7. 12 mm or 1.2 cm 9. 20 mm or 2 cm 11. kilograms 13. kilograms 17. liters 19. kiloliters 23. 0.001 25. 100 35. true 37. true 41. capacity 43. mass 55. 46°; 136° 57. 9°; 99° 59. 85 61. 528 63. $\frac{3}{\$5.67} = \frac{18}{\$34.02}$

Lesson 9-2   pp. 438–439
EXERCISES 1. 1,300 m 3. 600,000 cm 7. 2.06 m 9. 0.083 g 13. 2.4 m 15. 5.86 17. 4 23. about 299,792.458 km (or about 300,000 km) 25. 8,000 L 27. 240 m 33. 1,000x grams 45. acute triangle equilateral triangle 47. 1 : 61

Lesson 9-3   pp. 443–445
EXERCISES 7. P = 16 in., A = 16 in.² 9. P = 48 m, A = 128 m² 15. 25 m² 17. 25 cm² 21. 0.1147 in.² 23. 70 mm; 294 mm² 29. P = 14.4 m; A = 12.32 m² 31. $P = 3\frac{1}{10}$ in.; $A = \frac{3}{4}$ in.² 39. 75% 41. 65%

Lesson 9-4   pp. 448–450
EXERCISES 1. 24 ft² 3. 72 in.² 5. 31.5 m² 7. 25 cm² 9. 64 km² 11. 7 cm² 13. 25.2 in.² 15. 193.6 ft² 19. 36 ft²; 18 ft² 21. 24.5 m²; 12.25 m² 25. 13.2 in.² 33. 246 35. 18

Lesson 9-5   pp. 454–455
EXERCISES 1. $\overrightarrow{QR}$, $\overrightarrow{QS}$, $\overrightarrow{QT}$ 3. $\overrightarrow{RT}$, $\overrightarrow{ST}$ 5. 3.4 yd 7. 0.125 km 9. 16 in. 11. 57 cm 15. 88 mi 17. 44 m 21. 202.7 m; 405.2 m 23. 2.0 mi; 3.9 mi 25a. 150.79632 in. b. They cannot finish; the decimal π goes on forever. 33. 7.5

Lesson 9-6   pp. 458–459
EXERCISES 1. 201.0 mm² 3. 4,298.7 ft² 7. $17\frac{5}{8}$ mm² 9. $346\frac{1}{2}$ mi² 11. 12 in.² 13. 1,200 cm² 15. 3.8 mi² 17. 0.8 m² 21. A pan with a radius of 10 in., which has a diameter of 20 in.
31. 33.

Page 729

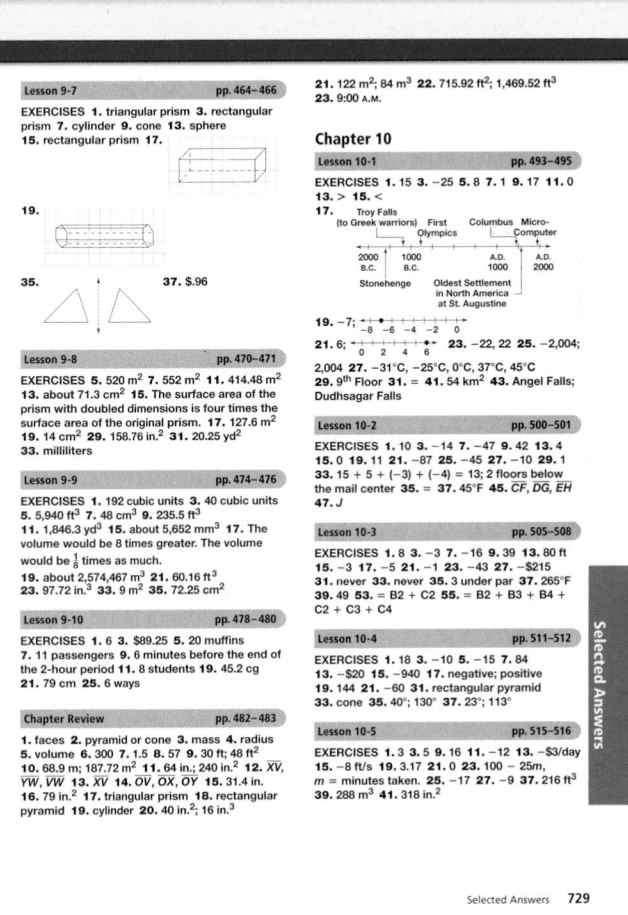

21. 122 m²; 84 m³ 22. 715.92 ft²; 1,469.52 ft³ 23. 9:00 A.M.

Lesson 9-7   pp. 464–466
EXERCISES 1. triangular prism 3. rectangular prism 7. cylinder 9. cone 13. sphere 15. rectangular prism 17.
19.
35. 37. $.96

Lesson 9-8   pp. 470–471
EXERCISES 5. 520 m² 7. 552 m² 11. 414.48 m² 13. about 71.3 cm² 15. The surface area of the prism with doubled dimensions is four times the surface area of the original prism. 17. 127.6 m² 19. 14 cm² 29. 158.76 in.² 31. 20.25 yd² 33. milliliters

Lesson 9-9   pp. 474–476
EXERCISES 1. 192 cubic units 3. 40 cubic units 5. 5,940 ft³ 7. 48 cm³ 9. 235.5 ft³ 11. 1,846.3 yd³ 15. about 5,652 mm³ 17. The volume would be 8 times greater. The volume would be $\frac{1}{8}$ times as much. 19. about 2,574,467 m³ 21. 60.16 ft³ 23. 97.72 in.³ 33. 9 m² 35. 72.25 cm²

Lesson 9-10   pp. 478–480
EXERCISES 1. 6 3. $89.25 5. 20 muffins 7. 11 passengers 9. 6 minutes before the end of the 2-hour period 11. 8 students 19. 45.2 cg 21. 79 cm 25. 6 ways

Chapter Review   pp. 482–483
1. faces 2. pyramid or cone 3. mass 4. radius 5. volume 6. 300 7. 1.5 8. 57 9. 30 ft; 48 ft² 10. 68.9 m; 187.72 m² 11. 64 in.²; 240 in.² 12. $\overrightarrow{XV}$, $\overrightarrow{YW}$, $\overrightarrow{VW}$ 13. $\overrightarrow{XV}$ 14. $\overrightarrow{OV}$, $\overrightarrow{OX}$, $\overrightarrow{OY}$ 15. 31.4 in. 16. 79 in.² 17. triangular prism 18. rectangular pyramid 19. cylinder 20. 40 in.²; 16 in.³

Chapter 10

Lesson 10-1   pp. 493–495
EXERCISES 1. 15 3. −25 5. 8 7. 1 9. 17 11. 0 13. > 15. <
17.

Troy Falls (to Greek warriors) | First Olympics | Columbus | Micro-Computer
| 2000 B.C. | 1000 B.C. | 1000 A.D. | 2000 A.D. |
Stonehenge | | Oldest Settlement in North America at St. Augustine |

19. −7;
21. 6; 23. −22, 22 25. −2,004; 2,004 27. −31°C, −25°C, 0°C, 37°C, 45°C 29. 9th Floor 31. = 41. 54 km² 43. Angel Falls; Dudhsagar Falls

Lesson 10-2   pp. 500–501
EXERCISES 1. 10 3. −14 7. −47 9. 42 13. 4 15. 0 19. 11 21. −87 25. −45 27. −10 29. 1 33. 15 + 5 + (−3) + (−4) = 13; 2 floors below the mail center 35. = 37. 45°F 45. $\overline{CF}$, $\overline{DG}$, $\overline{EH}$ 47. J

Lesson 10-3   pp. 505–508
EXERCISES 1. 8 3. −3 7. −16 9. 39 13. 80 ft 15. −3 17. −5 21. −1 23. −43 27. −$215 31. never 33. never 35. 3 under par 37. 265°F 39. 49 53. = B2 + C2 55. = B2 + B3 + B4 + C2 + C3 + C4

Lesson 10-4   pp. 511–512
EXERCISES 1. 8 3. −10 5. −15 7. 84 13. −$20 15. −940 17. negative; positive 19. 144 21. −60 31. rectangular pyramid 33. cone 35. 40°; 130° 37. 23°; 113°

Lesson 10-5   pp. 515–516
EXERCISES 1. 3 3. 5 9. 16 11. −12 13. −$3/day 15. −8 ft/s 19. 3.17 21. 0 23. 100 − 25m, m = minutes taken. 25. −17 27. −9 37. 216 ft³ 39. 288 m³ 41. 318 in.²

Selected Answers

Lesson 10-6 — pp. 520–521

EXERCISES 1. (−3, 1) 3. (3, 2) 5. A 7. J
15. grocery store 21. (−8, −3) 25. (0, 2), (1, 2), (1, 4), (0, 4), (2, 6), (2, 5), (4, 5), (4, 6), (6, 4), (5, 4), (5, 2), (6, 2), (4, 0), (4, 1), (2, 1), (2, 0) 27. Yes; answers may vary. Sample: The first coordinate tells you how far to move along the x-axis and the second coordinate tells you where to move along the y-axis. 35. The statistic is misleading because four of the five distances are less than 25 feet.

Lesson 10-7 — pp. 524–526

EXERCISES 1. −$2,256 3. $194 5a. Monday: $9; Tuesday: $18; Wednesday: −$9; Thursday: $17; Friday: −$12; Saturday: −$1
b.

c. Tuesday; Friday 7. 15 9. 23 13. Miami; Rochester 15. A company has made a profit if its total expenses are less than its total income. 23. acute 25. acute 31. 14

Lesson 10-8 — pp. 530–532

EXERCISES
1. [Input/Output table] 3. [Input/Output table]
5. [x y table with graph]

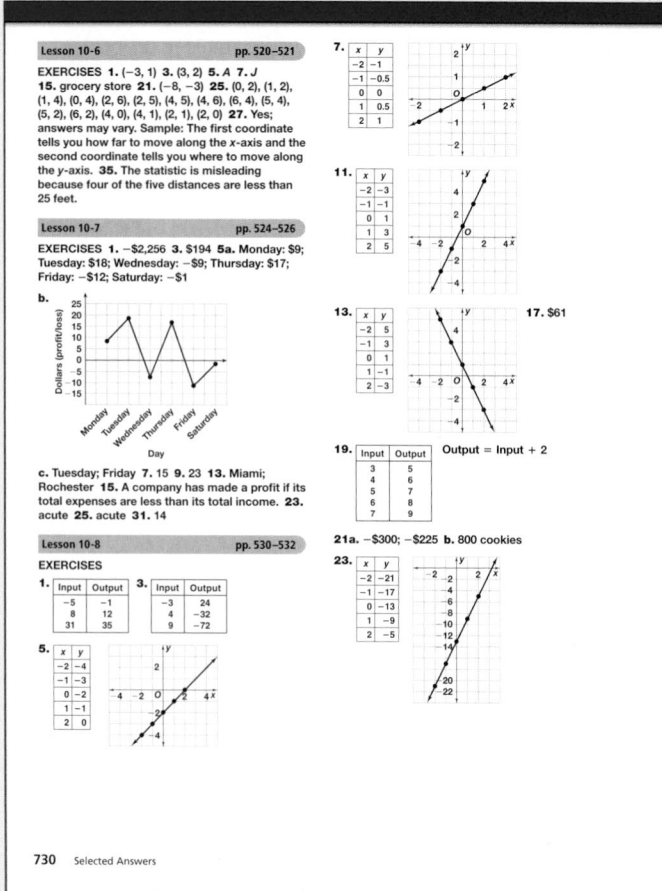

7. [x y table with graph]
11. [x y table with graph]
13. [x y table with graph] 17. $61
19. [Input/Output table] Output = Input + 2
21a. −$300; −$225 b. 800 cookies
23. [x y table with graph]

---

25. [x y table with graph]

27. Not linear; the graph is not a line. 37. 13 39. 25

Lesson 10-9 — pp. 534–535

EXERCISES 1. Answers may vary. Sample: about 360 lb/in.²

3. a–b. Answers may vary. Sample: a. about 60 mi/h b. 10
5. September 21 15. −6, 0, 3, 19 17. equilateral 19. isosceles

Chapter Review — pp. 538–539

1. function 2. ordered pairs 3. integers 4. quadrants 5. opposites 6. > 7. < 8. < 9. > 10. −2, −1, 1 11. −6, −4, 0, 5, 12. −7, −3, 5, 9 13. 11 14. −4 15. −2 16. −13 17. 8 18. 8 19. −11 20. −8 21. 36 22. −21 23. −10 24. 8 25. 4 26. −5 27. −4 28. 7
29–32. [graph]
33. $26,286 34. profit 35. 40

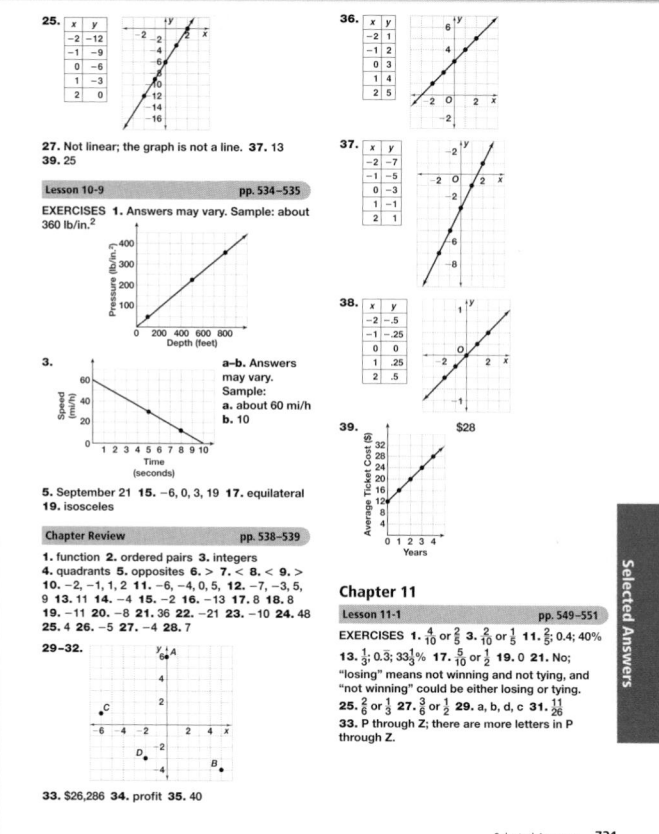

36. [x y table with graph]
37. [x y table with graph]
38. [x y table with graph]
39. $28

Chapter 11

Lesson 11-1 — pp. 549–551

EXERCISES 1. $\frac{4}{10}$ or $\frac{2}{5}$ 3. $\frac{2}{10}$ or $\frac{1}{5}$ 11. $\frac{2}{5}$; 0.4; 40%
13. $\frac{1}{3}$; 0.3; $33\frac{1}{3}$% 17. $\frac{5}{10}$ or $\frac{1}{2}$ 19. 0 21. No; "losing" means not winning and not tying, and "not winning" could be either losing or tying.
25. $\frac{2}{6}$ or $\frac{1}{3}$ 27. $\frac{3}{6}$ or $\frac{1}{2}$ 29. a, b, d, c 31. $\frac{11}{26}$
33. P through Z; there are more letters in P through Z.

---

35. [spinner] 47. −18 49. −2

Lesson 11-2 — pp. 555–557

EXERCISES 1. $\frac{3}{14}$ 3. 1 7. $\frac{3}{4}$ 9. Yes; the experimental probability of rolling a 1, 2, or 3 is $\frac{1}{2}$.
11. $\frac{2}{3}$ 13a. $\frac{3}{20}$ b. $\frac{13}{20}$ 15. It seems likely that the school will serve pizza every Friday. 17. 0
19. $\frac{2}{30}$ or $\frac{1}{15}$ 23. Spin it several times to see if it lands on each section about the same number of times. 39. −13 41. 10 45. congruent

Lesson 11-3 — pp. 560–562

EXERCISES 1. 2 3. 6 7. 200 students 9. 288 shirts 11. 192 belts 13. honesty 15a. about 11 times b. about 9 times 17. 24 blue; 56 red; 80 orange; 40 yellow 19. 30 blue; 70 red; 100 orange; 50 yellow 21. 60 pieces; experimental probability is usually more accurate with more trials. 23. $\frac{5}{16}$ 25. about 63 darts 33. −120 35. 96

Lesson 11-4 — pp. 565–566

EXERCISES 5. you: 11 pairs; friend: 22 pairs 7. 24 visits 17. R 19. S 25. centimeter

Lesson 11-5 — pp. 571–573

EXERCISES 1. $\frac{4}{8}$ or $\frac{1}{2}$ 3. $\frac{2}{8}$ or $\frac{1}{4}$
5.

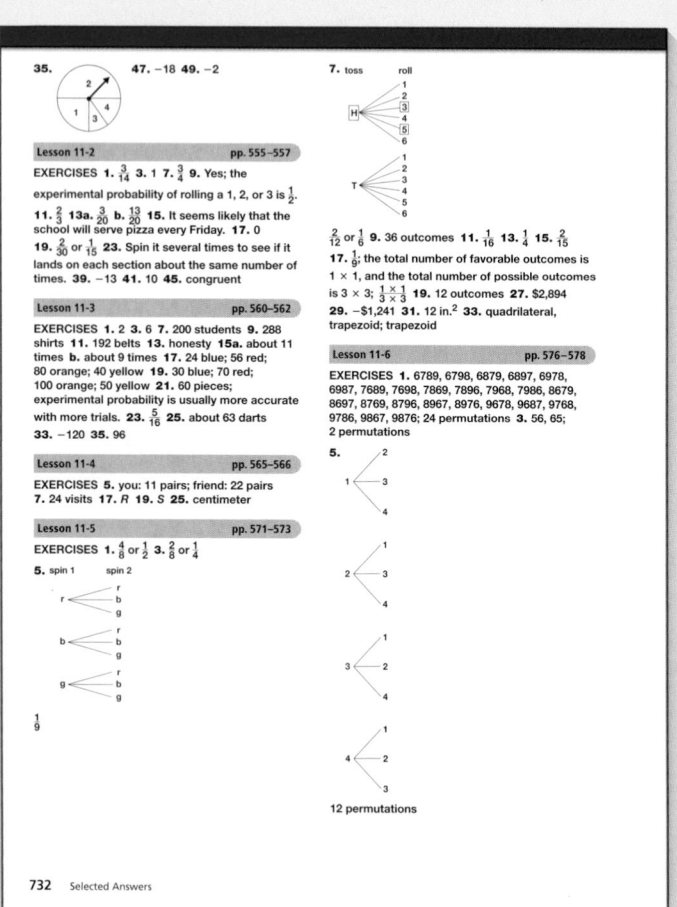

$\frac{1}{9}$

7.

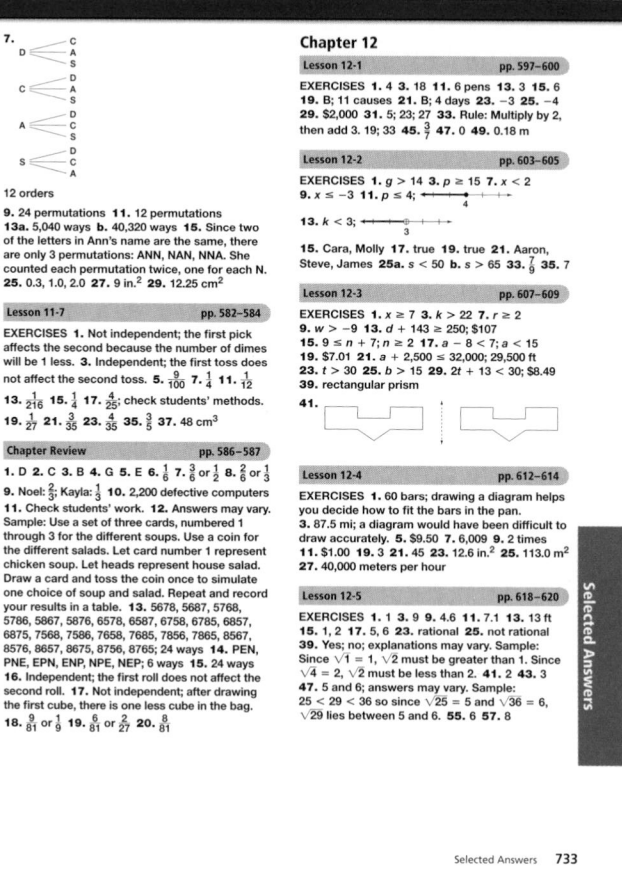

$\frac{2}{12}$ or $\frac{1}{6}$ 9. 36 outcomes 11. $\frac{1}{16}$ 13. $\frac{1}{4}$ 15. $\frac{2}{3}$
17. $\frac{1}{9}$; the total number of favorable outcomes is 1×1, and the total number of possible outcomes is 3×3; $\frac{1}{3} \times \frac{1}{3} = \frac{1}{9}$ 19. 12 outcomes 27. $2,894 29. −$1,241 31. 12 in.² 33. quadrilateral, trapezoid; trapezoid

Lesson 11-6 — pp. 576–578

EXERCISES 1. 6789, 6798, 6879, 6897, 6978, 6987, 7689, 7698, 7869, 7896, 7968, 7986, 8679, 8697, 8769, 8796, 8967, 8976, 9678, 9687, 9768, 9786, 9867, 9876; 24 permutations 3. 56, 65; 2 permutations
5. [tree diagram] 12 permutations

---

7. [tree diagram] 12 orders
9. 24 permutations 11. 12 permutations 13a. 5,040 ways b. 40,320 ways 15. Since two of the letters in Ann's name are the same, there are only 3 permutations: ANN, NAN, NNA. She counted each permutation twice, one for each N. 25. 0.3, 1.0, 2.0 27. 9 in.² 29. 12.25 cm²

Lesson 11-7 — pp. 582–584

EXERCISES 1. Not independent; the first pick affects the second because the number of dimes will be 1 less. 3. Independent; the first toss does not affect the second toss. 5. $\frac{9}{100}$ 7. $\frac{1}{4}$ 11. $\frac{1}{12}$
13. $\frac{1}{216}$ 15. $\frac{1}{4}$ 17. $\frac{5}{16}$; check students' methods.
19. $\frac{1}{27}$ 21. $\frac{3}{35}$ 23. $\frac{4}{35}$ 35. $\frac{3}{5}$ 37. 48 cm³

Chapter Review — pp. 586–587

1. D 2. C 3. B 4. G 5. E 6. $\frac{1}{6}$ 7. $\frac{3}{2}$ or $1\frac{1}{2}$ 8. $\frac{2}{6}$ or $\frac{1}{3}$
9. Noel: $\frac{2}{3}$; Kayla: $\frac{1}{3}$ 10. 2,200 defective computers 11. Check students' work. 12. Answers may vary. Sample: Use a set of three cards, numbered 1 through 3 for the different soups. Use a coin for the different salads. Let card number 1 represent chicken soup. Let heads represent house salad. Draw a card and toss the coin once to simulate one choice of soup and salad. Repeat and record your results in a table. 13. 5678, 5687, 5768, 5786, 5867, 5876, 6578, 6587, 6758, 6785, 6875, 6857, 7568, 7586, 7658, 7685, 7856, 7865, 8576, 8567, 8675, 8756, 8765, 8765; 24 ways 14. PEN, PNE, EPN, ENP, NPE, NEP; 6 ways 15. 24 ways 16. Independent; the first roll does not affect the second roll. 17. Not independent; after drawing the first cube, there is one less cube in the bag.
18. $\frac{9}{81}$ or $\frac{1}{9}$ 19. $\frac{8}{81}$ 20. $\frac{8}{81}$

Chapter 12

Lesson 12-1 — pp. 597–600

EXERCISES 1. 4 3. 18 11. 6 pens 13. 3 15. 6 19. B; 11 causes 21. B; 4 days 23. −3 25. −4 29. $2,000 31. 5; 23; 27 33. Rule: Multiply by 2, then add 3. 19; 33 45. $\frac{4}{5}$ 47. 0 49. 0.18 m

Lesson 12-2 — pp. 603–605

EXERCISES 1. $g > 14$ 3. $p \geq 15$ 7. $x < 2$
9. $x \leq -3$ 11. $p \leq 4$; [number line]
13. $k < 3$; [number line]
15. Cara, Molly 17. true 19. true 21. Aaron, Steve, James 25a. $s < 50$ b. $s > 65$ 33. $\frac{7}{9}$ 35. 7

Lesson 12-3 — pp. 607–609

EXERCISES 1. $x \geq 7$ 3. $k > 22$ 7. $r \geq 2$
9. $w > -9$ 13. $d + 143 \geq 250$; $107
15. $9 \leq n + 7$; $n \geq 2$ 17. $a - 8 < 7$; $a < 15$
19. $7.01 21. $a + 2,500 \geq 32,000$; 29,500 ft
23. $t > 30$ 25. $b > 15$ 29. $2t + 13 < 30$; $8.49
39. rectangular prism
41. [image]

Lesson 12-4 — pp. 612–614

EXERCISES 1. 60 bars; drawing a diagram helps you decide how to fit the bars in the pan.
3. 87.5 mi; a diagram would have been difficult to draw accurately. 5. $9.50 7. 6,009 9. 2 times 11. $1.00 19. 3 21. 45 23. 12.6 in.² 25. 113.0 m² 27. 40,000 meters per hour

Lesson 12-5 — pp. 618–620

EXERCISES 1. 1 3. 9 9. 4.6 11. 7.1 13. 13 ft 15. 1, 2 17. 5, 6 23. not rational 25. not rational
39. Yes; no; explanations may vary. Sample: Since $\sqrt{1} = 1$, $\sqrt{2}$ must be greater than 1. Since $\sqrt{4} = 2$, $\sqrt{2}$ must be less than 2. 41. 2 43. 3
47. 5 and 6; answers may vary. Sample: $25 < 29 < 36$ so since $\sqrt{25} = 5$ and $\sqrt{36} = 6$, $\sqrt{29}$ lies between 5 and 6. 55. 6 57. 8

T364

Lesson 12-6 — pp. 624–626

EXERCISES 1. 25 **3.** 5 **7.** 15 **9.** 5.7 **11.** 8 ft **13.** 1.3 **15.** 16.7 **17.** 75 ft **19a.** yes **b.** no **c.** no **d.** yes **21.** 22 in. **23.** No; the sum of the squares of the lengths of the legs in a right triangle is equal to the square of the length of the hypotenuse. The square of the length of the hypotenuse is greater than the square of either leg, so the hypotenuse is longer than either leg. **33.** $\frac{7}{25}$ **35.** $\frac{1}{4}$ **37.** 3 **39.** 84 **41.** > **43.** >

Chapter Review — pp. 628–629

1. E **2.** D **3.** B **4.** F **5.** A **6.** 3 **7.** 1 **8.** 125 **9.** no **10.** yes **11.** no **12.** yes **13.**

14. **15.** **16.** **17.** $q < 3$ **18.** $t < 5$

19. $v > 16$ **20.** $y \geq -20$ **21–22.** Explanations may vary. Samples are given. **21.** 21 people; drawing a diagram would be tedious. **22.** 184 strips; there are too many strips to include in a diagram. **23.** 9 **24.** 4.9 **25.** 5.5 **26.** 12 **27.** between 2 and 3 **28.** between 3 and 4 **29.** between 4 and 5 **30.** between 5 and 6 **31.** rational **32.** not rational **33.** rational **34.** rational **35.** 10 **36.** 8 **37.** 2.2 **38.** 5.3

Extra Practice

Chapter 1 — p. 642

1. eight hundred fifty-four **3.** seven thousand three hundred two **9.** 216 **11.** 0.2, 0.4, 0.7 **13.** 6.025, 6.05, 6.2, 6.25 **15.** about 7 **17.** about 770 **19.** 5; 4.874 **21.** 1; 1.489 **23.** 7.7436 **25.** 6,882 **27.** 3,850 **29.** 9.31 **31.** 0.8; repeating **33.** 5.8; terminating **35.** 21 **37.** 9

Chapter 2 — p. 643

1. 256; 1,024; 4,096; start with 1 and multiply by 4 repeatedly. **3.** 23, 27, 31; start with 7 and add 4 repeatedly. **5.** 2 **7.** 4 **9.** $b - 1$ **11.** $b + 4$ **13.** $3.50 **15.** true **17.** false **19.** 34 **21.** 17.8 **23.** 4 **25.** 8.6 **31.** $7 \times 10^4 + 2 \times 10^3 + 0 \times 10^2 + 0 \times 10^1 + 3 \times 1$ **33.** $8 \times 10^6 + 1 \times 10^5 + 2 \times 10^4 + 0 \times 10^3 + 4 \times 10^2 + 3 \times 10^1 + 2 \times 1$ **35.** 192 **37.** 85 **39.** 57 **41.** 188

Chapter 3 — p. 644

1. 2, 3, 9 **3.** 2, 3, 5, 9, 10 **7.** composite **9.** prime **13.** 10 **15.** 5 **19.** $\frac{1}{10}$ **21.** $\frac{3}{4}$ **25.** $\frac{15}{8}$ **27.** $\frac{100}{9}$ **31.** 8 **33.** 75 **37.** $\frac{4}{9}, \frac{4}{7}, \frac{1}{2}$ **39.** $\frac{7}{12}, \frac{2}{3}, \frac{5}{6}$ **43.** $1\frac{1}{4}$ **45.** $\frac{8}{25}$ **49.** $0.\overline{6}$ **51.** 0.25

Chapter 4 — p. 645

9. $\frac{3}{4}$ **11.** $1\frac{1}{3}$ **17.** $8\frac{1}{6}$ **19.** $11\frac{7}{12}$ **21.** $5\frac{17}{24}$ **23.** $5\frac{11}{15}$ **25.** $1\frac{3}{8}$ **27.** $3\frac{7}{9}$ **33.** 1 h 30 min **35.** 6 h 38 min **39.** $\frac{3}{4}$ of the tin

Chapter 5 — p. 646

1. $\frac{1}{3}$ **3.** $\frac{21}{32}$ **5.** 20 **7.** $13\frac{1}{8}$ **9.** $2\frac{1}{2}$ **11.** $1\frac{1}{4}$ **13.** 4 **15.** 7 **17.** $3\frac{3}{8}$ **19.** 30 **21.** 32 **23.** 168 **29.** 96 squares **31.** tons **33.** pounds **37.** 3 **39.** 4

Chapter 6 — p. 647

7. $.24 per ounce; $.25 per ounce; 8 ounces for $2.99 **9.** no **11.** no **13.** 2 **15.** 9 **19.** 130 km **21.** 500 km **23.** 0.96; $\frac{24}{25}$ **25.** 0.01; $\frac{1}{100}$ **29.** 32% **31.** 25% **35.** 3.375 **37.** 90

Chapter 7 — p. 648

1. mean: 22.25; median: 22.5; mode: 22 **3.** mean: 44.875; median: 43.5; mode: 29

5.

wpm	Tally	Frequency
35	IIII	4
40	III	3
45		0
50		0
55	II	2
60		0
65	II	2
70	I	1

```
x
x          x
x          x
x   x      x      x
x   x   x  x   x  x   x
35  40  45 50  55 60  65  70
```

7. vertical axis: hours of reading per year per person; horizontal axis: different forms of print material **9.** rent **11a.** 25 **b.** The United States

won 25 silver medals during the 2000 Summer Olympics. **13.**

```
6 | 9
7 | 2 4 7 8
8 | 5 6 9
9 | 1
Key: 6|9 means 69
```

```
65 70 75 80 85 90 95 100
```

15. Graphs may vary. Sample:

Daily Total Sales

(graph: Amount vs. Days M T W Th F)

Chapter 8 — p. 649

3. $\overline{AE}$ and $\overline{FB}$ **5.** obtuse **9.** complement: 62°; supplement: 152° **11.** complement: 33.7°; supplement: 123.7° **15.** equilateral **17.** true **19.** true **21.** similar **23.** not similar

25.

Chapter 9 — p. 650

1. mL **3.** cm **5.** 10,800 **7.** 1.008 **9.** about 18 cm² **11.** 52.25 ft² **13.** 144 cm² **15.** 33 ft; 88 ft² **17.** 69 mi; 380 mi² **19.** rectangular pyramid **21.** triangular prism **23.** 1,056 m²; 2,304 m³

Chapter 10 — p. 651

1. −2, −1, 0, 3 **3.** −8, −6, 7, 8 **5.** −4 **7.** −125 **11.** −4 **13.** 0 **15.** −40 **17.** −12 **23.** (2, 3) **25.** (−3, −1) **27.** G **29.** H **31.** $5,002 **33.** −$86

35.

m	1,000	1,500	2,000	2,500
km	1	1.5	2	2.5

(graph: Kilometers vs. Meters)

37. $2.64

Chapter 11 — p. 652

1. $\frac{2}{7}$ **3.** $\frac{1}{2}$ **5.** $\frac{6}{7}$ **7.** 3 **9.** 24 **13.** 1,324 students **15.** $\frac{1}{8}$

17.
```
6 < 7
  < 8
7 < 6
  < 8
8 < 6
  < 7
```
19. $\frac{3}{25}$ **21.** $\frac{16}{25}$

Chapter 12 — p. 653

1. 9 **3.** 6 **9.** $x > -2$ **11.** $x \geq 1$ **13.** $c \geq 5$ **15.** $m < 6$ **17.** $p \leq -14$ **21.** 7 **23.** 13 **27.** 1 and 2 **29.** 4 and 5 **33.** 34 **35.** 12

Skills Handbook

Place Value of Whole Numbers — p. 654

1. ten millions **3.** hundred millions **7.** 3 ten million **9.** 6 hundred million **13.** 6 hundred **15.** 6 ten million

Rounding Whole Numbers — p. 655

1. 70 **3.** 4,440 **7.** 300 **9.** 1,100 **17.** 16,218 is closer to 16,000 than to 17,000; 16,218 rounded to the nearest ten thousand is 16,000. **19.** 89,000

Adding Whole Numbers — p. 656

1. 76 **3.** 41 **7.** 393 **9.** 279 **13.** 2,894 **15.** 6,754

Subtracting Whole Numbers — p. 657

1. 44 **3.** 22 **7.** 346 **9.** 177 **13.** 6,828 **15.** 4,361

Multiplying Whole Numbers — p. 658

1. 243 **3.** 348 **9.** 852 **11.** 6,057 **17.** 1,150 **19.** 48,480

Multiplying and Dividing Whole Numbers by 10, 100, and 1,000 — p. 659

1. 850 **3.** 85,000 **17.** 32 **19.** 80 **31.** 7,600 **33.** 37

Dividing Whole Numbers — p. 660

1. 73 R2 **3.** 93 R1 **11.** 227 R13 **13.** 68 R17

Zeros in Quotients — p. 661

1. 30 R2 **3.** 90 R1 **7.** 70 R5 **9.** 20 R14 **17.** 503 **19.** 420 R2

Reading Thermometer Scales — p. 662

1. 36.8°C **3.** 38.4°C **7.** G **9.** F

Roman Numerals — p. 663

1. 11 **3.** 95 **11.** XV **13.** MDCXXXII

Additional Answers

CHAPTER 1

pages 6–7 Exercises

25.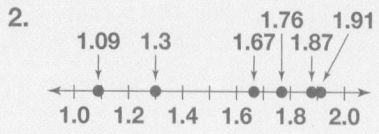

26. Answers may vary. Sample: 21,463;

pages 9–10 Check Understanding

2a. sixteen thousand, seven hundred two and three tenths

b. one thousand six hundred seventy and two hundred thirty-four thousandths

c. one and sixty-seven thousand twenty-three hundred-thousandths

pages 10–12 Exercises

13. two and sixty-one thousandths

14. three and eight ten-thousandths

15. forty hundredths

16. fifty and six thousand three ten-thousandths

21. 8 + 0.2; eight and two tenths

22. 90 + 1 + 0.9 + 0.01; ninety-one and ninety-one hundredths

23. 90 + 1 + 0.09 + 0.001; ninety-one and ninety-one thousandths

24. 1,000,000 + 600 + 50 + 0.02; one million, six hundred fifty and two hundredths

pages 13–14 Check Understanding

2.

pages 16–17 Exercises

1.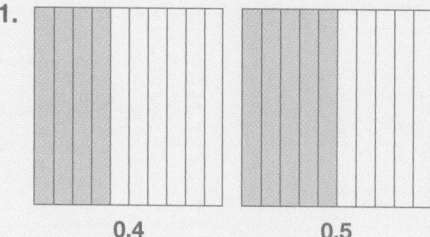

    0.4   0.5

0.5 is greater.

2.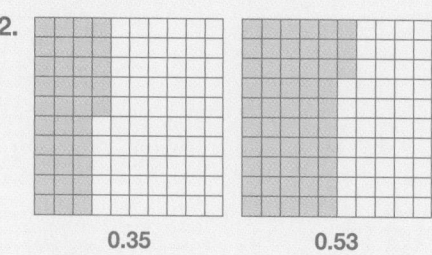

    0.35   0.53

0.53 is greater.

3.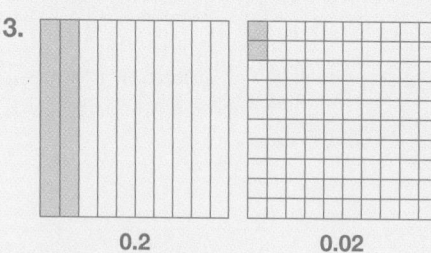

    0.2   0.02

0.2 is greater.

page 24 Investigation

4.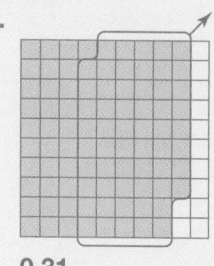

1.14

5.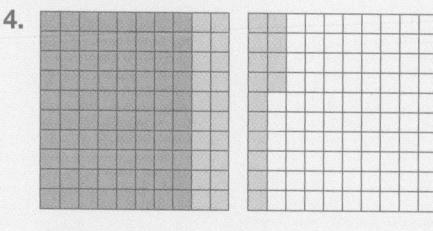

0.3

6.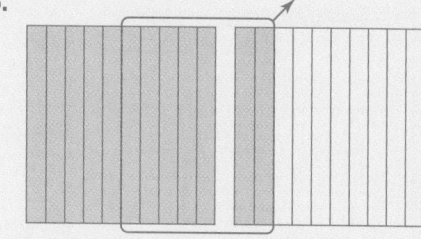

0.5

7.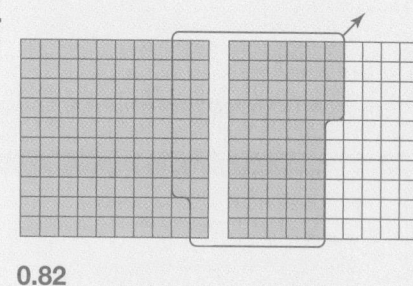

0.31

8.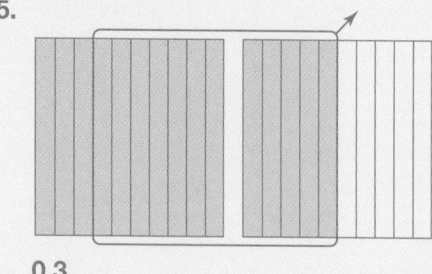

0.82

page 34 Investigation

1.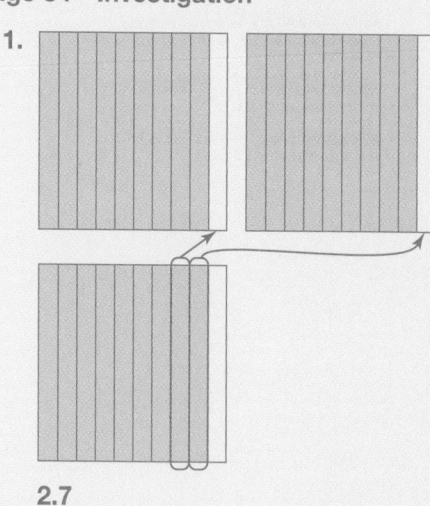

2.7

2.

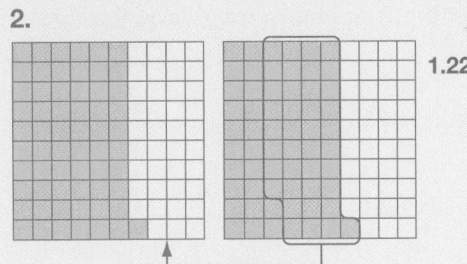

1.22

page 46 Exercises

22.

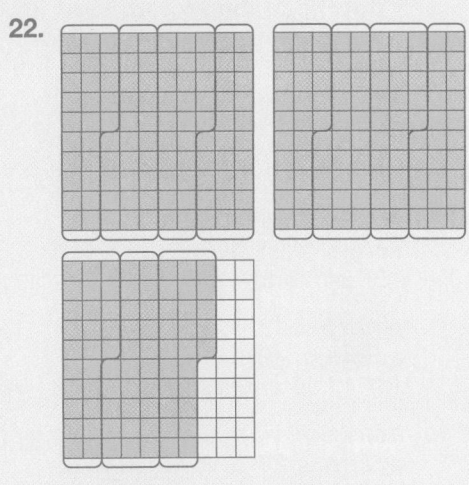

11 cards

CHAPTER 2

page 69 Check Understanding

1a.

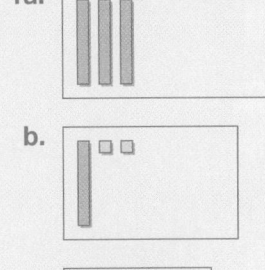

b.

c.

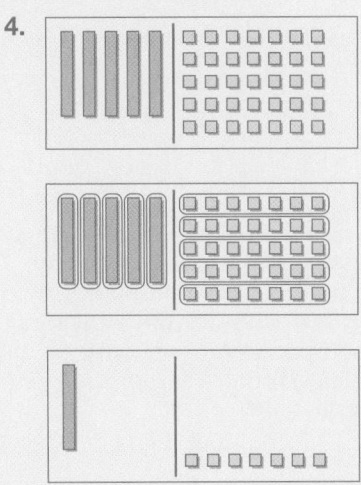

page 83 Writing in Math

2a. In the first rule, you find the product of the term number and itself.

The pattern is 1, 4, 9, 16, 25, 36, . . .

In the second rule, you start with 1 and find the next term by adding 3, the next by adding 5, and so on.

The pattern is 1, 4, 9, 16, 25, 36, . . .

b. Similarities and Differences:

Both rules result in the same pattern: 1, 4, 9, 16, 25, 36, . . .

The first rule uses the term number itself to find the new term.

The second rule uses the previous term to find the new term.

The first rule uses multiplication. The second term uses addition.

3a. "Simplifying an expression" means taking a numerical expression and performing operations to get the expression to its simplest form.

$(3^2 + 5) \times 2$ simplifies to 28.

"Evaluating an expression" means taking an algebraic expression, substituting for the variable, and performing operations to get the expression in its simplest form.

$4a - 15$ where $a = 8$ simplifies to 17 when you substitute for the variable.

b. Similarities and Differences:

Both terms involve performing operations to get an expression into its simplest form.

The first term involves only numerical expressions. The second term involves algebraic expressions and substituting for one or more variables.

page 89 Investigation

4.

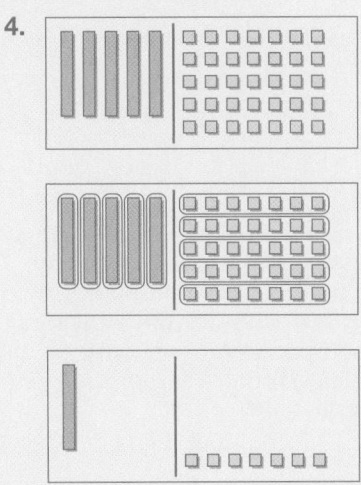

5.

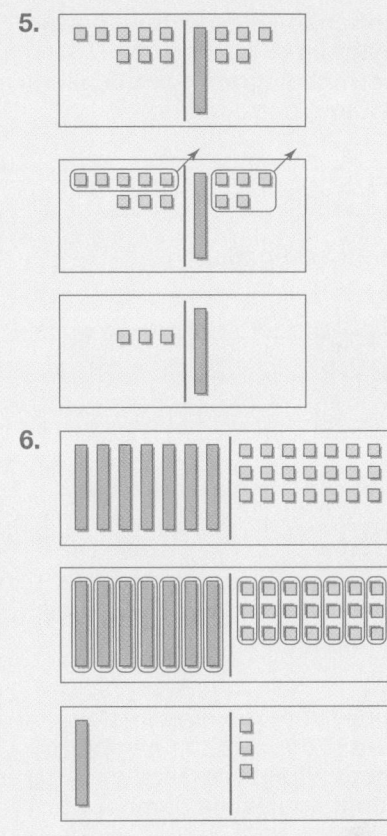

6.

page 107 Exercises

17. One way to find the total area is to find the area of each rectangle and then add the areas: $(6.8 \times 2.5) + (2 \times 2.5)$. Another way to find the total area is to multiply the total length of the rectangle by its width: $(6.8 + 2) \times 2.5$.

page 113 Test prep

15. [2] Draw a tree diagram.

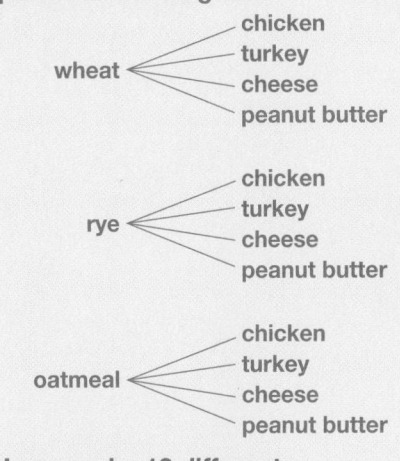

I can make 12 different sandwiches OR a correct explanation of choices.

[1] correct answer without correct diagram or explanation OR correct diagram or explanation without correct answer

CHAPTER 3

page 123 Investigation

1.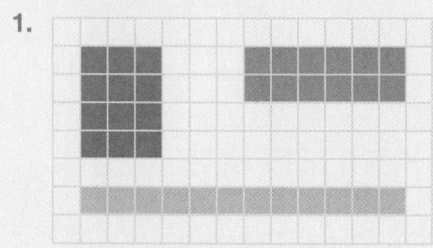

$1 \times 12, 2 \times 6, 3 \times 4$

2. four rectangles; two rectangles; one rectangle

3. Answers may vary. Sample: The number of rectangles that can be drawn is equal to the number of pairs of whole numbers whose product equals the number of squares.

pages 125–127 Exercises

17.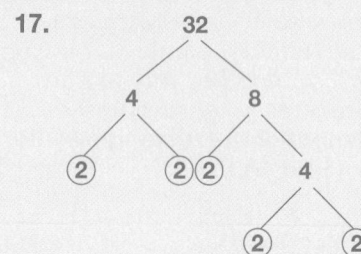

18.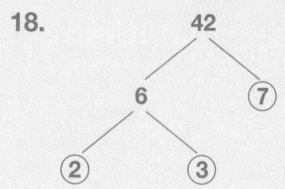

19.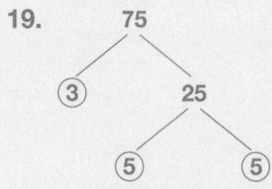

20.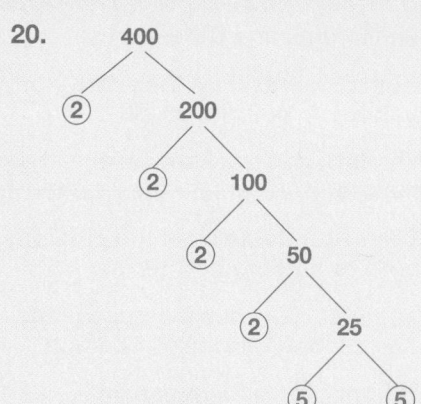

21.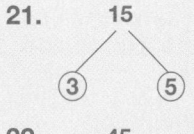

22.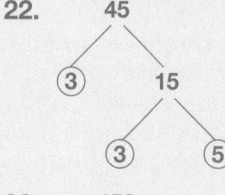

23.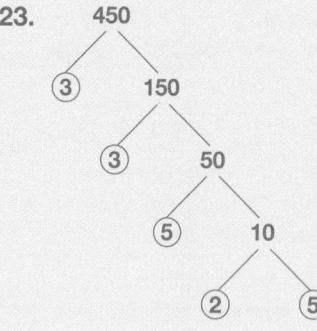

24.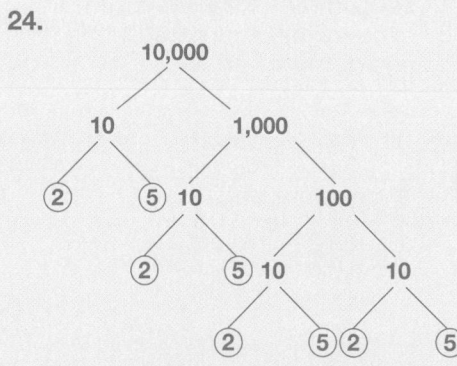

36. Answers may vary. Sample: Begin by testing 864 for divisibility by the smallest prime number, 2. $864 = 2 \times 432$. Continue dividing the composite factors until all remaining factors are prime. $864 = 2^5 \times 3^3$.

42. [2] Answers may vary. Sample: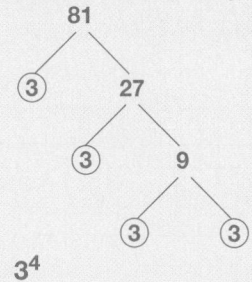

3^4

[1] The factor tree is complete, but the prime factorization is not written out OR there is a small computational error, but all the work is present.

pages 128–129 Check Understanding

1a. factors of 6: 1, 2, 3, 6
factors of 21: 1, 3, 7, 21
GCF of 6 and 21: 3

b. factors of 18: 1, 2, 3, 6, 9, 18
factors of 49: 1, 7, 49
GCF of 18 and 49: 1

c. factors of 14: 1, 2, 7, 14
factors of 28: 1, 2, 4, 7, 14, 28
GCF of 14 and 28: 14

3a.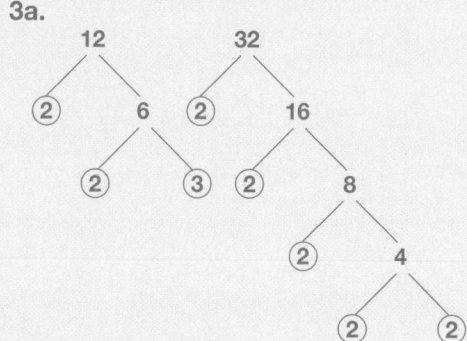

$12 = 2 \times 2 \times 3$
$32 = 2 \times 2 \times 2 \times 2 \times 2$
GCF = 4

b.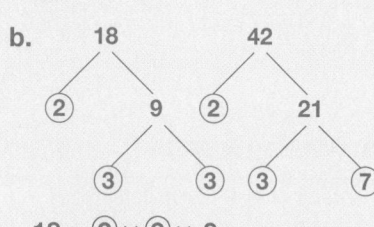

$18 = 2 \times 3 \times 3$
$42 = 2 \times 3 \times 7$
GCF = 6

pages 129–131 Exercises

1. factors of 14: 1, 2, 7, 14
factors of 35: 1, 5, 7, 35
GCF of 14 and 35: 7

T368

2. factors of 24: 1, 2, 3, 4, 6, 8, 12, 24 factors of 45: 1, 3, 5, 9, 15, 45 GCF of 24 and 45: 3

3. factors of 26: 1, 2, 13, 26 factors of 34: 1, 2, 17, 34 GCF of 26 and 34: 2

4. factors of 30: 1, 2, 3, 5, 6, 10, 15, 30 factors of 35: 1, 5, 7, 35 GCF of 30 and 35: 5

5. factors of 48: 1, 2, 3, 4, 6, 8, 12, 16, 24, 48 factors of 88: 1, 2, 4, 8, 11, 22, 44, 88 GCF of 48 and 88: 8

6. factors of 36: 1, 2, 3, 4, 6, 9, 12, 18, 36 factors of 63: 1, 3, 7, 9, 21, 63 GCF of 36 and 63: 9

12.
$$11\overline{)33\quad 55\quad 132}$$
$$\quad\;3\quad\;5\quad 12$$

GCF = 11

13.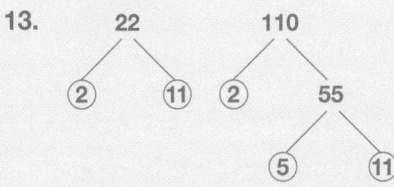

$$22 = 2 \times 11$$
$$110 = 2 \times 5 \times 11$$

14.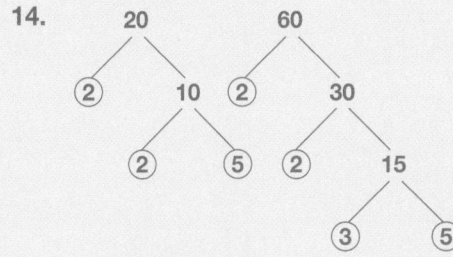

$$20 = 2 \times 2 \times 5$$
$$60 = 2 \times 2 \times 3 \times 5$$

15.
54
84
2   27   2   42
3   9   2   21
3   3   3   7

$$54 = 2 \times 3 \times 3 \times 3$$
$$84 = 2 \times 2 \times 3 \times 7$$

16.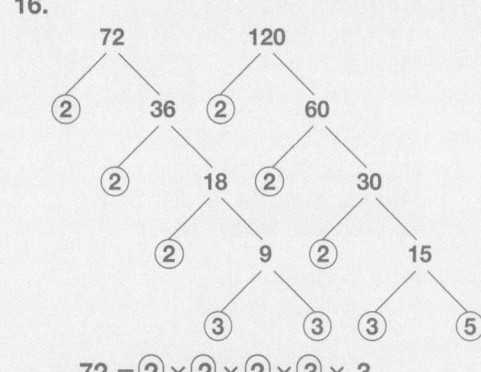

$$72 = 2 \times 2 \times 2 \times 3 \times 3$$
$$120 = 2 \times 2 \times 2 \times 3 \times 5$$

17.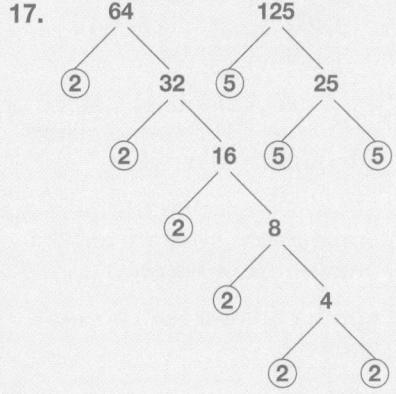

18.
117
130
3   39   2   65
3   13   5   13

$$117 = 3 \times 3 \times 13$$
$$130 = 2 \times 5 \times 13$$

19.
45
150
3   15   3   50
3   5   2   25
5   5

$$45 = 3 \times 3 \times 5$$
$$130 = 3 \times 2 \times 5 \times 5$$

page 139   Investigation

2. If the numerator is less than the denominator, then the fraction is less than 1. If the numerator and denominator are equal, then the fraction is equal to one. If the numerator is greater than the denominator, then the fraction is greater than 1.

3a–c. Check students' work.

d. 11 eighths, 22 eighths, 29 eighths; there are 8 eighths in each whole inch, so in $1\frac{3}{8}$ inches, there are $8 + 3 = 11$ eighths. The fraction $\frac{3}{4}$ is equivalent to $\frac{6}{8}$, so in $2\frac{3}{4}$ inches there are $2 \times 8 + 6 = 22$ eighths. In $3\frac{5}{8}$ inches, there are $3 \times 8 + 5 = 29$ eighths.

page 152   Exercises

46. [2] $1\frac{3}{16}$, $1\frac{7}{32}$, $1\frac{1}{4}$

$1\frac{1}{4} = 1\frac{8}{32}$

$1\frac{3}{16} = 1\frac{6}{32}$

[1] correct answer with no explanation

CHAPTER 4

page 179   Investigation

8.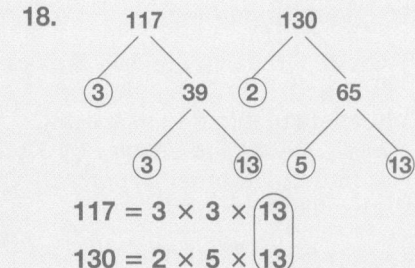

9.

CHAPTER 5

page 235   Writing in Math

2. The answer is wrong because $\frac{3}{10} + \frac{3}{10}$ is about 1, $\frac{2}{5}$ is about $\frac{1}{2}$, and $1\frac{1}{10}$ is about 1. So, the sum of $\frac{3}{10} + \frac{3}{10} + \frac{2}{5} + 1\frac{1}{10}$ is about 2. $2\left(\frac{3}{10}\right)$ means "2 times $\frac{3}{10}$," not "2 plus $\frac{3}{10}$." So, $2\left(\frac{3}{10}\right) + \frac{2}{5} + 1\frac{1}{10} = \frac{6}{10} + \frac{4}{10} + \frac{11}{10} = 2\frac{1}{10}$. Since $2\frac{1}{10}$ is closer to 2, this answer makes sense.

3. The answer is wrong because $\frac{5}{3}$ is almost 2, and $10 \div 2$ is 5. The setup is wrong. Only the divisor $\frac{5}{3}$ should be replaced with its reciprocal, $\frac{3}{5}$. So, $10 \div \frac{5}{3} = 10 \times \frac{3}{5} = \frac{30}{5} = 6$. Since 6 is much closer to 5 than $\frac{3}{50}$, this answer makes sense.

page 251 Check Understanding

Answers may vary. Samples are given.

3a. Gallons; a tanker truck holds more gasoline than can fit in a small bucket.

b. Fluid ounces or cups; a serving of yogurt is less than a pint.

c. Gallons; a bathtub can hold a few small buckets of water.

d. Fluid ounces; a bottle of cough syrup holds less than a pint.

page 252 Exercises

1–12. Explanations may vary. Samples are given.

1. Lots are usually measured in feet.

2. Any smaller unit would be too small, since the moon is thousands of miles from Earth.

3. A license plate is a little longer than a foot-ruler.

4. The width of a photograph is usually measured in inches.

5. One orange weighs less than a pound, so a bag of oranges would weigh more.

6. A package of chewing gum weighs about as much as a slice of bread.

7. A bowling ball weighs more than a loaf of bread.

8. A pickup truck is very heavy. Ounces are much too small.

9. A sample-size bottle of shampoo holds less than a cup.

10. A bowl can usually hold a cup of soup.

11. Lawnmowers usually hold about one gallon of gas.

12. A tube of toothpaste is usually measured in fluid ounces.

CHAPTER 6

pages 305–306   Exercises
16–18. Answers may vary. Samples are given.

16. Florida: $0.18, $3.18
Georgia: $0.12, $3.12
Massachusetts: $0.15, $3.15
Tennessee: $0.21, $3.21

17. Florida: $3.90, $68.90
Georgia: $2.60, $67.60
Massachusetts: $3.25, $68.25
Tennessee: $4.55, $69.55

18. Florida: $0.32, $5.62
Georgia: $0.21, $5.51
Massachusetts: $0.27, $5.57
Tennessee: $0.37, $5.67

32. [4] a. Alabama b.
$72.72 \approx \$73$,
$\$73 \times .04 = \$2.92$, $\$73 +$
$\$2.92 = \$75.92$; Mississippi:
$\$89.99 \approx \$90$,
$\$90 \times .08 = \$72$,
$\$72 \times .07 = \$5.04$
$\$72 + \$5.04 = \$77.04$
$\$75.92 < \$77.04$

[3] uses exact amounts instead of estimates OR has one minor computational error

[2] Steps are missing OR there are computational errors but the answer is still correct.

[1] correct answer with no work shown

page 315   Test Prep

15. [4] About 175 calls; multiply 5 days by 7 hours by 60 min to find how many minutes in a work week. Divide the answer by 12 to find the number of calls OR equivalent method.

[3] appropriate methods, but with one computational error

[2] appropriate methods, but with more than one computational error

[1] correct answer but no work shown

Additional Answers

Index

open-ended, 7, 16, 23, 137, 142, 271, 301, 329, 382, 412, 413, 419, 434, 444, 500, 549

Test Prep, 7, 12, 17, 23, 29, 33, 39, 42, 47, 51, 57, 67, 72, 78, 82, 88, 94, 98, 103, 108, 113, 122, 126, 131, 137, 142, 146, 152, 156, 160, 165, 174, 178, 184, 189, 194, 199, 205, 208, 213, 223, 228, 234, 240, 245, 249, 253, 257, 263, 272, 275, 281, 287, 291, 298, 302, 306, 309, 315, 325, 330, 334, 339, 345, 350, 355, 362, 367, 377, 383, 390, 396, 400, 404, 408, 413, 419, 425, 435, 439, 445, 450, 455, 459, 466, 471, 475–476, 479–480, 485, 495, 501, 508, 512, 516, 521, 526, 532, 535, 541, 551, 557, 570, 565, 573, 577, 582–583, 589, 600, 605, 608, 614, 620, 626, 631–633

See also Chapter Projects; Instant Check System; Mixed Review; Test-Taking Strategies

Assessment. See Alternative Assessment; Ongoing Assessment and Intervention; Prentice Hall Assessment System

Associative Property
of Addition, 25, 28, 54, 55, 86–88
of Multiplication, 36, 37, 54, 55, 86–88

Auditory Learners, Teacher's Edition pages 73, 133, 144, 177, 187, 193, 200, 209, 220, 231, 255, 349, 387, 453, 479, 493, 504, 556, 571, 613

Average, 322. *See also* Mean

Axes, of graphs, 518

B

Balance (profit and loss), 523

Bar graph, 334, 335, 337–339, 365, 390, 495

Base
defined, 99
of an exponent, 99, 110, 111, 146
of parallelogram, 446
of triangle, 447

Below Level Learner, Teacher's Edition pages 6, 10, 14, 20, 26, 31, 36, 41, 44, 49, 64, 69, 75, 81, 85, 91, 96, 100, 106, 120, 124, 129, 135, 140, 144, 149, 154, 158, 172, 176, 181, 186, 191, 197, 202, 207, 220, 225, 231, 237, 243, 247, 251, 255, 270, 274, 279, 284, 289, 295, 300, 304, 308, 323, 327, 333, 336, 342, 348, 353, 359, 374, 380, 387, 393, 398, 402, 406, 411, 416, 432, 437, 441, 447, 453, 457, 463, 468, 473, 478, 492, 498, 504, 510, 514, 519, 524, 528, 534, 548, 554, 559, 564, 569, 575, 581, 596, 602, 607, 612, 617, 623

Benchmark, 171, 172–174, 191, 210

Bisector
angle, 385
perpendicular, 384

Block Scheduling, 2B, 60B, 116B, 168B, 216B, 266B, 318B, 370B, 428B, 488B, 544B, 592B

Box-and-whisker plot, 356–357

Bug, 348

C

Calculator
with decimals, 241
exercises that use, 52, 101, 102, 125, 297, 302, 451, 618, 619
with exponents, 100
fraction, 138, 200
with fractions, 138, 200, 241
hints, 492
with mixed numbers, 200, 241
order of operations, 52
with percents, 302
with repeating decimals, 296
with square roots, 616
using, 52

Capacity
comparing, 252, 256, 261
customary units of, 250, 251
defined, 433
metric units of, 433, 434–435, 437, 438–439
See also Volume

Careers
accountant, 12
architect, 281
auto mechanic, 107
bicycle designer, 108
biologist, 323
board game designer, 584
carpenter, 236
cartoonist, 400
census taker, 28
clown, 204
collector, 128
costume designer, 256
event planner, 480
gymnastics instructor, 208
help-desk technician, 282
librarian, 576
meteorologist, 514
oceanographer, 188
package designer, 468
photographer, 382
primary care physician, 295
sales representative, 599
small business owner, 523
space engineer, 560
traffic engineer, 136
See also Math at Work

Cartesian plane. *See* Coordinate plane

Cell, 347, 365

Center, of a circle, 452

Centimeter, 431

Central tendency. *See* Measures of central tendency

Challenge, 7, 12, 17, 23, 29, 33, 38, 42, 47, 51, 67, 72, 77, 82, 88, 94, 98, 103, 107, 122, 125, 130, 137, 142, 146, 151, 156, 159, 174, 178, 183, 188, 194, 199, 204, 223, 227, 234, 239, 245, 249, 253, 257, 272, 276, 281, 287, 291, 297, 302, 305, 309, 325, 330, 332, 338, 345, 349, 355, 361, 376, 382, 389, 396, 399, 404, 409, 413, 419, 435, 439, 445, 450, 455, 459, 465, 471, 475, 479, 495, 501, 507, 512, 516, 521, 526, 531, 535, 551, 557, 561, 566, 572, 577, 583, 599, 605, 608, 614, 619, 625

Chance. *See* Probability

Chapter Projects
Celebration, 636
Crack It and Cook It!, 638
Go Fish, 640
Home Court Advantage, 637
Now Playing, 641
On Your Own Time, 639
Planet of the Stars, 638
Puzzling Pictures, 639
*See*ing Is Believing, 637
Stepping Stones, 636
The Time of Your Life, 640
Working for a Cause!, 641

Chapter Reviews. *See* Assessment

Chapter Tests. *See* Assessment

Checkpoint Quizzes. *See* Assessment

Check Skills You'll Need. *See* Instant Check System

Check Skills You'll Need, 2E, 60B, 16B, 168B, 216B, 266B, 318B, 370B, 428B, 488B, 544B, 592B, Teacher's Edition pages 5, 9, 13, 19, 25, 30, 35, 40, 43, 48, 63, 68, 74, 80, 84, 90, 95, 99, 105, 119, 123, 128, 134, 139, 143, 148, 153, 157, 171, 175, 180, 185, 190, 196, 201, 206, 219, 224, 230, 236, 242, 246, 250, 254, 269, 273, 278, 283, 288, 294, 299, 303, 307, 322, 326, 332, 335, 341, 347, 352, 358, 373, 379, 386, 397, 401, 405, 410, 415, 431, 436, 440, 446, 452, 456, 462, 467, 472, 477, 491, 497, 503, 509, 513, 518, 523, 527, 533, 547, 553, 558, 563, 568, 574, 580, 595, 601, 606, 611, 616, 622

Check Understanding. *See* Instant Check System

Choose a Method, 15, 28, 38, 70, 144, 192, 226, 280, 343, 380–381, 442–443, 529, 570, 572, 582, 597

Chord, 452, 483, 501

Circle
area of, 456–457, 458–459, 467, 521, 614
center of, 452
central angle of, 501
circumference of, 453, 454–455, 476, 521
defined, 452, 483
diameter of, 452, 453, 454–455, 501, 600
exploring, 451
identifying parts of, 452, 454
radius of, 452, 453, 454–455, 483, 501, 600

Circle graph, 341–342, 343–345, 365, 396

Circumference, 453, 454–455, 476, 483, 521

Classification
of angles, 380, 381–382, 392
of numbers, 617–618, 619, 629
of polygons, 397–398, 399–400
of triangles, 392–393, 394–396, 405, 423

Closure, Teacher's Edition pages 6, 10, 15, 21, 27, 31, 37, 41, 45, 49, 65, 70, 76, 81, 85, 92, 96, 101, 106, 120, 124, 129, 135, 140, 144, 150, 154, 158, 172, 176, 182, 186, 192, 197, 202, 207, 221, 226, 232, 237, 243, 247, 251, 255, 270, 274, 280, 284, 290, 296, 300, 304, 308, 323, 327, 332, 337, 343, 348, 353, 359, 375, 381, 388, 394, 398, 402, 407, 411, 417, 433, 437,

Index

Index

Index

Acknowledgments

Staff Credits

The people who made up the *Prentice Hall Mathematics Courses 1, 2, and 3* team—representing design services, editorial, editorial services, market research, educational technology, production services, product services, project office, and publishing processes—are listed below. Bold type denotes the core team members.

Amy Acer, Leora Adler, Scott Andrews, Carolyn Artin, Barbara Bertell, Suzanne Biron, Stephanie Bradley, **Judith Buice,** Christine Cannon, Ronit Carter, Justin Collins, Bob Cornell, Patricia Crotty, Patrick Culleton, Carol Dance, Sheila DeFazio, Marian DeLollis, Jo DiGiustini, Delphine Dupee, Emily Ellen, **Janet Fauser,** Debby Faust, Suzanne Feliciello, Steve Fenton, Michael Ferrio, Jonathan Fisher, Barbara Hardt, Richard Heater, Kerri Hoar, Jayne Holman, Karen Holtzman, Kate House, Alan Hull, **Nancy Jones,** Judie Jozokos, Melissa Kent, Russ Lappa, Lisa LaVallee, Christine Lee, Carolyn Lock, Rebecca Loveys, Catherine Maglio, **Cheryl Mahan,** Barry Maloney, Chris Maniatis, **Tim McDonald**, Autumn Mellor, Eve Melnechuk, Terri Mitchell, Janet Morris, Sandra Morris, Kyai Mullei, **Cindy Noftle,** Marsha Novak, Greg Oles, Marie Opera, Jill Ort, Michael Oster, Christopher Ott, Steve Ouellette, Joan Paley, Dorothy Preston, Roberto Portocarrero, John Reece, Sandy Roedel-Baker, Rashid Ross, Irene Rubin, Alan Ruffin, Donna Russo, John Saxe, JoAnne Sgroi, Vicky Shen, Dennis Slattery, Lisa Smith-Ruvalcaba, **Nancy Smith,** Emily Soltanoff, Debby Sommer, David Spangler, Cynthia Speranza, Karen Swanson, Mark Tricca, Michael Vogel, Nate Walker, Lisa Walston, Roberta Warshaw, Matthew Wilson, Helen Young, **Carol Zacny**

Cover Design

Peter Brooks, Brainworx Studios

Cover Photos

t, PhotoDisc, Inc./Getty Images, Inc.; **b,** Wolfgang Kaehler/Corbis

Technical Illustration

New England Typographic Services

Photo Research

Sharon Donahue, Sue McDermott, Kathy Beaura Ringrose

Illustration

Brucie Rosch: 20, 90, 580
Daniel Collins: 527
Joel Dubin: 158, 160, 201, 226, 269, 289, 321, 326, 440, 468, 470, 473, 520, 534
John Edwards: 22, 29, 65, 151, 204, 270, 298, 398, 468, 478, 479, 525, 569, 604
Kenneth Batelman: 133, 141, 225, 235, 257, 309, 432, 473, 613
Precision Graphics: 77
Roberta Warshaw: 7, 17, 27, 49, 132, 178, 228
Trevor Johnston: 28, 94, 103, 132, 204, 223, 342, 345, 351
Wilkinson Studios: 251, 257
XNR Productions: 204, 233, 245, 289, 290, 440, 521

Photography

Front Matter: Pages vii, L. Clarke/Corbis; **viii,** Jerry Lodriguss/Photo Researchers, Inc.; **ix,** Bill Miles/Corbis; **x,** Tony Freeman/PhotoEdit; **xi,** Alan Linda Detrick/Grant Heilman Photography, Inc.; **xii,** AP Photo/The Grand Rapids Press, Lance Wynn; **xiii,** Gary Braasch/Getty Images, Inc.; **xiv,** Barros & Barros/Getty Images, Inc.; **xv,** Tim Thompson/Getty Images, Inc.; **xvi,** Myrleen Gerguson Cate/Photo Edit; **xvii,** Layne Kennedy/Corbis; **xviii,** Pete Saloutos/Corbis

Chapter 1: Pages 2–3, Andrew Leyerle/Dorling Kindersley; **4,** D. Young-Wolff/PhotoEdit; **5,** Joseph Nettis/Photo Researchers, Inc.; **7,** Frank Siteman/Rainbow; **10,** AP Photo/Tom Gannam; **11,** Royalty-Free/Getty Images, Inc.; **12,** David Young-Wolff/PhotoEdit; **14,** Carl Purcell/Photo Researchers, Inc.; **15 both,** Richard Haynes; **16,** Getty Images, Inc.; **18,** Robert Burke/Getty Images, Inc.; **21,** Lisette Le Bon/Superstock, Inc.; **22 l,** Tom Stack & Associates, Inc.; **22 r,** U.S. Bureau of Engraving and Printing; **26,** Bob Daemmrich/The Image Works; **28,** Spencer Grant/PhotoEdit; **31,** Reuters NewMedia Inc./Corbis; **32 t,** Russ Lappa; **32 b,** Syracuse Newspapers/The Image Works; **34,** Tony Freeman/PhotoEdit; **36,** L. Clarke/Corbis; **37,** www.SellPhotos.CA; **38,** Russ Lappa; **41,** James Watt/Animals Animals/Earth Scenes; **43,** Chad Slattery/Getty Images, Inc.; **45,** John Moore; **46,** Liaison/Getty Images, Inc.; **48,** Lori Adamski Peek/Getty Images, Inc.; **50 t,** John Moore; **50 b,** Mitch Kezar/Getty Images, Inc.; **53,** Jeff Affleck/SuperStock, Inc.; **58 t,** The British Museum/Dorling Kindersley; **58 bl,** The Science Museum/Dorling Kindersley; **58 br,** Russ Lappa; **59 tl,** The Science Museum/Dorling Kindersley; **59 tr,** Steve Gorton/Dorling Kindersley; **59 b,** Alistair Duncan/Dorling Kindersley

Chapter 2: Pages 60–61, Vanessa Vick/Photo Researchers, Inc.; **62,** Bryn Colton/Corbis; **64,** Michael Rosenfeld/Getty Images, Inc.; **66,** Jerry Lodriguss/Photo Researchers, Inc.; **67,** Phil Degginger/Color-Pics, Inc.; **69,** Benelux Press/Index Stock Imagery, Inc.; **70 both,** Richard Haynes; **72,** Tom Prettyman/PhotoEdit; **75,** Alan Thornton/Getty Images, Inc.; **77,** David Young-Wolff/PhotoEdit; **81,** Michael S. Yamashita/Corbis; **82,** Eyewire/Getty Images, Inc.; **85,** Russ Lappa; **87,** Grant Heilman Inc.; **91,** Image Source/SuperStock, Inc.; **93,** Russ Lappa; **93 b,** Marc Muench/Corbis; **93 t,** Getty Images, Inc.; **97,** Dianna Blell/Peter Arnold, Inc.; **100 both,** Russ Lappa; **107,** Chris Salvo/Getty Images, Inc.; **108,** Mark Richards/PhotoEdit; **109,** Mark Thayer; **114 l,** R. P. Meleski; **114 tr,** Baum/Dorling Kindersley; **114–115 b,** Carlyn Iverson/Absolute Science; **114–115,** Denis Scott/Stock Boston; **115 t,** Grace Davies/Omni-Photo Communications, Inc.

Chapter 3: Pages 116–117, Blair Seitz/Photo Researchers, Inc.; **117,** C Squared Studios/Getty Images, Inc.; **118,** Dennis MacDonald/PhotoEdit; **120,** Wally McNamee/Corbis; **122,** Mark Richards/PhotoEdit; **125,** Joanna McCarthy/SuperStock, Inc.; **126 both,** Richard Haynes; **128,** Österreichische Post AG; **130,** Jeff Greenberg/PhotoEdit; **133 l,** Russ Lappa; **133 ml,** Russ Lappa; **133 mr,** Russ Lappa; **133 r,** Russ Lappa; **133 tl,** Art Wolfe/Getty Images, Inc.; **133 tr,** Davies + Starr/Getty Images, Inc.; **135,** TSI Pictures/Getty Images, Inc.; **136,** Bettman/Corbis; **137,** David Young-Wolff/PhotoEdit; **139,** Mark Burnett/Stock Boston; **140,** Russ Lappa; **142,** Steve Cohen/Getty Images, Inc.; **143,** Tom Stewart/Corbis; **144,** Pictor/Uniphoto; **144 l,** Richard Haynes; **144 r,** Richard Haynes; **146,** Tony Freeman/PhotoEdit; **149,** Bill Miles/Corbis; **151,** Tim Ridley/Dorling Kindersley; **155 br,** Alan Schein Photography/Corbis; **155 l,** AP/Wide World Photos; **155 t,** Alan Schein Photography/Corbis; **157,** Bob Daemmrich/Stock Boston; **159,** Mary Kate Denny/PhotoEdit; **166 b,** S. Wanke/Getty Images, Inc.; **166 t,** Geoff Brightling/Dorling Kindersley; **167 bl,** Andy Crawford/Dorling Kindersley; **167 br,** Richard Megna/Fundamental Photographs; **167 ml,** Dave King/Dorling Kindersley; **167 t,** Dorling Kindersley; **167 tl,** Andy Crawford/Dorling Kindersley

Chapter 4: Pages 168–169, Mark C. Burnett/Photo Researchers, Inc.; **170,** Terry Cosgrove/Getty Images, Inc.; **172,** David Young-Wolff/PhotoEdit; **173,** Russ Lappa; **176,** Superstock, Inc.; **177,** NIBSC/Photo Researchers, Inc.; **178 t,** C Squared Studios/Getty Images, Inc.; **178 bl,** John A. Rizzo/Getty Images, Inc.; **178 br,** David Toase/Getty Images, Inc.; **180,** Russ Lappa; **181,** Bob Daemmrich/Stock Boston; **183,** Faidley/Agliolol/International Stock; **185,** Russ Lappa; **186,** Ronn Maratea/Image State; **188 t,** Tony Freeman/PhotoEdit; **188 b,** John Moore; **190,** Renee Lynn/Corbis; **192 both,** Richard Haynes; **193,** Tony Freeman/PhotoEdit; **198 t,** Adam Smith/Getty Images, Inc.; **198 b,** Frozen Images/The Image Works; **204,** Vicki Silbert/PhotoEdit; **206,** Photo Edit; **207 l,** Pictor Uniphoto; **207 r,** Yuman/

The Image Works; **208,** Strauss/Curtis/Corbis; **214 t,** AP/Wide World Photos; **214 l,** AFP/Corbis; **214 r,** Russ Lappa; **215 t,** Robert Laberge/Getty Images, Inc.; **215 b,** AP/Wide World Photos

Chapter 5: Pages 216–217, The Image Works; **218,** Tom Stewart/Corbis Stock Market; **219,** John Moore; **221,** Silver Burdett Ginn; **222,** Brian Parker/Tom Stack & Associates, Inc.; **224,** Guinness World Records, Ltd.; **226,** Richard Haynes; **227,** John Moore; **228 both,** Richard Haynes; **229,** John Moore; **232,** Alan Linda Detrick/Grant Heilman Photography, Inc.; **233 b,** John Moore; **233 t,** Silver Burdett Ginn; **236,** Dan McCoy/Rainbow; **237,** Russ Lappa; **239,** Ariel Skelley/Corbis Stock Market; **240,** Alan Oddie/PhotoEdit; **243,** John Moore; **243,** Syracuse Newspapers/The Image Works; **246,** Owaki-Kulla/Corbis; **248 l,** Photodisc, Inc./Getty Images, Inc.; **248 ml,** Photodisc, Inc./Getty Images, Inc.; **248 mr,** Photodisc, Inc./Getty Images, Inc.; **248 r,** Photodisc, Inc./Getty Images, Inc.; **249,** John Moore; **250,** G. Biss/Masterfile Corporation; **252,** Past /Project Exploration; **255,** Bettmann/Corbis; **256,** AP/Wide World Photos; **259,** David Young-Wolff/PhotoEdit; **260,** 1995. Drabble by Kevin Fagan/United Feature Syndicate, Inc.; **264 b,** Annabelle Halls/Dorling Kindersley; **264 t,** James Muldowney/Getty Images, Inc.; **264–265,** Mike Powell/Getty Images, Inc.; **265 all,** James Jackson/Dorling Kindersley, Ltd.

Chapter 6: Pages 266–267, Tom Bean; **268,** Carl & Ann Purcell/Corbis; **271,** Russ Lappa; **272,** Frederick M. Brown/Getty Images, Inc.; **274,** Russ Lappa; **275,** AP Photo/The Grand Rapids Press, Lance Wynn; **278,** SW Production/Index Stock Imagery, Inc.; **279,** American Honda Motor Co., Inc.; **280,** Richard Haynes; **281 t,** OMNI-Photo Communication Inc.; **281 b,** Tony Latham/Getty Images, Inc.; **282,** SuperStock, Inc.; **285,** Ken O'Donoghue; **286,** AP/Wide World Photos; **290,** Pictor Uniphoto; **295,** David Hanover/Getty Images, Inc.; **297,** The Academy of Natural Science/Corbis; **299,** Dennis MacDonald/PhotoEdit; **303,** Russ Lappa; **304,** Russ Lappa; **307,** Michael Spingler/AP/Wide World Photos; **308,** Russ Lappa; **309,** Russ Lappa; **310,** Russ Lappa; **316 t,** Royal Tyrrell Museum/Alberta Community Development/Dorling Kindersley; **316–317 m,** Jim Channell/Dorling Kindersley; **317 tl,** Jeffrey Sylvester/Getty Images, Inc.; **317 tr,** Andy Crawford/Dorling Kindersley; **317 m,** John Paul Endress; **317 br,** Brady

Chapter 7: Pages 318–319, Mack Henley/Visuals Unlimited; **320,** International Stock/ImageState; **323,** Dick Blume/Syracuse Newspaper/Image Works; **325,** Gary Braasch/Getty Images, Inc.; **327,** Craig Lovell/Corbis; **329,** Nancy Sheehan/PhotoEdit; **330,** Jane Burton/Dorling Kindersley; **331,** Ryan McVay/Getty Images, Inc.; **337,** Lon C. Diehl/PhotoEdit; **338 l,** AP/Wide World Photos; **338 ml,** Eddie Adams/Getty Images, Inc.; **338 mr,** Homer Sykes/Woodfin Camp & Associates; **338 r,** Pascal Volery Reuters/Getty Images, Inc.; **343 both,** Richard Haynes; **344,** Bill Bachmann/Image Works; **347,** Spencer Grant/PhotoEdit; **349,** Bob Daemmrich/Stock Boston; **352,** Merritt Vincent/PhotoEdit; **354,** Richard Cummins/Corbis; **359,** Stone/Getty Images, Inc.; **360,** Royalty-Free/Corbis; **369,** David Robbins/Getty Images, Inc.

Chapter 8: Pages 370–371, Joseph Nettis/Photo Researchers, Inc.; **372,** Ronny Jaques/Photo Researchers, Inc.; **373,** Dennis Di Cicco/Peter Arnold, Inc.; **375,** Barros & Barros/Getty Images, Inc.; **376,** Russ Lappa; **377,** William H. Mullins/Photo Researchers, Inc.; **379,** David Brooks/Corbis; **380,** Richard Haynes; **381,** Richard Haynes; **382,** Howie Garber/Animals Animals/Earth Scenes; **387,** George Shelley/Corbis; **388,** Peter Menzel/Stock Boston; **389 l,** Corbis; **389 r,** Russ Lappa; **394 both,** Russ Lappa; **395,** Russ Lappa; **395,** Rob Crandall/Stock Boston; **397 l,** S. Wanke/PhotoDisc/Getty Images, Inc.; **397 m,** Ryan McVay/Getty Images, Inc.; **397 r,** Russel Illig/Getty Images, Inc.; **399,** Raphael Gaillarde/Gamma Liaison/Getty Images, Inc.; **400,** AP/Wide World Photos; **403 l,** C Squared Studios/Getty Images, Inc.; **403 ml,** Siede Preis/Getty Images, Inc.; **403 mr,** Siede Preis/Getty Images, Inc.; **403 r,** Siede Preis/Getty Images, Inc.; **403 b,** Tony Freeman/PhotoEdit; **405,** W. Cody/Corbis; **407,** AP/Wide World Photos; **410,** Corel; **413 l,** Andrew J. Martinez/Photo Researchers, Inc.; **413 r,** Rod Planck/Photo Researchers, Inc.; **415,** Corbis; **416,** Suzanne & Nick Geary/Getty Images, Inc.; **418,** Dallas & John Heaton/Stock Boston; **420,** M.C. Escher © 2003 Cordon Art B.V.-Baarn-Holland; **420 t,** Russ Lappa; **426 b,** Paul Barton/Corbis; **426 t,** Tony Freeman/PhotoEdit; **426–427 m,** David Jeffrey/Getty Images, Inc.; **427 b,** PhotoEdit; **427 t,** Jim Hiss/Hispanic Business Inc.

Chapter 9: Pages 428–429, Jeff Greenberg/Peter Arnold, Inc.; **430,** Corbis; **431,** Ken O'Donoghue; **432,** Russ Lappa; **433,** Russ Lappa; **434,** Topham/The Image Works; **437,** NASA/Goddard Flight Center; **438,** Warren Bolster/Getty Images, Inc.; **441,** AP Photo/Elise Amendola; **442,** Richard Haynes; **443,** Richard Haynes; **444,** George McLean/Cardinal Spellman Philatelic Museum; **447,** Tim Thompson/Getty Images, Inc.; **449,** Tony Hopewell/Getty Images, Inc.; **453,** Tony Freeman/PhotoEdit; **454,** Digital Vision/Getty Images, Inc.; **455,** Bill Amend/Universal Press Syndicate; **457,** Russ Lappa; **459,** Photo Researchers, Inc.; **463,** Bob Krist/Corbis; **465 bl,** Tony Freeman/PhotoEdit; **465 br,** John Elk III/Stock Boston; **465 tl,** Tony Freeman/PhotoEdit; **465 tr,** R.M. Arakaki/International Stock; **468,** Alan Klehr/Getty Images, Inc.; **475,** Robin Weiner/WIREPIX/The Image Works; **477,** Russell Illig/Getty Images, Inc.; **480,** Stephen Simpson/Getty Images, Inc.; **486 m,** Photo Courtesy of Northland College, Ashland, Wisconsin; **486 t,** Kim Sayer/Dorling Kindersley; **486–487 b,** Elfi Kluck/Index Stock Imagery, Inc.; **487 t,** Neil Setchfield/Dorling Kindersley

Chapter 10: Pages 488–489, Science VU/Visuals Unlimited; **491,** Neal Preston/Corbis; **493,** Tom Carter/PhotoEdit; **494,** Corbis; **499,** AP/Wide World Photo; **500,** Walter Bibikow/Index Stock Imagery/PictureQuest; **504,** Rid Catanach/Woods Hole Oceanographic Institution; **506,** Judith Canty/Stock Boston; **508,** John Moore; **509,** Tom Sanders/Corbis; **511,** Bob Daemmrich Photo, Inc.; **514 both,** Michael Schwartz/The Image Works; **517,** Spencer Grant/PhotoEdit; **520,** Myrleen Gerguson Cate/Photo Edit; **523,** Susan Van Etten/PhotoEdit; **524,** Tom Stewart/Corbis; **528,** Cary Wollinsky/Stock Boston; **529 both,** Richard Haynes; **531,** Sally & Derk Kuper; **533,** Yvette Californiardozo/Index Stock Imagery/PictureQuest; **534 l,** Siede Preis/Getty Images, Inc.; **534 ml,** C Squared Studios/Getty Images, Inc.; **534 mr,** C Squared Studios/Getty Images, Inc.; **534 r,** C Squared Studios/Getty Images, Inc.; **537,** Marc Romanelli/Getty Images, Inc.; **542 b,** Harald Sund/Getty Images, Inc.; **542 t,** Art Wolfe, Inc.; **542–543,** Planetary Visions, Ltd.; **543 bl,** David Muench/Getty Images, Inc.; **543 br,** Harvery Lloyd/Getty Images, Inc.; **543 ml,** Jeff Greenberg/Omni-Photo Communications, Inc.; **543 mr,** Getty Images/Eyewire, Inc.; **543 t,** Gery Randall/Getty Images, Inc.; **543 tr,** Peter Gridley/Getty Images, Inc.

Chapter 11: Pages 544–545, Richard Haynes; **546,** Anthea Sieveking/Petit Format/Photo Researchers, Inc.; **547,** Russ Lappa; **548 t,** Russ Lappa; **548 b,** David Young-Wolff/PhotoEdit; **550,** Elyse Lewin/Getty Images, Inc.; **553,** Russ Lappa; **554,** Tony Di Zinno/See Jane Run; **556,** Corbis; **559,** Paul Barton/Corbis; **560,** NASA/Dorling Kindersley Picture Library; **563,** Mark Burnett/Stock Boston; **566,** Joe McDonald/Corbis; **570 both,** Richard Haynes; **572,** Layne Kennedy/Corbis; **574,** Getty Images, Inc.; **575,** Rudi Von Briel/PhotoEdit; **576,** EyeWire/Getty Images, Inc.; **577,** United Media/United Feature Syndicate, Inc.; **581,** Syracuse Newpaper/The Image Works; **583 l,** Ken Ross/Getty Images, Inc.; **583 r,** Russ Lappa; **584,** Courtesy of Milton Bradley Co.; **585,** Russ Lappa; **590 t,** C Squared Studios/Getty Images, Inc.; **590 b,** Al Francekevich/Corbis; **591,** MMI Flash! Light/Stock Boston

Chapter 12: Pages 592–593, Ron Brown/Superstock, Inc.; **594,** AFP Photo/Don Emmert/Corbis; **595,** Pete Saloutos/Corbis; **595,** Ron Brown/Superstock, Inc.; **596,** Gary Conner/PhotoEdit; **597 both,** Richard Haynes; **598,** Tom & Dee Ann McCarthy/Corbis; **599,** (ZF) T. Knsselmann/Masterfile; **600,** Richard Haynes; **601,** 1986 James Mayo/Chicago Tribune; **603,** Tony Freeman/PhotoEdit; **604,** SuperStock, Inc.; **605,** Spokane Police Department; **606,** AP/Wide World Photos; **607,** Russ Lappa; **608,** Tim Thompson/Corbis; **611,** Bohemian Nomad Picturemakers/Corbis; **613,** David Young-Wolff/PhotoEdit; **616,** Ron Brown/Superstock, Inc.; **617,** Cynthia Hart Designer/Corbis; **619,** Roger Wood/Corbis; **623,** Zigy Kaluzny/Getty Images, Inc.; **625,** Jon Chomitz; **632 l,** Chris Bjornberg/Photo Researchers, Inc.; **632 t,** Tim Flach/Getty Images, Inc.; **632–633 b,** Amanda Friedman/Getty Images, Inc.; **633 b,** General Electric Lighting; **633 t,** Davies & Starr/Getty Images, Inc.

Teacher's Edition

Editorial and Production Services: The GTS Companies
Design Coordination: Susan Gerould/Perspectives